Take a closer look at key ecological co
Ecology in Depth and *Environmental*

ECOLOGY IN DEPTH

ENVIRONMENTAL APPLICATIONS

ECOLOGY

A Canadian Context

Second Edition

Bill Freedman
*Department of Biology,
Dalhousie University*

Jeffrey A. Hutchings
*Department of Biology,
Dalhousie University*

Darryl T. Gwynne
*University of Toronto in
Mississauga*

John P. Smol
*Department of Biology,
Queen's University*

Roger Suffling
*Faculty of Environment,
University of Waterloo*

Roy Turkington
*Department of Botany, and
Beaty Biodiversity Research
Centre, University of British
Columbia*

Richard L. Walker
*Department of Biological
Sciences, University of Calgary*

Dawn Bazely
*Biology Department, York
University*

1914–2014
Nelson Education celebrates 100 years of Canadian publishing

Ecology, Second Edition

by Bill Freedman, Jeffery A. Hutchings, Darryl T. Gwynne, John P. Smol, Roger Suffling,
Roy Turkington, Richard L. Walker, and Dawn Bazely

**Vice President, Editorial
Higher Education:**
Anne Williams

Publisher:
Paul Fam

Marketing Manager:
Leanne Newell

Developmental Editor:
Toni Chahley

**Photo Researcher/Permissions
Coordinator:**
Kristiina Paul

**Senior Production Project
Manager:**
Imoinda Romain

Production Service:
Integra Software Services Pvt. Ltd.

Copy Editor:
Karen Rolfe

Proofreader:
Integra Software Services Pvt. Ltd.

Indexer:
Integra Software Services Pvt. Ltd.

Design Director:
Ken Phipps

Managing Designer:
Franca Amore

Interior Design:
Dianna Little

Cover Design:
Jennifer Leung

Cover Image:
Paul Nicklen/National Geographic
Images

Box Images:
Ecology in Depth, Thinkstock;
Environmental Applications,
Evlakhov Valeri/Shutterstock;
A Canadian Ecologist,
© iStockphoto.com/Bart Coenders

Compositor:
Integra Software Services Pvt. Ltd.

Every effort has been made to
trace ownership of all copyrighted
material and to secure permission
from copyright holders. In the
event of any question arising as
to the use of any material, we will
be pleased to make the necessary
corrections in future printings.

**Library and Archives Canada
Cataloguing in Publication**

Freedman, Bill, author
    Ecology : a Canadian context /
Bill Freedman, Department of
Biology, Dalhousie University,
Jeffrey A. Hutchings, Department
of Biology, Dalhousie University,
Darryl T. Gwynne University of
Toronto in Mississauga, John P.
Smol, Department of Biology,
Queen's University, Roger Suffling,
Faculty of Environment, University
of Waterloo, Roy Turkington
Department of Botany, and Beaty
Biodiversity Research Centre,
University of British Columbia,
Richard L. Walker, Department
of Biological Sciences, University
of Calgary, Dawn Bazely, Biology
Department, York University.
— Second edition.

Revision of: Ecology : a Canadian
context / Bill Freedman ... [et al.].
    — Toronto : Nelson Education,
[2010], c2011.
Includes bibliographical references
and index.
ISBN 978-0-17-651014-5 (bound)

    1. Ecology—Canada—Textbooks.
I. Hutchings, Jeffrey Alexander,
1958-, author II. Gwynne, Darryl
T., author III. Smol, John Paul,
1955-, author IV. Suffling, Roger,
1948-, author V. Turkington,
Roy, 1951-, author VI. Walker,
Richard L. (Professor of biology),
author VII. Bazely, Dawn, author
VIII. Title.

QH541.E355 2014
577.0971   C2014-901290-X

ISBN-13: 978-0-17-651014-5
ISBN-10: 0-17-651014-1

About the Cover Image: This
image shows a Kermode bear
(*Ursus americanus kermodei*) in
its habitat of the Pacific coastal
forest of western and northern
British Columbia and the Alaskan
panhandle. The Kermode bear
is an uncommon subspecies
of the widespread black bear
(*U. americanus*); about one-tenth
of the black bear population has
a whitish pelage. Like other black
bears, animals in this population
are omnivorous in the feeding,

but when there is a seasonal run
of Pacific salmon (*Oncorhynchus*)
they focus on those fish as a highly
nutritious and energy-rich food. The
whitish fur is due to recessive genes
and is not an albino trait (the bears
do not have red eyes). The light
colour may be less visible to salmon
and so may confer a selective
advantage to the bears when they
are stalking that prey. In terms
of nutrient cycling, the migrating
salmon are a conveyor of marine
nitrogen and phosphorus to the

upper reaches of the watersheds
of the streams where they breed.
Feeding by the bears extends this
ecosystem function by transferring
nutrients in the form of partially
eaten fish carcasses and defecations
to terrestrial parts of the watershed.
The whitish Kermode bears are
also of cultural significance—they
are considered a "spirit" animal
by the local First Nations, whose
mythology includes stories about
them, and they are also the official
animal of British Columbia.

BRIEF CONTENTS

TABLE OF CONTENTS

CHAPTER 5

Population Ecology

CHAPTER 6

Behavioural Ecology

CHAPTER 7

Physiological Ecology

ABOUT THE AUTHORS

Sheldon Bowles

Bill Freedman

BILL FREEDMAN is an ecologist and environmental scientist. He was born in downtown Toronto and did all of his schooling there. He received his M.Sc. and Ph.D. degrees from the University of Toronto, where he studied in the Department of Botany. He has taught in the Department of Biology at Dalhousie University, Halifax, Nova Scotia, since 1979.

The conceptual framework of Bill's research has been the influence of environmental stressors on biodiversity and other structural and functional attributes of ecosystems. Understanding the influence of stressor regimes is of theoretical interest, and it also helps guide the management of ecological damage caused by disturbance and pollution. Bill's research has examined the effects of a wide range of industrial activities, with somewhat of a focus on forestry practices, as well as work on the environmental effects of acidification, eutrophication, metals, pesticides, and sulphur dioxide. Other interests include carbon storage in ecosystems, urban ecology, Arctic ecology, the biodiversity of Sable Island, the design of environmental monitoring programs, and ecologically sustainable systems of resource harvesting. More than 100 refereed publications in scientific journals have resulted from this work, plus several hundred book and encyclopedia chapters, research reports, and other documents.

Bill is also engaged in developing curriculum materials in support of higher education, and as part of that work he has written several textbooks, including *Environmental Ecology* (2nd edition, 1995), and *Environmental Science: A Canadian Perspective* (5th edition, 2010). Bill has served on the board of directors of the Nature Conservancy of Canada since 1992, was the chair of that board from 2007 to 2009, and wrote a retrospective of the organization (*A History of the Nature Conservancy of Canada*, 2013). He has also participated in environmental impact assessments of proposed and operating industrial facilities, and has served on advisory panels to government. In 2006, Bill received a Canadian Environment Award, Gold Medal Level, in the category of Community Awards for Conservation, from the Canadian Geographic Society. In 2007, he received a Careeer Achievement Award from the Canadian Council of University Biology Chairs. Beyond academics, Bill is a squash player, a collector of folk art and natural artifacts, and an enthusiastic naturalist and traveller who loves to spend time in wild places.

Jeff Hutchings

Jeffrey A. Hutchings

JEFFREY A. HUTCHINGS was born in Orillia, Ontario. He made his initial environmental forays into the landscapes of nearby Shield lakes and later the outports of Newfoundland. His maturing interests in ecology ultimately stemmed from field experiences ranging from mountainous terrain near Kispiox, British Columbia, to lakes and rivers adjoining Georgian Bay, Ontario, and from interior and coastal Newfoundland and Labrador to high-latitude lakes on Baffin and Ellesmere Islands in Nunavut. His current research centres on questions related to life history evolution, behavioural ecology, phenotypic plasticity, population dynamics, and conservation biology of marine and anadromous fishes, particularly Atlantic cod (*Gadus morhua*), Atlantic salmon (*Salmo salar*), and brook trout (*Salvelinus fontinalis*). From an applied perspective, this work has bearing on questions pertaining to the depletion, recovery, and sustainable exploitation of marine fish; interactions between wild and farmed Atlantic salmon; the biodiversity of Canadian fish; and the communication of science to decision makers and society.

Jeff is appointed as a Faculty of Science Killam Professor of Biology at Dalhousie University and Professor II in the Centre for Ecological and Evolutionary Synthesis at University of Oslo, Norway. He received his B.Sc. from the University of Toronto and his M.Sc. and Ph.D. from Memorial University of Newfoundland, and undertook postdoctoral research at the University of Edinburgh and Fisheries and Oceans Canada in St. John's, Newfoundland. In addition to Jeff's teaching and research responsibilities, he has served on many advisory and administrative committees for nongovernmental and governmental organizations. He was a member (2001–2012) and chair (2006–2010) of the Committee on the Status of Endangered Wildlife in Canada (COSEWIC), the national independent body responsible for advising the federal government on the status of species at risk in Canada. From 2009 to 2012, he chaired the Royal Society of Canada Expert Panel on Ocean Health and Marine Biodiversity. In 2012 and 2013 he served as the fourth president of the Canadian Society for Ecology and Evolution. He has been a member of the board of directors of WWF Canada since 2012.

Darryl T. Gwynne

DARRYL T. GWYNNE was born in Bristol, England, and moved to Canada in 1966. He is a professor of biology at the University of Toronto in Mississauga. He received a B.Sc. in Biology at the University of Toronto in 1974 and a Ph.D. in Zoology and Entomology from Colorado State University in 1979. After conducting postdoctoral research at the University of New Mexico, in 1981 he took up a Queen Elizabeth II Research Fellowship at the University of Western Australia. Since 1987 he has been at the University of Toronto, where he currently teaches animal behaviour and a fourth year "Topics in Ecology and Evolution" course.

Darryl's research seeks to understand the factors that control sexual selection and the "typical" sexual differences in behaviour and structure, such as ornaments and weapons. His studies and those of his students have investigated the consequences of mating systems as diverse as those with extreme sexual selection on males (harem defence and male weaponry in New Zealand weta (a group of cricket relatives) to the key study species, those that are rare examples of female competition for mates. The common element in the life histories of most of the study species are important goods and services offered by the males, such as prey used by dance flies, and specialized glandular secretions in other insects. The value of these gifts has led—for some species—to role reversals in behaviour, with females competing for access to gift-bearing males and occasionally the evolution of male-like ornamentation in females.

Darryl is author of over 100 scientific papers, several popular articles, and a book (*Katydids and Bush-Crickets: Reproductive Behavior and Evolution of the Tettigoniidae*, Cornell University Press, 2001). He is several chapters into a new book, a popular tome on sexual selection that focuses on the life histories of insects found in the area of his home in the Credit River Valley.

John P. Smol

JOHN P. SMOL is a professor in the Department of Biology at Queen's University, with a cross-appointment to the School of Environmental Studies, where he also holds the Canada Research Chair in Environmental Change. He received a B.Sc. from McGill University, an M.Sc. from Brock University, and a Ph.D. from Queen's University. Following postdoctoral work in the High Arctic with the Geological Survey of Canada, he became a faculty member at Queen's University. He has also held adjunct appointments at several other universities in Canada, the United States, and China.

John founded the Paleoecological Environmental Assessment and Research Lab (PEARL) in 1991—a group of about 30 researchers dedicated to the study of global environmental change, focusing primarily on lake ecology. An ISI Highly Cited Researcher, he has authored about 470 journal publications and book chapters, and completed 19 books, including his textbook *Pollution of Lakes and Rivers: A Paleoenvironmental Perspective*, now in its second edition and also being translated into Chinese. He has lectured on all seven continents, including as the 2008 Rutherford Lecturer at the Royal Society (London). He was the founding editor of the international *Journal of Paleolimnology* (1987–2007), is the editor of the journal *Environmental Reviews*, is editor of the *Developments in Paleoenvironmental Research* book series, and is on the editorial boards of additional journals.

Since 1990, he has received over 45 national and international research and teaching awards, including an NSERC Steacie Fellowship, the 1992 Steacie Prize (awarded to Canada's top young scientist or engineer), a Canada Council Killam Fellowship, the Geological Association of Canada Past-Presidents' Medal, the Botanical Society of America Darbaker Prize, the NSERC Herzberg Gold Medal as Canada's top scientist or engineer (2004), the Rigler Prize from the Society of Canadian Limnologists, the Royal Society of Canada Miroslaw Romanowski Medal for advances in the environmental sciences, an NSERC Award of Excellence, and the American Society of Limnology and Oceanography Hutchinson Award. The Royal Canadian Geographical Society named him as the 2008 Environmental Scientist of the Year (an honour shared with his brother, Jules Blais, of the University of Ottawa). In 2009, he was presented with the Killam Prize for the Natural Sciences from the Canada Council, as well as the Premier's Discovery Award for Life Sciences and Medicine. In 2013, he was awarded the inaugural Science Ambassador Award and the 2013 Weston Family Prize for Lifetime Achievement in Northern Research. He has received three honorary doctorates, from St. Francis Xavier University, the University of Helsinki, and the University of Waterloo.

John has received 10 teaching and scientific outreach awards from Queens University as well as outside agencies, including a 3M National Teaching Fellowship in 2009, considered to be Canada's top teaching honour. In 2010, following a nationwide search, *Nature* magazine named John Canada's Top Mid-Career Science Mentor.

In 2013, the Governor General named John an Officer of the Order of Canada.

Roger Suffling

ROGER SUFFLING came to the School of Planning at the University of Waterloo following the obtaining of degrees in botany, ecology, and weed science, and several years working in environmental consulting. He teaches ecology, park planning, ecological policy making, environmental impact assessment, landscape ecology, and ecological restoration. Roger's research interests centre on the landscape ecology and management of boreal forests, including the role of forest fires and global warming effects on the ecology and economy of Canada's mid-north. Equally, he and his students research the ecology and management of urban ecosystems. Roger has published numerous papers on these topics and has been a consultant for local, provincial, and national governments; a royal commission; private companies; and First Nations. He chaired an Ontario government scientific advisory committee on woodland caribou conservation, and for over 30 years has participated in numerous environmental assessments and conservation issues in northern Ontario. Many of these activities focus on applying ecological principles to management of incremental landscape change, whether caused by urban growth, forest fires, recreation, or forest harvesting. Roger has travelled to over 20 countries in his study of ecology but has a special passion for the ecosystems and people of northern Ontario. For a decade, through the Quetico Foundation, he co-organized a youth program for northern Ontario students to conduct landscape-scale research in Quetico Provincial Park, a large wilderness reserve. Roger's hobbies include a garden that manages to manage itself, family history, cross-country skiing, and wilderness canoeing. As an immigrant to Canada, Roger is profoundly grateful for the gifts that this vast and magnificent country has afforded him in friendships and beautiful landscapes. He is concerned that the next generation of Canadians must build a more sustainable society.

Roy and Evelyn Turkington

ROY TURKINGTON was born in Northern Ireland. After earning his B.Sc. (Hons) degree in Biological and Environmental Studies from the New University of Ulster and his doctorate from the University College of North Wales, Roy immigrated with his wife to Canada where he did postdoctoral research at the University of Western Ontario. Roy is a professor in the Department of Botany and the Beaty Biodiversity Research Centre at the University of British Columbia in Vancouver. He teaches two undergraduate courses in ecology and an undergraduate and graduate course in plant ecology. He is primarily an experimental field ecologist investigating population-level processes, such as competition and herbivory as influences on community structure, specifically species diversity and ecosystem function.

Roy's research, and that of his students, is supported primarily by the Natural Sciences and Engineering Research Council (NSERC) and has been conducted in a wide range of community types in the boreal forest in northern Canada, grasslands in western Canada and the United Kingdom, Garry oak ecosystems, the Negev desert in Israel, riverine forests in the Serengeti National Park in Tanzania, and subtropical forests in southern China.

Roy has published more than 150 papers and book chapters and has served on the editorial boards of *Agro-Ecosystems*, the *Canadian Journal of Botany*, and the *Israeli Journal of Ecology and Evolution*. He was on the editorial board of the Journal of Ecology for 20 years. One of his papers has been recognized by the British Ecological Society as one of the top 100 most influential papers ever published by the organization (1913–2012). In pursuit of his academic career, Roy and his wife have spent sabbaticals in Wales, Turkey, Northern Ireland, Israel, China, and Argentina.

In his spare time, Roy has a keen amateur interest in Middle Eastern and Biblical archaeology. He and his wife Evelyn are avid travellers and enjoy the outdoors. Together they have trekked the Annapurna circuit, the Mount Everest base camp, the High Atlas, the Inca trail, and climbed Kilimanjaro. For many years they have been involved in the AWANA children's ministry. Roy and Evelyn have two married children, Alistair and Andrea, and four grandchildren—and by the time this second edition is published, they will have five.

Richard L. Walker

RICHARD L. WALKER completed his Ph.D. in Animal Physiology at Michigan State University in 1975 and immediately accepted a faculty position at the University of Calgary in the Department of Biological Sciences. Richard retired in June 2012 and is now enjoying life as an Instructor Emeritus.

While in graduate school, Richard developed a keen interest in environmental physiology and the effects of pollutants on aquatic animals. He has had the privilege of working with some of Canada's leading environmental physiologists and has published journal articles on aluminum toxicity in brook trout.

Richard loves to teach and has received several teaching excellence awards from the Faculty of Science and from the Students' Union, and was recently inducted in Student's Union Teaching Excellence Hall of Fame. He is currently a sessional instructor in Human Physiology in the Faculty of Kinesiology.

As an avid hiker, backpacker, and skier, Richard considers himself very fortunate to live in the foothills of the Canadian Rockies. He also makes forays to the West Coast where he enjoys sailing with family and friends.

Dawn Bazely

DAWN BAZELY is professor of Biology in the Faculty of Science at York University, Toronto, where she has taught since 1990. She is also Director of IRIS, the university-wide Institute for Research and Innovation in Sustainability (2006–11 and 2012–13). At IRIS, Dawn's mission is to develop, lead, and support interdisciplinary research on diverse fronts. The student-led annual campus sustainability survey that she developed in 2007 is now a regular event. These surveys of the York community explore diverse topics ranging from climate change to local food and transportation preferences.

Dawn trained as an ecologist, in the field of plant–herbivore interactions, and has carried out field research in grasslands and forests, from temperate to arctic regions. Dawn has a B.Sc. in Biogeography and Environmental Studies and an M.Sc. in Botany from the University of Toronto. Her D.Phil. in Zoology, from Oxford University's Edward Grey Institute in Field Ornithology, looked at sheep grazing behaviour.

Since joining York University, Dawn has won the Faculty of Science and Engineering teaching award (2003) and the President's University-Wide Teaching Award (2013). As well as publishing dozens of journal articles, chapters, conference proceeding papers, and technical reports, Dawn wrote a textbook, *Ecology and Control of Introduced Plants: Evaluating and Responding to Invasive Plants*, (2003, with Judith Myers), and coedited *Environmental and Human Security in the Arctic* (2013). After nearly 20 years away from Arctic fieldwork, Dawn returned to the north in 2002 for fieldwork in Sweden. In 2006, she led the Canadian section of the International Polar Year project: GAPS (Gas, Arctic Peoples, and Security).

In 2011 Dawn received a Charles Bullard Fellowship from Harvard University, and spent her sabbatical at Harvard Forest, where she worked on a book examining conservation and ecological issues in southern Ontario, from scientific, policy, and political perspectives. This is the most heavily populated, industrialized, and farmed region of Canada, and it provides a case study for evaluating and responding to what lies ahead for other parts of the temperate forest region in the face of climate change and its associated issues and challenges.

PREFACE

The Context of Ecology

Ecology is a vital way of knowing. This is because its knowledge and predictions help us to understand how the natural world functions, the station of humans within that domain, and the means by which our use of its resources can be undertaken on a sustainable basis. For these reasons, the wisdom of ecology can beneficially inform key aspects of our society and economy.

Ecology has a global base of data and understanding and a universal set of principles that are relevant anywhere on Earth. A goal of any introductory textbook in ecology is to facilitate an understanding of that core of its knowledge. However, ecology also involves the study of wild species and their higher-level aggregations, such as populations, communities, and landscapes. In that sense, ecology has a profound spatial context that extends from relatively local situations to much larger regional scales, and ultimately, to the entire biosphere.

Within that context, however, the boundaries of countries are not ecoregional in their layout, meaning they were not designed according to natural ecological precincts. Nevertheless, national borders do specify particular expanses of land and sea. That spatial fact provides an important context for the ways that ecology is taught and learned in any country.

In this sense, Canada supports particular arrangements and dynamics of ecosystems and species, which are affected by the human economy in specific ways. The natural ecosystems of our country range from temperate Carolinian forest in extreme southern Ontario, to true desert in the southern Okanagan Valley of British Columbia, to High-Arctic tundra on the islands of Nunavut. On the Pacific coast there are humid temperate rainforests, while in the centre of Canada there are expansive montane and boreal forests and prairie grasslands, and on the Atlantic coast a mixture of temperate and boreal forests. The marine realms range from frigid and ice-covered waters north of Ellesmere Island to boreal and temperate ecosystems in more southerly reaches of the marine estate of Canada. The ecological communities that occur in these far-flung ecoregions of Canada, and the species they sustain, comprise the essence of the biodiversity of our country.

The peoples of Canada have always esteemed the natural values of their lands. First Nations and Inuit venerated animals and plants that were exploited as food, medicine, and materials, as well as the habitats that they all shared. An attitude of respect and awe of the natural world was also held by many early European and other immigrants to Canada, although those feelings may have been tempered by trepidation because of their often precarious circumstances of living in or at the edge of wilderness. Today Canada supports an astonishing cosmopolitan and multicultural society, but we still appreciate the natural world, as witnessed by its prominence in our art, coinage, literature, stamps, video, and other cultural expressions. Many of our students are newcomers to this country, and great numbers have been raised exclusively in urban environments. It is vitally important that they mature with a solid understanding of the ecological life support system, whether of the vast tundra and forest of the North or the more familiar parks and backyards of Canada's cities.

Notwithstanding the apparent high regard with which the peoples of Canada have always viewed the natural world, many of our native species and natural ecosystems are at great risk of disappearing. This damage has been caused by extensive conversions of natural habitats into human-dominated land uses, and by degradation caused by alien species and diseases, excessive resource harvesting, pollution, and other anthropogenic stressors. These are exceedingly important environmental damages, and also socioeconomic ones because they pose a grave threat to the longer-term sustainability of the Canadian economy. In large part those damages are ecological in character, as are their mitigations.

A Canadian Approach

Clearly, there is a Canadian context to learning about ecology. This obvious deduction is the reason that we have chosen to develop this textbook—*Ecology: A Canadian Context*, Second Edition—which you are now beginning to read. It is our belief that this new book will be helpful to Canadian students as they seek to learn about ecology, but in the context of our country. We also believe that this textbook will assist instructors of ecology in colleges and universities in Canada, in ways that books developed in other countries cannot do as well. We sincerely hope that you will appreciate, and benefit from, our efforts to achieve these goals.

It is important to recognize that this textbook has emerged from a process that is different from the more common procedure of "Canadianizing" versions of textbooks that were originally developed for use by students and instructors in a different country, usually the United States. Instead of taking the relatively easy path of modifying an existing textbook by inserting some Canadian content, we have created a totally new one, from the ground up. This book was specifically designed and written for Canadian students and their instructors in Canada, by Canadians well experienced in the ecology of our country.

In essence, the approach we took was to identify the core subject areas of ecology, which are relevant in all countries, and develop clear explanations of the basic principles. Wherever it was suitable, however, we illustrated those basics using data and case material relevant to Canada, and usually derived from studies by Canadian ecologists. This is not to say that our book does not also contain abundant international material, because it certainly does. The key point is that the essential approach of our treatment of introductory ecology is a balanced integration of global and Canadian contexts.

Ecology, Evolution, and Sustainability

This textbook is about the fundamentals of ecology within a Canadian context. However, evolution and sustainability also provide essential perspectives for the study of ecology, and we have endeavoured to integrate these themes into the book wherever they are relevant. The vitally important subjects of evolution and evolutionary relationships are examined across the curriculum, whenever they are helpful in understanding concepts and case material.

We have also used this approach to explore the vital intersection of ecology and sustainability and to integrate those links whenever subjects such as resource depletion, pollution, and the conservation of biodiversity are examined. In addition, there are two chapters that explore these imperative themes more comprehensively—one about resource ecology, and the other about the conservation of the natural world.

New to the Second Edition

We have worked hard to improve this second edition of the textbook. We engaged in a wide solicitation of instructors from universities and colleges across Canada to gather suggestions for improvements, and then diligently followed up with many constructive improvements in all chapters of the book. These improvements include:

- **Tone, Language, and Consistency:** We completed a comprehensive editorial review to improve the consistency of language and tone and diminish redundancy across the chapters.

- **Enhanced Instructional Imagery:** We have greatly enhanced the visual appeal of the book, with over **200 new and improved photos and illustrations** that illustrate key concepts.

- **Currency:** We have thoroughly updated the treatment of all time-sensitive information and issues across all of the chapters.

- **Plant Ecology:** In addition to enhancing our coverage of plant ecology throughout the book, we have introduced a greatly expanded chapter on physiological ecology that includes a major new section on plants, creating a more balanced treatment of that subject area.

- **Urban Ecology:** We have expanded the coverage of urban ecology throughout the book, including

increased coverage in Chapter 13, Landscape Ecology, and a new Environmental Applications Box 14.1—Feral Cats: Natural Born Killers.

- **Freshwater Ecology:** We have enhanced the coverage of freshwater ecosystems throughout the book, including new examples in Chapter 4, Nutrients and Their Cycling, and Chapter 9, Community Ecology.

- **New Boxes:** We have added an impressive number of new boxes that explain key concepts in greater detail, provide illustrative case material of the application of ecological knowledge, or feature the contributions of Canadian ecologists so that our students can understand our large national influence on the global endeavour of ecology. Among these new boxes is Ecology in Depth 16.1—The Paleoecology of Dinosaurs, contributed by Phil Currie, celebrated paleontologist at the University of Alberta.

- **Chapter Summaries:** We have also now included end-of-chapter summaries, which list the key learning outcomes that students are expected to have mastered.

We sincerely hope that you will appreciate our hard work in improving this textbook—in particular, because we had your needs foremost in our minds.

Organization

The field of ecology is wide and interdisciplinary, so much so that it cannot all be covered in an introductory-level class or in a textbook of a sensible length. When this book and its second edition were being planned, we consulted widely with colleagues and anonymous reviewers, who advised us that they wanted to see a textbook of modest length (and price) that covered the key themes of ecology, but not necessarily the entirety of its subject matter. To achieve that goal, we divided the field into 17 chapters, which are interconnected where relevant, but are still organized in ways that make them suitable for teaching and learning as independent units.

We have organized *Ecology: A Canadian Context*, Second Edition, into the following 17 chapters:

Chapter 1: Introduction to Ecology
BILL FREEDMAN

This chapter establishes the foundations of ecology, and examines its methodology within the context of the principles and practices of scientific investigation. One section examines evolution as an overarching theme of ecology, and another explains how ecological considerations are vital to framing the sustainability of the human economy.

Chapter 2: Environmental Influences
BILL FREEDMAN

Here we examine the environmental factors that influence species and ecosystems. While noting that ecosystems are always subjected to pervasive change, we examine considerations that might result in change being viewed as ecological or economic damage.

Chapter 3: Ecological Energetics

BILL FREEDMAN

This chapter explains the forms in which energy may exist and the laws of thermodynamics that govern their transformations. The energy budget of Earth is described, including the vital greenhouse effect that helps to maintain the planet within a temperature range appropriate for life and ecosystems. We then examine ecological energetics, beginning with the fixation of solar energy by primary producers, moving through the passage of fixed energy along food webs, and ending with the decomposition process that oxidizes dead organic matter to return degraded energy and simple inorganic molecules to the environment.

Chapter 4: Nutrients and Their Cycling

BILL FREEDMAN

Nutrients are explained as substances needed for the healthy physiology and growth of organisms. The cycling of carbon, nitrogen, phosphorus, and sulphur, and the bases calcium, magnesium, potassium, and sodium are examined. We also investigate soil as an ecosystem, including influences on the formation of dominant kinds of soils.

Chapter 5: Population Ecology

JEFFREY A. HUTCHINGS

This chapter describes the ways that populations may vary over time, including exponential and logistical changes and their explanatory models. The influences of age structure, competition, and trophic interactions on population change are explored, including their evolutionary contexts.

Chapter 6: Behavioural Ecology

DARRYL T. GWYNNE

Here, we examine interactions among behaviour, ecological relationships, and adaptive evolutionary change. The principal topics are foraging, defence against predators, sexual selection, and the evolution of social behaviour.

Chapter 7: Physiological Ecology

RICHARD L. WALKER

DAWN BAZELY

This field is examined through the adaptive physiological traits of animals and plants in relation to their environmental conditions. Particular attention is paid to thermobiology, water and ionic balances, gas exchange and transport, acid–base balances, and influences of environmental stressors.

Chapter 8: Life Histories

JEFFREY A. HUTCHINGS

This chapter distills the diverse life histories of species into sets of responses that are results of the dynamic interplay of biological variation and natural selection. The principal subject areas examined are the costs of reproduction, life histories and fitness, trade-offs between the numbers of offspring and their sizes, alternative life histories, and influences of anthropogenic harvesting.

Chapter 9: Community Ecology

ROY TURKINGTON

Ecological communities are examined as groups of species that live together and interact, directly or indirectly, through competition for scarce resources, herbivory, predation, disease, and facilitation. Environmental and biological influences on the structure and dynamics of communities are examined, including adaptive responses.

Chapter 10: Disturbance and Succession

BILL FREEDMAN

The causes and consequences of disturbances are explained, including those resulting from natural and anthropogenic influences. This is followed by consideration of the mechanisms and patterns of successional recovery, including case studies of both primary and secondary succession.

Chapter 11: Biomes and Ecozones

BILL FREEDMAN

The major terrestrial and marine biomes of the world are described, in both the terrestrial and marine realms, as are key habitats such as types of wetlands and anthropogenic ecosystems. The terrestrial and marine ecozones of both Canada and the rest of North America are examined.

Chapter 12: Biodiversity

BILL FREEDMAN

The hierarchical levels of biodiversity are explained, beginning with genetic variation, then species richness, and extending to community-scale patches on landscapes and seascapes. The ways of measuring biodiversity at these scales are also examined. Biodiversity's importance is explained, including its intrinsic value and the vital goods and services that are provided to humans and our economy.

Chapter 13: Landscape Ecology

ROGER SUFFLING

This chapter describes spatial approaches to the structure and dynamics of landscapes, including both natural and anthropogenic effects. The major ways of measuring the attributes of landscapes are explored, including the use of geographical information systems.

Chapter 14: Conservation of the Natural World

BILL FREEDMAN

The modern extinction crisis is examined and put into the context of previous mass extinctions caused by natural forces. The basic tenets of conservation biology are explained, including the design and stewardship of protected areas. Canada's biodiversity at risk is described, as are the conservation roles and responsibilities of governments and other organizations. The chapter ends with success stories involving cases of endangered species that have been rescued from the brink of extinction.

Chapter 15: Resource Ecology
BILL FREEDMAN

Ecological economics are explained as a foundation for understanding the concept of economic sustainability and its fundamental reliance on renewable resources rather than nonrenewable ones. Systems of harvesting and managing bioresources are explained, and international and Canadian case material is presented to illustrate the phenomenon of overharvesting. Improved management systems that would allow sustainable use are described, including integrated ones that accommodate both the economic values of resources as well as ecological considerations such as biodiversity and environmental services.

Chapter 16: Paleoecology: Lessons from the Past
JOHN P. SMOL

Longer-term ecological changes are described, as are the paleoecological methods that have allowed their causes and consequences to be examined. The importance of paleoecological studies to understanding environmental issues is also discussed.

Chapter 17: Ecology and Society
BILL FREEDMAN

This final chapter examines the concept of ecological integrity and the processes of ecological monitoring and research and environmental impact assessment. Ecological sustainability is also explained, as is the importance of the knowledge and wisdom of ecology, and the work of ecologists in guiding progress to that goal.

Features of the Text
In-Chapter Features and Learning Aids

The defining attributes of this textbook are the ways that it presents the fundamentals of ecology within a Canadian context, while integrating the concepts of evolution and sustainability wherever they are relevant. The book contains several features that help to further these goals:

- **Boxed Features.** All chapters have stand-alone boxed elements that present detailed examinations of selected important concepts or helpful case material. The three types of boxes are (1) **Ecology in Depth**, which is intended to provide a detailed investigation of important concepts; (2) **Environmental Applications**, an in-depth look at real-world applications of content discussed in the chapter; and (3) **A Canadian Ecologist**, which highlights prominent studies done by ecologists who have worked in Canada.

- **Tables, Figures, and Photos.** We have gone to great lengths to present easily digestible and abundant information in tables and figures, as well as plentiful and attractive photos that illustrate concepts, habitats, and species that are well communicated in a visual medium.

- **Key Terms.** Whenever we mention a word or phrase that is a core part of the lexicon of ecology, it is highlighted and defined. All of these terms are aggregated into a comprehensive **glossary** at the end of the book.

End-of-Chapter Learning and Review

Each chapter ends with a number of features that help to cultivate learning of the subject matter. These are:

- **Chapter Summary.** This is a bulleted list that summarizes the key concepts and learning outcomes that students are expected to master in each chapter. Each point is tied to one of the learning objectives outlined at the beginning of the chapter.

- **Questions for Review and Discussion.** A number of questions are presented for students to answer. These are intended to assist in review of the subject matter, while aiding comprehension and facilitating in-class discussion of certain topics. The *Instructor's Manual* for the book provides suggested answers for all of these questions.

End-of-Book Features

The following resources are found at the end of the book:

- **References.** All references cited in the chapter are listed in a comprehensive bibliography at the back of the book.

- **Glossary.** Definitions for all key terms are provided in this essential resource. Page references are included to help students review these key terms in the context of the original discussion.

- **Indexes.** Three types of index are included for readers' ease of reference. They consist of Name (of persons mentioned in the book), Species, and Subject indexes.

Instructor Ancillaries
About the Nelson Education Teaching Advantage (NETA)

 The **Nelson Education Teaching Advantage (NETA)** program delivers research-based instructor resources that promote student engagement and higher-order thinking to enable the success of Canadian students and educators. To ensure the high quality of these materials, all Nelson ancillaries have been professionally copyedited.

Be sure to visit Nelson Education's **Inspired Instruction** website at http://www.nelson.com/inspired to find out more about NETA. Don't miss the testimonials of instructors who have used NETA supplements and seen student engagement increase!

- **Planning Your Course.** *NETA Engagement* presents materials that help instructors deliver engaging content and activities to their classes. **NETA Instructor's Manuals** not only identify the topics that cause students the most difficulty, but also describe techniques and resources to help students master these concepts. Dr. Roger Fisher's *Instructor's Guide to Classroom Engagement* accompanies every Instructor's Manual.

- **Assessing Your Students.** *NETA Assessment* relates to testing materials. **NETA Test Bank** authors create multiple-choice questions that reflect research-based best practices for constructing effective questions and testing not only recall but also higher-order thinking. Our guidelines were developed by David DiBattista, psychology professor at Brock University and 3M National Teaching Fellow, whose research has focused on multiple-choice testing. All Test Bank authors receive training at workshops conducted by Prof. DiBattista, as do the copyeditors assigned to each Test Bank. A copy of *Multiple Choice Tests: Getting Beyond Remembering*, Prof. DiBattista's guide to writing effective tests, is included with every Nelson Test Bank.

- **Teaching Your Students.** *NETA Presentation* has been developed to help instructors make the best use of Microsoft® PowerPoint® in their classrooms. With a clean and uncluttered design developed by Maureen Stone of StoneSoup Consulting, **NETA PowerPoints** features slides with improved readability, more multi-media and graphic materials, activities to use in class, and tips for instructors on the Notes page. A copy of *NETA Guidelines for Classroom Presentations* by Maureen Stone is included with each set of PowerPoint slides.

- **Technology in Teaching.** *NETA Digital* is a framework based on Arthur Chickering and Zelda Gamson's seminal work "Seven Principles of Good Practice In Undergraduate Education" (*AAHE Bulletin*, 1987) and the follow-up work by Chickering and Stephen C. Ehrmann, "Implementing the Seven Principles: Technology as Lever"(*AAHE Bulletin*, 1996). This aspect of the NETA program guides the writing and development of our **digital products** to ensure that they appropriately reflect the core goals of contact, collaboration, multimodal learning, time on task, prompt feedback, active learning, and high expectations. The resulting focus on pedagogical utility, rather than technological wizardry, ensures that all of our technology supports better outcomes for students.

Instructor Resources

All NETA and other key instructor ancillaries are provided on the Instructor Companion Site at **http://www.nelson.com/ecology2e**, giving instructors the ultimate tool for customizing lectures and presentations.

- **NETA Test Bank.** This resource includes multiple-choice questions written according to NETA guidelines for effective construction and development of higher-order questions. The Test Bank was copyedited by a NETA-trained editor. Also included are true-and-false questions.

- The NETA Test Bank is available in a new, cloud-based platform. **Testing Powered by Cognero®**[*] is a secure online testing system that allows you to author, edit, and manage test bank content from any place you have Internet access. No special installations or downloads are needed, and the desktop-inspired interface, with its drop-down menus and familiar, intuitive tools, allows you to create and manage tests with ease. You can create multiple test versions in an instant, and import or export content into other systems. Tests can be delivered from your learning management system, your classroom, or wherever you want.

- **NETA PowerPoint.** Microsoft® PowerPoint® lecture slides have been created for every chapter. Features include key figures, tables, and photographs from *Ecology: A Canadian Context*, Second Edition. NETA principles of clear design and engaging content have been incorporated throughout, making it simple for instructors to customize the deck for their courses.

- **Image Library.** This resource consists of digital copies of figures, short tables, and photographs used in the book. Instructors may use these jpegs to customize the NETA PowerPoint or create their own PowerPoint presentations.

- **NETA Instructor's Manual.** This resource is organized according to the textbook chapters and addresses key educational concerns, such as typical stumbling blocks student face and how to address them.

- **DayOne.** Day One—Prof InClass is a PowerPoint presentation that instructors can customize to orient students to the class and their text at the beginning of the course.

---

[*]Cognero and Full-Circle Assessment are registered trademarks of Madeira Station LLC.

- **TurningPoint®**: Another valuable resource for instructors is **TurningPoint® classroom response software** customized for *Ecology: A Canadian Context*, Second Edition. Now you can author, deliver, show, access, and grade, all in PowerPoint, with no toggling back and forth between screens. With JoinIn you are no longer tied to your computer. You can walk about your classroom as you lecture, showing slides and collecting and displaying responses with ease. If you can use PowerPoint, you can use JoinIn on TurningPoint. (Contact your Nelson publishing representative for details.)

- **CengageNOW™** connects students to assignable content matched to their text. CengageNOW is an interactive learning solution that helps students focus on what they need to learn. It improves academic performance by increasing students' time on task and giving them prompt feedback. With a focus on active learning, concept mastery, and automatic grading, CengageNOW is an easy-to-use digital resource designed to get students involved in their learning progress and be better prepared for class participation and assessment. CengageNOW for *Ecology: A Canadian Context*, Second Edition, can be used for self-study or assigned as homework.

  This online tutorial and diagnostic tool identifies each student's unique needs with a pretest that generates a Personalized Study Plan for each chapter. The CengageNOW study plan helps students focus on concepts they're having the most difficulty mastering. It refers to the accompanying e-book and provides a variety of learning activities designed to appeal to diverse ways of learning. After completing the study plan, students take a post-test to measure their understanding of the material. Instructors can track and monitor student progress by using the instructor Gradebook.

Ancillaries for Students

CengageNOW™ includes access to interactive learning resources that will help you get the most out of your course. Interactive learning resources include tutorials, videos, animations, games, other multimedia tools, and in most cases an integrated e-book.

Using CengageNOW, you can:

- evaluate your knowledge of the material covered in your textbook;

- prepare for exams with a prep quiz;

- generate a Personalized Learning Plan to identify the areas you should study and target resources for your review; and

- gain access to rich, interactive learning modules tied to each chapter of your textbook.

Visit NELSONbrain.com to start using CengageNOW. Enter the access code included with your text or buy instant access at NELSONbrain.com.

Take your ecology experience to the next level with our **Cengage Learning e-book**! The CL e-book gives students access to an integrated, interactive learning environment with advanced learning tools and a user interface that lets students control their learning experience. An innovative offering will be online growth models that allow students to interact with content to show computer-simulated cause-and-effect models of ecological systems using varying parameters.

Acknowledgments

A number of our colleagues and friends generously provided their time and effort to review drafts of the material in various chapters. These ecologists and other scientists pointed out informative case material of which we were unaware, corrected inadvertent errors in our work, improved our writing and presentation, or helped us in other important ways.

In addition, the publisher commissioned a number of reviews from instructors of ecology classes at several universities and colleges in Canada. These people also provided invaluable commentary on the structure of the textbook, on the book proposal plan, and on draft chapters.

For the second edition:

Yuguang Bai, University of Saskatchewan

Kerri Finlay, University of Regina

Hugh Henry, Western University

Christopher J. Lortie, York University

Heike Lotze, Dalhousie University

Cynthia Paszkowski, University of Alberta

Danijela Puric-Mladenovic, University of Toronto

Curt Stager, Paul Smith's College

William Tonn, University of Alberta

Jana Vamosi, University of Calgary

We also gratefully acknowledge the assistance of the following people for their assistance with the first edition of this book:

Maydianne Andrade, University of Toronto

James Basinger, University of Saskatchewan

Dawn Bazely, York University

Christine Beauchamp, Dalhousie University

Stephen Beauchamp, Environment Canada

Paul Bentzen, Dalhousie University

Hugh Broders, Saint Mary's University

Paul Catling, Biosystematics Research Institute, Agriculture Canada

Brian Cumming, Queen's University

Terry Curran of Dryden, Ontario

Les Cwynar, University of New Brunswick

Eva Dodsworth, University of Waterloo

Nancy Flood, Thompson Rivers University

Gail Fraser, York University

Angelo Gioviazzo of Guelph

Richard Harington, Canadian Museum of Nature

Greg Henry, University of British Columbia

Tom Hutchinson, Trent University

Leland J. Jackson, University of Calgary

Dan Krause, Nature Conservancy of Canada

John Lewis, University of Waterloo

Ian McLaren, Dalhousie University

Dennis Lehmkuhl, University of Saskatchewan

John Markham, University of Manitoba

Matt Meston, University of Waterloo

Curt Meine, Aldo Leopold Foundation

Neal Michelutti, Queen's University

Ron O'Dor, Dalhousie University

Michael Paterson, Department of Fisheries and Oceans

David Patriquin, Dalhousie University

Michael Pisaric, Carleton University

Trevor Pitcher, University of Windsor

Helen Rodd, University of Toronto

Alexandra Rouillard, Queen's University

Kathleen Rühland, Queen's University

Daniel Ruzzante, Dalhousie University

James Savelle, McGill University

Janet Silbernagel, University of Wisconsin, Madison

Graham Stinson, Natural Resources Canada

Josef Svoboda, Erindale Campus, University of Toronto

John Theberge, University of Waterloo, and Wolf
    Ecosystem Research

Mary Theberge, Wolf Ecosystem Research

William Tonn, University of Alberta

Nigel Waltho, Carleton University

Scott Wilson, University of Regina

Stephen Woodley, Parks Canada

Boris Worm, Dalhousie University

Steve Xu, University of Waterloo

Roger Suffling would like to thank class members of ENVS469, 2008 and 2009, University of Waterloo, Ontario.

Dawn Bazely would like to thank Prof. Roger Lew, Biology, York University, who currently teaches BIOL 2010 Plants, for letting me use all of your plant physiology books and, together with Bill Freedman and Toni Chahley, for endless conversations about how best to integrate plant ecophysiology into an existing chapter on animals. And, most of all, I thank the three of you for your patience with me as I went through the process of joining an existing team: we all have more grey hair to show for it.

Thanks are also due to the many people who worked on the production of Ecology: A Canadian Context, Second Edition, including Karen Rolfe, copyeditor; Barbara Booth for her substantive edit of the text; Kristiina Paul, permissions, photograph, and art researcher; Dianna Little, designer; Indhumathy Gunasekaran, Project Manager at Integra; and staff at Nelson Education, including Paul Fam, Publisher; Toni Chahley, Developmental Editor; Imoinda Romain, Senior Production Project Manager; Deanna Anderson, Manufacturing Manager; Franca Amore, Managing Designer; Suzanne Peden, Asset Coordinator, for her art direction; and Leanne Newell, Senior Marketing Manager. Bill Freedman also acted as lead editor, having the responsibility of editing all chapters and working toward a common style and language.

Finally, a word about the chapter-opening photographs. Bill Caulfeild-Browne has been taking pictures for 50 years. From his base in Tobermory, Ontario, Bill travels across Canada and the world to explore and capture the beauty of nature. His photographs have been featured in one-man exhibitions in Mississauga and Toronto and in books, calendars, websites, fine art prints, and the Toronto Star. We are pleased to present Bill's work at the start of each chapter of Ecology: A Canadian Context, Second Edition and invite you to view his galleries at http://www.billcaulfeild-browne.ca.

We would be most grateful if any readers of this book could send us any suggestions they might have for improvements.

We sincerely hope that this book will be helpful as you learn about ecology.

Bill Freedman, Dalhousie University

Jeffrey A. Hutchings, Dalhousie University

Darryl T. Gwynne, University of Toronto

John P. Smol, Queen's University

Roger Suffling, University of Waterloo

Roy Turkington, University of British Columbia

Richard L. Walker, University of Calgary

Dawn Bazely, York University

YOUR TOUR OF *ECOLOGY*

Each chapter of *Ecology: A Canadian Context,* Second Edition, engages students from beginning to end.

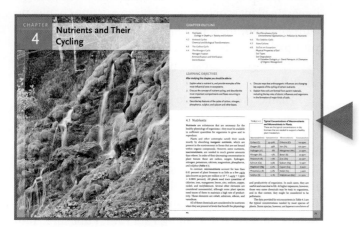

Each chapter begins with a list of **Learning Objectives** for the chapter. Use these objectives to guide your study and test your understanding of important topics. The **Chapter Outline** shows the main topics and boxes—a useful tool for reviewing the chapter.

A **Canadian Ecologist** profiles Canadian ecologists, from historical role models such as John Macoun to the work of Chris Pielou, Diane Srivastava David Schindler, Charles Krebs, and others. Learn about the exciting research being done in Canada!

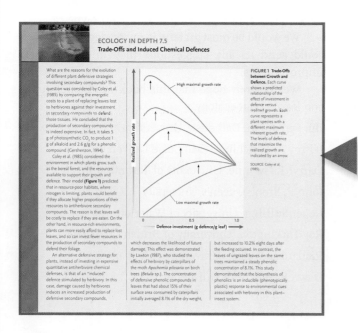

Ecology in Depth boxes examine important concepts in close detail. Explore topics such as genes and individuals in conflict, and conservation of carbon stocks of natural ecosystems.

ENVIRONMENTAL APPLICATIONS 14.1
Feral Cats: Natural Born Killers

The domestic cat (*Felis catus*) makes a wonderful pet, and for this reason millions of them live with people as companion animals. Some of them are "working" pets that help to keep the populations of mice and rats from becoming too abundant, especially on farms. However, many other cats live as feral animals in the wild, where they make their living by killing and eating small mammals and birds **(Figure 1)**. Feral cats are causing some native animals to be much less abundant than formerly, even to the point of being endangered.

This problem is especially acute on isolated islands and other places where cats or other placental predators did not originally occur, such as Australia and New Zealand. Even in Europe and North America, however, free-ranging pet and feral cats are among the most important predators of small native animals. A recent study in the United States estimated that these abundant predators were killing 1.4–3.7 billion birds and 6.9–20.7 billion mammals annually (Loss et al., 2013). Most of the mortality was caused by un-owned feral cats, as opposed to pets that were allowed to spend some time

outdoors. Overall, the cat-related deaths are thought to be the largest anthropogenic cause of mortality of birds and small mammals in North America.

The authors of this study, and those of comparable research elsewhere, strongly recommend that the numbers of feral cats be greatly reduced as a necessary measure to conserve native animals.

However, many people love cats and as a result there is intense opposition to proposed culls of these animals in the wild. This is an example of an ethical dilemma associated with affection for animals—in this case, a love of domestic cats is pitted against a love of native birds and mammals that are being severely affected by these alien natural-born killers.

FIGURE 1 Domestic Cats Are Extremely Effective Predators, and They Are Responsible for Killing Large Numbers of Native Birds and Other Small Animals.

SOURCE: http://whyfiles.org/2011/the-secret-life-of-cats

What can forestry learn from wildfires? How does eutrophication—pollution by nutrients—happen? How do mountain pine beetles produce antifreeze to survive winters in central BC? You'll find the answers to these and other questions in the **Environmental Applications** boxes throughout the text.

Many concepts in ecology tend to be abstract and theoretical. **Stunning, full-colour visuals** throughout the book will consolidate key points and indicate their relationships so that you better understand these concepts.

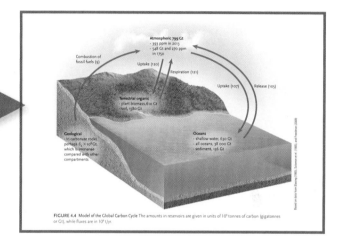

FIGURE 4.4 Model of the Global Carbon Cycle The amounts in reservoirs are given in units of 10⁹ tonnes of carbon (gigatonnes or Gt), while fluxes are in 10⁹ t/yr.

CHAPTER SUMMARY

(LO 13.1)
- Landscape ecology examines spatial elements ecology by using hierarchical scales in space and time.

(LO 13.2)
- European and North American approaches to landscape ecology have developed separately but they are now coming together. Both have been applied in Canadian urban, rural, and wilderness settings.

(LO 13.3)
- Landscape elements describe the type, size, shape, number, and arrangement of distinct communities within a landscape. They may be patches, corridors, or networks that together form spatial mosaics with dominant matrices.

(LO 13.4)
- Landscape metrics are widely applied to quantify measurements of landscape elements, and thus to allow inferential statistics to be applied.

NEL   CHAPTER SUMMARY   **339**

Chapter Summary is an end-of-chapter feature that contains bulleted summary points that are tied to the chapter objectives.

Questions for Review and Discussion help you check your understanding of the key issues and think beyond basic concepts.

Three indexes have been developed to aid your navigation of the text: a Name Index, a Species Index, and a Subject Index.

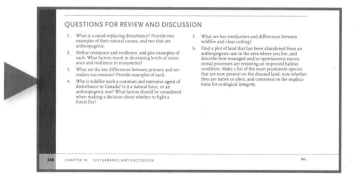

QUESTIONS FOR REVIEW AND DISCUSSION

1. What is a stand-replacing disturbance? Provide two examples of their natural causes, and two that are anthropogenic.
2. Define resistance and resilience, and give examples of each. What factors result in decreasing levels of resistance and resilience in ecosystems?
3. What are the key differences between primary and secondary successions? Provide examples of each.
4. Why is wildfire such a common and extensive agent of disturbance in Canada? Is it a natural force, or an anthropogenic one? What factors should be considered when making a decision about whether to fight a forest fire?
5. What are key similarities and differences between wildfire and clear-cutting?
6. Find a plot of land that has been abandoned from an anthropogenic use in the area where you live, and describe how managed and/or spontaneous successional processes are restoring an improved habitat condition. Make a list of the most prominent species that are now present on the disused land, note whether they are native or alien, and comment on the implications for ecological integrity.

246   CHAPTER 10   DISTURBANCE AND SUCCESSION   NEL

Introduction to Ecology

LEARNING OBJECTIVES

After studying this chapter you should be able to:

1. Define ecology and explain its interdisciplinary nature and where its subject areas fit within the hierarchical organization of the universe.

2. Explain the main subject areas of ecology, including their scales of interest in space, time, and levels of organization of the biosphere.

3. Explain the geological structure and dynamics of planet Earth.

4. Describe the nature and methodologies of scientific investigation, and explain why it is vital to understanding the natural world.

5. Outline the theory of evolution, including the key role of natural selection, and explain why it provides a pervasive context for knowledge in ecology.

6. Understand why the wisdom of ecology is vital to guiding the process of sustainable economic development.

1.1 Foundations of Ecology

Ecology and the Natural World

Some of the most important questions that scientists ask are existential, meaning they examine how the natural world came to exist and be organized. Examples of such questions are:

- What are the connections among the astonishingly diverse components of nature, both living and non-living, and how and why do they change over time?

- What sources of energy drive the processes by which matter is moved about and reorganized into different forms, including the biochemicals that are synthesized by organisms?

- What physical laws govern these processes and relationships?

Clearly, the physical sciences, especially physics and chemistry, are fundamental to answering these questions. This is because all matter and energetics are physical attributes, even when they occur in organisms. Moreover, virtually all the universe is inanimate, meaning it is devoid of life **(Figure 1.1)**. There is, however, one tiny bit of the cosmos (relatively speaking) where life and ecosystems are known to exist—it is the biosphere of Earth. Within that

biosphere, the sciences of biology and ecology are central to understanding the natural world. Knowledge of biology is essential to understanding the genesis of life, its functioning, and its evolution over time. Ecology is specifically relevant to **ecosystems**, which are spaces where groups of organisms are interacting and evolving under the influence of myriad environmental factors, including other organisms.

Because of its context within the realm of the greatest questions of science, the knowledge of ecology has intrinsic worth—it allows us to better understand the organization of the natural world. In fact, most ecologists took up their profession because of their enchantment with fundamental questions about organisms, ecosystems, the universe, and everything.

Ecological knowledge is also important for practical, day-to-day reasons that are related to the inherent need of people to have access to the necessities and amenities of life—for resources such as food, materials, energy, and shelter, and for the aesthetics of pleasure and satisfaction. The knowledge of ecology can be applied to the solution of vital problems related to the supply and quality of resources and the sustainability of their use. Applied ecological knowledge is also crucial to conserving the biodiversity of Earth, which must be done even while our economy harvests necessary resources over extensive areas.

Earth: a pale
blue dot.

NASA

FIGURE 1.1 The "Pale Blue Dot" This is an image of Earth taken in the 1990s by the spacecraft *Voyager 1* from about 5.9 billion km away. This furthest-ever, barely perceptible image of Earth shows our planet against the incredible vastness of space, and it reminds us of the lonely and precarious existence of the only place in the universe that is known to sustain life and ecosystems. Earth is the tiny light-coloured spot at the centre-right, within the vertical light-purple band. The phrase "pale blue dot" was coined by Carl Sagan (1934–1996), an astronomer and author who wrote a book with that title.

Research in applied ecology also involves big questions, particularly those related to the use of natural resources and the damage that human activities are causing to ecosystems and biodiversity—these are vital considerations with respect to the sustainable limits of the human economy. Ecologists and other environmental specialists have useful professional advice to offer with respect to these aspects of sustainable development. That counsel is received by decision makers in government and private-sector businesses, and also by ordinary citizens, who consider it when making choices about their actions that carry a risk of causing environmental damage. We examine these subjects in more detail in Chapters 15 and 17.

It is vitally important that the economy of Canada, and of all countries, operates in ways that are truly sustainable **(Figure 1.2)**. This means that the economy does not degrade its essential resource base, or cause wanton ecological damage, even while it enables large numbers of people to have healthy and productive lives. Sustainable development is among the most important of national and global issues, and its only alternative, which is unacceptable, is nonsustainability. However, by many measures we are currently on that latter pathway, and if it is followed much longer the economy could collapse because of the inexorable effects of insufficient resources and environmental deterioration. That catastrophe would result in misery for a shocking number of people and would be also be terrible for other species and natural ecosystems. Such an awful outcome can yet be avoided, and one of the keys to that happening is for society to consider the advice offered by ecologists and other environmental specialists about prudent use of the natural capital of Earth. At the same time, we must do all that is necessary to conserve the planet's natural heritage of biodiversity. These are huge challenges, but they can and must be met.

FIGURE 1.2 The Knowledge of Ecology Can Be Applied to the Management of Natural Resources Because trees can regenerate after timber is harvested from a forest, their biomass can be viewed as a renewable natural resource. However, the kind of regeneration that occurs, and the environmental effects of forestry operations, are profoundly affected by the kind of forestry being practised. These are important considerations with respect to the sustainability of timber harvesting. In this image, a timber-harvesting machine is being used to clear-cut and de-limb trees at a site near Truro in Nova Scotia.

Bill Freedman

Organisms and Environment

A simple working definition of **ecology** is "the study of the relationships of organisms and their environment." The word was first used (as *oekologie*) in 1869 by Ernst Haeckel (1834–1919), a German biologist and philosopher, to mean "the study of the natural environment including the relations of organisms to one another and to their surroundings" (Odum and Barrett, 2005). The etymology of the word is from the Greek words *oikos* ("house") and *logos* ("the study of").

As a means of systematic investigation of the natural world, the roots of ecology are much older than the word itself, extending to early inquiries by ancient philosophers, such as the Greeks, Hippocrates (*ca.* 460–377 BCE) and Aristotle (384–322 BCE). Today, the kinds of studies that those philosophers undertook would be labelled as **natural history**—the investigation of organisms in their wild habitats, but also extending to an interest in all natural phenomena, including physical ones. Investigations in natural history are relatively simple—usually, few or no quantitative observations (such as measured data) are collected and a rigorous scientific methodology is not used (see Section 1.2). The study of natural history is still popular today—it is undertaken by many people who are fascinated by wild plants, birds, invertebrates, and other marvels of nature, often with a view to collecting unique observations or specimens.

In contrast to natural history, ecology is a scientific branch of learning—it is a systematic and quantitative enterprise. Ecologists work by proposing testable hypotheses that are related to some aspect of the organization or functioning of the natural world. They design and undertake methodical research to investigate those questions, usually by studying patterns that have been observed in nature and by using experimental techniques. Ecologists also apply statistical approaches to analyze the significance of differences they have observed along natural gradients in nature or among experimental treatments; these can involve variations in the abundance of organisms or in the strength and influence of environmental factors. Once ecologists have gained a quantitative understanding of apparent controls of the system they are studying, they may develop conceptual or mathematical models that predict the likely results of manipulations of variables, or the consequences of other kinds of environmental change.

Ecologists may use extremely sophisticated tools in their research, such as high-capacity computing systems, advanced instrumentation for chemical and genetic analysis, remote-sensing technology, and tracking devices suitable for animals as large as whales or as small as songbirds. However, this is not always the case—much ecological research uses less-sophisticated measurements of the natural world, such as estimates of the abundance of trees or birds in a woodlot, or measurements of temperature using a thermometer. Even simple methodologies can be useful in ecological research, so long as they yield data that are reasonably accurate and repeatable, and are gained in the context of a properly designed investigation.

Fundamentals

A higher goal of ecology is to understand how variations in the distribution and abundance of species are affected by **environmental factors** (or **influences**; **Figure 1.3**).

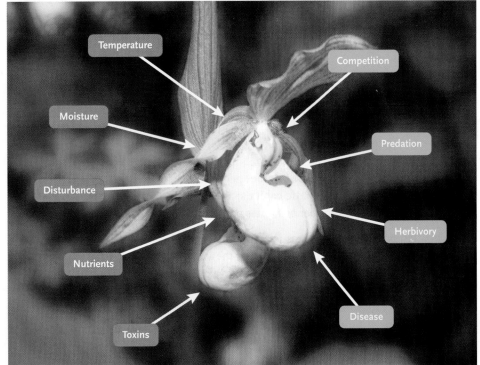

FIGURE 1.3 Organisms and Environment Ecology is the study of the relationships of organisms and their environment. Environmental influences can be biotic (green) or abiotic (orange), and the relationships are reciprocal, meaning that organisms also exert an influence on environmental factors. The organism depicted is a yellow lady's slipper orchid (*Cypripedium pubescens*), which occurs in moist calcium-rich habitats in many regions of Canada and elsewhere in the Northern Hemisphere.

Temperature

Competition

Moisture

Predation

Disturbance

Herbivory

Nutrients

Disease

Toxins

Bill Freedman

The factors may be **inorganic** (**abiotic** or **nonliving**), such as moisture, nutrients, temperature, wildfire, and wind, or they may be **organic** (**biotic**) and associated with the influences of other organisms. The biotic influences include interactions such as:

- **competition**, in which organisms interfere with one another as they vie for access to resources whose supply is less than the biological demand; this interaction may occur among individuals of the same species (*intraspecific competition*) or between species (*interspecific*);
- **herbivory**, which involves animals feeding on the tissues of plants;
- **predation**, in which one species of animal kills and eats another kind; and
- **parasitism** and **disease**, which are also feeding relationships but do not necessarily result in the host being killed.

The word **ecosystem** (**ecological system**) is often used in the context of ecological research and writing. It is, however, a generalized term that cannot be precisely defined; rather, an ecosystem is a space in which organisms interact with one another and with environmental factors, and it is delimited for the purposes of studying it. In this sense, a tiny ecosystem might be identified as existing within a container formed by a pitcher plant (such as *Sarracenia purpurea*, the provincial flower of Newfoundland and Labrador), which includes retained rainwater, algae, and a few specialized invertebrates **(Figure 1.4)**. The largest ecosystem we know of is the biosphere, which is bounded by the presence of all organisms on Earth and includes the environmental factors with which they interact, such as sunlight.

Ecosystems are said to have **structural attributes**, which are typically reported in units of quantity per unit of habitat, such as the following:

- biomass: this is the weight of organic matter, often stated in kilograms per square metre (kg/m²) or tonnes per hectare (t/ha), usually on a dry-weight basis to avoid the vagaries of water content, which may change depending on hydration;
- density: the abundance of individuals per unit of habitat, often expressed as the number per m² or per ha on land or per m³ in aquatic habitats; and
- species richness: the number of species per unit area.

When studying a large area, as is often done, ecologists use subsampling procedures to estimate the average values of structural measures. However, they also pay close attention to estimates of the spatial variation of the attributes being measured, which is itself an important structural feature.

The **functional attributes** of ecosystems are rates of change of the structural ones, and they are typically

Bill Freedman

FIGURE 1.4 An Ecosystem An ecosystem is a space in which organisms interact with one another and with environmental factors, and it is delimited for the purposes of studying it. Even the space within the cup-shaped leaf of this pitcher plant (*Sarracenia purpurea*) can be studied as an aquatic ecosystem that contains algae and invertebrates and sustains productivity, decomposition, and nutrient cycling, while being connected to the rest of the biosphere and also beyond through the absorption of solar energy.

measured as change of the amount per unit area and time, such as the following:

- productivity, or the rate of increase of biomass, often measured as g/m²·year or t/ha·yr;
- nutrient fluxes, or the rate of movement of vital chemicals, such as the fixation of atmospheric nitrogen in kg/ha·yr; and
- water flow, for example in a stream, as m³/ha·yr.

Ecologists are often interested in knowing about past changes in the structural and functional attributes of ecosystems—these provide a historical context for the present circumstances, as well as for likely future values. Sometimes the change is rapid, as occurs when a forest is disturbed by a wildfire or a clear-cut. **Disturbances** like these are followed by a period of ecological recovery, known as **succession**, which has its own longer-term dynamics. These subjects are examined later in this section and again in more detail in Chapters 9 and 10.

Ecology within the Hierarchy of Organization

The natural world comprises the universe and all things in it. Within that inestimable space, the amazing complexity of nature may be more easily understood if we first consider it in a hierarchical manner **(Figure 1.5)**.

The universe is the biggest entity within this layered system. It includes billions of stars (one estimate is 10^{21} or 1000 billion billion) and probably an even larger number of planets. These are incomprehensibly large numbers, but the universe is an enormous place.

Earth is one particular celestial body. It orbits the Sun, a medium-sized star, as do seven additional planets along with various comets, asteroids, and other objects that together compose a seemingly ordinary solar system. Earth is the third-closest planet to the Sun, orbiting it every 365 days at an average distance of 149 million km, and rotating on its own axis every 24 hours. Earth is a spherical body, with a solid diameter of 12 700 km. About 70 percent of its surface is covered by liquid water and the rest by terrestrial rocks, sand, ice, and vegetation. With so much of the planetary surface covered with water, we might wonder why Earth was not in fact named "Water" or "Ocean" **(Figure 1.6)**.

Like all celestial bodies, Earth has unique characteristics. But what makes the planet particularly exceptional is the fact that its environments have supported a spontaneous genesis and subsequent evolution of organisms. Life first appeared about 3.6 billion years ago, within only one billion years of the formation of the planet during the nativity of the solar system. We do not know how life first sparked from inanimate matter, although it is believed that natural genesis somehow occurred spontaneously, as a consequence of appropriate conditions of chemistry, temperature, solar radiation, pressure, and other critical factors.

The complexity of the universe is expressed at scales that range from the unimaginably vast, such as galaxies and the universe itself, to the infinitesimally minute, such as subatomic entities. The realm of life occupies intermediate levels of the hierarchy, ranging from biochemicals to the biosphere, but it is important to understand that these are connected to all of the other levels. The realm of ecology encompasses the following levels:

- **individual organisms**: living entities that are genetically and physically discrete;
- **populations**: individuals of the same species that co-occur in space and time;
- **species**: individuals (and populations) that are capable of interbreeding and producing fertile offspring;

FIGURE 1.5 Hierarchical Organization of the Universe To study its extraordinary complexity, we can organize the universe in an ordered manner, which in this diagram proceeds from smaller at the top to larger at the bottom. Note, however, that all of the elements are intrinsically connected. The realm of ecology is shown in the green font.

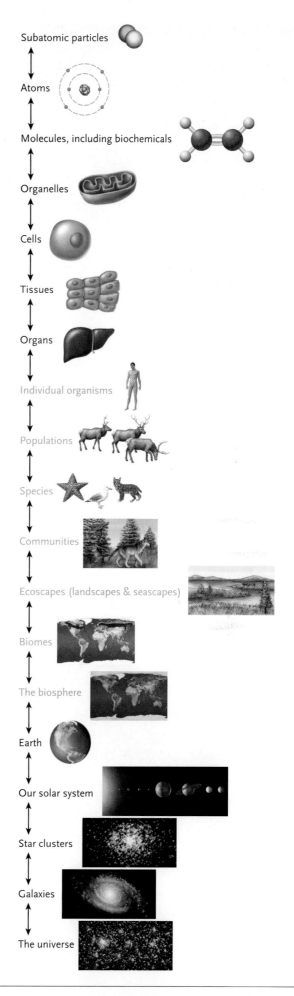

Subatomic particles

Atoms

Molecules, including biochemicals

Organelles

Cells

Tissues

Organs

Individual organisms

Populations

Species

Communities

Ecoscapes (landscapes & seascapes)

Biomes

The biosphere

Earth

Our solar system

Star clusters

Galaxies

The universe

FIGURE 1.6 **Planet Earth** With so much of the planetary surface covered with water, we might wonder why Earth was not in fact named "Water" or "Ocean." This image was taken by a satellite on 25 August 1992, as Hurricane Andrew was making landfall on the coast of Louisiana (it is the spiral-shaped cloud system approaching the southern United States).

- **communities**: populations of various species that occur together in the same space and time **(Figure 1.7)**;
- **ecoscapes**: mosaics of various kinds of community-level patches over large areas, which are known as **landscapes** in terrestrial environments and as **seascapes** in marine ones; and
- the **biosphere**: all space occupied by life on Earth.

FIGURE 1.7 **An Ecological Community** A community is made up of populations of various species that are present at the same place and time and that are interacting with each other to varying degrees. This intertidal community dominated by marine invertebrates was photographed at Pacific Rim National Park, on western Vancouver Island, British Columbia.

Individual organisms connect with lower levels of the hierarchy through their biochemistry and the physiology of their cells and organs. The biosphere connects with higher levels, and most especially with the Sun, through the continuous input of solar radiation that sustains almost all ecological productivity and that influences other environmental factors such as weather and climate.

Connections and Constraints

Much of the subject matter of ecology is about understanding connections—of interactions of organisms with other organisms and also with nonliving environmental factors. The connections among organisms are diverse and web-like and involve contacts related to feeding, competition, and other behaviours. Interactions with abiotic factors are also complex, with diverse influences operating at the same time, although at different intensities. Connections are so important in ecology that environmental philosopher Barry Commoner (1971) formulated a "law" based on the observation that "everything is connected to everything else."

Ecologists view the multifarious connections among the components of ecosystems in a holistic manner. This so-called **ecosystem approach** does not regard an ecological system as being a haphazard grouping of individuals, populations, communities, and environments—rather, these are considered to all be connected and interdependent, although in varying degrees. This is a necessary approach, because life and ecosystems have **emergent properties** that cannot be predicted from knowledge only of their parts, and which exist only in systems that are operating as an integrated whole.

A computer is a physical system with emergent properties. However, you could not predict its remarkable operating capabilities based only on knowledge of its chemical composition, or even from an inventory of its parts. A computer works properly only if its components are manufactured and assembled correctly, the software is loaded, and it is operated by someone who understands how to use it.

An ecosystem also has emergent properties. For example, a forest consists of an assemblage of abiotic elements (rocks, water, gases) and diverse organic ones (species of trees and other plants, animals, microorganisms, and dead organic matter). From knowledge of only those components, it would be impossible to predict the productivity, nutrient cycling, and feeding relationships that occur within the forest.

Another ecological principle is that organisms are sustained by resources—the "goods and services" that are provided by ecosystems. All species have particular necessities, which they acquire from the specific habitats that they use. Plant species, for example, must have an adequate supply of sunlight, water, nutrients such as carbon and nitrogen, and space. Other aspects of their environment must also be suitable, including the kinds of disturbances that occur, as well as biotic influences such as competition and herbivory. Likewise, animals must have sufficient access to appropriate food and habitat.

However, vital resources are not always sufficient to meet the biological demand. Suboptimal access to those needs results in physiological stress that constrains the growth, development, and reproduction of individual organisms, and therefore of their populations, communities, and larger ecosystems. For example, a plant may experience an inadequate nutrient supply because it is growing in infertile soil, or light may be insufficient because of competition with nearby plants. An outcome of this environmental stress could be that the plant develops few or even no seeds during its lifetime. The lack of offspring (seeds) is an important result because evolutionary success is related to an organism leaving progeny that carry its genetic lineage into future generations of its kind (see Section 1.3 for a more detailed explanation of fitness). Likewise, the productivity and development of animals (including humans) may be limited by their environmental circumstances. An individual that must deal with stresses caused by a shortage of food or difficult relations with competitors, predators, or diseases may have little success in life.

The greatest level of ecosystem development occurs in regions in which environmental conditions are not excessively stressful to organisms. For example, in terrestrial environments, old-growth tropical forest represents the maximal degree of ecosystem development because it sustains enormous biodiversity and other forms of complexity. That ecosystem develops in environments that provide an adequate supply of moisture and nutrients and are consistently warm, and in which severe disturbances caused by wildfire, wind storm, or disease are rare. The marine analogue is coral reefs, which support more species and biological complexity than any other oceanic ecosystem, again because they exist in environments that are consistently well supported by vital resources. Other kinds of environments are more stressful, and in those places ecological development may be limited to prairie, tundra, desert, or other ecosystems with relatively low levels of complexity and productivity.

Change is a pervasive attribute of ecosystems. Some are particularly dynamic, regularly experiencing large changes in their species composition, biomass, and rates of productivity and nutrient cycling. This occurs in ecosystems that experience seasonally cold or dry climates, so that distinct growing seasons are followed by periods of dormancy during which there is little or no productivity. All Canadian ecosystems are like this, albeit to varying degrees—a warm and productive growing season is followed by a cold and wintry dormant period. Animals survive the hard times of winter by feeding on plant biomass that accumulated during the growing season, or they hibernate or migrate to a warmer clime.

Intense ecological change is also caused by disturbances by wildfires, windstorms, or biological factors, such as an acute pathogen that may kill the dominant organisms of an ecosystem. Those events of severe ecological damage are followed by an extended period of recovery that is referred to as succession (see Chapter 10 for a detailed examination of disturbance and succession). Some natural disturbances can affect millions of hectares, as occurs with large wildfires and irruptions of tree-killing insects, such as bark beetles and budworm moths **(Figure 1.8)**. Other disturbances are more local, perhaps associated with the death of a large tree caused by a lightning strike.

Some ecosystems are rarely disturbed and so they are relatively stable. Nevertheless, if they are closely monitored for a long time, they will also be found to be changing. At the very least, these and all ecosystems are influenced by changes in regional climate and by other long-term and pervasive dynamics, such as evolution.

Environmental stressors have always affected organisms and ecosystems. However, ecosystems are not only influenced by "natural" stressors but also by **anthropogenic** ones (associated with human activities). Like any species, *Homo sapiens* affects other species with which we interact and the ecosystems of which we are a component. Anthropogenic stressors have intensified enormously in modern times, and throughout much of the world they are now the major influence on the productivity of species and on the structure and function of ecosystems.

People and their economic activities affect species and ecosystems in several key ways:

- by harvesting useful biomass, such as trees and hunted animals;
- by converting natural ecosystems into land uses for agricultural, urbanized, or industrial purposes;
- by introducing alien species that invade natural habitats and cause ecological damage;
- by causing toxicity through pollution; and
- by emitting large amounts of greenhouse gases, causing the global climate to change.

These influences also engender a great variety of indirect effects. For example, clear-cutting trees from an area will devastate conditions for the plants and animals that need forested habitat, which causes their abundance to decline on affected sites. At the same time, however, other species will be favoured by these environmental changes. Moreover, timber harvesting indirectly affects functional properties of the ecosystem, such as productivity, streamflow, and erosion. These indirect ecological influences are important, and they are cumulative on any direct effects.

The population of our species in 2014 was about 7.2 billion individuals, and we are living in almost all of the habitable places on Earth. Directly or indirectly, more than half of the net terrestrial production of the planet is being diverted to the human economy (Vitousek et al., 1986).

Bill Freedman

FIGURE 1.8 **Disturbance** A disturbance can affect a relatively large area and kill the dominant species. It is then followed by community-scale regeneration. This area of boreal forest dominated by black spruce (*Picea mariana*) in central Labrador was affected by a wildfire several years previously. The linear unburnt areas are moist habitats along streams, while the larger tract of intact forest at the top of the image likely survived because of luck and wind direction.

Moreover, overconsumption is rapidly depleting important renewable and nonrenewable natural resources. The risk to humans is that the resource mining cannot be sustained for very long. The risk to the natural world from the unprecedented and wanton influence of a single species (humans) is irreversible damage from the endangerment and extinction of species and of entire ecosystems. One of the great challenges of ecology is to provide timely advice that is needed to help transform the human economy into a sustainable enterprise that will support both itself and the natural world. We examine this subject in more detail in Chapters 15 and 17.

The Biosphere

The biosphere is the spatial envelope within which life occurs, and Earth is the only place in the universe where this is known to exist. The biosphere is the largest possible ecosystem, encompassing all of life and its immediate environments. It extends from at least 3 km into the crust to as high as 41 km in the stratosphere—

microorganisms have been recovered from both of those extreme environments (see Ecology in Depth 2.1). Of course, the biosphere is also intimately connected to influences originating far outside its boundaries, particularly through the continuous inputs of solar radiation that drives the photosynthesis that is the basis of almost all ecological productivity (Chapter 4).

The biosphere originated as early as about 3.6 billion years ago, upon the genesis of life. The first life forms were bacteria-like organisms that fed on a soup of organic chemicals that had gradually accumulated in primordial aquatic environments. Those chemicals might have been synthesized during lightning-sparked reactions involving simple inorganic compounds, such as ammonia, carbon dioxide, methane, and water. The earliest bacteria were **heterotrophic** organisms that could survive only if they had access to organic matter as a source of nutrition.

The first **autotrophic** microorganisms, which feed themselves through biosynthesis, evolved about 3.1 billion years ago. They were probably **chemosynthetic** bacteria that could oxidize sulphide compounds and use some of the energy released to power a biosynthesis of sugars from carbon dioxide and water (Chapter 4). The evolution of chemosynthesis was an extremely important evolutionary outcome because it resulted in the production of much more organic matter than had the previous inorganic reactions.

The first **photosynthetic** organisms, which were likely cyanobacteria (blue-green bacteria), evolved around 2.5 billion years ago. These were **phototrophs** (or **photoautotrophs**, meaning "light self-feeding") that used solar energy to biosynthesize sugars from CO_2 and H_2O, releasing O_2 as a metabolic by-product. The evolution of photosynthesis further amplified the ability of the biosphere to produce biomass and so to support the evolution of many kinds of heterotrophic organisms.

The discharge of large amounts of biogenic oxygen during photosynthesis resulted in enormous environmental change. The atmosphere became transformed over several hundred millions of years from being essentially anaerobic (devoid of O_2) to having a concentration similar to the present value of 21 percent. This meant that the dominant chemical reactions in the environments of life were changed from being reducing in character (which result in an increase in the number of electrons) to oxidizing reactions (fewer electrons) similar to those of present times.

The development of predominantly oxidizing conditions would have been catastrophic for most of the existing species and so a mass extinction resulted. The only survivors would have persisted in relatively uncommon anaerobic habitats, plus those few original species that were capable of tolerating oxygen. Those initially rare O_2-tolerant microbes then multiplied throughout the habitable parts of the planet and underwent an evolutionary radiation, or a proliferation of newly evolved species. Most species that are alive today are their descendants.

The abiotic components of the biosphere are exceedingly complex, and for the purposes of study it is helpful to divide them into three major environments—the atmosphere, hydrosphere, and solid portions of planet Earth.

Atmosphere

The **atmosphere** is an envelope of gases that surrounds the solid Earth, and is retained by gravitational attraction. It also contains much smaller amounts of suspended particulates and droplets. The major gases are nitrogen (N_2; 78.08%, by volume), oxygen (O_2; 20.95%), argon (Ar; 0.93%), carbon dioxide (CO_2; 0.039%), and neon (Ne; 0.002%). The water content is highly variable, but it averages about 1 percent (in the lower atmosphere). The density of the atmosphere decreases rapidly with increasing distance from the surface (sea level), with half of its mass occurring within 5.6 km of the surface, and three-quarters within 11 km. The atmosphere extends to at least 120 km, beyond which is the void of outer space. The two lower

strata of the atmosphere, the troposphe[...] are most important to functioning of [...]

The **troposphere** is the lowest laye[...] at the poles and 17–20 km at the [...] boundary, the tropopause, is rather [...] affected by extreme weather systems) [...] heated by sunlight, an effect that var[...] tude, being greatest in the tropics. T[...] tion of atmospheric heat content becomes dispersed by vertical mixing and by lateral air flows or winds, which are sometimes manifest in the extreme phenomena of hurricanes and tornadoes. The jet stream is a particularly vigorous, meandering, ribbon-like, westerly (in the northern hemisphere) airflow that occurs near the tropopause. Because of the continuous turbulence within the troposphere, it is sometimes called the "weather atmosphere." In general, air temperature decreases with increasing altitude; between sea level and about 11 km the average lapse (or cooling) rate is about 6.5°C per 1000 m.

The **stratosphere** extends from the tropopause to about 50 km above the surface. Unlike in the troposphere, temperature generally increases with height. The stratosphere is essentially devoid of H_2O and it contains a distinct "ozone layer" with a high O_3 concentration [2–8 parts per million (ppm), compared with about 0.08 ppm at the surface]. The O_3 is produced by a complex of ultraviolet-driven photochemical reactions. The stratospheric O_3 provides a crucial environmental service by absorbing much of the high-energy solar ultraviolet radiation and thereby preventing it from reaching the surface, where it would harm organisms by damaging crucial biochemicals such as DNA and photosynthetic pigments.

Hydrosphere

The **hydrosphere** consists of water occurring in various compartments—on the surface of the planet, in rocks, and in the atmosphere. About 98.5 percent of global water is in the oceans. Almost all the rest is in glaciers (which cover about 10 percent of the planet's land surface), although this has varied enormously over geological time—at the peak of the most recent ice age, more than 12 000 years ago, sea level was about 120 m lower than today because so much water was present in glacial ice **(Figure 1.9)**. About 0.32 percent of global water is groundwater, occurring in cracks and other interstices in soil and rocks, while only 0.2 percent is in surface waters (lakes, rivers, and wetlands), and 0.1 percent is in the atmosphere.

The **hydrological cycle** (or **water cycle**) refers to movements of water among the various compartments in which it occurs **(Figure 1.10)**. These fluxes are powered by the energy of absorbed solar radiation, plus gravitational potential for downward flows. A key aspect of the hydrological cycle is **evaporation** of water to the atmosphere from the oceans, inorganic surfaces on land, and

FIGURE 1.9 **Glaciers** Glaciers are solid water present on land. They currently cover about 10 percent of the terrestrial surface, and are the largest reservoir of freshwater on the planet. This glacier is on Ellesmere Island in Nunavut.

Bill Freedman

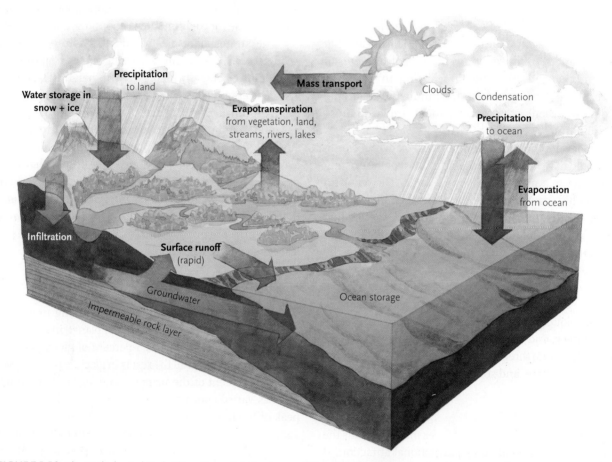

FIGURE 1.10 **The Hydrological Cycle** The water cycle refers to quantities present in various compartments as well as movements occurring among those reservoirs. The absorbed energy of sunlight powers the evaporation of water and its transport by wind and oceanic currents, while downward movements occur in response to gradients of gravitational potential.

SOURCE: From DRAPER/REED. Our Environment, 4E. © 2009 Nelson Education Ltd. Reproduced by permission. www.cengage.com/permissions

vegetation (the latter is called **transpiration**; the combined effect is **evapotranspiration**).

About 90 percent of water evaporated to the global atmosphere is from the oceans, even though only 70 percent of Earth's surface is marine. The atmospheric water may be transported by winds over long distances, but eventually it cools and forms droplets or ice crystals, which if large enough will settle gravitationally from the atmosphere as **precipitation** (rain or snow). Some of the deposited water percolates through soil and may join longer-term stores of groundwater deep in the ground (known as aquifers) or erupt to the surface at springs that feed streams, rivers, lakes, and wetlands. Eventually, the freshwater is returned to the oceans by riverflow, completing the hydrologic cycle.

Solid Earth

The solid Earth consists of several concentric layers. The innermost region is the core, with a diameter of 3500 km and comprising molten metals, predominantly iron and nickel. The heat of the **core** is generated by the decay of unstable isotopes of uranium and other radioactive elements.

The **mantle** occurs above the core and is about 2800 km thick and composed of less-dense minerals in a semi-liquid state known as magma, which contains large amounts of silicon, oxygen, magnesium, and other lighter elements. Magma from the upper mantle may erupt at the surface at volcanoes, and the lava that spews forth cools to form basaltic rock.

The **lithosphere** is the top layer, averaging 80 km thick. It consists of the uppermost mantle plus basaltic, granitic, and sedimentary rocks of the topmost layer called the **crust**. Oceanic crust averages 10–15 km in thickness, while continental crust is 20–60 km thick. The mineralogy of the crust is highly complex, in contrast to the relatively uniform mantle and core. The most abundant crustal elements are oxygen (45%), silicon (27%), aluminum (8.0%), iron (5.8%), calcium (5.1%), magnesium (2.8%), sodium (2.3%), potassium (1.7%), titanium (0.86%), vanadium (0.17%), hydrogen (0.14%), phosphorus (0.10%), and carbon (0.032%).

Biotic Habitats

The biosphere is a complex mosaic of biotic environments, which support characteristic assemblages of species that develop collective structural and functional attributes. At the global scale, the most extensive kinds of natural ecosystems are referred to as **biomes** (Chapter 11). Biomes of the terrestrial realm include forests, ranging from tropical to boreal, as well as grassland, tundra, and desert. In the marine realm, the dominant biomes involve the open ocean, at the surface and at all depths, as well as coastal ones, such as coral reefs, estuaries, and continental shelves. These are all natural ecosystems whose distinctiveness is due to:

- the particular species that have assembled into communities;
- their biological interactions; and
- the prevailing abiotic environmental conditions.

Of course, the modern world also supports extensive anthropogenic ecosystems, which have their own distinctive environmental conditions and biodiversity. These include various agricultural ecosystems, as well as urbanized and industrial ones. Anthropogenic ecosystems are vital to the human economy, and they include the places where almost all people live. However, their biodiversity is generally degraded (alien species being notably abundant), as is their ecosystem functioning (see Chapters 15 through 17).

1.2 The Science of Ecology

Ecology is highly **interdisciplinary**, meaning it incorporates and crosses the boundaries of many subject areas. Biology is central to ecology, but knowledge of chemistry, computer science, earth sciences (geology), geography, mathematics, meteorology, oceanography, physics, statistics, and other fields is also important **(Figure 1.11)**.

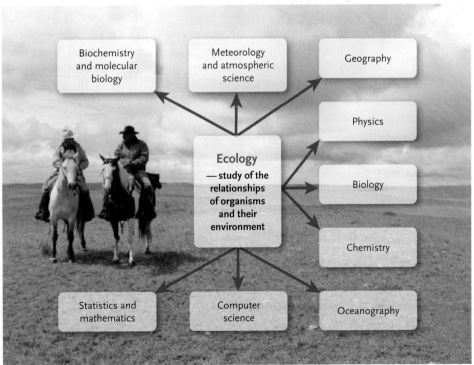

FIGURE 1.11 Ecology Is a Highly Interdisciplinary Field of Knowledge The knowledge bases and methodologies of various kinds of science-related disciplines are relevant to the study of ecosystems. The background image shows range-management specialists riding in shortgrass prairie of the Old Man on His Back Prairie and Heritage Conservation Area in southwestern Saskatchewan, a protected area of the Nature Conservancy of Canada.

In a general sense, ecologists seek to understand the organization and functioning of the natural world and to determine environmental influences that result in observed patterns of:

- the phylogenetic relationships of species, including their past and ongoing evolutionary changes;
- the life-history attributes of species and of functional groups (the latter are clusters of species that are similar in their life history but are not necessarily closely related);
- the dynamics of populations, including limits to their growth;
- the assembly of species into distinctive ecological communities, and the interactions among those co-occurring species;
- the spatial patterns and temporal dynamics of the various communities that occur on landscapes and seascapes;
- the rates of ecosystem functions, such as productivity and nutrient cycling;
- structural attributes of ecosystems, such as the storage of biomass and nutrients and biodiversity at its various levels;
- the importance of biodiversity and ecosystem functions to sustaining the human economy; and
- the influence of the human economy on the structure and functioning of ecosystems and their components.

However, the natural world is a notoriously complex system, and for this reason it is difficult to accurately describe its past and present conditions, and even more so its future ones. This differs from the physical sciences, such as chemistry and physics, where it is often possible to make exact measurements of conditions and to make accurate predictions of future ones.

For example, chemists can foretell the chemical and thermodynamic consequences of handling many substances in a laboratory. These, for instance, are the consistent and inviolate properties of sodium chloride: 1 mole weighs 58.44 g (1 mole is 6.02×10^{23} atoms or molecules); the density is 2.16 g/cm³; the melting point is 801°C; the boiling point is 1465°C; solubility in water is 35.9 g/100 mL (at 25°C); and when NaCl is dissolved into water, a small energy release (known as the enthalpy of solution) of 5 kJ per mole occurs, which will slightly warm the solution.

Another example is the ability of physicists to predict the rate at which the intensity of radiation will diminish with increasing distance from a point source of its emission. For example, the Sun is a point source of electromagnetic radiation, and its intensity can be calculated at various distances. At the average distance of Earth from the Sun, the rate of energy input is 8.21 J/cm²-min (this is known as the *solar constant*). At that intensity of insolation, the average temperature of the surface of the

Earth would be about −33°C, as a consequence of the warming input of solar visible and near-infrared wavelengths and the cooling output from the planet of long-wave infrared. (Fortunately, however, Earth has a natural greenhouse effect and the *actual* average surface temperature is about 15°C; see Chapter 4.)

Some aspects of the physical and chemical world are so well understood that universal and inviolate "laws" have been formulated to explain them and to predict the future values of relevant variables. For example, the first law of thermodynamics states that although energy can be transformed from one state to another, it cannot be created or destroyed, so its net quantity is always constant (see Section 3.3 in Chapter 3).

Similarly, a number of universal physical constants have been identified. One example is the speed of electromagnetic radiation (the speed of "light"), which is always 2.9979×10^8 m/sec, regardless of the velocity of the emitting body. Hard rules in geometry are also important, such as the ratio of the circumference of a circle to its diameter, which always has a value of 3.14159 (symbolized as pi or π).

It is rare, however, for ecologists to be able to make such accurate predictions about changes in the components or functioning of ecosystems. This is the reason that ecology has no true "laws," and why ecologists are sometimes alleged to have "physics envy."

The awesome complexity of organisms and ecosystems, and the corresponding difficulties that biologists and ecologists have in making accurate measurements and predictions, are due to three major circumstances. First, the inorganic environment can be highly variable, and as a result some abiotic factors are exceedingly complicated and unpredictable, such as the systems that redistribute energy in the atmosphere—winds and storms. This is why weather forecasting is often inaccurate, as are predictions of future climatic conditions. The heat-distribution systems of the oceans—currents and upwellings—are also difficult to accurately measure or foretell. Seemingly capricious variations of the spatial and temporal values of abiotic factors contribute to the complexity of biological and ecological responses to them.

Second, biological systems are also unpredictable, in part because of genetic variations that result in differential responses to environmental conditions. The biological responses may involve aspects of biochemistry and physiology, anatomical development, productivity, fecundity, or behaviour. The genetic variations may be among individuals within a population, as well as among different species. Moreover, the genetic attributes of populations change over time (this is evolution), and species may become extinct if they cannot cope with changes in environmental conditions.

Third, as we previously noted, organisms and ecosystems have emergent properties that are difficult to predict. These synergetic qualities exist in an intact whole, but they cannot be predicted from knowledge only of the parts.

Ecological Data

Many ecological data are based on somewhat inaccurate and imprecise measurements of environmental or biological variables. Because those data are only approximations of the "true" values of the natural phenomena, predictions based on them are subject to some degree of uncertainty. **Accuracy** is the degree to which an observation or measurement reflects the true value of a subject. **Precision** is the degree of repeatability of those measurements.

Imagine the difficulty of estimating the number of trees or their biomass over a remote forested landscape, or the number of caribou present in a huge area of boreal forest, or of sandpipers in a big flock **(Figure 1.12)**. Total direct counts cannot be made if the study area is immense or the animals are too abundant, so subsampling procedures must be used. Those methods have an inherent inexactness, based on factors such as the size and number of the sampling plots—in general, however, a larger number of bigger samples will provide data that have better accuracy and precision. Of course, the numbers and sizes of plots are themselves partly determined by how much effort is available to conduct a study, which is reflected in the funding and amount of technology and person-power that can be used to achieve reliable measurements.

Accuracy and precision are also relevant to environmental variables, such as determining the concentrations of nutrients or pollutants in samples of water, soil, or organisms, or when measuring climate-related factors.

FIGURE 1.12 Uncertainty of Measurement Because of the large areas involved and other complexities, many ecological data are based on somewhat inaccurate and imprecise measurements of environmental or biological variables. How many semi-palmated sandpipers (*Calidris pusilla*) are in this migratory flock in the Bay of Fundy in New Brunswick? Note that there are many birds flying, but many are also roosting densely on the ground. Moreover, the image captures only part of the flock.

Imagine the difficulty of estimating the average carbon storage or surface temperature of a stand of old-growth forest in coastal British Columbia, or of mixedgrass prairie in Saskatchewan, or an estuary on the Atlantic coast.

Problems associated with accuracy and precision are unavoidable aspects of doing ecological studies in the real world. Ecologists cope with this circumstance in several ways. First, they use the best sampling methodology and technology that their research budget can afford. Second, they do not report observations using excessive numbers of **significant figures**. Because ecological data are typically highly variable, they are usually reported with only 2–3 significant figures. This is most easily explained by a simple example: all of the following numbers have three significant figures: 444; 4.44; 0.00444; and 4.44×10^3.

Finally, the sampling variation of ecological data is typically reported using statistical parameters, such as the observed *range* of values about the calculated *average* (or *mean*), and the *standard deviation* (SD) or *standard error* (SE is the SD divided by the square root of the sample size). In an experiment, the statistical significance of differences of the averages among treatments is analyzed using *t-tests* or *analysis of variance* (*ANOVA*) if the data distribution is normal, or by chi-square or other nonparametric tests for non-normal data.

Environmental and biological complexities can be daunting to ecologists, but they do echo the reality of the natural world. In essence, all work in ecology is intended to make progress in sorting out these hard-to-know attributes of ecosystems and to eventually discover their organizing principles.

Subject Areas of Ecology

Many ecologists work out of curiosity—their interest is to better understand the natural world. This "pure" science has intrinsic value, and it often results in knowledge that is of economic value. Other ecologists, however, are more directly interested in "applied" research that is related to important issues such as:

- finding improved ways of managing biological resources that are of economic importance, such as in agriculture, fisheries, forestry, and hunting;
- preventing or repairing ecological damage that has been caused by pollution, disturbances, or other causes of degradation;
- planning and management for biodiversity, including ways of conserving species at risk, as well as taking care of protected areas;
- managing ecosystem functions, such as erosion, hydrology, nutrient cycling, and productivity, including ways to promote carbon storage in biomass as an offset to the emissions of greenhouse gases.

Ecology is a complex and diverse subject area. Some decades ago it was divided into two main subject areas that differed according to the level of integration at which they were pursued:

- **autecology** is the study of the relationships of environment influences on individual organisms, or of specific populations or species, often with particular reference to factors affecting their life history, distribution, and abundance; and
- **synecology** is the study of relationships occurring among groups of species, and their biotic influences, along with those of abiotic factors, on community dynamics and ecosystem functions.

Today, however, these are considered archaic terms that have been replaced by a wider diversity of specialized, but somewhat overlapping fields within ecology **(Figure 1.13)**. Some of these fields have their own specialist journals and societies. The major subject areas of ecology are the following:

- **Conservation** ecology is the application of ecological knowledge to the stewardship of biodiversity and protected areas.
- **Syste**ms ecology uses a holistic approach to investigate the attributes of ecosystems.
- **Paleoecology** deals with populations, communities, and ecosystems that existed in the distant past, while **historical ecology** examines more recent changes.

- **Evolutionary ecology** is an overarching approach that provides context for much of ecology; the core theme is evolutionary aspects of adaptive ecological change, including interactions with selective forces.
- **Statistical ecology** involves the application of statistical methodologies to examining and explaining patterns and processes, while **mathematical ecology** involves the use of quantitative models.
- **Theoretical ecology** involves the identification of theories regarding the organization and functioning of ecosystems, and the use of rigorous methodologies to test their veracity; the field is particularly relevant to population ecology and biogeography.
- **Landscape ecology** examines the structural and functional attributes of ecosystems at large scales, including influences on the spatial and temporal dynamics of their communities.
- **Environmental ecology** is the study of the ways that the components and functions of ecosystems are affected by stressors, such as disturbances, pollution, and climate change, usually with a focus on stressors that are anthropogenic.
- **Applied ecology** is the integration of ecological knowledge with economic needs, such as finding improved ways to cultivate crops or to mitigate environmental damage.

FIGURE 1.13 Ecology Is a Complex Subject Area Broadly defined, ecology is the study of the relationships of organisms and their environment. However, it is a complex subject and is pursued within the context of a diversity of specialized but overlapping fields. The background image is red maple (*Acer rubrum*) in its fall colouration.

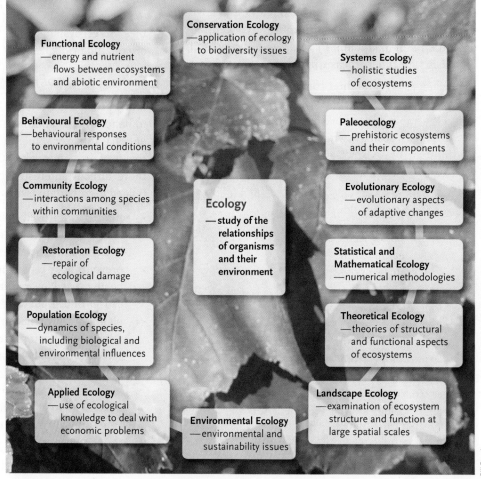

- **Population ecology** is the study of the dynamics of the abundance of species, including environmental influences on those changes.
- **Restoration ecology** involves the use of ecological knowledge and practices to repair environmental damage, such as by establishing vegetation on derelict land or by re-creating endangered natural ecosystems.
- **Community ecology** examines interactions occurring among populations of species within an ecological community.
- **Behavioural ecology** examines the ways that behaviour adapts to changes in environmental conditions.
- **Physiological ecology** (or **ecophysiology**) studies the adaptive biochemistry and physiology of organisms in response to variations of environmental conditions.
- **Ecosystem ecology** (**functional ecology**) studies the flows of energy and nutrients among organisms and the abiotic environment.
- **Molecular ecology** (or **ecological genetics**) is a recently emerged field in which the methodologies of molecular biology (in population genetics, phylogenetics, and genomics) are used to investigate certain kinds of ecological and evolutionary questions in a field setting.

The subject areas of ecology can also be segregated according to the kinds of organisms that are being examined. In this sense, major subject areas are:

- **Animal ecology**, which is the study of the populations, ecophysiology, productivity, and behaviour of wild animals and their communities;
- **Plant ecology**, which covers similar fields but with respect to plants and vegetation; and
- **Microbial ecology**, which is again similar, but often the focus is on functional processes, such as decomposition and nutrient cycling.

A further way to segregate fields of study in ecology involves major kinds of habitats and environments:

- **Marine ecology** is the study of any aspects of ecology in the oceanic realm.
- **Forest ecology** investigates tree-dominated ecosystems, including nontreed successional stages that are recovering from a recent disturbance of a mature forest.
- **Freshwater ecology** is the study of lakes (limnology), ponds, rivers, streams, and wetlands.
- Arctic ecology, tropical ecology, desert ecology, and similar focal areas involve studies of those natural environments.
- **Urban ecology** studies biodiversity and processes in urbanized habitats, with a focus on problems that can be mitigated by naturalization and the establishment of protected areas.

Ecologists

An **ecologist** is a specialist who studies some aspect of ecology. Ecologists are highly qualified scientists, meaning they have at least an undergraduate degree in science, although many also have graduate degrees, up to the Ph.D. However, other than their university degrees, very few ecologists are certified as being a specialist practitioner of ecology, in the way that doctors are licensed to practise medicine or lawyers to practise law.

Nevertheless, it *is* possible to become a certified ecologist. For example, the Ecological Society of America, a prestigious U.S. organization, will certify qualified people at various professional levels of ecology. Typically, this is done only by people working in the private sector, such as in a consulting firm that provides services related to environmental planning or impact assessment. Interestingly, very few professors who are specialized to teach ecology—including the authors who wrote this text—are certified as being ecologists. However, we are all highly qualified practitioners.

An ecologist is not the same thing as an *environmental scientist*. The latter is an interdisciplinary generalist who uses and applies science-related knowledge that is relevant to environmental issues. This might include atmospheric and water chemistry, climatic influences, and damage caused by pollution or disturbance to both human systems and natural ones. An ecologist is also not the same thing as an *environmentalist*, who is any person having a significant involvement with environmental issues, especially in advocacy, which means taking a strong public stance on issues. Nevertheless, many ecologists might refer to themselves as being environmental scientists, and most would also be concerned with environmental issues and so would consider themselves to be environmentalists. But the reverses are not necessarily true.

Ecologists work in all parts of the world, although most reside in relatively wealthy countries, such as Canada. Although the general methodologies and knowledge of ecology are universal in their scope, a great deal of local and ecoregional context is needed. In fact, it was in recognition of that ecoregional perspective that the authors undertook to prepare this text about ecology within the context of the biodiversity and environments of Canada. We believe that the learning of ecology should, in part, be informed by the context of the species and ecosystems with which students are most familiar.

Many ecologists have careers as professors working in universities and colleges, or as scientists in government agencies, the private sector, or nongovernmental organizations (NGOs or environmental charities, such as Ducks Unlimited Canada, the Nature Conservancy of Canada, and World Wildlife Fund). Some ecologists working in Canada have become well known in their field of study—as researchers, authors, and advocates for

FIGURE 1 Chris Pielou

E. C. (Chris) Pielou (b. 1924) earned her Ph.D. (and later the higher doctorate, D.Sc.) from the University of London (England) **(Figure 1)**. She began her career in Canada in 1963, as a research scientist in what was then the federal Ministry of Forestry and Agriculture, before shifting to academia. She has been a professor at Queen's University (1968–1971), a Killam Professor at Dalhousie University (1974–1981), and an Environmental Research Professor working out of the University of Lethbridge (1981–1986). She also held visiting professorships at North Carolina State University, Yale University, and the University of Sydney, Australia.

Pielou is best known for her research and books about the application of mathematics to ecological investigations, including the use of advanced probability theory. In fact, her explanations and demonstrations of those methodologies have been so significant that she is considered the originator of the field of mathematical ecology. Perhaps her most influential book is *Introduction to Mathematical Ecology* (1969), and its second edition *Mathematical Ecology* (1977), which essentially sparked the genesis of that field by inspiring many ecologists to use and further develop techniques that she identified and advocated. Her contributions have been recognized by the E. C. Pielou Award, given annually by the Statistical Ecology Section of the Ecological Society of America. Pielou's overall contribution to ecology has also been recognized by awards such as the Lawson Medal of the Canadian Botanical Association in 1984; in 1986 she was the second woman to win the Eminent Ecologist Award from the Ecological Society of America.

Although "retired" since 1986, Pielou remains extraordinarily active, writing books about ecology at an impressive pace. She has also served on various scientific boards, among them the Clayoquot Sound Scientific Panel, which recommended better forestry practices for the forests around the Sound on the west coast of Vancouver Island, and a National Research Council (USA) study on the effects of oil and gas activities on Alaska's North Slope. Pielou's extraordinary career and ideas have been inspirational to ecologists worldwide, perhaps more so because some of her greatest contributions occurred during a time when women were relatively uncommon among the practitioners of ecology.

science and for conserving the natural world. A selection of these people is highlighted in each chapter of this book, in the special boxes titled "A Canadian Ecologist."

The Scientific Method

In view of the exceeding complexity of the natural world—and especially those aspects that involve biology and ecology—it is necessary to adopt a rigorous scientific approach to investigations in those fields. But what is meant by a scientific approach?

Origins of Science

The word **science** originates from the Latin word *scientia*, which means "knowing" or "knowledge." The purview of science is to further a lofty goal of achieving knowledge—to use systematic and objective methodologies to better understand the natural world. A key goal is the discovery of general principles that can provide insight into factors which control the structure and function of nature and so would allow predictions to be made about the future. Science is also characterized by a rapidly growing body of knowledge that is based on empirical (observational), theoretical, and practical (applied) ideas and observations.

Thinking people have always wondered about "big questions," such as existence and the place of humans within the natural world. The initial ways of knowing about these problems involved belief (or faith-based) systems based on religion, morality, and aesthetics. Even today, many people choose faith-based understanding associated with religion or philosophy as a preferred alternative to knowledge gained from scientific investigation. This is particularly the case of highly contemplative issues, such as the existence of God, discovering a meaning of life that goes beyond mere survival, the differences between right and wrong, and understanding the inherent value of art and other aesthetic expressions.

However, science is the best system to use when investigating questions about past, present, and future conditions of the natural world. This includes the origin of life, its evolutionary changes, the ecological context of humanity, and the characteristics and functioning of ecosystems. Many people have answered these questions to their own satisfaction through the received wisdom of belief systems. However, their faith-based interpretations may be diametrically opposed to conclusions derived from rational scientific investigations, a circumstance that has resulted in controversy and conflict. This is an ongoing difficulty and context in our society—it involves disagreements between belief systems and science about important issues in biology, medicine, and the environment. While acknowledging this discordant fact, we must understand that science-based investigations are fundamental to the pursuit of knowledge in ecology.

The modern practice of science developed from a much older endeavour known as natural philosophy. This was a way of learning used by classical Greeks and other ancients who were interested in rational enquiries into the meaning of observed phenomena and of existence itself. Of course, their old-time investigations were relatively unsophisticated in the methodologies that were used, which often involved only the application of logic. Modern science is considered to have begun with the methodical studies of several well-known practitioners of the 16th and 17th centuries, such as:

- Nicolaus Copernicus (1473–1543), a Polish astronomer who originated a heliocentric theory of the solar system, in which planets orbit the Sun;
- Galileo Galilei (1564–1642), an Italian who worked in astronomy and investigated the physics of objects in motion; and
- Isaac Newton (1642–1727), an Englishman who formulated laws about the motion of objects, including the role of gravity, as well as the nature of light, and who invented the mathematics of calculus.

Goals and Methods of Science

A higher goal of scientific enquiry is to formulate general principles about the workings of the universe (e.g., see Chapter 3 for an explanation of the laws of thermodynamics that govern transformations of energy). However, many natural phenomena involve extremely complex systems that may never be fully understood in terms of physical laws. This is particularly true of much of the organization and functioning of organisms and ecosystems.

Scientists undertake systematic observations of natural phenomena and conduct experiments to try to determine their controlling influences. These scientific investigations may be pure or applied. Pure science is driven by curiosity—it is a search for knowledge without regard to its immediate usefulness, including to human welfare. Applied science, in contrast, deals with questions that are economically important. Applied scientists might work to fund cures for diseases, to discover new machines or other technologies, to determine improved ways of managing natural resources, or to reduce pollution or deal with other environmental problems.

Logic

Francis Bacon (1561–1626), an English philosopher, was a promoter of the then-emerging methodologies of rational scientific investigations. His greatest influence was as an advocate of the use of inductive logic, in which conclusions about phenomena are reached by considering accumulating evidence based on observations of nature and the results of experiments. Consider the following application of **inductive logic**, applied to an ecological question:

- *Observation 1:* Plants are observed to increase their biomass even though they do not feed on other organisms.
- *Observation 2:* If plants are kept in the dark, they do not grow larger; rather, they eventually die.
- *Observation 3:* If deprived of water, plants do not grow—they desiccate and perish.
- *Observation 4:* If deprived of nutrients, such as carbon dioxide, nitrate, phosphate, or potassium, plants do not grow, or they do so extremely slowly.
- *Inductive conclusion:* Plants are able to grow only if they have access to light, moisture, and nutrients.

Deductive logic is a different way of reasoning that involves making one or several assumptions and then drawing logical conclusions. With this process, the veracity of the initial assumptions determines the truth of any subsequent inferences. Therefore, if assumptions are based on incorrect belief, or on wrong information, then any deduced conclusions are likely to be in error. Here is an example of the use of deductive logic, applied to an ecological question:

- *Assumption:* Sunlight captured by photosynthetic organisms is the foundation of ecological productivity, because that energy drives the biosynthesis of simple sugars from carbon dioxide and water.
- *Deduced conclusion:* Biological energy fixation cannot occur in a dark environment.

For a long time, the above assumption and deduction were considered to be true. In 1892, however, Sergei Winogradsky (1856–1953), a Russian scientist, discovered that certain bacteria could link their autotrophic productivity to energy released during the oxidation of sulphide chemicals (Chapter 3). This process, now known as chemosynthesis, occurs in environments where sulphide compounds become exposed to oxygen; for example, where coal mining exposes iron sulphide (FeS_2) to the atmosphere. This allows chemosynthetic *Thiobacillus* bacteria to grow while generating sulphate and acidity and sometimes causing a severe environmental problem known as acid-mine drainage.

In general, inductive logic plays a much stronger role in the conduct of science than deductive logic does. However, conclusions based on either kind of logic depend on the accuracy of the data or presumed knowledge that is used. Deductive logic works well only if the original assumptions are correct, and inductive conclusions based on faulty data will be erroneous.

Facts, Hypotheses, and Experiments

A **fact** is an event or a thing that is true—it is known to have happened or to exist. Facts are confirmed as being genuine on the basis of evidence from experience and scientific investigations. By comparison, a **hypothesis** is a proposed explanation of a phenomenon or its cause. Logic, inference, statistics, and mathematics may be used to formulate a hypothesis, usually as a statement that can be tested by experiments or other kinds of research.

A hypothesis should be designed in a way that allows it to be proven wrong. If a hypothesis cannot be refuted, then the methods of science cannot test its predictions. Here is an example of a faulty hypothesis of that sort: "Cats are so intelligent that they are able prevent people from discovering their cleverness." A better hypothesis would be "cats are intelligent," because it can be examined in various ways, including by standard methodologies in ethology (the science of animal behaviour).

A **theory** is a bigger idea that relates to a unifying principle—one that explains a large body of knowledge, such as facts based on observational and experimental evidence and any laws that are based on them. Examples of celebrated theories in science are:

- gravitation, which was first proposed by Isaac Newton;
- evolution by natural selection, published in 1858 by its codiscoverers, English naturalists Charles Darwin (1809–1882) and Alfred Russel Wallace (1823–1913); and
- relativity, originating with the German–Swiss physicist Albert Einstein (1879–1955).

These well-established theories have been examined by a great deal of research and so they are supported by increasingly large bodies of scientific evidence. This does not mean, however, that future research will not refute these theories and by so doing prove them to be false. In fact, the intent of most scientific research is to test whether the predictions of a hypothesis or a theory can be disproved (or falsified).

In practice, the **scientific method** begins with a researcher identifying a question about a phenomenon—about some aspect of the organization or functioning of the natural world. Often, the question is developed from the "bottom" upward, using inductive logic and an existing body of knowledge **(Figure 1.14)**. The question is interpreted in terms of existing theory, and hypotheses are formulated to test predictions of the theory. The hypotheses are then reformulated as **null hypotheses**, which seek to disprove the hypotheses. Research is then undertaken to test the null hypotheses. This research can employ controlled experiments, as well as careful observations of patterns in nature. If a null hypothesis is proven to be correct, then the original hypothesis must be incorrect and so it is discarded. However, if research disproves a null hypothesis, it is still necessary to conduct further research that retests the original hypothesis by formulating additional null hypotheses. Eventually, if a large body of evidence accumulates that fails to falsify a hypothesis, it helps to substantiate the original theory.

Because null hypotheses seek to disprove rather than support a question, they are an efficient way to conduct research. Consider a case in which a hypothesis has been

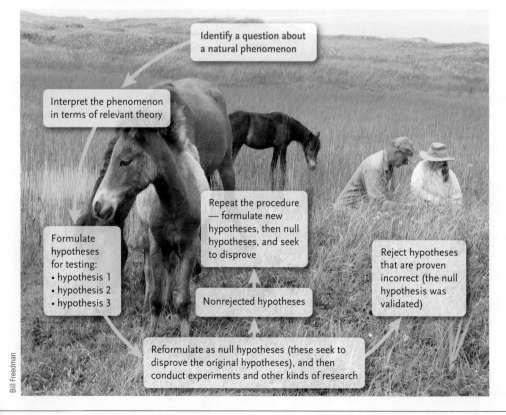

Identify a question about a natural phenomenon

Interpret the phenomenon in terms of relevant theory

Formulate hypotheses for testing:
- hypothesis 1
- hypothesis 2
- hypothesis 3

Repeat the procedure — formulate new hypotheses, then null hypotheses, and seek to disprove

Nonrejected hypotheses

Reject hypotheses that are proven incorrect (the null hypothesis was validated)

Reformulate as null hypotheses (these seek to disprove the original hypotheses), and then conduct experiments and other kinds of research

FIGURE 1.14 Diagrammatic Representation of the Scientific Method The process is to formulate a question about the natural world, interpret it using the existing theory, then develop hypotheses, and reformulate them as null hypotheses, which are tested by research. If a null hypothesis is found to be correct, then the original hypothesis must be rejected. However, if the null hypothesis is proven incorrect, the original hypothesis is not necessarily proven to be correct. Rather, it is subjected to additional examination, but again with the intent of disproving it. The background shows ecologists studying wetland plants and environmental factors affecting their communities on Sable Island, Nova Scotia, while several wild horses study them.

Bill Freedman

FIGURE 1.15 A Manipulative Experiment This kind of experiment involves the modification of factors that are hypothesized to influence a natural phenomenon, with the results compared against a nonmodified control. This plot of sedge tundra on Ellesmere Island received nitrogen fertilizer, while control plots (not shown) did not. The stimulation of plant growth is apparent in the greener colour and larger biomass of the treated plot compared with the surrounding vegetation.

subjected to a great deal of research and is supported by numerous confirming experiments and observations. This circumstance may support a conditional acceptance of the hypothesis, but no amount of confirming evidence can ultimately "prove" it. In fact, as soon as well-defined research confirms a null hypothesis, the original hypothesis is disproved. This is why it is more efficient to do research that proceeds immediately to examine null hypotheses, and why the scientific method seeks to disprove the predictions of hypotheses.

An **experiment** is an investigation that is designed to provide evidence that tests a hypothesis. A **manipulative experiment** involves modifications of one or more **variables** (i.e., values that may change) that are hypothesized to influence a natural phenomenon **(Figure 1.15)**. The results of manipulated treatments are compared against a **control**, which was not modified and therefore sets the baseline condition. For example, tree seedlings growing in the understorey of a forest might be exposed to the following set of experimental manipulations:

- *Treatment 1:* This is the control, with no experimental modification of environmental factors.
- *Treatment 2:* Nitrogen fertilizer is added.
- *Treatment 3:* Phosphorus fertilizer is added.
- *Treatment 4:* Water is added.

If the seedlings grow better in response to any of the additions (compared with the control), then that factor would be judged to be limiting the productivity. On the other hand, if none of the treatments resulted in higher productivity than the control, the conclusion would be that some other environmental factor is limiting, perhaps

inadequate light because of a shading overstorey of tree foliage.

Natural experiments involve studying gradients in nature or other variations of environmental conditions and ecological change, and then developing explanations for the observed patterns using statistical analyses. If significant relationships are discovered among variables, it suggests a possible cause-and-effect mechanism. That observation could be followed up by developing hypotheses whose predictions are then tested by manipulative experiments. An application of this process is illustrated in Environmental Applications 1.1.

Great advances in understanding occur when theories are rejected through new discoveries of science. Thomas Kuhn (1922–1995), a philosopher of science, believed that **scientific revolutions** occur whenever a well-established theory is rigorously tested and then collapses under the weight of new facts and observations that it cannot explain. The obsolete theory is then replaced by a new, more informed **paradigm** (a set of assumptions, concepts, practices, and values that constitutes an understanding of the natural world and is shared by an intellectual community).

There are many examples of these sorts of scientific revolutions. For instance, once mariners discovered that the Earth is not flat, they could courageously sail beyond the horizon without dread of falling off the edge of the world. It was also once believed that all bodies in the solar system, and even all of those in the universe, revolved around the Earth, but the realization by Copernicus of a heliocentric organization overthrew that and other incorrect astronomical ideas of the time.

The explanation of scientific methodology that we just examined suggests an orderly and objective progression of the formulation of ideas and hypotheses, objective empirical studies, and comparison of alternative hypotheses. However, scientists are creative and experienced people with personal insights and biases that may affect their research. Scientists often design research that they think will "work," such as experiments that are likely to yield useful results and thereby contribute to an orderly improvement of knowledge. Karl Popper (1902–1994), a philosopher of science, believed that scientists design experiments according to their "imaginative preconception" of how the natural world functions. In this sense, scientists are not merely technically competent and knowledgeable people—they are also insightful and creative in the development of ideas, hypotheses, and programs of research.

Be Objective and Critical

Ecological science is replete with uncertainty, and many data and models are only approximations of the actual reality. Consequently, there are uncertainties in

The study of spatial gradients of environmental influences and the ecological responses to them can be an effective way to examine cause-and-effect relationships. This methodology can be illustrated by a chain of studies that were made of the effects of pollution on vegetation around a large metal smelter near Sudbury, Ontario. The smelter was a point-source of emissions of many pollutants.

Studies of air and soil pollution showed that high concentrations of sulphur dioxide (SO_2) were in the atmosphere close to the smelter, and the metals nickel (Ni) and copper (Cu) were greatly elevated in soil (Freedman, 2010). In addition, soluble aluminum (Al) was high because of severe acidification. With increasing distance from the smelter, the environmental concentrations of SO_2, Ni, Cu, and other toxic stressors rapidly decreased (Freedman and Hutchinson, 1980a) (**Figure 1**; note that zinc is a "reference" metal that was not emitted by the smelter).

Studies of vegetation showed a comparable spatial pattern of damage caused to plants (Freedman and Hutchinson, 1980b). There were strong statistical correlations between the pollutants (SO_2, Ni, Cu, Al, and acidity) and damage caused to plants, which suggests a potential causal mechanism for the harm **(Figure 2)**. The field studies of environmental and ecological gradients were complemented by laboratory experiments in which plants were grown in polluted soil collected near the smelter but in the absence of SO_2. This work proved that the metals and acidity contributed to the plant damage at the intensities of exposure that were observed in the field (Whitby and Hutchinson, 1974).

In 1972, a very tall "superstack" was built at the smelter, which had the effect of widely dispersing the SO_2 emissions and greatly alleviating the local pollution. When this happened, a few species of grasses rapidly increased in abundance, even though the local soil remained polluted with nickel and copper. Subsequent research showed that the grasses had evolved a genetically based tolerance to the toxic metals in soil, but not to atmospheric SO_2, which explained why they did not become abundant until after the SO_2 pollution was alleviated (Cox and Hutchinson, 1979).

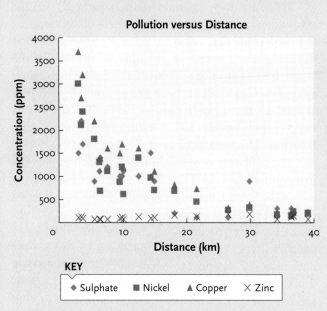

FIGURE 1 Environmental Gradients The concentrations of nickel and copper in soil are indicators of the spatial patterns of pollutants with increasing distance from the smelter, which is a point-source of emissions. Atmospheric SO_2 is not shown, but its pattern is similar. Zinc is not emitted by the smelter and is provided as a "reference" metal.

SOURCE: Based on data from Freedman, B. and T. C. Hutchinson. 1980. "Pollutant inputs from the atmosphere and accumulations in soils and vegetation near a nickel copper smelter at Sudbury, Ontario, Canada," *Canadian Journal of Botany*, 58: 108 132.

FIGURE 2 Vegetational Gradients Gradients of vegetation response are indicated by three measures: (a) basal area of shrubs and trees (m²/ha) is the sum of the cross-sectional areas of all stems in sampling plots; (b) ground cover is the percentage of the surface that is obscured by the foliage of low-growing ground vegetation; and (c) species richness is the average number of plant species per 1 m² sampling quadrat.

SOURCE: Based on data from Freedman, B. and T. C. Hutchinson. 1980. "Long term effects of pollution near a nickel copper smelter at Sudbury, Ontario, Canada on surrounding forest communities," *Canadian Journal of Botany*, 58: 2123 2140.

our estimations of past, present, and future ecological variables. Because of this, information and predictions in ecology should always be critically interpreted. This should be done when we are learning about ecology by listening to a speaker; reading a text, journal article, or webpage; and acquiring information through any other medium, such as video and the Internet.

Ecological knowledge is clearly important to the welfare of humans and other species—it helps to identify key issues, investigate their causes, and provide a degree of understanding of their consequences. Nevertheless, the explanatory value of ecology has limitations (as does much scientific endeavour), and these constraints must be acknowledged and addressed to the degree that is possible. Critical analysis and skepticism are important aspects of that process.

One place to begin this scrutiny is with primary ecological research—original studies that are based on novel information. The best primary research is published in refereed journals—these have a process by which qualified reviewers are asked to scrutinize the work, suggest changes, and recommend whether it should be published. However, much primary research is also published in governmental reports, in theses by graduate students, on websites, and in other less-well-refereed formats. Key aspects of the critical analysis of primary research are the following:

- Are clear hypotheses formulated, and are they relevant to the existing body of ecological theory and knowledge?
- Are the study design, field and laboratory methodology, and data analyses appropriate to resolving the questions being asked?
- Were the results and conclusions of the work compared with pertinent research that has been published by other ecologists, and were the similarities and differences discussed?

Secondary ecological research involves the synthesis of work that has been published by others. This research may occur in texts that are written to support the teaching of ecology, in literature reviews published in a refereed journal, and as overviews intended to support policy development or advocacy about an environmental issue. These works assemble information and attempt to reach over-arching conclusions about the state of knowledge of ecological science pertinent to some topic or issue. Important aspects of the critical analysis of secondary research are:

- Is the study published in a refereed journal, or is it otherwise heavily scrutinized for its methodology and objectivity?
- If the work is an analysis of a controversial issue, or based on incomplete or possibly inaccurate information, was a precautionary approach used to accommodate the uncertainty that is inherent in the recommendations?

Much ecological knowledge is relevant to managing important problems related to the sustainable use of natural resources, the conservation of biodiversity, and the prevention and repair of environmental damage. These issues engender controversy, and both sides of a problem may use a selection of scientific information to bolster their position. Moreover, today we live in a globalized world with remarkably abundant information and ease of communication. We can swiftly exchange ideas and data over vast distances and through diverse networks. In this sense, the world is a "global village" along the lines envisioned by Marshall McLuhan (1911–1980), a Canadian philosopher who wrote about the emerging phenomenon of universal networking enabled by communications technology. This is also the case of ideas and information related to ecology.

The users of any scientific knowledge have an obligation to critically evaluate what they are learning—they must decide whether the theory is appropriate, the methodologies reliable, and the conclusions robust and consistent with what is already known. This process is vital in science, and it is required if ecologists are to advance their field of knowledge and to provide helpful advice about issues that are important to society and to conservation of the natural world.

1.3 Evolutionary Ecology

Evolutionary ecology is a fusion of the subject matter of ecology and evolutionary biology. It has become an encompassing theme in much of the study of ecology. It does this by promoting interpretations of the evolutionary history of species and of their interactions with one another and with abiotic influences. Evolutionary considerations and interpretations are especially relevant to studies of the life history of species, their behaviour and sociobiology, and interactions such as herbivory, predation, parasitism, disease, and symbioses, such as mutualism and cooperation.

Environmental factors affect organisms by modifying their physiology, development, growth (productivity), behaviour, and reproduction. Organisms that live in an environmental regime that is sufficient to meet their needs will have a higher likelihood of maximizing their genetic potential. Barring accidents, they would be more likely to have as many offspring as is biologically possible, being limited only by their inherent genetic potential, as encoded in their **genome**. The genome of an organism is the specific genetic information that is embedded within the base sequences of its DNA (deoxyribonucleic acid, a nucleic acid that stores the genetic coding of most organisms; exceptions are viruses and some bacteria, which utilize RNA, or ribonucleic acid, for this purpose).

The genome of an individual is a fixed entity, apart from a relatively minor influence of mutations that might occur during its lifetime. However, the actual expression of the genetic potential, known as the **phenotype**, may vary considerably, depending on the circumstances that an organism experiences. In this sense, the phenotype is the anatomy, physiology, behaviour, and other characteristics that an individual expresses and shows to the world. The term **phenotypic plasticity** refers to the variable expression of the genotype, occurring in response to vagaries of environmental conditions. Although organisms may exhibit considerable phenotypic plasticity, any observed variations are still constrained by the flexibility allowed by the genome.

It is important to understand that individual organisms do not evolve, and that phenotypic plasticity does not represent an evolutionary change. **Evolution** is a change in the collective genetic information of a population or of a higher-order grouping (such as species), occurring from generation to generation. For evolution to happen, genetic variation must exist among individuals within a population (as is generally true of large populations, especially of species that reproduce sexually; it is not necessarily the case of those that propagate by asexual means).

In evolutionary biology, **fitness** is the proportionate contribution that an organism makes to the genetic make-up of subsequent generations. Fitness is related to the number of offspring that is produced (more offspring leads to higher fitness), as well as their own success in breeding and contributing their genetic information to succeeding generations, and also that of their own progeny, and so on.

Natural selection is an important cause of evolutionary change. The theory of natural selection predicts that individual organisms are more likely to have descendants (i.e., to achieve higher fitness) if their phenotypic attributes are better suited to coping with the constraints and opportunities presented by their environment, compared with other individuals in their population. If the adaptive advantages (or **adaptations**) of an individual are determined by its genotype, they can be passed to descendants. And if an individual has a relatively large number of descendants (because of higher fitness), this will result in population-level genetic change, or evolution. Natural selection is the principal driving mechanism of evolution, although additional means exist, such as polyploidy and random genetic drift occurring within small populations. Cultural selection of desired traits by humans is yet another cause of evolution, leading to the development of domestic varieties of economically or socially important species **(Figure 1.16)**.

Both abiotic and biotic factors may act as agents of natural selection, and evolution may occur in response to the conditions of benign environments, or to more stressful ones. Individuals whose genetically based phenotypic qualities render them better adapted to coping with a specific environmental regime will be more likely to have relatively high fitness, compared with others in

Bill Freedman

FIGURE 1.16 Natural Selection Natural selection is a process that affects the evolution of species, including humans (*Homo sapiens*). Cultural selection is a variant that involves humans selecting for desirable traits, such as in varieties of domestic dog (*Canis lupus familiaris*).

their population. In a sense, a higher level of fitness could be interpreted as achieving greater "success" in life, which is ultimately represented by an individual having a disproportionately large representation in the collective genetic information of subsequent generations of its kind.

Natural selection and resulting evolutionary changes are often studied using the techniques of molecular ecology, which include population genetics, phylogenetics, and genomics. Many of these studies use molecular techniques to investigate basic questions, such as the ecological and evolutionary relationships of species. Many others are applied to questions related to conservation, such as the identification of species present in natural habitats, and the forensic documentation of body parts of endangered species that may have been illegally killed and traded. The key distinction of these leading-edge studies is that they use advanced molecular techniques to investigate evolutionary and practical questions in a field setting, rather than in the laboratory.

Although the subject area is controversial, ideas related to evolution have also been used to ask questions related to the characteristics of higher-order parts of the ecological hierarchy, such as communities and even the biosphere. For instance, some kinds of natural forests and other ecosystems are highly flammable in their mature condition, and although a wildfire may be catastrophic to their dominant organisms, the disturbance imposes a degree of rejuvenation on the system by speeding up rates of nutrient cycling and other functions. Often, these fire-prone ecosystems are dominated by plants whose biomass is extremely combustible. Canadian examples include white birch (*Betula papyrifera*), jack pine (*Pinus banksiana*), and black spruce (*Picea mariana*), which have explosively flammable bark or foliage. Is it possible that these species have evolved a high degree of flammability that, while lethal to the individuals in a wildfire, is favourable to their longer-term populations because this kind of disturbance is needed if their stands are to rejuvenate and regenerate?

The notion of **group selection** has been developed to help conceptualize this sort of population or community-level evolutionary process. It involves genetic information becoming more widespread in a population because of the benefits realized by a group, beyond effects on the fitness of the individuals involved. Group selection is an interesting idea, but it has not yet progressed very far in terms of theory development, largely because of the difficulty of doing empirical studies—most of the work on this subject has been conceptual or theoretical.

Even at the level of the biosphere it has been suggested that life, as an integrated whole, has somehow evolved mechanisms that provide a degree of regulation of environmental conditions, so as to maintain them within a favourable range for continued survival. It has even been suggested that there is a degree of homeostatic control, which in this case would suggest that when change is detected there is an ability to force steady conditions through compensating mechanisms of planetary physiology.

These ideas originated with James Lovelock, a British scientist who suggested that all life in the biosphere integrates into a "superorganism" that he named Gaia (after an ancient Greek mother goddess that is said to metaphorically personify Mother Earth). According to Lovelock, Gaia may have evolved mechanisms to maintain its atmospheric concentration of oxygen at an optimal level of 21 percent, which is comfortable for organisms that rely on an oxidative metabolism but not so high that it would promote an excessive flammability of biomass and disastrous conflagrations. Along the same lines, he suggested that Gaia somehow maintains the intensity of its atmospheric greenhouse effect at a level that keeps the global climate comfortable, principally by having mechanisms to control the concentrations of water, carbon dioxide, and methane.

These are intellectually titillating ideas, but few scientists believe them. The problem is that evolution at that scale would exceed the possibilities of group selection, and any emergent hypotheses are essentially nontestable because we know of only one replicate of planetary life.

1.4 Ecology and Sustainability

The knowledge of ecology is important for many reasons. First and perhaps foremost, there is great intrinsic value to understanding the influences of environmental factors on organisms and ecosystems. In fact, some of the greatest questions in science are about the existence and functioning of life and ecosystems.

Knowledge of ecology is also vital for reasons beyond understanding the organization of the natural world. Humans are organisms, albeit with unique cognitive ability and astonishing cultural and technological abilities that empower us to have an unprecedented ability to harvest, manage, and damage components of the biosphere. Like any species, if humans are to survive, then individual people and their collective economies must have access to resources that are harvested from nature—these provide us with food, materials, energy, and other necessities.

Within that context, the knowledge of ecology is crucial to the design of a human enterprise that can harvest natural resources in ways that do not diminish their availability to future generations—this is what is meant by a **sustainable economy**. Such an economy must ultimately be founded on the wise use of renewable resources. **Renewable resources**, such as sunlight and biomass, are capable of regenerating and so can potentially be harvested forever. In contrast, **nonrenewable resources**, such as metals and fossil fuels, are present in a fixed quantity and do not regenerate after they are mined from the environment **(Figure 1.17)**.

The link to ecology is that many of the most vital renewable resources are goods and services provided by ecosystems, such as biomass in its many forms, clean flowing water, and nutrient cycling. To be sustainable, an economy must not use those necessities faster than the rate at which they are being produced by the natural world. Moreover, even while conserving its essential base of natural resources, an **ecologically sustainable economy**

FIGURE 1.17 Ecology Is Useful We need the knowledge and skills of ecologists to help deal with environmental problems. Once this immense open-pit oil-sand mine near Fort McMurray, Alberta, is played out, the intent is to rehabilitate the land to an acceptable ecological condition, such as forest and wetlands.

must avoid causing the endangerment or extinction of other species and of entire natural ecosystems.

Ultimately, it is renewable resources that are the vital basis of a sustainable human economy. The most prominent kinds of renewable resources are related to sunlight, which may be used directly or transformed and made available in other forms, including:

- direct (or passive) solar, which can be absorbed as useful heat;
- photovoltaics, in which sunlight is converted to electricity;
- wind and oceanic currents, which are large-scale movements of mass that are driven by thermal gradients created by regional differences in the absorption of solar energy;
- hydroelectricity, which is generated using gravitational flows of water that are energized by the solar-powered hydrological cycle; and
- biomass in its many forms.

Some additional renewable resources are nonsolar in origin, including:

- tidal movements of water, which are driven by the gravitational attraction among the Sun, Earth, and Moon, and that can be used to generate electricity; and
- geothermal energy, which is produced by the heat of radioactive decay occurring in the core of Earth.

Of the various kinds of resources noted above, biomass is most directly a product of ecosystems. We harvest and use biomass as the source of all of our food, much of our medicine and materials, and a source of energy. Ecological knowledge is crucial to fostering the productivity of biological resources, to setting appropriate harvest limits, and to dealing with environmental damage that is inevitably caused by the use of any natural resource, including to ecosystems and the biodiversity they sustain. Clearly, ecological considerations and knowledge are vital to the sustainable development of the human economy. This subject matter is dealt with in various parts of this book, but especially in Chapters 15 through 17.

What is the role of ecologists and their knowledge in helping society to deal with problems related to natural resources, biodiversity, and other environmental issues? Essentially, it is to provide sage and objective advice to decision makers, who are generally politicians, governmental bureaucrats, or leaders in the private sector or in the nongovernmental community (such as environmental charities). The advice of ecologists and other scientists helps people to understand the causes and consequences of environmental problems, and to then choose appropriate actions that would help to avoid or repair those damages.

It is important to understand, however, that the advice of ecologists and other scientists is only one consideration for decision makers, who are also concerned with cultural, economic, and political contexts of environmental problems. In fact, when making decisions about how to deal with an environmental problem, decision makers may give greater weight to social and economic considerations than to scientific ones.

This is particularly the case if there is scientific uncertainty about an issue, which is often the case. Because of ongoing controversy about concerns such as global climate change, the endangerment and extinction of biodiversity, the diminishment of natural resources, and the importance of various kinds of pollution, decision makers are receiving scientific advice that is to some degree contrary or ambiguous. Moreover, decision makers often worry about short-term implications of their decisions on their own chances for re-election or continued employment, or on the economic activity of their company or of society more generally. They may view those considerations as being more important than the consequences of ecological and other kinds of environmental damage (see Chapter 17); if so, this will have a great influence on how seriously they consider advice offered by ecologists or other scientists.

It is obvious that the knowledge of ecology is crucial to the development and implementation of a sustainable human economy. However, ecologists must work hard to ensure that their well-considered advice is having an appropriately serious influence on societal-level decisions that carry the risk of causing environmental damages. Ultimately, this goes beyond the conduct of excellent research—it also requires a deep engagement of some ecologists in consultative and advocacy activities. Ecologists and their knowledge are too important to remain coolly detached from important issues about which their advice is required and should be heeded.

CHAPTER SUMMARY

(LO1.1)

- Ecology is the science-based study of the relationships of organisms and their environment. Its research is interdisciplinary, in the sense that although ecology mostly involves biology, it includes other aspects of science, such as chemistry, geology, meteorology, mathematics, physics, and statistics. Work in ecology may be undertaken at various scales, ranging from individual organisms to populations, communities, landscapes, and ultimately the entire biosphere, but there are also connections to levels below and above these ones

(LO1.2)

- Ecology is a diverse subject area with many specializations that range in their scales of interest from individuals to the biosphere, in addition to certain environments (such as the marine, freshwater, and terrestrial realms), as well as specific biomes (such as certain kinds of forest, grasslands, and aquatic ecosystems), including their inherent dynamics of space and time.

(LO1.3)

- The Sun is one of many billions of stars in the universe, and Earth is one of eight planets in a heliocentric solar system. While recognizing that all elements of the universe are unique in various characteristics, the singularity of Earth is that it is the only place known to support life and ecosystems.

(LO1.4)

- Ecology uses scientific methodologies, which involve making observations and analyses based on careful and objective studies of patterns in the structure and functioning of the natural world, as well as controlled experiments to test the predictions of hypotheses. This approach distinguishes science from belief systems, and ecology from natural history.

(LO1.5)

- The theory of evolution provides an underlying context for much of ecology, particularly in the sense of understanding how populations and higher-order groupings of organisms are able to adapt to changes in environmental conditions.

(LO1.6)

- The study of ecology is vital to guiding the human economy along a pathway that is sustainable for both people and the natural world. It provides necessary advice for the sustainable use of natural resources, particularly renewable ones, as well as for the maintenance of biodiversity and ecosystem functions.

QUESTIONS FOR REVIEW AND DISCUSSION

1. What is the subject matter of ecology? Explain the difference between curiosity-driven and applied work in ecology.

2. Make a list of important environmental factors, including abiotic and biotic ones. Explain how they influence the productivity of organisms and ecosystems.

3. Which levels of the hierarchical organization of the universe are most relevant to ecology? Provide a brief explanation of each of them, including how they are linked to the levels above and below.

4. What is fitness, and how is it related to evolution by natural selection?

5. Why do ecologists have "physics envy"?

6. What is the scientific method? Explain a case in which that methodology is applied to investigating a question in ecological research.

7. Explain how the knowledge of ecology is important to the sustainability of the human economy.

Environmental Influences

LEARNING OBJECTIVES

After studying this chapter you should be able to:

1. Explain how abiotic and biotic environmental influences affect organisms and the structure and function of ecosystems.

2. Describe the kinds of environmental stressors, how they may change over space and time, and the ways they limit the productivity and fitness of organisms and the development of ecosystems.

3. Understand the concepts of tolerance, resilience, disturbance, succession, and stability and how they relate to regimes of environmental stressors.

4. Explain the principle of limiting factors and its application to the environmental problem of eutrophication.

5. Discuss extreme environments and how they help to define the limits of tolerance of organisms and thereby the dimensions of the biosphere.

2.1 Environmental Influences

We previously examined a working definition of ecology as "the study of the relationships of organisms and their environment." Within that context, a core subject matter of ecology is examination of the kinds of **environmental influences** (or **environmental factors**) that affect organisms and ecosystems.

Depending on their relative importance at a particular place or time, those influences can have profoundly beneficial or damaging consequences. Those effects may be exerted on the components of ecosystems, such as individual organisms, populations, communities, or ecoscapes (landscapes or seascapes), as well as on vital functions such as productivity, decomposition, and nutrient cycling. As such, the study of environmental factors helps ecologists to better understand the influences that affect, and perhaps even control, the structural and functional attributes of ecosystems.

Biotic and Abiotic Influences

Environmental factors may be classified as being **abiotic** (or **inorganic**), meaning they are exerted by nonliving agencies, or **biotic** and associated with the influences of organisms (see also Section 1.1). Abiotic factors may act through a physical influence, as is the case of moisture, radiation, temperature, water currents, and wind, or they may be chemical, as with nutrients and toxic substances.

The influence of either kind of environmental factors may be direct or indirect. For example, on a sunny day, plants may receive abundant solar radiation that directly supports their photosynthesis. However, there are also indirect effects of the insolation, such as warming of the environment and rapid evaporation of water, both of which have important physiological consequences (Chapter 7). Another case might involve a forest fire, which directly kills or damages vegetation by scorching or consuming its biomass, while also indirectly affecting the habitat for plants and animals for the decades that it might take for recovery to occur (Chapter 10).

Biotic factors may also have a direct influence. These occur when a beaver creates a pond-like habitat by damming a stream, or when a moose feeds on willow stems and thus affects the biomass and productivity of the shrubs, or when a pack of wolves kill and eat the moose.

Those and other biotic factors also exert indirect influences. For instance, when trees and shrubs have absorbed most of the water from the soil, a result is droughty conditions for seedlings and other low-growing plants in the understorey. Another case might involve a dense population of deer that has eaten most of the forage available to them in a local habitat, resulting in food deprivation for themselves as well as other herbivores. Yet another example could be physiological stress endured by fish in a shallow lake because the decomposition of dead plant and algal biomass has resulted in low-oxygen conditions. Note that it is common for the indirect influences of biotic factors to be exerted through changes in abiotic ones, such as moisture, nutrients, or oxygen.

Environmental Influences May be Optimal or Suboptimal

If a habitat is to support life and ecosystems, its environmental conditions must satisfy the needs of organisms. However, species vary greatly in their optimum and ranges of tolerance of environmental factors. For example, plants growing in the Arctic tundra must be capable of tolerating an extremely protracted and cold winter, whereas those of tropical forest require more evenly warm and moist growing conditions.

In general, environmental factors affect organisms by modifying their physiology, development, growth (productivity), reproduction, and behaviour. Organisms that are fortunate to live in an environmental regime in which abiotic and biotic factors are optimal to meeting their needs will have a higher likelihood of growing well and achieving their genetic potential **(Figure 2.1)**. They will be more likely to grow quickly and have as many offspring as is biologically possible, being limited only by constraints inherent in their genome. Organisms that meet these "performance" criteria are more likely to maximize their fitness, and so to disproportionately contribute to the evolution of succeeding populations, and ultimately of their species (see Section 1.3).

It is rare, however, for the natural world to provide such agreeable conditions that organisms can routinely achieve a high level of reproductive fitness. It is much more usual for environmental conditions to be suboptimal (or stressful) to some degree, meaning they pose constraints on the potential biochemistry, growth, behaviour, and fitness of organisms. For example, a particular

FIGURE 2.1 Performance of Individuals Individuals that experience relatively good environmental conditions are more likely to be productive and to achieve reproductive success and a higher level of fitness. In this case, a low-growing shrub of northern blueberry (*Vaccinium boreale*) growing in a relatively open, moist, and fertile site near Goose Bay, Labrador, has produced an impressive biomass of fruit. While there are no guarantees, consistent fruit crops like this are likely to result in higher fitness than would be achieved by the same plant if growing under more stressful environmental conditions.

maple seedling might have established itself in a suboptimal place on the forest floor that does not provide much light, moisture, or nutrients. Under those tough conditions the seedling will be less productive than its genetic potential would have allowed, and it may never reach maturity (the point at which it produces seeds) and so might have no fitness during its life. On the other hand, a luckier seedling that establishes in a site with easier access to vital resources may quickly grow to maturity and produce many seeds (although it will still be exposed to the vagaries of unpredictable disturbances).

This example highlights the fact that the inherent potential of an organism is set by its genotype, but the actual expression of that capacity (the phenotype) varies depending on circumstances that it has experienced, a phenomenon referred to as phenotypic plasticity (Section 1.3). Clearly, environmental context and opportunity are important factors that influence success in life, and this is true of all organisms.

Of course, the influences of environmental factors are also relevant at ecological scales beyond that of individual organisms—such as populations, communities, and landscapes. The least stressful environments are distinguished by conditions of moisture, nutrients, temperature, and biotic interactions that are not unduly constraining to ecosystem functions, and damage caused by disturbances, such as wildfire and disease, is rare. Relatively beneficial conditions such as these allow for a high degree of ecosystem development, in the sense of attaining relatively high biodiversity (in terms of species per unit area), high structural complexity, and rapid

FIGURE 2.2 Environmental Stress Varies Relatively benign environmental conditions allow for greater ecological development, while stressful habitats permit less. The image on the left shows an area of tropical rainforest in Tambopata National Park, Peru, a habitat that represents the zenith (peak) of ecosystem development on land. The image on the right is of high-altitude tundra-forest near Whitehorse, Yukon, where severe climatic stress and thin soil restrict ecosystem development in terms of biodiversity, biomass, and the rates of productivity and nutrient cycling.

productivity and nutrient cycling. In this sense, the least developed ecological communities occur in desert and oceanic abysses, and the most diverse and highly developed ones are tropical rainforest and coral reefs **(Figure 2.2)**.

Conversely, difficult environmental conditions may result in ecosystems with low biodiversity and productivity. At the greatest extremes the conditions are sufficiently harsh that no life or ecosystems are viable. As far as we know, those inhospitable conditions occur everywhere beyond the limits of Earth's biosphere, but even on this planet lifeless places are widespread—they occur deep within the crust, on top of mountains, in volcanic fumaroles, and in other utterly barren places. Nevertheless, some forms of life manage to exist in remarkably hostile conditions (see Ecology in Depth 2.1).

The Principle of Limiting Factors

Environmental factors are complex and highly situational—at any particular time and place they exist as an intricate array, and the relative strength of their influence can vary greatly. Typically, however, in any circumstances only one or a few factors are exerting a dominant influence, with others having a relatively minor effect.

This idea was first expressed by Justus von Liebig (1803–1873), a German chemist who developed the "law of the minimum." In his original expression, the principle stated that the productivity of an agricultural crop is determined not by the total supply of all necessary resources, but rather by the factor that is most scarce. In ecology, this idea is known as the **principle of limiting factors**. It states that certain ecological processes are controlled by whichever environmental factor is present in the least supply relative to the demand for it (see **Figure 2.3** and Environmental Applications 2.1 for a case study).

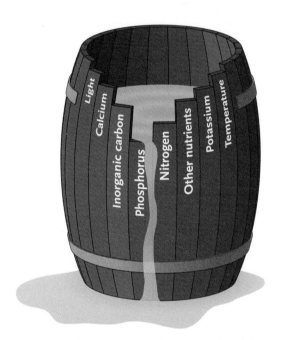

FIGURE 2.3 Liebig's Law of the Minimum Liebig explained his idea using the metaphor of an old-time barrel, which was constructed of vertical wooden slats (called staves) bound by metal hoops. In his metaphor, the length of the staves is uneven, and so the limiting factor for the water-holding capacity of the barrel is set by the height of the shortest stave. In this example, which is meant to illustrate the environmental factor that usually limits the productivity of freshwater lakes, the limiting factor is phosphorus.

The intensity (or availability) of many environmental factors varies continuously from values as low as zero to much higher levels. Within this range, zones can be defined in terms of their effect on the rates of various ecological functions—such as the metabolism of organisms, the growth of populations, or ecosystem-level processes such as productivity or decomposition **(Figure 2.4)**. The optimal range of any environmental factor will support the highest possible rates, although this effect is subject to constraints imposed by other

ECOLOGY IN DEPTH 2.1
Extreme Environments

Virtually all the universe consists of lifeless environments—the only known exception is the relatively miniscule biosphere of Earth, the bounds of which are defined by the presence of organisms. Even on our habitable planet, however, much of the physical space is devoid of life—this extends from places deep in the crust to soaring tracts in the atmosphere, as well as diverse places in between. The outer limits of the biotic envelope, where life and ecosystems are barely viable, are referred to as extreme environments. The highest and lowest of these **extreme environments** where life occurs are:

- *The stratosphere*, where viable microorganisms have been recovered from atmospheric samples collected as high as 41 km, where ultraviolet radiation is intense and the temperature about −20°C (Wainwright et al., 2003).
- *In fissured geological formations in the crust*, as deep as 3 km (Golubic et al., 1981), in which endolithic ("within-rock") bacteria survive in a warm, high-pressure environment by oxidizing sulphides and sparse organic matter (see Chapter 3 for an explanation of chemosynthesis).

Extreme environments also occur in more intermediate places where conditions are intense because of geological or other circumstances, such as:

- *Environments of severe acidity or alkalinity*, as in the case of pHs less than 3 that are associated with the oxidation of sulphide minerals by acidophilic ("acid-loving") *Thiobacillus* bacteria (see Chapter 4), or those with pH more than 9 that support specialized alkaliphilic ("alkali-loving") microbes.
- *Hot environments* associated with geothermal heat, such as eruptions of searing water at geysers on land or at deep-sea vents, or in deep crustal places, in which thermophilic ("heat-loving") archaean microbes may survive at temperatures exceeding 100°C.
- *Extremely dry habitats*, such as the most arid deserts, which may support only xerotolerant ("dry-tolerant") microbial crusts, such as that formed by *Microcoleus* cyanobacteria in salt desert (Campbell, 1979).
- *High-altitude habitats* above the alpine tundra, where extreme climatic and rocky conditions allow only a meagre productivity of lichens and bryophytes, a sparse abundance of invertebrates, and constrained microbial activity.

Sometimes pollution can be intense enough to represent an extreme environment. For example, seams of bituminous oil-shale have spontaneously ignited and burned for centuries at the Smoking Hills, a remote place in the western Northwest Territories (see Ecology in Depth 2.2).

This has resulted in "natural pollution" of the nearby tundra with sulphur dioxide, which is toxic to plants and causes severe acidification of soil and water, to the degree that the worst affected habitats are nonvegetated. This natural damage is similar to that caused by smelters that emit SO_2, such as the ones near Sudbury, Ontario (Freedman, 2010).

For that matter, many habitats constructed by people are extreme environments. This includes any tracts of asphalt or concrete, where few organisms are able to survive. Interestingly, this does not have to be the case, because many of those anthropogenic habitats could be naturalized to a degree, for example, by allowing some vegetation to establish and grow. Increasingly, that goal is being pursued through a naturalization approach to horticulture and also by the eco-technology of "green roofs," in which vegetation is grown on flat rooftops instead of covering the roof with asphalt. The improved ecological conditions provide some habitat for biodiversity and also fosters ecological services, such as heat retention during the winter, cooling in summer, and carbon-storage benefits associated with vegetation. This improved urban management illustrates a general point—that stressful environmental conditions can often be alleviated as a way of improving ecosystem development to benefit both people and biodiversity.

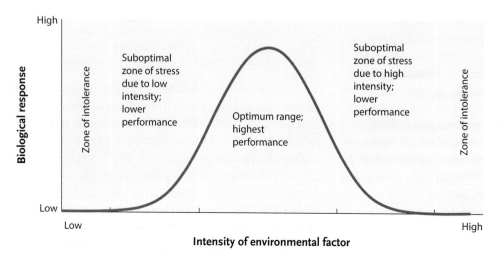

FIGURE 2.4 Ecological Responses to the Intensity of Environmental Factors Organisms, populations, and ecosystem functions have certain zones of tolerance and optima for environmental factors, although their relative influence may vary if other factors are limiting.

The principle of limiting factors can be readily appreciated by examining an important environmental problem known as **eutrophication**, in which the productivity of lakes or other waterbodies increases as nutrients are added **(Figure 1)**. When high rates of nutrient loading cause severe eutrophication to occur, the increased productivity may result in noxious algal blooms, a lack of oxygen in deep water, fish kills, tainting of drinking water, and other problems. When eutrophication became recognized as an important problem in the 1960s, its cause was difficult to mitigate because the limiting nutrient was not yet known.

The controversy about the potentially limiting nutrients for eutrophication focused on the roles of three candidate factors—the supplies of nitrogen [(N) as nitrate or ammonium], phosphorus [(P) as phosphate], and carbon [(C) as bicarbonate or carbon dioxide]. Some of the crucial ecological research that resolved this question was performed in the Experimental Lakes Area (ELA), located near Kenora in northwestern Ontario. This is a region of northern forest where scientists have been conducting longer-term studies related to limnology (the study of lakes), particularly questions related to environmental problems. The ELA scientists used a novel technique known as a "whole-lake experiment" to investigate eutrophication. Essentially, they manipulated conditions in an entire lake, by adding nutrients to it, and comparing any ecological responses to conditions in a nonmanipulated "control" lake. The natural condition of the ELA lakes is oligotrophic (or unproductive), but when fertilized with certain nutrients they could become eutrophic (highly productive). Some of the key whole-lake experiments related to eutrophication were the following (Schindler, 1990; Schindler et al., 1990):

- Lake 304 was fertilized for two years with N, P, and C and it quickly became eutrophic. Soon after the addition of P was stopped, the lake returned to its original oligotrophic condition, even though N and C were still being added.
- Lake 226 is an hourglass-shaped lake with two basins connected by a narrow channel **(Figure 2)**. The sections were separated by a vinyl barrier, and one half was treated with C, N, and P and the other with C and N. Only the basin that received phosphorus became eutrophic. When the nutrient additions were stopped, the lake recovered its oligotrophic condition within a year.
- Lake 302 was also fertilized with P, N, and C. However, the nutrients were injected into its deep water during the summer, a time when lakes develop a thermal stratification that prevents warmer surface water (the epilimnion) from mixing with cooler water below (the hypolimnion). Eutrophication did not occur because phytoplankton in the surface water did not have access to nutrients that had been added to the deeper water.
- Lake 227 became highly eutrophic after it was fertilized with P and N, and it remained so over a 37-year period during which the annual P addition remained constant but the inputs of N declined. This experiment demonstrated that naturally occurring fixation of atmospheric N_2 (see Chapter 4) can provide enough inorganic N to satisfy the needs of phytoplankton. As a result, the P addition by itself was sufficient to cause eutrophication.

These whole-lake experiments at the ELA, along with research in other regions of Canada and elsewhere, provided convincing evidence that phosphorus is usually the limiting nutrient for primary

FIGURE 1 Eutrophication Eutrophic waters are highly productive because the nutrient supply is abundant. This fertile shallow-water wetland in southern Ontario has a profuse growth of aquatic plants. When their dead biomass sinks to deeper water, most of the oxygen is consumed by decomposition, which can make the habitat unsuitable for aquatic animals.

(Continued)

FIGURE 2 **A Whole-Lake Experiment** Lake 226 is an hourglass-shaped lake in the Experimental Lakes Area. Its two basins were separated with a vinyl partition, and only the basin that received phosphorus became eutrophic, showing that phosphorus was the limiting nutrient to eutrophication.

Courtesy of David Schindler

phate, this is not true of other aquatic ecosystems. Coastal marine waters, for example, are usually limited by nitrate. In any situation, however, knowledge of the limiting nutrients is useful because it shows a way to prevent eutrophication by taking actions to reduce the loading of the limiting nutrient. Where these mitigations have been pursued, such as for cities on the Great Lakes, eutrophication is much less of an environmental problem than it once was.

This is not to say, however, that eutrophication is no longer an important environmental problem—it is severe and even worsening in places where nutrient dumping to lakes is not well controlled. In Canada, the most important problems today are occurring in Lake Winnipeg, which has been suffering from worsening blooms of blue-green algae (cyanobacteria) for several decades. The cause is large inputs of nitrogen and phosphorus, with the latter considered the primary limiting factor for the eutrophication. The source of the nutrients is mostly drainage from agricultural fields that have been excessively fertilized with those nutrients, but there are also sizeable inputs from sewage wastewaters. The algal blooms make the lake much less suitable for use as a source of drinking water (the cyanobacteria release distasteful compounds as well as toxins) and they also poses a threat to recreational use of the lake and a commercial fishery, which are important economic activities. Ultimately, resolution of the eutrophication of Lake Winnipeg will require a watershed-scale approach to reduce the nutrient loading, including requiring urban areas to remove nutrients from their treated sewage effluents, and agricultural interests to control their overuse of fertilizers.

productivity in freshwaters. This knowledge pointed the way to an effective management strategy to control eutrophication, which has focused on reducing or eliminating the phosphorus content of detergents, treating sewage to reduce its phosphorus concentration before wastewaters are released to the environment, and finding ways to reduce inputs of agricultural fertilizer to lakes and rivers.

While the primary limiting nutrient for algal productivity in almost all freshwaters is the availability of phos-

influences, which according to the principle of Liebig may be more limiting than the one being considered.

In comparison, the suboptimal range of an environmental factor may be capable of supporting individuals, populations, or ecosystem functions, but at reduced levels of performance. As such, suboptimal conditions are tolerable, but because the intensity of the factor is too low, or too high, the resulting stress causes a less-than-optimal performance to occur. At higher intensities of an environmental factor that exceed the limits of tolerance,

survival is not possible. These ideas of tolerance and optima were first expressed by the American ecologist Victor Shelford (1877–1968).

Almost always there will be some degree of genetically based variation among individuals in the tolerances and optima of environmental conditions. As a result, population-level evolutionary change may result when the intensity of environmental factors changes, as long as the influence remains within the zone of tolerance of the population.

Natural Pollution at the Smoking Hills

The Smoking Hills are a natural phenomenon at a remote coastal location beside the Beaufort Sea near Cape Bathurst in the Northwest Territories. The region has a sedimentary geology, and seams of bituminous shale occur in the seacliffs. When the shale becomes exposed to atmospheric oxygen, as occurs when erosion causes slumping of the coastal cliffs, sulphide minerals (such as iron sulphide, FeS_2) are oxidized by chemosynthetic *Thiobacillus* bacteria (see Chapter 4), which produces sulphate and heat as metabolic by-products. In certain insulated situations the heat accumulates to the degree that the bituminous shale spontaneously ignites. The material may then smoulder for years, releasing sulphur dioxide (SO_2) to the atmosphere, which is blown inland by the prevailing winds as ground-level plumes. The SO_2 is toxic to plants, and additional environmental damage is caused when the gas deposits to soil and water and causes severe acidification, with pH less than 3 occurring in some places. At such low pHs, naturally occurring metals become highly soluble in water, which greatly increases the toxicity of the environment.

The Smoking Hills are an ancient phenomenon, at least thousands of years old, although the first historical reference was in 1826 by John Richardson, an early explorer. The case of the Smoking Hills represents "natural pollution" because neither the presence of the bituminous shale nor its ignition have anything to do with people.

The SO_2, extreme acidity, and metal availability have caused intense ecological damage in the vicinity of the plumes **(Figure 1)**. The ecological effects have been studied by Tom Hutchinson and colleagues from the University of Toronto. In the worst-affected places there is total devastation—no plants can survive and the land and water are essentially barren. However, with increasingly further distances from the edge of the seacliffs, the plumes become progressively diluted by ambient air and the pollution becomes less severe.

The first vegetated community that is encountered supports only a few plants that are tolerant of the chemically stressful habitats—including a wormwood (*Artemesia tilesii*) and a polar-grass (*Arctagrostis latifolia*). These are wide-ranging species, but their local

populations are likely specifically adapted to tolerating the pollution. As one moves several kilometres further inland, the normal tundra vegetation is encountered, which supports a much richer plant community of more than 70 species. Tundra ponds are also common at the Smoking Hills—those affected by severe acidity and metals support only a few tolerant species, while the reference ponds have much more biodiversity and higher productivity.

As a natural phenomenon, the pollution and ecological damage at the Smoking Hills are of interest to ecologists. They also provide insight into the longer-term patterns of damage that might be expected from anthropogenic emissions of SO_2; for example near a large smelter, such as those at Sudbury, Ontario (Environmental Applications 1.1). These effects include severe acidification and toxic metals, a rapid decrease in the intensity of pollution with increasing distance from sources of emissions, severe damage caused to the biota of terrestrial and aquatic habitats, and the evolution of local populations (known as ecotypes) that are relatively tolerant of the toxic stressors.

FIGURE 1 Natural Air Pollution at the Smoking Hills The sulphurous plumes are emitted by spontaneously ignited bituminous shale, and they damage the tundra by SO_2 toxicity, acidification, and solubilized metals.

Bill Freedman

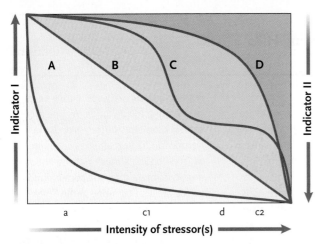

FIGURE 2.7 Stressors and Biological or Ecological Responses
The curves are hypothetical SER relationships, and they depict variations in the resistance to biological or ecological change when faced by a change in environmental stress. The response variables may either a decrease (Indicator I) or increase (Indicator II) in value. A, B, C, and D represent different relationships between increased stress and change in a biological or ecological indicator. Model A would be valuable as an early-warning indicator because it exhibits an initial rapid change, but this slows after a threshold of tolerance (a) has been exceeded. Model B responds steadily and is a consistent measure of response throughout the range of the stressor. Model C exhibits a stepwise response with rapid change at one threshold of tolerance (c1) followed by relative stability, and then rapid response at another threshold (c2). Model D provides a late-warning signal because it shows a strong response only after an extended range of tolerance is exceeded at threshold (d), which could be at a relatively advanced stage of damage. The shape of the response curves may differ substantially for increased and decreased stress because of differences in resilience (hysteresis) in the stressor–response function.

SOURCE: Based on Freedman (1995) and Lapaix et al. (2009).

Stability refers to how constant a population, community, or landscape remains over time. Biological and ecological stability may be due to a number of factors. Strong resistance to environmental change contributes to stability, as does a high degree of resilience after a perturbation. The subjects of tolerance, resilience and stability are examined in more detail in Chapter 10 in the contexts of disturbance and succession. Our intent here is to introduce the concepts as fundamental ways of thinking about the ecological effects of environmental influences.

2.3 Ecological Responses to Changes in Environmental Stress

An ecosystem that has been affected by a disturbance typically suffers mortality of some individuals, along with changes to its structural (e.g., species composition, biomass distribution) and functional (e.g., decomposition and nutrient cycling) properties. A process of successional recovery then begins, and if it proceeds for a long enough time, a mature ecosystem will be restored, perhaps one that is similar to that existing before the disturbance.

Chronic stressors, which influence ecosystems relatively continuously, include many climatic and chemical influences. Depending on their intensity, organisms may suffer a loss of productivity, or acute effects such as tissue damage, or ultimately death. At the community level, relatively vulnerable species will be reduced or eliminated if there is a large enough increase in the intensity of stress. Part of their function in the community (i.e., their niche) may then be assumed by more-tolerant species of the original community, or by invaders that can exploit a stressful but weakly competitive habitat. Increased exposure to environmental stressors can also result in evolutionary changes if individuals vary in their tolerance and those differences are genetically fixed. Under such conditions, natural selection may eventually result in increased tolerance at the population level.

Longer-term ecological change may result from a prolonged intensification of chronic stress. This might occur, for example, if a new metal smelter emits pollutants such as sulphur dioxide and metals that affect an initially forested landscape. The toxic stressors may damage the tree-sized plants of the original forest and eventually cause it to give way to communities dominated by shrub-sized and herbaceous vegetation. If the stress from pollutants is severe enough, the landscape may lose its plant cover entirely. Ecological damage of this sort has occurred around many older smelters that, because of lax environmental legislation at the time, were allowed to cause excessive pollution. Well-known examples include a number of smelters near Sudbury (see Environmental Applications 1.1) and "natural" pollution at the Smoking Hills (Ecology in Depth 2.2).

Because a smelter is a point-source of emissions (i.e., emissions are released from a discrete place, such as a smokestack), the intensity of pollution decreases in a more-or-less exponential pattern with increasing distance (Environmental Applications 1.1 and **Figure 2.8**). As a consequence, the ecological responses will radiate outward from the source of pollution and eventually become manifest as a persistent spatial gradient of community change.

Other spatial changes in stressors also result in corresponding patterns of ecological responses. For instance, a linear source (such as a highway) of pollutants will establish a perpendicular (orthogonal) gradient that parallels the source. Road de-icing salt and vehicular tail-pipe emissions are distributed along roads in this way. A stepcline is a result of an immediate change at a boundary,

FIGURE 2.8 Gradients of Toxic Stress In this case, historical emissions of SO_2 from a smelter near Sudbury, Ontario, have created gradients of toxic stress that resulted in corresponding changes in the structure and function of affected ecosystems, including damage to vegetation because of acidification and toxicity. The pollution and damage were most intense near the source of emissions, as shown by the blackened bedrock and lack of vegetation close to the smokestack. The pollution became rapidly less with distance, as suggested by the shrubby vegetation in the foreground about 5 km from the smelter. Eventually, with increasing distance, the nonaffected (reference) conditions of mature mixed-species forest and clean lakes are reached.

Bill Freedman

for instance, between a lake and its surrounding terrestrial upland, or between a dump of toxic industrial wastes and the surrounding land. Often, environmental gradients result in a transitional zone, known as an **ecotone**, between distinctive community types (see Section 13.2).

As environmental stress intensifies over time, the following patterns of ecological responses are commonly observed:

- Depending on the sensitivity of species, there will be decreases of productivity, increased mortality, and reproductive failure. If there are genetically based differences in tolerance within a population, then natural selection may result in evolutionary change and the development of ecotypes that are more resistant to the stressor.
- Changes occur in the community as sensitive species are replaced by others that are more tolerant of the intensifying stressor regime.
- Top predators and large-bodied species may be selectively lost from the ecosystem.
- Species diversity and richness are decreased.
- Community-level respiration exceeds production, so the net production becomes negative and the amount of biomass decreases.
- Nutrient capital becomes depleted by leaching and other losses.
- Rates of productivity, decomposition, and nutrient cycling are decreased.

If the intensified regime of stressors becomes stabilized at a high intensity, then the longer-term ecological change will reflect these kinds of responses. Compared with the original communities, the affected ecosystem will be simpler in structure and function, will sustain less biodiversity, will be dominated by relatively small species, and will have low rates of productivity and slower decomposition and nutrient cycling. In the worst cases, no biota can survive.

In general, these changes would be interpreted as representing ecological "damage," in the sense of impaired quality and natural condition of the ecosystem (or *ecological integrity*; see Section 17.2). The ability of the ecosystem to supply the human economy with natural resources will also be generally degraded. Judgments of the quality of change—whether it is "good" or "bad"—are important in ecology. In general, however, changes are more likely to be considered as being damage if they are caused by an intensified stressor regime that has resulted from a human influence, such as an industrial activity. If the stressors are natural in origin, then the ecological change might not be viewed as being damage. These considerations are highly relevant to the intersection of ecology with environmental planning and impact assessment (Section 17.5), and are a key aspect of the applied relevance of the knowledge of ecologists.

The intensity of environmental stress may also decrease over time. When this happens, the ecological responses are in many respects the reverse of those observed when stress intensifies (but not necessarily exactly so—resilience is the degree to which succession recovers the original community). These changes represent a process of ecological recovery after the relaxation of stress.

For example, bans on the manufacturing and use of organochlorine insecticides and PCBs since the early 1970s have allowed a recovery to occur in the populations of birds that had been affected by those toxic chemicals, such as the bald eagle (*Hlaiaeetus leucocephalus*), peregrine falcon (*Falco peregrinus*), and double-crested cormorant (*Phalacrocorax auritus*). Similarly, the cessation of commercial hunting of grey whales (*Eschrichtius robustus*) has allowed their greatly depleted population on the Pacific Coast to recover to about their pre-exploitation abundance. In the case of the smelters near Sudbury, large reductions have occurred in the emissions of SO_2 and metals and this has also resulted in a substantial ecological recovery.

These cases all show that prudent actions to reduce the intensity of anthropogenic stressors can often result in great improvements of ecological conditions. However, there is always some degree of lingering damage, and in some cases the degradation is so severe that a substantial recovery may take centuries.

A CANADIAN ECOLOGIST 2.1

Tom Hutchinson: An Environmental Ecologist

FIGURE 1 Tom Hutchinson

Tom Hutchinson is a plant ecologist, educated in England, whose research initially involved fundamental questions about the ability of certain plant species to occur over a wide range of soil environments **(Figure 1)**. After he immigrated to Canada to take up a faculty position at the University of Toronto, he became interested in the damaging effects that pollution was having on vegetation near several large smelters at Sudbury. When he started that work in the late 1960s, not many academic ecologists were studying anthropogenic damages in ecosystems—most were engaged in "curiosity-driven" research about natural environmental influences on organisms and ecosystems. Therefore, Hutchinson was a leader in the emerging field of "environmental ecology," or research into ecological problems that are caused by industrial activities and other aspects of the human economy.

Hutchinson's conversion to applied work was sparked by a visit to Sudbury, where he was inspired by the sight of landscapes that had been devastated by several decades of intense pollution from metal-processing industries. He recognized the possibility of doing research that would examine fundamental questions about the structure and function of ecosystems, but in the context of steep gradients of toxic stressors. Tom engaged many enthusiastic students in research examining the patterns and causes of ecological damage in terrestrial and aquatic habitats, including the evolution of local plant ecotypes that have a genetically based tolerance of high concentrations of metals in their soil.

Subsequent to that work, Tom expanded his interests to other research areas relevant to environmental problems, including studies of pollution by metals and gases in various environmental contexts (smelters, recycling facilities, tailings disposal sites, urban areas), oil spills, declines of sugar maple forest, and climate change, including the potential effects of "nuclear winter" (a severe climatic deterioration that might follow a nuclear war).

In addition to his research interests, Hutchinson focused his teaching at the University of Toronto, and later at Trent University, on environmental ecology and sustainability, thereby influencing the outlook and knowledge of thousands of students. His impressive career has helped to legitimize the research and teaching of academic ecologists who are interested in these sorts of applied subject areas, which are important to sustainable development of the Canadian and global economies.

CHAPTER SUMMARY

(LO2.1)

- Environmental factors have a profound influence on the distribution and abundance of organisms and ecosystems, and on the rate of ecosystem functions.

(LO2.2)

- Environmental factors may be biotic or abiotic, and natural or anthropogenic, and they may vary continuously over space or time or in a more discrete fashion. If present at an intensity that is insufficient to meet their biological or ecological needs, or that is intolerable, then the productivity and reproductive fitness of individuals will be degraded, and ecosystem development will be constrained.

(LO2.3)

- Key ecological ideas related to environmental factors are tolerance (the ability of an organism or an ecological variable to function in a "healthy" manner within a range of intensities of environmental stressors, without undergoing changes that would be judged as representing damage), resilience (the speed and degree to which an organism, population, community, or ecoscape can recover to its original condition following a disturbance or after an intense stressor relaxes), disturbance (an event of damage that disrupts a population or community), succession (the process of community-level recovery following a disturbance), and stability (constancy over time, including resistance to environmental change and the degree of resilience after a perturbation).

- The principle of limiting factors states that, at any time, a particular environmental factor is present in the least supply relative to the demand, and it is the constraining influence on ecosystem functions. Within this context, all environmental factors have ranges of availability that are optimal, suboptimal, or intolerable, although the relative influence may be affected by other factors that are more limiting.

- Extreme environments define the limits of tolerance of organisms for environmental influences, and thereby the dimensions of the biosphere. Extreme environments can be associated with natural conditions, as well as anthropogenic influences such as severe pollution and asphalt or concrete surfaces.

QUESTIONS FOR REVIEW AND DISCUSSION

1. What are environmental factors? How do they affect the development of organisms and ecosystems?

2. What is the principle of limiting factors, and how does it help us to deal with certain environmental problems, such as eutrophication?

3. What are environmental stressors? Describe the major types of stressors.

4. Explain the key differences in the ecological effects of a disturbance and a chronic stressor.

5. Compare the ecological effects of a stand-replacing disturbance and a microdisturbance.

6. What ecological changes are observed following a large and persistent increase in the intensity of environmental stress?

Ecological Energetics

LEARNING OBJECTIVES

After studying this chapter you should be able to:

1. Define energy and describe the states in which it might exist.

2. Explain the laws of thermodynamics that govern the transformations of energy, including their ecological context.

3. Explain how the Earth is a flow-through system for solar energy.

4. Identify the major components of the energy budget of the Earth.

5. Explain the mechanism and importance of the Earth's natural greenhouse effect, and how it may be intensified by anthropogenic emissions of greenhouse gases.

6. Describe energy relationships within ecosystems, beginning with the fixation of solar energy by primary producers, through to the passage of that fixed energy to herbivores, carnivores, and decomposers, and eventually back to the nonliving environment.

7. Explain why there are large differences in productivity and standing crop among the major kinds of terrestrial and aquatic ecosystems.

8. Explain why the trophic structure of ecological productivity is pyramid shaped, and why ecosystems cannot support many top predators.

3.1 Energy in Ecosystems

All physical processes occurring anywhere in the universe are driven by flows of energy. As far as we know, however, Earth is the only place where there is a biological fixation of energy, principally of solar radiation by photosynthetic organisms. This phenomenon imparts the energetic basis for almost all of life (the only exceptions are related to chemically derived energy through a process called chemosynthesis, which is also examined in this chapter).

The field of **ecological energetics** is the study of the ways that solar energy becomes fixed by plants and other photosynthetic organisms and is then available to be transferred to other species. Important aspects of ecological energetics are the amounts of energy and biomass that are stored and transferred among the various trophic (or feeding) levels of ecosystems, and how certain physical and biological principles influence those structural and functional characteristics.

In this context, the term **biomass** (or **standing crop**) refers to the weight of the accumulated production of organic matter by an organism or by an ecosystem. **Productivity** refers to the rate at which energy is being fixed (in autotrophs), and also the rate at which biomass is accumulating (in all organisms and ecosystems). Because the water content of biomass can be highly variable, this material is usually measured on a dry-weight basis (typically after drying at about 100°C). Biomass data are often standardized to area (such as tonnes dry weight per hectare; t/ha), while productivity is further standardized to time (such as t/ha-year).

Ecological energetics is based on the principle that organisms and ecosystems are **open systems** with respect to energy, rather than closed ones. This means that energy flows into ecosystems, where some of it is fixed and used in various ways, and then eventually discarded in a degraded form (such as heat; these ideas are examined later in more detail in the section on thermodynamics). A corollary of this principle is that organisms and ecosystems are not self-sustaining: they require an ongoing supply of energy from the Sun or another source if they are to function and survive.

In almost all ecosystems, solar radiation is the key resource that supports the existence of organisms and ecological productivity. **Autotrophs** (self-feeding organisms), such as plants and algae, absorb solar energy and

Bill Freedman

FIGURE 3.1 **Autotrophs** Plants are autotrophs that absorb sunlight and use some of that energy to drive photosynthesis. Plants are green because their chlorophyll absorbs blue and red wavelengths of visible radiation, but reflect most of the green. This is a low-growing coastal plant known as sea sandwort (*Honckenya peploides*), growing on a beach in Nunavik, an arctic region of northern Quebec.

use it to fix carbon dioxide and water into simple sugars while generating oxygen as a waste **(Figure 3.1)**. This process, known as **photosynthesis**, is summarized by the following equation:

(3.1) $$Sunlight + 6\ CO_2 + 6\ H_2O \rightarrow C_6H_{12}O_6 + 6\ O_2$$

The energy content of the sugar produced by photosynthesis is the organic fuel for a vast complex of biochemical reactions by which autotrophs synthesize an enormous diversity of carbohydrates, proteins, fats, and other compounds that are needed for their growth and reproduction. The biomass accumulated by autotrophs is also a vital food for **heterotrophs**—organisms such as animals, fungi, and most bacteria that can subsist only by feeding on the biomass of other organisms.

In this chapter we will first examine energy as a physical entity—one that exists in various forms or states (Section 3.2). We then look at two laws of physics that govern the transformations of energy among its alternative states, and how it flows through and is stored in physical systems, including Earth and its ecosystems (Section 3.3). We then examine energy flows and budgets at the planetary level, including the warming mechanism known as the greenhouse effect (Sections 3.4 and 3.5). Finally, we examine and compare the energy fixation and accumulation of biomass in major kinds of ecosystems (Sections 3.6 and 3.7).

3.2 Fundamentals of Energy

Energy is defined as the capacity of a body or a system to perform work. In turn, **work** is defined as the consequence of a force that is applied over a distance. In this physical sense, examples of work being accomplished include the following:

- Solar radiation is absorbed and warms a dark pavement.
- Wind blows a leaf through the air.
- Trees are burned during a wildfire.
- A bicycle is driven along a road.
- A plant uses sunlight in photosynthesis.
- An animal metabolizes the absorbed energy of its food to run its physiology.

Energy may exist in various states (which are explained below). Under suitable conditions energy can be converted from any one of those states to another (Section 3.3). The examples noted above all involved changes of the state of energy. For instance, sunlight is electromagnetic energy, but if absorbed by an asphalt surface it is transformed into thermal energy. During a forest fire, the potential energy of biomass is converted into heat and electromagnetic energy. And during photosynthesis, solar electromagnetic energy is absorbed by chlorophyll, a pigment in foliage, and used to join carbon dioxide and water to form a sugar that stores potential energy.

The joule (J) is the standard measure of energy content according to the Système Internationale d'Unités (SI), which is the international scheme by which scientific units are established. One joule is defined as the amount of energy needed (or work done) in applying a force of one newton through a distance of one metre (because $1\ N = 1\ kg.m/sec^2$, this is equivalent to accelerating 1 kg of mass at 1 metre per second per second (m/s^2) over a distance of 1 m). Another commonly reported unit of energy is the calorie (cal or gram-calorie), which is equivalent to 4.18 joules and is defined as the energy needed to heat one gram of water from 15°C to 16°C. However, this is not the same as the "Calorie" by which dieticians measure the energy content of foods, which is actually 1000 calories (10^3 cal = 1 kilocalorie or kcal = 1 Calorie).

States of Energy

The states of energy can be assembled into three fundamental types: electromagnetic, kinetic, and potential, each of which is described in the following sections.

Electromagnetic Energy

Electromagnetic energy (or **electromagnetic radiation**) is associated with fundamental entities known as photons, which display characteristics of both particles and waves. Photons move through space at an unvarying velocity of 3.0×10^{10} cm/s, which is known as the "speed of light." Electromagnetic energy occurs in the form of a continuous spectrum that extends from extremely long wavelengths to very short ones. The wavelength ranges are arranged into discrete segments, which are known as gamma, X-ray, ultraviolet, visible (or "light"), infrared,

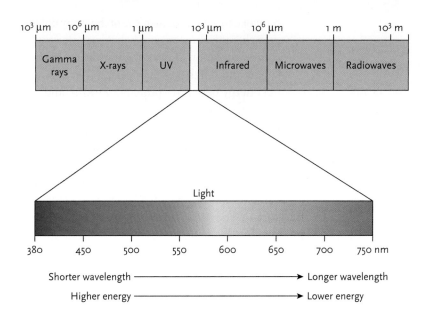

FIGURE 3.2 The Electromagnetic Spectrum
The spectrum is a continuum, but it is divided into sectors based on wavelength of the radiation (or on its inverse, frequency). The spectrum is presented in units of nanometres (1 nm = 10^{-3} μm = 10^{-9} m) on a logarithmic scale ($\log_{10}$). The visible component is expanded to show the wavelength ranges for the prismatic colours of the rainbow: red, orange, yellow, green, blue, and violet.

SOURCE: From RUSSELL/WOLFE/HERTZ/STARR. *Biology*, 1E. © 2010 Nelson Education Ltd. Reproduced by permission. www.cengage.com/permissions

microwave, and radio **(Figure 3.2)**. Shorter electromagnetic wavelengths are more "energetic" in that their higher frequency embeds a greater density of energy. Visible radiation is the most familiar portion of the electromagnetic spectrum—it is perceived by the human eye as "light" and ranges from about 0.4 to 0.7 micrometres (1 μm = 10^{-6} m).

Any object (or matter) whose surface temperature exceeds −273°C or "absolute zero" (this is 0 degrees on the Kelvin scale and is the coldest possible temperature) will radiate (or emit) electromagnetic energy. Moreover, the surface temperature of the object directly controls both the spectral quality and the rate of emission; hotter bodies have much greater emission rates than cooler ones, and the spectral quality is more strongly dominated by shorter, higher-frequency wavelengths.

The Sun, for instance, has a surface temperature of about 5500°C, and its emitted radiation is mostly ultraviolet (0.2–0.4 μm), visible (0.4–0.7 μm), and near-infrared (0.7–2 μm) **(Figure 3.3)**. In contrast, Earth has a much cooler surface that averages about 15°C, and so it radiates much less energy and of lower frequencies (longer wavelengths) that peak at about 10 μm in the longer-wave infrared part of the spectrum.

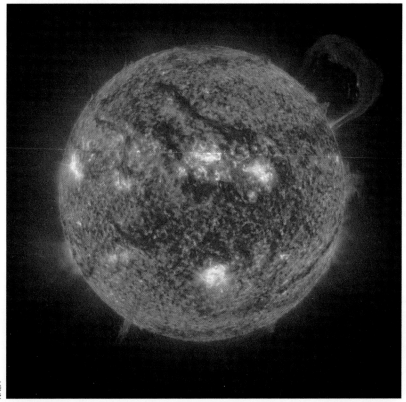

FIGURE 3.3 Energy from the Sun Drives Almost All Ecological Productivity This is an image of the Sun taken on 14 September 1999, using a telescope based on ultraviolet radiation. The immense handle-shaped prominence on the upper-right is an irruption of dense plasma suspended in the hot corona of the Sun. The hottest regions on the surface of the Sun appear as whitish, while the darker reddish areas are somewhat cooler.

NASA

Kinetic Energy

Kinetic energy exists in two basic forms, both of which involve mass in motion, but at different scales of space:

- **Thermal energy**, also called sensible energy or "heat," is associated with the rate of vibration and rotation of atoms or molecules and of their internal components (such as electrons and the nucleus). This kinetic movement occurs only at temperatures above $-273°C$ ($0°$ K). As temperature rises, the rates of vibration and rotation also increase rapidly and this accounts for gains in the amount of heat.

- **Mechanical energy** is associated with objects that are in motion, such as a planet moving through space, water flowing in a river, or a caribou strolling across a tundra. The mass and velocity of the moving object determine the amount of mechanical kinetic energy that is present.

Potential Energy

Potential energy represents a capacity to perform work when it becomes transformed into kinetic or electromagnetic energy. Potential energy may exist in various states:

- **Chemical energy** is stored in the bonds that link atoms within molecules. This kind of potential energy is mobilized by chemical reactions that lead to a release of kinetic or electromagnetic energy (if thermal energy is released, the reaction is referred to as *exothermic*). Examples of these sorts of reactions include the following:

  - If sodium chloride ($NaCl$) or other salts are dissolved into water, potential energy inherent in their ionic bonds is released, in the process generating heat that slightly warms the water.

  - When iron sulphide (FeS_2) is oxidized, some of the potential energy of its inter-atomic bonding is released; specialized bacteria known as *Thiobacillus* have the ability to tap the chemical potential of sulphides to support their productivity—this autotrophic process is known as *chemosynthesis* (see Section 3.6).

  - If organic compounds, such as hydrocarbons (molecules that contain only C and H atoms), are combusted in the presence of oxygen, the chemical potential of their inter-atomic bonds is released; for example, the combustion of gasoline in an engine releases its chemical potential, some of which is converted into the kinetic energy of moving pistons, which is transferred to other machinery and results in motion of the vehicle.

  - When biochemicals produced by organisms are oxidized by metabolic processes, energy is provided to support all aspects of their physiology, growth, reproduction, and behaviour, along with some generation of heat; carbohydrates such as sugars and starches contain about 17 kJ of potential energy per gram; proteins, 21 kJ/g; and fats or lipids, 39 kJ/g.

- *Gravitational energy* is a product of gravity, or the attractive forces that exist among all objects. Water that is situated at any height above sea level contains gravitational potential energy. If there is a pathway to a lower altitude, the potential energy is converted into kinetic energy of flowing water. Hydroelectric power plants are designed to convert some of the kinetic energy of flowing water into electricity.

- *Compressed gases* store potential energy by virtue of their compactedness, which is much greater than the lower pressure of the ambient atmosphere. This potential energy can do work if the gases are permitted to expand—for example, within the piston chamber of an automobile engine.

- *Elasticity* is a kind of potential energy that is inherent in the physical qualities of certain materials and that can perform work when released, as occurs when a drawn bow is used to shoot an arrow.

- *Electrical potential* exists when there are differences in the densities of electrons between regions. Electrons are negatively charged, subatomic particles. If a conducting material, such as a copper wire, connects two zones with higher and lower electron densities—and therefore different electrical potentials—electrons will flow down the gradient. When this happens, the electrical energy can be harnessed by various devices and machines that produce light, heat, or mechanical work. Voltage is a measure of the difference in electrical potential.

- *Nuclear energy* is by far the densest kind of energy—it results from the enormously strong binding forces that exist within (rather than between) atoms. In essence, nuclear reactions convert matter into energy. Compared to all other energy-releasing processes, nuclear reactions release immensely larger amounts of kinetic and electromagnetic energies per unit of fuel consumed. Potential energy is released through two different kinds of nuclear reactions:

  - *Fission reactions* occur when the nuclei of certain isotopes of unstable (radioactive) atoms, such as the heavy metals uranium-235 and plutonium-239 (^{235}U and ^{239}Pu), are split to produce lighter elements plus an immense quantity of energy. The reactors of nuclear power plants use controlled fission reactions to generate electricity. However, an uncontrolled fission reaction may result in a massive explosion, a fact that has been harnessed to manufacture devastating nuclear weapons.

- *Fusion reactions* occur when certain light elements, such as hydrogen, combine to form heavier atoms, in the process unleashing an immense amount of energy. Hydrogen bombs produce enormous nuclear explosions based on hydrogen-fusion reactions. Natural fusion reactions fuelled by hydrogen occur in stars, resulting in the production of enormous amounts of electromagnetic and kinetic energies, most of which is radiated into space.

3.3 Laws of Thermodynamics

Energy that exists in one state, such as electromagnetic, kinetic, or potential energy, can be transformed into another state. These transformations may occur spontaneously or human-made devices may enable them. However, all energy transformations must obey certain constraints whatever the circumstance. These constraints, or limiting conditions, are physical principles that are known as the laws of thermodynamics.

First Law of Thermodynamics

The **first law of thermodynamics** states *that energy can be transformed among its various states, but it is never created or destroyed, and so the energy content of the universe stays constant.* Because the amount of energy is conserved, in any particular system there is a zero-sum energetic balance among the inputs of energy, the amount stored within the system, and the outputs.

An example of this concept is an airplane that consumes fuel in order to fly, an energy input that can be measured. The engines and other machinery convert the chemical potential of the fuel into other states, such as movement of the aircraft (kinetic energy), power for lights (electrical energy), friction with the atmosphere (thermal energy), and hot exhaust gases (thermal energy). Overall, however, the first law of thermodynamics dictates that, while these and many other energy transformations occur as an airplane flies through the atmosphere, an exact accounting of all the reactions involving energy storage and outputs would show that the initial energetic content of the fuel was conserved.

A more ecological example concerns the energy budget of Earth (see Section 3.4 for more details). The planet receives an input of solar energy. That incoming electromagnetic radiation is either reflected back to outer space, absorbed by the atmosphere or by the surface of the planet, or absorbed by chlorophyll and used to drive photosynthesis. However, there are also energy outputs that balance the amounts of incoming solar energy that are absorbed. The outputs include the dissipation of increased heat content of both the atmosphere and surface by a radiation of infrared energy to outer space, and the eventual oxidation of the potential energy of any accumulated biomass by the respiration of organisms or perhaps by a wildfire. An accurate budgeting of these processes, plus additional transformations not mentioned, would find that although solar energy was converted into numerous other forms, the total amount of energy in the system or flowing through it was conserved.

Second Law of Thermodynamics

The **second law of thermodynamics** states that *energy transformations can occur spontaneously only under conditions in which the entropy in the universe is increased.* **Entropy** is a physical property that is linked to disorder, and it relates to the randomness and uncertainty of the distributions of matter and energy. Negative entropy results in a decrease in disorder (or an increase in order).

To understand the idea of entropy and the second law, think about a balloon. Experience tells us that the highly dispersed gases of the atmosphere would never spontaneously relocate and compress to inflate a balloon. That would be an exceedingly improbable event that, in a physical sense, would represent a gain of negative entropy. However, if person blows forcefully into a balloon, it can be inflated. That results in a local accumulation of negative entropy, which is made possible because energy has been put into the system to do the work of compressing gases. Once a balloon is inflated, it contains potential energy inherent in its compacted gases, and it may undergo a slow deflation or a fast one if it is punctured. Those decompression events can occur spontaneously because compressed gases in a balloon are in a highly ordered state, and they become more disordered when they return to the atmosphere—that change represents an increase in entropy. The key lesson here is that increases in entropy can occur spontaneously, but gains of negative entropy require an expenditure of energy through some kind of work.

Entropy also increases when sunlight (shorter-wave electromagnetic energy) is absorbed by a surface, converted to thermal energy (increased temperature), and then dissipated by a reradiation of longer-wave infrared energy. The solar energy that continuously irradiates Earth is composed primarily of visible and near-infrared wavelengths. The atmosphere and Earth's surface absorb much of that radiation and convert it to an increasing thermal content, which is eventually dissipated to outer space by a spontaneous emission of long-wave infrared. However, the overall planetary function of absorption and reradiation corresponds to an increase in entropy. This is because the original shorter-wave radiation has less entropy than the reradiated longer-wave type.

An important consequence of the second law is that energy transformations can never be totally efficient.

FIGURE 3.4 Entropy, Life, and Ecosystems Although life and ecosystems are "islands" of negative entropy, the second law of thermodynamics is not contravened because there are continual inputs of energy that power the work necessary to maintain these highly ordered systems. Almost all biological and ecological functions are driven by solar energy, either directly or indirectly. This includes the energy needed for photosynthesis by plants and other autotrophs, the foods needed by heterotrophic organisms (including people), and even the energy needed for activities such as bird-watching (in this case occurring in Point Pelee National Park, Ontario).

Bill Freedman

In technological applications, this means that some of the initial energy content of a fuel must be converted into heat, which is a relatively low grade form of energy, so that there is an increase of entropy. In a power plant, only about 40 percent of the energy of a fuel, such as coal or natural gas, can be converted into electricity, even if the best available technology is used. Similarly, the thermodynamic efficiency of an automobile is only about 30 percent (calculated as the kinetic energy of the moving vehicle divided by the potential energy of its fuel).

The productivity of ecosystems is also inefficient in this sense. Even if plants are living in optimal environmental conditions, their photosynthesis captures very little of the energy of the incoming solar radiation. In fact, natural ecosystems typically fix less than 1 percent of incident sunlight into biochemicals, although dense algal cultures in a laboratory may attain an efficiency of up to 6 percent.

It is interesting to contemplate how the existence of life and ecosystems satisfies the need for an increase in entropy from any spontaneous energy transformation, as is required by the second law of thermodynamics. Initially, solar radiation (a diffuse form of energy) is absorbed during photosynthesis and used to drive the fixation of simple inorganic compounds— readily available but widely dispersed carbon dioxide and water—into simple sugars. That initial ecological productivity is followed by an astonishing complex of biochemical reactions in both autotrophic and heterotrophic organisms. Some of those reactions use additional simple compounds (such as ammonium, nitrate, and phosphate) and ions (such as potassium, calcium, and magnesium) to synthesize organic substances having a dense energy content and a great diversity of molecular and physical structures. In this sense, organisms and ecosystems are built upon a foundation of multitudinous transformations of diffuse energy and mass into much denser and more highly organized structures that represent intense bioconcentrations of negative entropy.

That reduction in entropy might seem to contravene the second law of thermodynamics. However, the ostensible contradiction can be logically resolved in this way: Although organisms and ecosystems represent local bioconcentrations of negative entropy, this is thermodynamically feasible because of biological work that is made possible by harnessing some of the continuous input of solar radiation that is received by the biosphere. If this external energy subsidy were to somehow be terminated, all organisms and biomass would spontaneously disintegrate and release simple inorganic compounds and heat back into the environment. That would increase the entropy of the universe by a larger amount than that of the negative entropy that was gained by the original biofixation.

In this sense, therefore, the biosphere represents a localized "island" of negative entropy, which is continually fuelled by the Sun **(Figure 3.4)**. Moreover, as far as we know, Earth is the only place in the vast universe where the negative entropy of life and ecosystems exists.

3.4 Energy Flows and Budgets

The Sun is the focal point of its solar system, accounting for almost all of its energy and mass. Earth is the third-closest of eight planets that revolve around that star. The Sun provides energy that heats the surface of Earth,

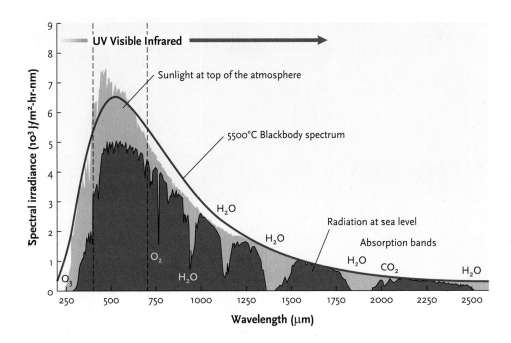

FIGURE 3.5 The Solar Spectrum The solid line shows the radiative spectrum that would be exhibited by a theoretical black body with a surface temperature of 5500°C (similar to that of the Sun). The overlying coloured area is the similar quality of solar radiation as it is received at the outer limits of Earth's atmosphere. The jagged curve beneath is the typical spectrum of sunlight that is received at Earth's surface, following the complex of wavelength-specific reflections and absorptions by atmospheric gases, particulates, and clouds.

SOURCE: Based on *Reference Solar Spectral Irradiance: Air Mass 1.5* (http://rredc.nrel.gov/solar/spectra/am1.5/)

promotes the circulation of its atmosphere and oceans, causes water to evaporate, and drives photosynthesis. In due course, all of the solar energy that Earth absorbs is dissipated back to outer space by an emission of long-wave infrared radiation. Because the inputs and outputs of electromagnetic radiation are in an essentially perfect balance, Earth is a **flow-through system** with respect to solar energy.

The input of energy to Earth is known as the **solar constant**. This insolation has a value of 8.21 J/cm².min (1.96 cal/cm².min), measured at the average distance from the Sun in Earth's elliptical orbit, and just beyond the atmosphere **(Figure 3.5)**. Visible radiation (ranging from about 380–750 μm in wavelength) and near-infrared (750–2500 μm) each account for about half of the incoming solar energy. Ultraviolet radiation accounts for less than 1 percent of the insolation, but it is biologically important because it can cause severe injuries to organisms.

Earth has an **energy budget**, which describes how the input of sunlight is reflected, absorbed, temporarily stored in different ways, and then eventually reradiated back to space **(Figure 3.6)**. Important aspects of Earth's energy budget are examined below.

- *Reflection* refers to incoming sunlight that is not absorbed by either the atmosphere or the surface of Earth. An average of 30 percent of the incoming solar radiation is reflected back to space. The reflectivity (or **albedo**) is affected by a number of factors:

  - *the amounts of cloud cover and suspended atmospheric particulates*, both of which are highly reflective, and also extremely variable over time and space;

  - *the character of the surface at a place or region*, with snow and ice being especially reflective and dark-coloured vegetation (such as boreal forest),

recently burnt areas, and asphalt being highly absorptive; and

  - *the angle of incidence* of the insolation (a lower angle means greater reflectivity); because Canada occurs at relatively high latitudes, the relative amount of reflection is generally higher during the winter and lower in the summer, and also higher around dawn and dusk and lower at noon.

- *Absorption of certain wavelengths of solar radiation by atmospheric constituents*, such as certain gases and vapours, results in heating of their mass and causes thermal gradients to develop. The gradients become partially dissipated by winds (atmospheric mixing) and by the reradiation of longer-wave infrared. The atmosphere absorbs about 25 percent of the incident solar radiation, with H_2O vapour and CO_2 gas being especially important in this function, particularly in the infrared part of the spectrum.

- *Absorption of solar radiation by the surface* accounts for about 45 percent of the solar energy received by Earth, but this varies greatly from place to place, depending on the local albedo. The absorptive surfaces include nonliving ones such as water, rocks, and buildings, as well as living matter such as vegetation. Dark-coloured surfaces are particularly effective at absorbing solar radiation.

- *Evaporation of water* occurs from both nonliving surfaces, such as oceans, lakes, wetlands, and moist soil, and also from organisms. Evaporation occurring from all surfaces is called **evapotranspiration**, and that from organisms, principally from vegetation, is **transpiration**. During evaporation, water changes from a liquid state to a gaseous state. This process absorbs energy, known as the latent heat (or enthalpy)

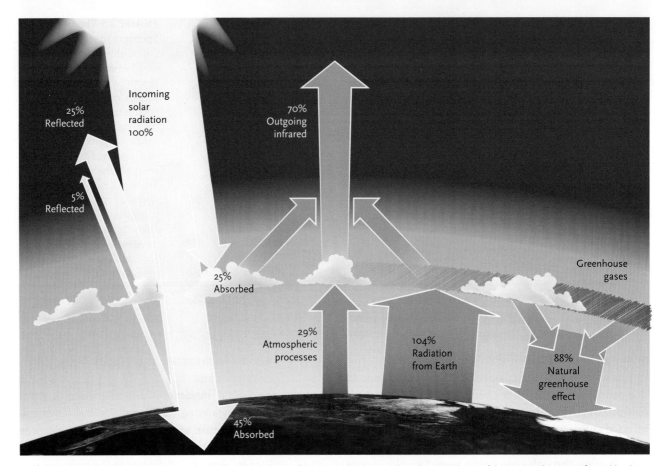

FIGURE 3.6 The Planetary Energy Budget About 25 percent of the sunlight that reaches the outer limit of the atmosphere is reflected back to space by clouds and atmospheric particulates. An additional 5 percent is reflected away by the surface. The other 70 percent is absorbed and mostly heats the atmosphere and the surfaces of terrestrial and aquatic environments. The absorbed energy is eventually dissipated by a reradiation of longer-wave infrared energy. Greenhouse gases in the atmosphere interfere with this reradiation, and that phenomenon keeps the surface warmer than it would otherwise be. The numbers in the figure are "percentage of incoming solar radiation."

SOURCE: Based on S.H. Schneider, "Climate Modeling," *Scientific American*, 256, 72-80. Copyright © 1987 by Scientific American.

of vapourization, which has a value of 2.26 kJ per g of H_2O at 100°C. However, it takes more energy to evaporate water that is at a cold temperature compared with a warm one. It also takes less energy to evaporate water at a higher altitude or at a lower barometric pressure (water boils at 100°C at sea level, but at only 68°C at 8848 m on the summit of Mount Everest). Because the evaporation of water is endothermic (i.e., an energy input is needed to make it happen), this process helps to dissipate the heat content of the surface and so results in cooling **(Figure 3.7)**. In contrast, the condensation of water is exothermic, so it releases heat; this happens when water vapour condenses into ice particles or water droplets higher in the atmosphere, and when dew or frost occurs.

• *Melting of snow and ice* also absorbs energy, known as the latent heat of fusion and having a value of 0.33 kJ/g at a temperature of 0°C. Melting helps to dissipate the heat of absorbed solar energy, as does any subsequent increase in the temperature of the liquid water. For example, it takes about 4.19 J to raise the temperature of 1 g of water by 1°C (or 83.8 J to increase the temperature from 0°C to 20°C).

• *Wind and water currents* are large-scale phenomena by which the highly uneven distributions of heat content in the atmosphere and oceans become more evenly dispersed. In general, these processes involve convective flows of mass and thermal energy from lower-latitude regions, which are warmer because they have a much larger absorption of solar radiation, to cooler regions at higher latitudes.

• *Biological fixation* occurs when energy within the visible part of the solar spectrum, principally red and blue wavelengths, is absorbed by chlorophyll, a pigment that occurs in plants and algae. The absorbed energy is used to drive photosynthesis, a biochemical process by which CO_2 and H_2O are combined to form glucose, a simple sugar (monosaccharide) with a molecular formula of $C_6H_{12}O_6$, with gaseous O_2 being released as a waste product. The fixed energy of glucose is then used to drive an astonishing complex of biochemical processes that support the metabolism of the plants and algae and allow them to accumulate biomass and to reproduce. The biomass of these autotrophs is then available to support animals and other heterotrophs, which are unable to directly use

FIGURE 3.7 Evaporation The evaporation of water from ecological surfaces is one way that the absorbed energy of sunlight becomes dissipated. Transpiration refers to the evaporation of water from plants, while evapotranspiration occurs from both vegetation and abiotic surfaces. This is a view of a slow-flowing reach of a prairie river and its fringing riparian habitat in Moose Jaw in southern Saskatchewan.

Bill Freedman

solar energy. Although biological fixation accounts for only a small fraction of the solar radiation absorbed by Earth's surface (averaging less than 1 percent) it is obviously crucial to the functioning of ecosystems.

Virtually all of the solar energy absorbed by Earth's surface is eventually reradiated back to space, and so the planet as a whole represents a zero-sum flow-through system. This is also true of particular areas or places over longer periods of time, such as years and decades. However, during any particular day or between seasons, the net storage of thermal energy can significantly change. Daily changes may include warmer temperatures at noon than at midnight. Seasonal changes may include conditions that are much warmer during the summer than in winter, as is typical of temperate and higher latitudes, including all of Canada. Over an entire year, however, seasonal variations of energy absorption are evened out because they are dissipated by a reradiation of long-wave infrared.

A small exception to the generalization of Earth being a zero-sum flow-through system involves a relatively tiny amount (at the planetary scale) of longer-term net storage of biologically fixed solar energy. Dead plant biomass accumulates over long periods of time in bogs and other wetlands in which sub-surface oxygen is limited, so there is a slow rate of decomposition. Initially, the organic matter may accumulate as peat, at a rate of 20–100 cm per century in bogs. Over geologically long periods of time (millions of years), some of that peat may become deeply buried beneath layers of sediment. In that environment, chemical reactions occurring under conditions of high pressure, high temperature, and a lack of oxygen may form natural gas, petroleum, coal,

and oil-sand. Those fossil fuels represent a miniscule fraction of the solar energy that arrived to Earth, was fixed by autotrophs, and then accumulated over geological time at an exceedingly slow rate. Nonetheless, they are vital resources for the modern human economy (see Chapter 15).

3.5 The Greenhouse Effect

Earth's energy budget has a crucial influence on environmental conditions on or near the surface of the planet. One of these influences is exerted by the so-called **greenhouse effect**, a natural phenomenon that exists because of the presence of certain gases in the atmosphere. These **greenhouse gases (GHGs)** absorb some of the long-wave infrared that is reradiated by the surface of Earth as it cools itself of absorbed solar radiation. The atmospheric GHGs are warmed by that absorption, which causes them to reradiate even longer-wave infrared energy in all directions, including back to Earth's surface. The overall effect is to slow the rate of cooling of the surface, in a sense acting as a thermal blanket over the planet. Because of this greenhouse effect, Earth has an average surface temperature of about 15°C, which is 33°C warmer than the −18°C that it would otherwise be.

Clearly, the natural greenhouse effect has a beneficial influence on environmental conditions on Earth. In the absence of this phenomenon, the planet would be much colder and almost all water would be frozen. A primordial ice-covered planet would have been inhospitable to the genesis of life and to its subsequent evolution in ways that have allowed myriad forms of life to diversify and flourish, including the species that survive today. This is because liquid water is necessary for almost all physiological functions, such as the action of enzymes, while also providing much of the mass of organisms. Abundant liquid water is also crucial to many ecosystem functions—it is a key aspect of the matrix of the environment and is essential to certain mass-flows essential to nutrient and material cycling, such as those occurring in rivers and oceanic currents.

The most important greenhouse gas is water vapour (H_2O), which is responsible for about 36 percent of the warming influence (IPCC, 2007). Next in importance is carbon dioxide (CO_2), followed by methane (CH_4), nitrous oxide (N_2O), ozone (O_3), carbon tetrachloride (CCl_4), and chlorofluorocarbons (CFCs). Of these various substances, CFCs are the most radiatively powerful, because on a per-molecule basis they are 4000 to 8000 times more effective at absorbing infrared than is CO_2 (this number is known as the *greenhouse warming potential*). By comparison, CCl_4 is 1400 times as strong as CO_2, N_2O 310 times, CH_4 20 times, and O_3 17 times.

The above explanation of the greenhouse effect is not particularly controversial, and the following facts are widely acknowledged:

- Earth has a flow-through energy budget.
- The planet has a natural greenhouse effect caused by certain gases in the atmosphere.
- This phenomenon has been crucial in setting the environmental stage for biological genesis and evolution.
- The concentrations of GHGs, with the exception of water vapour, have been rapidly increasing during the past several centuries.
- This important environmental change is occurring because of anthropogenic emissions of the GHGs.

Overall, the concentration of CO_2 has increased from about 280 ppm in 1750 to 393 ppm in 2013 **(Table 3.1)**.

TABLE 3.1	**Increases in Concentration of Greenhouse Gases in the Atmosphere**

The lifetime refers to the residence time in the atmosphere (years). The increased radiative forcing (W/m^2) refers to the higher intensity of the greenhouse effect that can be attributed to increased concentrations of the gas since 1750. The ozone data are for the lower atmosphere (troposphere).

Greenhouse Gas	Concentration 1750	Concentration 2013	Lifetime	Increased Radiative Forcing
CO_2 (ppm)	280	393	100	1.85
CH_4 (ppm)	0.7	1.8	12	0.51
N_2O (ppm)	0.27	0.32	114	0.18
O_3 (ppb)	25	34	<1	0.35
CFCs (ppb)	0.0	1.2	45–100	0.25

SOURCE: Blasing, T.J. 2013. *Recent greenhouse gas concentrations*. Carbon Dioxide Information Analysis Center, U.S. Department of Energy, Oak Ridge, TN. http://cdiac.ornl.gov/pns/current_ghg.html

During the same period, CH_4 increased from 0.7 to 1.8 ppm, and changes have also occurred in other GHGs. The increases are coincident with the massive growth of both the human population and industrialization during the past several centuries. These increases have been observed at many places around the world in addition to Mauna Loa and Alert **(Figure 3.8)**, and they represent one of the best-documented changes in global environmental chemistry caused by anthropogenic influences.

The causes of the increases of CO_2 are particularly well understood. Principally, they are due to the combustion of fossil fuels and the clearing of forests, which have contributed roughly comparable amounts of emissions during the past several centuries. To a much lesser degree, the manufacturing of cement has also been significant.

FIGURE 3.8 Recent Increases of Atmospheric CO_2 Concentration The data are from environmental observatories located on Mauna Loa, Hawaii, and at Alert, Ellesmere Island, Nunavut. Despite one station being tropical and the other in the High Arctic, they show the same increase of CO_2 during the shared time period of monitoring.

SOURCE: Based on data from Keeling, R.F., S.C. Piper, A.F. Bollenbacher and J.S. Walker. 2009. *Atmospheric CO₂ Records from Sites in the SIO Air Sampling Network*. Oak Ridge National Laboratory, Carbon Dioxide Information Analysis Center, Oak Ridge, TN. http://cdiac.ornl.gov/trends/co2/sio-keel.html

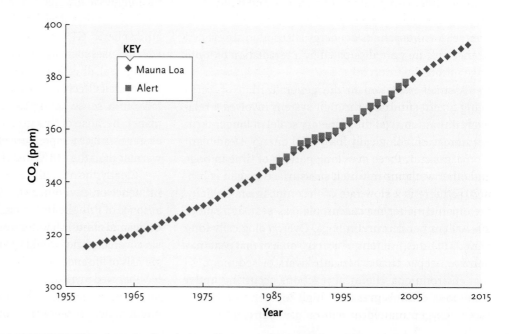

Although GHGs help to maintain the temperature of Earth's atmosphere in a roughly equilibrium condition, it is widely believed that their increasing concentrations are intensifying the natural greenhouse effect. According to the Intergovernmental Panel on Climate Change (IPCC), an international organization that works under the auspices of the United Nations Environment Program, there is abundant evidence that the global climate has been warming for more than 100 years and this change is being caused by anthropogenic emissions of GHGs (IPCC, 2007, 2013). For example, see the data on increased radiative forcing since 1750 (**Table 3.1**). The higher concentrations of CO_2 are responsible for about 59 percent of the anthropogenic warming, CH_4 for 16 percent, O_3 for 11 percent, CFCs for 8 percent, and N_2O for 6 percent.

Nevertheless, the fact and causes of anthropogenic global warming remain controversial. A strong majority of environmental scientists believes that global warming has been occurring for about 150 years and that it is caused by anthropogenic emissions of GHGs. However, a minority of specialists believes that anthropogenic warming has not yet been proven, and hence there is ongoing debate about the issue.

To generate predictions about climate change, atmospheric scientists use supercomputers to run three-dimensional climatic models. The models are based on highly complex calculations that involve dynamics of solar radiation inputs as well as their absorption in the atmosphere and at the surface, in various regions of the globe and at different times of year, plus the development of atmospheric thermal gradients and mixing by winds, along with other influences on temperature and additional climatic variables. Once the models can be demonstrated as being effective at predicting climatic conditions in the present and in the recent past (the latter is called backcasting), they can be used to perform "virtual experiments." These involve reparameterization to "modify" atmospheric conditions by increasing the strength of the greenhouse effect to see what changes might occur in future climates. Commonly examined scenarios have included atmospheric CO_2 concentrations increasing by 50–100 percent or more (if recent rates of increase are projected into the future, the concentration of atmospheric CO_2 would double in about two centuries).

In general, these models predict that the average global surface temperature is likely to be 1–4°C warmer in 2050 than today. However, the warming will not be even over the surface of the planet. It will be less in the tropics, and will occur faster and be progressively more severe at higher latitudes—in temperate regions and even more so in boreal and arctic latitudes (see Ecology in Depth 3.1).

It is also probable that there will also be large changes in precipitation regimes, including the interior of continents becoming generally drier than they are

FIGURE 3.9 Melting Glaciers Since about 1850, one of the effects of a warming climate has been the widespread melting of glaciers. This glacier on Ellesmere Island is melting back by several metres each year, exposing new till substrates for colonization by tundra plants.

today. It is also predicted that alpine and high-latitude glaciers will melt back and in many places disappear, a phenomenon that will decrease the flow of water in many rivers, which are fed by glacial meltwater (**Figure 3.9**). If these and other predicted climatic changes occur, they will result in enormous challenges to vital economic activities, such as agriculture, while also causing massive ecological damage.

Forecasts of anthropogenic global climate change, and of the economic and ecological consequences, are of course fraught with uncertainty. Climatic conditions, economies, and ecosystems are extraordinarily complex phenomena, and their responses to future environmental changes cannot be predicted with accuracy. Nevertheless, there is a rapidly emerging consensus among environmental scientists that anthropogenic climate change is already occurring and is likely to intensify in the near future. The consequences of this global change could be dire. As a result, there is a surge of popular and political support for actions to slow down the increase of GHGs in the atmosphere, and to eventually reduce their concentrations.

Some of the proposed solutions to this environmental problem are ecological. One of them is focused on conserving existing forests and other ecosystems that store large amounts of biomass, in order to prevent their organic carbon from ending up in the atmosphere as CO_2. Another tactic is intended to withdraw CO_2 that is already in the atmosphere, for example, by extensively planting trees on disused agricultural land to increase the amount of carbon stored in biomass (this is known as **afforestation**; see Ecology in Depth 3.2).

Anthropogenic climate change is an extremely important issue—it has huge implications for the structure and sustainability of the human economy and for the

ECOLOGY IN DEPTH 3.1
Warming the Tundra

There is increasing evidence that anthropogenic increases in the concentrations of GHGs in the atmosphere, particularly CO_2, are changing Earth's climate. However, the effects will not be distributed evenly over the globe. For example, global warming is predicted to be much more intense at higher latitudes, such as in the Arctic region. Signals of this climate change are already being observed, including glaciers that have been rapidly melting during the past century, a much longer and more extensive ice-free season over vast regions of the Arctic Ocean, and the recent appearance of relatively southern birds, such as American robins (*Turdus migratorius*), in some places in the Arctic.

Ecologists working in the Arctic believe that climatic warming is likely to have a number of effects on the vegetation of northern climes. These might include increased productivity and more prolific flowering due to a longer growing season, faster decomposition and nutrient cycling due to microbial activity being stimulated by warmer soil and an increased depth of the seasonally thawed active layer, and eventually the migration of boreal plants into currently tundra habitats. These predictions appear to be sensible, but they are conjectural, meaning they are based on an extrapolation of existing ideas and incomplete knowledge, rather than being derived from experimental work that is designed to test hypotheses about warming in the Arctic.

But there *are* ways of doing realistic experiments related to the effects of climate warming on Arctic vegetation. One method is remarkably low-tech—it involves enclosing small areas of natural tundra within open-topped frames covered with clear material (such as plexiglas or greenhouse fibreglass sheeting) that passively warms the interior microclimate by reducing wind speeds, thereby slowing the dissipation of heat of absorbed sunlight. Ecosystem processes such as plant growth and nutrient cycling are then compared with nonenclosed reference plots. Because the method is simple and inexpensive, it is feasible to examine various kinds of plant communities and to have good replication within all of them.

This undemanding yet elegant experimental method was pioneered by Greg Henry of the University of British Columbia. Once he and others demonstrated that it is an effective way to do research on warming in the Arctic, it was adopted by ecologists in other northern countries. They established a collaborative network called the International Tundra Experiment (ITEX) to compare their results and develop predictions about the ecological effects of climate warming.

Comparisons among 11 ITEX locations in Alaska, Canada, Russia, and Scandinavian countries found that the open-top warming chambers **(Figure 1)** raised the ground-level air temperature by 1–3°C, which stimulated the productivity and flowering of dwarf shrubs, grasses, and sedges (Arft et al., 1999). A general increase in the cover of shrub species in response to warming was found across the tundra biome (Walker et al., 2006).

These experimental results suggest that observed increases in shrub abundance in many areas of the Arctic are a result of recent warming. However, the increased competition from these favoured plants may be decreasing the abundance of slower-growing species, such as lichens and bryophytes, resulting in an overall loss of species diversity. In addition, studies of CO_2 fluxes at four ITEX locations found that the warming has caused a general increase in primary production (photosynthesis) and an increase in ecosystem-level respiration, with the greatest responses occurring in dry tundra communities (Oberbauer et al., 2007).

The observed responses of tundra vegetation to experimental warming were not always consistent among far-flung locations or among habitats that varied in soil moisture within particular study areas. This observation highlights the difficulty in making general predictions about the ecological responses to climate warming—ecosystems are just too complex in their structure and function, and in their reactions to changes in environmental conditions, to provide straightforward answers regarding these sorts of issues.

FIGURE 1 Warming the Tundra These ITEX frames were established by Greg Henry and collaborators in several plant communities at Alexandra Fiord on Ellesmere Island. They have been monitored for more than 20 years in order to study the potential effects of climate warming on tundra vegetation.

Greg Henry

viability of many wild species and natural ecosystems. Although the details of this issue are beyond the scope of this ecology text, it is important to know that recent climate warming appears to be forced by an intensification of the planet's natural greenhouse effect, and this influence is likely anthropogenic.

3.6 Energy Fixation in Ecosystems

The fixation of solar radiation by photosynthetic organisms, and the subsequent transfer of the organic energy of biomass through trophic systems, is a key subject area of ecological energetics. Ecologists classify organisms according to the manner in which they access energy, as follows:

Autotrophs

Autotrophs are organisms that use an external source of energy to drive their fixation of water and inorganic carbon (usually CO_2) into glucose, a simple sugar. The glucose is then used to power their other metabolic functions, such as the synthesis of a great variety of biochemicals, growth through an increase of biomass, and reproduction. Because autotrophic organisms provide the biological foundation of ecological productivity, they are also referred to as being **primary producers**.

Autotrophs are divided into two groups depending on the source of energy they use to accomplish the initial biosynthesis of glucose. **Photoautotrophs** are the most abundant kinds of autotrophs and are responsible for almost all of the productivity of the biosphere (see **Equation 3.1**). The most prominent groups of photoautotrophs are plants in terrestrial environments and algae and blue-green bacteria in aquatic ones **(Figure 3.10)**. These organisms have pigments, especially chlorophyll, that absorb visible solar electromagnetic radiation for use in photosynthesis. Because chlorophyll is a strong absorber within the red and blue ranges of visible light but is reflective of green, the photosynthetic tissues of these autotrophs (such as the leaves of plants) are green in colour (for an interesting exception see **Figure 3.11**).

Chemoautotrophs are a less-prominent group of autotrophs. They are specialized bacteria that have the ability to harness energy released by the oxidation of certain inorganic chemicals to power their **chemosynthesis** metabolism. One example is *Thiobacillus thiooxidans*, a bacterium that has the capability of oxidizing sulphide minerals (such as iron sulphide, FeS_2) according to the following reaction:

(3.2) $4\,FeS_2 + 15\,O_2 + 14\,H_2O \rightarrow$
$$4\,Fe(OH)_3 + 16\,H^+ + 8\,SO_4^{2-}$$

FIGURE 3.10 Almost All Plants are Photoautotrophs Plants use the green pigment chlorophyll to capture sunlight that is used to power their photosynthesis. This cinnamon fern (*Osmunda cinnamomea*) produces two kinds of fronds: sterile green ones that are photosynthetic, and brown ones that produce the spores necessary for reproduction.

Because this reaction is exothermic, some of the released energy can be harnessed by the chemoautotrophs to drive their biosynthesis of $CO_2 + H_2O$ to form glucose. As with photoautotrophs, the fixed energy is then available to fuel all other aspects of the metabolism of the bacteria, as well as organisms that may feed upon their accumulated biomass.

The total amount of energy that is fixed by all of the autotrophs in an ecosystem is referred to as **gross primary production (GPP)**. Some of the GPP is used to support the **respiration (R)** of the primary producers, which is needed to maintain their metabolic health and to allow them to grow. In essence, respiration involves an oxidation of biochemicals through metabolic reactions, and it requires O_2 and releases CO_2 and H_2O as wastes. In its simplest expression, respiration is the opposite of photosynthesis, as follows:

$C_6H_{12}O_6 + 6\,O_2 \rightarrow 6\,H_2O + 6\,CO_2$
$$+ \text{energy to support metabolism} \quad (3.3)$$

Net primary production (NPP) is calculated as the difference between GPP and R. Therefore, NPP is the

Mike Apps: Carbon in Ecosystems

FIGURE 1 Mike Apps

Mike Apps was a research scientist (now retired) with the Canadian Forest Service (CFS) whose work focused on the relationships between boreal forest and the global carbon budget, and on the implications of management for emissions of GHGs **(Figure 1)**. Apps collaborated with many Canadian and international experts in the field of carbon cycling, beginning to work with boreal ecologists from North America, Europe, Russia, and China at a time when such international relationships were uncommon.

Apps and his coresearchers have advanced our understanding of the dynamics of biomass-carbon in the terrestrial landscapes of Canada and other northern regions, particularly in forests. They have improved our understanding of the implications of forest management for biomass storage and productivity—including timber harvesting, plantation establishment, and the creation of protected areas. Canadian forests are important in these regards. About 400 million hectares, or half the land area of Canada, is forested—representing 10 percent of the global forest estate. Apps and his colleagues have shown that, while northern forests sometimes serve as a net carbon sink (i.e., the amount of CO_2 fixation exceeds its release by respiration, decomposition, and disturbances), at other times they are a net source (CO_2 releases exceed fixation). The "source" years are related to times when wildfires are extensive or insect damage is severe, as is now occurring because of damage caused to western forests by the mountain pine beetle (*Dendroctonus ponderosae*). Apps and his colleagues have helped both scientists and policy makers to appreciate the role that natural disturbances play in the carbon budget of the boreal forest.

The ongoing work of Apps, Werner Kurz (also a CFS scientist), and other colleagues is now focused on improving our models of carbon storage and dynamics in forest ecosystems across Canada, including in tree biomass and the dead organic matter of litter and soil. Moreover, their simulation models can predict effects of management activities and environmental change. Their *National Forest Carbon Monitoring, Accounting and Reporting System* is an ongoing collaboration led by CFS that involves other agencies and many scientists (see Natural Resources Canada, 2013). One of the key components of this system is the Carbon Budget Model of the Canadian Forest Sector (CBM-CFS3), which has become a widely used tool for researchers and forest managers. The CBM-CFS3 helps us understand climate change and the environmental consequences of economic and stewardship choices that potentially affect immense tracts of the Canadian forest estate.

Apps has also played a lead role in the work of the Intergovernmental Panel on Climate Change (IPCC), an agency of the United Nations Environment Program. The IPCC is charged with leading a global effort to understand the causes and consequences of anthropogenic climate change. Apps and many other IPCC participants shared in the 2007 Nobel Peace Prize, which was co-awarded to the IPCC and former U.S. Vice-President Al Gore "for their efforts to build up and disseminate greater knowledge about man-made climate change, and to lay the foundations for the measures that are needed to counteract such change."

---

cannot support a large productivity of top predators, such as mountain lions, timber wolves, orcas, or great white sharks. In general, high-level carnivores can be sustained only by ecosystems that are highly productive or very extensive. This is well illustrated by the savannas and grasslands of Africa, which may support numerous species of large-mammal predators: cheetahs, leopards, lions, hyenas, and wild dogs. The savanna is an extensive and—when there is no drought—a productive habitat that supports an abundance of top predators. In contrast, the tundra and boreal forest of northern Canada can support only one natural top predator, the wolf, because although these are vast habitats, they are not productive. During the past century, much of the area of African savanna and grassland has been settled and converted to agricultural land use. It is difficult for so many top-predator species to survive in such a greatly diminished natural ecosystem.

Prior to their integration with the commercial economy, the Arctic Inuit and the boreal-dwelling Indian peoples of Canada had a diet that was primarily carnivorous, so those indigenous cultures functioned as top predators in their ecosystem. As a consequence of feeding at a high level of their food web, these Aboriginal peoples did not maintain large populations. In modern times, most people feed as omnivores and are participating in an increasingly globalized economy that harvests a wide range of foods derived from microbes, fungi, algae, plants, and invertebrate and vertebrate animals. Having access to such a wide array of foodstuffs is allowing humans to maintain an extremely large population—more than 7.1 billion in 2013. However, with the rapid depletion of natural resources, it remains to be seen whether this global enterprise can be sustained for very long.

CHAPTER SUMMARY

(LO3.1)

- Energy is a physical attribute that is related to the ability to perform work and it can exist in various states, including electromagnetic, kinetic (thermal and mechanical), and potential (chemical, gravitational, compressed gases, elasticity, electrical, and nuclear).

(LO3.2)

- The first law of thermodynamics states that although energy can be transformed, it is never created or destroyed, and so the energy content of the universe stays constant. In an ecological context, this means that there is a perfect balance between energy coming into an ecosystem, energy stored within it, and energy leaving. The second law of thermodynamics states that energy transformations will spontaneously occur only under conditions in which the entropy in the universe is increased. However, if energy is put into a system, then negative entropy can be developed, and this is the essential basis of the existence of life and ecosystems, with sunlight being the key source of external energy.

(LO3.3)

- The energy inputs and outputs on Earth are in an essentially perfect balance; therefore, the energetics of the planet is a flow-through system.

(LO3.4)

- At a global level the major input of energy to the Earth is solar radiation in the visible and near-infrared ranges. Some of that energy is reflected to outer space by atmospheric particulates and clouds and by high-albedo surfaces. The rest of the solar input is absorbed by atmospheric gases and by relatively dark surfaces. Some of the absorbed energy becomes dissipated by evaporation and other means, but most of it heats the absorbing surfaces, which then cool themselves by reradiating long-wave infrared wavelengths.

(LO3.5)

- The natural greenhouse effect occurs because some of the long-wave infrared emitted by the surface of the planet is absorbed by greenhouse gases in the atmosphere (especially by water vapour and carbon dioxide). This slows down the rate of planetary cooling and, as a consequence, the average surface temperature is maintained at about 15°C instead of the −18°C it would otherwise be. Because human activities are increasing the atmospheric concentrations of greenhouse gases, the natural greenhouse effect is likely being intensified and is resulting in global climate warming and other changes.

(LO3.6)

- Autotrophs (primary producers) are organisms that use a nonbiological energy source (such as sunlight) to synthesize sugars from carbon dioxide and water. The productivity of autotrophs supports their own growth and reproduction and their accumulated biomass is also available to be fed upon by hetertotrophs such as herbivores (primary consumers), carnivores (secondary consumers), and detritivores (decomposers).

(LO3.7)

- The most productive ecosystems, such as tropical forests and coral reefs, occur in environmental situations where primary production is not unduly constrained by the availability of sunlight, moisture, or nutrients. In contrast, lower-productivity ecosystems such as deserts and tundra are constrained by limitations posed by any of those factors. In stable ecosystems, a large standing crop of biomass may accumulate, as occurs in old-growth forests.

(LO3.8)

- The pyramid-shaped trophic relationship is due to energy-conversion inefficiencies that are inherent in the second law of thermodynamics. Trophic inefficiencies are also the reason that top predators can only be sustained by high ecological productivity or by very extensive ecosystems. However, pyramids of the biomass or numbers of individuals in an ecosystem may form different kinds of structures, even ranging to an inverted pyramid.

QUESTIONS FOR REVIEW AND DISCUSSION

1. What are the various states in which energy can exist? How can they be transformed from one to another?

2. What are the first and second laws of thermodynamics? Explain their implications for energy transformations and for life and ecosystems.

3. What is meant by an energy budget? Explain the major aspects of the energy budget of Earth.

4. What is the greenhouse effect? Why does it exist? How might it be affected by anthropogenic influences?

5. Explain why tropical forests and coral reefs are considered to be the most highly developed ecosystems on Earth. What are the environmental circumstances that allow this to happen?

6. Describe a food web for a Canadian ecosystem with which you are familiar.

7. From an energetic perspective, why would it be more efficient for a person to feed as a vegetarian?

CHAPTER

4

Nutrients and Their Cycling

LEARNING OBJECTIVES

After studying this chapter you should be able to:

1. Explain what a nutrient is, and provide examples of the most influential ones in ecosystems.

2. Discuss the concept of nutrient cycling, and describe the most important compartments and fluxes occurring in ecosystems.

3. Describe key features of the cycles of carbon, nitrogen, phosphorus, sulphur, and calcium and other bases.

4. Discuss ways that anthropogenic influences are changing key aspects of the cycling of certain nutrients.

5. Explain how soils are formed from parent materials, including the key roles of abiotic influences and organisms in the formation of major kinds of soils.

4.1 Nutrients

Nutrients are substances that are necessary for the healthy physiology of organisms—they must be available in sufficient quantities for organisms to grow and to reproduce.

Plants and other autotrophs satisfy their needs mostly by absorbing **inorganic nutrients**, which are present in the environment in forms that are not bound within organic compounds. However, some nutrients, referred to as **macronutrients**, are needed in much greater amounts than others. In order of their decreasing concentration in plant tissues these are carbon, oxygen, hydrogen, nitrogen, potassium, calcium, magnesium, phosphorus, and sulphur **(Table 4.1)**.

In contrast, **micronutrients** account for less than 0.01 percent of plant biomass to as little as a few $\mu g/g$ (also known as parts per million or 10^{-6}; $1 \mu g/g = 1$ ppm = 0.0001 percent). All plants need trace quantities of chlorine, iron, manganese, boron, zinc, sodium, copper, nickel, and molybdenum. Several other elements are considered nonessential, although some plant species need traces of them to maintain a high rate of productivity. These elements are cobalt, selenium, silicon, and vanadium.

All of these chemicals are considered to be nutrients when they are present at levels that benefit the physiology and productivity of organisms. In such cases, they are useful and essential to life. At higher exposures, however, these very same chemicals may be toxic to organisms, and in that context, they might be considered to be pollutants.

The data provided for micronutrients in **Table 4.1** are the typical concentrations needed by most species of plants. Some species, however, are hyperaccumulators of

TABLE 4.1	**Macronutrients and Micronutrients in Plants**

These are the typical concentrations in dry biomass that are needed to support a healthy plant metabolism.

Macronutrients	Concentration (%)	Micronutrients	Concentration (ppm)
Carbon (C)	45–50	Chlorine (Cl)	100
Oxygen (O)	45	Iron (Fe)	100
Hydrogen (H)	6	Manganese (Mn)	50
Nitrogen (N)	1.5	Boron (B)	20
Potassium (K)	1.0	Zinc (Zn)	20
Calcium (Ca)	0.5	Sodium (Na)	10
Magnesium (Mg)	0.2	Copper (Cu)	6
Phosphorus (K)	0.2	Nickel (Ni)	3
Sulphur (S)	0.1	Molybdenum (Mo)	0.1

A chemical is deemed to be a nutrient if organisms need it to have a healthy metabolism. But any chemical, including one that may be a nutrient, is also capable of causing toxicity if it is present in too high an exposure. It can act as a poison by disrupting physiology in some way, or by damaging organs, and may even cause death. According to Paracelsus (1493–1541), a Swiss natural scientist who is considered to be the "father" of toxicology (the science of the study of poisons): *It is the dose alone that determines poisoning.*

This means that even a material as seemingly innocuous as liquid water can be poisonous. In fact, if too much water is drunk too quickly the electrolyte concentration of the blood plasma is diluted to the degree that a heart attack may result (see Environmental Applications 2.2 in Chapter 2).

Therefore, any chemical can cause toxicity if its exposure overwhelms the tolerance of organisms. For example,

certain metals may be naturally present in high concentrations in places that are affected by an unusual mineralogy, such as an ore body occurring at the surface. One such habitat occurs where serpentine minerals are abundant—these are rich in nickel and cobalt and deficient in key nutrients such as calcium and nitrogen. The resulting soil conditions are hostile to most plants because of metal toxicity and nutrient deficiency. Serpentine-influenced habitats occur in various places in the world, including western Newfoundland and the Gaspé region of Quebec. In eastern Canada, the serpentine vegetation typically is low-growing and tundra-like in appearance, and some arctic species are present even though the regional climate is capable of supporting boreal forest (see Figure 13.6 in Chapter 13). The constrained ecological development is due to chemical stresses associated with the serpentine minerals.

Some plants of serpentine habitats have a genetically based tolerance of the toxic soil conditions. This suggests that locally adapted populations of wide-ranging species, known as **ecotypes**, have evolved as a result of natural selection in favour of individual genotypes that are relatively tolerant of toxic metals and nutrient imbalance. In older serpentine habitats, such as those in California and some tropical places, this evolutionary process has progressed much further and has resulted in many locally adapted species, or *endemics*.

Certain industrial activities may result in severe pollution by metals, as often occurs around metal-processing facilities such as smelters. For example, soil in the vicinity of smelters at Sudbury, Ontario, has been polluted by nickel and copper (see Environmental Applications 1.1 for background information). The vegetation at certain moist sites is dominated by metal-tolerant ecotypes of grasses, such

---

particular chemicals, meaning they absorb and store them in unusually high concentrations in their tissues. For instance, some halophytic or "salt-loving" plants that are tolerant of saline habitats will amass high concentrations of sodium and chloride in their tissues. *Salicornia* is a genus of herbaceous plants that grow in salt marshes and other saline wetlands, and they can accumulate more than 1 percent sodium in their biomass. One of the common names for this species is pickleweed, because of its tasty saltiness when added to salad or eaten as a steamed vegetable. There are also metal-accumulating species and ecotypes that grow in soils with high concentrations of nickel, copper, or other minerals (see Ecology in Depth 4.1).

Inorganic nutrients, such as carbon, oxygen, hydrogen, nitrogen, phosphorus, and others, are absorbed by plants and other autotrophic organisms in a variety of ways. Carbon is an abundant constituent of all organic compounds and it may be viewed as the chemical "backbone" of life. In fact, organisms are sometimes referred to as "carbon-based life forms" (to separate them from other conceivable forms of life that are the subject matter of science fiction). Land plants absorb inorganic carbon

as gaseous carbon dioxide (CO_2) from the atmosphere, and they fix it by photosynthesis into glucose, a simple sugar (for some plants, malic acid is the first stable product of photosynthesis; see Chapter 7). Aquatic autotrophs may use CO_2 dissolved in water, or the ion bicarbonate (HCO_3^-).

Molecular oxygen (O_2) is needed for metabolic oxidations during cellular respiration, and it is obtained as gaseous O_2 from the atmosphere or dissolved in water. The same gas is also released as a "waste" during photosynthesis. Hydrogen is obtained from liquid water (H_2O), which dissociates into hydrogen and oxygen during photosynthesis.

Nitrogen is a key constituent of amino acids and therefore of all proteins and enzymes, as well as many other biochemicals. It is mostly absorbed as the dissolved ions nitrate (NO_3^-) and/or ammonium (NH_4^+), either in aquatic environments or in water taken up from the soil. The atmospheric gases NO or NO_2 can also be taken up and used by some plants, and N_2 can be fixed by certain microorganisms.

Phosphorus is important in various aspects of physiology but especially in bioenergetics as a component of

as hairgrass (*Deschampsia caespitosa*)
(Figure 1) and redtop (*Agrostis gigantea*).
Roger Cox and Tom Hutchinson (1979)

of the University of Toronto studied
the tolerance of hairgrass by growing
it in laboratory solutions containing

the metals, or not, and comparing the
growth of populations from metal-
polluted sites with more than 400 ppm
of both nickel and copper with reference sites having less than 20 ppm of
each. They observed that plants from
the metal-rich sites were much more
tolerant of these metals than the reference grasses. Plants from the metal-
rich sites were also more tolerant of
aluminum, which is not associated with
smelter emissions but is made more
available for plant uptake because of
acidic conditions. An unexpected result
was the tolerance of the ecotypes to lead
and zinc, which do not occur in high
concentrations in their native soil. This
observation suggests a physiological
cotolerance among various heavy metals.
This research demonstrates that natural
selection has resulted in the evolution
of local ecotypes that are tolerant of
toxic site conditions that were created by
anthropogenic pollution.

FIGURE 1 **Hairgrass** Hairgrass (*Deschampsia caespitosa*) growing near Sudbury.

adenosine triphosphate (ATP), a key energy-transporting molecule. Phosphorus is mostly absorbed as phosphate (PO_4^{-3}) dissolved in water. Calcium phosphate is an important biomineral, and a key component of bones.

Potassium, calcium, magnesium, and sodium help to regulate various aspects of physiology, and they are mostly absorbed as the cations Ca^{2+}, Mg^{2+}, K^+, and Na^+ dissolved in water. These are sometimes referred to as "base cations" because they are associated with alkaline (or basic) environmental conditions. Calcium carbonate (or calcite) is an important biomineral and is abundant in the shells of mollusks and other invertebrates.

Sulphur is a component of certain amino acids and other biochemicals. It is mostly absorbed as dissolved sulphate (SO_4^{-2}) and sometimes as sulphur dioxide (SO_2) from the atmosphere.

As we examined in Chapter 2, the **principle of limiting factors** suggests that productivity is controlled by whichever environmental factor is present in the least supply relative to the biological demand for it. Therefore, if key factors such as the availability of light and moisture are not limiting, it is likely that at any particular time, only one nutrient constrains the productivity of an ecosystem.

In general, the primary productivity of freshwater ecosystems is most often limited by the supply of phosphorus, especially by the phosphate ion. Coastal marine waters are usually limited by nitrate, and terrestrial habitats by nitrate and/or ammonium **(Figure 4.1)**.

This chapter is primarily about inorganic nutrients and the ways that they cycle in ecosystems. We will focus on the most influential nutrients: carbon (Section 4.3), nitrogen (Section 4.4), phosphorus (Section 4.5), sulphur (Section 4.6), and calcium and other base cations (Section 4.7). It should be pointed out, however, that from the perspective of animals and other heterotrophs, organic chemicals (biochemicals) can also be considered to be a sort of nutrient that is needed as food. Depending on the species, they may feed on the living and/or dead biomass of autotrophs and/or of other heterotrophs (see Chapter 3). The organic nutrition they need includes the many kinds of carbohydrates, proteins, fats (or lipids), and other substances, including inorganic chemicals. The physiology of nutrition deals with the complex needs of animals for a balanced diet of these chemicals, but we do not examine the subject in this chapter; rather, the focus is on inorganic nutrients and their ecological cycling.

FIGURE 4.1 A Phytoplankton Bloom off Vancouver Island This satellite image shows areas of high density of phytoplankton cells, or "blooms." In this region the blooms occur during the growing season when winds from the north push surface waters westward, causing bottom waters to rise to the surface as nutrient-rich upwellings that fertilize a high rate of algal productivity. The concentrated densities of cells are visible as bluish-green swirls of coloured surface water. The image was taken on 25 June 2006.

NASA

4.2 Nutrient Cycles

Earth is a flow-through system with respect to its energetics, meaning that there is a large and continuous input of solar electromagnetic radiation, which is balanced by a large output, mostly occurring as long-wave infrared (Chapter 3). In contrast, Earth is essentially a **closed system** with respect to its mass because almost no matter is received from outer space, and none is lost to it **(Figure 4.2)**. (In reality, this is not exactly true because there are some gains of extraterrestrial stuff from meteorite impacts and similar sources; however, these inputs are infinitesimally small in comparison with the mass of Earth.)

Although Earth has essentially unchanging quantities of nutrients and other materials, they do circulate in diverse ways. The processes and pathways by which nutrients are transferred, chemically transformed, and reused in ecosystems are referred to as **nutrient cycling**. Research on nutrient cycling can be undertaken at various spatial scales, ranging from individual organisms, to small areas, to ecosystems that have been defined for the purpose of studying them (such as a lake, a watershed, or a stand of forest, prairie, or tundra), and even at the level of the entire biosphere. In this practical context, nutrient cycling may be studied by examining:

- *inputs* of nutrients, such as the amounts arriving with rain and dustfall, by the absorption of atmospheric gases, and in migrating animals;
- *transformations* of chemical compounds within the ecosystem, such as the recycling of organically bound nutrients into inorganic forms through the complex

It is also possible to damage soil of natural habitats in various ways. For example, heavy traffic by off-road vehicles, and sometimes even by large numbers of hikers, may cause considerable damage on slopes and in wet areas. Severe pollution can also cause damage to soil (and to all biota) through toxicity and a reduction of plant cover, which can lead to erosion and other problems. The appropriate management of soil is an important issue in both anthropogenic and natural ecosystems, and it is one of the keys to maintaining healthy terrestrial ecosystems.

CHAPTER SUMMARY

(LO4.1)

- Nutrients are substances that are needed for the healthy physiology of organisms. Plants and other autotrophs absorb nutrients from their environment, while animals and other heterotrophs obtain them from the food they eat. The most important nutrients needed to support ecosystems are carbon, nitrogen, phosphorus, potassium, sulphur, and calcium.

(LO4.2)

- Nutrients are stored in various compartments of ecosystems (such as in the biota, water, soil, and atmosphere) and are transferred among compartments. Many transformations involve chemical changes of the nutrients from one molecular form to others.

(LO4.3)

- The chapter describes key features of the cycles of carbon, nitrogen, phosphorus, sulphur, and calcium and other bases. Similarities and differences are examined in terms of the importance of the atmosphere, water, and soil in providing these nutrients to autotrophs, as well as the ways that the organic forms of nutrients become recycled through the processes of decomposition.

(LO4.4)

- Human activities are changing the rates of cycling of certain nutrients, which may result in pollution and the depletion of natural resources. These influences are mostly associated with the production and excessive use of synthetic fertilizer in agriculture, along with the dumping of waste materials such as sewage and gaseous compounds of sulphur and nitrogen into the environment.

(LO4.5)

- Soil is formed from original parent materials by the actions of climatic factors such as precipitation, leaching, and freeze-and-thaw cycles, as well as biological processes that are mostly associated with microorganisms and plants. There are distinctive kinds of soils, each of which develops under particular environmental regimes associated with climate and the kinds of vegetation that dominate the ecosystem.

QUESTIONS FOR REVIEW AND DISCUSSION

1. What are the basic elements of a nutrient cycle, including the roles of key compartments and fluxes?
2. Compare key aspects of the cycles of carbon, nitrogen, phosphorus, and sulphur.
3. Choose a major nutrient (carbon, nitrogen, phosphorus, or sulphur) and explain how human influences are changing the rates of certain aspects of its cycling.
4. How do climatic and biological influences affect the formation of soil from parent material?
5. Choose a type of soil, and use information in the text and from other sources to prepare a detailed description of its physical and biological qualities, as well as the ecological circumstances that influence its development.
6. How do your daily activities intersect with key aspects of the carbon cycle? Are there ways that you could decrease the size of your carbon footprint—the amounts of carbon dioxide that are emitted to the atmosphere as a result of your personal activities, especially through your energy use, that involve the combustion of fossil fuels?

LEARNING OBJECTIVES

After studying this chapter you should be able to:

1. Define population growth rate and explain how it is used to describe past, present, and predicted changes in the abundance of a species or a population.

2. Forecast changes in abundance given assumptions concerning the effects of density, age, and developmental stage on population growth rate.

3. Apply simple models for theoretical and applied purposes, such as predicting the recovery of depleted populations or the growth of newly established ones.

4. Interpret graphs of population abundance trends, and understand how state-space graphs are used to predict outcomes of interspecific interactions.

5. Understand how interactions with other species, such as competition and predation, can affect the growth rate and likelihood of persistence of populations or species.

6. Discuss why per capita population growth is of fundamental importance to population ecology, resource management, and conservation biology.

5.1 Models in Ecology

At its core, the study of ecology is founded on observation and experimentation. This is how knowledge of the factors responsible for patterns in the distribution and abundance of organisms is obtained. But empirical data, whether collected in the field or the laboratory, are insufficient, in and of themselves, to be of much utility if we might wish to generalize research undertaken on one species or population to other species and populations. Models can be used to achieve such generality. Simple descriptions of past or present conditions experienced by organisms cannot be used, on their own, to forecast or predict how the trajectories of populations will change in the future. Models can be used to generate such predictions. For conservation biologists wishing to understand how habitat destruction might affect a species' chance of extinction (Chapter 14), or for scientists wishing to determine the percentage of a population that can be sustainably harvested over the long term (Chapter 15), one requires models. Furthermore, one requires not qualitative or verbal models, but quantitative mathematical models to ensure that the model's implicit assumptions, structure, and components are clear and not open to subjective interpretation.

The best models are often those that are able to explain something adequately, or to predict something reliably, using the fewest number of variables and parameters. As you will see, trajectories in the abundance of bacteria, plants, and animals can be very reliably explained by a model that has one parameter (rate of increase) and one variable (numbers of individuals at given time). The ways in which the survival of an organism changes as it grows older can be modelled by one of three patterns—three models that adequately describe survivorship patterns for all species. Simple models can also be surprisingly good in explaining patterns of change in the abundance of species competing with one another for the same source of food or interacting with one another as predator and prey (see also Chapter 9).

An introduction to the relevance and importance of models to population ecology can best be illustrated by considering how populations change in abundance through time.

5.2 Population Change

The abundance of any species may increase or decrease because of natural and anthropogenic influences. Some years there are far more mosquitoes and rabbits than in other years. One of the most fundamental challenges in ecology lies in understanding how various biotic and abiotic factors affect the rates of change of populations. A population is a group of conspecific individuals (i.e., of the same species) that inhabits a particular area (Section 1.1). Because they interact within their habitat, members of a population have a greater probability of reproducing among themselves than they do with conspecifics of other populations.

Examples of population change include the following:

- Some plant species proliferate in areas that have been recently disturbed, perhaps by a forest fire or clear-cut, while other species adapted to more stable habitats decline in those same places.
- Native herbivores will sometimes increase rapidly (an **irruption**) in abundance, as occasionally happens with mountain pine beetle (*Dendroctonus ponderosae*) in western pine forest and green sea urchin (*Strongylocentrotus droebachiensis*) in Atlantic kelp habitats.
- Certain non-native species exhibit huge increases in abundance following their introduction to Canada, such as zebra mussel (*Dreissena polymorpha*) in the Great Lakes beginning in the late 1980s, the starling (*Sturnus vulgaris*) in the late 19th century, and the dandelion (*Taraxacum officinalis*) in the 17th century.

Long-term reductions in abundance can be particularly dramatic. For example, declines of over 80 percent have been experienced by many overharvested species, such as the Atlantic cod (*Gadus morhua*) and porbeagle shark (*Lamna nasus*) on the Atlantic coast; the bowhead whale (*Balaena mysticetus*) in the eastern Arctic; plains bison (*Bison bison bison*) in the prairies; and ginseng (*Panax quinquefolius*) in southern Quebec and Ontario. Other native species have experienced persistent declines because their habitat has been destroyed [e.g., the northern spotted owl (*Strix occidentalis caurina*) in southern British Columbia], or because of competition from invasive species [e.g., the eastern pondmussel (*Ligumia nasuta*) in southern Ontario]. Climate change is a factor for species, such as the Peary caribou (*Rangifer tarandus pearyi*) on the Arctic islands of Nunavut **(Figure 5.1)**.

FIGURE 5.1 Peary Caribou This subspecies of caribou is found only in the Canadian Arctic and coastal northwestern Greenland. Having declined by 83 percent from 1961 to 2001, these endangered animals are threatened by increased amounts of snow and freezing rain associated with climate change, which limits their access to food.

Jim Brandenburg/Minden Pictures/Getty Images

In addition to increases or decreases in abundance caused by a disturbance or a slower change in environmental conditions, all populations fluctuate to some degree. Some populations are cyclical, such as those of the snowshoe hare (*Lepus americanus*) and one of its major predators, the lynx (*Lynx canadensis*).

Before we can tease apart the factors that affect changes in the abundance, we need to understand how population growth is modelled. General models are often more useful because they will apply to more species and as a result they will identify general principles that underlie the diverse patterns of population change that are observed in ecosystems.

5.3 Exponential Population Growth

Populations change in abundance when individuals are added to or removed from the population. For a **closed population** that is isolated from other groups, such that no individuals move between them, changes in abundance are determined by the difference in the numbers of births (M) and deaths (D). In a closed population, the number of individuals, N, increases from one time unit (t) to the next ($t + 1$) when M exceeds D, and it decreases when D is greater than M. (An additional implicit assumption is that the spatial area of the closed population remains constant.) For an **open population**, from which individuals may enter or leave, N is additionally influenced by the numbers of immigrants (I) and emigrants (E). In an open population, changes in population size between time units t and $t + 1$ can be described as:

(5.1)
$$N_{t+1} = N_t + (M_t - D_t) + (I_t - E_t)$$

The change in population size (ΔN) over a given change in time (Δt) describes a rate, which is measured in individuals per unit time, and that can be described as:

(5.2)
$$\Delta N / \Delta t = (N_{t+1} - N_t)/(t + 1 - t)$$

For simplicity, models of population growth often incorporate the assumption that there is no immigration or emigration, so that changes in N are a consequence only of the numbers of births and deaths. This assumption is usually reasonable.

The time frame over which changes in abundance are measured can be either:

- continuous, meaning that changes in population occur over extremely small intervals of time, also known as instantaneous change, or
- discrete and occurring at distinct intervals, such as once every year.

In general, however, neither continuous nor discrete intervals perfectly capture the time frames during which births and deaths actually take place, and thus when they alter the abundance of a population. For example, although births might occur at a similar time within the year for species that breed during a particular season, such as in the autumn for brook trout (*Salvelinus fontinalis*), in the early summer for white-throated sparrow (*Zonotrichia albicollis*), or in spring for the pollination of sugar maples (*Acer saccharum*), deaths do not follow such predictability in timing in these species.

Density-Independent per Capita Growth Rate (r_{max})

The exponential model of population growth is also termed the **density-independent model of population growth** because it assumes that per capita growth rate does not vary with population density. Mathematically, it is convenient to simplify population growth as a process that occurs continuously, because this allows us to use differential equations for the purposes of modelling. As noted above, Δt under this circumstance represents an infinitesimally short period of time, ∂t, so the rate of change in population size would be $\partial N/\partial t$. In continuous time, the number of births, M, will be the product of the population size, N, and the instantaneous birth rate, m (measured as births per individual per unit of time), such that:

$$M = mN$$

or

(5.3)
$$m = M/N$$

Similarly, the number of deaths will be a function of population size and the instantaneous death rate, d, such that:

$$D = dN$$

or

(5.4)
$$d = D/N$$

In a closed population, changes in abundance are equal to the difference in the number of births and deaths: $N = M - D$. Thus, in continuous time,

$$\partial N/\partial t = mN - dN$$

and

(5.5)
$$\partial N/\partial t = (m - d)N$$

The difference between the instantaneous rates of birth and death represents the **intrinsic rate of population growth** (r) in continuous time, such that $r = m - d$.

The intrinsic rate of increase is a per individual or per capita rate of population growth. An **exponential model of population growth** can thus be described by the equation:

(5.6)
$$\partial N/\partial t = rN$$

Note also that:

(5.7)
$$r = \partial N / N \partial t$$

in which r is measured as *individuals per individual per unit of time*. For an exponentially growing population, the per capita rate of increase does not change with either time or variations in the population size (although it does for populations that experience logistic growth, as is explained below). Rather, it remains constant at a value equal to the **maximum per capita rate of growth** for that population. Therefore, we will let the intrinsic rate of increase, which is equivalent to the maximum per capita rate of population growth, be r_{max}.

Continuous-Time, Exponential Population Growth

The growth rate of a population that is increasing continuously and exponentially can be expressed by the following model:

(5.8)
$$\partial N / \partial t = r_{max} N$$

Often, equations can be more easily interpreted when they are plotted as a figure that shows abundance, N, plotted against time, t. If this is done for different values of r_{max}, various patterns of exponential population growth are seen. As the value of r_{max} increases, and because their growth is exponential, populations grow by increasingly larger amounts and $\Delta N / \Delta t$ increases over time. Compare, for example, the increases in N (from a starting point, N_0, of 10 individuals) exhibited by various species with hugely different r_{max} values **(Figure 5.2)**.

Each of the curves plotted in **Figure 5.2** describes how population size increases over time. Under these different values of r_{max}, the number of individuals at any time t, or N_t, depends on two **parameters** (numbers that remain constant) and one **variable** (a number that can vary), such that N_t depends on the starting population size (N_0, a parameter), the intrinsic rate of increase (r_{max}, also a parameter), and time (t, a variable):

(5.9)
$$N_t = N_0 \exp(r_{max} t)$$

This basic equation is used to model exponential changes in abundance with changes in time. The phrase $exp(r)$ means to exponentiate the bracketed term r. It can also be written as e^r (as will be done in this book), although exp can be more convenient when the bracketed terms contain superscripts or subscripts.

Using the rules of calculus, Equation 5.9 can be obtained by integrating Equation 5.8. For specific rates of growth, one can use Equation 5.9 to calculate the time required for a population to double, treble, and so on, over time. For example, the **doubling time** is the time required for a population to increase from N_0 to $2N_0$. Following on from Equation 5.9,

$$2N_0 = N_0 \exp(r_{max} t_{double})$$

and, after dividing through by N_0,

$$2 = \exp(r_{max} t_{double})$$

Taking the natural logarithm of both sides of the equation yields the following expression:

$$\ln(2) = r_{max} t_{double}$$

which, following rearrangement, yields an equation for calculating the doubling time:

(5.10)
$$t_{double} = \ln(2)/r_{max}$$

Similarly, the trebling time for a population would be:

(5.11)
$$t_{treble} = \ln(3)/r_{max}$$

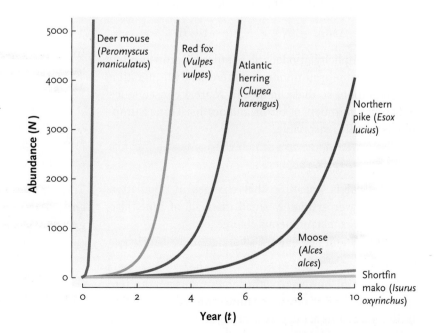

FIGURE 5.2 Exponential Growth Curves These curves are for species that are increasing at their maximum rate of per capita growth, r_{max}. In all populations, the starting abundance, N_0, is 10 individuals.

SOURCE: Estimates of r_{max} are from Hutchings et al. (2012).

Linear and exponential growth rates yield extremely different patterns of growth. Although the abundance of a population may increase steadily (in the density-independent case) with time, the rate at which it increases is extraordinarily faster under exponential growth than under linear growth.

An excellent analogy of exponential population growth rate is the compounded rate of interest that is received on a bank account or by financial instruments, such as a guaranteed interest certificate (GIC) or a Canada Savings Bond. In this analogy, "compounded" means that the interest rate (the rate of growth) is applied to both the initial investment plus all of the accrued interest, so that their total increases exponentially over time. With an initial investment of $1000, and with interest accruing annually at a compounded rate of 5 percent, the value of the asset would double after only 13.8 years. However, if the interest was accruing in a linear fashion (5 percent of the original principal being added every year, as opposed to 5 percent of the accumulated amount), it would take 20 years to double the funds. After 50 years of compounded interest, the exponentially growing account would total $12 182, according to our continuous exponential population growth model (Equation 5.9). In contrast, a linearly growing account would contain only $3500 after 50 years. Clearly, exponential growth is a powerful force in both economics and population biology.

As **Table 5.1** shows for the species in **Figure 5.2**, small changes in r_{max} can result in large differences in doubling times. See Ecology in Depth 5.1 for an analogy of linear versus exponential growth.

Discrete-Time, Exponential Population Growth

The continuous-time model of exponential population growth assumes that births and deaths occur continuously through time. However, this assumption is reasonable for relatively few organisms, mostly simple ones, such as bacteria and yeasts. Instead, most populations experience discrete pulses of births, especially if breeding occurs in a particular season. Deaths may also be seasonal in some species, perhaps occurring during a difficult time of the year, such as during the winter. Under these circumstances of discretely timed events, the number of individuals at a particular time $t + 1$ will be a function of the abundance at time t multiplied by a growth rate parameter λ, which is termed the finite rate of increase:

$$N_{t+1} = \lambda N_t \tag{5.12}$$

Therefore, the population at any time t will be equal to the abundance at time $t - 1$ multiplied by λ, meaning that:

$$N_1 = \lambda N_0$$

and

$$N_2 = \lambda N_1 \quad \text{or} \quad N_2 = \lambda(\lambda N_0)$$

and

$$N_3 = \lambda N_2 \quad \text{or} \quad N_3 = \lambda[\lambda(\lambda N_0)]$$

In general, then, the abundance at any time t for a population growing exponentially at discrete time intervals can be calculated as:

$$N_t = \lambda^t(N_0) \tag{5.13}$$

When the discrete time interval is infinitesimally brief, Equation 5.13 is equivalent to Equation 5.9, meaning that r is mathematically related to λ as:

$$\lambda = e^r \tag{5.14}$$

or, taking the natural logarithm of both sides,

$$r = \ln(\lambda) \tag{5.15}$$

TABLE 5.1	**Doubling Times**

These are the estimated population doubling times for six species of vertebrate animals. The doubling times are calculated using the equation $t_{double} = \ln(2)/r_{max}$.

Common Name	Binomial	r_{max}	Doubling Time (years)
Deer mouse	*Peromyscus maniculatus*	15.9	0.04 (~2 weeks)
Red fox	*Vulpes vulpes*	1.78	0.39 (~5 months)
Atlantic herring	*Clupea harengus*	1.08	0.64 (~8 months)
Northern pike	*Esox lucius*	0.60	1.16
Moose	*Alces alces*	0.27	2.57
Shortfin mako	*Isurus oxyrinchus*	0.12	5.78

SOURCE: Data from Hutchings et al. (2012) (unpublished).

Therefore, a population's abundance will:

- increase exponentially when $r > 0$ and $\lambda > 1$
- decrease exponentially when $r < 0$ and $\lambda = 1$
- remain unchanged when $r = 0$ and $\lambda = 1$

Relevance of r to Evolutionary Ecology, Resource Management, and Conservation

Models of exponential population growth can seem too simplistic to be of much practical use. In actual practice, however, these models are extremely useful. Indeed, a strong argument can be made that the intrinsic rate of population growth, r, is one of the most unifying parameters in all of ecology. There are several reasons to support this assertion.

First, r can represent individual fitness, thereby reflecting the rate at which a particular genotype is increasing relative to others in the same population. Under this circumstance, r represents a genotypic rate of increase. In this sense, it is the average of all per capita genotypic rates of increase that yields a population-level per capita increase (either r_{max} or r). This provides a link between evolutionary change (in genetically based individual fitness) and demographic change (per capita population growth rate).

Second, for commercially valuable species, the rate at which individuals can be sustainably harvested is larger if the per capita growth rate is higher. In other words, the sustainable **harvest rate** (i.e., the number of individuals removed from a population relative to the number available) is greater for populations with relatively high values of r_{max}. That is why the stocks of Atlantic cod on Georges Bank off southern Nova Scotia (with $r_{max} = 0.67$) can be harvested at a higher rate than those off northeastern Newfoundland ($r_{max} \sim 0.09$ to 0.26) (Myers et al., 1997; Hutchings, 1999).

Finally, r is of fundamental importance in the context of conservation biology. Because r_{max} describes the maximum per capita rate of population increase, which is also the growth rate at a relatively low level of abundance, this parameter suggests the rate at which a depleted population might recover. Populations with a relatively high r_{max} will generally recover faster than those with a lower r_{max}. Indeed, the exponential population growth model often provides an excellent representation of the changes in population size when the initial abundance is low (**Figure 5.3**).

5.4 Logistic Population Growth

Under the density-independent model (exponential growth), birth and death rates are assumed to be constant—neither m nor d changes as N increases or decreases. In reality, however, there are limits to the growth of populations. As N increases, competition for resources such as food and space intensifies (see Section 5.5 for more information on competition). Competition has the effect of reducing the per capita birth rate, m, and increasing the per capita death rate, d. In the density-dependent logistic model, birth and death rates are described as follows:

$$m = m_0 - aN \tag{5.16}$$

and

$$d = d_0 + cN \tag{5.17}$$

According to these equations, as the population increases, the per capita rates of birth and death decline and

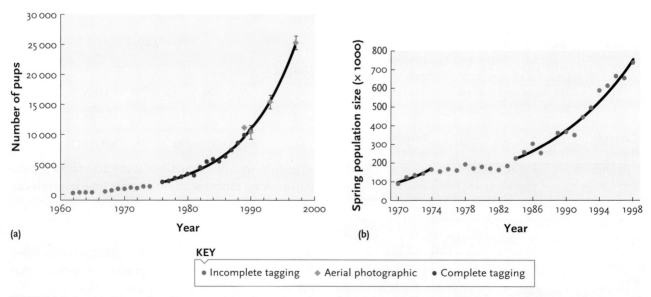

KEY

• Incomplete tagging   ◆ Aerial photographic   • Complete tagging

FIGURE 5.3 Empirical Examples of Exponential Population Growth (a) The numbers of grey seal (*Halichoerus grypus*) pups on Sable Island, Nova Scotia; (b) greater snow goose (*Anser caerulescens atlanticus*) in southern Quebec.

SOURCE: (a) Bowen, W.D., J. McMillan, and R. Mohn. 2003. "Sustained exponential population growth of grey seals at Sable Island, Nova Scotia," Oxford University Press, *ICES Journal of Marine Science*, 60: 1265–1274 (Figure 3, p. 1272). Reproduced by permission of Oxford University Press. (b) Menu, S., G. Gauthier, and A. Reed. 2002. "Changes in survival rates and population dynamics of greater snow geese over a 30-year period: Implications for hunting regulations," *Journal of Applied Ecology*, 39: 91–102. Used with permission of Blackwell Publishing Ltd.

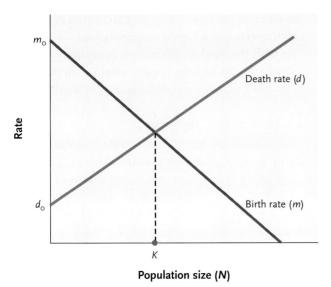

FIGURE 5.4 Linear Changes This diagram shows linear changes in per capita birth rate (m) and death rate (d) with changes in density (N).

increase, respectively, at rates determined by the slopes a and c, in a linear manner with increases in N **(Figure 5.4)**.

Density-Dependent per Capita Growth Rate (r)

In the presence of density dependence, per capita population growth is affected by changes in density. For populations growing exponentially, we previously let r_{max} be the maximum per capita rate of growth. This is the fastest rate that a population can increase in abundance:

$$(5.18) \qquad r_{max} = m_0 - d_0$$

In practical terms, r_{max} is realized when the population abundance is small relative to the maximum abundance that can be supported in a given environment, that is, its **carrying capacity**, K.

Recall Equation 5.8, which describes the exponential model for population growth:

$$\partial N/\partial t = r_{max} N$$

To incorporate an effect of increasing density (higher N) on population growth, the instantaneous rate of change in population size ($\partial N/\partial t$) can be reduced by an amount that is proportional to the unused portion of the carrying capacity (K). Given this condition and the fact that the per capita rate of increase will be highest when N is about 0, we now have:

$$(5.19) \qquad \partial N/\partial t = r_{max} N (1 - N/K)$$

This equation describes a basic, continuous-time, **logistic model of population growth**. Note that the population growth rate, $\partial N/\partial t$, initially increases with increasing N, reaching a maximum value at $N/K = 0.5$, and then declines and eventually reaches 0 when $N = K$ **(Figure 5.5)**.

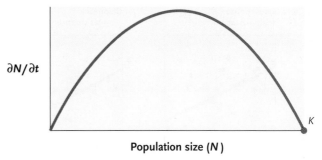

FIGURE 5.5 A Dome-Shaped Relationship This diagram shows the dome-shaped relationship between population growth rate ($\partial N/\partial t$) and population density (N) for the logistic population growth model. Note that population growth rate, $\partial N/\partial t$, initially increases with increasing density, reaches a maximum value at $N/K = 0.5$, and then declines and eventually reaches 0 when the carrying capacity has been reached.

Recall that the per capita rate of population growth ($\partial N/N\partial t$) for the exponential model is equal to the maximum per capita growth rate, that is, r_{max}. However, in the logistic model the per capita rate of population growth changes with density. This can be shown by rearranging Equation 5.19 such that we now have:

$$\partial N/N\partial t = r_{max} (1 - N/K) \qquad (5.20)$$

Note that, unlike the exponential model, the per capita rate of population growth ($\partial N/N\partial t$) is no longer a constant value. This allows us to define r, the **realized per capita rate of population growth** and to distinguish it from r_{max}. For the logistic growth equation, the realized per capita rate of population increase is:

$$r = r_{max} (1 - N/K) \qquad (5.21)$$

This equation informs us that as population size N gets larger, the realized per capita growth rate, r, becomes smaller **(Figure 5.6)**. John Fryxell and colleagues (1998) of

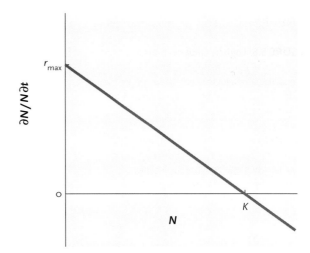

FIGURE 5.6 Growth Rate and Population Size This is the relationship of realized per capita growth rate $(1/N)(\partial N/\partial t)$ as a function of population size (N) for the logistic population growth model. Realized per capita growth rate (r) declines with increases in population size, reflecting the depressing influence of density on r. Note, r is negative when N exceeds K.

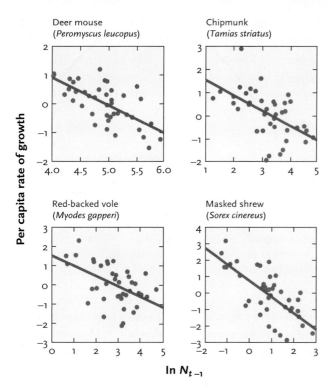

FIGURE 5.7 Growth Rate and Population Density These diagrams illustrate linear reductions in per capita population growth rate (r) with increasing density (N) for four small mammals in Algonquin Provincial Park, Ontario.

SOURCE: Used with permission of the Ecological Society of America, from Fryxell, J. M., J. B. Falls, E. A. Falls, and R. J. Brooks. 1998. "Long-term dynamics of small-mammal populations in Ontario," *Ecology*, 79(1): 213–225; permission conveyed through Copyright Clearance Center, Inc.

the Universities of Guelph and Toronto studied wild populations of small mammals in central Ontario and found good evidence that per capita growth rates decline linearly with population size **(Figure 5.7)**. Although the logistic model implicitly assumes that r continues to increase as N declines **(Figure 5.6)**, there can be circumstances in which r begins to decline once N has fallen below a "threshold" population size. This phenomenon is of concern from a

conservation perspective because such declines in r would inhibit the recovery of a depleted population.

As with the model of density-independent growth, Equation 5.19 can be integrated to produce an equation that describes changes in population N growth with time:

$$N_t = \frac{K}{1 + [(K - N_0)/N_0] \exp(-r_{max}t)} \tag{5.22}$$

A plot of density-dependent growth versus time yields a graph in which N increases with t until N is equal to $0.5K$, after which the rate declines until $\partial N/\partial t = 0$ when $N = K$ **(Figure 5.8)**. This "S-shaped" pattern of population increase is termed a "sigmoidal" or "logistic growth curve," and it provides good fit to changes in abundance of real populations over time. For example, **Figure 5.9** shows the population growth of breeding merlins (*Falco columbarius*) near Saskatoon, using data compiled by researchers at the University of Saskatchewan (Oliphant and Haug, 1985; Lieske, 1997).

Time Lags and Oscillations of Abundance

From a modelling perspective, it is useful to think of K as a point estimate because it represents a population that has reached its carrying capacity but is not fluctuating around it. However, the reality is different—in nature, populations may oscillate about their carrying capacity to varying degrees, sometimes exceeding it or falling below. One of the factors that can contribute to the overshooting and undershooting of K is a **time lag**. A time lag occurs when a population does not immediately respond to a variable.

The logistic growth model presented in Equation 5.22 assumes that there is no time lag between changes in N and in $\partial N/\partial t$—that is, $\partial N/\partial t$ is assumed to be instantaneous. In most populations, however, a time lag separates the time at which an increase in abundance occurs and that when negative effects of the increased density

FIGURE 5.8 Logistic Growth This is an illustration of how a population grows in accordance with a logistic population growth model. The sigmoidal or S-shaped curve is a characteristic feature of logistic growth. The growth rate of the population increases (as reflected by an accelerating slope) until abundance reaches half of the carrying capacity (K), after which the growth rate declines (reflected by a decelerating and slope) until the abundance equals K (when the slope is flat).

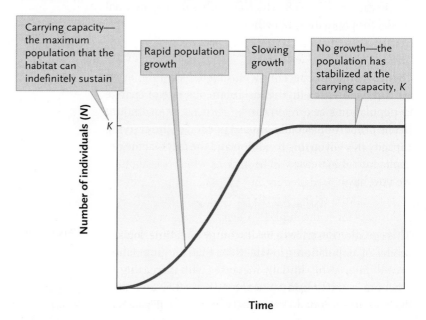

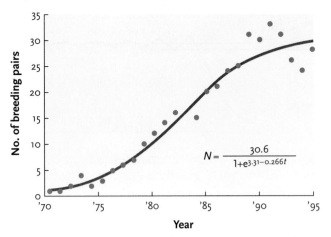

$$N = \frac{30.6}{1+e^{3.31-0.266t}}$$

FIGURE 5.9 Logistic Growth This figure shows the patterns of logistic population growth exhibited by merlins (*Falco columbarius*) along the south Saskatchewan River, Saskatchewan. From an initial abundance of fewer than five breeding pairs in the early 1970s, the number of merlins increased approximately six-fold until the early 1990s, when the growth rate declined, which may mean that the population has reached its carrying capacity for this particular area.

SOURCE: Neal, D. 2004. *Introduction to Population Ecology*. Cambridge University Press, Cambridge, UK. Reprinted with the permission of Cambridge University Press.

decreases the per capita survival and/or birth rate. Consider, for example, a population of Arctic grayling (*Thymallus arcticus*) in a creek flowing into Great Slave Lake, Northwest Territories. Although those fish may spawn in the early summer (June) of year t, the consequences of an increase in density on per capita birth rate may not be realized until the offspring reach maturity and compete with one another for spawning sites. If the age at maturity is three years, then the density-dependent effects of an increase in N in year t will not be realized until year $t + 3$.

A time lag, τ, can be incorporated into the logistic growth model (Equation 5.19) as follows:

(5.23) $$\partial N/\partial t = r_{max} N (1 - N_{t-\tau}/K)$$

Robert May examined the dynamics of population models in his 1976 book, *Theoretical Ecology: Principles and Applications*. He showed that the degree to which populations fluctuate about their carrying capacity, and the likelihood that they would ever stabilize at K, depends on the time lag and the **response time** of a population, which is defined as $1/r_{max}$ (populations with fast maximum per capita rates of growth have correspondingly short response times). May demonstrated that population growth can be predicted by the ratio of the time lag to the response time: $\tau(1/r_{max})^{-1}$, which simplifies to τr_{max}.

In essence, the higher the maximum rate of per capita population growth, or the longer the time lag, the more likely it will be that a population will oscillate around its carrying capacity. When τr_{max} is relatively small (between 0 and 0.37), the population grows to its carrying capacity and remains at that level of abundance

(Figure 5.10a). For our grayling example above (for which $\tau = 3$), r_{max} would have to be 0.12 or less for the population to grow to, and to not fluctuate about, its carrying capacity. For values of τr_{max} larger than 0.37 but less than 1.57, the growth dynamics are such that the population initially overshoots its carrying capacity, then undershoots it, and then continues to oscillate about K but by increasingly smaller amounts before the abundance becomes constant at the carrying capacity **(Figure 5.10b)**. This is termed a **damped oscillation**. For values of τr_{max} greater than 1.57, the population enters a **stable limit cycle** during which it indefinitely fluctuates above and below its carrying capacity by a constant amplitude **(Figure 5.10c)**.

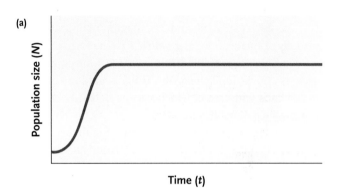

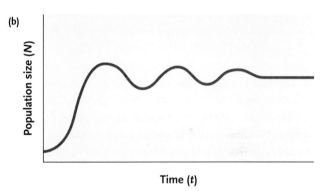

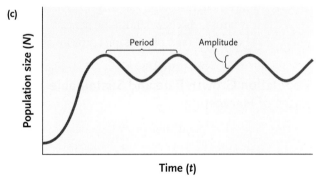

FIGURE 5.10 Effects of Time Lags These are examples of continuous-time, logistic population growth curves having different time lags. (a) A population for which the ratio of time lag to response time (r) is small (0.00 to 0.37) will grow in accordance with the classical logistic growth curve; (b) a population for which r is between >0.37 and <1.57 leads to damped oscillations whereby the abundance fluctuates with increasingly reduced amplitude about the carrying capacity; (c) large values of r (>1.57) lead to stable limit cycles in which populations continually oscillate about, but never persistently remain at, the carrying capacity.

The discrete version of the logistic population growth model represents a slightly modified form of the continuous model (Equation 5.19):

(5.24) $$N_{t+1} = N_t + r_{max} N_t (1 - N_t/K)$$

It has an implicit lag τ of 1 time unit t, so that the effects of a change in density in year t are not manifested until year $t + 1$. Thus, given that the dynamics in the presence of a time lag is reflected by $\tau\, r_{max}$, the degree to which a population stabilizes at its carrying capacity depends solely on r_{max} for the discrete model.

Similar to the continuous model, a population following the discrete version of the logistic model will reach its carrying capacity after experiencing a series of damped oscillations if r_{max} is less than 2 **(Figure 5.11a)**. If r_{max} ranges between 2.0 and 2.6, the population will continually oscillate above and below K in the form of either two or four-point stable limit cycles (a four-point limit cycle is shown in **Figure 5.11b**). If r_{max} is greater than 2.6, then **chaos** will ensue, which can be defined as a non-repeatable pattern **(Figure 5.11c)**.

Population biologists were among the first scientists to appreciate the fact that simple deterministic equations (meaning the parameters are held constant and do not vary) can generate complex, chaotic patterns. Gotelli (2008) commented on this, but also cautioned that chaos should not be confused with **stochasticity**, which refers to patterns that are unpredictable. Chaotic patterns are, in fact, predictable and repeatable because they depend solely on the initial values of the parameters and variables in an equation. However, a maximum population growth rate of 2.6 (above which chaos results) is high and occurs infrequently in nature. If time t was measured in years, such a population would be increasing in abundance by more than 12 times per year! This is why chaotic population dynamics, in the absence of strong regulatory factors such as predation (see Section 5.6), are thought to be limited to the simplest organisms, such as viruses, bacteria, and some parasites, which tend to have very high rates of per capita growth.

Population Growth Rate and Sustainable Rates of Harvesting

Density-dependent population growth models are usually used to predict the effect of harvesting biological resources. Resource managers often want to identify a quota that will result in the largest, but sustainable, long-term harvest **(Figure 5.12)**—this is known as the **maximum sustainable yield**, or MSY. Resource managers want to maintain populations at the abundance or biomass at which the MSY can be taken. In a fishery, this population target is termed B_{MSY}, meaning the biomass (often in terms of the total weight of individuals in a population) from which the MSY can be obtained **(Figure 5.13)**. In some jurisdictions, there are legal consequences for failing to attain this

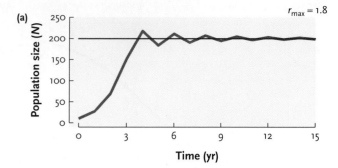

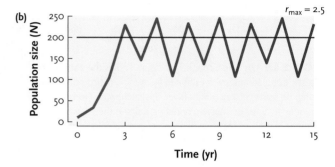

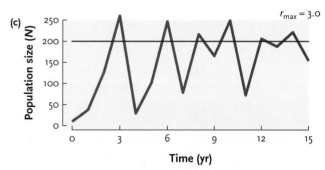

FIGURE 5.11 Different Values of r_{max} These are examples of discrete-time, logistic population growth curves having different time lags. (a) Populations for which r_{max} is less than 2 exhibit damped oscillations; (b) populations for which r_{max} is between 2.0 and 2.6 exhibit either 2- or 4-point stable limit cycles (the example illustrated here is a 4-point cycle); (c) populations for which r_{max} exceeds 2.6 exhibit chaos.

reference point (MSY) or some percentage thereof. Under federal law in the United States, for example, the term "overfishing" is interpreted in terms of the capacity of a fishery to produce the MSY on a continuing basis. If an overexploited fish stock falls below 0.5 B_{MSY}, by law a fishery rebuilding plan must be developed by the federal Secretary of Commerce. Such a legal requirement to rebuild overfished stocks does not exist in Canada, although comparable actions are often attempted.

The theoretical criteria for MSY originate from the logistic growth model. Recall that, according to Equation 5.19, there is a population size N, or in the case of a fishery, a population biomass B, at which the population growth rate ($\partial N/\partial t$) is at a maximum. For illustrative purposes, let us assume that t equals 1 year, and that we can use Equation 5.24, the discrete model for logistic population growth:

$$N_{t+1} = N_t + r_{max} N_t (1 - N_t/K)$$

FIGURE 5.12 Predicting Sustainable Harvests Pacific sardine (*Sardinops sagax*) have been commercially fished in British Columbia's waters since 1917. Its numbers have been subject to huge fluctuations in abundance and catch, which are driven primarily by fishing and environmental change.

goldenangel/Shutterstock.com

Within an MSY context, it is best to harvest a population when $(N_{t+1} - N_t)$ is at its maximum. According to the logistic growth model, this would occur at $0.5K$, although for many fisheries it is estimated that the maximum population growth rate might actually occur between $0.3K$ and $0.5K$ (Garcia et al., 1989). The maximum number of fish produced in a given year would correspond to the middle shaded area in **Figure 5.13**. During that year, $(N_{t+1} - N_t)$ would be at its maximum. The growth in population size $(N_{t+1} - N_t)$ is considered to be surplus from a fisheries perspective (but not from the perspective of the fish population) and therefore available to be harvested (this is the basis for *surplus yield models* in fisheries science).

If fishery managers could maintain a population at B_{MSY}, they would be able to produce the maximum yield that could be sustained over the long term. Today, however, many of the world's commercial fisheries have

FIGURE 5.13 Logistic Growth of a Commercially Harvested Fish Population This figure shows how the yearly increase in total fish biomass (*B*) changes with population size, being higher when *B* is near *K*/2, and smaller when *B* is small or large, relative to *K*. The highest "surplus population growth" (meaning surplus from a fisheries perspective, but not from that of a fish population) is represented by the shaded areas and represents the maximum sustainable yield. The biomass at which MSY is attained is termed B_{MSY}.

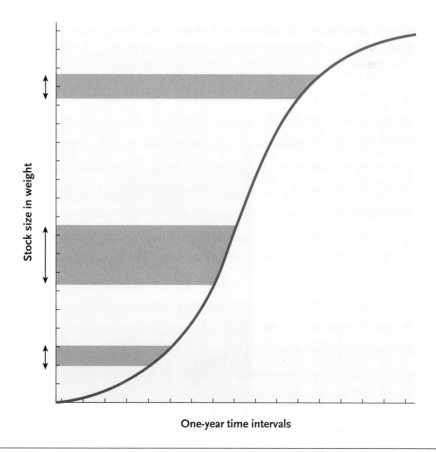

5.4 LOGISTIC POPULATION GROWTH

hapter 15), so that many fish populations are $_{MSY}$. This means that the sustainable yields ler than could be attained at or near B_{MSY} 2009). Compare, for example, the yield that ically be sustained at B_{MSY} (middle shaded **5.13**) with that corresponding to a population size considerably less than B_{MSY} (lowest shaded area). You will learn more about harvesting and managing bioresources in Chapter 15.

5.5 Age- and Stage-Structured Population Growth

So far, the population growth models we have considered have depended on birth and death rates and, for logistic growth, density (or abundance). For most organisms, however, the patterns of birth and survival vary with age. Body size and developmental stage might also affect birth and death rates, and models can be constructed to accommodate their influence. For the most part, we will consider age-specific effects, because of their generality and the fact that the age of organisms is often positively correlated with their size and life stage. Nonetheless, we will consider a simple stage-specific model and examine how it might be applied in a conservation context.

Age-Specific Schedules of Fecundity and Survival

Our objective initially will be to estimate the growth rate of an age-structured population that is undergoing exponential growth. Species whose individuals typically reproduce more than once in their lives are termed **iteroparous**, such as Atlantic salmon (*Salmo salar*), humans (*Homo sapiens*), and sugar maple (*Acer saccharum*) in eastern Canada. In contrast, individuals of **semelparous** species die after a single reproductive event, such as Pacific salmon (*Oncorhynchus* spp.), short-finned squid (*Illex illecebrosus*) off Atlantic Canada, and soapweed (*Yucca glauca*) in southern Alberta. For iteroparous species, it is necessary to determine at what age species begin to reproduce.

Age will be denoted by x and will represent years. We will also assume that individuals begin to reproduce as soon as they reach given age of maturity. The age-specific birth rate, also referred to as **age-specific fecundity** or **fertility**, is denoted m_x. This represents the average number of offspring (e.g., seeds of a plant, eggs of a fish or bird, newborns of a live-bearing mammal) that are born to a female at age x. Values of m_x need not be integers (whole numbers). For example, bighorn sheep (*Ovis canadensis*) females (*ewes*) in the mountains of western Canada have a litter size of one lamb (Bérubé et al., 1999), but not all of them breed every year **(Figure 5.14)**. Therefore, the m_x value for bighorn sheep is calculated as 1 multiplied by the age-specific probabilities of breeding. Researchers at the Université de Sherbrooke have estimated the values of m_x for ewes aged 2, 3 and 4 years to be 0.36, 0.76, and 0.86, respectively, in the region of Sheep River, Alberta (Loison et al., 1999).

The fecundity schedule of bighorn sheep is typical of species that experience **determinate growth**, which means that individuals stop growing after a certain age. Once maturity is attained, fecundity tends to be relatively constant from one age to the next, as typically occurs in birds and mammals. However, for organisms with **indeterminate growth** that continues throughout their

FIGURE 5.14 Bighorn Sheep (*Ovis canadensis*) These animals reside in alpine meadows and foothills near rocky cliffs in southern British Columbia and southwestern Alberta. These animals are adapted to extreme ranges of elevation and temperature.

© iStockphoto.com/Tom Tietz

lives, such as fish, reptiles, and many long-lived plants, the number of offspring produced tends to increase as age (and body mass) increases.

We can define **age-specific survival** (l_x), such that l_5 represents the probability of survival from birth until the beginning of the breeding season at 5 years of age (that is, at the beginning of age class 6). It is useful to distinguish *age* from *age class*, as follows:

Age: 0   1   2   3   4   5
      |--------|-------- |----- ---|---------|----------|
Age class: 1   2   3   4   5

A newborn individual is of age $x = 0$. It is in the first age class ($x = 1$) until it reaches the age of 1, at which time it enters the second year class. If the ages in a population range from 0 to k, the age classes range from 1 to k.

Schedules of age-specific survival typically follow one of three patterns **(Figure 5.15)**. **Type I Survivorship Curve** is characteristic of species that exhibit relatively high survival during young and intermediate ages, after which survivorship declines steeply as the maximum longevity is approached (e.g., bighorn sheep and humans; **Figure 5.16a**). **Type II Survivorship Curve** is characteristic of the relatively few species that have a constant rate of mortality throughout their lives [e.g., some turtles and birds, such as the black-capped chickadee (*Poecile atricapilla*) **Figures 5.16b** and **5.17**]. **Type III Survivorship Curve** is characteristic of species in which mortality is exceedingly high in early life until individuals attain an age when their vulnerability to risks of death declines, after which they experience relatively high survival, as is the case of plants with wind-dispersed seeds, marine

invertebrates, and fish that broadcast their eggs in the water during spawning (e.g., Atlantic cod, **Figure 5.16c**)

Life Tables

The data required to estimate survivorship and the exponential rate of growth in an age-structured population are often compiled in a **life table**. The age-specific survival and fecundity (or fertility) data are the core of a life table. The survival data may be obtained in one of two ways. When the relative numbers of individuals in each age

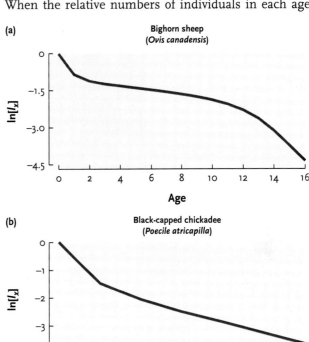

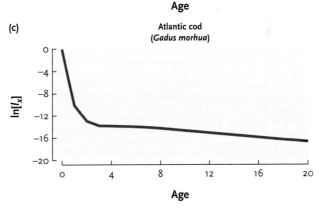

FIGURE 5.16 Examples of Type I, II, and II Survivorship Curves in Natural Populations (a) A Type I curve is shown for bighorn sheep in Alberta (Loison et al., 1999). (b) A Type II curve corresponds well to data for black-capped chickadees (Loery et al., 1987). (c) A Type III curve is illustrated by survival data for Atlantic cod (Hutchings, 1999). Age is in years.

SOURCE: Based on data from Loison, A., M. Festa-Bianchet, J.-M. Gaillard, J.T. Jorgenson, and J.-M. Jullien. 1999. "Age-specific survival in five populations of ungulates: Evidence of senescence," *Ecology*, 80: 2539–2554; Loery, G., K.H. Pollock, J.D. Nichols, and J.D. Hines. 1987. "Age-specificity of black-capped chickadee survival rates: Analysis of capture-recapture data," *Ecology*, 64: 1038–1044; Hutchings, J.A. 1999. "The influence of growth and survival costs of reproduction on Atlantic cod, Gadus morhua, population growth rate," *Canadian Journal of Fisheries and Aquatic Sciences*, 56: 1612–1623.

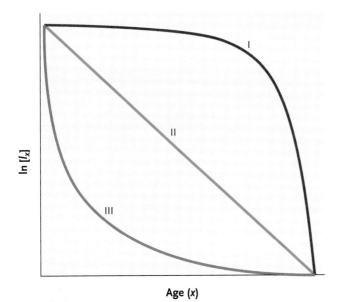

FIGURE 5.15 Three General Types of Survivorship Curves The natural logarithms of age-specific survival (l_x) are plotted against age (x). The Type I curve reflects survival that is comparatively high in early life, but increasingly lower later on. The Type II curve reflects a relatively constant survival throughout life. The Type III curve reflects high mortality in early life, followed by decreasing mortality as individuals age.

FIGURE 5.17 The Black-Capped Chickadee (*Poecile atricapilla*) Ranging throughout all of Canada, it is a common inhabitant of deciduous and mixed forests and open woodlands. It exhibits a Type II survivorship curve.

class are similar from one generation to the next (i.e., they have a **stable age distribution**) a population can be sampled to determine the age and abundances of individuals, that is, the estimation of N_x. Estimates of age-specific survival, l_x, based on such abundance data are most reliable. Second, when it is not possible to reliably estimate the age-specific abundance because the age distribution is not stable from one generation to the next, researchers can determine annual survival (from one age, or year, to the next) using a mark-recapture analysis. This involves marking a group of individuals of a given age x in one year, and then resampling the population one year later to determine the numbers that have survived.

Using these data, a life table can be assembled that describes the age-specific survival probabilities and fecundities that the average individual in a population can expect to experience from birth until death.

One means of obtaining these data is to monitor the fate of all of the individuals born at the same time, meaning they are all from the same **cohort**. The age-specific survival and fecundity schedules obtained from such a monitoring program comprise a **cohort life table**. Rather than following the fate of a single (or multiple) cohort(s), which can take several years, an alternative means of obtaining these data is to estimate them for all individuals in a population at a single point in time, thereby producing a **static life table**. One key assumption that is made when constructing a life table is that the data that are collected—either over the life span of a single cohort or at a single point in time—are representative of age-specific schedules for other cohorts or time periods.

The black-capped chickadee is one of the most common birds in Canada, breeding in all provinces and territories except Nunavut **(Figure 5.18)**. Despite its commonness, a life table for this bird has never been assembled for a particular population. However, a life table can be assembled using various sources of information. The first challenge is to estimate survival during the first year of life, a parameter that requires data on:

- the number of eggs laid by an average female;
- the percentage that hatch (hatching survival);
- the percentage of hatchlings that fledge from the nest (nestling survival); and
- and the percentage of fledglings that survive to maturity at age 1 year.

Mahoney et al. (1997) studied black-capped chickadees in central Ontario and found that the clutch size averaged 6 eggs per female, of which 86 percent hatch. Half of the hatchlings are expected to be female (Ramsay et al., 2003). A nestling survival estimate of 74 percent is available from Albano (1992), although this is for an Illinois population of the closely related Carolina chickadee (*Poecile carolinensis*). Smith (1995) provides an estimate of over-summer survival of 1-year-old female black-capped chickadees of 65 percent, based on a 10-year-study, while Loery et al. (1987) estimates that 45 percent of fledged birds survived to the following year, based on a 26-year study. Based on these estimates of survival, we can calculate the probability of surviving to age 1, l_1, as $0.86 \times 0.74 \times 0.65 \times 0.45 = 0.19$. A life table for female black-capped chickadees is presented in **Table 5.2**.

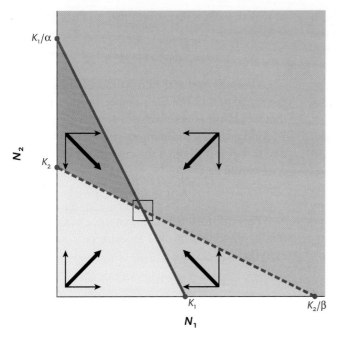

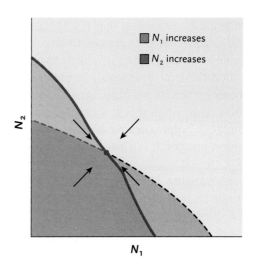

FIGURE 5.28 Competitive Exclusion The Lotka–Volterra competition model predicts stable coexistence of both competitors in a stable equilibrium. For the reasons explained in the caption to Figure 5.25, both species decline in the orange zone and increase in the green zone. In the dark blue zone, only species 2 can increase because the combined abundance of competitors is below its isocline but above that for species 1. In the light blue zone, only species 1 can increase because the combined abundance of competitors is below its isocline but above that for species 2. The point of intersection of the two species isoclines represents a combined abundance at which both competitors are at equilibrium. This equilibrium is stable because any divergence from this point of intersection will result in a return of the combined abundances to the point of intersection of the species isoclines. The diagram on the right is Figure 1 from MacArthur (1958).

SOURCE: Modified with permission of the Ecological Society of America, from MacArthur, R.H. 1958. "Population ecology of some warblers of northeastern coniferous forests," *Ecology*, 39(4): 599–619; permission conveyed through Copyright Clearance Center, Inc.

FIGURE 5.29 Warblers The black-throated green, Blackburnian, and bay-breasted warblers often share the same breeding habitat in coniferous forests. They are three of the five species of warblers studied by Robert MacArthur in his classic 1958 study in community ecology.

Following the methods of a study by MacArthur (1972), we can gain insight into the conditions that predict the persistence of species 1 and 2 by examining the algebraic solutions to the equations that he formulated.

We begin by assuming that if a species is able to increase in abundance under conditions that are less favourable to its needs, then it is likely to persist there. These conditions can reasonably be presumed to exist for species 1 when its per capita growth rate $(\partial N_1/N\partial t)$ is positive, even when it is at an exceedingly low level of abundance (approximated by zero), and when its competitor, species 2, is close to its carrying capacity $(N_2 \sim K_2)$.

By rearranging Equation 5.42 to have per capita growth rate on the left side, and then substituting 0 for N_1 and K_2 for N_2, we obtain the following:

(5.46)
$$(\partial N_1/\partial t \times 1/N_1 = r_1 [(K_1 - 0 - \alpha K_2)/K_1]$$

For per capita growth to always be positive, the following must hold true (given that r_1 is always positive):

(5.47)
$$K_1 - \alpha K_2/K_1 > 0$$

which means that

(5.48)
$$K_1/K_2 > \alpha$$

This inequality stipulates the condition that species 1 can persist only if its carrying capacity (relative to that of species 2) is greater than the competitive effect of species 2 on species 1. Expressed another way, if species 1 is to persist in the face of stiff competition (large α), then its carrying capacity must be relatively large. We can follow the same logic, and an analogous set of substitutions into Equation 5.43 to show that species 2 will persist when

(5.49)
$$K_2/K_1 > \beta$$

We can use the inequalities specified by Equations 5.48 and 5.49 to identify conditions under which coexistence at a stable equilibrium can exist. For both species to coexist,

$$K_1/K_2 > \alpha \text{ and } K_2/K_1 > \beta \text{ or } K_1/K_2 < 1/\beta$$

Placing these inequalities into a single expression that specifies the conditions for stable coexistence yields:

(5.50)
$$\alpha < K_1/K_2 < 1/\beta$$

This expression allows us to address a question of fundamental importance to ecology: How similar can competitors be and still coexist?

Recall that if competitors are interchangeable in their respective effects on the population growth rate of each other, then the competition coefficients would be equal to unity: $\alpha = \beta = 1$. Therefore, if competitors are dissimilar in terms of their competitive abilities, the competition coefficients would be less than one. Let us set

$\alpha = \beta = 0.05$. Substituting these values into Equation 5.50 we get

$$0.05 < K_1/K_2 < 20$$

This tells us that if competitors are highly dissimilar, the range in ratios of their respective carrying capacities that would support stable coexistence is extremely large. By contrast, if the competitors are extremely similar, such that $\alpha = \beta = 0.95$, then the conditions for stable coexistence would be

$$0.95 < K_1/K_2 < 1.05$$

This informs us that coexistence of similar competitors is possible only over an extremely narrow range of carrying capacities.

Character Displacement

Our exploration of algebraic constraints implicit to the Lotka–Volterra competition model tells us that the greater the similarity in resource use by potential competitors, the lower the likelihood that they will be able to coexist and the greater the probability that one of them will not persist (Gause, 1934). This necessity of divergence for the stable coexistence of competitors is reflected in the concept of **character displacement**, or a divergence in the phenotypic attributes of similar species as a result of competition occurring when they co-occur in a habitat. This idea was first championed by the British ornithologist David Lack (1910–1973) in his research on Darwin's finches (*Geospiza* spp.), which breed on the Galápagos Islands (Lack, 1947) **(Figure 5.30a)**.

Since then, the role of competition in phenotypic and genotypic divergence of close relatives sharing habitats has been explored in a wide variety of species. Dolph Schluter, an evolutionary biologist at the University of British Columbia, defines character displacement as a general process of phenotypic change that is induced or maintained by resource competition (Schluter, 2000). During this process a character changes from being represented by a single, unimodal, phenotypic distribution for a species (or a feeding morph) in **allopatric** populations (which occupy geographically separate ranges) to being represented by a bimodal or even multi-modal phenotypic distribution in **sympatry** (within a shared range; see **Figure 5.31**).

Schluter and colleagues have provided several examples of character displacement in fish populations, most notably those of the three-spined stickleback (*Gasterosteus aculeatus*), in which comparisons were made between competing feeding types of differing morphology **(Figure 5.30b)**. The key difference is in the lengths of their gill rakers, which are structures attached to the gills that help to prevent small invertebrates from escaping past the opercular opening and then out of the

FIGURE 5.30 **Character Displacement** This evolutionary process has been studied in Darwin's finches and in stickleback fish. (a) The Small Ground Finch (*Geospiza fuliginosa*) is one of four species of ground finch on the Galápagos that have bills of the "crushing" variety that are used to feed on seeds. (b) The Three-Spined Stickleback (*Gasterosteus aculeatus*) exists as different feeding morphs within some lakes in British Columbia.

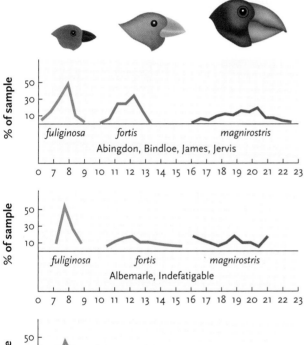

fish, when these foods are swallowed from the mouth cavity to the gut—the longer the rakers, the smaller the size of food items that are retained. In British Columbia lakes contain two morphs of sticklebacks. The benthic morph (bottom-feeding benthivore) generally has shorter gill rakers than the limnetic morph (open-water feeding planktivore) with which it co-occurs (**Figure 5.32**; Schluter and McPhail, 1992).

5.7 Predator–Prey Interactions

Thus far, we have considered the effects of density, age, developmental stage, and interspecific competition on the rate at which a population can change in abundance over time. These factors can be identified as being ecological (e.g., competition, density) or biological (e.g., age, size) in nature. Although we have not dealt explicitly with physical environmental factors, such as light or temperature, we have been incorporating their effects implicitly whenever we considered the carrying capacity (see Chapter 7 on physiological ecology).

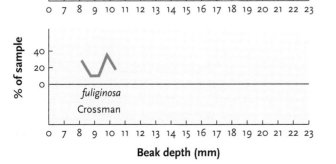

FIGURE 5.31 **Character Displacement in Darwin's Finches** The histograms show the phenotypic distributions of beak depth for three species of finches that either compete for seeds on the same island (are sympatric) (top three sets of histograms) or exist in allopatry (bottom two sets of histograms). Note two things: (1) the beak depths of *Geospiza fuliginosa*, *Geospiza fortis*, and *Geospiza magnirostris* do not overlap; (2) there is a divergence in the beak-depth distributions of *G. fuliginosa* and *G. fortis* when they occur sympatrically on Charles and Chatham Islands, but not when allopatric on Crossman and Daphne Islands.

SOURCE: Based on Lack, D. 1947. *Darwin's Finches.* p. 82. New York: Harper and Brothers.

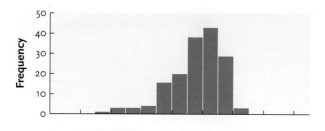

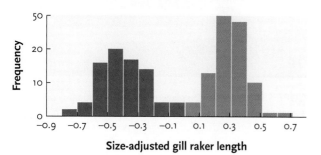

Size-adjusted gill raker length

FIGURE 5.32 Gill Rakers in Sticklebacks The data are frequency distributions of size-adjusted gill raker length in coastal British Columbia lakes with one or two trophic (feeding) morphs of three-spined stickleback. The upper panel represents data for sticklebacks inhabiting Cranby Lake, which supports only one feeding morph. The lower panel shows data for the benthic morph (green) and the limnetic morph (orange), which coexist in Paxton Lake.

SOURCE: Schluter, D. and J. D. McPhail. 1992. "Ecological character displacement and speciation in sticklebacks," *American Naturalist*, 140: 85–108, p. 91, Figure 3.

Predation is an additional major ecological factor that affects population growth. As an aside, we are referring to interspecific predation, in which the predator and the prey are different species. Intraspecific predation, or cannibalism, is also somewhat common, occurring, for instance, in at least 10 percent of fish families (Smith and Reay, 1991) and being an important factor affecting population growth in some of them (e.g., Claessen et al., 2000). However, cannibalism is not considered to be a general determinant of population growth for most species of animals. In this section we focus on interspecific predation.

Influence of Predator–Prey Interactions on Population Growth

Predation affects the population growth rates of both predator and prey. For a predator, the consumption of prey can increase the predator's birth rate and/or reduce mortality, both of which may help to increase population growth. C. S. (Buzz) Holling (1959), a Canadian ecologist doing research on the population dynamics of injurious insects, described four reactions of predators to changes in the density of their prey:

- The **numerical response** is an increase of the abundance of predators in response to their consumption of prey.
- The **functional response** describes the ways that the consumption of prey increases with its density.

- The **aggregative response** refers to a spatial shift in the distribution of predators as they move into an area where their prey is abundant.
- The **developmental response** is related to changes in the consumption of prey as a result of variations of the developmental state of a predator as it gets older.

In addition to models of interspecific competition, Lotka and Volterra developed models that describe the population dynamics of predator–prey interactions. They considered that the instantaneous population growth rate of a predator (P) will, to a first approximation, be a function (f) of the abundance of other members of its species and of their prey (p), such that

$$\partial P / \partial t = f(P, p)$$

As an additional simplification, it is assumed that the predator is a specialist that feeds only on a particular species of prey. In the absence of that prey, the predator will decline exponentially at a rate corresponding to its inherent death rate, d_p, such that:

$$\partial P / \partial t = -d_p P \qquad (5.51)$$

We can modify Equation 5.51 to describe the growth rate of the predator population when the prey is present, such that

$$\partial P / \partial t = \theta p P - d_p P \qquad (5.52)$$

In Equation 5.52, θ is a measure of the **conversion efficiency** of a predator, which is the ability to convert the energy of its food into growth plus investment in offspring. The product of θp is directly related to the numerical response of a predator.

Similarly, we can assume that the population growth rate of the prey will be a function of its abundance plus that of its predator, as follows:

$$\partial p / \partial t = f(P, p)$$

In the absence of the predator, and to a first approximation, the prey (p) can be expected to increase in accordance with the exponential growth model (Equation 5.6), such that:

$$\partial p / \partial t = rp \qquad (5.53)$$

However, in the presence of a predator, a negative influence can be expected on the population growth rate of the prey because of the increased mortality it suffers, such that:

$$\partial p / \partial t = rp - \phi P p \qquad (5.54)$$

In Equation 5.54, the constant ϕ is termed the **capture efficiency**, which is defined as the effect of a single predator on the per capita growth rate of its prey, that is, $(\partial p / \partial t)(1/p)$.

There are two simplifying assumptions to Equation 5.54. The first is that predators and prey move randomly within their shared habitat. This means that the movement of prey is not conditional on that of the predator, and vice versa. The second assumption is that the reduction in $\partial p / \partial t$ that is attributable to predation is related to the likelihood that predators and prey will encounter one another. This encounter rate is related to the product of the abundances of the predators and prey (Pp). This makes sense, especially if predators and their prey are moving randomly throughout their habitat, and is illustrated in the examples below:

Number of Predators:	P	1	1	3
Number of Prey:	p	1	2	2
Predators × Prey:	Pp	1	2	6

Therefore, the greater the probability of encounter between predators and prey (i.e., the larger the value of Pp), the greater the reduction in the population growth rate of the prey.

Turning back to the capture efficiency, the larger ϕ is, the more the prey population is negatively affected by the addition of a single predator. For example, consider what ϕ might be for a 12-metre basking shark (*Cetorhinus maximus*), the largest fish to occur in Canada. This species feeds by swimming forward slowly and steadily with its mouth wide open, capturing small prey known as zooplankton, and using its gill rakers to filter them from the water. A single basking shark might have a high value of ϕ because of the tremendous numbers of prey that it can consume per feeding episode. By contrast, a fish-eating osprey (*Pandion haliaetus*) might be expected to have a lower value of ϕ because it can capture only one prey item at a time and is not successful on every feeding attempt.

Functional Responses of Predators

As previously noted, the manner in which the consumption of prey increases with its density is called the functional response of a predator. Holling (1959), in a study of the effects of predation by small mammals on sawflies (hymenopteran insects that can damage certain trees), described several of these functional responses (**Figure 5.33**).

The Type I functional response describes a linear relationship between the prey density and the rate at which they are consumed by predators. This is the type of functional response that might be expected of predators that catch their prey using passive means, such as spiders that use a web to snare flies and other prey species. As the number of flies caught per unit area of web increases, the predatory spider can increase its feeding rate (number of flies consumed per unit of time). In a graph of prey density versus their rate of consumption by

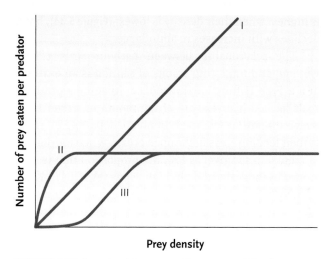

FIGURE 5.33 Functional Responses These are models of Types I, II, and III functional groups by predators to changes in the density of their prey.

predators, the slope identifies the predation-related mortality rate of the prey. This allows us to interpret a Type I functional response as being one for which the proportion of the prey population consumed by the predators (the prey mortality rate) remains constant with changes in prey density (**Figure 5.34**).

The Type II functional response identifies a relationship in which the slope of the functional response is highest near the origins of the x and y-axes, and then declines gradually as the prey density steadily increases (**Figure 5.34**). This is thought to typify predator–prey relationships, where the searching time required to locate an individual prey item declines as prey density increases. Because there is less searching time at high levels of prey density, the consumption rate by predators is limited by how long it takes to capture, subdue, and consume each food item—this is the handling time. The steadily declining slope that is characteristic of a Type II functional response means that the mortality rate of the prey

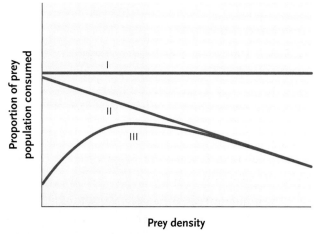

FIGURE 5.34 Prey Consumption The models show the proportion of the prey that is consumed by predators at different levels of prey density, in accordance with functional responses I, II, and III.

is highest when their density is lowest (**Figure 5.34**), but it declines with increases in abundance.

The relationship between harbour seals (*Phoca vitulina*) and migrating smolts of salmon is an example of a a Type II functional response. Imagine a group of seals located just seaward of the mouth of a river from which migrating Atlantic salmon are departing en route to their feeding areas in the open ocean. When the density of smolts in the river is low, the proportion that is consumed by the seals might be high. However, if the number of migrating smolts is higher, the consumption rate of each seal is no longer limited by the time required to locate a fish, but rather by the handling time. At an even higher abundance of smolts, the proportion of the fish that is consumed by the predators will steadily decline, as is reflected by the negative linear function in **Figure 5.34**. Eventually, the predators may become satiated by the high abundance of their prey. Another example of a Type II functional response is the relationship between the densities of wolves and their prey of moose, as documented by François Messier of the University of Saskatchewan (**Figures 5.35** and **5.36**).

The Type III functional response (**Figure 5.34**) has a shape that resembles the sigmoidal logistic growth curve that we examined earlier. An important mechanism by which a Type III functional response can arise is through prey-switching. Here, the rate of feeding per predator increases slowly when prey are at a low density, and then occurs much more rapidly at intermediate levels of abundance. Within the context of prey abundance, the mortality attributable to predation is relatively low at low densities, and it reaches a maximum at an intermediate levels, when the slope of the Type III functional response is at its greatest (**Figure 5.34**).

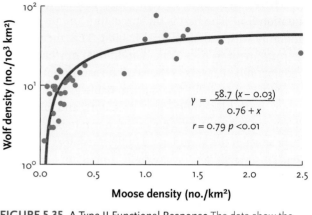

$$y = \frac{58.7\,(x - 0.03)}{0.76 + x}$$

$$r = 0.79 \; p < 0.01$$

FIGURE 5.35 A Type II Functional Response The data show the response of wolves to changes in the density of moose. Based on data from studies conducted in a broad region extending from Quebec to Alaska.

SOURCE: Used with permission of the Ecological Society of America, from Messier, F. 1994. "Ungulate population models with predation: A case study with the North American moose," *Ecology*, 75(2): 478–488; permission conveyed through Copyright Clearance Center, Inc.

Although the link might not be readily apparent, this functional response is part of the Equation 5.54 that describes how the growth rate of a prey population is affected by predation. Recall that Equation 5.54 stipulates that:

$$\partial p/\partial t = rp - \phi Pp$$

where ϕ is the capture efficiency. This parameter has units of $p/(Pp)$, meaning the number of prey consumed per predator per prey. If we multiply ϕ by p, the product has the same units as the functional response, **that is**, prey consumed per predator. Therefore, the functional response in Equation 5.55 is the product ϕp.

FIGURE 5.36 Predation of Moose by Wolves This interaction represents one of the classic predator–prey relationships between mammals in Canada's boreal forests.

Population Dynamics of Predator–Prey Interactions

When examining the dynamics associated with interspecific competition, the population growth rates of both predators and prey are set to zero to determine the equilibrium solutions for their respective models—the abundances of predators and prey at which the population growth rates are nil.

Returning to the Lotka–Volterra population growth models for predators and prey, we have:

$$\partial p / \partial t = rp - \phi Pp \qquad \text{for prey}$$

and

$$\partial P / \partial t = \theta pP - d_p P \qquad \text{for predators}$$

To find the equilibrium solutions of these equations, we set $\partial p / \partial t$ and $\partial P / \partial t$ to zero, giving us:

(5.55) $$P = r/\phi \qquad \text{for prey}$$

and

(5.56) $$p = d_p/\theta \qquad \text{for predators}$$

The equilibrium solution for the prey is specified in terms of the number of predators that is required to keep the prey population growth rate at zero. Similarly, the equilibrium solution for the predators is specified in terms of the number of prey required to maintain the predator population growth rate at zero.

The prey isocline (along which $\partial p / \partial t = 0$) is a horizontal line that separates the predator–prey state space into two regions **(Figure 5.37a)**. The number of predators required to keep the prey population at equilibrium is equal to r/ϕ. This ratio has a fairly straightforward biological interpretation—it means that at a higher per capita growth rate of the prey, and a lower capture efficiency of the predator, the greater the number of predators that is required to maintain the prey at equilibrium. An oversimplification of the Lotka–Volterra model that is associated with the horizontal isocline is that the number of predators required to maintain the prey at zero growth rate does not depend on the abundance of prey (we will revisit this issue later). If the number of predators falls above the prey isocline, the prey will decline; but if the number of predators falls below the isocline, the prey will increase **(Figure 5.37a)**.

The predator isocline is defined in terms of the numbers of prey that are required to maintain the predator at an abundance at which it is neither increasing nor decreasing. This is a vertical line in **Figure 5.37b** that intercepts the x-axis at d_p/θ, meaning that the greater the death rate of the predator, or the lower the conversion efficiency of the predator, the higher the number of prey that is required to keep $\partial P / \partial t = 0$. If the number of prey exceeds that required to support the predator population, the predator will increase in abundance (as indicated by

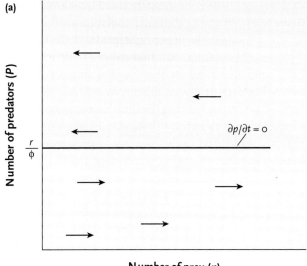

(a)

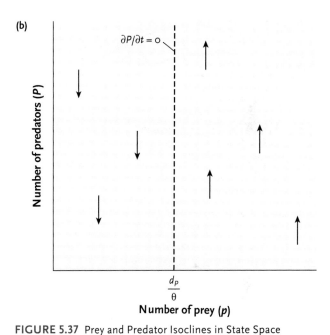

(b)

FIGURE 5.37 Prey and Predator Isoclines in State Space
(a) Directional changes in prey density, depending on whether the number of predators is above (prey decrease) or below (prey increase) the horizontal prey isocline (at which $\partial p / \partial t = 0$); (b) directional changes in predator density, depending on whether the number of prey is above (predators increase) or below (predators decline) the vertical predator isocline (at which $\partial P / \partial t = 0$).

the upward-facing arrows to the right of the vertical isocline in **Figure 5.37b**). Alternatively, the predator will decline if the number of prey is less than that specified by the isocline.

On their own, neither of these equilibrium solutions to the Lotka–Volterra predator–prey models is particularly helpful in providing insights into the population dynamics of predator–prey interactions. However, when we combine them into a single state-space graph, some interesting properties emerge from these simple models.

The isoclines divide the state space into four regions **(Figure 5.38)**. When the starting population sizes of predator and prey are in the upper-right quadrant, the number of predators is greater than that required to control the prey population, and so the number of prey can be expected to decline (for simplicity, we will use the word "control" when considering the number of predators that is required to keep $\partial p/\partial t = 0$; we will use the word "sustain" when identifying the number of prey required to keep $\partial P/\partial t = 0$). By contrast, an excessive number of prey is required to sustain the predator, meaning they will increase in the upper-right quadrant. The joint vector of predators and prey will move their combined abundance into the upper-left quadrant. Here, there are insufficient prey to sustain the predator (we are to the left of the vertical predator isocline), and there are more predators than are required to control the prey, meaning that both will decline.

Once the combined abundances fall below the horizontal prey isocline in the lower-left quadrant, the prey can increase because the number of predators is insufficient to control them. When the prey increase to a level of abundance greater than that required to sustain the predator (i.e., greater than dP/θ), both predator and prey can increase (lower-right quadrant of the state space). The joint vector is now directed toward the upper right. And when the abundance of predators exceeds r/ϕ, the combined abundance of predators and prey will be, once again, in the upper-right quadrant. The combined abundances will then cycle through the four quadrants in the form of an ellipse on the state-space graph.

If we wish to predict the abundance of predators and prey through time, we find that these elliptical trajectories yield a cyclical pattern of troughs and peaks **(Figure 5.39)**. The abundance peaks of predators occur when the joint vector crosses from the upper-right to the upper-left quadrants, when the prey are approximately halfway through their decline. Similarly, the peak prey levels (at the transition of the lower-right and upper-right quadrants) occur when the predator is at its midpoint of increase. The troughs of prey and predator abundance occur when the joint abundances shift from the upper to lower-left, and from the lower-left to lower-right quadrants, respectively. These patterns yield population cycles that are similar to those depicted in **Figure 5.39**.

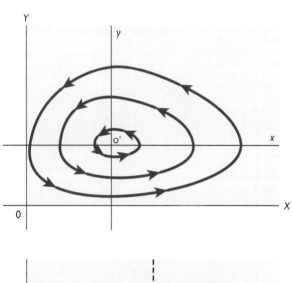

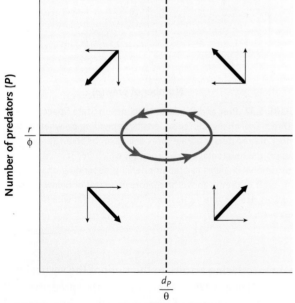

Number of prey (p)

FIGURE 5.38 Neutrally Stable Cyclical Population Dynamics This is a relationship of predators and prey resulting from the Lotka–Volterra predator–prey model. The top panel shows the same state-space graph as it originally appeared in Lotka (1925). He used the state-space graph to display the cyclical dynamics that he predicted would be associated with a parasite infecting an insect host.

SOURCE: Based on Lotka, A.J. 1925. *Elements of Physical Biology*. Williams and Wilkins, Baltimore, MD.

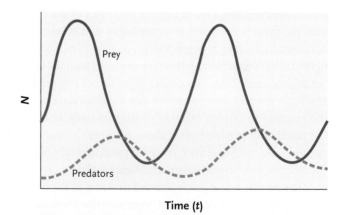

Time (t)

FIGURE 5.39 Population Cycles These are cyclical increases and decreases in the abundance of predators and prey through time, as predicted by the Lotka–Volterra predation model. Note the time lag in the peak abundances of predators and prey. Given that the predators are tracking the increased abundance of their prey, their rise in abundance can be expected to follow that of the prey. The prey decline as their predators approach their peak abundance. Thereafter, the predators decline because of a lack of prey, and the cycles repeat themselves.

The amplitudes of the cycles are determined by how close the combined abundances are to the point of intersection of the two isoclines, at which the predators and prey will not cycle because both $\partial p/\partial t$ and $\partial P/\partial t$ equal 0. The farther away the combined abundance is from the intersection, the greater will be the amplitude of the population cycles. Indeed, if the starting point is too far away from the isoclinal intersection point, the combined abundance vector will eventually meet one of the axes (resulting in either predator or prey abundance declining to zero), and the species will not cycle.

There are a number of real-world predator–prey systems where their abundances fluctuate in cyclical patterns similar to those predicted by the simple Lotka–Volterra model. The best–known example may be those of the snowshoe hare and lynx (**Figures 5.40** and **5.41**). Nonetheless, there are other predator–prey systems that do not appear to cycle in response to their reciprocal abundances. This may reflect the simplicity of the Lotka–Volterra model. For example, there are isoclines whose shapes lead to the prediction of stability, rather than cyclical fluctuation, in the abundances of predators and prey.

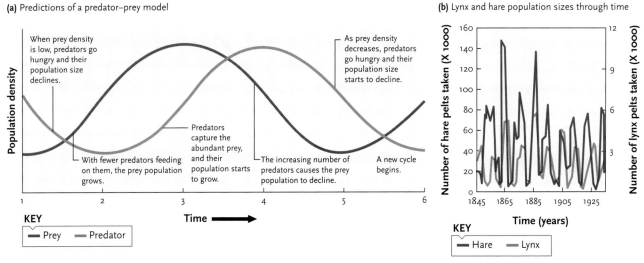

(a) Predictions of a predator–prey model

When prey density is low, predators go hungry and their population size declines.

With fewer predators feeding on them, the prey population grows.

Predators capture the abundant prey, and their population starts to grow.

The increasing number of predators causes the prey population to decline.

As prey density decreases, predators go hungry and their population size starts to decline.

A new cycle begins.

Population density

Time

KEY
— Prey — Predator

(b) Lynx and hare population sizes through time

Number of hare pelts taken (X 1000)

Number of lynx pelts taken (X 1000)

Time (years)

KEY
— Hare — Lynx

FIGURE 5.40 Lynx and Hares The data show cyclical increases and decreases in the abundance of lynx and snowshoe hare, based on pelt records maintained by the Hudson's Bay Company. The abundance of pelts is thought to be a good reflection of the abundance and possibly reflective of the predator–prey cycles predicted by the Lotka–Volterra model depicted in Figure. 5.39. The fit is particularly good from approximately 1910 to the early 1930s, with increases in hare (prey) abundance followed by increases in their predator (lynx), followed by reductions in prey and then reductions in the predator until the cycle begins anew.

SOURCE: From RUSSELL/WOLFE/HERTZ/STARR. *Biology*, 1E. © 2010 Nelson Education Ltd. Reproduced by permission. www.cengage.com/permissions.

FIGURE 5.41 Predation of Snowshoe Hare by Lynx Data on this relationship provide the most widely cited empirical example of the cyclical population dynamics predicted by the Lotka–Volterra predator–prey model.

Variations in Predator–Prey Isoclines

One way in which greater realism can be achieved is if a carrying capacity is incorporated into the prey isocline (the Lotka–Volterra model includes the assumption that the abundance of predators is the only factor regulating prey density, rather than, for example, intraspecific competition occurring among the prey themselves). Recall the prey population growth model:

$$\partial p / \partial t = rp - \phi Pp \tag{5.57}$$

and the logistic growth model:

$$\partial N / \partial t = rN(1 - N/K)$$

To incorporate the negative effects that increasing prey density can have on their own population growth through intraspecific competition, we can modify Equation 5.54 to yield:

$$\partial p / \partial t = rp(1 - p/K) - \phi Pp \tag{5.58}$$

To obtain the prey isocline, we again set $\partial p / \partial t = 0$, which yields:

$$0 = rp(1 - p/K) - \phi Pp$$

or

$$0 = p[r(1 - p/K) - \phi P] \tag{5.59}$$

The case where $p = 0$ is not of interest, because we are trying to understand the dynamic interactions of *both* predators and prey. However, if we set the bracketed term on the right-hand side of the equation to zero, we have:

$$0 = r(1 - p/K) - \phi P$$

which, following rearrangement, yields the prey isocline:

$$P = r/\phi - p(r/\phi K) \tag{5.60}$$

Notice that the form of this equation is analogous to that of a straight line with a negative slope, where the *y*-intercept is r/ϕ (after setting $p = 0$) and the *x*-intercept is K (after setting $P = 0$).

Plotted in state space, this new prey isocline, along with the unchanged vertical predator isocline, leads to a situation in which the combined abundances of predators and prey converge on a stable equilibrium. This is represented by the intersection of the two isoclines **(Figure 5.42)**. So, by incorporating additional factors (intraspecific competition and predator density) that can influence prey abundance, we reduce the probability that the predators and prey will cycle in response to one another's abundance.

Michael Rosenzweig and Robert MacArthur (1963) proposed an additional modification to the isoclines that can render them more realistic—they argued that the prey isocline should be dome-shaped **(Figure 5.43)**.

They reasoned that relatively few predators would be required to control the prey when they are at a low density, leading to a downward shape in the lower left part of the state space. They further suggested that if the prey are experiencing density-dependent growth, such that the relationship between $\partial p / \partial t$ and p is dome-shaped, then the maximum number of predators required to control the population growth of the prey would occur at half of their carrying capacity. The necessary number of predators would decline thereafter

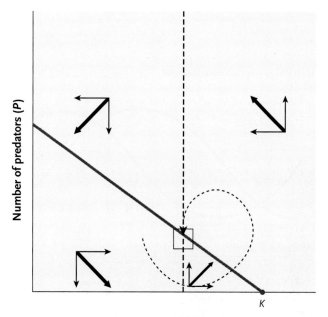

FIGURE 5.42 Influence of Carrying Capacity This is a model of predator–prey population dynamics associated with a prey isocline that incorporates a prey carrying capacity. The point of intersection of the two isoclines presents a stable equilibrium.

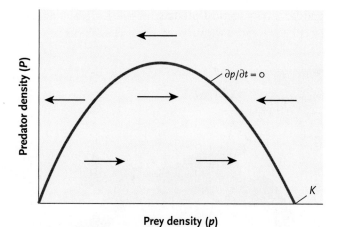

FIGURE 5.43 A Dome-Shaped Prey Isocline This is an example of this kind of isocline, as originally envisaged by Rosenzweig and Macarthur (1963). Inside the dome, the prey is expected to increase because the number of predators is less than that required to control the prey population. Outside the dome, there are more predators than required to maintain the prey at an equilibrium, resulting in a decline in the abundance of their prey.

SOURCE: Neal, D. 2004. *Introduction to Population Ecology*. Cambridge University Press, Cambridge, UK. Reprinted with the permission of Cambridge University Press.

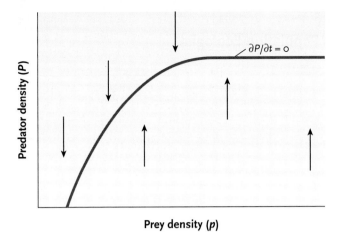

FIGURE 5.44 An Asymptotic Predator Isocline This model also follows Rosenzweig and Macarthur (1963). Here, the number of predators that can be supported would increase with increasing prey density, until the effects of intraspecific competition prevents the population of predators from increasing further. Predator densities would increase in the state space below the isoclines, but decline in the state space above them.

SOURCE: Neal, D. 2004. *Introduction to Population Ecology.* Cambridge University Press, Cambridge, UK. Reprinte.d with the permission of Cambridge University Press.

with increasing prey densities, as the production of prey per unit of time declines as they approach their carrying capacity. Rosenzweig and MacArthur also reasoned that the predator isocline should be asymptotic in shape **(Figure 5.44)**, such that the number of predators that could be supported would increase with increasing prey density until the effects of intraspecific competition among predators prevented their population from increasing further.

Different outcomes for both predators and their prey can be yielded by various combinations of Rosenzweig and MacArthur's dome-shaped prey isocline with Lotka and Volterra's vertical predator isocline. If the predator isocline is located within the right half of the area below

the prey isocline, a stable equilibrium will result **(Figure 5.45a)**. However, if the predator isocline is located within the left half, the prey are predicted to become extirpated **(Figure 5.45b)**. And if the predator isocline perfectly divides the area under the prey isocline, predators and prey will cycle in accordance with the original prediction made by the Lotka–Volterra model **(Figure 5.45c)**.

Altered Predator–Prey Interactions Resulting from Overfishing

Many commercially exploited populations of marine fish have been reduced to historically unprecedented low levels of abundance. These ecological and economic catastrophes have raised concerns that the resulting changes in predator–prey interactions may slow, or even prevent, the recovery of the depleted populations. One example is provided by predator–prey relationships among species of fish in the southern Gulf of St. Lawrence. Atlantic cod in this region, which had the largest cod stock in the world in the mid-1980s, have declined to such low levels that Swain and Chouinard (2008) have predicted they could become effectively extirpated from the southern Gulf of St. Lawrence by 2050.

One of the factors that is hypothesized to be retarding the recovery of cod in the southern Gulf of St. Lawrence is the increase in abundance of other fish, such as mackerel (*Scomber scombrus*) and herring (*Clupea harengus*). These are smaller species that cod formerly preyed heavily upon. In recent years, the decline in cod may have released the herring and mackerel from intensive predation by cod. However, these smaller fish prey heavily upon the eggs and larvae of cod, likely reducing the rate of offspring production by cod. The loss of offspring may compromise the recovery of this once-abundant predator and the economically important fishery (Swain and Sinclair, 2000).

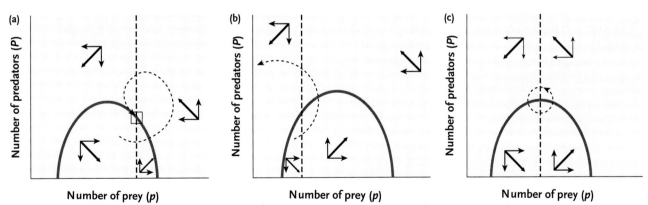

FIGURE 5.45 Location of the Vertical Predator Isocline These models of predator–prey dynamics associated with dome-shaped prey isoclines depend on the location of the vertical predator isoclines. (a) The predator isocline is to the right of the hump in the prey isocline (suggestive of a relatively inefficient predator), resulting in stable coexistence between predator and prey; (b) the predator isocline is to the left of the hump in the prey isocline (suggestive of a relatively efficient predator), resulting in extinction of the prey and eventual starvation of the predator; (c) if the predator isocline intersects the prey isocline at a right angle, the predators and prey are predicted to exhibit stable cycles characteristic of the traditional Lotka–Volterra predation model.

FIGURE 1 Charles Krebs

Charles (Charley) J. Krebs has had a large influence on the development of the science of ecology **(Figure 1)**. Born in St. Louis, Missouri, he undertook his postgraduate degrees at the University of British Columbia (UBC). Since 1970,

following six years at Indiana University, Charley Krebs has been a member of the faculty of the Department of Zoology of UBC, where he is now Professor Emeritus.

The title of Krebs' first scientific publication, in the journal *Arctic* in 1961, carried several harbingers of his future research endeavours: *Population dynamics of the Mackenzie Delta reindeer herd, 1938–1958*. The recurrent themes of population ecology in his work, notably cyclical dynamics, as well as Arctic research, mammals, and long-term studies, are all reflected there. More than 240 scientific publications later, Krebs and his colleagues are still working on the population dynamics of snowshoe hare, mice, voles, and their predators at Kluane Lake in southwestern Yukon (where he has been doing research since 1973), and of lemmings at several sites in arctic Canada including Herschel Island off the north Yukon coast (begun in 1987). In addition to his work in northern Canada, Krebs has undertaken studies of the dynamics of terrestrial mammals in Australia and in the United States.

Among the most prominent contributions of Krebs to ecology and teaching are his books (seven titles), which include two widely used textbooks: *Ecology: The Experimental Analysis of Distribution and Abundance* (6th edition, 2009) and *Ecological Methodology* (2nd edition, 1999). Moreover, he has effectively communicated the results and implications of ecology and ecological research to many elements of society, both in Canada and globally. This includes helping to foster educational programs in developing nations (he has taught ecology and pest management in China and the Philippines) as well as participating on international expert panels in the developed world, such as the Cooperative Research Centre for Vertebrate Biocontrol in Australia.

Krebs' research achievements have been recognized by numerous notable award including the inaugural President's Award from the Canadian Society for Ecology and Evolution (2009), the Ecologist Award from the Ecological Society of America (2002), and fellowships in the Norwegian and Australian Academies of Science.

CHAPTER SUMMARY

(LO5.1)

- Populations change according to the difference of the numbers of (births + immigration) minus (deaths + emigration), or $N_t + 1 = N_t + (M_t - D_t) + (I_t - E_t)$. The intrinsic rate of increase (r) is a per individual or per capita rate of population growth.

(LO5.2)

- Population abundance trajectories can be predicted using simple population growth models. Depending on the species, the abundance, and the available survival and fecundity data, these forecasts can be made by incorporating the effects of density, age, and developmental stage, using logistic and age-/stage-structured models.

(LO5.3)

- Population growth models can be used from a theoretical and practical perspective. One example of the former would

be predictions regarding the probability of establishment and future increase of an invasive species. An applied example would include predictions regarding the timeframe required for depleted populations to attain a recovery target.

(LO5.4)

- Simple models of population growth examine species in isolation of their interactions with other species. Yet competition with other species for space, for food, or for other resources can negatively affect a population's ability to grow. Similarly, the ability of a species to grow, or even persist, will depend on the abundance of that species' predators and prey.

(LO5.5)

- One means of predicting whether a competitor or predator will displace another species, or whether the interacting species will coexist, is through the use of state-space graphs. To predict the outcome of competition between competing species, these simple graphs incorporate factors such as carrying capacity and the impact of competition on each species' per capita population growth rate. State-space graphs can also be used to identify conditions under which predators can, and cannot, coexist.

(LO5.6)

- The parameter r can be described as being one of the most fundamental parameters in ecology. Being a metric of species and population growth rate, this parameter can be used to establish targets for the sustainable harvesting of wild populations and for the predicting the recovery trajectories of depleted populations.

QUESTIONS FOR REVIEW AND DISCUSSION

1. Canada's human population attained an abundance of 35 million in 2013. At current rates of natural birth and immigration, it has been estimated that the population will double in 78 years. Calculate r for the Canadian human population. What will Canada's population size be in 2050?

2. Regarding population growth, which of the following statements is not true?

   a. Birth (plus immigration) and death (plus emigration) rates must be equal for population size to remain constant over time.

   b. Net recruitment is highest at intermediate densities when populations experience density-dependent growth.

   c. $(K–N)/K$ represents the proportion of habitat or resources that remains available.

   d. A time lag may cause a population to temporarily overshoot K and to oscillate above and below K.

   e. Carrying capacity increases as population size decreases.

3. Using the following hypothetical life table for a population of cedar waxwings (*Bombycilla cedrorum*), answer the following questions:

Age (x)	Age-Specific Survival (l_x)	Age-Specific Fecundity (m_x)
0	1	0
1	0.167	2
2	0.083	3
3	0.048	3
4	0.016	4
5	0	–

   a. This population will:
      i. eventually become extinct
      ii oscillate about its carrying capacity
      iii. increase exponentially
      iv. experience logistic population growth
      v. remain constant in abundance over time

   b. What is the average number of offspring produced by each female in her lifetime? What is the generation time for this population?

   c. If the survival of waxwings from birth to age 1 were to increase by 50 percent, would this affect the long-term prognosis of the population?

4. In 2007, basking sharks off the Pacific coast of Canada were assessed as endangered by the Committee on the Status of Endangered Wildlife in Canada (COSEWIC). These are the largest fish in Canadian waters, and tens to hundreds of individuals were once observed in the bays and inlets of coastal British Columbia. However, only six have been observed since 1996. The species declined primarily because of a "pest eradication" program undertaken by Canada's Department of Fisheries and Oceans from 1954 to 1971. A large blade fitted to a DFO patrol vessel was used to kill basking sharks because their tendency to feed near the surface would cause them to sometimes become entangled in salmon gill nets, resulting in lost economic opportunities for commercial salmon fishers. In comparison, basking sharks in eastern Canadian waters are thought to number between 5000 and 10 000 individuals. Assuming exponential growth by the species on the West Coast and an estimated $r_{max} = 0.03$ individuals per individual per year, how many years would it take for basking sharks to reach a presumably sustainable population abundance of 7500 individuals from an initial abundance of 100 individuals?

5. Two species of rodents that compete with one another in their native distribution have invaded a previously unoccupied patch of habitat. The carrying capacity of species 1 is 5000 individuals, whereas the carrying capacity for species 2 is 15 000. The competition coefficients a and b are 0.5 and 2.0, respectively. Draw the state-space isoclines for these two species. If the initial population size of species 1 is ($N_1 = 4000$) and is double that of species 2, what is the predicted outcome of interspecific competition between these two species?

6. Canadian lynx and their primary prey, snowshoe hare, exhibit 9- to 11-year cyclical patterns in their abundance in Canada's boreal forests (see **Figure 5.40b**). These cycles are assumed to be directly linked to one another because the lynx is a specialist predator of snowshoe hare. However, lynx are absent on Anticosti Island at the mouth of the St. Lawrence River, yet the hare still exhibits cyclical patterns in abundance. Given the absence of lynx, what factors might be responsible for the regulation of snowshoe hare on Anticosti Island?

Behavioural Ecology

LEARNING OBJECTIVES

After studying this chapter you should be able to:

1. Understand that there are different levels of questioning with regard to biological traits; these are related to the difference between ultimate and proximate "why" questions.

2. Explain that natural selection acts mainly on individuals. This includes fitness conflicts between individuals of the same species, with these conspecifics representing an important part of the selective environment.

3. Describe how conflicts between the fitness interests of males and females in mating, and between competing

males, can promote the evolution of costly ornamental traits by sexual selection, even when those characters may decrease individual survival.

4. Understand that, given certain genetic and ecological factors, selection can favour a decrease in fitness conflict within social groups, which can lead to the evolution of castes in which individuals reduce or give up their personal reproduction to aid the reproduction of other group members.

6.1 Behavioural Ecology

Behavioural ecology investigates why animals in the wild behave the way they do. The "why" relates to the evolutionary adaptiveness of behaviour in relation to natural environments (**Ecology in Depth 6.1**). Examples of topics include foraging for food and avoidance of natural enemies (predators, parasites, or pathogens). Of particular importance, however, are social behaviours that serve as adaptations when organisms interact with individuals of the same species (**conspecifics**). Adaptations evolve by Darwinian **natural selection** (see Section 1.3) that favours "behaviour patterns which maximize an individual's chance of surviving and passing copies of its genes to future generations" (Davies et al., 2012).

Social behaviours are typically related to the competitive struggles to reproduce. They include the use of ornaments or armaments by males competing to acquire mates (**sexual selection**) and competitive interactions

among females when there are limited opportunities to breed within a social group.

Interactions with natural enemies and conspecifics may impose intense selection pressures that result in continuous evolutionary change. The interaction of pathogens and parasites with their host species is one example of this dynamic process. Most pathogens and parasites have a short generation time that allows them to quickly evolve strategies to adapt to the defences of their longer-lived hosts, which then must evolve new protections. The mating preferences of females for ornamented males (such as male birds with showy plumage) is another example of biological interactions changing over evolutionary time. This preference has been a powerful force favouring the evolution of male adaptations. However, sexual selection for ornamentation is partly opposed by **viability selection** against ornaments, which may reduce the likelihood of survival of the individual. For example, the bright courtship colours of male guppies are be easily located by predators (see Section 6.4).

Scientific investigation proceeds by testing potential answers (hypotheses) to a question using experiments, observations, and comparisons. In evolutionary studies, however, some of the potential answers are not alternatives. For example, answers to the question "Why do red-winged blackbirds (*Agelaius phoeniceus*) fly north in the springtime?" can be both:

- *ultimate, or related to fitness, such as: "in order to breed successfully";*

- *and proximate, or mechanistic: "because they are cued by increasing day-length to migrate northward"*

Behavioural ecologists ask ultimate "why" questions, but proximate levels of analysis can also inform the evolutionary answers. For example, consider the question: "Why do crickets (*Nemobius sylvestris*) that are parasitized by a hairworm (*Paragordius tricuspidatus*) jump into water?" Proximate evidence supports the hypothesis that the host cricket is manipulated by the parasite to migrate to the aquatic breeding habitat of the free-living hairworm adults. It has been shown that hairworm neurotransmitters occur in the brain of a parasitized cricket, and they interfere with its normal behaviour. Such chemicals are not predicted by an alternative ultimate hypothesis: that parasitized crickets seek water because they are ill, that is, the cause is thirst alone (Biron et al., 2006).

Adaptation, Selection, and Behaviour

Adaptive **traits** enhance an individual's survival or reproduction, but ultimately an increase in evolutionary **fitness** requires that copies of genes that underlie those traits are passed on to the next generation (see Section 1.3). Organisms usually display **optimal behavioural** traits that enhance their fitness. However, some organisms appear to behave suboptimally, such as when changes in the biotic or abiotic environment are too rapid for an adaptive response to occur (Davies et al., 2012). Behavioural ecologists often evaluate fitness by examining the relative **reproductive success** of individuals that differ in certain behavioural traits. This is a different approach from that used by population geneticists, who might examine fitness through changes in the relative abundance of various alleles in subsequent generations.

Behavioural ecologists examine fitness by asking "why" questions about the traits of interest (**Ecology in Depth 6.1**). Behavioural traits that would seem to decrease fitness are particularly challenging. One example is suicide: why do male redback spiders (*Latrodectus hasselti*) copulate and then somersault into the lethal jaws of their cannibalistic mate? Why does the use of a barbed stinger in defence of the hive by a worker honeybee (*Apis mellifera*) invariably result in its fatal self-evisceration? And why do crickets that are parasitized by a hairworm jump into a pool of water, where they drown? As we will see later, there are fitness-enhancing behavioural answers to all of these questions. The point being made here is that, although the answers to ultimate "why" questions of this sort may be difficult to fathom, they do reveal specific links between interesting behaviours and enhanced fitness (Ecology in Depth 6.1).

A focus on the fitness of individuals rather than on populations or species was eloquently argued in G. C. Williams' book *Adaptation and Natural Selection* (1966), and was furthered by Richard Dawkins in books such as The *Selfish Gene* (1976) (for additional discussion of the conceptual tension between selection on genes and on individuals, see Ecology in Depth 6.2). Dawkins (1995) made an obvious but perceptive argument: each and every ancestor of all living organisms must have matured, mated, and produced at least one offspring. However, many or even most of the contemporary conspecifics of the ancestors did not achieve that fitness. They may have been felled by a pathogen while young or failed to find a mate. An evolutionary consequence of this ancestral filtering mechanism—*natural selection*—is that organisms have inherited many "successful" (or adaptive) traits. As a consequence, to the degree that is possible, organisms are expected to choose the best mates and habitat, to make appropriate choices of food, and to avoid natural enemies. Occasionally, however, individuals may show adaptations that are more difficult to interpret, such as those that seem to decrease immediate personal survival but that enhance their reproductive success, or subversive tactics that decrease the fitness of other individuals, such as hosts in the case of parasites, and, in certain situations, even mating partners.

Two final points can be made about genes and behavioural adaptations. First, discussion of "genes for" a particular behaviour does not imply that a single gene underlies the trait. In fact, adaptive behaviour is usually the result of numerous genes (Fitzpatrick et al., 2005). Second, variations in behaviour that have differing consequences for fitness do not necessarily reflect genetic differences at all; they may also be due to phenotypic plasticity (see Section 1.3). For example, male insects that have had ample food as larvae typically grow to be relatively large adults, which may increase their mating

In nature, individual organisms are adapted to survive and reproduce. Thus, behavioural ecologists ask questions about how certain traits may affect the fitness of individuals. Copies of genes underlying adaptive traits are passed along to offspring, so behavioural ecologists are also interested in the relative success of genes replicating. For example, genes that support altruism are passed on via relatives (Davies et al., 2012) (Section 6.5).

Occasionally, successfully replicating genes are selfish in the sense of enhancing their own replication (fitness) at the cost of decreasing the fitness of the individual (and thus of other genes in the genome). One such example is the case of the stalk-eyed fly (*Cyrtodiopsis dalmanni*), named for the bizarrely long

eye-stalks of males. This species has an "outlaw" selfish allele on the X chromosome, which during meiosis in males inactivates Y-bearing sperm (Wilkinson et al., 1998a). Inactivation enhances the fitness of the outlaw gene because all of the fertilizing spermatozoa carry the X allele. At the same time, however, the fitness of the individual fly is decreased because there is diminished fertility of the ejaculate and a strong daughter bias in females that mate with these males.

Antagonistic selection occurs when alleles interfere with the replication of other alleles. This type of selection on individuals has produced suppressor alleles that in males disable the Y-inactivating outlaw genes. Because the suppressor genes are genetically linked to other genes that code for longer eye

stalks, there is also female-choice sexual selection for "good genes" that provide genetic fitness benefits to offspring (see Section 6.4). This occurs because females prefer to mate with long-stalked males—those less likely to carry outlaw alleles.

In addition to the good-genes benefits of mating with long-stalked males, there is evidence that runaway sexual selection (Section 6.4) may also play a role in amplifying the trait of longer eye-stalks (Wilkinson et al., 1998b). Artificial selection experiments were set up to produce genetic lines of both long- and short-stalked males, and it was found that females preferred males with the stalk length that was characteristic of their own lineage. It appears, therefore, that female preference and male trait genes have coevolved.

success if they must defend access to a female against rivals. Conversely, smaller males may adopt an alternative tactic that involves mating surreptitiously. These alternative ways of acquiring mates are partly conditional on environmental conditions that were experienced as larvae. Genetic variation may underlie both of the behaviours, which may be phenotypically plastic responses to environmental situations. The ability to exhibit a plastic response is itself an adaptation that is evolving in response to unpredictable environments (see also Chapter 8 and Ecology in Depth 6.2).

6.2 Foraging for Food

Optimal foraging theory describes how food choices and intake are enhanced to increase fitness. Foraging strategies have been shown to do this in many ways, including how food items and patches are chosen and handled. A simple prediction is that animals will consume every edible item that they encounter. In many situations, however, it is better to be selective when foraging. For example, if items or patches of food differ in quality, fitness may be increased by focusing the foraging effort on targets of higher quality.

Preferences for items of higher quality are expected to occur whenever effort is expended to find or process food. This might be relevant if there is a cost of travelling

between patches of food (e.g., a sparrow flying between seed sources), if an animal needs to manipulate items before consuming them (e.g., birds needing to remove the husk of a sunflower seed), or if it must return to a particular location with the food (e.g., a bird that is feeding nestlings).

A field study of foragers that prefer higher-quality food patches was conducted by Ralph Cartar (2004) of the University of Calgary. He decreased the quality of patches by stressing plants to diminish the amount of nectar in their flowers and thus decreasing food available to foraging bumblebees (*Bombus* species). He examined two hypotheses to explain the preference of bumblebees for the patch types: (1) local experience, in which bees stay longer when receiving more nectar in a particular patch, and (2) remembering the locations of higher-quality patches. The hypotheses were examined by studying the foraging times and habits of individually marked bumblebees. Both of the hypotheses received empirical support, with evidence for the second (memory) hypothesis coming from bees that were observed to pass by lower-quality plants, and to then return frequently and spend disproportionate time in those providing higher nectar rewards. Cartar concluded that remembering the location of the higher-quality plants indicates sophisticated cognitive processing in the bumblebees, especially considering the hundreds to thousands of individual plants that might be visited in a single foraging trip.

FIGURE 6.1 **FIGURE 6.1** A Grey Squirrel (*Sciurus carolinensis*) Lima et al. (1985) observed that individuals carried food only if it was obtained close to cover, and were more likely to carry large pieces because they took longer to eat, which if done in the open would expose them to greater danger from predators.

Foraging While Threatened by Enemies

Animals that are actively foraging and thus exposed to an increased risk of predation or parasitism are expected to forage less optimally when risk increases. This prediction has been supported in many studies. In a study of grey squirrels (*Sciurus carolinensis*; **Figure 6.1**), Lima et al. (1985) varied both food value (small or large pieces of cookie) and the costs of carrying food back to a safe area (distance from tree cover). They observed that squirrels carried food only if it was close to cover, and were more likely to carry large pieces because they took longer to eat, which if done in the open would expose them to more danger from predators.

Animals also tend to decrease their activity when in the presence of predators. Frank Macchiusi and Robert Baker (1992) of the University of Toronto studied the aquatic tube-dwelling larvae of a midge (*Chironomus tentans*). The larvae must leave their refuge to feed, but they reduced the time spent outside their tube when predatory sunfish (*Lepomis gibbosus*) were present. As such, the presence of sunfish had a direct impact on midge fitness because it reduced their food intake. As a result, the number of larvae that moulted to the next instar was also reduced.

Tradeoffs have also been noted between foraging behaviour and risks of parasitism. Hutchings et al. (2002) studied lambs of wild sheep (*Ovis aries*) that were grazing in areas in which experimental differences had been created in the risk of being parasitized. Lambs that foraged in habitats that were well fertilized with manure had a food intake that was 1.5 times greater, but they were also exposed to more than five times the abundance of a helminth parasite that was present in dung and could be transmitted to the lambs while eating. Some of the lambs were treated with an antiparasite medicine partway through the experiment, and their foraging was com-pared to a control group. At first, all of the lambs rejected the high-parasite/high-quality forage. Although lambs of both groups eventually began to graze on this conflicted food, the treated lambs grazed on it more often; these healthy, parasite-free lambs could apparently afford risking greater contact with the parasites.

6.3 Natural Enemies and Adaptive Behaviour

Animals may face many types of risk at once, and there are tradeoffs among the behaviours to avoid disparate risks. For example, Baker and Smith (1997) of the University of Toronto examined larval dragonflies (*Ishnura verticalis*) that were faced with a conflict between grooming movements to remove parasitic mites, and remaining still when predatory fish were nearby. When the researchers manipulated fish presence and the number of mites, the only significant effect was more grooming movements by the dragonfly larvae exposed to a higher density of mites. This behaviour had fitness consequences because moving made the larvae conspicuous and more likely to be eaten by fish. These results suggest that the costs of parasitism are so high that the dragonfly larvae will tolerate an increased risk of predation.

A **brood parasite** is a species that lays its eggs in a nest of another individual or species for incubation and raising the young. By doing this the brood parasites exploit the provisions of their host, but their virulence may be further increased if they remove or kill the offspring of the host. Examples include slave-making ant species that raid the nests of other ants to capture eggs or larvae for recruitment into their worker force, and certain wasps and flies whose larvae kill those of host solitary-wasps and bees.

Perhaps the best-studied example of the impact of a brood parasite on host adaptations is that of the Eurasian cuckoo (*Cuculus canorus*), which eats the egg of a host bird and then lays one of its own in the nest. **Coevolution** is revealed in studies of cuckoo races, each of which is specialized in laying eggs that mimic those of a particular species of host. Clearly, host discrimination against poorly matched eggs is a powerful selective force that maintains traits in the eggs of cuckoo host-races. Remarkably, the host-races maintain the adaptive genetic differences that underlie egg patterns despite the fact that all of the races appear to freely interbreed. The mystery of this complex adaptation was solved by Lisle Gibbs et al. (2000) of McMaster University, who demonstrated that the cuckoo races are restricted to female lineages. Genes influencing egg type may be carried on the female-specific sex chromosome, which is inherited from mother to daughter. Unlike many animals, in birds the female and not the male is the heterogametic sex.

Certain invertebrate parasites are extremely proficient at channelling the resources of their host into their own fitness. In a bizarre example, the parasitic larva of the ichneumonoid wasp *Zatypota percontatoria* modifies the normal web-spinning habits of its host spiders so that they spin cocoons that protect the wasp's pupa (Korenko and Pekár, 2011). This occurs just before the spider is killed and eaten by the larva. Some invertebrate parasites have a complex life history that involves them passing through several intermediate host species and/or habitats. In such cases, the parasite may adaptively manipulate host behaviour to ensure that its life cycle is completed. For example, birds, the final hosts of a certain nematode, are fooled into eating ants that are infected by the parasite larvae because the ants resemble the colour of fruit (see Ecology in Depth 6.1) **(Figure 6.2)**.

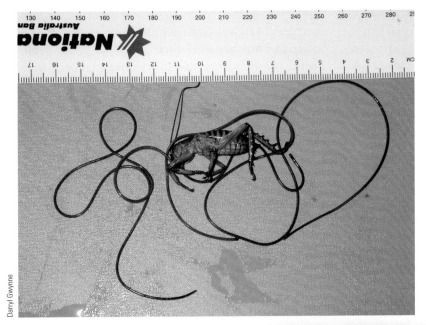

Darryl Gwynne

FIGURE 6.2 Parasites and Behaviour Top: A tree weta (an orthopteran insect in the family Anostostomatidae) with two hair worms that emerged when it was placed in a pool of water.

Right: An ant, *Cephalotes atratus*, whose abdomen resembles the colour of a ripe berry when parasitized by the nematode *Myrmeconema neotropicum*. This increases the likelihood that the ant will be detected and eaten by a fruit-eating bird, which is the final host of the nematode.

Stephen P. Yanoviak

The manipulation of host behaviour is particularly common in species of spiny-headed worms (Acanthocephala) that parasitize crustaceans as their intermediate host and vertebrates as the final host (both hosts must be parasitized if the nematode is to complete its life cycle). Parasitized crustaceans are often modified in their colour and behaviour. Cézilly et al. (2000) experimented with two species of spiny-headed worms that manipulate an intermediate host, the amphipod *Gammarus pulex*, in different yet adaptive ways. Noninfected *Gammarus* would remain sheltered in poorly lit areas close to the river bed. However, *Gammarus* infected by one species of spiny-headed worm are attracted to open, well-lit areas where they are at greater risk of being eaten by fish, the final host. In contrast, *Gammarus* infected by the other species of spiny-headed worm move up in the water column, which places them near the water surface where the final hosts—aquatic birds such as ducks—are likely to be foraging.

Changes in host behaviour may simply be a symptom of a parasite-induced illness, or a defensive reaction to parasitism. When testing the proposition that a parasite is adaptively manipulating its host, it is important to rule out alternative hypotheses (see Ecology in Depth 6.1). Moreover, modified behaviour must be shown to be a result of parasitism rather than the cause, in the sense that a host behaving differently might be more likely to become parasitized. Robert Poulin (2006) suggested that support for the adaptive manipulation hypothesis should include evidence that:

- phenotypic alteration of the host is complex in character;
- there is an increased likelihood of encountering the next stage in the parasite's life cycle; and
- the parasite's fitness is increased.

All of these criteria are satisfied by experiments that examined the effects of a single-celled pathogen, the protozoan *Toxoplasma gondii*, on the behaviour of its intermediate rodent hosts. Berdoy et al. (2000) showed that rats (*Rattus norvegicus*) with toxoplasmosis are no longer repelled by the scent of their cat (*Felis domesticus*) predators, the final host of the *Toxoplasma*. Instead, the scent of cats becomes a fatal attraction for the infected rats. By the way, toxoplasmosis also occurs in humans, in which the effects are usually harmless in adults (but can be adverse for a developing fetus), although there is intriguing evidence of personality changes.

6.4 Interacting with Sexual Competitors

Foraging and avoiding natural enemies are critical to survival, but for such adaptations to evolve their genetic potential must be passed along to offspring. Reproductive success is therefore key to fitness, and struggles among conspecifics to mate and reproduce are central areas of study in behavioural ecology. A compelling example of the importance of reproduction over individual survival in enhancing fitness comes from research on adaptive suicide involving the Australian redback (*Latrodectus hasselti*), one of a group of species known as the widow spiders, Maydianne Andrade (1996) of the University of Toronto showed that during copulation the male somersaults into the jaws of his mate and as a consequence increases his reproductive success **(Figure 6.3)**.

Sexual selection is a general theory of selection in the context of mating. It most commonly involves selection on males to mate with as many partners as they can. In contrast, multiple matings can be less than optimal for the fitness of females. This sexual conflict over the female mating rate that is optimal for fitness is central to understanding sex differences in the intensity of sexual selection.

Sexual selection results from competition for matings. In males this is about fertilizing more ova, and it is reflected in a greater variation in the production of offspring (**reproductive skew**) among males than among females; some males sire more offspring than others (e.g., **Figure 6.3**). Therefore, compared to females, males are usually adapted to maximizing their numbers of matings with different partners. Because copulation typically has costs for any females that re-mate, interactions between the sexes should reflect sexual differences in the optimal mating rate. This is expected to result in selection for salesmanship among displaying males, and in sales discrimination

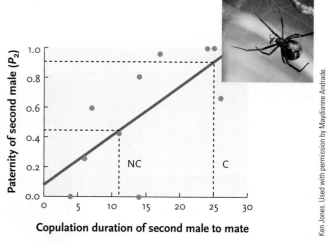

FIGURE 6.3 **Fitness and Duration of Copulation** This graph shows the fitness (proportion of eggs they fertilized) of male redback spiders (*Latrodectus hasselti*) following a mating with a nonvirgin female, as a function of his copulation duration. The slope of the line was used to estimate paternity from copulation duration (dotted lines): cannibalized males (C) had greater average paternity than noncannibalized males (NC). In the top right corner, a female looms over the partially eaten body of her much smaller mate.

SOURCE: From Andrade, M.C.B. 1996 "Sexual selection for male sacrifice in the Australian redback spider," *Science*, 271: 70-72 Reprinted with permission from AAAS.

FIGURE 6.4 Sperm Competition in Bullfrogs, *Lithobates catesbeiana* The several males are physically competing for access to the female, but there is also competition among their sperm to fertilize her ova as they are laid (these frogs have external fertilization).

Kevin Judge

and/or resistance to re-mating by females. It is the greater intensity of sexual selection on males that Darwin viewed as the evolutionary force that underlies structures such as ornaments and weapons, features that are called **secondary sexual characters**. These characters are usually absent or not expressed to the same degree in females, resulting in sex differences or **sexual dimorphism**.

The nature of sexual selection varies greatly. Because sexually active males typically seek matings, there is **intrasexual selection**, or competition between members of the same sex. For males this can involve aggression between rivals **(Figure 6.4)** and/or competition among gametes in the rivals' ejaculates stored in a female **(sperm competition)**. These interactions can result in the evolution of aggressive behaviour, risk taking, weaponry (such as caribou antlers and the horns and elongate mandibles of some insects; **Figure 6.7**), and devices to remove or displace the sperm of rivals stored in the female's reproductive tract.

In addition, **intersexual selection** (between the sexes) occurs when females show mating preferences. This female choice has led to the evolution of ornamentation in males, which can include visual displays as well as acoustical and pheromonal signals. Female choice is adaptive when the costs of being choosy (e.g., of movements among potential partners) can be offset by the acquisition of a genetically superior mate or one that provides better resources, such as paternal care.

Traits that evolve by intrasexual or intersexual selection may have survival costs. In the classic Darwinian model, sexual selection on male ornaments is often opposed by **viability selection**. For example, the extent of ornamentation may be limited by natural selection due to increased risks of predation, as in the colouration patterns of male guppies (*Poecilia reticulata*). Viability selection from predators or other sources may also

influence behaviour in that species, as revealed by Jean-Guy Godin and Stephanie Briggs of Mount Allison University (1996), who showed that in the presence of a predator, female guppies from high-predation-risk environments took fewer risks by reducing their choosiness for the most colourful males.

An increased risk of predation can also mediate sexual selection via **sexual conflict**, especially over the number of matings. There are costs of re-mating, typically for females that have already been inseminated, either because of cumulative risks of predation or because copulation itself is costly. Examples of the latter are an increase in the added risk of infection by sexually transmitted diseases or in receiving additional "toxic" ejaculates. For example, male fruit flies (*Drosophila melanogaster*) ejaculate chastity-inducing chemicals that prevent the female from copulating with rival males, but they also have a toxic side effect of reducing female fitness (Chapman et al., 2008). The outcome of sexual conflict over re-mating is either female rejection of males, or **convenience polyandry** when the costs of struggling with a male are sufficiently high that females will allow copulation.

Before discussing the various forms of sexual selection, we will first address the central question of why males are typically more sexually competitive than females.

Why Is Sexual Competition Greater in Males?

Charles Darwin argued that sexual selection on males explains the evolution of both behavioural and structural differences between the sexes. The factors that determine the typically greater sexual selection on males stem from sexual differences in the underlying strategy of maximizing reproductive success.

As mentioned previously, in contrast to males, female success rarely comes from maximizing the number of matings. This is because females have a relatively large **parental investment** in each individual offspring compared with males, and that limits the number of young they can produce. This greater investment by females is due to the much larger material contribution of the egg to the fertilized zygote, compared with the sperm of males, and also in some species because of the maternal effort of time and energy in caring for offspring. Compared to males, the large parental investment of females results in a lower potential rate of reproduction, a greater time-out from mating activities, and thus fewer individuals available for mating (i.e., a negative female bias in the **operational sex ratio**). In part, the limited number of females available for mating induces reproductive competition among males.

The theory of sexual differences predicts that the typical roles of the sexes in mating will reverse, with greater sexual selection on females, in cases where males invest more than females in the offspring. Such large male investments can come from the delivery of goods and services that enhance the survival of his mate or her offspring. Examples include costly paternal care or nutritious substances given by the male to the female. These latter are known as mating or **nuptial gifts**. For example, prey items are proffered by the males in certain species of birds, spiders, dance-flies (dipterans in the family Empididae), and scorpionflies (Mecoptera). Some insects also offer nuptial gifts of nutritious secretions from external glands or internal organs that produce spermatophores. Gifts may also be specialized chemicals that, when ejaculated into the female and translocated to her eggs, protect them from predation (such as pyrrolizidine alkaloids in certain moths) (Gwynne, 1997).

The prediction of role reversal has been supported in species that show paternal care and nuptial gifts. For species with parental care, role reversal occurs when male investment decreases their potential reproductive rate to below that of females (Clutton-Brock and Vincent, 1991). This occurs in certain birds such as jacanas (*Jacana*) and phalaropes (*Phalaropus*) in which males incubate the eggs and raise the young, while the female does not share these responsibilities. In one katydid species (family Tettigoniidae), not only do males feed their mate, but there is also phenotypic plasticity in the mating roles (**Figures 6.5** and **6.6**). When high-protein food is scarce, hungry females will compete to obtain nuptial meals from courting males (Gwynne and Simmons, 1990). Manipulations of food availability in laboratory and field experiments have supported the theory that role reversal and sexual selection on females is caused by a change of the usual relative parental investment in offspring and a subsequent reversal in the operational sex ratio.

Direct Competition between Rivals

Direct competition between males is a form of selection that influences the evolution of weaponry and certain aspects of complex life histories. Male weapons used in sexual combat include exaggerated structures used in combat between rivals, such as large horns or mandibles that function to lift or flip in horned scarab beetles (family Scarabaeidae) and weta (family Anostostomatidae in the order Orthoptera) (**Figure 6.7**). Comparable structures in antlered deer and horned bison and rhinoceros are also used in fights and other tests of rival strength. The structures may also function as signals of the potential to win fights, and may result in smaller-weaponed males prudently withdrawing from a fight and so avoiding combat-related injury.

Direct male–male competition has been linked to the evolution of alternative life histories. In bluegill sunfish (*Lepomis macrochirus*), territorial males become mature at about seven years old and defend a nest, whereas "cuckolder males" that parasitize the parental care provided by territorial males mature after only two years. A cuckolder bluegill follows a "sneaker" mating strategy whereby he swims in quickly and ejaculates just as a female and a territory-holding male are spawning on the nest. Territorial and sneaker males represent different genetic and reproductive strategies. Comparable alternative strategies have been documented in coho salmon (*Oncorhynchus kisutch*; see also Chapter 8).

If the fitness of one genetically based mating strategy is consistently greater than that of another, then over evolutionary time sexual selection is expected to eliminate the alternative. However, studies have found that differences in fitness are common and persistent among alternative mate-locating behaviours. This suggests the existence of mating systems in which alternatives are conditional on environment circumstances (i.e., they exhibit behavioural phenotypic plasticity) rather than being genetically based.

The scarab beetle *Onthophagus acuminatus* is one example; larger-bodied males use their cephalic horns to defend the nest entrance of their mate from rival males. In contrast, smaller hornless males use a lower-fitness tactic of sneaking matings by tunnelling into the side of the nest and breeding with the female. If these smaller males possessed horns, their tunnelling movements would be hindered. Neither body size nor mating tactic (horn versus no-horn sneak) is inherited (Emlen, 1997; Emlen et al., 2005). Instead, the amount and quality of food eaten by the larva (monkey dung provisioned by the mother) determines its size and thus whether it will become large enough to develop a horn. Remarkably, the horned attribute of a male is conditional not only on its own body size, but also on a cue of the level of sexual competition that a larval male will likely encounter as an adult. Because dung quality is somewhat predictable

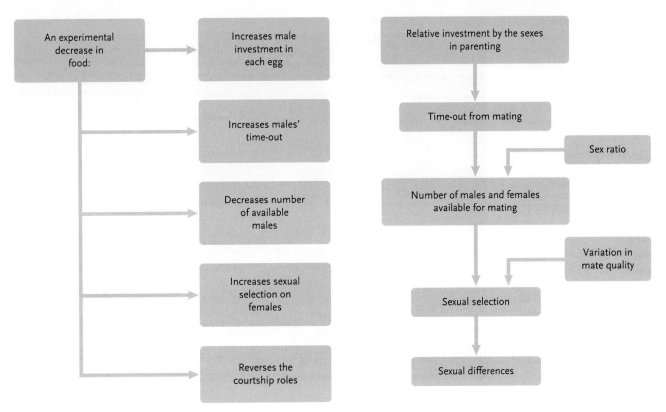

FIGURE 6.5 Nuptial Feeding in Katydids: A Test of Factors Controlling the Typical Sexual Differences Factors hypothesized to control sexual selection and sexual differences (on the right) were examined in laboratory and field experiments (results on left) with a katydid species (Orthoptera: Tettigoniidae). When less food was available, females received more nutrients from the male in the form off nuptial gifts (radiolabelled proteins) (Figure 6.6). This reversed the usual direction of sexual selection and sex differences as hungry females competed for matings with the few males that were able to produce costly nuptial gifts. Increased variation in mate quality can also increase choosiness by the opposite sex, which in turn imposes sexual selection on the variable sex. A key factor is the number of sexually active males and females that are available (operational sex ratio), which can also be affected by large changes in the primary sex ratio—the ratio of all adult females to males.

SOURCE: Material adapted from Darryl T. Gwynne, *Katydids and Bush-crickets: Reproductive Behavior and Evolution of the Tettigoniidae.* Copyright © 2001 by Cornell University. Used by permission of the publisher, Cornell University Press.

FIGURE 6.6 Nuptial Gifts
A female Mormon cricket (*Anabrus simplex*) is eating a large spermatophylax secretion that was transferred by a male as a nuptial gift during mating.

FIGURE 6.7 Weapons Fights between rival males have provided selection pressure for the evolution of weapons in many animals, particularly certain insects and ungulates. In a study of caribou (*Rangifer tarandus caribou*), Cyrille Barrette and Denis Vandal of Laval University (1990) reported that males commonly spar with their antlers but there usually is little risk of injury. Fights for access to females will escalate, however, when antlers are similar in size, and this can lead to injury or even death. Similarly, for males of a large orthopteran from New Zealand, the Wellington tree weta (*Hemideina crassidens*), Clint Kelly (2006a) of the University of Quebec at Montreal showed that males use their sword-like mandibles to fight for access to harems of females living in tree holes. Again, when males are evenly matched with respect to weapon size, combatants can receive fatal injuries, such as a crushed head.

Darryl Gwynne

(being high when seasonally abundant fruit is a large part of the monkey diet) male beetles can vary their development adaptively. When high-quality dung is abundant, male larvae of a certain body size are more likely to mature hornless because the high-quality food has signalled that rival males also have access to that resource. Thus the population-wide body size of rival males will on average be larger. Even though the horn/hornless traits are not heritable, the threshold body size at which male *O. acuminatus* larvae switch into a horned phenotype is determined by genetic differences as well as by diet quality.

Mating Preferences

In addition to direct competition, Darwin proposed female choice as a mechanism that imposes sexual selection among males. In this sense, females can choose among males; for example, by "shopping" among a series of their displays before mating with one of them. Given the potential costs required to make such a choice, what kinds of selection pressures caused female choice to evolve, and what are the benefits in terms of fitness?

In some cases, females may not benefit because preference for the displays of certain males actually results from female behaviour that evolved in other contexts. For example, Heather Proctor (1991) of the University of Alberta showed that a leg vibration display by male water-mites (order Hydracarina) evolved to mimic the tremors of zooplankton prey. Therefore, males attract mates by

exploiting female sensory systems that evolved in a food-seeking context (see also **Figure 6.8**).

Sensory exploitation can provide an impetus for the evolution of mating preferences that benefit females, as well as male signals that advertise those benefits (Kokko et al., 2003). For example, a possible benefit to female water-mites mating with males whose display vibrations mimic those of prey is the production of "sexy sons" that inherit their father's ability to attract mates. Offspring of these fitter males, and the females that prefer to mate with them, inherit genes for both the male trait and for the female preference. If there is an association between genes for the preference and genes for the male display (e.g., if they are closely linked on a chromosome), a result can be a process of **runaway sexual selection**. This was first described by the early population geneticist R.A. Fisher (1930)—with each ensuing generation, the male traits become more elaborate and females prefer males with increasingly exaggerated traits (see Ecology in Depth 6.2).

The production of sexy sons is just one of a number of potential benefits to choosy females. Attractive male traits such as ornaments can evolve as indicators of any fitness benefit that may be passed to a male's offspring that is genetically linked with his level of ornamentation (Kokko et al., 2003). For example, females might prefer ornaments or displays that indicate "good genes" for male vigour that can be inherited by sons and daughters.

This was demonstrated in a study of *Hyla* tree frogs in which males with a series of long calls in their song

Anna Price

FIGURE 6.8 Colouration Differs among Male Trinidadian Guppies (*Poecilia reticulata*) This variation is related to both sexual and viability selection. More-colourful males are preferred by females, possibly because they are of higher genetic quality, but a drawback is they are also more vulnerable to predation. Moreover, a hypothesis supported by Helen Rodd et al. (2002) of the University of Toronto is that the colourful spots mimic food, and so may be a form of sensory exploitation whereby males can attract females.

were both preferred by females and sired better offspring (Welch et al., 1998). By comparing maternal half-siblings (i.e., from the same clutch of eggs) that were fertilized with sperm by males with either long or short calls, offspring of long-call males were shown to perform better (e.g., they grew faster) during larval and juvenile development. Because fertilization occurs after egg laying in this species, an alternative hypothesis was ruled out in which effects on tadpole fitness are due to greater investment by females in the eggs fertilized by higher-quality males.

The question of how low-quality males are prevented from faking high-quality signals was addressed by Zahavi (1975). He argued that indicators of quality are kept honest by their high cost, so that the vigour of a male is demonstrated by the "handicaps" of exaggerated traits developed through sexual selection. Jean-Guy Godin of Mount Alison University and Lee Dugatkin (1996) tested this by showing that colourful male guppies engage in high-risk behaviour when they leave their school to inspect a nearby predatory fish **(Figure 6.8)**. They found that females preferred males that were experimentally manipulated to show boldness, that is, the males that were positioned closest to a predator.

The production of sexy sons or other kinds of offspring that survive better are "indirect benefits" to a choosy female. This is because she gains no immediate benefit, such as an increase in her own survival. Examples of parasite avoidance illustrate the difference between indirect and direct benefits of mate choice. Hamilton

and Zuk (1982) suggested that bright male colouration in many species of birds signals low levels of infection by blood parasites, so that a female mating with a colourful male would gain indirect benefits in offspring with paternal resistance traits. In contrast, female barn swallows (*Hirundo rustica*) obtain direct benefits in avoiding ectoparasite infection when they prefer mates with longer tail-streamers; these males tend to have fewer blood-sucking mites than those with a shorter tail (Moller, 1991).

Direct benefits that enhance female survival include male provision of care to offspring, as well as nuptial gifts of food. Female tree-crickets (*Oecanthus nigricornis*) prefer the lower-pitched songs of larger males that provide bigger nuptial gifts. Direct benefits from males also include more-fertile ejaculates (see Ecology in Depth 6.2).

These examples of female choice suggest that sexual selection—and thus evolutionary change in ornaments and displays—is directional. This is because in each generation, females consistently prefer males with larger or more elaborate ornamental traits. Eventually, however, opposing natural selection for viability must limit further elaboration of the trait, for example, because excessively ornamented males are overly vulnerable to predators.

Directional sexual selection does not occur when choosy females obtain good-genes benefits by mating with genetically compatible males, because the preferred mate for any particular female can differ. For example, females in many groups of animals (insects, fish, lizards, and mammals) prefer to mate with males that have dissimilar genetic loci in a series of genes known as the major histocompatibility complex (MHC; Milinski, 2006). These genes are important for an effective immune system, particularly in individuals that are more heterozygous at these loci. Preferences for MHC-dissimilar mates is expected to increase heterozygosity in offspring. This may be the case in marsupial mice (*Antechinus agilis*), in which females prefer the scent of genetically dissimilar males (Parrott et al., 2007).

The Sexes in Conflict

In the sexy-son model of female choice, paternal genes increase the fitness of sons but not daughters. Studies of insects and vertebrates have also demonstrated that paternal genes that benefit sons can harm daughters, a case in which these genes are **sexually antagonistic**. Julien Mainguy of Laval University and his colleagues (2009) provided evidence for this in a study of mountain goats (*Oreamnos americanus*). In this species, heavyweight males perform best in the jousts that are competition for mates. In fact, body mass was a better predictor than a male's horn length of his success in siring progeny. However, although heavyweight fathers produced larger sons, the opposite was true for their daughters, whose body

FIGURE 1 Bridget Stutchbury

Ron Mumme

Bridget Stutchbury, a professor of biology at York University, has devoted her career to studying the behaviour, ecology, and conservation biology of migratory songbirds (**Figure 1**). Her research includes the use of radio telemetry and molecular markers to understand the mating and migration patterns of songbirds. Research in her lab has shown that female hooded warblers (*Wilsonia citrina*) produce young that were fathered by neighbouring males, and not just the partner (Chiver et al., 2008). Those male neighbours had more vigorous song displays than the one the females were paired with.

Recent work by Stutchbury uses tiny devices that are attached to songbirds using a "backpack" device and record their location based on time and the length of daylight in order to track their amazing migratory journeys between

mass was negatively correlated with that of their sire. These daughters would almost certainly have lower success in breeding because body mass is important to the fitness of both sexes in this species.

A second type of sexual antagonism is the conflict that occurs when a male gains paternity at a cost to his mate's lifetime reproductive success, for example, by coercing a nonreceptive female into mating (Kokko et al., 2003). This form of sexual conflict can impose selection on males for traits that function to overcome female resistance to unwanted matings. At the same time, however, there is selection on females for stronger resistance. An example of this concerns water striders, insects in the family Gerridae that live on the surface of ponds. Locke Rowe of the University of Toronto and colleagues (1994) have shown that male water striders have clasping devices that grasp and subdue females during copulation, but that females of certain species have coevolved devices that serve to prevent attempts of males to copulate with them. For one such species, *Gerris incognitus*, Arnqvist and Rowe (1995) experimentally lengthened the female devices, which increased their ability to thwart unwanted grasping attempts by males.

Sexual Selection Continues after Copulation

Behavioural ecologists often estimate male fitness by determining the number of matings obtained. However, mating does not necessarily equate to reproductive success because there may be differential fertilization by the sperm of rivals in competition within the female's reproductive tract (Parker, 1970). This phenomenon of sperm competition is thought to have led to the evolution of male structures that flush out (e.g., in some moths) or brush out (e.g., some dragonflies) the stored sperm of rivals. **Postcopulatory sexual selection** between males can be revealed with the use of molecular markers of paternity.

Postcopulatory sexual selection has been documented in wild sheep (*Ovis aries*) living on an island off Scotland (Preston et al., 2001). Dominant rams had the highest mating success at the beginning of the rutting season. Later on, however, frequent copulation by the dominants had depleted their supplies of sperm and their paternity was equalled or slightly exceeded by lower-status males.

Studies of the relative siring success of males have also been carried out on species of birds, in which paternity is controlled mainly by female preference. Dan Mennill and colleagues (2002), working at the Queens University Biological Station, found that female black-capped chickadees (*Poecile atricapilla*) eavesdrop on song contests and judge the "winners." Moreover, the females increase the extra-pair paternity of their offspring (i.e., sired by a male other than the partner) if their partner male is observed to have "lost" a singing contest (this was determined by experiments in which the researchers played a recorded song of a high-ranking male, to which the resident male would respond but could not dominate). The results of this study supported the eavesdropping hypothesis over one in which females responded to any postplayback change in the behaviour of her partner.

Biased paternity may result when females manipulate the ejaculate of certain males. This is an example of intersexual selection by "cryptic" or postcopulatory female choice. For example, a male of the fly *Dryomyza anilis* courts the female during courting by tapping his genitals on hers during times when they are not actively copulating (Otronen, 1990). A higher tapping rate tends to increase his paternity because it stimulates the female to favour his sperm over that of rivals.

Postcopulatory sexual selection occurs across the animal kingdom, even in hermaphrodite species. In the brown garden snail (*Cantareus aspersus*), insemination is

Canada and Central or South America. This research has been done with wood thrush (*Hylocichla mustelini*), purple martin (*Progne subis*), and red-eyed vireo (*Vireo olivaceous*). When the birds return to their breeding grounds in the springtime, information downloaded from the geolocators reveals their daily locations on their migratory journey and in the overwintering habitat. This technology shows that the birds migrate to particular locations for the winter, and then return to the vicinity of places where they had been born, or had previously bred. In addition to being useful in understanding the complex life histories of these migratory songbirds, this kind of knowledge can be used to develop strategies for their conservation because it reveals their full annual range and critical habitats. These species are all declining in abundance, likely because of decreases of their overwintering habitat caused by deforestation to develop agricultural land uses.

In addition to her scientific papers, Stutchbury has written two popular books to inform the general public about the fascinating biology and conservation needs of migratory birds. These books are *Silence of the Songbirds* (2007) and *The Bird Detective* (2010).

influenced by long calcite "love darts" that are used to stab the partner during copulation. Ron Chase and Katrina Blanchard (2006) of McGill University showed that if the stab location is near the partner's genital pore, mucus on the dart has a hormonal influence that results in more sperm being transferred to the partner. The apparent cause is a reduction in the otherwise high level of digestion of sperm in the genital tract of the recipient. Changes in paternity are likely a result of competition between the male functions of the two hermaphroditic individuals.

6.5 Social Behaviour

Members of the same species represent an important part of the environment for any organism. Selfish interactions between conspecifics are common and we have already examined cases of interactions between competing males. In selfish interactions, one individual (the actor) gains in fitness and the recipient loses. W. D. Hamilton (1964) classified three additional kinds of social interactions with differing fitness consequences. In mutually beneficial interactions, both the actor and recipient have an increase in fitness. In **altruistic** interactions, the actor loses and recipient gains. The fourth type is a spiteful interaction in which the fitness of both actor and recipient decreases.

Mutually Beneficial Acts and the Advantages of Group Life

Selfish interactions are common within social groups. Examples include competition within groups for food and mates. Competition is just one of the costs of sharing space with conspecifics, along with additional factors such as greater risks of infection by pathogens. Given

these costs, there must be compensating fitness benefits to all individuals that join a group. For some species there are mutually beneficial advantages, including locomotion efficiency noted in some in caterpillars **(Figure 6.9)**,

FIGURE 6.9 A Cluster of Forest Tent Caterpillars (*Malacosoma disstria*) in Southern Ontario These insects cluster together as they move between temporary bivouacs and feeding locations. Emma Despland and Sarah Hamzah (2004) of Concordia University have shown that the close presence of other caterpillars keeps individuals quiescent and allows for efficient locomotion when the group moves.

thermoregulation in certain bats, and maintaining hydration in terrestrial isopod crustaceans. Individuals in groups can also gain mutual benefits by coordinating their foraging and hunting activities (e.g., pack hunting of large prey by wolves, *Canis lupus*), and this may be a reason for the grouping and flocking behaviours of many birds and mammals.

Another mutual benefit is safety in numbers, which can occur when the risk of predation on an individual is reduced due to increased vigilance of groups or to confusion of predators by the movements of many prey items. There are numerous examples of the beneficial effects of increasing group size. For example, when group size of the black grouse (*Tetrao tetrix*) was increased experimentally, the numbers of black flies (Simuliidae) biting individual birds was reduced (Rätti et al., 2006). Another case involves massive groups of adult periodical cicadas (*Magicicada septendecim*) that synchronously emerge in the trillions every few years in the northeastern United States (Lockwood, 2004). Karban (1982) found that cicada density correlated positively with female reproductive fitness because of a decrease in individual risk of capture by predators at high densities. Some of the most striking behaviours observed in groups of animals are the intimately coordinated movements that occur among individuals within flocks of certain birds or schools of fish. This is apparently a result of individuals continuously replacing others in safer locations, typically closer to the centre of the group.

Changing roles can also be seen in social interactions that at first glance appear to be altruistic, but in the long run are actually mutually beneficial in terms of their consequences for fitness. For example, vampire bats (*Desmodus rotundus*) bite their host (such as a cow) and lap its blood as food. The bats need to feed at least every second night, but unsuccessful foragers may receive regurgitated blood from well-fed individuals in their colony. However, regurgitation turns out to be a type of reciprocal social exchange in that donors will be repaid if they in turn are unsuccessful in obtaining a blood meal. A factor that selects for this **reciprocity** is that the relative value of an amount of blood received by a bat at risk of starvation is much higher than the same quantity donated by a well-fed individual. Other factors that select for the behaviour are frequent pairwise interactions between individuals, so that bats take turns in helping each other, along with a system whereby cheats are recognized and punished (Wilkinson, 1984).

Altruism: Why Do Some Organisms Help Others?

Selfish and mutualistic interactions increase individual fitness. In contrast are fitness-decreasing altruistic behaviours, such as the worker honeybee whose barbed sting, when used to defend the hive, results in the individual's evisceration and death. Altruism in the social insects and certain other species appears to be a challenge to natural selection; in fact, Charles Darwin (1859; Chapter 8) regarded it as "one special difficulty, which at first appeared to me insuperable, and actually fatal to my theory."

The pinnacle of altruism occurs in the **eusocial** species **(Table 6.1)**, in which sterile **castes** such as "workers" are developmentally specialized for helping the "queen" reproduce **(Figure 6.10)** or for defending the nest **(Figure 6.11)**. Eusociality occurs in a variety of animals, including a number of different insects, a few crustaceans, two mammals, certain birds (see Ecology in Depth 6.3), and even some unicellular organisms **(Table 6.1)**.

Altruism is best known in the hymenopteran insects, in part because ants and eusocial species of bees and wasps are so ecologically successful (there are over 9000 species of ants alone; Holldobler and Wilson, 1994). Remarkably, eusociality has evolved in at least eight separate lineages within the Hymenoptera (Hughes et al., 2008) **(Figure 6.12)**. This fact inspired evolutionary theorist William D. Hamilton to examine natural selection working at the genetic level (Ecology in Depth 6.2). He noted the unusual genetic system of the Hymenoptera in which unfertilized eggs hatch into haploid males, thus producing asymmetries in sibling relatedness as measured by the **coefficient of relatedness** (*r*) (Harpending, 2002): whereas females share 50 percent of their genes with their daughters, they share 75 percent with sisters, with 50 percent coming from their haploid father and another 25 percent from their diploid mother. In contrast, full sisters in diploid species share only 50 percent of their genes. Thus, Hamilton reasoned that a female worker in a haplo-diploid species can obtain greater fitness returns on an investment that produces a full sister than one generating a daughter.

Kin selection refers to natural selection that favours genetic contributions to future generations through altruism to close relatives. This is an important concept because it expands the definition of fitness beyond that of successful direct ancestry (see Ecology in Depth 6.3): **inclusive fitness** comprises both **direct fitness** via offspring and **indirect fitness** gained by helping close relatives. For altruism to evolve Hamilton argued that its costs (*C*) to the actor, such as any loss of direct fitness, must be outweighed by its indirect benefit (*B*) weighed by the relatedness (*r*) of the actor and recipient. Therefore, any gene causing an actor to become altruistic will increase in frequency if:

$$B/C > 1/r, \text{ thus } rB - C > 0 \qquad (6.1)$$

Although kin selection is central to our understanding of altruism and the evolution of eusociality, recent theory shows that haplo-diploidy is not important (Gardner et al., 2012). One consideration involves the

TABLE 6.1	**Species with Reproductive and Specialized Nonreproductive Castes**				
	Workers feed the young, unless otherwise stated.				

Species	Class (Order)	Sex-Determining System	Genetic Factors That Increase Relatedness	Ecological Factors	Weaponry for Nest Defence
Mole-rats, *Heterocephalus glaber* and *Cryptomys damarensis*	Mammalia	Diplo-diploid	High levels of inbreeding	Fortress defenders of subterranean burrow system and need to cooperate in foraging	Teeth of nonreproductives (both sexes)
Snapping-shrimp, *Synalphaeus* species (three evolutionary origins)	Crustacea	Diplo-diploid	Monogamy	Fortress defenders of a sponge within which they feed on organic matter	Enlarged pincer claws
Termites (all species of the order Isoptera)	Insecta (Isoptera)	Diplo-diploid	Inbreeding	Fortress defenders of gallery systems within wood, their food source, or in hard clay nests	Various elaborated body structures of soldiers (both sexes)
Certain aphids (Aphidae)	Insecta (Homoptera)	Diplo-diploid	Clonal reproduction	Fortress defenders of a plant gall within which they feed. No nurturing workers	Piercing mouthparts and specialized legs
Certain thrips	Insecta (Thysanoptera)	Haplo-diploid	Inbreeding	Fortress defenders of a plant gall within which they feed. No nurturing workers	Enlarged forelegs of soldiers (both sexes)
Curculionid beetle, *Austroplatypus incompertus*	Insecta (Coleoptera)	Diplo-diploid	Unknown	Fortress defenders of gallery systems within wood, where they feed on fungi	Not studied
Many Hymenoptera: ants, bees, and wasps, with many independent evolutionary origins	Insecta (Hymenoptera)	Haplo-diploid	Monogamy	Forager-defenders that eat insects (ants, wasps), pollen (bees and a few wasps), and nectar	Sting of females

FIGURE 6.10 Castes in a Species of Termite (*Macrotermes bellicosus*) The enormous queen is the egg-laying breeder in the colony, and she is attended by several nonbreeding castes: large-headed soldiers and smaller workers. Above the queen is a dark-brown male. This species occurs in Ghana.

wonderisland / Shutterstock.com

Scientists formulate hypotheses and then test them using experiments or comparisons. In an experiment, variables are controlled through manipulation, whereas in a comparison variables are statistically removed. In a bird example, Australian grey-crowned babblers (*Pomatostomus temporalis*) exhibit helping behaviour when nonbreeding individuals in a social group help to feed the nestlings of a breeding pair. This is a kind of altruism because it enhances the reproductive success of another individual at a cost to one's own reproduction. This kind of behaviour can evolve through kin selection if the helpers are close relatives of the breeders.

This hypothesis predicts that helpers will increase the success of raising young birds to which they are related. However, a simple positive correlation between helping and success might also be explained by a confounding variable, such as the higher-quality territory that may be held by a larger social group. Nevertheless, studies in which the number of helpers is experimentally reduced, as well as comparisons in which confounding variables are statistically controlled, both support the hypothesis that helpers increase the success of raising young birds (Brown et al., 1982; Blackmore and Heinsohn, 2007).

The theory of kin selection also predicts that altruism will originate in species that

have social systems in which the altruist and recipient individuals are closely related. However, comparisons between species require phylogenetic controls in which the similarity due to common ancestry is removed statistically from the effects of adaptive evolution. Such comparisons can determine the number of independent origins of a trait, as well as correlations among traits and environmental variables; the latter allows comparative tests of how environmental variables influence the evolution of traits [see the books by Dan Brooks and Deborah McLennan (1991 and 2002) of the University of Toronto]. Moreover, the variation in traits can be displayed on evolutionary trees to determine their ancestral states (e.g., **Figure 6.12**).

Darryl Gwynne

FIGURE 6.11 A Large Mound of the Termite *Nasutitermes triodae* in Northwestern Australia The mound contains a large colony of this eusocial insect.

raising of haploid brothers, which have only 25 percent relatedness to worker females, so that much of the advantage of raising closely related sisters is lost. Although it was suggested that the haplo-diploid argument could be

rescued if workers raised many more sisters than brothers, that reproductive strategy would have resulted in the population sex ratio becoming so female biased that the fitness value of each brother would increase greatly with so many available mates (Davies et al., 2012; Gardner et al., 2012).

Instead of haplo-diploidy, monogamy of the hymenopteran queen is considered the key trait in maintaining the high level of relatedness that is necessary for eusociality to evolve through kin selection (Hughes et al., 2008; Gardner et al., 2012). If a queen mates with more than one male, the presence of many half-sibling reproductive individuals in a nest or hive would negate the relatedness advantage of workers helping to raise reproductive sisters.

The key prediction from the queen monogamy hypothesis is that, at the evolutionary *origins* of eusociality from a solitary ancestral lifestyle, females mated only once. This key prediction was supported using comparative tests that traced the origins of eusociality onto a phylogeny of Hymenoptera (see Ecology in Depth 6.3) (Hughes, 2008); for the eight independent origins of eusociality, a single-mating female (queen) was indeed ancestral **(Figure 6.12)**.

Monogamy is a more general explanation for high relatedness and the origins of eusociality because it also occurs in the ancestors of many eusocial diplo-diploid species: the termites, a beetle, some marine crustaceans, and two species of mole-rats **(Table 6.1; Figure 6.12)** (Hughes et al., 2008). Inbreeding is another mechanism that can increase the relatedness necessary for

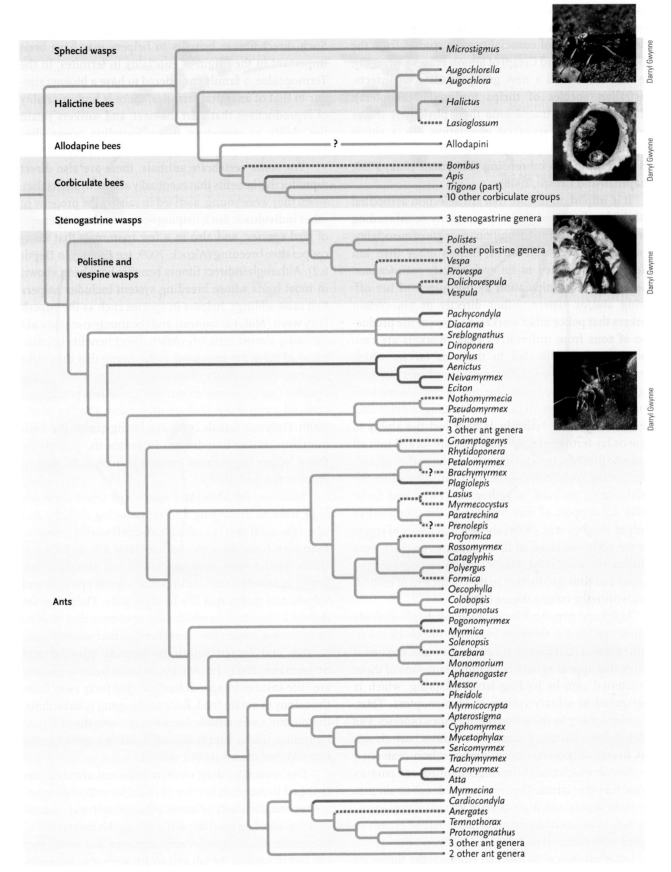

FIGURE 6.12 Phylogeny of the Order Humenoptera This evolutionary tree shows phylogenetic relationships among ants and the eusocial bees and wasps. Two independent origins of eusociality are shown, with green and yellow areas denoting separate clades (parts of the tree in which the taxa (genera) share a common ancestor). Clades in which females mate more than once are in red (> 2 mates in solid red, 1 -2 mates dashed). Solid green lines denote single mating females.

SOURCE: Based on W. O. H. Hughes, et al. 2008. "Ancestral Monogamy Shows Kin Selection Is Key to the Evolution of Eusociality," *Science*, 320: 1213.

Behavioural ecologists also study the fitness consequences of behaviour in humans and some of this work has practical applications. Methods involve fieldwork with both "traditional cultures" that have been little influenced by globalization, and research on people living in urbanized and industrial societies (Hames, 2001). Studies include optimal foraging in traditional cultures (Borgerhoff Mulder, 2005), but other areas of research focus on the social environment and include topics such as mate choice and parent–offspring interactions.

This research can have practical applications. For example, Margo Wilson and Martin Daly (1997) of McMaster University examined the relationship between parenting and the fitness value of offspring. They found that, as predicted from theory, child abuse was directed more at stepchildren than to genetic offspring. Daly and Wilson (1997) have also used life-history theory to understand violent behaviour and homicide in male humans. Using data from Chicago, they found that men from neighbourhoods with a high risk of death from natural causes showed an apparently adaptive "discounting of the future" by having a higher likelihood of engaging in high-risk lifestyles that can lead to success, but that also increased the chance of being murdered.

6.9 Future Directions

Behavioural ecology has sometimes been criticized for its lack of robust hypothesis testing. Some researchers have been accused of "adaptive storytelling"—of outlining hypotheses but not rigorously testing them. However, most papers in leading journals such as *Behavioral Ecology* and *Behavioral Ecology and Sociobiology* do contain rigorous empirical tests of hypotheses. In fact, the field of behavioural ecology represents an exciting "synergy between evolution, ecology and behaviour" (Alonzo, 2008, p. 600).

An additional criticism is that behavioural ecologists rarely study the genetic mechanisms underlying models of adaptation. Although we have learned that behavioural variation is not necessarily expected to map onto genetic variation, in many models of adaptation—including adaptive phenotypic plasticity—there are assumptions about genetic mechanisms. Some models have explicit assumptions, such as in the association between genes for ornamentation and preference in runaway sexual selection.

As a research direction, Owens (2006) urged behavioural ecologists to take advantage of model systems, by using classic species used in laboratories such as the fruit fly (*Drosophila melanogaster*) and house mouse (*Mus musculus*), in which genetic mechanisms are well known. These species are useful because replication of studies (which is rare in behavioural ecology: Kelly, 2006b) is more feasible than in most behavioural-ecological research, and these model systems can guide research with other species. For example, as emphasized by Mark Fitzpatrick and colleagues (2005) of the University of Toronto, *candidate genes* in very different animal systems (species) have been shown to underlie complex behaviours such as foraging. These genes may therefore be useful in understanding broader genetic mechanisms that control adaptive behaviour.

It is also important to recognize that the strength of behavioural ecology—as in all sectors of ecology—is in making predictions that are supported by the study of complementary systems. Therefore, an important direction for behavioural research is to be able to replicate the results of studies with "novel systems," such as in species where behavioural knowledge is lacking but that appear to have a life history which is appropriate for examining a particular hypothesis.

CHAPTER SUMMARY

(LO 6.1)

- "Why" questions about adaptive traits can be answered in two ways that represent different levels of explanation. Proximate answers concern mechanisms, such as the genetic or neural mechanisms underlying a trait. However, ultimate answers address fitness, such as how variation in a trait increases survival or reproductive success.

(LO 6.2)

- Behavioural ecology investigates the adaptive (fitness) value of traits to individual organisms, because selection acts on individuals, not on social groups or populations. This view of selection explains survival adaptations to the biological environment, such as avoiding natural enemies, as well as to the social environment of conspecifics. Social interactions may lead to conflict between the fitness interests of individuals, not only between members of the same sex (such as females competing for the egg-laying role in a social nest), but also between the sexes (as when a male coerces a female into a copulation that compromises her fitness).

- Conflicts over fitness interests and other forms of sexual selection have produced extravagant or ornamental adaptations that reduce survival but are selected for because they enhance reproductive success. Examples include structures such as the tail of a male peacock, a display that is important in attracting females, as well as weapons that also function in reproductive competition for breeding rights within a social group.

- Some social groups are exceptional in that conflict between individuals is reduced as some individuals reduce their fitness while helping others to reproduce. This altruistic behaviour is highly evolved in eusocial species in which altruists form distinct morphological castes that differ from the reproductive ones. The evolution of eusociality is explained by ecological factors that favour group life as well as kin selection.

QUESTIONS FOR REVIEW AND DISCUSSION

1. Explain reciprocity and how it differs from altruism.
2. Given your understanding of the concept of individual (direct) fitness, explain why organisms might compromise their survival while enhancing their reproductive success.
3. What sorts of changes in an animal's environment might select for a decrease in optimal foraging behaviour?
4. Selection theory predicts that plants will not evolve to communicate the presence of herbivores to nearby plants of other species or even of the same species. Given what we know about the evolution of altruism in animals, what conditions would be necessary for plants to evolve the ability to communicate such information to members of their own species?
5. What ecological, behavioural and genetic factors led to the origin of eusociality?
6. Explain how a way of obtaining mates has lower fitness returns than an alternative. In other words, why has selection not led to the loss of the low-fitness behaviour?

Physiological Ecology

CHAPTER OUTLINE

LEARNING OBJECTIVES

After studying this chapter you should be able to:

1. Compare ectothermy and endothermy, and also the responses of heterotherms and homeotherms to changes and extremes of ambient temperature, including the roles of torpor and hibernation in energy conservation.

2. Compare the water-balance and ionic problems faced by marine animals with those of freshwater and terrestrial ones, and describe how these animals cope with their aqueous environments.

3. Compare gas exchange in water-breathing animals and air-breathing ones, including the role of respiratory pigments in blood gas transport, and explain how oxygen binding is affected by carbon dioxide and acidity of the blood, and by acidification of the environment.

4. Describe basic strategies used by plants to cope with extremes of temperature and water availability, including the roles of the photosynthetic systems C3, C4, and CAM.

5. Explain how plant hormones affect development and anatomy, and the roles of secondary compounds in protecting against herbivory and other stressors.

7.1 Introduction to Physiological Ecology

Physiology is the branch of biology that examines the functioning of organisms. Physiologists are interested in the internal processes that are essential to survival, and how those biological functions are regulated. This may be studied at various levels: biomolecules, cells, organs, and whole organisms.

Physiological ecology (or **ecophysiology**) is the study of how organisms function in their environment. Ecophysiology looks at ecological questions concerning how animals and plants interact with their physical, chemical, and biotic environments, but in terms of functional mechanisms that determine growth, reproduction, and survival. Within this context, Lambers et al. (1998) wrote that "ecology provides the questions, while physiology provides the tools to determine the mechanisms." (p. 2)

Ecophysiology is a challenging subject area. This is because researchers must think about mechanisms at lower levels of biotic integration, such as biochemistry and biophysics, and then scale the resulting knowledge to higher levels, such as individuals, populations, and even communities. Major advances in physiological ecology during the past century have led to fascinating discoveries about the ways that organisms have evolved to exploit the variety of environments in the biosphere—from the tops of the highest mountains to the abyssal depths of the oceans, and from the frigid poles to the torrid tropics. By determining ecophysiological mechanisms and patterns, ecologists can learn about the functionality of specific traits of organisms, as well as their evolutionary heritage.

Much of what we know about physiology comes from research done under controlled conditions in the laboratory. However, ecophysiology also involves field studies, where organisms interact with real-world environmental factors. It is a great challenge to integrate knowledge gained from laboratory and field studies to build a realistic understanding of the ways that organisms survive and thrive in the natural world.

This chapter looks at the physiological ecology of animals and plants. While there are similarities between these groups, there are also important differences. First, plants are autotrophs that synthesize their own food using an external source of energy (sunlight) to create simple sugars from inorganic compounds (initially carbon dioxide and water), as well as nitrate, phosphate, potassium, and others. In contrast, animals are heterotrophs that feed on the existing biomass of other organisms.

Second, plants are typically rooted in a fixed place, and so their ecophysiology is strongly influenced by the need to deal with opportunities and constraints associated with local abiotic and biotic factors. In contrast, most animals can move from extremes of environmental conditions to places that may be more favourable to their physiological and ecological needs.

The physiological ecology of plants and animals is an extremely diverse and complex subject area, and in an introductory text not all of that scope can be examined. However, there are key subject areas that are relevant to all organisms, and we examine them in the following sections on plant and animal ecophysiology:

1. *thermobiology*, or the physiological mechanisms and behavioural choices that are used to achieve a favourable energy balance;
2. *water and ion balances* that must be maintained to avoid stresses associated with extremes of wet and dry;
3. *gas exchange* to procure gases needed for healthy metabolism and to void others that are wastes;
4. *acid–base balancing* to maintain ideal intracellular and extracellular pH for a variety of physiological functions; and
5. *secondary metabolites* that are important intermediaries affecting competition and predation.

7.2 Physiological Ecology of Animals

Thermobiology

Metabolism and other physiological functions involve a diversity of chemical reactions, all of which are to some degree sensitive to temperature. Despite this, organisms are adept at occupying environments that are extreme in terms of temperature—certain species are adapted to the extreme heat of deserts, while others survive in the icy cold of polar regions. Thermobiology is the study of the ways that organisms have adapted to cope with the range of temperatures that occur in their environment, including extreme conditions. In the following sections we examine temperature-related adaptations that influence the physiological ecology of animals.

Aerobic and Anaerobic Metabolism

The consumption and digestion of organic foods occurs primarily by **aerobic metabolism**, in which oxygen (O_2) is involved in biochemical reactions by which some of the energy of carbohydrates, fats, and proteins is converted into adenosine triphosphate (ATP; this is the principal molecule used to store and transfer energy in cells) via oxidative processes (glycolysis, Krebs cycle, and oxidative phosphorylation). Organelles known as mitochondria are the sites where aerobic metabolism occurs, and the larger their number within the cells of a tissue, the greater is its **oxidative capacity** (this is the ability to use O_2, which is typically measured as mL O_2 per gram of tissue per minute). However, when the O_2 supply is limited compared with the physiological demand for that gas, animals may also use **anaerobic metabolism** to maintain the production of ATP. Anaerobic metabolism is much less efficient than aerobic in terms of converting the energy of food into ATP, but it is crucial in maintaining biological functions when the O_2 supply is limited. Both aerobic and anaerobic metabolisms produce heat as a major waste product.

Metabolic Rate

The **metabolic rate** is usually determined as the rate of oxygen consumption, largely because this is a relatively easy measurement for physiologists to make. However, O_2 is consumed only during aerobic metabolism, so for animals with a substantial anaerobic capacity alternative measurements of metabolic rate must be made. One way to do this is to measure the rate of heat production or the difference in the caloric contents of ingested food and excreted feces (these are also relevant to aerobic metabolism). Because animals differ in size and shape, it is important to standardize measurements of metabolic rate, such as by expressing it per unit of body mass, such as O_2 consumed per kg per hour, also known as **mass-specific metabolism**. There is generally an inverse relationship between the mass-specific metabolic rate (O_2/kg.hr) and the body mass—the smaller the animal, the faster the metabolism. This is particularly apparent in small mammals and birds, for reasons that we examine later in this section.

Heat and Cold

As we examined in Chapter 3 heat is thermal kinetic energy, and cold is a lack of heat. Both are measured as temperature. When objects (including organisms) having different temperatures make contact, the colder one gains heat from the warmer, but according to the first law of thermodynamics, the total amount of energy is conserved.

Animals exchange heat with their environment by several transfer mechanisms, which integrate into a

FIGURE 7.1 Mechanisms of Heat Exchange with the Environment Endothermic animals like this wolf (*Canis lupus*) exchange heat with their environment by conduction, convection, evaporation, and radiation. They gain heat via the absorption of solar energy and by producing metabolic heat.

Sun

Radiation from Sun

Convection of air currents

Evaporation of water vapour from nostrils and tongue transfers heat energy

Conduction of heat energy to ground

Photos.com

thermal energy budget **(Figure 7.1)**. The most important components of such a budget are the following:

- *Absorption* is the conversion of solar radiation into thermal energy; for instance, by a lizard basking in the sun.
- *Radiation* is the emission of electromagnetic energy by any body with a heat content (meaning a temperature that exceeds absolute zero, or $-273°C$); the Sun does this, as do all organisms, but at rates that depend on their temperature (actually, it is a nonlinear dependence related to the surface temperature raised to the fourth power, or T^4).
- *Conduction* is heat transfer by the direct contact of masses that differ in temperature—the warmer one loses heat to the cooler.
- *Convection* is heat transfer from an organism to cooler air or water passing over its warmer body surface.
- *Evaporation* is the dissipation of heat by energy needed to convert water from a liquid state to a gaseous one; the specific heat of vaporization of water is 2.4 kJ/g (580 cal/g), so its evaporation from the body surface is an effective way for an animal (or plant) to cool itself.

Animals can variously heat or cool themselves by any or all these mechanisms. They may relax in the shade or a breeze if it is hot, or bask in the sun if it is cold, or evaporate moisture from their body surface. All of these mechanisms

are also relevant to plants, although they are not able to move about seeking a more comfortable thermal environment.

The Concept of Q_{10}

All biochemical reactions and physiological functions (such as muscle contraction and neurotransmission) are affected by temperature. In general, the warmer the temperature at which a reaction is occurring, the faster it will run, although the relationship is logarithmic **(Figure 7.2)**.

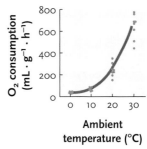

FIGURE 7.2 The Logarithmic Relationship of Physiological Reactions and Temperature The oxygen consumption of tiger moth (*Arctia caja*) caterpillars was measured at four temperatures. The data show a logarithmic increase in oxygen consumption with an increase in ambient temperature (if O_2 consumption was plotted as a logarithm, this would be a straight line).

SOURCE: P.F. Scholander, Walter Flagg, Vladimir Walters, and Laurence Irving. "Climatic Adaptation in Arctic and Tropical Poikilotherms," *Physiological Zoology*, 26: 67–92. © 1953 University of Chicago Press.

Metabolic rate and body mass are directly related—as the mass increases, so does the rate of oxygen consumption. However, the relationship is not linear: an animal weighing 100 g does not have 10 times the metabolic rate of a 10 g one. The relationship between metabolic rate and body mass is logarithmic and is described by the following equation:

$$\log M = \log a \times b \log W$$

where

- M = the metabolic rate, measured as mL of O_2 consumed per gram of body mass
- W = the body mass (g)
- a = a parameter that is particular to each species
- b = the mass exponent

The average value of b is 0.75, and it is similar for most species. This equation, also called an allometric equation, is not restricted to metabolic rate. Most physiological traits, such as heart and ventilation rates, are also related to body mass as described by this relationship.

The mass-specific metabolic rate (mL O_2/unit time/unit mass) varies inversely with mass. This is true for all ectotherms and endotherms. In fact, on a per-gram basis, a shrew has about 100 times the metabolic rate of an elephant. At one time the higher metabolic rate of smaller mammals was explained on the basis of their larger ratio of surface area to volume,

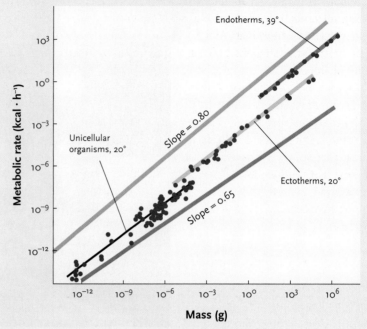

FIGURE 1 The Relationship between Body Mass and Metabolic Rate in a Variety of Animals
This plot shows a broad relationship between body mass and metabolic rate across a wide range of organisms, from microbes to large mammals. The three lines are closely parallel, and all of them have an approximate slope of 0.75.

SOURCE: Based on Randall, D., W. Burggren, and K. French. 2002. *Animal Physiology: Mechanisms and Adaptations.* 5th ed. W.H. Freeman and Co., New York, NY. After Hemmingsen, 1969.

which means that they have a faster loss of heat and so need to maintain a higher metabolism to remain homeothermic **(Figure 1)**. However, this argument is weakened by the fact that ectotherms also show this relationship—smaller ones have a greater mass-specific metabolic rate. So

why, then, is the mass-specific metabolic rate inversely related to mass? A number of alternative hypotheses have arisen, but none are adequate to explain the relationship in ectotherms, so the issue is not yet resolved. It is likely that multiple causes contribute to the phenomenon.

This relationship holds true for all biochemical reactions, at least within the range of temperatures suitable for the functioning of typical **enzymes** (proteins that catalyze biochemical reactions).

Because metabolic rate is a function of all biochemical reactions occurring in an organism, it also shows a logarithmic relationship with temperature, as do particular functions such as heart rate and the velocity of nerve conduction. The relationship between temperature and the rate of a function is described by an equation known as the Q_{10}:

$$Q_{10} = K_2(t + 10°C)/K_1(t°C)$$

where k_1 is a reaction velocity at temperature t and k_2 is the velocity at $t + 10°C$.

The usual range of the Q_{10} values for physiological functions and metabolic rate is 2 to 3, which means that there is a 2- to 3-fold increase in rate for a 10°C increase in temperature (within a temperature range of about 10°C–20°C). The value of Q_{10} tends to be more than 3 at temperatures below 10°C, and less than 2 if above 20°C. However, the Q_{10} values may vary among physiological functions being examined, and also among species whose metabolic adaptations reflect different climatic regimes.

Ectothermy and Endothermy

Ectotherms are animals with a relatively slow metabolic rate, so they rely on the external environment, rather than their internal metabolic one, as a source of heat.

Many vertebrate animals, such as fish, amphibians, and reptiles, and almost all invertebrates, must warm themselves by basking in sunlight or by seeking other sources of environmental heat before they can comfortably move about. Ectotherms that live in cool or cold environments, including all climatic regions of Canada, have evolved enzymes that function well at relatively low temperatures, thus allowing their metabolism, locomotion, nerves, and other physiological functions to operate and sustain life.

Other animals, such as birds and mammals (and a few others), have the capacity to produce and retain enough heat from their own metabolism to create a body temperature appropriate for their physiology and biochemical reactions. These animals are **endotherms**—organisms that produce their "heat from within." As we examine later, endotherms have evolved ways of conserving their metabolic heat by insulation and adaptive modifications of their circulatory system.

Heterothermy and Homeothermy

Animals also vary in terms of their ability to maintain a steady body temperature. **Homeotherms** can maintain a constant body-core temperature independent of that of their environment. **Heterotherms** (or **poikilotherms**) cannot do this—their body temperature changes with that of their environment.

Generally speaking, endotherms are also homeothermic, as is the case of mammals and birds. However, some animal species are "partial" endothermic homeotherms. For example, prior to flight on a cool day, bumblebees and large moths actively warm themselves by "shivering"—they rapidly contract and relax their flight muscles in order to generate body heat. Moreover, while flying they also generate metabolic heat, which maintains their body temperature above that of the environment. **Figure 7.3** illustrates a range of organisms that are ectothermic homeotherms or endothermic heterotherms, as well as others that are ectothermic heterotherms or endothermic homeotherms.

Thermoregulation

The physiological functions that are involved in maintaining a relatively constant body temperature over a wide range of ambient temperatures are referred to as **thermoregulation**. If an animal is to thermoregulate for a sustained period of time, it must have a high oxidative

FIGURE 7.3 Examples of Ectothermy, Endothermy, Heterothermy, and Homeothermy Animals occur in all four quadrants, and some species may move from one quadrant to another depending on the environmental conditions. MR = metabolic rate; T_a = ambient temperature; T_b = body temperature.

SOURCE: Willmer, P., G. Stone, and I. Johnston. 2000. *Environmental Physiology of Animals*. Blackwell Science, Oxford, UK. Copyright © 2004, John Wiley and Sons.

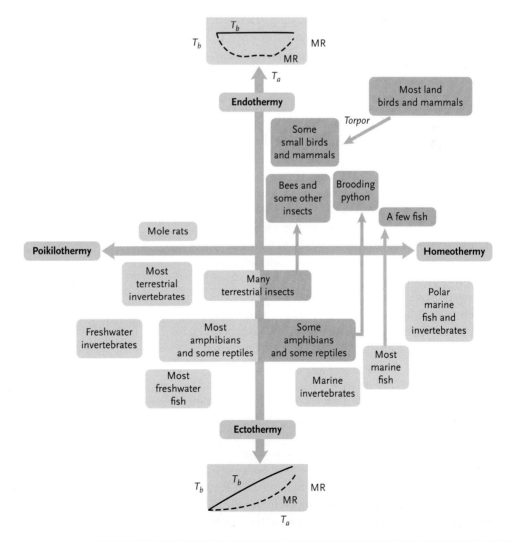

capacity, thermal insulation, a closed circulatory system (in which the blood is enclosed within a series of vessels), and a nervous system that can sense changes in body temperature. In this section we emphasize thermoregulation by metabolic functions—behavioural responses such as choosing to bask in the sun or to cool in the shade are also means of thermoregulation, but this is more so the subject of behavioural ecology (Chapter 6).

HIGH OXIDATIVE CAPACITY—HOW DOES METABOLISM PRODUCE HEAT?

About 75 percent of the energy released by the metabolism of glucose is typically released as heat, and only 25 percent generates ATP. Because endotherms have much higher metabolic rates than ectotherms, they generate a lot more heat.

A number of small mammals, such as rodents and bats, use brown adipose tissue (also known as brown fat) as a key source of energy. The brown colour is due to the rich blood supply to the tissue and the yellowish colour to the high concentration of mitochondria in the cells. Consequently, the cells have a high oxidative capacity. However, the oxidation of fat stored in these cells does not produce ATP—all of the embedded energy is liberated as heat. How does this happen? In normal oxidative metabolism, protons are pumped into intermembrane spaces of the mitochondria during electron transport, and they then diffuse into the matrix inside those organelles. This process is coupled to the action of ATP synthase, and it thereby liberates energy needed to produce ATP. However, during times of increased demand for heat production, protons diffuse directly into the mitochondrial matrix through an alternative membrane protein called thermogenin (this occurs only in the mitochondria of brown fat cells). No ATP is synthesized in this process, and so all of the energy liberated is in the form of heat.

This source of heat is vital for small mammals, which have a high ratio of surface area to body mass and so must generate a lot of heat to stay warm (for a similar reason, human infants also oxidize brown fat as a crucial source of heat). The oxidation of brown fat is also important to animals that enter daily or seasonal torpor, and also hibernation, during which the body temperature decreases. As much as 30 kJ/kg•min (500 W/kg) of heat production can result from the metabolism of brown fat. This is about 10 times the thermal energy gained from the contraction of skeletal muscles during shivering.

INSULATION—KEEPING THE HEAT IN

In addition to having a capacity for a high oxidative metabolism, thermoregulation requires a means to conserve metabolic heat (to limit its loss). This is accomplished by having a layer of insulation between the body core and the environment. Various tissues may be used for this purpose, including subdermal fat (just under the skin), as well as feathers in birds and hair in mammals **(Table 7.1)**.

TABLE 7.1	The Insulating Properties of Feathers, Fur, and Fat	
Material	Insulating Ability (°C m² W⁻¹)
Ice	2.9
Water	11
Dry soil	20
Fat	38
Pigeon feather (flat)	99
Sheep wool	102
Goose-down feathers	122
Husky dog fur	157
Lynx fur	170
Still air	270

SOURCE: Willmer, P., G. Stone, and I. Johnston. 2000. *Environmental Physiology of Animals*. Blackwell Science, Oxford, UK. Copyright © 2004, John Wiley and Sons.

Hair and feathers work in much the same way as fibreglass insulation—the idea is to trap a layer of stagnant air among the fibres. Because still air is not a good conductor of heat, a trapped layer just above the skin reduces the rate of exchange with the environment. When air temperatures are cold, most birds and mammals "fluff up" their feathers or fur to trap additional air. This is done by contracting muscles attached to the base of the feather or hair to cause it to "stand up," a process known as piloerection (in mammals) or ptiloerection (in birds).

Fat is also a good form of insulation, although not as effective as fur or feathers. A thick layer of subcutaneous fat is especially important in mammals that have little fur or hair covering their body, such as whales, seals, and humans. The thermal conductivity of the blubber of a minke whale (*Balaenoptera acutorostrata*) is about 0.25 W/mK (watts per metre per degree Kelvin), compared with 0.20 W/mK for human fat (Kvadsheim et al., 1998).

REGULATION OF BODY TEMPERATURE—CONTROL OF HEAT PRODUCTION AND LOSS

To thermoregulate, the nervous system must monitor and react to changes in body temperature. This sensory function is an example of a **negative feedback system** and it involves the following elements **(Figure 7.4)**:

- a thermo-detector, which is composed of thermo-sensitive receptors;
- an optimal body temperature, known as the set point;
- an integrator that compares the actual body temperature to the desired one; and
- a set of outputs to the cardiovascular system, skeletal muscles, and endocrine system, which stimulate them to generate more or less heat to bring the temperature closer to the set point.

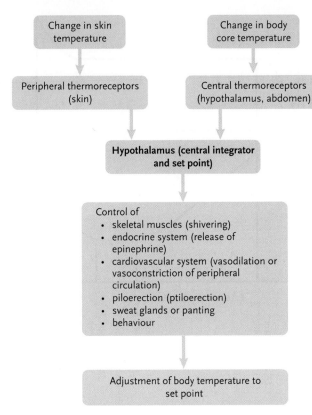

FIGURE 7.4 Negative Feedback Control of Body Temperature
Thermosensitive receptors detect changes in the body-surface or core temperature and relay this information to a central integrator (the hypothalamus, a part of the brain), which compares it to the desired set point. Adjustments are made to the cardiovascular and endocrine systems and to skeletal muscles to bring the body temperature closer to the set point.

SOURCE: Davenport, J.A. 1992. *Animal Life at Low Temperature*. Chapman and Hall, London, with kind permission from Springer Science+Business Media B.V.

This physiological system works much like that of a thermostat and furnace in a home, which maintains the interior temperature within a comfortable range. The thermostat is set to a desired temperature (a set point). A thermometer feeds information about the room temperature back to the thermostat. If the room temperature is cooler than the set point, the thermostat sends an electric signal to turn on the furnace, which runs until the room reaches the desired warmth.

In a homeothermic animal, the corresponding function of a thermostat is played by temperature-control centres within the hypothalamus. The set point, which is also set by the hypothalamus, is the desired body temperature. Thermoreceptors located on the body surface and within the core send information about the temperature of those regions to the hypothalamus. The hypothalamus integrates information about "temperature" relayed by the thermoreceptors, compares it with the set point, and makes compensating adjustments to key physiological functions that help adjust skin and core temperatures closer to the set point, such as:

- the activity of skeletal muscles, which can be stimulated by neural output from the hypothalamus via motor neurons;
- adjustments of insulation by piloerection (or ptiloerection), also stimulated by output from the hypothalamus;
- circulation of the blood, for example, by vasodilation or vasoconstriction to adjust the blood supply to the skin;
- evaporative water loss by sweating or panting;
- the metabolic rate, which is influenced by release from the adrenal gland of the powerful, stress-related hormone epinephrine (or adrenaline), which stimulates metabolism; and
- behavioural functions, such as seeking a warmer or cooler environment.

RESPONSES TO COLD Physiological actions taken to correct a drop in the temperature of the body surface or core all involve the generation of metabolic heat or its conservation. One of the faster responses is shivering, or the rapid contraction and relaxation of skeletal muscles to generate metabolic heat in the body core. Shivering is not a process that can be consciously controlled—it is an automatic response to cold.

Vasoconstriction is another rapid response. It is controlled by the sympathetic nervous system, and is activated by commands from the hypothalamus in response to lowering of the body temperature. Vasoconstriction is accomplished by smooth muscle surrounding the arterioles that supply the skin. It slows the flow of blood to the surface, which reduces the heat lost to the environment by convection, conduction, and radiation of infrared.

The fluffing of fur or feathers is also controlled by the hypothalamus, and helps to reduce heat loss by trapping air to enhance the cover of insulation over the body.

The above three mechanisms are rapidly deployed when the body temperature drops below the set point. An additional compensating mechanism is slower to affect the body temperature—it is **nonshivering thermogenesis**, which involves the endocrine system. Nonshivering thermogenesis is stimulated by release of the hormone epinephrine from the adrenal gland, which is activated by the hypothalamus via the sympathetic nervous system. The epinephrine is released into the blood where it stimulates metabolism mainly by increased lipolysis, which allows lipids to be used as an energy source. Nonshivering thermogenesis is prevalent in animals that have stores of brown fat, including young placental mammals. It is less prevalent in birds.

Animal behaviour also changes in response to cooling. Individuals tend to seek out microhabitats such as warm and windless places where they will lose less heat by convection. They may also curl up to lessen the area of body surface exposed to cold air, thereby reducing heat loss by radiation and convection.

Some mammals and a few birds may undergo torpor or hibernation during cold periods. **Torpor** is a relatively short-term condition of decreased activity—it is usually characterized by reduced metabolism, slower breathing, and often a lower body temperature (some bats do this at night, as do tiny hummingbirds). **Hibernation** lasts a longer time, and it involves similar physiological adjustments that are intended to maintain life during a period of prolonged cold temperatures, but at relatively low energy costs to the animal. Many rodents such as ground squirrels hibernate during the winter, as do some bats.

RESPONSES TO HEAT A rise in body temperature above the set point results in the activation of various cooling mechanisms. One response is increased sweating and panting, which provide cooling by the evaporation of water—2.43 kilojoules (580 calories) of thermal energy are dissipated per gram of water evaporated. This is an effective means of cooling if humidity of the atmosphere is low, but not if it is high because evaporation is constrained by the low diffusional gradient.

An animal can also cool itself by vasodilation to shunt more blood flow to the body surface, which increases heat loss by conduction and convection to the environment. In addition, fur or feathers may be flattened closer to the body to reduce their insulating effect. The amount of epinephrine in the blood circulation also decreases, which helps to reduce the metabolic rate so that less heat is generated. Muscular activity is also reduced, again to avoid the generation of metabolic heat.

There are also behavioural responses to heating of the body, such as moving to a cooler environment in a shaded place, burrowing underground, or orienting the body to lessen the surface area exposed to the sun.

EFFECT OF AMBIENT TEMPERATURE ON THE METABOLIC RATE OF ENDOTHERMIC HOMEOTHERMS The metabolic rate of mammals and birds varies inversely with the ambient temperature, at least within a certain range. This effect varies among species depending on the body size, the amount of insulation, and the ratio of surface area to body volume. **Figure 7.5** is a typical plot of metabolic rate versus ambient temperature. Note that endothermic homeotherms maintain a constant body temperature over a wide range of ambient temperatures, the extremes of which are known as the upper and lower incipient lethal limits. If the ambient temperature goes beyond those limits, the animal will become either **hypothermic**, with a dangerously lowered body temperature, or **hyperthermic**, with an excessively elevated one. An animal in those extreme circumstances has exceeded its capacity to thermoregulate and will soon die if it cannot find a more habitable thermal environment.

Between the incipient lethal limits, however, the metabolic rate can be adjusted to thermoregulate by the mechanisms previously described. The **thermoneutral zone** defines a temperature range where metabolism is

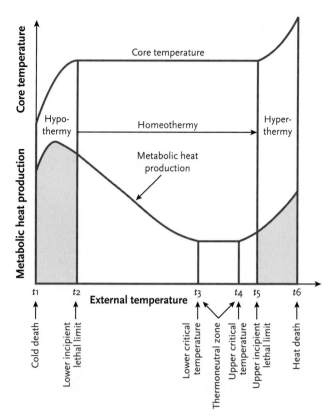

FIGURE 7.5 Influence of Ambient Temperature This diagram shows the body core temperature and metabolic heat production as a function of ambient temperature in a typical homeothermic endotherm.

SOURCE: This article was published in *Comparative Biochemistry*, Vol I (Florkin & Mason, eds.), Hoar, W.S., Copyright Academic Press, 1960.

at its lowest and independent of ambient temperature. Within that zone the body temperature is maintained by simply adjusting heat exchange by vasodilation, vasoconstriction, and/or adjusting the fur or feathers. These mechanisms are not energetically costly, so the metabolic rate is not significantly affected.

The limits of the thermoneutral zone are called the upper and lower critical temperatures (UCT and LCT, respectively). Metabolism increases when the ambient temperature rises above the UCT because of increased energy demands for sweat production or panting to decrease body temperature. In humans, for example, sweat production can increase by 50-fold during sustained aerobic exercise, such as while running a marathon, from about 0.1 to 5.0 litres per day. Because sweating is an active process that involves the use of ATP, a large increase in sweat production will increase the metabolic rate. Metabolism increases below the LCT because of shivering and nonshivering thermogenesis required to provide heat.

The presence of surface insulation has a large influence on the temperature range of the thermoneutral zone. Increasing the amount of insulation extends the thermoneutral zone by lowering the LCT **(Figure 7.6)**. Increased insulation also reduces the rate of increase of the metabolism in response to lowering of the ambient temperature. In a broader context, the effectiveness of

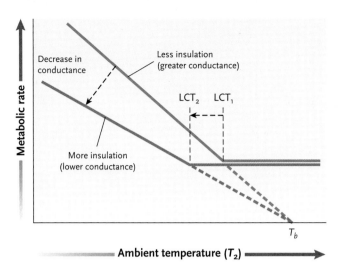

FIGURE 7.6 Surface Insulation This diagram shows surface insulation helps to reduce heat loss, decreases the Lower Critical Temperature (LCT), and increases the breadth of the thermoneutral zone.

SOURCE: From Eckert's ANIMAL PHYSIOLOGY, 5e. Copyright © 2002 by W. H. Freeman & Co. Used by permission of the publisher.

ADAPTATIONS TO TEMPERATURE EXTREMES The cold of winter is a thermoregulatory challenge for birds and mammals. The difficulty is particularly acute in the boreal and arctic zones, where ambient temperatures can fall below −40°C and wind chills to −60°C. Having a thick layer of insulation is essential at these frigid temperatures. Heterothermy is an additional adaptation, in which the temperature of the body core is maintained while that of the extremities may drop to nearly 0°C.

Some mammals hibernate, such as the grizzly bear (*Ursus arctos*) and arctic ground squirrel (*Spermophilus parryii*). However, others such as the arctic fox (*Alopex lagopus*) and caribou (*Rangifer tarandus*) remain active in winter and must have sufficient food or fat reserves to provide energy to maintain their body core temperature and other necessary functions. They are also heterotherms, using adaptations such as those explained in the following paragraphs.

Much of the mass of body appendages consists of bone, cartilage, tendons, and skin, which have minimal metabolic rates and so do not produce much heat. There is a small heat production if the muscles are active, but the main source of warmth in appendages is from the flow of blood. Little blood flow is needed to maintain the most essential function—that of keeping tissues supplied with nutrients and oxygen. Therefore, restricting the blood flow to appendages is an effective adaptation that helps to prevent the loss of precious heat to the environment, as long as the extremities are not allowed to actually freeze. This is a common physiological trait of many endotherms that live in a cold climate. For example, the temperature of the foot pads of sled dogs may be only slightly above 0°C during the winter, which is enough to prevent frostbite even if the ambient temperature is close to −50°C.

insulation is evident when comparing the thermoneutral zones and changes in metabolic rate of tropical versus arctic mammals in response to temperatures below the LCT **(Figure 7.7)**. The grey wolf has an enormous natural range in North America, extending from the northern tip of land on Ellesmere Island to as far south as Mexico (although it is now extirpated from the latter country). The southernmost animals are relatively lean and have a high ratio of surface area to body volume, and also a less-dense fur, both of which facilitate cooling. In contrast, the northern animals are bigger and have a lower ratio of surface to volume and much denser underfur to conserve body heat.

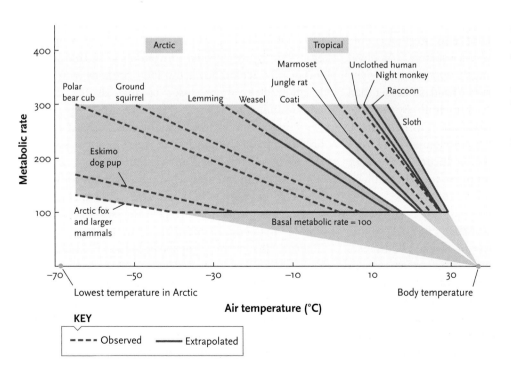

FIGURE 7.7 Range of the Thermoneutral Zones for Tropical and Arctic Mammals Mammals living in a colder climate have a broader thermoneutral zone and a lower critical temperature.

SOURCE: Figure 10 from Scholander, P. F., et al. 1950. *Biol. Bull.* 99: 237–258. Reprinted with permission from the Marine Biological Laboratory, Woods Hole, MA.

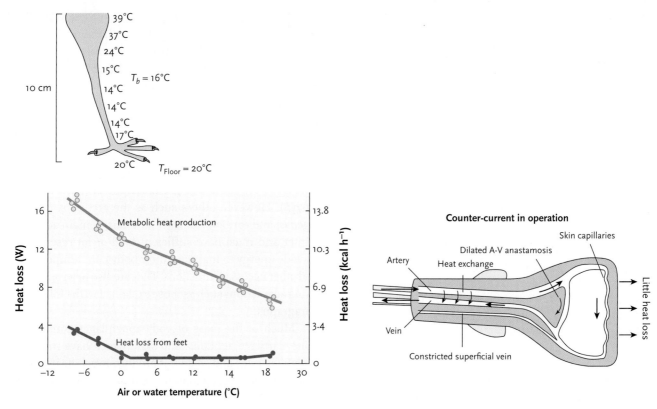

FIGURE 7.8 Counter-Current Heat Exchange The artery and vein supplying the limb are in close proximity, so heat is exchanged between the two. As warm blood passes down the artery, heat is lost to the cooler venous blood returning from the distal end, thus reducing the amount of heat lost in the limb.

SOURCE: (1) Graph: Kilgore, D.L. and K. Schmidt-Nielsen. 1975. "Heat Loss from ducks' feet immersed in cold water," *The Condor*, 77:475–478. (2) Drawings: Willmer, P., G. Stone, and I. Johnston. 2000. *Environmental Physiology of Animals*. Blackwell Science, Oxford, UK. Copyright © 2004, John Wiley and Sons.

Another adaptation that reduces heat loss in limbs is the presence of a **counter-current heat exchange**. This function involves the major artery that supplies blood to the extremity, and the corresponding vein that drains back to the body **(Figure 7.8)**. The artery supplying warm blood lies in close proximity to the vein draining cooler blood, and the flow is in opposite directions in the two vessels, hence the term "counter-current." As blood travels down the artery, heat moves from it to blood in the vein; this occurs because the arterial fluid is warmer than the venous all along the length of the limb. By the time the venous blood reaches the body at the upper end of the limb, there is only a slight difference in temperature from the arterial blood coming from the body core. At the other end (the distal one), the temperature of the arterial blood approaches that of the venous in the foot.

TORPOR, HIBERNATION, AND ESTIVATION—
CONTROLLED HYPOTHERMIA In an energetic sense, it is "costly" to maintain a constant core temperature. To conserve energy, the body temperature of some species will decrease when they are sleeping and not behaviourally active. This function is known as regulated hypothermy. Daily bouts of hypothermy are referred to as daily torpor, and they occur in many small mammals that live

in temperate regions, such as rodents and bats (see Ecology in Depth 7.2). Alternatively, some homeotherms that live in boreal and arctic latitudes may undergo extended periods of hypothermy during the winter months, which is referred to as seasonal torpor or hibernation. Some animals even undergo prolonged periods of hypothemia during part of the summer, a phenomenon known as **estivation**. In all of these conditions—torpor, hibernation, and estivation—the body temperature is allowed to drop closer to that of the ambient environment.

Hibernation is used by mammals from six different orders, including species of bats, ground squirrels, marmots, and mice. During the winter months in nonhibernating mammals, there is a steep thermal gradient between the body core and the ambient environment, which is energetically costly to maintain. Rather than doing this, the body temperature of hibernating mammal drops to just above freezing (about 5°C) for weeks on end **(Figure 7.9)**, with the animal arousing only occasionally, perhaps to maintain its immune system (Prendergast et al., 2002). The heart rate and breathing frequency also fall dramatically. By the way, bears are not true hibernators because they do not undergo these dramatic changes in their physiology—in

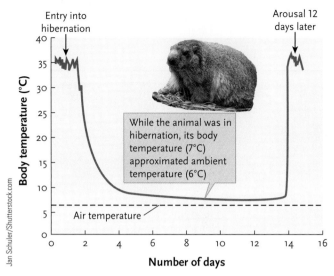

FIGURE 7.9 Effect of Hibernation on Body Temperature Body temperature decreases with the onset of hibernation in the woodchuck (*Marmota monax*) and is maintained just above the ambient temperature.

SOURCE: Hill, R.W., G.A. Wyse, and M. Anderson. 2008. *Animal Physiology*. Sinauer Associates, Sunderland, MA.

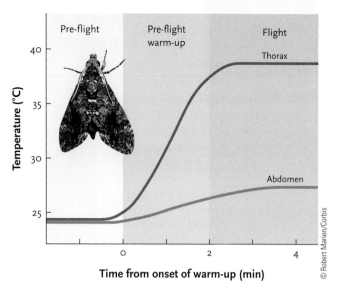

FIGURE 7.10 Pre-Flight Warm-Up in the Hawkmoth (*Manduca sexta*) Rapid contraction and relaxation ("shivering") of thoracic flight muscles helps to warm the animal to a high enough temperature to allow it to fly.

SOURCE: Republished with permission of The Company of Biologists Ltd, from Heinrich, B and G.A. Bartholomew. 1971. "An analysis of pre-flight warm-up in the sphinx moth Manduca sexta," *Journal of Experimental Biology*, 55:233–239; permission conveyed through Copyright Clearance Center, Inc.

essence, they just enter a long and deep sleep during the winter.

Estivation is similar to hibernation in that homeotherms allow their body temperature and other physiological functions to decrease substantially. Unlike hibernation, however, estivation occurs when the environment becomes exceedingly hot and dry. Estivation is beneficial because reduced metabolism means less demand for oxygen, so there is less water loss associated with breathing. Estivation is relatively common among small mammals and a few birds of desert regions, as well as in many reptiles and amphibians.

In mammals the arousal from torpor or hibernation involves shivering and nonshivering thermogenesis using stores of brown fat. The energetic cost of arousal is significant and is a factor in the overall cost–benefit equation of controlled hypothermia.

ENDOTHERMY AND HOMEOTHERMY IN INSECTS

Most insects are ectothermic heterotherms. However, there are a few exceptions that are endothermic during flight, owing to heat generated during vigorous muscle contractions. A few larger insects might also be considered to be homeothermic, because they can maintain their thorax temperature within a narrow range somewhat independent of that of the air. The homeothermic insects include species of sphinx moths (family Sphingidae), bumblebees (*Bombus species*), and the honeybee (*Apis mellifera*), all of which vigorously shiver their thoracic muscles in a "pre-flight warm-up" if their body is too cool to allow them to fly **(Figure 7.10)**.

Tolerance of Extreme Cold

In regions with a seasonal climate that includes a cold winter, such as anywhere in Canada, many aquatic heterothermic animals burrow into mud at the bottom of ponds. This avoids freezing temperatures, because freshwater bodies deeper than 10–30 cm (depending on the local climate) do not freeze to the bottom. However, some heterothermic animals do have to cope with exposure to subfreezing temperatures.

One that has been well studied is the wood frog (*Rana sylvatica*), a wide-ranging species in Canada that occurs in almost all forested areas, even in the boreal zone. This amphibian is remarkable for its ability to survive being frozen solid. The physiological mechanism that allows it to do this was discovered by Ken Storey and his collaborators at Carleton University (Storey and Storey, 1996). In wood frogs, ice forms in the extracellular fluids of tissues, but not in the intracellular fluids (i.e., within cells). If ice did form within cells, then their sharp crystals would pierce the membranes, which would rupture the cells and cause them to die.

Wood frogs and other animals that can tolerate freezing produce antifreeze compounds that enter the intracellular and extracellular fluids. These compounds are called **cryoprotectants**. Glucose is one such antifreeze compound—it is produced in abundance from glycogen stores in the liver. A high concentration of glucose lowers the freezing point of aqueous fluids, which can prevent freezing from occurring (as in intracellular fluids) or at least slow the rate of freezing so that only small ice

ECOLOGY IN DEPTH 7.2
Torpor in Bats

The western long-eared bat (*Myotis evotis*) and big brown bat (*Eptesicus fuscus*) are examples of homeotherms that exhibit daily torpor **(Figure 1)**. These bats are common along cliffs of the South Saskatchewan River in southeastern Alberta, where they have been studied by Robert Barclay and his students at the University of Calgary (Lausen and Barclay, 2003). The bats roost in cracks and crevices during the day and leave those refuges in the early evening for a night of hunting flying insects, which they find by echolocation. When the bats return to the roost in the early morning, their body temperature drops to close to that of ambient environment. Females of both species that are not pregnant or lactating use daily torpor more frequently than those that are reproductively active. However, the

FIGURE 1 Big Brown Bat (*Eptesicus fuscus*)

Ivan Kuzmin/Shutterstock.com

additional energy expenditure of nontorpor is offset by the need for these females to bring their pregnancy to term, and to feed and raise their young during the short breeding season.

---

crystals form, which are much less deadly to cellular membranes.

When a wood frog initially encounters cold in early winter (slightly less than the freezing point of water at 0°C) there is a slow formation of ice in the extracellular fluids, which triggers the abundant release of glucose into the blood circulation. Some of this glucose becomes absorbed into cells, building to a high concentration that lowers the freezing point of the intracellular fluid. As more ice forms in the extracellular fluid, the unfrozen solution becomes increasingly more concentrated in solutes and thus, by the process of osmosis, draws water out from the cells. This causes the concentration of osmotically active chemicals in the intracellular fluid to increase to the degree where it does not freeze even in the slightly subzero temperatures that may occur in the benthic environment. From this point on, as much as 80 percent of the extracellular fluid may freeze into ice, but the physical integrity of the cell is maintained because ice crystals do not form within the cells.

In the springtime, as temperatures slowly rise, the frozen wood frogs thaw. However, they do this from the inside outward, rather than the other way around. This occurs because the concentration of extracellular glucose is highest in vital internal organs, such as the heart and circulatory system, which have the lowest freezing point

and so thaw first. In fact, wood frogs are the first amphibians, and among the first heterothermic animals, to emerge in the springtime.

Freeze tolerance is quite widespread among animals that inhabit frigid environments. Many insects overwinter by tolerating extremely cold temperatures, and then come to life in the spring to resume a new season of reproduction and growth (Danks et al., 1994; Danks, 2004—see Environmental Applications 7.1). Most species use cryoprotectants of various kinds to protect their tissues, often low-molecular-weight compounds such as polyhydric alcohols (e.g., glycerol). However, some species can **supercool**, meaning their body water remains unfrozen even in subzero temperatures because of the absence of seed crystals (or nuclei) around which ice crystals can form. Some arctic gall midges (tiny flies in the family Cecidomyiidae) may remain unfrozen even at temperatures as low as −62°C.

Similarly, many bony fish (teleosts) that live in polar waters, in which the temperature may be below zero much of the year, produce antifreeze compounds (proteins and glycoproteins) or undergo supercooling, or both, to avoid freezing (see Ecology in Depth 7.3). Polar marine fish living in shallow water typically rely on an accumulation of antifreeze compounds to lower the freezing point of their body fluids, while deep-water ones use supercooling. As long as a supercooled fish does not

The Convergent Evolution of Cryoprotectants in Fish: Similar Solutions to Similar Problems

The evolution of cryoprotectants in a number of different species of fish, insects, plants, and even bacteria appears to be a fairly recent event, perhaps occurring in response to ice ages that have sporadically occurred over the past 30 million years. This represents an example of convergent evolution, in which unrelated organisms living in similar environments have evolved comparable traits.

An example of convergent evolution is the development of antifreeze glycoproteins in Arctic cod (*Boreogadus saida*) and Antarctic toothfish (*Dissostichus mawsoni*) (Chen et al., 1997; Ewart et al., 1999). Both of these fish thrive in polar waters where the temperature is below the freezing point of oceanic saltwater ($-1.9°C$). Remarkably, although they are literally "poles apart" in terms of their biogeography and phylogeny (they are classified in different orders and superorders), the antifreeze glycoproteins that they produce are almost identical in molecular structure. However, the genes that encode the sequences of amino acids for these glycoproteins have different origins, and the codons within the genes are different. The molecular evidence for convergent evolution in these fish is also supported by morphological, paleontological, and paleoclimatic evidence. The two species appear to have diverged from a common ancestor at least 40 million years ago, which is well before the first glaciations of the Antarctic (10–14 million years ago) and Arctic regions (2.5 million years ago) that apparently led to their separate evolutions of antifreeze compounds.

encounter ice crystals in its environment, it will remain unfrozen. However, as soon as ice is encountered, rapid freezing occurs and so does death.

Adaptations of Ectotherms to Changes in Temperature

Most ectotherms are at the mercy of their environmental temperature, any changes of which directly affect their metabolism. Nevertheless, there are tactics that ectotherms can use to decrease the effects of changes in ambient temperature. These tactics include certain behaviours, acclimatization, the production of specific enzymes, and changes to the properties of their cell membranes.

Behavioural Thermoregulation

Behavioural thermoregulation involves moving between a cooler to a warmer one, or vice versa. For example, reptiles and amphibians can raise their body temperature above that of the ambient environment by basking in the sun. Desert-dwelling reptiles are especially adept at behavioural thermoregulation, moving in and out of the sun, or flattening or raising their body off a substrate to maintain a comfortable temperature. This does not mean that these animals are homeothermic, because they do not have the capacity to maintain a constant body temperature regardless of ambient conditions. However, on a sunny day they may be able to keep their temperature within a range that allows their muscles to contract rapidly, which is an advantage when trying to capture fast prey or when avoiding their own predators.

Some aquatic animals, such as lake trout (*Salvelinus namaycush*), will change their location to select cooler or warmer waters in order to maintain a comfortable body temperature. In most Canadian lakes, a warmer layer of water up to two metres deep (called the epilimnion) develops at the surface during the summer. The epilimnion sits upon the cooler hypolimnion, and remains intact until the autumn, when the surface cools and the stratification is dispersed by strong winds. The trout may feed in the epilimnion during the summer, but retreat to the hypolimnion if they become uncomfortably warm.

There are constraints to behavioural thermoregulation. On cloudy or otherwise cool days, ectotherms may have difficulty finding a warm place where they can raise their body temperature. Similarly, fish may not be able to find an ideal water temperature if their lake does not stratify during the summer.

Acclimatization

Acclimatization is a process of adjustment that occurs in animals that are living in conditions outside their comfort zone but within their physiological limits (the related term **acclimation** is used when only one environmental factor is involved). A familiar example involves people who live at high altitudes (about 3000 m above sea level), who have little difficulty exerting themselves in physical activity despite the relatively low atmospheric pressure and constrained oxygen supply to their blood and muscles. People who live closer to sea level may feel weak and dizzy at high altitudes, and they are vulnerable to a circulation-related sickness called pulmonary edema. This is the reason that mountain climbers prudently spend some time acclimatizing to high-altitude conditions before they ascend to even higher ones.

ENVIRONMENTAL APPLICATIONS 7.1
The Mountain Pine Beetle and Antifreeze

Since its beginning in the late 1990s, an infestation of the mountain pine beetle (*Dendroctonus ponderosae*) has devastated vast tracts of pine forest in the interior of British Columbia. When abundant, the larvae of this native beetle kill trees because their feeding tunnels destroy the cambium, the growing tissue located just under the bark that produces new wood. Eventually they girdle the tree, meaning water can no longer be transported upward to the foliage or sugars downward to the roots. Other than cutting infested trees, there is little that forest managers can do to mitigate outbreaks. As of 2013, more than 16 million hectares of pine forest had been severely damaged, greatly affecting the economically important forest industry **(Figure 1)**.

The beetle thrives in the hot and dry conditions of the summer. The adults emerge from mid-July to late August and fly to seek uninfested trees, where they mate and lay eggs under the bark, especially on lodgepole pine (*Pinus contorta*). After about two weeks, the eggs hatch and the larvae bore into the cambium, where they overwinter. During the late fall, the larvae produce antifreeze compounds, mostly glycerol, which help them to survive at temperatures as low as about −20°C during the winter months (Regniere and Bentz, 2007).

However, if the ambient temperature falls to −35°C or lower for several days in a row, large numbers of the larvae are killed.

These kinds of deadly temperatures occurred routinely during most winters and they kept populations of the beetle in check. More recently, however, winter temperatures in the central interior of British Columbia have moderated—this may be a regional signal of global warming (see Chapter 3). Because beetle-killing temperatures have become uncommon, many larvae survive the winter to further the infestation. In addition to warmer winters, the beetle irruption has likely been promoted by forest-management practices, especially the routine control of forest fires, which promotes the widespread occurrence of mature pine forests—just the kind of menu that this pest favours.

FIGURE 1 Aerial View of Extensive Attack by Mountain Pine Beetle

A similar phenomena affects ectothermic animals that are acclimated to a particular ambient temperature. Many fish and aquatic invertebrates adjust to new habitats by acclimating their cellular biochemistry to allow for normal physiological functioning. Much of the research on thermal acclimation has been done in the laboratory, where temperature, photoperiod, and other factors can be controlled. Usually, the investigations measure the ability of animals to acclimate to sudden changes in ambient temperature.

Dawson and Bartholomew (1956) did a classic series of experiments in which the western fence lizard (*Sceloporus occidentalis*) and side-blotched lizard (*Uta mearnsi*) were acclimated to either 16°C or 33°C **(Figure 7.11)**. Following initial measurements of metabolic rate at the temperature of acclimation, the lizards were subjected to a rapid change

in ambient temperature and the metabolic rate was measured again. This was repeated over a series of temperature changes—for example, lizards initially acclimated to 33°C experienced rapid changes to 28°C and then to 16°C. Likewise, animals acclimated to 16°C were rapidly exposed to 28°C and then 33°C. The lizards acclimated to 16°C had a significantly higher metabolic rate at all temperatures than did the animals acclimated to 33°C.

What is remarkable about this study is that the *difference* in metabolic rates of the animals tested at their acclimation temperature was less than what was predicted by the sudden change in ambient temperature. In other words, something had occurred during acclimation that kept the metabolic rate of the two groups closer. Subsequent research by other investigators revealed that the acclimation of metabolic rate is attributable to changes

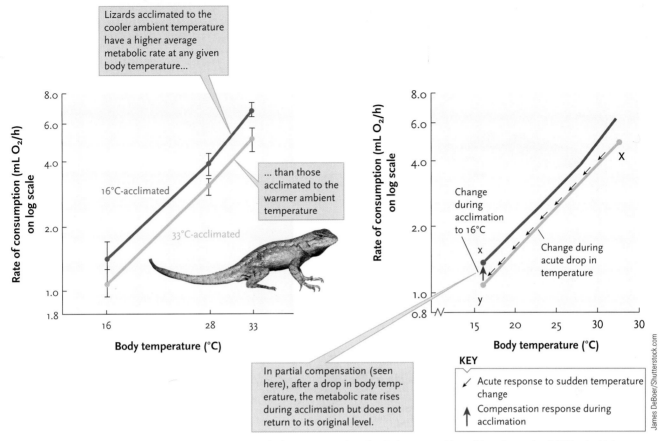

Lizards acclimated to the cooler ambient temperature have a higher average metabolic rate at any given body temperature...

... than those acclimated to the warmer ambient temperature

16°C-acclimated

33°C-acclimated

In partial compensation (seen here), after a drop in body temperature, the metabolic rate rises during acclimation but does not return to its original level.

Change during acclimation to 16°C

Change during acute drop in temperature

KEY

Acute response to sudden temperature change

Compensation response during acclimation

James DeBoer/Shutterstock.com

FIGURE 7.11 Effect of Acclimation Temperature on Metabolic Rate Fence lizards (*Sceloporus occidentalis*) acclimated to 16°C had a higher metabolic rate than those acclimated to 33°C at all temperatures tested.

SOURCE: Dawson, W. R. and Bartholomew, G. A. (1956). "Relation of oxygen consumption to body weight, temperature, and temperature acclimation in lizards Uta stansburia and Scelopwus occidentalis," *Physiological Zoology*, 29: 40–51, the University of Chicago Press.

in the activity of key enzymes that are involved in oxidative metabolism. Members of the same species acclimated to cooler temperatures have higher activity of these enzymes than do those acclimated to warmer conditions. This means that animals acclimated to cooler temperature are able to boost their metabolic rate, thus reducing the potentially negative effect of ambient temperature on their metabolism.

Isozymes

Isozymes (or **isoenzymes**) are slightly different versions of a particular enzyme, and they may vary in their efficiency at different reaction temperatures. This is important because enzyme–substrate affinity is vital to the efficiency of biochemical reactions, and that relationship is affected by temperature. The relationship is indirect, in that enzyme–substrate affinity is lower at higher temperatures and higher at lower ones. Ideally, a biochemical reaction would be more efficient if the enzyme–substrate affinity did not change. However, during the acclimation process, the enzyme–substrate affinity relationship can be changed by producing various isozymes of key enzymes, each functioning optimally within a particular temperature range.

Peter Hochachka and George Somero of the University of British Columbia were among the first ecophysiologists to study the influence of isozymes in ectothermic animals. Their research on lactate dehydrogenase (LDH) showed that fish acclimatized to different ambient temperatures produced different isozymes of LDH. When they compared the enzyme–substrate affinities of the isozymes, it was apparent that they were similar when tested at their acclimation temperature **(Figure 7.12)**. Therefore, the efficiency of the biochemical reactions mediated by the LDH was maintained, reducing the effects of temperature on metabolic rate.

Properties of Cell Membranes Can Also Be Affected by Body Temperature

Cellular membranes are composed largely of phospholipids, proteins, and cholesterol. Typically, when oils or other liquids containing lipids (animal fats) are subjected to cold, they solidify. When this occurs to the lipids in cell membranes, it changes their properties, which affects the viscosity (or fluidity) and flexibility of the membrane. This can be a physiological challenge for ectotherms when they are exposed to large changes in ambient temperature.

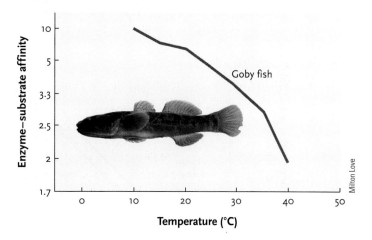

(a) Enzyme–substrate affinity as a function of temperature in a goby

Enzyme–substrate affinity

Goby fish

Milton Love

Temperature (°C)

(b) Enzyme–substrate affinity as a function of temperature in six species of poikilotherms

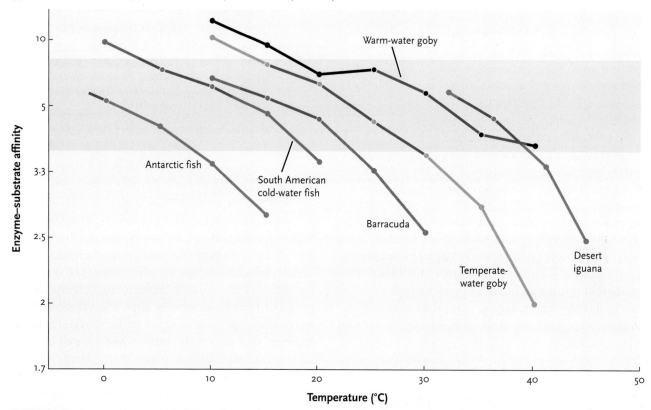

Enzyme–substrate affinity

Warm-water goby

Antarctic fish

South American cold-water fish

Barracuda

Temperate-water goby

Desert iguana

Temperature (°C)

FIGURE 7.12 Lactate Dehydrogenase Enzyme Substrate Affinity versus Acclimation Temperature in Fish Note that the affinity for pyruvate (the substrate) is similar within the normal acclimated range of ambient temperature typical for each fish [shown in blue in part (b)].

SOURCE: Hochachka, P.W. and G.N. Somero. 2002. *Biochemical Adaptation: Mechanism and Process in Physiological Evolution*. Oxford University Press, New York, NY. By permission of Oxford University Press, Inc. Data from Graves and Somero, 1982, Holland et al., 1997, and Fields and Somero, 1997, 1998.

Membrane fluidity can be altered by changing the composition of the phospholipids in cell membranes, particularly by adjusting their content of unsaturated fatty acids. In another study by Hochachka and Somero (1984), membrane fluidity was compared among fish species that were adapted to different temperatures. They found that the unsaturated fatty acid content of phospholipids is higher in membranes of animals that live in colder temperatures. Because of this adaptation, the membrane fluidity of the cells of cold-water fish is close to that of warm-water species. In fact, the similarities of membrane fluidity are as close as those of species of endotherms, such as mammals and birds. This effect is referred to as homeoviscous adaptation.

Water and Ion Balance

Liquid water is essential for life. All animals must have a source of water to replace fluids lost due to evaporation, urination, and defecation. Animals obtain water by drinking, absorbing it by osmosis across their integument (body coating), or as a product of their own oxidative metabolism (e.g., when glucose is oxidized, carbon dioxide and water are by-products). Water typically composes 60–90 percent of the body mass of an animal, and it is compartmentalized into intracellular and extracellular fluids. In this section, we will examine the ways that animals regulate their water content to prevent overhydration or dehydration. The intake of water must balance its loss; otherwise intracellular or extracellular volume might expand or contract excessively, either of which could be problematic.

Water enters cells via proteinaceous channels known as aquaporins, which extend through the phospholipid bilayer of the cellular membrane. The net direction of water movement is determined by the relative concentrations of solutes (mostly ions and proteins) dissolved in water on either side of the membrane. Because membranes are selectively permeable to some solutes but not others, an imbalance in the concentration of dissolved substances inside and outside a cell may be corrected fairly quickly by simple diffusion across the membrane until an equilibrium is reached. However, because nondiffusible solutes, such as certain large proteins, cannot pass through cell membranes, an imbalance in their concentration results in the movement of water molecules until the osmotic concentration (or osmolarity) of particles becomes equal on either side. Osmosis is the diffusion of water through a semipermeable membrane along a gradient from a lower concentration of solutes (or low osmolarity of nondiffusible solutes) to a higher one; this is also known as an osmotic gradient.

Most cells cannot tolerate much change in their volume. Therefore, animals must limit the amount of difference in the solute concentrations between their extracellular and intracellular fluids in order to prevent large differences in osmotic concentration from occurring across cell membranes. This is done mostly by regulating two physiological variables: (1) the ionic composition of the extracellular fluid, and (2) the amount of water in the extracellular fluid.

Regulation of the ionic composition of body fluids is essential for proper functioning of both the nervous system (even in animals in which it is rudimentary) and muscles (skeletal, cardiac, and smooth). A variety of mechanisms is used to regulate the ionic composition of the body fluids. For example, mammals have sensors that monitor both the volume (via indirect means, such as by monitoring vascular pressure) and ionic concentrations of Na^+, K^+, and Ca^{2+} in their extracellular fluids. Physiological adjustments that regulate volume and ions

mostly involve adjusting functions of the renal organs (kidneys) and digestive tract. In aquatic animals, the respiratory system also plays a role in regulating the ionic concentration and volume of extracellular fluids.

Role of the Renal Organ

Most animals have a renal organ, also known as a kidney or excretory organ, which regulates ions and water in their extracellular fluids. The structure of the renal organ varies among animals, depending on their phylogenetic relatedness, but all perform the same basic functions. These include the filtration of extracellular body fluids, reabsorption of essential ions and nutrients from the filtrate, secretion of dissolved substances into the filtrate, and excretion of excess ions, nitrogenous wastes, and water **(Figure 7.13)**.

The simplest renal organs are tube-shaped (or tubiform) structures, such as the metanephridia found in each segment of an earthworm, and the antennal glands of crustaceans. One end of the tube is porous to

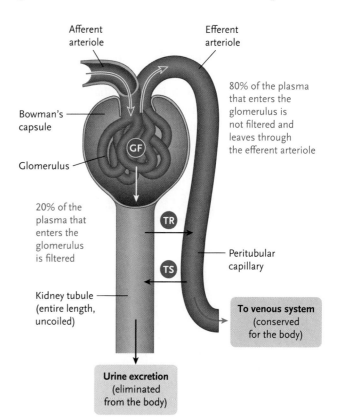

FIGURE 7.13 Filtration, Reabsorption, Secretion, and Excretion in a Kidney Tubule, or Nephron

ions, various nutrients, small peptides, and water, but large proteins such as albumens cannot move into the organ. Sometimes the filtrate is referred to as an ultrafiltrate because its concentration of proteins and other large solutes is so low. As the filtrate passes along the tube, ions, nutrients (such as glucose), and water are reabsorbed back into the extracellular fluid, leaving behind excess water, ions, and nitrogenous waste products of metabolism, such as ammonia or urea. These "excess" materials are excreted into the environment.

The kidneys of vertebrate animals contain many small nephrons, which are basic structural and functional units that are responsible for filtration, reabsorption, secretion, and excretion (a human kidney typically contains more than one million nephrons). A nephron is divided into different regions, each of which performs a slightly different function (Figure 7.14). The first region is called Bowman's capsule and it is the site where the ultrafiltrate of the extracellular fluid (the blood plasma) accumulates. It is surrounded by a capillary network called the glomerulus, from which there is a filtration of fluid moving into Bowman's capsule by **bulk flow** (this is the movement of fluid from one compartment to another due to differences in pressure). Because the fluid pressure in Bowman's capsule is much less than that of the blood plasma within the glomerulus, liquid moves from the blood into the lumen of the capsule. The rate of water flow

changes if the blood pressure in the glomerulus is altered—an increase that results in more rapid filtration, and a decrease in less.

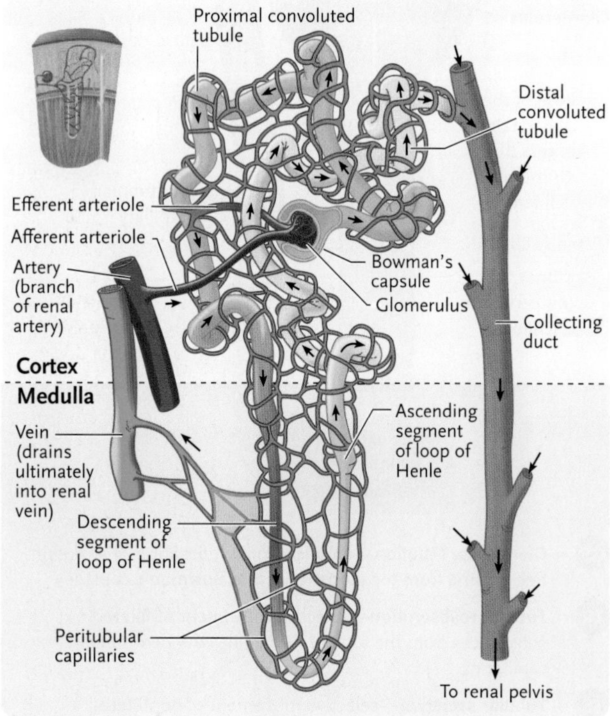

The next region of the nephron is called the proximal tubule, which is where about 70 percent of the reabsorption of valuable ions, nutrients, and water occurs. There are specialized transport mechanisms that selectively move ions and nutrients (such as glucose and amino acids) from the lumen of the proximal tubule back into the blood; osmotic water flows track the movements of these solutes.

The loop of Henle is a U-shaped region of the nephron that connects the proximal tubule to the distal end (Figure 7.14). The length of the "loop" is variable, being short in cortical nephrons and long in juxtamedullary ones. Juxtamedullary nephrons are an adaptation for more efficient reabsorption and conservation of water, and so their proportion is greater in mammals that live in drier habitats, such as desert. Note that this structure occurs in birds and mammals; it is lacking in fish, amphibians, and reptiles, which instead have the proximal tubule connected to the distal end by a short connecting length.

Essentially, the loop of Henle reabsorbs more salt from the filtrate than it does water because of the impermeability of portions of the loop to water. The reabsorbed salt is concentrated in a portion of the kidney called the renal medulla, through which the loop travels. A more distal portion of the nephron, called the collecting duct, traverses the medulla and encounters the high salt concentration. The permeability of the collecting duct to water can be adjusted—therefore, if an animal needs to conserve water, its ducts become more permeable to that fluid, which moves into the medulla by osmosis and eventually back into the blood plasma.

The rate of reabsorption can be regulated to compensate for changes in ionic composition and volume of the extracellular fluid. This involves increasing or decreasing the rate of reabsorption of selected ions and water. Both the endocrine system and nervous system are involved in the control of this regulation.

Life in Aquatic Environments

Aquatic environments present big challenges to the maintenance of water balance and ionic composition of body fluids. This is because the extracellular fluids of aquatic animals are different in ionic and osmotic concentrations from their aquatic environment. To maintain those biotic conditions their regulatory biology must deal with the tendency for either an osmotic influx or efflux of water. Consequently, there must be physiological mechanisms to maintain the osmotic and ionic integrity of body fluids. Some marine organisms actually conform to the osmotic concentration and ionic composition of seawater, and thereby avoid the physiological issues associated with nonconformity.

FIGURE 7.14 Anatomical Regions in Mammalian Cortical and Juxtamedullary Nephrons Note that the loop of Henle in juxtamedullary nephrons is much longer and extends deeper into the renal medulla than do the tubules of cortical nephrons.

SOURCE: From Eckert's ANIMAL PHYSIOLOGY, 5e. Copyright © 2002 by W. H. Freeman & Co. Used by permission of the publisher.

MARINE ENVIRONMENTS Animals that match the osmotic characteristics of their environment are called **osmoconformers**. There are many examples in marine habitats, but none in freshwater because its low osmotic concentration would be lethal in organisms. Most osmoconformers are also **ionoconformers**, in that they have an extracellular ionic composition similar to that of their aquatic environment **(Table 7.2)**. Many pelagic marine invertebrates are both osmoconformers and ionoconformers, thus eliminating the need to have special regulatory mechanisms to maintain the ionic composition or osmotic strength of their body fluids.

Unlike pelagic marine invertebrates, bony fish and sharks (teleosts and elasmobranchs, respectively) are **osmoregulators** and **ionoregulators** that maintain a different extracellular ionic composition from that of seawater **(Table 7.2)**. Note that the ionic concentrations of the extracellular fluids of these fish are much less than that of seawater. These animals therefore face an osmotic and ionic challenge because they tend to lose water to their environment and to gain salt ions, primarily via their gills.

To cope with the problem of water loss by osmosis, teleost fish drink seawater and absorb it across their gut, and then excrete the overload of ions via their renal organ and gills. This physiological system allows them to replenish water lost via osmosis while also maintaining themselves **hyposmotic** to the seawater (i.e., they have a

lower osmotic strength). The excretion of ions via the gills involves specialized epithelial chloride cells, which are packed with mitochondria and therefore have a high oxidative capacity.

The ATP generated by the mitochondria is used to power the transport of Na⁺, Cl⁻, and K⁺ from the extracellular fluid across the basolateral membrane of the chloride cells **(Figure 7.15)**. The Na⁺ is actively transported

TABLE 7.2	**Ionic Concentrations in Extracellular Fluids**

The jellyfish Aurelia is an osmoconformer, while the teleost flounder Pleuronectes and dogfish shark Squalus acanthias are osmoregulators. The data for the Aurelia jellyfish are for the extracellular matrix, while those for the fish are for blood plasma. The ion concentrations are in millimoles/L (mmol/L) and osmotic concentration in milliosmoles/L (mosm/L).

	Ionic Concentration					
	Na⁺	K⁺	Ca⁺²	Mg⁺²	Cl⁻	Osmolarity
Seawater	460	10	10	53	540	1000
Aurelia	454	10	10	51	554	1000
Paralichthys	180	4	3	1	160	337
Squalus	269	4	3	1	258	1075

SOURCE: From Eckert's ANIMAL PHYSIOLOGY, 5e. Copyright © 2002 by W. H. Freeman & Co. Used by permission of the publisher.

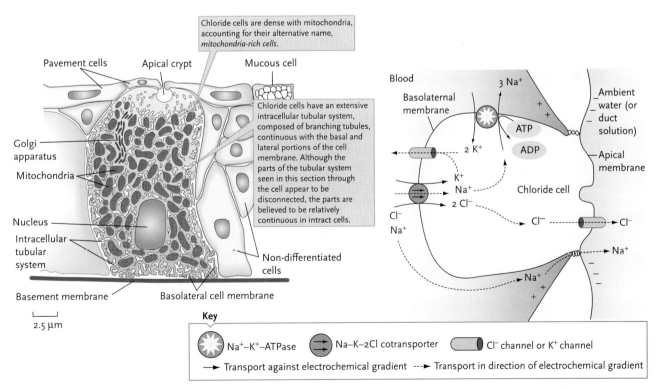

FIGURE 7.15 Chloride Cell Function in the Marine Teleost Gill A Na⁺/2Cl⁻/K⁺ co-transporter moves these ions into the chloride cell across the basolateral membrane. Na+ is then actively pumped back out into the extracellular fluid via Na⁺/K⁺ ATPase. The Cl⁻ diffuses into the environment via a specialized Cl⁻ channel. Na⁺ follows via the intercellular pathway between the epithelial cells due to the electrical attraction of the Cl⁻.

SOURCE: Degnan, K.J., K.J. Karnaky, and J.A. Zadunaisky. 1977. "Active chloride transport in the in vitro opercular skin of a teleost (Fundulus heteroclitus), a gill-like epithelium rich in chloride cells," *Journal of Physiology*, 271: 155–191. Used by permission of Blackwell Publishing Ltd.

back into the extracellular fluid (in exchange for K⁺) via Na⁺/K⁺ ATPase, which is also found in the basolateral membrane. The potassium ions diffuse back into the extracellular fluid via specialized K⁺ channels. The chloride ions do not move back into the extracellular fluid; instead, they move out of the chloride cells via Cl⁻ channels in the apical membrane, which faces the seawater. Because the movement of Cl⁻ ions does not involve an active transport mechanism, the concentration gradient between the chloride cell and seawater must be large enough to favour efflux by diffusion. As Cl⁻ accumulates on the outside of the apical membrane, the environment immediately around the outer surface becomes negatively charged. This attracts Na⁺ to move from the extracellular fluid into the environment by passing between the chloride cell and its neighbouring cells. In this way, teleost fish can get rid of excess Na⁺ and Cl⁻ ions that have been taken in by drinking or leaked into the fish across the gills.

Marine elasmobranch fish use different mechanisms in their **osmoregulation** and **ionoregulation**. Like teleost fish, they maintain the concentration of ions in their extracellular fluid at a much lower concentration than in seawater, and they also gain excess ions by diffusion from their marine environment. But instead of using chloride cells to remove excess monovalent ions, elasmobranchs use cells in structures called rectal glands that perform the same function. The rectal glands excrete excess ions into the hind gut, and they are eventually eliminated with the feces. The gills are not involved in ionoregulation in elasmobranchs. Despite their body fluids having smaller ionic concentrations than seawater, elasmobranchs maintain a slightly higher osmolarity than occurs in their aqueous environment **(Table 7.2)**. They are able to do this by maintaining a high concentration of urea in their blood (about 376 mmol/L in the dogfish shark; this would be toxic to bony fish). Therefore, the high osmotic concentration in the extracellular fluids of elasmobranches is attributed to both inorganic ions and urea. Because these animals are slightly **hyperosmotic** to seawater (having a higher osmotic strength), they actually gain water by osmosis, thus eliminating the need to drink seawater.

FRESHWATER ENVIRONMENTS In contrast to seawater, life in freshwater is challenging because that matrix is dilute in its ionic composition. This means that all freshwater animals are hyperosmotic and **hyperionic** to their environment **(Table 7.3)**. Because of this condition they tend to gain substantial amounts of water by osmosis and also tend to lose ions by diffusion. To maintain the osmotic and ionic gradients, freshwater animals must osmoregulate and ionoregulate their body fluids.

Excess water that seeps into the body fluids of freshwater teleosts by osmosis is excreted as copious and

TABLE 7.3	Comparison of Blood Plasma of a Trout (*Salmo trutta*) and Its Freshwater Environment

Ion concentrations are in mmol/L, and osmotic concentrations in mosm/L.

	Ionic Concentration					
	Na⁺	K⁺	Ca⁺²	Mg⁺²	>Cl⁻	Osmolarity
Freshwater	0.4	0.1	0.8	0.2	0.2	0.5–10
Salmo	161	5.3	6.3	0.9	119	326

SOURCE: Hill, R.W., G.A. Wyse and M. Anderson. 2008. *Animal Physiology.* Sinauer Associates, Sunderland, MA.

dilute urine by the renal organ, which also reabsorbs ions from the filtrate to conserve their extracellular concentrations. However, most ionoregulation occurs in the gills, which absorb ions from the aqueous environment (instead of pumping them out, as in marine teleosts). The gill cells that are responsible for ion uptake are similar to the chloride cells of marine teleosts, except the transporters are different. On the apical (inward) side of these cells, two kinds of transport proteins are involved in ionic exchange with the environment **(Figure 7.16)**. One transporter excretes HCO_3^- (bicarbonate) into the water in exchange for Cl⁻. This involves HCO_3^- moving down a concentration gradient into the ambient water, and Cl⁻ into the cell against a gradient. The other transporter

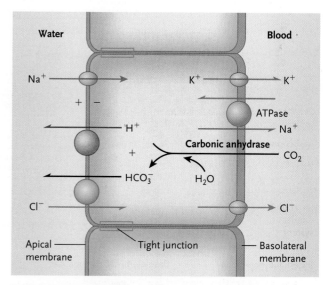

FIGURE 7.16 Transport Mechanisms for Ion Uptake in the Freshwater Teleost Gill Na⁺/K⁺ ATPase in the basolateral membrane plays a key role in maintaining low gill epithelial cell Na⁺ concentration by actively transporting this ion into the blood plasma (hemolymph) in exchange for K⁺. Intracellular K⁺ eventually diffuses back into the hemolymph via a K⁺ channel. Na⁺ is exchanged for H⁺ across the apical membrane and Cl⁻ is exchanged for HCO_3^-. The Cl⁻ moves across the basolateral membrane through a Cl⁻ channel.

SOURCE: From Eckert's ANIMAL PHYSIOLOGY, 5e. Copyright © 2002 by W. H. Freeman & Co. Used by permission of the publisher.

exchanges H^+ or NH_4^+ for Na^+. In this case, the H^+ or NH_4^+ move down a concentration gradient into the water, and Na^+ against a gradient into the cell. Once inside the cell, the Cl^- diffuses across the basolateral membrane into the extracellular fluid via a Cl^- channel. The Na^+ is actively transported out of the cell using energy liberated by Na^+/K^+ ATPase found in the basolateral membrane.

Freshwater crustaceans, such as crayfish, use similar tactics as teleosts to osmoregulate and ionoregulate. They excrete a dilute urine via an antennal gland, which reabsorbs ions from the filtrate of the extracellular fluid before releasing the excess as urine (similar to the renal organs of freshwater fish). The gills of crayfish are also efficient at extracting Na^+ and Cl^- from the water in exchange for H^+ and HCO_3^-, respectively. Amphibians, such as frogs and salamanders, use transport mechanisms in the skin to ionoregulate. The transporters used are the same as those found in freshwater teleosts and crayfish.

Water and Ions in Terrestrial Environments

All terrestrial organisms have to deal with a basic problem: conserving water. The main ways that animals lose water to the environment are excretion with the urine and feces and evaporation from the respiratory surfaces and integument (skin). Particularly in dry environments, the usual physiological strategy is to:

- reduce water loss by concentrating the urine and making the feces as dry as possible;
- dehumidify exhaled air during the ventilation cycle to reduce water loss, while hydrating the air during inhalation to keep the respiratory surface moist; and
- make the integument impermeable to water.

CONCENTRATING THE URINE AND FECES The renal organs of terrestrial mammals and birds have the capacity to concentrate urine so that its osmotic concentration is higher than that of the extracellular fluid. The ultrafiltrate that enters Bowman's capsule has a similar osmotic strength as the blood plasma, but due to reabsorption of water by the collecting tubules, the osmolarity of the urine is higher. The desert-dwelling kangaroo rat (genus *Dipodomys*) can do this very efficiently—the ionic concentration of its urine is up to 16 times that of the blood plasma, thus conserving scarce body water (Table 7.4). The urine-concentrating ability is often measured as the ratio of urine to plasma (U:P ratio). Mammals that live in habitats where water is readily available have lower U:P ratios than those living where it is scarce.

The ability to concentrate urine is a function of the numbers of juxtamedullary nephrons (those with a long loop of Henle). In desert-dwelling mammals, almost all of the nephrons are of this type, and they reach deep into the renal medulla. The renal medulla is also proportionally

TABLE 7.4	**Ability of Mammals to Concentrate Urine** A higher urine:plasma (U:P) ratio indicates a greater physiological efficiency at conserving water.	
Animal	Maximum Urine Osmotic Concentration (mosm/L)	U:P Ratio
Beaver (*Castor canadensis*)	520	1.7:1
Human (*Homo sapiens*)	1200	4.0:1
Rat (*Rattus norvegicus*)	2900	9.0:1
Vampire bat (*Desmodus rotundus*)	4650	14:1
Kangaroo rat (*Dipodomys sp.*)	5000	16:1

SOURCE: Based on data from Willmer et al. (2000).

thicker than that of nondesert mammals to allow for the length of the loop of Henle.

The production of dry fecal pellets is also a way to conserve water in mammals. Most of the water reabsorption occurs in the large intestine (or hindgut or colon). **Table 7.5** shows the water content of the fecal materials of two ruminant mammals—the dromedary camel is adapted to dry habitats, and the cow is not.

REDUCING WATER LOSS IN EXHALED AIR Humans are not efficient at conserving water by trapping its vapour from air that we exhale to the atmosphere—this is why our breath is "visible" as condensed vapour on a cold day. In contrast, some birds and mammals are very economical in conserving water vapour from their respiratory tract. As they inhale air, it passes through moist nasal passages and becomes warmed and humidified as it travels to the lungs. The nasal passages are cooled as moisture evaporates from their surface, and the warmed air is capable of absorbing more water vapour than the inhaled cooler air. By the time the inhaled air reaches the

TABLE 7.5	**Maximum U:P Ratio and Fecal Water Content in Two Ruminant Mammals** The fecal water content is in grams H_2O per kilogram of feces.	
	Maximum U:P Ratio	Fecal Water Content
Cow (*Bos primigenius*)	4	750
Dromedary (*Camelus dromedarius*)	8	440

SOURCE: Based on data from Hill et al. (2008).

respiratory surface where gas exchange occurs, it is almost fully saturated with water vapour.

When the stale air is exhaled, the reverse happens—the warm moist air travels outward over the cooler nasal passages, thus condensing vapour on their surface and conserving water by dehumidification. Animals that are exceptionally good at this function have narrow and convoluted nasal passages, which increases the surface area for efficient humidification and dehumidification of the air that they breathe. The desert-dwelling kangaroo rat is a champion of water conservation by dehumidification of its exhaled air **(Figure 7.17)**. It can actually lower the temperature of its expired air below that of the ambient environment by condensing its load of water vapour—no other animal is known to do this to such a degree.

REDUCING WATER LOSS ACROSS THE SKIN The skin is another avenue of water gain or loss. Unless an animal lives in a humid environment, it is in jeopardy of losing water by evaporation across its integument. Amphibians are especially vulnerable to water loss from their skin and this is why most species must have easy access to aquatic habitats to survive. However, toads (genus *Bufo*) have a thicker skin and their epidermis is keratinized, which helps to prevent water loss through the skin. Terrestrial arthropods, such as insects, have a comparable solution—they secrete a water-conserving layer of wax over their exoskeleton (or cuticle, which is composed of chitin and protein).

METABOLIC WATER Some desert-dwelling rodents have a remarkable ability to survive without drinking any water. Instead, they meet their needs by using water from their food, plus that generated by oxidative metabolism. Even dry seeds will yield so-called **metabolic water** when their biomass is oxidized. This occurs during metabolism in mitochondria, when each atom of oxygen used in oxidative phosphorylation obtains two protons to form water at the end of the electron-transport chain. There is also some content of free water even in seemingly dry seeds, which also contributes to the needs of desert herbivores.

All organisms have the capacity to make metabolic water, but desert mammals are highly efficient at retaining this vital substance. The kangaroo rat is exceptionally competent in its water conservation, having a very low **obligatory water loss** to breathing, feces, and urine (see Ecology in Depth 7.4). Its fecal pellets are extremely dry, and its urine very concentrated in salts and nitrogenous wastes. This animal can survive without drinking.

WATER CONSERVATION IN INSECTS Insects are excellent at water conservation: their waxy cuticle greatly reduces water loss across their integument, their respiratory system is efficient at preventing evaporation, and they produce highly concentrated excretions. Their fecal wastes are mixed with a product formed by their Malpighian tubules, which occur at the junction of the midgut and hindgut **(Figure 7.18)**. The tubules are analogous to the nephron of vertebrates in that they process extracellular fluid to remove waste products of metabolism.

Ions (especially K^+) are pumped into the lumen of the tubules, and water and other solutes then follow. For example, Cl^- is drawn into the tubules by electrical attraction to K^+. The K^+-rich solution then travels down the tubules and enters the hindgut, where Cl^- and K^+ (and Na^+) are absorbed back into the hemolymph (this extracellular fluid is a blood analogue in arthropods and many other invertebrates with an open circulatory system; there is no distinction between their interstitial fluid and blood, and the hemolymph fills the interior of the body and surrounds all cells). Water then flows into the hemolymph by osmosis, leaving behind a pasty, highly

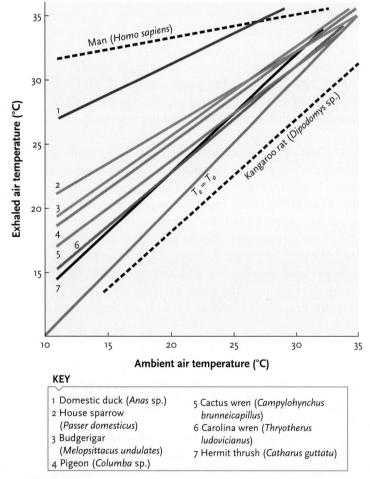

KEY

1 Domestic duck (*Anas* sp.)	5 Cactus wren (*Campylohynchus brunneicapillus*)
2 House sparrow (*Passer domesticus*)	6 Carolina wren (*Thryotherus ludovicianus*)
3 Budgerigar (*Melopsittacus undulates*)	7 Hermit thrush (*Catharus guttatu*)
4 Pigeon (*Columba* sp.)	

FIGURE 7.17 Temperature of Exhaled Air as a Function of That of Inhaled Air The bold line ($T_e = T_a$) represents equality between the two temperatures. All birds and mammals, except for the kangaroo rat, are above the line of equality. Humans are well above the line and are not efficient at trapping moisture from their expired air. T_e = exhaled air; T_a = inhaled air.

SOURCE: Reprinted from Schmidt-Nielsen, K., F.R. Hainsworth, and D.E. Murrish. 1970. "Countercurrent heat exchange in the respiratory passages: Effect on water and heat balance," *Respiration Physiology*, 9 (2):263–276 with permission from Elsevier.

The kangaroo rat (*Dipodomys merriami*) of the southwestern desert of the United States has been studied for its remarkable ability to conserve water (**Figure 1**; Schmidt-Nielsen and Schmidt-Nielsen, 1951). In a series of experiments, kangaroo rats were provided with a diet of barley seed but were not allowed to drink water. The experiments were conducted under a variety of relative humidities, ranging from 5 to 90 percent. These desert-adapted mammals remained healthy even at the lowest humidity.

Based on the amounts of carbohydrate, fat, and protein found in the grain, an estimate was obtained of the amount of "metabolic water" available to the kangaroo rats (this is water formed during the metabolic oxidation of food). The gross production from 1 g of barley was 0.54 g of H_2O (at 25°C and 33 percent relative humidity). As long as the ambient relative humidity was greater than 10 percent, kangaroo rats were capable of meeting all of their water needs from a diet of barley seeds.

The total water loss by the kangaroo rats was 0.47 g per g of barley, equivalent

FIGURE 1 A Kangaroo Rat (*Dipodomys merriami*)

to 86 percent of the water gained, as follows:

- Ventilation = 0.33 g of H_2O per g of barley consumed (this number is based on the O_2 needed to oxidize the barley, and therefore the amount of air passing in and out of the lung).
- Urinary = 0.14 g of H_2O per g of barley (this is water needed to excrete the

urea produced as a nitrogenous waste).
- Fecal = less than 0.01 g of H_2O.

Therefore, the net amount of water gained from the metabolism of 1 g of barley is 0.07 g, or about 14 percent of the H_2O actually produced.

concentrated excretory product that is a combination of urine and feces.

EXCRETING NITROGENOUS WASTE
All animals metabolize proteins, and so they must deal with nitrogenous wastes that arise from the deamination of amino acids (removal of the amino functional group), and from metabolism of nucleic acids. There are three common forms of nitrogenous waste: ammonia (NH_3), urea [$(NH_2)_2CO$], and uric acid ($C_5H_4N_4O_3$).

Most animals that live in aquatic environments (except for elasmobranchs and marine mammals) excrete ammonia as their nitrogenous waste. The ammonia does not take much energy to produce, and it is excreted rapidly to prevent it from accumulating to toxic levels in body fluids. Animals that produce ammonia as the primary nitrogenous waste are referred to as **ammonotelic**.

However, terrestrial animals must conserve water, and so they tend to excrete nitrogenous waste in concentrated forms, but they cannot do this with

ammonia because it is too toxic. Instead, they produce urea or uric acid, which are much less toxic, although there is a trade-off because these compounds are energetically costly to produce. Mammals and most terrestrial amphibians are **ureotelic**, meaning they produce urea as a nitrogenous waste. Almost all birds and reptiles (except for some ureotelic turtles) produce uric acid as their nitrogenous waste, and thus are **uricotelic**. Most terrestrial invertebrates, including insects, are also uricotelic.

Unlike ureotelic animals that produce a liquid urine containing urea, uricotelic ones make a paste with a high concentration of uric acid, or they excrete a dry fecal pellet high in that substance. Normally in uricotelic animals, the product of the renal organ (Malpighian tubules in the case of insects) is mixed with fecal matter in the hindgut before being expelled through the cloaca (this is a shared passage for urine and feces). Water is reabsorbed in the hindgut and cloaca, causing the uric acid to precipitate as a fine crystal, and a paste or solid waste is excreted.

- Exposure of the gas-exchange surface to water results in osmotic and ionic challenges if the body fluids are not isosmotic to the water.
- If there is a thermal gradient between the body and the aqueous environment, heat is lost or gained across the gas-exchange surface.

Despite these challenges, aquatic animals have employed water-breathing for hundreds of millions of years, in both marine and freshwater environments. Their gas-exchange surface is called a gill (except for marine reptiles and mammals, which have lungs). Gills are filamentous structures with a single layer of epithelial cells that form a barrier between circulating body fluids and the environmental water. The filaments provide a very large surface area for gas exchange. Either water is drawn over the surface of the gill to ventilate the filaments and achieve a more efficient gas exchange, or the animal moves through the water to pass it over the gills.

Some vertebrate animals, such as certain salamanders, have external gills and rely mostly on water currents and diffusion for gas exchange. Others, such as teleost fish, mollusks, and crustaceans, have internal gills within a protective chamber. Although internalization requires a specialized mechanism to ventilate the gills by passing water over them, these vital organs are relatively protected from damage by contact with objects in the environment and also from predators.

GILL VENTILATION There are a variety of ways of ventilating internalized gills. Bivalve molluscs (such as clams and oysters) have abundant cilia that cover the surface of their inhalant siphon, and their constant beating causes a water current to pass over the gills. Cephalopod molluscs (octopi and squids) are much larger animals, and they use a pumping action of their inhalant siphon to force water over their gills. Crustaceans have their gills enclosed in a chamber within the thorax, where a structure called a gill bailer creates pulses of negative pressure that draw water over their gills.

Teleost fish have their gills enclosed by a rigid operculum. Ventilation of their gills involves the coordinated action of pumping structures that creates both suction and pressure. At the start of a ventilatory cycle, the mouth opens, the floor of the buccal (mouth) cavity drops, and the operculum bulges slightly outward while maintaining a seal with the body wall, thus increasing the volume of the buccal and opercular cavities. This increase in volume lowers the pressure in those areas and results in a flow of water into the mouth and over the gills by suction. Next, the mouth closes, the floor of the buccal cavity rises, and the operculum opens to allow water to be pushed over the surface of the gills, working in the manner of a pressure pump. Note that the gills are ventilated during both the expansion and contraction phases.

Although gills come in different shapes and sizes, they all share the function of acting as the interface between the circulating body fluids and the aquatic environment. The direction of the flow of water is opposite to that of blood flow in the gills. This creates a **counter-current flow** that it is important to the efficiency of gas exchange across the surface of the gills. Because of the counter-current flow, the gradient of oxygen partial pressure between the blood and environmental water favours diffusion into the blood. This means that blood continuously picks up oxygen as it travels through the gill lamellae. If the blood and water were flowing in the same direction, the diffusion gradient would quickly disappear prior to full oxygenation of the blood—this would be much less efficient than a counter-current flow.

Animals That "Breathe" Air

All terrestrial animals are air-breathing, as are aquatic mammals and reptiles. Air is a much less dense medium than water, so less energy is expended to ventilate the gas-exchange surface, compared with pumping water over gills. Also, the concentration of oxygen in air (about 21 percent) is much greater than in water (typically 7 ppm in freshwater at 20°C). The key challenge faced by air breathers is the evaporation of water at their gas-exchange surface and possible desiccation of the body fluids. This effect is reduced by internalization of the gas-exchange surface and humidification of the air as it is inhaled.

Most vertebrate animals rely on "lungs" for the exchange of oxygen and elimination of carbon dioxide, although semi-terrestrial amphibians can also exchange gas across their skin. Terrestrial insects, the most diverse group of animals on the planet, rely on an internal tracheal system for gas exchange.

VERTEBRATE LUNGS The lungs of amphibians consist of a pair of simple air sacs that develop as extensions of the pharynx. Amphibians ventilate their lungs by forcing air into them by a pumping action of the buccal cavity. At the start of the ventilatory cycle, air is drawn in through the two nares (nostrils) as the buccal cavity is expanded by lowering its floor. During this time the opening to the lungs, called the glottis, is closed. Next, with the nares still open, the glottis opens and air from the previous inhalation is expelled along the roof of the buccal cavity and out the nares by elastic recoil of the lungs, in much the same way that air leaves an open balloon. The nares then close and the floor of the buccal cavity is raised, pushing fresh air through the open glottis and into the lungs. Importantly, the anatomical structure and function of the buccal cavity inhibits the mixing of fresh air in the ventral (lower) portion with stale air exhaled from the lungs as it passes along the dorsal aspect. The cycle then starts again as the nares are opened and the next charge of fresh air is drawn into the buccal cavity, and so on. This method of breathing is known as **positive-pressure ventilation** because air is forced into the lungs by the pumping action of the buccal floor.

Reptiles, birds, and mammals fill their lungs by **negative-pressure ventilation**. Their lungs are contained within a thoracic (or chest) cavity that is forced to expand by contraction of the diaphragm as well as muscles between the ribs. When the thorax expands so do the lungs, resulting in their inner pressure falling below that of the atmosphere. This draws air in via the nostrils or the mouth, and through the airways (tubular passages) that connect to the lungs. During quiet breathing, exhalation occurs as the muscles of the thorax and diaphragm relax, which allows the thorax to recoil and increase pressure in the lungs to force air out the airways. However, during times of excitement or exercise, a different set of thoracic muscles will contract to force larger volumes of air out of the lungs during exhalation.

The gas-exchange surface of the lungs of reptiles, birds, and mammals is much more complex than in amphibians. The inner lung surface of mammals is composed of plentiful alveolar sacs, which are located at the end of a series of branched airways (terminal bronchioles). Each alveolar sac is an aggregation of tiny individual alveoli, superficially resembling a cluster of grapes. Taken together, the alveoli have a very large surface area—in a human it would be about 75 m². Each alveolus receives its own blood supply, giving ample opportunity for gas exchange with the blood.

Birds are the champions of negative-pressure ventilation. Bird lungs are composed of a series of air sacs at either end of the gas-exchange surface. That surface is made up of a number of tubes called parabronchi, whose surrounding tissue comprises sponge-like material consisting of small "air capillaries" intermingled with blood vessels. Inhalation caused by expansion of the thorax results in enlargement of the air sacs, which causes fresh air to move along the airways into the posterior air sac, and air from the parabronchi is drawn into the anterior air sac. Upon exhalation, the air sacs are squeezed so that the fresh air from the posterior air sacs is forced into the parabronchi. At the same time, air from the previous breath, which is stored in the anterior air sacs, is squeezed out of the airways and into the atmosphere. This system results in a continual flow of fresh air over the parabronchi throughout the ventilatory cycle, and not just during inhalation as occurs in mammalian lungs.

VENTILATION BY INSECTS Terrestrial insects do not have lungs or gills. Instead, they use a series of tubes (each called a trachea) to take oxygen deep within the muscles of their abdomen and thorax. The opening to each trachea on the body surface is guarded by a structure known as a spiracle, which can open and close. The tracheae are branched

and eventually give rise to tiny, thin-walled, blind-ended tubules known as tracheoles, where gas exchange occurs with the body tissues. No ventilatory muscles are associated with the tracheal system, and the movement of gases is simply by diffusion. Although this might seem to be an inefficient way to get oxygen to the working muscles, it works well enough with small animals such as insects. However, the largest insects may increase their ventilation by contracting and relaxing abdominal muscles, which indirectly pumps their tracheal system. Flight muscles also increase tracheal ventilation in flying insects.

Like all air breathers, terrestrial insects have the problem of loss of body water by evaporation, in this case via openings to the tracheal system. To reduce this problem, insects open their spiracles only periodically to allow fresh air in; the build-up of CO_2 in the tracheae and surrounding tissue fluids is a key stimulant for opening the spiracles.

Gas Transport: The Role of Respiratory Pigments

Animals that transport gases using a circulatory system have a **respiratory pigment** that allows much more gas to be carried than can simply dissolve in the circulating fluid. Hemoglobin is the most common respiratory pigment, but there are also others: hemerythrin, hemocyanin, and chlorocruorin. All vertebrates and certain invertebrates use hemoglobin to increase the O_2-carrying capacity of their blood.

To illustrate the advantage of respiratory pigments, we can examine the O_2-carrying capacity of human blood, which carries about 3 mL O_2/L dissolved in the plasma, but up to 200 mL/L in association with its hemoglobin content. Therefore, 98.5 percent of the O_2 is carried bound to hemoglobin and only 1.5 percent is dissolved in plasma. Animals with a high metabolic rate are especially dependent on respiratory pigments to maintain the oxygenation of their hard-working muscles.

Hemoglobin is made up of four protein subunits called globulins, each with a porphyrin ring containing iron. Because one O_2 molecule can bind to the iron in each porphyrin ring, a hemoglobin molecule can transport up to four molecules of O_2. Moreover, the binding of one molecule of O_2 facilitates the binding of others, a phenomenon known as cooperativity, although usually fewer than four molecules of O_2 are bound at any time. The effect of partial pressure of O_2 (PO_2) on the binding process and on O_2-saturation of hemoglobin is illustrated by an oxygen binding curve (or O_2 dissociation curve; **Figure 7.21**). Note that at very low PO_2, the curve is relatively slow-rising and less than 20 percent of the O_2-binding sites are occupied with O_2. At intermediate pressures there is a rapid increase in the rate of binding as cooperativity occurs and the hemoglobin loads more and more oxygen. Then at higher PO_2 the curve slowly approaches saturation, giving it a sigmoidal shape.

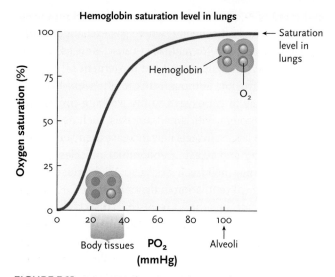

Hemoglobin saturation level in lungs

← Saturation level in lungs

Hemoglobin

O_2

Body tissues   **PO_2**   Alveoli
(mmHg)

FIGURE 7.21 Oxygen Binding Curve The curve has a similar shape for all animals that use a respiratory pigment, but the O_2-carrying capacity varies depending on the type of pigment used.

SOURCE: From RUSSELL/WOLFE/HERTZ/STARR. *Biology*, 1E. © 2010 Nelson Education Ltd. Reproduced by permission. www.cengage.com/permissions.

How does this affect the delivery of oxygen to the tissues? The typical PO_2 of tissue fluid in mammals is 4.0–5.3 kPa (30–40 mmHg), depending on the rate of O_2 consumption by aerobic metabolism in the cells. The blood that leaves the gas-exchange surface has undergone

O_2 loading and its hemoglobin is steeped with that vital gas. As the blood passes through the organs and other tissues of the body, where the PO_2 is lower, the diffusion gradient favours the movement of O_2 off the hemoglobin and into the tissues. Ultimately, 60–70 percent of the O_2 bound to hemoglobin will dissociate and move into the tissues.

COMPARATIVE ASPECTS OF RESPIRATORY PIGMENTS
Respiratory pigments differ in the amount of oxygen they can carry as well as their affinity for that gas **(Figure 7.22)**. Even animals that use hemoglobin do not necessarily show the same binding characteristics. The affinity characteristics of respiratory pigments are expressed in terms of the P_{50}, which is the partial pressure of the blood at 50 percent saturation of the pigment with O_2. The higher the affinity, the lower is the P_{50} of the pigment.

Generally, the blood P_{50} tends to be relatively low in animals that live in an O_2-poor environment, such as low-O_2 water, in an underground burrow, or at high altitude. For example, the blood P_{50} of carp (*Cyprinus carpio*) and catfish (order Siluriformes), which can live in O_2-poor water, is lower than that of trout and salmon (Salmonidae) that cannot tolerate a low-O_2 environment. The blood of carp and catfish is able to load O_2 more readily than can that of trout at low PO_2.

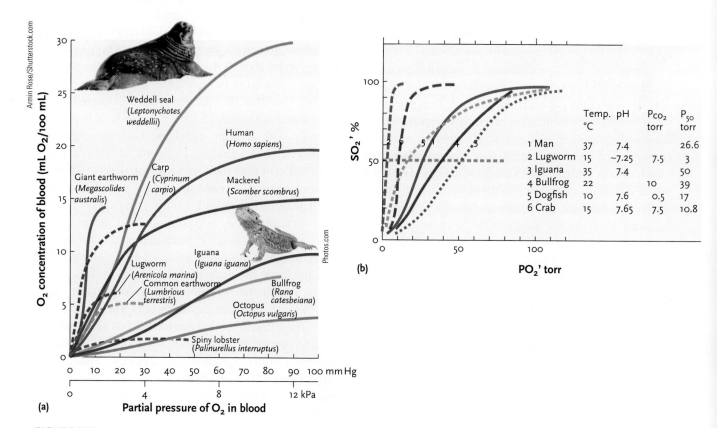

	Temp. °C	pH	Pco₂ torr	P_{50} torr
1 Man	37	7.4		26.6
2 Lugworm	15	~7.25	7.5	3
3 Iguana	35	7.4		50
4 Bullfrog	22		10	39
5 Dogfish	10	7.6	0.5	17
6 Crab	15	7.65	7.5	10.8

FIGURE 7.22 Oxygen-binding Curves of the Respiratory Pigments of Various Animals The partial pressure of O_2 at 50 percent saturation is referred to as the P_{50} of the blood. The lower the P_{50} value, the greater is the affinity for O_2.

SOURCES: (a) Hill, R.W., G.A. Wyse, and M. Anderson. 2008. *Animal Physiology*. Sinauer Associates, Sunderland, MA. (b) Dejours, P. 1975. *Principles of Comparative Respiratory Physiology*. North Holland Publishing. Amsterdam.

Conversely, there is a trend among mammals for the O_2-affinity of the respiratory pigment to decrease with diminishing body mass, that is, the blood P_{50} tends to be higher in smaller mammals regardless of environmental conditions. If the availability of O_2 is not a limiting factor for pigment saturation, then the advantage of higher blood P_{50} is a greater ease of unloading O_2 at the tissue level. Recall that smaller mammals have a higher mass-specific metabolism, which is required to maintain their body temperature. Therefore, the more efficient the unloading of O_2 is at the tissue level, the greater the ability to maintain a higher metabolic rate. In general, it is advantageous to have a lower blood P_{50} in environments where O_2 is limited, in order to saturate the respiratory pigment. In contrast, it is better to have a higher blood P_{50} in situations where O_2 is not limiting, because it helps to unload more O_2 at the tissue level.

Gas Transport and Exchange in Diving Mammals

Certain marine mammals can dive to great depths and stay submerged for a long time. The deepest dives are to astonishing depths: Cuvier's beaked whale (*Ziphius cavirostris*) has been recorded to 1885 m, elephant seal (*Mirounga angustirostris*) to 1640 m, and sperm whale (*Physeter catodon*) to 1200 m (Reynolds and Rommel, 1999; Whitehead, 2002; Tyack et al., 2006). The dive times may be as long as two hours.

PHYSIOLOGICAL FEATURES OF DIVING MAMMALS

Marine mammals that can remain deeply submerged for a long time have adaptive physiological characteristics **(Figure 7.23)**. First, their blood has a particularly large carrying capacity for oxygen. For example, the blood of the harbour seal (*Phoca vitulina*) at saturation can carry 26–29 mL of O_2/100 mL (this is known as the volume % oxygen), while that of the sperm whale is 31 volume %, and the Weddell seal (*Leptonychotes weddellii*) 29–36 volume % (Hill et al., 2008). In comparison, human blood, and that of other terrestrial mammals living at altitudes below 3000 metres, typically carries 17–22 volume % O_2. The high volume % O_2 of deep-diving mammals is partly due to a higher concentration of hemoglobin and greater density of erythrocytes in their blood.

In addition, the blood volume of some deep-diving mammals (such as Weddell seal, elephant seal, and sperm whale) is 2 to 3 times greater than that of nondiving mammals (200–250 mL/kg of body mass versus a more typical 60–110 mL/kg) (Butler and Jones, 1997; Kooyman and Ponganis, 1998). Considering both the high O_2-carrying capacity and blood volume of deep-divers, the total maximum oxygen store is about 60–85 mL O_2/kg body weight, or 4–6 times that of terrestrial mammals (14–15 mL O_2/kg).

Skeletal muscle contains a respiratory pigment known as myoglobin, which serves as an O_2-storage compound that may be used during activities that require a sustained high consumption of O_2. The concentration of myoglobin in the muscle tissue of deep-diving mammals is 55–70 mg/g muscle (wet weight), compared with 4–9 mg/g in typical mammals. Therefore, deep-diving mammals have a far superior capacity to store oxygen in their muscles.

Other physiological adaptations that aid in deep and sustained diving include the following (Kooyman and Ponganis, 1998):

- The lungs and thorax are collapsible, which prevents injury from high pressure while also decreasing buoyancy.

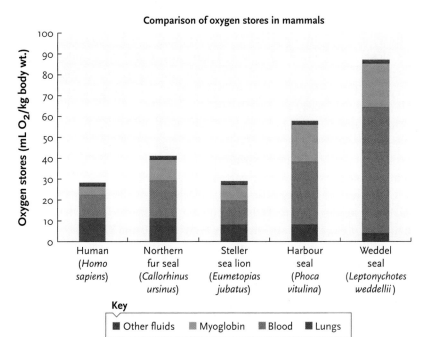

Comparison of oxygen stores in mammals

Oxygen stores (mL O_2/kg body wt.)

Human (*Homo sapiens*), Northern fur seal (*Callorhinus ursinus*), Steller sea lion (*Eumetopias jubatus*), Harbour seal (*Phoca vitulina*), Weddel seal (*Leptonychotes weddellii*)

Key
Other fluids ■ Myoglobin ■ Blood ■ Lungs

FIGURE 7.23 Comparison of Oxygen Stores in Mammals Northern fur seal (*Callorhinus ursinus*) and Steller sea lion (*Eumetopias jubatus*) dive for relatively short periods of time, while harbour seal (*Phoca vitulina*) and Weddell seal (*Leptonychotes weddellii*) dive for longer times.

SOURCES: Based on Lenfant, C, K. Johansen and J.D. Torrance. 1970. "Gas transport and oxygen storage capacity in some pinnipeds and the sea otter," *Respiration Physiology*, 9: 277–286; Ponganis, P.J., G.L. Kooyman, and M.A. Castellini. 1993. "Determinants of the aerobic dive limit of Weddel seals: Analysis of diving metabolic rate, postdive end tidal PO_2's and blood and muscle oxygen stores," *Physiological Zoology*, 66:732–749.

- Blood is shunted away from non-used muscles and visceral organs (liver, kidney, spleen, stomach, and pancreas), while the brain and heart are provided with more circulation.
- The heart rate is reduced to decrease the oxygen consumption (this is called diving bradycardia).
- During a dive, the hematocrit may increase (this is the proportion of the blood volume that is composed of erythrocytes)—the Weddell seal has a hematocrit of 38 percent on the surface, but it may increase to 52 percent during a dive. Erythrocytes are added to the blood from the spleen over a 20-minute period (during a sequence of dives), and are removed during periods of prolonged rest.

METABOLISM DURING DIVING Because oxygen is conserved for heart and brain function during diving (by shunting blood away from muscles), anaerobic (glycolytic) metabolism becomes important in muscle tissue. This leads to a large accumulation of lactic acid and CO_2 in muscle tissue and blood, but deep-diving mammals can sustain this. For example, their lactate concentration may exceed 22 mmol/L of blood, about a 40-fold increase from that at rest. In comparison, during periods of intense physical activity in a human, such as sprinting, the muscle and blood may accumulate 15 mmol/L of lactate. When a deep-diver rests on the surface, the lactic acid is metabolized, but the longer the dive, the more time it takes to remove the accumulated lactate. In fact, to avoid having to spend long periods on the surface trying to metabolize lactate, seals will choose to engage in shorter dive times so as to not exceed their "aerobic dive limit."

Acid–Base Balance

The acid–base balance in an animal refers to its physiological ability to regulate the pH of intracellular and extracellular fluids within narrow limits close to neutrality (pH 7.0). There are several reasons for this tight regulation, including the sensitivity of enzymes to changes in pH and its effect on nerve and muscle function and on transport of oxygen by hemoglobin. The pH of body fluids is largely determined by the amount of dissolved CO_2 as well as the concentrations of volatile (or fixed) organic acids (such as lactic and keto acids). Carbonic acid, formed from the hydration of CO_2 (i.e., $CO_2 + H_2O \leftrightarrow H_2CO_3$), is considered a volatile acid because its concentration varies depending on the rate of CO_2 loss across the gas-exchange surface (lung or gill) as well as its production by metabolism. The greater the rate of ventilation of the gas-exchange surface, the more CO_2 is removed from the body and the lower the concentration of H_2CO_3 in body fluids. Organic acids are produced during metabolism and are considered nonvolatile because they are not affected by gas exchange with the environment.

A lowering of the pH of body fluids to below the normal range is called an **acidosis**, and an increase of pH is **alkalosis**. The normal pH range mostly depends on the temperature of the animal and its metabolic rate. Disruptions of the acid–base balance are classified according to the source of the excess acid or base. Those caused by the addition or removal of CO_2 in the blood are referred to as **respiratory disturbances** (or **disorders**). Those caused by the addition of fixed acids or bases to the blood are called **metabolic disturbances** (or **disorders**). The addition of a fixed acid results in a reduction in the concentration of bicarbonate (HCO_3^-) in the blood, since the HCO_3^- is consumed as it neutralizes the H^+ (the reaction is: $H^+ + HCO_3^- \leftrightarrow H_2CO_3$). Therefore, metabolic disturbances of the acid–base balance are sometimes characterized by changes in the blood HCO_3^- concentration by means other than those in ventilation.

If the production of CO_2 exceeds the rate at which it is removed by ventilation, a **respiratory acidosis** is generated. Conversely, if the rate of ventilation is such that CO_2 removal exceeds its rate of production, a **respiratory alkalosis** results. A metabolic acidosis is generated when fixed acids are added to the blood, and a metabolic alkalosis is caused by the addition of a base (or alkali) to that fluid.

pH and Temperature

The pH of neutrality is defined as the pH of "pure" water, which is neither acidic nor basic—it has a neutral pH of 7.0 because the concentration of H^+ is equal to that of OH^- (both have an identical concentration of 10^{-7} moles/L). Note, however, that this refers to distilled water that has not had contact with the atmosphere, so there is no dissolved CO_2 (if distilled water is in equilibrium with atmospheric CO_2 at 390 ppm, the resulting carbonic acid equilibrium would generate a pH of about 5.6). In addition, the pH of neutrality varies slightly with temperature—it rises above 7.0 at temperatures below 25°C and it falls above 25°C. Consequently, the pH of intracellular and extracellular fluids of animals is affected by their body temperature **(Figure 7.24)**. Ectotherms living in cooler environments tend to have a higher blood pH than those at warmer temperatures.

Regardless of the temperature, the normal blood pH of animals is slightly more alkaline than the pH of neutrality—typically between 7.40 and 7.80 depending on whether the animal is air-breathing or water-breathing. A typical arterial blood pH of a trout at 15°C is 7.7, while that of an air-breathing mammal is 7.4 (body temperature 37°C). This is mainly due to the presence of **buffers** in the blood and intracellular fluid. Buffers are chemicals that cause the pH to remain at a particular value.

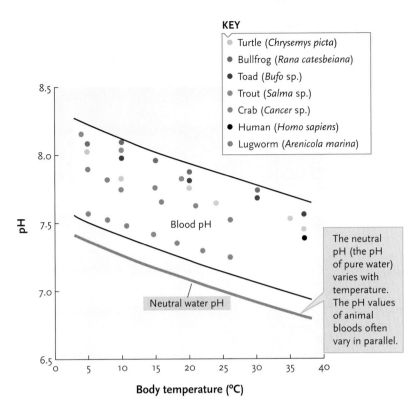

FIGURE 7.24 Effect of Temperature on the pH of Water and Extracellular Fluid in a Variety of Animals There is an inverse relationship between body temperature and the pH of extracellular fluids. Pure water shows a similar effect. Note that the extracellular fluid is slightly more alkaline than water at all temperatures.

SOURCE: Dejours, P. 1975. *Principles of Comparative Respiratory Physiology.* North Holland Publishing. Amsterdam.

Regulation of Acid–Base Status

There are three lines of physiological defence against changes in the acid–base status of an animal. They are (1) buffers, (2) control of ventilation of the gas-exchange surface, and (3) regulation of acid excretion and bicarbonate reabsorption by the renal organ.

Strong acids are readily buffered by proteins, such as hemoglobin, which occur in the intracellular or extracellular fluids, and by HCO_3^-, which combines with H^+ to form H_2CO_3, a weak acid. These buffers do not necessarily prevent changes in blood pH, but they do reduce the amount of the change.

A change in the blood pH or Pco_2 can stimulate changes in ventilation of the gas-exchange surface. Chemoreceptors located in the cardiovascular system can detect changes in blood pH and Pco_2. This information is relayed to the control centre in the brain for ventilation, resulting in an adjustment in its rate. Additionally, in mammals, the pH of the cerebral spinal fluid is sensitive to changes in blood Pco_2. An increase in the Pco_2 of the blood results in diffusion of CO_2 into the spinal fluid, where it combines with water to form H^+ and HCO_3^-. Chemoreceptors in the brain detect the drop in pH and stimulate ventilation. The normal response to an acidosis, therefore, is an increase in ventilation, which lowers the blood Pco_2 and drives the pH to a more alkaline condition. Decreasing the CO_2 drives the reaction to the left, thereby reducing the H^+ concentration (and so raising the pH). Alkalosis is dealt with in the opposite way—as the pH rises or Pco_2 falls, ventilation is reduced, resulting in an accumulation of H^+ and lowering of the pH.

Although control of ventilation is a rapid way of correcting an acid–base disruption, it cannot always return the balance to normal. However, the renal organ can also help to correct an acid–base disturbance, although the changes take place more slowly **(Figure 7.25)**. The tubules of the renal organ can excrete acids and increase the rate of HCO_3^- reabsorption to compensate for an acidosis, or reduce the H^+ excretion and HCO_3^- reabsorption to compensate for an alkalosis.

Effects of Environmental Acidification

Large regions of Canada and extensive areas of other countries have suffered from an acidification of surface waters and sometimes also of soil. These environmental damages are often caused by the deposition of acidifying substances from the atmosphere by the following mechanisms:

- acidic precipitation (acidic rain and snow);
- the dry deposition (or direct uptake) of gaseous sulphur dioxide (SO_2), which generates acidity when it becomes oxidized to sulphate (SO_4^{-2}) in the receiving ecosystem—because the SO_4^{-2} is electrochemically balanced by H^+, acidity is generated; and
- the dry deposition of gaseous oxides of nitrogen (NO_x, composed of NO and NO_2), which becomes oxidized to nitrate (NO_3^-) that is electrochemically balanced by H^+.

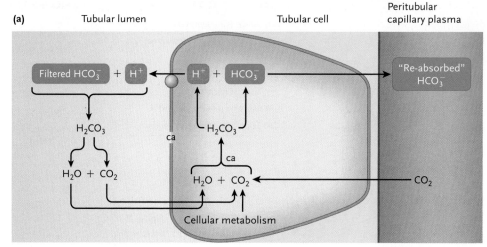

FIGURE 7.25 H⁺ Excretion and HCO₃⁻ Reabsorption by Renal Tubules Some of the H⁺ secreted by the renal tubules is used in the reabsorption of HCO₃⁻, and other secreted H⁺ is trapped in the form of monobasic phosphate. In the process, a new molecule of HCO₃⁻ is added to the bloodstream.

SOURCE: From SHERWOOD. *Human Physiology*, 1E. © 2010 Nelson Education Ltd. Reproduced by permission. www.cengage.com/permissions.

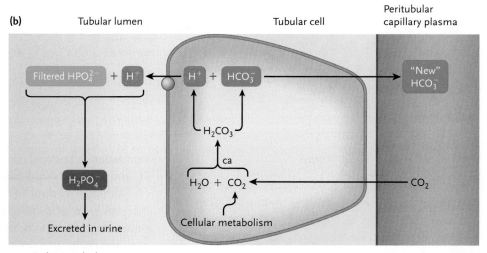

Surface waters (lakes, rivers, and streams) are vulnerable to acidification if they have a low concentration of calcium (Ca^{2+}; this ion is mostly derived from calcium carbonate, $CaCO_3$, in bedrock and soil of the watershed; Section 4.7). The importance of the Ca^{2+} is in its relationship with alkalinity (HCO_3^-) in the water, which is the key source of acid-neutralizing capacity (ANC) in fresh waters—if the concentration of Ca^{2+} is high, so will be the alkalinity and ANC, and there is much greater resistance to becoming acidified.

Calcium is also important in protecting aquatic animals from acid-induced loss of ions from their body fluids. Species living in low-calcium water, therefore, are more susceptible to acid stress (low-Ca water is sometimes called "soft," while high-Ca is "hard" water). In addition, acidification results in metals dissolving from minerals in soil and sediment, causing them to occur in high ionic concentrations in surface waters. In terms of causing toxicity to aquatic animals, the most important of the ionic metals is aluminum, occurring in the form of Al^{3+}. Chris Wood (McMaster University) and Gordon MacDonald (Guelph University) have studied the

physiological effects of acidification on fish (Wood and McDonald, 1982; Wood and Rogano, 1986; Wood, 1989). Wood and his students were the first to identify cardiovascular collapse as the immediate cause of death in fish living in highly acidic waters. That finding has been important in understanding the global problem of acid rain, as well as its mitigation.

Strangely enough, acidification of soft water does not result in an acidosis in fish, but instead it causes a major loss of key cations across the gills, such as Na^+ and Cl^-. In hardwater lakes, cation loss is not as large a problem, but aquatic animals may experience a metabolic acidosis. In either situation, the Na^+ loss occurs partly because of an inability to exchange Na^+ for H^+ across the gills. Normally, H^+ is moved into the environment in exchange for Na^+ uptake in a 1:1 ratio, but in acidified water the H^+ gradient is too great and the exchange is significantly reduced. As mentioned in the previous section on ionoregulation, freshwater animals face the problem of ion loss by diffusion to the environment because their body-fluid ion concentrations are so much greater than that of the water in which they live. Therefore, continued ion leakage to the environment, coupled with a reduction in uptake, results in steady ion depletion and is a cause of death in fish in acidified soft waters (toxicity from Al^{3+} ions is also important).

Calcium seems to help protect the gills of fish and aquatic invertebrates against ion loss, and as a result many animals in hard waters can recover from acid exposure once the metabolic acidosis has been compensated. However, the low-Ca concentrations of soft water offer no such protection and upward of 30 percent ion loss is normally lethal to aquatic animals. The actual cause of death is likely due to circulatory failure. Dilution of the extracellular fluid because of the ion loss results in water movement into the intracellular fluid, which reduces the circulating blood volume and raises its viscosity. In addition, the erythrocytes tend to swell due to the movement of water into those cells from the blood plasma. The combination of increased blood viscosity and red blood cells swelling greatly increases stress on the heart, and that vital organ may fail.

The increased solubility of metals such as Al^{3+} at low pH (<5.5) adds to the problems faced by aquatic animals in soft-water conditions. Aluminum may accumulate on the surface of gills as a diffuse precipitate (or flocculate) of $Al(OH)_3$, which may cause an inflammatory response that thickens and distorts the lamellae and results in a mucous accumulation on the gill surface. This greatly reduces the ability to exchange gases with the environment, and results in both hypoxia (low O_2) and hypercapnia (high CO_2). Coupled with the ion losses, the hypoxia and hypercapnia may prove fatal to fish in acidified waters and can contribute to their populations becoming extirpated.

7.4 Physiological Ecology of Plants

Like animals, plants must be able to take advantage of the opportunities presented by their environment, while at the same time dealing with disturbances and other stressors. In this section, we examine the basic ecophysiological strategies that plants use to cope with changes in temperature and water availability, including the roles of several photosynthetic systems. We also examine how plant hormones affect development and anatomy, and how secondary compounds protect against herbivory and other stressors. While some aspects of plant ecophysiology are rather similar to that of animals, the stationery nature of plants has led to some remarkable adaptations that enhance their fitness and survival.

Photosynthesis

The energetic basis of almost all life is the fixation of carbon through photosynthesis (Chapter 3). According to Albert Szent-Györgyi (1960), 1937 Nobel Laureate in Physiology: "What drives life is thus a little electric current, set up by the sunshine. All the complexities of intermediary metabolism are but the lacework around this basic fact." With photosynthesis playing such a vital role in life and ecosystems, a central aspect of plant ecophysiology is the study of various adaptations that have evolved to perform this function in different kinds of species and environments.

In photosynthesis, a leaf receives sunlight and absorbs photons from specific wavelengths of its spectrum. The key absorbing pigment is chlorophyll, which is highly absorptive of red and blue wavelengths, the energy of which is used to drive photosynthesis. At the same time, chlorophyll is reflective of green light, which is the reason foliage is that colour: in other words, green light is not absorbed by leaves. There are also a number of secondary pigments that absorb photons, such as yellow carotenes and red anthocyanins, but these are much less prominent in determining leaf colour. The chlorophyll and secondary pigments occur within specialized organelles within cells called chloroplasts, which is where photosynthesis occurs. The basic chemical equation for photosynthesis is:

$$Sunlight + 6\ CO_2 + 6\ H_2O \rightarrow C_6H_{12}O_6 + 6\ O_2$$

There are two stages of the photosynthetic reaction. The first is a **light-dependent reaction** in which photons absorbed by chlorophyll and other pigments cause those molecules to become "excited" (this happens in the thylakoid membranes, present in stacks known as grana in the chloroplasts). This is followed by **dark reactions** in which the absorbed energy is transferred in the form of electrons to various molecules, eventually producing six-carbon sugars (this occurs in the stroma, or fluid matrix surrounding the grana).

The basic dark-reaction pathway is the Calvin or C3 Cycle, so-named because its initial product is 3-phosphoglycerate (or PGA). A subsequent reaction produces glyceraldehyde-3-phosphate (or G3P), a three-carbon sugar-phosphate molecule that enters a range of pathways that synthesize 6-carbon sugar molecules, such as glucose, along with starches and other products.

C3 Photosynthesis

Most plants have C3 photosynthesis, especially species of temperate, boreal, and arctic ecosystems. However, as we examine in the following section, two additional photosynthetic pathways are used by plants that are adapted to hotter and drier environments, in which the C3 physiology is somewhat inefficient, especially in terms of the water balance.

The dark reactions of C3 photosynthesis take place in the chloroplasts of plant cells **(Figure 7.26)**. In those organelles, carbon is reduced in a series of steps that

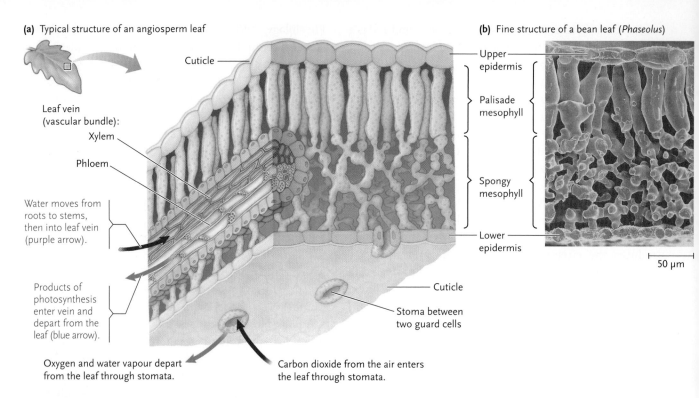

(a) Typical structure of an angiosperm leaf

(b) Fine structure of a bean leaf (*Phaseolus*)

Cuticle

Leaf vein (vascular bundle):

Xylem

Phloem

Water moves from roots to stems, then into leaf vein (purple arrow).

Products of photosynthesis enter vein and depart from the leaf (blue arrow).

Oxygen and water vapour depart from the leaf through stomata.

Carbon dioxide from the air enters the leaf through stomata.

Upper epidermis

Palisade mesophyll

Spongy mesophyll

Lower epidermis

Cuticle

Stoma between two guard cells

50 μm

FIGURE 7.26 Gas Exchange and Leaf Anatomy The internal structure of a leaf provides an anatomical system that allows carbon dioxide to enter and reach the surfaces necessary for gas exchange and water loss. (a) Diagram of a typical leaf structure for many kinds of flowering plants. (b) Scanning electron micrograph of tissue from the leaf of a kidney bean plant (*Phaseolus*), transverse section. Notice the compact organization of epidermal cells.

SOURCE: (a) From RUSSELL/WOLFE/HERTZ/STARR. *Biology*, 1E. © 2010 Nelson Education Ltd. Reproduced by permission. www.cengage.com/permissions (b) With kind permission from Springer Science+Business Media: Planta, "Water droplets and ice deposits in leaf intercellular spaces: redistribution of water during cryofixation for scanning electron microscopy," vol. 172 (1):20-37, C.E. Jeffree, et al, 1987.

convert it from CO_2 to a component of an organic molecule. A key compound in this reaction is a five-carbon sugar with two phosphate groups, called ribulose 1,5-bisphosphate (RuBP). RuBP is present at both the beginning and end of the dark reactions, because the steps leading to carbon fixation form a cycle, named the Calvin cycle after Melvin Calvin, who first described it and for that accomplishment received a Nobel Prize in 1961. Glyceraldehyde 3-phosphate (or G3P) is a three-carbon sugar-phosphate molecule that is produced by three turns of the Calvin cycle. Most of the G3P molecules are exported from the chloroplast to the cytoplasmic matrix (or cytosol) of the cell, within which the nucleus and organelles are suspended, where it is converted to sucrose, a six-carbon sugar.

The first step of the dark reaction is the process of carbon fixation. As long as enough CO_2 molecules are available, molecules of RuBP are carboxylated by the enzyme ribulose bisphosphate carboxylase (or Rubisco; this may be the most abundant protein and enzyme in the biosphere; Cooper 2000). However, Rubisco is not only a carboxylase enzyme, but also an oxygenase, meaning that it acts in both ways—in the presence of O_2 as well as CO_2.

The resulting competition between O_2 and CO_2 for Rubisco alters the first step of the Calvin cycle, which should produce two molecules of 3-phosphoglycerate

(PGA) from RuBP. Instead, the cycle does something different **(Figure 7.27)**. Only one molecule of PGA and one molecule of phosphoglycolate are produced, which then follow a metabolic pathway in which CO_2 is eventually given off, in a process known as **photorespiration**. In some plants, up to half of the CO_2 that is initially fixed by the dark reactions is lost through photorespiration. The process is favoured under conditions that cause O_2 to accumulate in plant leaves, such as when it is hot and dry, which causes the stomata to close to reduce water loss.

Although photorespiration is energetically wasteful, it is required in order to remove excess phosphoglycolate, which can be toxic.

C4 and CAM Photosynthesis

Plants have evolved additional means of reducing their losses of fixed carbon, through alternate photosynthetic pathways. In the systems called C4 and CAM photosynthesis, there is a temporal and spatial separation of different steps in photosynthesis **(Figure 7.27** and **Table 7.6)**.

In C4 photosynthesis, oxaloacetate, a 4-carbon molecule, is the first product, rather than PGA (a 3-carbon molecule). The enzyme phosphoenolpyruvate carboxylase (PEP carboxylase), rather than Rubisco, catalyzes the photosynthetic reaction, in which CO_2 is fixed to

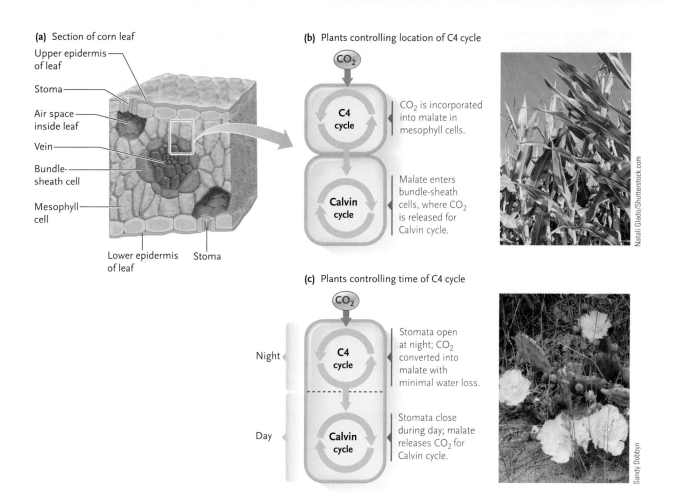

(a) Section of corn leaf

Upper epidermis of leaf
Stoma
Air space inside leaf
Vein
Bundle-sheath cell
Mesophyll cell

Lower epidermis of leaf   Stoma

(b) Plants controlling location of C4 cycle

CO₂

C4 cycle

CO₂ is incorporated into malate in mesophyll cells.

Calvin cycle

Malate enters bundle-sheath cells, where CO₂ is released for Calvin cycle.

Natali Glado/Shutterstock.com

(c) Plants controlling time of C4 cycle

CO₂

Night

C4 cycle

Stomata open at night; CO₂ converted into malate with minimal water loss.

Day

Calvin cycle

Stomata close during day; malate releases CO₂ for Calvin cycle.

Sandy Dobbyn

FIGURE 7.27 Variations on the Basic Photosynthetic Pathway (a) Shows the physical separation involved in the C4 photosynthetic cycle. In the first phase, carbon is initially fixed as the molecule oxaloacetate. (b) In a second step, the oxaloacetate may be converted to either malate or aspartate, and these molecules concentrate in bundle sheath cells where they are decarboxylated and eventually incorporated into the Calvin cycle. (c) By contrast, in the CAM cycle, carbon is fixed in the same location in the plant cell, and the C4 cycle operates at night, and the Calvin cycle during the day.

SOURCE: From RUSSELL/WOLFE/HERTZ/STARR. *Biology*, 1E. © 2010 Nelson Education Ltd. Reproduced by permission. www.cengage.com/permissions

TABLE 7.6 | **Key Characteristics of Basic Photosynthetic Pathways**

Photosynthetic Pathway	Name	First Product	Location	Time
C3	Calvin cycle	3-Phosphoglycerate	Mesophyll cells	Daylight
C4	Hatch-Slack pathway	Oxaloacetate	Mesophyll cells	Daylight
C4	Calvin cycle	3-Phosphoglycerate	Bundle sheath cells	Daylight
CAM	Hatch-Slack pathway	Oxaloacetate	Mesophyll cells	Night
CAM	Calvin cycle	3-Phosphoglycerate	Mesophyll cells	Daylight

SOURCES: Based on Evert & Eichhorn. 2013. *Raven Plant Biology*, 8th edition Freeman and Mooney, H.A., Chapter 11 on Photosynthesis in Crawley, MJ (ed) 1986 Plant Ecology pp 345–373.

phosphoenolpyruvate (PEP). This means of carbon fixation is called the C4 or Hatch-Slack pathway, named after two Australian physiologists who first determined the pathway.

Plants that fix carbon via both the Calvin (C3) cycle and the Hatch-Slack pathway are known as C4 plants. Unlike plants that use only the Calvin cycle for

photosynthesis, in which reactions occur in the leaf mesophyll cells, in C4 plants the C4 pathway occurs in the mesophyll and the C3 reactions in specialized bundle-sheath cells located around the foliar vascular tissue (the xylem and phloem). In addition, the Calvin cycle in C4 plants uses CO₂ molecules derived from the Hatch-Slack pathway.

In C4 plants, the spatial separation of photosynthetic stages C4 and C3 reduces the amount of photorespiration, which represents a gain of efficiency. At the same time, however, photosynthesis in C4 plants is energetically more costly compared with that in C3 plants. This is because C4 plants require five ATP molecules (these are units of energy currency) to fix one molecule of CO_2 (to PGA), while only three ATPs are required for this fixation in C3 plants. Nevertheless, there is a net benefit to C4 plants from the reduction of photorespiration, which occurs because the movement of CO_2 molecules to the bundle-sheath cells maintains high levels of that gas compared with O_2. Under these conditions, the enzyme Rubisco acts as a carboxylase and not as an oxygenase.

Crassulacean acid metabolism, or CAM photosynthesis, represents yet a different separation of photosynthetic steps, in which carbon is fixed in the dark. This photosynthetic system occurs in many tropical and subtropical species, such as in the families Cactaceae (cacti), Crassulaceae (succulents), and Bromeliaceae (bromeliads) **(Figure 7.27).**

Unlike C4 plants, the various steps in CAM photosynthesis all take place in the mesophyll leaf and stem cells, similar to C3 plants. The same enzyme as in the C4 pathway, PEP carboxylase, is involved, and it produces the same 4-carbon molecule, oxaloacetate, but this happens in the dark, at night. Immediately on formation at night, the oxaloacetate is reduced to malate, which is stored in large cellular vacuoles until the next morning, when it is light again. The malate accumulation in the large vacuoles in mesophyll cells of CAM plants gives the tissues a thick, succulent anatomy.

When it is light again the CO_2 is released from malate through decarboxylation. The CO_2 then enters the Calvin cycle, and produces the RuBP molecule of step one. This C3 cycle occurs in the same cells as the PEP carboxylase activity of the previous night. PEP carboxylase, present in C4 and CAM photosynthesis, has a greater activity at low CO_2 concentrations than does Rubisco. The functional outcome of PEP carboxylase activity is to concentrate CO_2 and increase carbon fixation by Rubisco.

In CAM plants, photosynthesis relies on CO_2 that enters the leaves through stomata that open at night. However, the CO_2 is stored overnight in malate, and is not fixed in photosynthesis until the following day. Because the CO_2 is liberated from compounds that are already inside the leaf, the stomata can be closed during the day, which is a water-conserving tactic for plants living in hot and dry environments. This is the principal advantage of CAM metabolism.

Both CAM and C4 plants are well adapted to high light intensities, hot temperatures, and drought. These photosynthetic systems both occur in various plant families and are thought to have evolved on numerous occasions from the C3 pathway (Ehleringer and Monson, 1993).

For instance, the grass family Poaceae has many C3 species, but also many of hot climates that are C4, such as maize (*Zea mays*) and crabgrass (*Digitaria* spp.). In a mixed-species Canadian lawn, the difference between C3 and C4 grasses becomes obvious when temperatures rise and drought increases over the summer and plants become increasingly stressed. The patches of bright green in the lawn are often hairy crabgrass (*Digitaria sanguinalis*), which continues to photosynthesize under the hot and dry conditions, while C3 species such as bluegrass (*Poa pratensis*) wither.

C3 plants are more competitive than C4 plants at cooler temperatures. However, as predicted climate warming occurs, C4 and CAM plants are expected to migrate northward and become increasingly prominent in Canadian habitats. Nevertheless, Rowan Sage (2004), an ecophysiologist at the University of Toronto, has pointed out that many C3 species also grow in arid zones, alongside C4 plants. He suggests that C4 photosynthesis should be viewed as an adaption that compensates for high levels of photorespiration and carbon deficiency, rather than as an adaption to hot and dry conditions.

So what are the likely implications of climate warming for plants in Canada? Most species in the boreal forest have C3 photosynthesis, including the dominant trees, such as black spruce (*Picea mariana*). Way and Sage (2008) examined photosynthesis in seedlings of that species growing under lower and higher temperature experimental conditions. They found that seedlings of black spruce have some ability to acclimate to warmer temperatures, with net photosynthesis increasing and respiration showing an especially large response. Nevertheless, black spruce does not perform well during growing seasons that are unusually hot and dry, which suggests that it may be vulnerable to predicted climate warming.

Many crops grown in Canada are C3 species, but it has proven hard to generalize about the likely effects of climate change on them. Some species will respond positively to increased CO_2 concentrations, although field research of crop responses to higher CO_2 has found lower than expected yields (Long et al., 2006). However, most C3 crop species are likely to suffer if the predictions of intensified droughts and high temperatures occur in some regions (Minorsky, 2002). Although C4 crops are generally expected to be favoured in warmer and drier climates, many of the specifics are not known and so there may be risks to food security (Tubiello et al., 2007).

Water Balance

Plants are mainly composed of water, which makes up 80–95 percent of the "fresh" biomass of foliage and flowers, and about half that of woody tissues such as the trunks and branches of trees (Lambers et al., 1998). In particular, water is an essential part of the protoplasm,

Diane Srivastava: Scaling Up from Miniature Food Webs to Global Biodiversity

Photography by T. Zulkoskey

FIGURE 1 Diane Srivastava

Diane Srivastava is a Canadian ecologist who addresses big questions by conducting experiments in miniature ecosystems **(Figure 1)**. Based at the University of British Columbia in Vancouver, Srivastava and her students use tiny but natural ecosystems—such as aquatic habitats present in the leaf rosettes of bromeliads **(Figure 2)** or in treeholes, or the communities of mites in moss patches—as locations for experiments that examine how food webs work. Although the research is done at a small scale, it yields theoretical insights that can be transferred to larger ecoscapes where comparable experiments are not possible for logistical or ethical reasons (for instance, it would be extremely controversial to conduct an experiment in which wolves or orcas were removed from a large-scale food web).

Tropical bromeliads are one such miniature ecosystem, because many species impound pools of water among their leaves. This provides a microhabitat for a food web of aquatic animals, dominated by insects and microbes and fuelled by exogenous detritus that falls into the bromeliad. In research done in Costa Rica, Srivastava has tracked how the physiological constraints of a keystone predator, a damselfly larva, affect the functioning of the food web. Unlike their fast-developing prey of detritivores, the damselflies require months to reach maturity and so are restricted to larger bromeliads that rarely dry out. Bromeliads with damselflies present have fewer of the prey detritivores, and thus less organic detritus is consumed and respired as CO_2. In addition, detrital nitrogen is incorporated

Photo courtesy of D. Srivastava

FIGURE 2 The Bromeliad (*Werauhia sanguinolenta*) This tropical epiphytic plant from Costa Rica forms pools of water at its leaf bases that provide aquatic microhabitats. These can be studied as miniature ecosystems and experimentally manipulated to examine hypotheses related to food webs.

into the bodies of detritivores, but then lost from the bromeliad ecosystem when the aquatic larvae transform into terrestrial adults. By consuming detritivores before they emerge, damselflies keep much of the detrital nitrogen within the aquatic ecosystem, where it can be slowly absorbed by the bromeliad.

Changing regimes of precipitation in the humid tropics may result in altered distributions of drought-sensitive species such as this damselfly, as well as the bromeliads, and thereby cause shifts in ecosystem functioning to occur. Srivastava is leading an international consortium that is studying the effects of climate change on bromeliad ecosystems throughout South and Central America.

Srivastava has also been part of global networks that use simulation models and **meta-analyses** (the latter involves mathematical analysis of results from many different studies in various parts of the world) that examine how losses of biodiversity affect ecosystem services, including those important to

the human economy. The integration of approaches, from small-scale experiments to large-scale synthesis, is a signature of her research. In 2010, she was awarded a prestigious NSERC Steacie Memorial Fellowship in recognition of her contributions.

Srivastava's interest in ecology was sparked when, as an undergraduate at Dalhousie University, she became engaged in research on lakes. Her MSc (University of Toronto) demonstrated how overgrazing by abundant snow geese on saltmarshes fringing Hudson Bay, coupled with physiological constraints in their forage plants, caused a collapse of the ecosystem. Her PhD (Imperial College at Silwood Park, UK) used aquatic insects in treeholes to examine the interplay of ecological and biogeographic limits to species diversity. Like most academic ecologists, Srivastava's career started at a smaller scale and then built to a much larger and influential one, which in her unique case also parallels the kinds of research that she and her students are now doing.

the living part of cells, where it provides a vital matrix into which biochemical and inorganic compounds can be dissolved or otherwise mobilized for transport within the cell or throughout the organism. Water also plays a role in many of the metabolic reactions that go on in cells. For instance, H_2O and CO_2 are combined during photosynthesis to produce glucose ($C_6H_{12}O_6$), a simple sugar. In the reverse process of respiration, organic molecules are oxidized and the ultimate "wastes" of those reactions include H_2O and CO_2.

Within a plant, water plays a role similar to that of blood in animals: it circulates and transports gases and solutes that are raw materials for growth and reproduction. Water does this within cells, among others located in close proximity, and also over longer distances within the plant—in the tallest trees this distance is more than 100 m from soil to the highest foliage. Water also transports the **phytohormones** that regulate growth and development (plant hormones are examined in a later section).

Finally, the hydrostatic pressure of water within cells (called turgor) plays a key role in holding plants upright. This is especially true of herbaceous plants, which lack the rigid woody tissues of shrubs and trees. When plants such as sunflowers and grasses suffer from extreme drought, they develop floppy (or wilted) leaves and stems as a response to desiccation **(Figure 7.28)**. If they have not dried out too excessively, meaning they have not passed the **permanent wilting point**, the dehydrated tissues can recover if watered. However, if that "point of no return" has been exceeded, then the wilting is lethal for affected leaves and stems, and often for the entire plant, which may become so weakened physically that it falls to the ground. Hydrostatic pressure is less necessary to keep trees and shrubs erect, because even during a severe drought they will continue standing because of the strength of their woody tissues, although their foliage may have been weakened or killed by wilting.

Plant cells have a rigid cell wall, which is lacking in animal cells and is an important difference between these groups of organisms. Because plant cells accumulate and concentrate soluble inorganic salts, sugars, organic acids, and amino acids within their protoplasm, there is an osmotic gradient between the aqueous solutions inside and outside their bounds. This results in water being spontaneously absorbed into the cell by osmosis. Because the cell wall is rigid, there is a build-up of hydrostatic pressure as a result of the accumulation of water within the plasma membrane. In addition, as leaves age there is a further strengthening of the cell wall with compounds such as lignin, so that older foliage is less vulnerable to wilting.

FIGURE 7.28 Wilting Occurs When Dehydration Results in a Loss of Turgor Pressure in Leaves or Stems The permanent wilting point represents dehydration that is so severe that the tissues cannot recover when watered. These images compare well-hydrated and wilted foliage of the tulip tree (*Liriodendron tulipifera*), a species in the Magnolia family that occurs in southwestern Ontario.

Plant cells are able to maintain turgor because their interior is an environment with a relatively high osmotic strength due to large concentrations of dissolved solutes in their vacuoles (this is related to water potential, which is explained below). As a plant cell absorbs water by osmosis, the internal hydrostatic pressure increases, and the membrane pushes against the enclosing cell wall, creating a force known as turgor. In contrast, if a cell loses water, perhaps because of drought, the loss of turgor can result in wilting, a potentially lethal effect.

How Much Water Is Needed?

Plants need a lot of water and they are constantly absorbing it through their roots and transporting it to their aerial parts, especially to the leaves, where it is evaporated to the atmosphere by transpiration. In fact, only 1–3 percent of absorbed water is typically retained in plant tissues, which is far different from the more than 90 percent retention of absorbed nitrogen, phosphorus, and potassium (Lambers et al., 1998).

The reason for the enormous flow-through of water in plants is related to their need to take in the atmospheric CO_2 needed for photosynthesis, and also to the strong water-concentration gradient that exists between the inside and the outside of leaves. The CO_2 absorption occurs at the moist surface of foliar cells known as mesophyll, which is located in a space beneath tiny pores in their leaves called **stomata** (the singular is stoma; **Figure 7.29**). However, those mesophyll surfaces also freely evaporate water to the sub-stomatal cavity, which then diffuses into the atmosphere through open stomata.

Therefore, there is a trade-off between adaptations related to (1) the vital need to absorb CO_2 for photosynthesis, and (2) the need to conserve H_2O, especially when its availability is limited. To the degree possible, plants manage this conflict by reducing or closing their stomata to conserve water during times of drought, and also at night when photosynthesis does not occur (except in CAM plants, as we examined previously). However, this is an imperfect solution and leaves and even entire plants may die of desiccation during an extended drought.

Measuring Water Content

The water content of a plant tissue is measured as its weight as sampled in the field (i.e., its "fresh weight" or FW), divided by the dry weight (DW, after drying in an oven at 95°C). Of course, the water content of plants growing in the field varies greatly depending on such factors as how moist the soil is and the rate of transpiration, which is greatly affected by temperature and winds. Plant ecophysiologists may accommodate these variations of fresh weight by expressing the water content on the basis of the saturated weight (SW) of fully hydrated tissue, as follows:

Relative Water Content (RWC) = [(FW − DW)

$$\div \ (SW − DW)] \times 100$$

Many kinds of plants have been measured for their relative water content. Under well-watered conditions, the RWC is close to 100 percent, but it is less than that during sunny days because of losses through transpiration. For drought-susceptible plants such as most annual and biennial species (such as lettuce), the RWC can quickly decline to lethal values during prolonged dry conditions. However, some species are tolerant of drought and can maintain their RWC at viable levels even during times of extreme water scarcity. Loik and Nobel (1993) studied the prickly-pear cactus (*Opuntia fragilis*) over a wide range from Peace River, Alberta, south to Albuquerque, New Mexico, and found that the plants typically had a RWC of

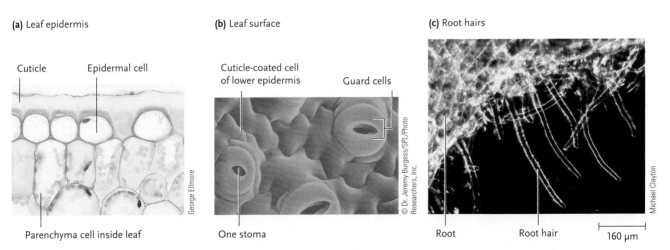

(a) Leaf epidermis

Cuticle   Epidermal cell

Parenchyma cell inside leaf

George Ellmore

(b) Leaf surface

Cuticle-coated cell of lower epidermis   Guard cells

One stoma

© Dr. Jeremy Burgess/SPL/Photo Researchers, Inc.

(c) Root hairs

Root   Root hair   160 µm

Michael Clayton

FIGURE 7.29 Structure and Examples of Epidermal Tissue (a) Cross-section of leaf epidermis from a bush lily (*Clivia miniata*). (b) Scanning electron micrograph of a leaf surface, showing cuticle-covered epidermal cells and stomata. (c) Root hairs, an epidermal specialization.

48 to 63 percent, but that declined to about 34 percent during the dry and cold conditions of winter.

Water Potential

Water potential is the potential energy of a sample of water per unit volume, relative to that of pure water in reference conditions (the latter refers to distilled water with no dissolved substances and at one atmospheric pressure and 20°C). Water moves along gradients from high to low potential. The gradients may result from differences in

- osmotic strength: if two solutions have different concentrations of dissolved substances they differ in osmolarity, and if they are separated by a water-permeable membrane then water will move from the higher to the lower until there is no longer a gradient of water potential;
- gravity: if a pathway exists, water will spontaneously move from an elevated position to one lower down, as when streamwater flows from the top to the bottom of a watershed, and then onward to the ocean if a conduit (such as a river) is present;
- mechanical pressure: if a bag filled with water is squeezed, the water potential increases and will result in an outward flow if there is a channel; and
- surface tension: as we examine below, this can produce lifting forces in small capillaries.

Water potential is usually expressed in pascals (Pa), and it is measured as the amount of pressure that is required to stop the movement of water by exerting a comparable but opposite hydrostatic pressure.

Ecophysiologists use the concept of water potential to predict how water will move in a plant. Gradients of the partial pressure of water vapour, and capillary action, play key roles in this water movement.

From Roots to Stomata

The vascular system of plants consists of two specialized tissues: (1) the xylem that transports water and inorganic nutrients absorbed by roots from the soil upward to the leaves, and (2) the phloem that transports food (photosynthate dissolved in water) from leaves to other parts of the plant. The upward flow in the xylem happens mostly during the day, and it involves a "pumping" system that has no moving parts and is based on capillarity.

The concept of capillary action is often demonstrated using a fine-diameter (about 1 mm) glass tube that, if inserted into a beaker of water, will draw some of the liquid upward against the force of gravity. The capillary forces are due to the formation of a curved meniscus all around the junction of the water and the hydrophilic ("water-loving") surface of the glass tube. The curved meniscus exerts an upward force because of an intensification of the local surface tension (an attractive force that exists among water molecules). Because the tube has such a small diameter, the meniscus occupies a large fraction of its cross-sectional surface, and this is sufficient to raise a column of water—the smaller the diameter, the higher the column is raised against the downward force of gravity.

In essence, plants raise water upward using a comparable physical system—their xylem consists of multitudinous long and thin hydrophilic tubes that form a continuous water column that reaches all the way from their roots to the surface of the mesophyll cells in their foliage. It is at the junctions of the mesophyll cells that the critical tiny meniscuses exist with the atmosphere, and these exert the upward force that lifts the column of water. In the case of the tallest trees, that column is lifted as high as about 155 m (that is the height of a particular redwood, *Sequoia sempervirens*, in Redwood National Park, California, which may be the tallest tree in the world).

Photosynthesis and Water

Even if there were no need to cool leaves in sunny weather, plants would still transpire water to the atmosphere. The reason is that when stomata open to allow the intake of CO_2 needed for photosynthesis, large amounts of H_2O exit because its concentration in the sub-stomatal cavity is usually much higher than in the ambient environment, creating a steep gradient of water potential. Overall, the photosynthetic reactions require about the same number of molecules of CO_2 and H_2O. However, the use of CO_2 is relatively efficient because about 40 percent of the amount taken into the leaf is fixed into glucose, compared with only 1 percent of the water (Lambers et al., 1998).

The ecophysiology of how plants cope with drought highlights the trade-offs that are taking place inside foliage. When their environment is dry, plants close their stomata to conserve water, but this reduces the availability of CO_2 for photosynthesis. As we learned earlier, plants have evolved several photosynthetic systems to cope with this situation, known as C4 and CAM, in which the function of photosynthesis is separated in either space or time from the intake of CO_2.

Water Stress, Drought, and Winter Snow

Much of Canada receives enough precipitation to allow soil moisture to be adequate for plants during most of the growing season. There are exceptions, however, such as:

- in the southern Okanagan Valley of British Columbia, where there is an area of semi-desert habitat;
- over much of the southern Prairie Provinces in some years, which may experience widespread drought; and
- in much of the High Arctic islands, where there is polar desert and semi-desert because of sparse precipitation.

Another consideration is the wintertime drought that is routinely experienced in boreal and temperate forests. During the winter, H$_2$O is present as snow and ice, and the liquid form needed by plants is not available, so plants experience water stress. Research on spruce has shown that its evaporation of water during the winter is about 10 times greater than what would have been possible unless the tree had somehow replenished its losses by transpiration (Marchand, 1996). Where does that water come from? Although this question has not yet been fully resolved, it is thought that trees use their own stored water in the trunk, redistributing it during the winter. It may also be possible for plants to somehow absorb water from an unfrozen film that occurs around soil particles because of a high solute concentration that depresses the freezing point, although that uptake has not yet been documented by research.

In any event, the relative water content of tree tissues varies during the winter **(Figure 7.30)**. Marchand and Chabot (1978) studied winter desiccation in trees growing at the tree-line on Mount Washington, in New Hampshire, by tracking the relative water content of branches above the snow pack over two winters. They observed that the RWC could increase even during the winter, indicating that some degree of rehydration is possible then, and that recovery from low water content occurs rapidly in the spring. They also found that water loss is especially rapid from damaged tissues, such as where needles and stems were broken off. The loss of water from damaged branches was most likely due to exposure of the vascular tissue.

Another wintertime problem can arise when branches and large limbs accumulate large snow loads, creating a heavy weight that can damage the tree. The conical growth form of coniferous tree species that inhabit regions with heavy snow makes them somewhat less vulnerable to this kind of damage. This is because their steep-sided profile allows much of the snow load to be discarded. Seasonally deciduous trees that shed their foliage for the winter are also less apt to accumulate snow, because their wintertime canopy has a small surface area on which snow can build up to a heavy weight.

Under certain atmospheric conditions, highly damaging wintertime events called ice storms can occur. This happens when a cold rain is falling and the atmospheric temperature is less than zero, a phenomenon that results in the supercooled water freezing onto the surfaces of trees and also buildings and power lines. The build-up of rime ice can be quite substantial **(Figure 7.31)** and the accumulated weight can result in extensive breakage. A severe example occurred in 1998, when an intense ice storm caused massive damage to trees (and power lines) in eastern Ontario and southern Quebec.

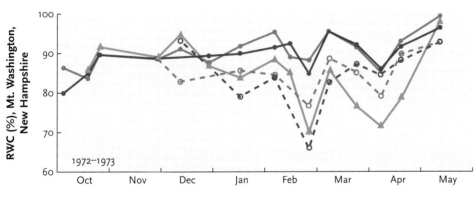

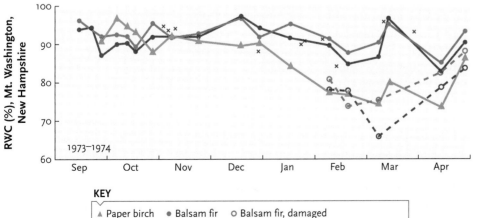

FIGURE 7.30 Seasonal Changes of the Relative Water Content (RWC) The figure compares how the RWC of exposed branches of paper birch (*Betula papyrifera*), black spruce (*Picea mariana*), and balsam fir (*Abies balsamea*) changed from the autumn through to the springtime. Data are also shown for damaged branches.

SOURCE: Peter J. Marchand and Brian F. Chabot, "Winter Water Relations of Tree-Line Plant Species on Mt. Washington, New Hampshire," *Arctic and Alpine Research* Vol. 10, No. 1 (Feb., 1978), pp. 105–116. Copyright © by the Regents of the University of Colorado.

KEY
▲ Paper birch · Balsam fir ○ Balsam fir, damaged
● Black spruce ○ Black spruce, damaged × Balsam fir, Madbury, NH

FIGURE 7.31 Rime Ice This twig accumulated a 2.5-cm thick layer of ice during the great ice storm that affected much of eastern Canada in 2008.

SOURCE: National Oceanographic and Atmospheric Administration

Mike Barker

Duguay et al. (2001) of McGill University studied the damage and recovery in tree species on Mont St. Hilaire, near Montreal, after that ice storm. Enormous numbers of trees and branches were broken due to the ice formation, estimated at over 20 tonnes of woody biomass per hectare. The openness of the forest canopy greatly increased, to the degree that the amount of open sky nearly doubled. Certain species of trees were more vulnerable to suffering damage, largely as a result of their canopy architecture. Deciduous species, such as beech (*Fagus grandifolia*) and sugar maple (*Acer saccharum*), experienced much heavier crown damage, compared with eastern hemlock (*Tsuga canadensis*), a conifer. The recovery potential of the different species was partly based on an ability of damaged branches to resprout, as in sugar maple; however, hemlock cannot do this.

Adaptations for Conserving Water

Plants have evolved many adaptations for conserving water in dry environments. An avoidance strategy used by annual plants of desert habitats is to survive the dry season in a persistent diapause condition. They do this as seeds that patiently wait in the soil for the rains to eventually come, which is followed by an exuberant flourishing of germination, growth, flowering, and dispersal of another seed crop. Aronson et al. (1992) studied desert annuals such as pink mustard (*Erucaria hispanica*) and false brome (*Brachypodium distachyon*) and found that they could complete their life cycle in only two to three months. However, longer-lived species cannot do this; to maintain their perennial tissues they need to have anatomical and physiological adaptations to cope with the stresses of dry environments over the longer term.

The classical anatomical adaptations are those of desert plants, such as species of cacti. These and other drought-tolerant plants (or xerophytes) usually have a greatly reduced biomass of leaves, or none at all, instead conducting photosynthesis in their green stems. Although they grow in dry environments, many xerophytic plants have stout juicy stems, which have a thick waxy cuticle that prevents much transpiration, and they are often well armed with spines to deter herbivores. Many xerophytes also have deep perennial roots that allow them to tap underground water. They may also have a whitish-hairy surface whose high albedo (reflectance) helps to reduce a build-up of heat in tissues during the day and so reduces the need for evaporative cooling. Finally, they may open their stomata only at night for gas exchange, as was previously explained for CAM plants.

Many plants of arid grasslands, such as the shortgrass prairie, are also well adapted to coping with periodic drought. The most abundant plants in grasslands are graminoids—meaning grass-like plants in families such as the true grasses (Poaceae), sedges (Cyperaceae), and rushes (Juncaceae). Most of their biomass is located belowground, especially during the dry season when their leaves and flowering shoots have senesced and died back **(Figure 7.32)**. They also have a spreading and often deep root system that allows them to effectively access water and nutrients; a mature individual of the grass species, rye (*Secale cereale*), was estimated to have a root system with a surface area of 639 m² and occupying 6 litres of soil volume; its root area was 130 times larger than that of its aboveground shoot and leaves (Dittmer, 1937; Evert and Eichhorn, 2013).

So called "evergreen" plants that retain their foliage in the winter also have adaptations for tolerating the drought of that season. Conifer needles have a thick waxy cuticle that helps to prevent evaporation; water loss from conifer foliage in the winter is about 40 times less than during the growing season (Marchand, 1996). Additional adaptations of conifer needles include a

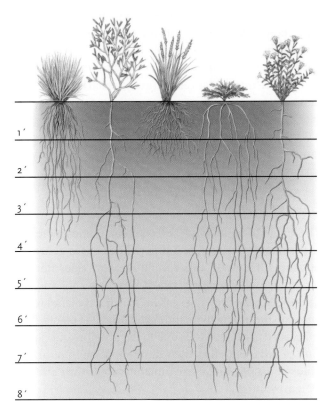

FIGURE 7.32 Roots of Prairie Plants Perennial species of Prairie plants have spreading and/or deep root systems as an adaptation to absorbing water from their periodically dry habitat. Arranged from left to right, the species are little bluestem (*Andropogon scoparius*), lance-leaved psoralea (*Psoralea lanceolata*), June-grass (*Koeleria cristata*), ground plum (*Astragalus crassicarpus*), and false prairie boneset (*Brickellia eupatorioides*).

multilayered epidermis that reinforces the effect of the waxy cuticle, and stomata that occur in pits, which increases the thickness of the boundary layer through which water vapour must move by the relatively slow process of diffusion.

Waterlogging Is Also a Problem

In wetlands and in soil after a heavy rainfall, spaces in the soil matrix are filled with water instead of air, a condition known as waterlogging. When this happens the environment quickly becomes anaerobic because of O_2 depletion by root respiration and decomposition. Such habitats are dominated by species that can function without access to oxygen—usually this is a facultative ability in the sense that they can switch from aerobic to anaerobic metabolism as conditions require. The chemistry of the soil solution also changes, typically with an increase in the production of methane (CH_4), hydrogen sulphide (H_2S), and other reduced compounds, and often an increase in the pH (meaning a decrease in acidity).

While some species can survive periodic flooding, even a short period of waterlogging will kill many plants that are intolerant of that environmental condition. Of course, plants living in permanent wetlands such as marshes and swamps can tolerate having their roots immersed in water over long periods. These differences in tolerance of flooding are illustrated by certain tree species. Among maples, the silver maple (*Acer saccharinum*) naturally occurs in swamps that are flooded for all or most of the growing season. Although this species can grow well in better-drained conditions, and in fact is commonly planted as a street tree in urban areas, in nature it is restricted to wetter habitats because it is not a strong competitor against other trees that are better adapted to nonflooded habitats. An example of the latter is sugar maple (*Acer saccharum*), which is intolerant of prolonged flooding but is a strong competitor on well-drained sites. Red maple (*Acer rubrum*) has a broader tolerance, occurring over a wide range of conditions from wet swamps to drier uplands.

There are many other such variations of tolerance of wet conditions among closely related groups of plants. For instance, the aquatic sedge (*Carex aquatilis*) occurs in wet mucky sites, while bristleleaf sedge (*Carex eburnea*) needs dry sandy habitat. Among grasses, the common reed (*Phragmites australis*) occurs in marshes, while poverty-grass (*Danthonia spicata*) grows in well-drained places. An example from dicotyledonous plants is the water-knotweed (*Polygonum amphibium*) of marshes and ponds, compared with the fringed bindweed (*Polygonum cilinode*) of drier sites.

The ecophysiology of wetland plants can be examined by looking at the conditions and adaptations of species that grow in peat bogs. Bogs are a major kind of wetland in Canada, being especially widespread in the boreal and low-tundra regions and occupying 12 percent of the land area of our country (Tarnocai, 2009). The most abundant plants in bogs are peat mosses (*Sphagnum* spp.), which, like all mosses, lack vascular tissue (xylem and phloem) and do not have a cuticle over the surface of their leaves. *Sphagnum* moss is extremely proficient at extracting nutrient cations such as K^+ and Ca^{2+} from the water, for which they release H^+ in exchange; this is the primary reason bogs are acidic habitats, typically with a pH less than about 4.5.

Sphagnum can hold up to 20 times its dry weight in water. It can do this because its foliage consists of two kinds of cells: (1) green- or red-coloured living cells that are photosynthetically active, and (2) larger dead hyaline cells that have a spongy quality. A single layer of photosynthetic cells surrounds each of the hyaline ones, whose cell walls contain pores that allow water to easily flow into them. Once *Sphagnum* biomass is well hydrated (either living plants or dead peat), it tends to hold on to its water content, which is a reason bogs are hard to drain in order to develop agricultural land. This is also the reason that peat bogs can remain wet even after they have grown in height to the degree that their surface is elevated above that of the surrounding well-drained terrain (these are called raised bogs).

Peat accumulates dead biomass, at about 20–100 cm per year, so that the deepest bogs in Canada have peat depths that exceed 12 m (Gorham et al., 2003). Huge amounts of organic carbon are stored in *Sphagnum* peatlands. One of the predicted effects of global warming is that long-term frozen peat in northern latitudes could thaw and release their encapsulated CH_4 and CO_2 gases to the atmosphere, and then become dried and exposed to oxygen and rapidly decompose to release much more CO_2 (Tarnocai, 2009). These processes could result in a self-accelerating boost to climatic warming by an intensification of the planetary greenhouse effect.

Heat and Cold

Plants living in especially hot or cold places have physiological adaptations that allow them to tolerate those extreme temperature conditions. In addition, all regions of Canada have a strong seasonality of climate. A popular view is that we live in a cold country, as is voiced in the opening line of the song "Mon Pays (My Country)" by Gilles Vigneault: *Mon pays, ce n'est pas un pays, c'est l'hiver* ("My country is not a country, it is winter"). In fact, however, the summer can be quite hot in most of Canada, even briefly in the Arctic. Nevertheless, the length of the growing season is generally much longer in southern regions of Canada, and shorter in the north, although it has also been steadily lengthening in both regions because of climate change.

It is important to remember that plants are autotrophs, meaning they absorb solar energy and use it to drive the biosynthesis of CO_2 and H_2O to form a simple sugar, which provides the energetic basis of their subsequent metabolism as well as that of all heterotrophs. Temperature has a strong effect on photosynthesis, the rate of which increases with both warming and higher CO_2 concentration, and then declines at higher temperatures that exceed the tolerance of the enzyme systems **(Figure 7.33)**.

Growing-Degree Days

The length of the growing season is sometimes indicated as the frost-free season of uninterrupted above-zero temperatures. However, this simple measure does not differentiate well enough between relatively cool and hot days during the growing season, which have large influences on the productivity and development of plants. This is because plant growth is due to the division and expansion of cells, as well as their differentiation into various kinds of tissues, and those functions are greatly affected by temperature.

The concept of **growing-degree days (GDDs, or growing-degree units, GDUs)** is a better way of capturing temperature-related influences on plant growth and development. GDDs are related to the cumulative heat available during a day, or over a longer period, extending even to the entire growing season. Because GDDs have a marked effect on plant growth, they provide an indicator that allows ecologists (and farmers and gardeners) to compare this important aspect of environmental conditions across regions and over time. A GDD is measured using the following equation (Ahrens, 2012):

$$\text{daily GDD} = (T_{max} + T_{min})/2 - T_{base}$$

where: T_{max} = the maximum air temperature on a particular day

T_{min} – the minimum air temperature on that same day

T_{base} = the base temperature for plant growth, which varies by species but is commonly set to a value of 10°C

When calculating an annual GDD, any temperatures colder than the T_{base} are given a value equal to the T_{base} before doing the calculation, and the T_{max} is usually capped at 30°C because most plants do not grow faster above that warm temperature. Here is a sample calculation for a day with a low temperature of 10°C and a high of 24°C: $(10 + 24)/2 - 10 = 7$ degree-days. If that calculation were repeated for all days in a year and the values summed, the result would be the annual degree-days. To calculate a climatic "normal" for GDDs, the average of at least 30 years of data are needed.

Plant species vary greatly in the GDDs needed to influence events in their **phenology**, which means the

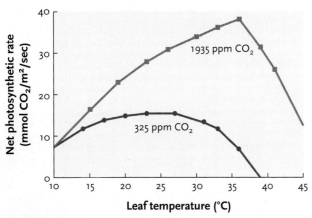

FIGURE 7.33 Effect of Leaf Temperature and CO_2 Concentration on the Rate of Photosynthesis of Large-toothed Aspen (*Populus grandidentata*)

SOURCE: Based on Jurik et al. (1984). Jurik, T.W., J.A. Weber, and D.M. Gates. 1984. "Short-term effects of CO_2 on gas exchange in leaves of big-toothed aspen (*Populus grandidentata*) in the field," *Plant Physiology*, 75: 1022–1026.

seasonal progression of developmental events, such as the timing of production of leaves or of flowers (this term may also be used in reference to comparable events in animals, such as when the young are born). For instance, red maple (*Acer rubrum*) begins to flower once about 27 GDDs have accumulated in the springtime, whereas white ash (*Fraxinus americana*) needs 30–50, black locust (*Robinia pseudoacacia*) 140–160, elderberry (*Sambucus canadensis*) 330–400, and staghorn sumac (*Rhus typhina*) 450–500 (Wikipedia, 2013).

Cooling the Leaf

Many physiological functions occur inside leaves, most of which are biochemical, such as photosynthesis, respiration, and other aspects of metabolism. These processes result in the production of an astonishing diversity of organic chemicals. There are also physical aspects of plant physiology, such as the evaporation of water by transpiration and its diffusion through stomata into the atmosphere. As was noted earlier, transpiration is an inevitable consequence of the need for gas exchange, but it also plays a helpful energetic role on sunny days by providing cooling and preventing the occurrence of potentially lethal hot temperatures inside leaves. On a summer day when there is no wind, leaf temperatures can be 10°C or more warmer than the ambient atmosphere. Temperatures of 40°C have been measured in leaves of white oak (*Quercus alba*) (Vogel, 2009), which is much warmer than the optimal range for photosynthesis **(Figure 7.32)**.

An additional mechanism by which leaves are cooled is by the conduction of thermal energy (heat) to the surrounding atmosphere. All surfaces, including leaves, have a thin film of stagnant (nonmoving) air on their surface, which is called the boundary layer. This layer is relatively thin under windy conditions when the atmosphere is turbulent, perhaps only 1 mm, and it is thicker under calm conditions, up to 3 mm or so. The importance of the boundary layer is that heat moves through it by diffusion, or molecular contact, which is a much slower process than the mass transport of air volumes. Some plants have evolved anatomical adaptations that help to maintain a thinner boundary layer over the surface of their leaves, thereby increasing the rate of heat loss. For example, the foliage of most species of poplars, such as trembling aspen (*Populus tremuloides*), is attached to the twig by a flattened petiole that does not have much resistance to sideways forces, so even the slightest wind will cause the leaves to flutter. This has the effect of creating turbulence over the leaf surface, which causes the boundary layer to be thinner than it would be if the leaf was still. This results in an increase of heat loss by thermal conductance, which enhances the cooling function.

An additional foliar adaptation that increases cooling takes advantage of the fact that boundary layers are thinner close to an edge, such as the boundary of a leaf. This means that any leaf shape that deviates from a circle (which has the smallest ratio of edge to area of all two-dimensional shapes) will have, on average, a thinner boundary layer. The leaves of some species have taken this adaptation to rather extreme bounds by having highly complex and deeply cut leaf shapes. A native example is the black oak (*Quercus velutina*), and another familiar one is the cut-leaf philodendron (*Philodendron bipinnatifidum*), a tropical plant that is commonly grown as a houseplant.

Clearly, leaf shape is important for promoting water loss and cooling. Often, there is variation in leaf shape on the same tree—the sun leaves of white oak are smaller and more deeply indented, while shade leaves from cooler parts of the same tree are larger and less indented (Vogel, 2012).

Additionally, the rate of leaf cooling is influenced by humidity of the atmosphere. The air inside the leaf usually has relative humidity close to 100 percent. The stomata and their patterns of opening and closing determine the rate of water loss to the atmosphere. Many factors, including the illumination or light level, internal CO_2 concentration, local wind speed, and external humidity affect the extent to which the stomata are open. When the ambient humidity is high, evaporation slows down because the gradient from inside to outside the leaf is relatively low, and as the rate of water loss from the cell surfaces decreases, the evaporative cooling effect also slows. Clearly, the humidex reading is as relevant for the cooling of leaves as for the comfort of humans.

Coping with Cold

Plant tissues must be able to deal with potentially lethal cold temperatures when the growing season is over and their environment progressively cools and reaches freezing and even colder temperatures. One common response is for plants to drop their foliage in preparation for the winter.

Leaf drop occurs in all trees and shrubs, including both conifers and angiosperms. However, seasonally deciduous species drop all of their foliage in the autumn. This group includes almost all angiosperms and a few gymnosperms such as larch (*Larix* spp.) and gingko (*Gingko biloba*). So-called evergreen conifers also drop their oldest foliage in the autumn (typically aged five or more years), while retaining the younger leaves for reuse in the following summer (however, their foliage-of-the-year has the greatest efficiency in performing photosynthesis, an attribute that progressively declines over the years, which is a reason the oldest multiyear leaves are not retained).

The process of leaf drop involves the formation of an impermeable layer of corky cells (the abscission layer) between the leaf petiole and its twig. That layer prevents the movement of water into the leaf, and sugars produced by ongoing photosynthesis out of it. The formation of the abscission layer is stimulated by environmental cues related to falling temperatures and a decreasing ratio of the lengths of day:night, which stimulates the synthesis of certain phytohormones that cause the corky cells to be grown. This results in the leaf drying out and eventually falling from the plant, to be replaced by new foliage in the following springtime when increasing temperatures and an increasing ratio of the lengths day to night stimulates a different hormonal regime.

The same autumnal hormone regime stimulates leaves to slow and then stop their production of chlorophyll. This is the key photosynthetic pigment, and when chlorophyll is abundant it is the dominant influence on leaf colour, which is typically green. Once the production of chlorophyll stops, and its existing amount becomes degraded by oxidation by solar ultraviolet radiation, the colours of other pigments in the leaves become unmasked, resulting in the lovely foliar palettes of the autumnal season. The most important of those secondary pigments are carotenoids (which are orange, red, or yellow), anthocyanins (blue-red), and betalains (red; these do not co-occur in species that produce anthocyanin). The amounts of these various pigments vary among plant species, and this accounts for the different colours that their foliage develops in the autumn.

Other less-obvious chemical changes also occur in leaves before they are dropped. Foliage is a highly nutrient rich tissue. In order to retain the vital and limited stocks of nitrogen and phosphorus, most of those nutrients are reabsorbed (resorbed) from the foliage into the twigs, to be reused the next spring when a new crop of leaves is grown. Typically, seasonally deciduous woody plants resorb about 54 percent of the nitrogen content of their leaves before they are dropped in the autumn, and 51 percent of the phosphorus (Aerts, 1996). Evergreens are slightly less efficient, resorbing 47 percent of the nitrogen from the older leaves before they are dropped, and 50 percent of the phosphorus. This nutrient retention is important, because nitrogen and phosphorus are commonly in short supply in terrestrial ecosystems, with nitrogen being the more frequently limiting nutrient to plant productivity. Moreover, because foliage is a nutrient-rich tissue compared with other parts of trees, such as wood and bark, it accounts for a much larger fraction of the nutrient capital than it does of the biomass (Table 7.7). For that reason, it is advantageous to hold on to as much of that content as possible by resorbing it from foliage before it is shed in the autumn.

| TABLE 7.7 | The Importance of Foliage Stores of Nitrogen and Phosphorus in Trees |

The data are the quantities of biomass, nitrogen, and phosphorus in the foliage of a selection of tree species (kg per tree), expressed as a percentage of the total in the aboveground biomass (roots are not included). The data are for trees with stem diameters greater than 15 cm.

Species	Biomass	Nitrogen	Phosphorus
Sugar maple (*Acer saccharum*)	2.0	16.5	16.5
Trembling aspen (*Populus tremuloides*)	2.1	14.6	14.5
White birch (*Betula papyrifera*)	1.9	16.1	15.8
Black spruce (*Picea mariana*)	8.5	28.7	33.0
Red spruce (*Picea rubens*)	7.7	34.9	34.0
Balsam fir (*Abies balsamea*)	15.8	48.9	38.6

SOURCE: Based of data from Freedman et al. (1982). Freedman, B., P.N. Duinker, H. Barclay, R. Morash, and U. Prager. 1982. *Forest Biomass and Nutrient Studies in Central Nova Scotia. Part 1. Biomass and Nutrient Standing Crop Equations. Information Report M X 134.* Maritimes Forest Research Centre, Canadian Forestry Service. Fredericton, N.B. 100 pp.

Of course, any tissues that remain on the plant must be capable of withstanding the effects of freezing wintertime temperatures as well as drought caused by frozen water in their environment. This is true of evergreen foliage, and also of the cylindrical layers of cambium that underlie the bark and are the only living parts of the stems and roots of trees and other woody plants. (The heartwood at the centre of tree trunks, which makes up most of the biomass of large trees, is actually a physiologically dead tissue that has accumulated from past years of outward radial growth.)

The greatest challenge that plants face from freezing temperatures is the formation of ice crystals within their cells. As Vogel (2012) puts it, "Ice is bad news" for several reasons that involve stressful plant ecophysiology:

- A given weight of ice occupies less volume than the liquid water from which it formed, which affects the hydrostatic pressure on enclosing cell walls and on tissues in general; water is densest at 4°C, and less so on either side of that temperature—1 g of liquid water at 20°C occupies a volume of 1 cm³, but 1 g of ice would take up about 0.92 cm³ (it is because of this difference in density that ice floats);

- When ice forms, most of the gas dissolved in the previous liquid water is forced out of solution and into the atmosphere, or it may remain within the ice as trapped bubbles—this is why ice taken from an iceberg or glacier and used to cool a drink will make popping sounds as its trapped gas bubbles escape;

- Similarly, as ice freezes, dissolved inorganic substances become excluded into small briny volumes that remain unfrozen because salty water freezes at lower temperatures than 0°C (the freezing point of seawater is about –2°C), and more highly concentrated solutions freeze at even lower temperatures; and

- As water begins to freeze, sharp ice crystals are formed, which can pierce membranes and cause the death of affected cells—this is why lettuce leaves turn mushy when they are frozen and then thawed.

To deal with these potentially lethal cold-temperature stressors, plants undergo a process of seasonal **acclimation** in which they adjust aspects of their physiology to cope with the anticipation of winter. One aspect of acclimation is shown by blueberry shrubs, which have a similar respiration rate when growing in 10°C conditions as do plants acclimatized to 20°C **(Figure 7.34)**. However, if plants acclimated at 20°C are placed in 10°C growing conditions, their respiration rate drops. Eventually, the respiration rate of the plants initially acclimated at 20°C, if kept at 10°C, will rise as they become reacclimated to the cooler conditions.

Drought hardening, in which plants are exposed to moderate water stress, is also an acclimation process, and so is cold hardening, the process by which plants tolerate cooler temperatures in anticipation of winter conditions. The latter involves plant cells transforming their aqueous matrix into a condition that does not freeze as easily as pure water. This is done by producing high concentrations of "antifreeze" proteins and sugars. In effect, this change allows the cellular water to supercool, or reach temperatures below 0°C without freezing. The decreases in relative water content described earlier in the cactus *Opuntia fragilis*, when plants were acclimated to cooler temperatures, are an example of changes that occur during acclimation and that allow survival in cold winter temperatures.

In addition, various evergreen plants of tundra and boreal habitats allow their leaves to severely dehydrate in terms of the water content of their extra- and intra-cellular fluids. The remaining sugary fluid enters a "vitrified" state, which, like silica glass, lacks a crystalline structure and so is an extremely viscous liquid rather than a solid (Strimbeck et al., 2008).

7.5 Phytohormones

The growth and development of plants follow pronounced seasonal rhythms. As warming occurs in the springtime, woody plants thaw and begin to push sugar-laden sap to their aboveground tissues, including their extremities of high twigs from which leaves and flowers will eventually grow. Certain environmental cues serve as triggers for the synthesis of plant hormones (or phytohormones) that cause the sap flow to occur. The cues are related to the relative lengths of the light of day and the dark of night, in conjunction with the accumulating degree-days that thaw the plant and soil and make liquid water available as a transport medium for the sugars. When enough sugar and heat (as degree-days) have accumulated, the buds of twigs will break their long-held winter dormancy (this process is also controlled by phytohormones) and leaves will begin to grow. This will be followed by other seasonal events, such as flowering and the production and dissemination of fruits (also controlled by phytohormones).

Unlike in animals, whose hormones are produced in specific glands by specialized cells, and have targeted physiological influences on other cells, phytohormones are produced by tissues that have additional purposes and they are much less specific in their influences. The production of a specific phytohormone may be influenced by several environmental factors, and it may trigger more than one physiological or developmental response. There are many plant hormones, but the major ones are:

- Abscisic acid influences many plant developmental processes, especially by inhibiting the growth of buds and seeds and in so doing maintaining their dormancy, and in some plants affecting the timing of leaf drop (or abscission).

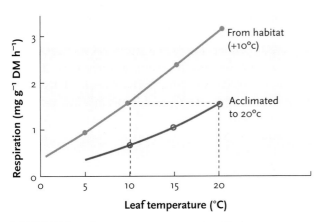

FIGURE 7.34 Acclimation to Temperature in a Blueberry (*Vaccinium mytilloides*) The plants exhibit different respiration rates depending on the environmental temperature to which they are acclimated.

SOURCE: Körner, C. & Larcher, W. 1988. "Plant life in cold environments." In: S.P. Long and F.I. Woodward (eds), *Plants and Temperature. Symposium of the Society of Experimental Biology*, Vol 42, pp 25–57.

- Auxins influence cell growth and enlargement, the formation of buds, and the initiation of root growth. They work with other hormones, especially cytokinins, to control the growth and development of stems, roots, flowers, and fruits, and also to stimulate leaf abscission in the autumn. When the flow of auxins from a distal bud is stopped (perhaps by an injury, such as being eaten by a herbivore), the loss of the apical dominance stimulates buds lower on the stem to break dormancy and begin growing.
- Cytokinins influence cell division and shoot formation, affect leaf growth and their internodal spacing along shoots, help to regulate the seasonal aging of tissues, and mediate the transport of auxins throughout the plant. Cytokinins and auxins occur in a consistent ratio and work in concert to exert a synergistic influence. Cytokinins also work in conjunction with ethylene to promote the seasonal abscission of leaves, flower parts, and fruits.
- Ethylene affects cell growth and shape, delays leaf growth, stimulates plants to grow upward, and affects the ripening of fruits.
- Gibberellins influence the physiology of seed germination, the timing of flowering in some plants, and counter the inhibition of shoot growth and dormancy induced by abscisic acid.

Responding to changes in environmental conditions, phytohormones are synthesized in appropriate quantities and ratios to have a controlling influence on the seasonal phenology of development of plants and their tissues. For instance, in the springtime, cytokinins promote the initiation and expansion of leaves, while in the autumn ethylene gas (and sometimes abscisic acid) help to regulate foliar senescence and abscission.

Sometimes the action of phytohormones is countered by other influences. For example, delayed senescence may be induced in leaves of deciduous trees that are colonized by small moth larvae known as leaf miners (Figure 7.35). The miners affect the cytokinins of their host leaves to delay leaf senescence, thereby prolonging their access to the foliar microhabitat deeper into the autumn (Giron et al., 2007; Kaiser et al., 2010). However, the interaction is further complicated by the presence of *Wolbachia*, a bacterial symbiont in the gut of the leaf miner, which is the agent that produces the cytokinin analogues that are the means by which the physiology of leaf senescence is manipulated. The effect of this influence of the leaf miners is to prolong the suitability of their within-leaf habitat by causing "islands" of green tissue to linger on leaves whose surface has otherwise senesced.

Secondary Compounds

Plants synthesize a range of molecules that are referred to as **secondary compounds** (or **secondary metabolites**). They range from quite small molecules to others that are large and complex. Early research into secondary compounds found that they do not occur in all cells, unlike primary metabolites such as sugars, amino acids, proteins, and nucleic acids. This observation suggested that secondary compounds had no obvious primary biochemical functions in plant growth, such as in photosynthesis or respiration.

Nevertheless, secondary compounds do appear to play an important role in plant growth and survival. Many are toxic chemicals that help to defend the plant against being eaten by an herbivore. They may also be toxic to other plants and so help in competitive interactions, a biotic interaction called **allelopathy**. Additional roles played by secondary compounds include acting as chemical signals that trigger plant responses to environmental change, protecting against ionizing radiation, and being involved in the dispersal of pollen and seeds.

There are many kinds of secondary compounds. Depending on the chemical and plant species, the compounds may be restricted to certain tissues, or be found throughout the plant, and their concentrations may be stable or fluctuate daily or seasonally. Often, the concentrations of these compounds are inducible, in that their production is triggered by damage to the plant, such as when leaves are eaten by an herbivore or when there is a pathogenic infection. During the past several decades there has been considerable research into the costs and benefits to plants of synthesizing these often energetically costly molecules, as well as understanding how their production is regulated and triggered by environmental cues.

Secondary compounds are synthesized by modifications of primary met°abolic pathways, the latter being vital to core aspects of plant biochemistry. Greatly improved molecular techniques have resulted in a much more detailed understanding of the biochemical pathways associated with the synthesis of secondary compounds, and we now know that there are many overlaps between primary and secondary pathways (Seigler, 1998).

There are three major groups of secondary metabolites (Table 7.8):

- **Alkaloids** are a class of nitrogen-containing plant secondary compounds. They have a cyclic molecular structure and contain at least one nitrogen atom in their molecular structure. About 10 000 alkaloid compounds are known, many of which are specific to particular kinds of plants (Southon and Buckingham, 1989).

(a)

G₁ from untreated insects　　　　G₁ from antibiotic-treated insects

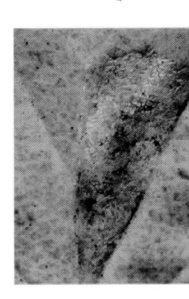

FIGURE 7.35 Effect of Leaf-Miner Moths (*Phyllonorycter blancardella*) on Delaying Senescence of Leaves of Apple (*Malus domestica*) This hormone-mediated interaction maintains "island of green" areas of foliage that extend the feeding season for the leaf miners. The leaf on the left has been affected by a leaf miner, while on the right the influence has been prevented by administering an antibiotic that kills the bacterial symbiont that lives in the gut of the larva and that produces the hormone mimic that affects the plant.

SOURCE: Kaiser W., E. Huguet, J. Casas, C. Commin, and D. Giron, Plant green-island phenotype induced by leaf-miners is mediated by bacterial symbionts. Proceedings B, 2010, 277 (1692): 2311–2319, by permission of the Royal Society.

(b)

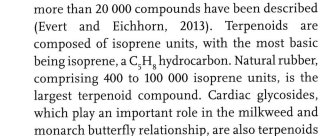

EFI-α
(control)

16S
(universal bacterial detection)

wsp
(*Wolbachia* detection)

EFI-α
(control)

16S
(universal bacterial detection)

wsp
(*Wolbachia* detection)

- **Terpenoids** (or *terpenes*) occur in all plants, and more than 20 000 compounds have been described (Evert and Eichhorn, 2013). Terpenoids are composed of isoprene units, with the most basic being isoprene, a C_5H_8 hydrocarbon. Natural rubber, comprising 400 to 100 000 isoprene units, is the largest terpenoid compound. Cardiac glycosides, which play an important role in the milkweed and monarch butterfly relationship, are also terpenoids (see page 209).
- **Phenolics** are a large group of compounds that are characterized by the presence of a hydroxyl (–OH) group. Phenolics occur in all plant groups, and include flavonoids, lignins **(Figure 7.36)**, tannins, and salicylic acid (a natural base of acetylsalicylic acid, which is the active ingredient in aspirin).

Allelopathy

Allelopathy is akin to chemical warfare among competing plants. It involves one species producing toxic secondary compounds and releasing them into the local environment, where they poison other plants and so confer a competitive advantage (the

TABLE 7.8 Classes of Plant Secondary Compounds

Class of Secondary Compound	Examples of Compounds	Characteristics	Functions in the Plant	How Widespread?
Alkaloids (N-containing compounds)	Caffeine, cocaine, morphine, nicotine, quinine, theobromine	Highly mobile within the plant; toxic or otherwise biologically active at low concentrations	Antiherbivore defence; absorb UV radiation.	Found in ~20% of angiosperm, absent from mosses, ferns, and conifers
Cyanogenic glycosides (N-containing compounds)	Amygdalin, linamarin	Cyanide gas is released when the compound is triggered by a physical disturbance and the necessary enzymes are present	Antiherbivore defence	~2000 plant species
Glucosinolates (N- and S-containing compounds)	Sinigrin	A mustard oil glycoside	Antiherbivore defence	Mostly in Brassicaceae, the mustard family
Terpenoids	Cannabinoids, crotenes, isoprene, terpene	Volatile oils; many are toxic, some are photosynthetic pigments, hormones, or components of membranes	Antiherbivore defence; antimicrobial against fungi and bacteria; attract pollinators; mimic pheromones	All plants contain these biochemicals
Flavonoids (Phenolics)	Anthocyanin	Flower and leaf colours	Attract pollinators; mediate plant-bacteria interactions	Widespread
Tannins (Phenolics)	Flavone	Sequestered in vacuoles	Bitter taste deters herbivores	Widespread
Lignin (Phenolics)	Lignin	Deposited in cell walls	Strengthens cell walls to allow plants grow upright and to transport water	Second most abundant organic compound, after cellulose

SOURCES: Based on Harborne (1997), Lambers et al. (1998), Evert and Eichhorn (2013).

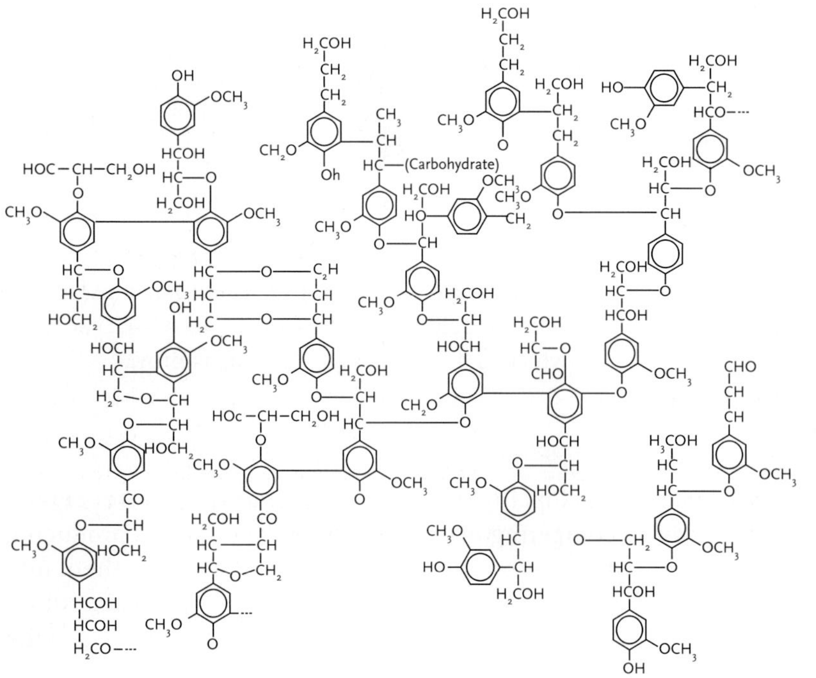

FIGURE 7.36 The Molecular Structure of Lignin, a Highly Complex Phenolic Compound

species that produces the allelochemical is not susceptible to its toxicity).

One of the best-studied examples of this biological interaction involves a polyphenol called juglone, which is synthesized by the black walnut (*Juglans nigra*), a tree native to the eastern deciduous forest. It has long been observed that many species of plants cannot grow beneath the canopy of a black walnut tree, and research has shown that this is an allelopathic effect. In the living tissues of walnut, juglone is present as hydrojuglone, a nontoxic form, but when that is leached by rain to the ambient environment that compound becomes oxidized to its toxic form (Rietveld, 1983). In experiments, juglone was found to affect the oxygen uptake in mitochondria of other plants, and that is the likely cause of its toxicity (Hejl et al., 1993).

Protection from Herbivores

Plants cannot run away from their predators, and herbivores need to consume a large amount of vegetation to grow and reproduce. For example, sheep typically graze from 8 to 12 hours per day (Valentine, 2001). Many plants produce secondary compounds that are distasteful or poisonous, which helps to deter the predators of their tissues. This is reflected in the observation that herbivores typically prefer to eat certain plant species, while avoiding others because of their secondary compounds (and sometimes because of armaments, such as spines; see also Ecology in Depth 7.5).

Secondary compounds that are involved in deterring herbivory can be grouped into two categories, qualitative and quantitative. Qualitative defences are toxins that are active even when occurring in low concentrations in plants (Lambers et al., 1998). Examples include alkaloids, cardiac glycosides, cyanogenic glycosides, glucosinolates, nonprotein amino acids, and certain proteins. On the other hand, the quantitative defensive compounds of plants tend not to be directly toxic, but instead interfere with either digestibility or palatability, which also affect the choice of food plants by herbivores. The secondary compounds that act in this quantitative way are mainly phenolic compounds, including tannins, which block the activity of digestive enzymes, while both lignins and tannins affect the toughness of leaves.

Certain herbivores have evolved ways of detoxifying secondary compounds, and in some cases of accumulating the chemicals for use as their own defence against predators. Perhaps the best known case of this involves the monarch butterfly (*Danaus plexippus*) and its larval food plant, species of milkweed (*Asclepias* spp.) (**Figure 7.37**). The milkweeds are herbaceous perennial angiosperms that defend themselves against most herbivores by producing a whitish latex in their sap that contains high concentrations of cardiac glycosides, a kind of alkaloid. These chemicals are toxic, and also sticky, both of which deter most herbivores, but not the larvae of monarchs, which can tolerate the alkaloids, and in fact milkweeds are their only food plants. Moreover, the larvae accumulate the alkaloids in their own tissues, a characteristic that renders them distasteful and toxic and so helps to protect them from their own predators. The adult monarchs also contain the alkaloids, although they do not feed on milkweed (they rely on nectar obtained from the flowers of a wide range of plant species; they retain the alkaloid residues from their larval stage). Both the larvae and adult monarch butterflies are boldly marked and brightly coloured as a warning to their predators. Interestingly, another butterfly known as the viceroy (*Limenitis archippus*) is marked and coloured similar to the monarch, a mimicry that helps to protect it even though it does not contain the milkweed-derived cardiac glycosides.

The ongoing interactions between the defences of plants and the tolerance of herbivores is sometimes referred to as an "evolutionary arms race." Natural selection exerted by herbivores forces plants to evolve increasingly toxic secondary metabolities, even while the herbivores respond by evolving mechanisms for dealing with the toxins.

FIGURE 7.37 The Monarch Butterfly (*Danaus plexippus*) This species accumulates the secondary compounds from milkweed eaten by its larvae, making the insect toxic to potential predators.

© Bill Brooks/Alamy

What are the reasons for the evolution of different plant defensive strategies involving secondary compounds? This question was considered by Coley et al. (1985) by comparing the energetic costs to a plant of replacing leaves lost to herbivores against their investment in secondary compounds to defend those tissues. They concluded that the production of secondary compounds is indeed expensive. In fact, it takes 5 g of photosynthetic CO_2 to produce 1 g of alkaloid and 2.6 g/g for a phenolic compound (Gershenzon, 1994).

Coley et al. (1985) considered the environment in which plants grow, such as the boreal forest, and the resources available to support their growth and defence. Their model **(Figure 1)** predicted that in resource-poor habitats, where nitrogen is limiting, plants would benefit if they allocate higher proportions of their resources to antiherbivore secondary compounds. The reason is that leaves will be costly to replace if they are eaten. On the other hand, in resource-rich environments, plants can more easily afford to replace lost leaves, and so can invest fewer resources in the production of secondary compounds to defend their foliage.

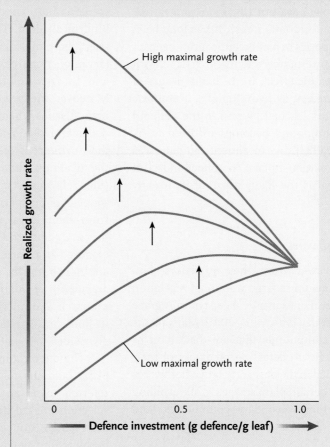

FIGURE 1 Trade-Offs between Growth and Defence Each curve shows a predicted relationship of the effect of investment in defence versus realized growth. Each curve represents a plant species with a different maximum inherent growth rate. The levels of defence that maximize the realized growth are indicated by an arrow.

SOURCE: From Coley, P.D., J.P. Bryant, and F.S. Chapin, "Resource availability and plant anti-herbivore defense," *Science*, 230: 895–899. Reprinted with permission from AAAS.

CHAPTER SUMMARY

(LO7.1)
- Key aspects of the ecophysiology of animals related to temperature are ectothermy and endothermy, as well as the responses of heterotherms and homeotherms to changes and extremes of ambient temperature.

(LO7.2)
- Animals must manage their water balance and ionic concentrations, and the physiological systems for dealing with these issues vary between freshwater and marine species, as well as terrestrial ones.

(LO7.3)
- The means of gas exchange differs greatly between water-breathing and air-breathing animals, including the role of respiratory pigments and acidity of the blood and the environment.

(LO7.4)
- Plants exhibit a number of basic strategies to cope with extremes of temperature and water availability, including the photosynthetic systems known as C3, C4, and CAM.

(LO7.5)
- Plant hormones affect development and its outcome in terms of anatomy, while secondary compounds are important in helping to protect against herbivores as well as other environmental stressors.

An alternative defensive strategy for plants, instead of investing in expensive quantitative antiherbivore chemical defences, is that of an "induced" defence stimulated by herbivory. In this case, damage caused by herbivores induces an increased production of defensive secondary compounds, which decreases the likelihood of future damage. This effect was demonstrated by Lawton (1987), who studied the effects of herbivory by caterpillars of the moth *Apochemia pilosaria* on birch trees (*Betula* sp.). The concentration of defensive phenolic compounds in leaves that had about 15% of their surface area consumed by caterpillars initially averaged 8.1% of the dry weight, but increased to 10.2% eight days after the feeding occurred. In contrast, the leaves of ungrazed leaves on the same trees maintained a steady phenolic concentration of 8.1%. This study demonstrated that the biosynthesis of phenolics is an inducible (phenotypically plastic) response to environmental cues associated with herbivory in this plant–insect system.

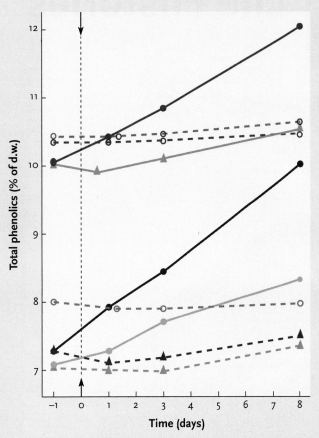

FIGURE 2 Induction of Chemical Defences by Herbivores The data show changes in the total phenolic compounds in leaves of six birch trees after damage caused to three of them by allowing larvae of the moth *Apochemia* to eat about 15 percent of their foliar area. The solid dots refer to grazed leaves, the solid triangles to ungrazed leaves on grazed trees, and the open circles are control trees lacking the moth larvae.

SOURCE: J.H. Lawton 1987. "Food-shortage in the midst of apparent plenty: the case for birch feeding insects." In Proceedings of the Third European Congress of Entomology. Ed. H.W. Velthius, pp. 219–228 Nederlandse Entomologische Verening, Amsterdam.

QUESTIONS FOR REVIEW AND DISCUSSION

1. Explain why ectothermic animals tend to be hetero-thermic (or poikilothermic), and endotherms tend to be homeothermic. Can endotherms be heterothermic? Can ectotherms be homeothermic?

2. Explain the importance of insulation and metabolism in endothermic homeotherms.

3. What is the difference between torpor and hibernation? What is the advantage of daily torpor in small mammals such as mice or bats?

4. Explain how marine fish, both teleosts and elasmobranchs, deal with the osmotic and ionic problems they face in their environment.

5. Compare and contrast the advantages and disadvantages of being a water breather versus an air breather.

6. Compare and contrast positive-pressure and negative-pressure ventilation in air-breathing organisms.

7. Describe the gas-exchange system in insects. Why isn't a circulatory system necessary to transport gases in these animals?

8. Describe basic strategies used by plants to cope with extremes of temperature and water availability, including the roles of the photosynthetic systems C3, C4, and CAM.

9. Explain how plant hormones affect development and anatomy, and the roles of secondary compounds in protecting against herbivory and other stressors.

Life Histories

LEARNING OBJECTIVES

After studying this chapter you should be able to:

1. Describe how organisms differ in the means by which they propagate genes to future generations (i.e., fitness).

2. Explain how life histories are constrained by trade-offs between life-history traits and costs of reproduction.

3. Predict how age at maturity and reproductive effort are affected by changes in the mean and variance in survival rates.

4. Understand why some organisms produce many small offspring, while others produce only a few large ones.

5. Explain why mating and reproductive strategies can differ dramatically within a population.

6. Understand how anthropogenic harvesting can generate evolutionary changes in life-history attributes of wild populations.

7. Explain how life histories are linked to individual fitness, population growth, resource management, and conservation biology.

8.1 Fundamentals of Life History Theory

The striking heterogeneity of the Canadian landscape coupled with strong seasonal variability in the factors that affect the pace of life, such as temperature and light, have contributed to an extraordinary palette of differences in how organisms reproduce. Female polar bears (*Ursus maritimus*), weighing several hundred kilograms, reach sexual maturity at 4–6 years of age and produce 1–2 cubs, each weighing less than 1 kg, every 3 years or so; few live longer than 25 years. Whitebark pine (*Pinus albicaulis*), a 5–20 m high western Canadian inhabitant of high-elevation forests, doesn't start to reproduce until 30–50 years of age, producing tens of thousands of 7–11 mm seeds every 1–2 years for as many as 1000 years. Banded killifish (*Fundulus diaphanus*), living in eastern Canadian rivers and estuaries, spawn at a young age (1 yr) and small size (5–10 cm) and live no more than 3–4 years, producing 200–400, 1.5 mm-diameter eggs per year. These differences in the age and size at which organisms reproduce, the number and size of their young, and the number of years they can expect to live reflect organismal differences in **life history**.

A life history describes the attributes of the life cycle through which an individual organism (or more precisely, a genotype) passes, with particular reference to strategies that influence its survival and reproduction. Life-history traits typically vary with the age of an individual and are expressed through behaviour, physiology, and anatomy. Life-history traits are limited to the possibilities allowed by the genotype, but their expression is influenced by environmental conditions (this is known as phenotypic plasticity; see Section 1.3). Within groups of organisms, such as a population or species, there may be commonalities of life-history traits that differentiate certain groups from others and are subjected to the adaptive influences of natural selection. The evolution of life-history traits may also be influenced by anthropogenic selection.

The life history of an organism is analogous to a biography, because it examines and interprets life events and how they may have contributed to success or failure. In ecology, the life-history characteristics of a species can be distilled to a set of responses, influenced by natural selection, that affect the reproductive success of individuals. Within this context, life-history theory provides an explanatory and predictive framework for understanding why organisms differ so extraordinarily in the means by which they propagate their genes to future generations (i.e., in their fitness). Here are some examples of those differences that occur among species:

- *Age at maturity*: Individuals of some species reproduce at a young age, which can be only minutes in some bacteria, a few days for many invertebrates, and several months for small mammals such as white-footed mouse (*Peromyscus leucopus*), while in other species sexual maturity is delayed to a much later age, such as several decades in the humpback whale (*Megaptera novaeangliae*) and dogfish shark (*Squalus acanthias*).
- *Reproductive events*: Some organisms may reproduce many times during their life (iteroparity), such as snapping turtle (*Chelydra serpentine*) and rockfish (*Sebastes* spp.), whereas others do so only once and then die (semelparity), such as Pacific salmon (*Oncorhnychus* spp.), annual plants such as Indian tobacco (*Lobelia inflata*), and perennial evergreens such as bamboo (Poaceae).
- *Size and numbers of offspring*: Some species have many small offspring, as occurs in swordfish (*Xiphias gladius*) that produce hundreds of millions of 1.7-mm-wide eggs, while others have only a few but large offspring, as is the case of the great white shark (*Carcharodon carcharias*), which births only 2–14 pups at a time, each about 1.5 m long, and the coconut (*Cocos nucifera*) which typically produces fewer than 50 fruits per year.

- *Parental care*: Some parents invest a great deal of energy in caring for their young, such as female grey seals (*Halichoerus grypus*), which lose about 40 percent of their body mass during a 16–18-day lactation period as they transfer exceedingly rich milk (containing 60 percent fat) to their single pup. Other species (including all plants) provide no parental care at all, such as Atlantic cod (*Gadus morhua*) that release eggs and sperm directly into oceanic water, with the survival of the offspring depending entirely on environmental conditions and circumstances.

A life history is often examined in terms of the expenditure of reproductive effort, which may be defined as the proportion of total energy that is devoted to reproduction (Hirshfield and Tinkle, 1975). There are physiological, anatomical, and behavioural aspects of reproductive effort. In animals, reproductive effort might be measured as gonad development, migration to the breeding grounds, changes in feeding rate or preference, and energetic demands associated with competition for mates, nest construction, or parental care. In plants, reproductive effort is typically measured by the allocation of energy (often measured as biomass) to flowers or fruits.

Ecological studies of life history often examine changes in age-specific survival and fecundity of individuals and groups (such as a population) and how those traits have been influenced by factors based on genetics and environmental conditions. In fact, much of this chapter will examine *age-specific* schedules of survival and fecundity of certain animals. In other species, however, these data might be appropriately expressed as *developmental stage-specific* schedules, such as in insects (the stages may be egg, larva, pupa, adult), vascular plants (seed, seedling, pre-reproductive, flowering, fruiting), or mushrooms (spore, haploid hyphae, dikaryotic mycelium, and basidiocarp or mushroom). See Chapter 5 for a review of survivorship.

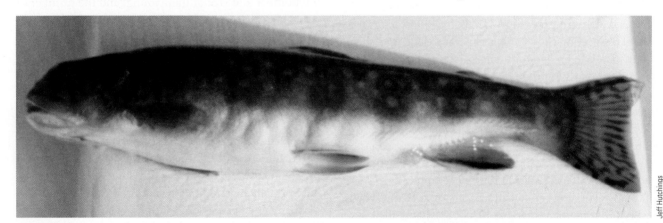

FIGURE 8.1 The Allocation of Resources to Reproduction The eggs produced by this 12 cm long female brook trout (*Salvelinus fontinalis*) can be seen "bulging" along the ventral side of the fish. This is a visually striking example of high reproductive effort, in terms of the proportional allocation of body tissue to gonad development. The fish is from Freshwater River, located on Cape Race in southeastern Newfoundland. Photograph courtesy of Jeffrey Hutchings.

The life history of an individual ultimately determines its fitness, as well as the persistence and growth rate of populations and the ability of commercially important species to sustain various levels of exploitation by humans. The study of life histories is a vital field in ecology—it is at the core of research addressing evolutionary ecology, conservation of biodiversity, and harvesting of bioresources.

Life-History Traits

Life histories reflect the expression of traits that are closely related to fitness, such as

- **age at maturity** and **size at maturity**, or the age and size at which an organism reproduces for the first time;
- **fecundity** or **fertility**, or the number of offspring produced by an individual in a single breeding season;
- offspring size, such as that of an egg, embryo, newborn, or seed; and
- **longevity (lifespan)**.

The analytical link between life history and fitness can be expressed by the discrete-time version of the Euler–Lotka equation (examined in Chapter 5), in which the fitness of genotype i (r_i) can be calculated from:

$$(8.1) \qquad 1 = \sum_{x=\alpha}^{x=\tau} l_x m_x \exp(-r_i x)$$

where l_x represents the probability of surviving from birth until age x, fecundity at age x is given by m_x, and age ranges from maturity (α) until death (τ).

The links between life-history traits and fitness are evident from close examination of the Euler–Lotka equation. For example, age at maturity (α) and longevity (τ) are explicitly denoted below and above the summation sign, respectively. Age-specific fecundity (m_x) is a function of the number and size of offspring that an individual produces. The influence of size at maturity on life history is less explicit. However, it becomes clear that the size at which an individual first reproduces (its size at maturity) can affect its age-specific schedules of survival and fecundity if we acknowledge that:

- the age-specific survival (l_x) of an individual often depends on its size, because larger individuals often have a higher likelihood of survival than smaller ones, and
- fecundity (m) usually increases with body size; for instance, larger fish typically produce more eggs, and larger plants more seeds.

Parity (the number of breeding events in a lifetime) and individual growth rate are two additional traits that are commonly linked to life histories. Emelparous organisms reproduce once in their life and then die (semelparity), while iteroparous organisms reproduce more than once (iteroparity). The link between life history and growth rate lies in the determination of an individual's body size at a given age. This connection is usually more relevant for organisms with **indeterminate growth** (meaning they increase in size, albeit at a declining rate, throughout their life, as occurs in most plants, fish, and amphibians) than for those that cease to grow following the attainment of maturity (determinate growth, as occurs in most insects, mammals, and birds).

Trait Variability

The variability of life histories is typically studied at three levels of biological organization: (1) among species; (2) among populations within a species; and (3) among individuals within a population. The diversity of expression of life-history traits among species is extraordinary. For example, the age at maturity can vary from minutes in bacteria to decades, such as 14 to >30 years in the white sturgeon (*Acipenser transmontanus*), an endangered fish of the Fraser River in British Columbia. Even within a single class of vertebrate animals, the age at maturity can range widely (**Figure 8.3**). The range of size at maturity is also huge, varying over seven orders of magnitude in vertebrate animals. Among the smallest is the 6.2-mm male anglerfish (*Photocorynus spiniceps*), a sexually dimorphic deep-sea fish whose much larger females are about 5 cm long and serve as sexual hosts for the tiny parasitic males (Pietsch, 2005). At the larger end of the spectrum of size at maturity is the blue whale (*Balaenoptera musculus*), which matures at about 23 m or longer and grows as big as 33 m (Sears, 2002; **Figure 8.2**). The size of offspring can range from seeds and eggs less than 1 mm in diameter to newborn blue whales, which weigh about 7 tonnes. In fact, seed size in plants varies by more than 10 orders of magnitude, with the smallest being orchid seeds weighing only 1 μg and the largest being those of the coco de mer (*Lodoicea maldivica*) of the Seychelles Islands, whose individual seeds weigh up to 18 kg (Westoby et al., 1992). The numbers of offspring per breeding episode can also vary enormously, by up to nine orders of magnitude, as is shown for three groups of vertebrate animals in **Figure 8.4**.

Second, there can be considerable variation of life-history traits within a species (e.g., Hutchings and Jones, 1998). Among populations of Atlantic salmon (*Salmo salar*), the age at maturity can range 10-fold, from only 1 year for males in the southern rivers of New Brunswick and Nova Scotia to as much as 10 years for females in Arctic Nunavik in northern Quebec. The size at maturity varies by more than 14-fold, from less than 7 cm for males in Newfoundland to more than 1 m among females in southern Norway. The number of eggs laid per female per breeding season ranges from tens to tens of thousands, while egg diameter ranges from 4.5 mm in Ouananiche Beck, a tributary of Bristol Cove River in southeastern

FIGURE 8.2 A Blue Whale (*Balaenoptera musculus*) This is the largest animal ever to have lived. It matures at a length of 23 m or more and can attain sizes exceeding 33 m and 180 tonnes.

Mark Carwardine/Peter Arnold/Getty Images

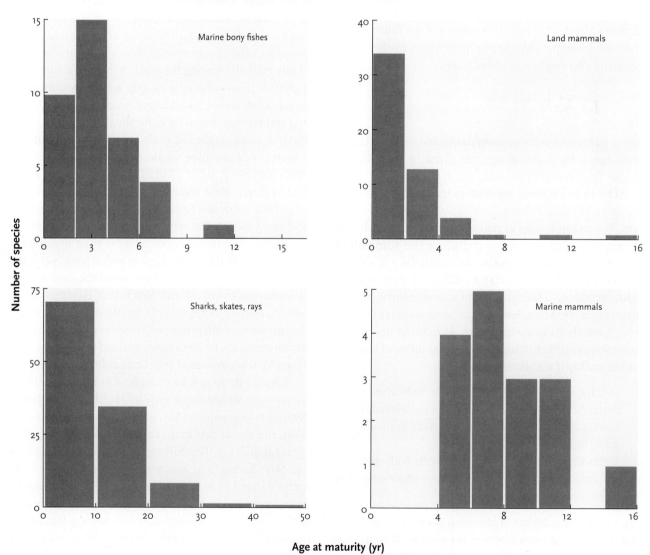

FIGURE 8.3 Age at Maturity The graphs show the distributions of age at maturity (years) for various kinds of vertebrate animals.

SOURCE: Hutchings et al. (2012).

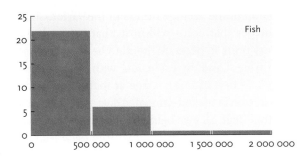

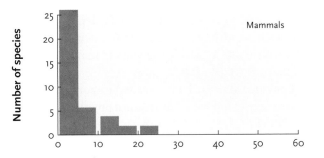

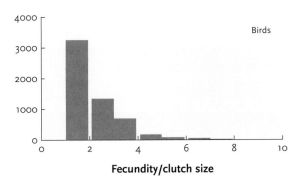

FIGURE 8.4 Numbers of Offspring per Breeding Episode
Distributions of fecundity, or clutch size, for marine teleost fish, terrestrial and marine mammals, and landbirds.

SOURCE: (Top, middle) Hutchings, J.A., R.A. Myers, V.B. Garcia, and L.O. Lucifora. 2010. *Life history correlates of extinction risk in vertebrates*. (Bottom) Jetz W, Sekercioglu CH, Böhning-Gaese K (2008) The Worldwide Variation in Avian Clutch Size across Species and Space. *PLoS Biol*, 6(12): e303. doi:10.1371/journal.pbio.0060303

Newfoundland, to 7.0 mm in the Restigouche River, northern New Brunswick.

Third, if environmental conditions are different enough, natural selection can result in surprisingly local differences in life-history traits among individuals within a species. This has been illustrated by studies initiated in 1987 by Jeff Hutchings, then of Memorial University of Newfoundland, on populations of brook trout separated by distances ranging from only a few hundred metres to 19 km on Cape Race in southeastern Newfoundland (Hutchings, 1991, 2006; Wilson et al., 2003; Purchase and Hutchings, 2008; see **Figure 8.5**). The most divergent populations are in Freshwater River and Cripple Cove River, where the trout are nonmigratory, occur at a similar density, are not affected by competition or predation from other species of fish, and are also not fished so the population is in a natural condition. Despite these similarities, females in Freshwater River mature about one year earlier (at 3.1 years on average) than those in

Cripple Cove River (4.2 years), and at a five-fold smaller weight (**Figure 8.6**). The smallest lengths at maturity—62 mm for males and 70 mm for females in Freshwater River—are the shortest recorded for this wide-ranging species. In addition, females in Freshwater River allocate about double the percentage of their body mass to gonadal tissue compared with those from Cripple Cove River, and they produce 30 percent more eggs for their size, each of which is almost double the volume (**Figure 8.6**). These differences in life-history traits between populations can been interpreted as representing adaptive responses to local environmental conditions, particularly in the food supply and quality of overwintering habitat, on age-specific survival, fecundity, and growth rate of the trout.

Linking Life-History Traits to Population Growth Rate

The link between life history and individual fitness is made explicit in the Euler–Lotka equation. In that context, a population's per capita rate of increase, *r*, is simply a

Jeff Hutchings (top and bottom)

FIGURE 8.5 A Stream at Cape Race This habitat is located on the southeastern tip of the island of Newfoundland. Brook trout inhabit more than 20 small streams and rivers across a 19-km distance. Freshwater River (lower photo) is where the bulk of the trout life-history research on Cape Race has been undertaken.

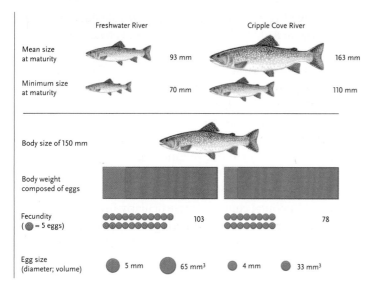

Freshwater River   Cripple Cove River

Mean size at maturity	93 mm	163 mm
Minimum size at maturity	70 mm	110 mm

Body size of 150 mm

Body weight composed of eggs

Fecundity ($\bullet$ = 5 eggs)   103   78

Egg size (diameter; volume)   5 mm   65 mm³   4 mm   33 mm³

FIGURE 8.6 Variations of Life History Species may exhibit considerable variations of life history across small geographic scales. In this case, brook trout inhabiting rivers only 9 km apart on Cape Race, Newfoundland, differ in the expression of many life-history traits, including size at maturity, proportional allocation of body mass to gonads, fecundity, and egg size (the data on eggs are for 150 mm-long females, to control for their body size).

SOURCE: Based on Hutchings (1993, 1996)/Dorling Kindersley/Getty Images

function of the average fitness of the various individual genotypes that occur within it, that is, μ (r_i). Two life-history traits in particular tend to be strongly associated with fitness and, by extension, with population growth rate. The first of these is age at maturity. Lamont Cole (1954), who modelled simulated data, was the first to demonstrate that, all else being equal, the fitness of individuals (r) increases as age at maturity declines. This link between r and age at maturity provides one reason populations that are characterized by a relatively young age at maturity tend to be more resistant to decline and are more resilient when recovering from a depletion, compared with those in which individuals mature at older ages (Reynolds et al., 2005).

Body size at maturity is a second important life-history correlate of individual fitness and population growth rate. Hutchings et al. (2010) performed an empirical study of how life-history traits can be correlated with one another and with maximum per capita population growth rate, r_{max}. They examined life-history data and estimates of r_{max} for 199 species (421 populations) of vertebrate animals (bony and cartilaginous fish and terrestrial and marine mammals (**Figure 8.7**). While age at maturity

FIGURE 8.7 Variations of Life History Traits These Canadian vertebrate animals vary tremendously in terms of life-history traits such as age at maturity and fecundity. Top row: Meadow voles (*Microtus pennsylvanicus*), found across Canada, mature at less than two months of age, whereas the endangered porbeagle (*Lamna nasus*) off eastern Canada matures at 8 (males) to 13 years (females). Bottom row: The Pacific halibut (*Hippoglossus stenolepis*) produces hundreds of thousands to several millions of eggs annually, whereas the humpback whale (*Megaptera novaeangliae*) bears a single calf every two to three years.

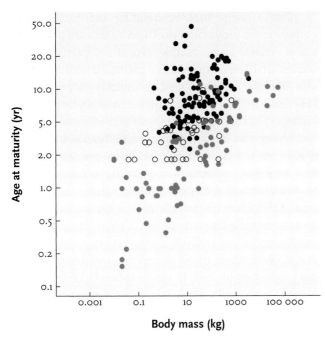

FIGURE 8.8 Age at Maturity with Respect to Body Size At the species level, age at maturity increases with body size in vertebrate animals such as bony fish (open circles), cartilaginous fish (sharks, skates and rays; black circles), and terrestrial and marine mammals (orange circles).

SOURCE: Based on data from Hutchings, J.A., R.A. Myers, V.B. Garcia, and L.O. Lucifora. 2010. *Life history correlates of extinction risk in vertebrates.*

increased with body size among these animals (**Figure 8.8**), fecundity was positively associated with body size only in bony fish (**Figure 8.9**). The researchers also examined

whether age at maturity, maximum body size, or fecundity was the best predictor of maximum population growth rate (r_{max}). They found that body size had the strongest correlation, and that the association between size and r_{max} was similar among the groups examined (**Figure 8.10**). In contrast, there was no correlation between r_{max} and fecundity across seven orders of magnitude (ranging up to 5×10^8 eggs in swordfish) in bony fish (**Figure 8.11**).

It is not surprising to find that offspring production can be unrelated to r_{max} (as was first noted by Cole, 1954), given that (1) fecundity is only one of several traits that contribute to individual fitness (and thus to population growth rate) and (2) various trade-offs (reflected by negative associations among traits) often prevent selection from increasing the value of one fitness-related trait without diminishing that of another (Roff, 2002). Nonetheless, Hutchings et al. (2010) found that r_{max} increased with litter size across the relatively low fecundities that are characteristic of cartilaginous fish and mammals (**Figure 8.11**). This suggests that the narrower the range and the lower the absolute value of fecundity, the greater the potential influence on fitness of the addition of a single offspring. For example, in a mammal that typically produces two offspring, the addition of an additional one offspring represents a 50 percent increase in fecundity, whereas there would be a negligible contribution to the fitness of a bony fish that produces 100 000 eggs.

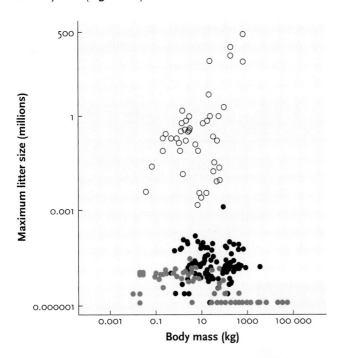

FIGURE 8.9 Fecundity with Respect to Body Size At the species level, fecundity increases with body size in bony fish (open circles) but not in cartilaginous fish (black circles) or in mammals (orange circles).

SOURCE: Based on data from Hutchings, J.A., R.A. Myers, V.B. Garcia, and L.O. Lucifora. 2010. *Life history correlates of extinction risk in vertebrates.*

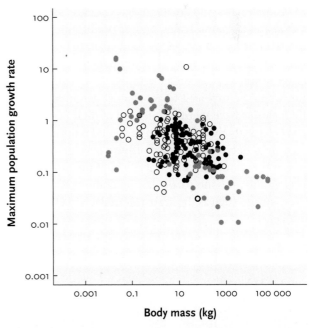

FIGURE 8.10 Population Growth and Body Size This graph shows how the maximum per capita rate of population growth (r_{max}) declines as body size increases across a range of vertebrate animals. This pattern of association does not differ among bony fish (open circles), cartilaginous fish (black circles), and mammals (orange circles).

SOURCE: Based on data from Hutchings, J.A., R.A. Myers, V.B. Garcia, and L.O. Lucifora. 2012. *Life history correlates of extinction risk in vertebrates.*

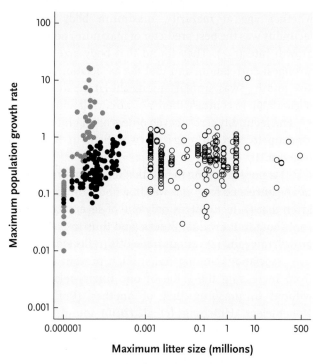

FIGURE 8.11 Population Growth and Fecundity This graph shows divergent associations between the population growth rate and fecundity in a range of vertebrate animals. Maximum per capita rate of population growth (r_{max}) is not associated with fecundity in bony fish (open circles), but it does increase with litter size in cartilaginous fish (black circles) and in mammals (orange circles).

SOURCE: Based on data from Hutchings, J.A., R.A. Myers, V.B. Garcia, and L.O. Lucifora. 2012. *Life history correlates of extinction risk in vertebrates.*

Bet Hedging

Environments vary to greater or lesser degrees across all spatial and temporal scales. In less predictable environments, selection pressures are more likely to result in life histories that spread the risk of reproductive failure over space or time. Under such circumstances, natural selection would be expected to act against genotypes whose life histories have them placing "all of their eggs in one basket." In other words, selection should reduce the variance in genotypic/individual fitness over generations, even if this would entail a "sacrifice" of the expected fitness within any one particular generation (Roff, 1992). Life histories such as these are referred to as **bet-hedging strategies**.

One strategy that bet-hedging individuals often employ is the production of offspring that are phenotypically variable in traits that can affect survival in an unpredictable environment. In plants, for example, variable size and timing of seed germination are traits that have been implicated as components of bet-hedging life histories. As summarized by Andrew Simons of Carleton University and Mark Johnston of Dalhousie University (2006), both of these traits affect fecundity and survival, and seed size influences the timing of germination. Within-plant variability in the size of seeds produced has been interpreted as an adaptive response to variable environments (Capinera, 1979). If some environmental conditions favour individuals that emerge from larger seeds, while others favour those from smaller ones, then the production of seeds of various sizes by an individual plant in a particular season may be favoured by natural selection.

In bacteria, variability in the translucence of colonies produced by a single genotype is an analogue of seed-size variability in plants, as has been observed for *Pseudomonas fluorescens* by Beaumont et al. (2009) (**Figure 8.12**). In response to a selection regime in which the environment varied unpredictably from one generation to the next, they found that several populations of *P. fluorescens* evolved a bet-hedging strategy whereby populations stochastically switched their colony morphology, facilitating their persistence to the selection regime. This response represents phenotypic plasticity—a variable expression of genotypic potential depending on the environmental conditions that are experienced.

Even under controlled environmental conditions, the time of germination can vary considerably in plants, as was shown by Simons and Johnston (2006) for successive generations of the annual dicot *Lobelia inflata* (**Figures 8.13** and **8.14**). Most interesting, however, is the observation that the variation in germination time can differ among genotypes within the same population (**Figure 8.15**). This suggests that natural selection can act on the *variance* in germination timing, rather than simply on the *mean* time, a finding that is consistent with the prediction that such diversification bet hedging can be an evolved strategy.

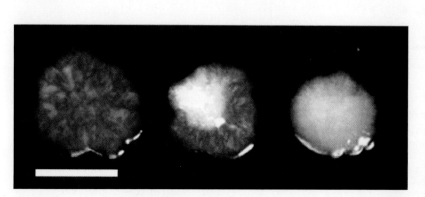

FIGURE 8.12 Unpredictably Variable Environments *Pseudomonas fluorescens* responds to unpredictably variable environments by evolving a bet-hedging strategy that produces bacterial colonies of differing morphology. Translucent, sectored, and opaque colonies produced by a single bet-hedging genotype of the bacterium *P. fluorescens* (scale bar is 2 mm).

SOURCE: Beaumont, H.J.E., J. Gallie, C. Kjost, G.C. Ferguson, and P.B. Rainey. 2009. "Experimental evolution of bet hedging," *Nature*, 462: 90-93. (Figure 1(b) on page 91). Reprinted by permission from Macmillan Publishers Ltd.

FIGURE 8.13 Bet Hedging in a Semelparous Plant The timing of seed germination in *Lobelia inflata* can vary more than 10-fold from one generation to the next, even under controlled environmental conditions in a growth chamber.

SOURCE: Simons, A.M. and M.O. Johnston. 2006. "Environmental and genetic sources of diversification in the timing of seed germination: Implications for the evolution of bet hedging," *Evolution*, 60: 2280-2292. Reprinted with permission from John Wiley and Sons, Inc.

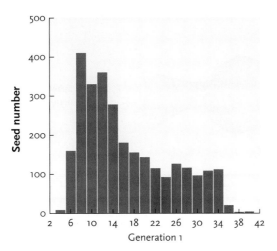
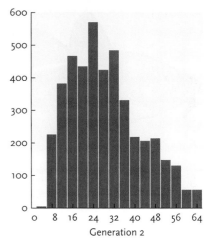

Generation 1 Generation 2

Days to germination

FIGURE 8.14 Indian Tobacco (*Lobelia inflata*) This semelparous or monocarpic plant inhabits fields and thickets from Newfoundland to central Ontario. The seed germination of *Lobelia inflata* was studied by Simons and Johnston (2006); see also Figure 8.13.

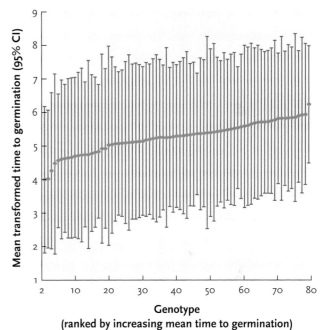

Genotype
(ranked by increasing mean time to germination)

FIGURE 8.15 Germination Time This graph shows how germination time varies within and among 79 genotypes from a single population of *Lobelia inflata* growing under controlled environmental conditions. Variation within genotypes (which are ranked in order of increasing mean time to germination; orange diamonds) is represented by the vertical bars (95 percent confidence intervals). Variation among genotypes is represented by the differences in the heights of the bars.

SOURCE: Simons, A.M. and M.O. Johnston. 2006. "Environmental and genetic sources of diversification in the timing of seed germination: Implications for the evolution of bet hedging," *Evolution*, 60: 2280-2292. Reprinted with permission from John Wiley and Sons, Inc.

Bet hedgers can also spread their reproductive risks by reproducing multiple times throughout their lives, or within a single breeding season, and even numerous times within the same location (almost always with multiple mates, which spreads the risk even further). The Atlantic cod is an example of a species that bet hedges by spreading its reproductive risks. Presumably in response to the high temporal and spatial unpredictability of the environments in which cod larvae find themselves, natural selection has favoured the evolution of a life history in which females release their eggs in multiple batches (typically every four to seven days) during a breeding season. The longer the spawning period, the greater the likelihood that larvae will hatch at a time when the food availability is high **(Figure 8.16)**,

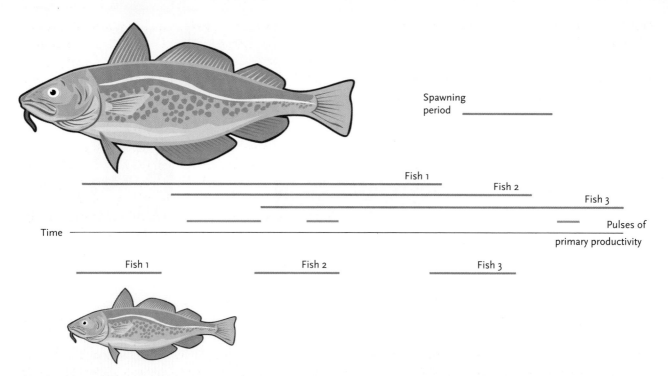

FIGURE 8.16 Bet-Hedging in Atlantic Cod This marine fish exhibits a bet-hedging life-history strategy by producing multiple batches of eggs throughout a protracted spawning period. Large females spawn over longer periods of time (indicated by the three horizontal orange lines above the time axis) than small females (indicated by the three horizontal lines below the time axis). Because of longer spawning periods, the larvae produced by large cod are more likely to begin feeding in the presence of a pulse of food productivity (e.g., an algal bloom with associated zooplankton) than are those produced by small females. This is reflected by the general lack of overlap between temporal pulses of primary productivity (green lines) and the spawning periods of small females.

SOURCE: patrimonio designs ltd/Shutterstock.com

which lowers the chance of unusually poor reproductive success by a particular female. It addition, larger individuals spawn over longer periods of time than smaller ones (Hutchings and Myers, 1993). In theory, this would mean that a population comprising large spawners would have reduced temporal variability in offspring survival (this is termed "recruitment" in fisheries science) when compared to a population composed of small spawners.

Another way to think about bet-hedging life histories is to consider that the fitness associated with a particular genotype is best estimated as a geometric mean calculated across several generations (a geometric mean is the nth root of the product of the values in a sample; it is used to determine the typical value or central tendency of a group of numbers). Use of the geometric mean makes explicit the fact that fitness is determined by a multiplicative process: the total number of descendants left by an individual after n generations depends on the product of the number surviving to reproduce in each generation (Seger and Brockmann, 1987). Therefore, the geometric mean fitness of genotype i after n generations can be calculated as:

$$(r_{i(1)}) \times (r_{i(2)}) \times (r_{i(3)}) \times (r_{i(4)}) \times \ldots \times (r_{i(n)})^{(1/n)}$$

Note that in this formula the geometric mean is strongly influenced by unusually low values. The more variable a set of values is, the lower is the geometric mean, which underscores the tenet noted above and is best exemplified by bet-hedging life-history strategies—that natural selection should act to reduce the variance in fitness over generations.

8.2 Trade-Offs and the Costs of Reproduction

Trade-Offs

The concept of a **trade-off** is fundamental to understanding the evolution of life histories and to predicting how organisms might respond to environmental change. A trade-off implies that an increase in the value of one life-history trait (and its potential importance in terms of influencing fitness) can be achieved only if there is a concomitant reduction in that of another one. In other words, it is not possible for an organism to maximize simultaneously all traits that are positively associated with fitness. A theoretical organism that can maximize all aspects of fitness concurrently can be termed a "Darwinian demon," and could exist only if its evolution was unconstrained.

That is, in a life-history sense it might be capable of maturing as early in life and at as large a size as possible, while also producing maximal numbers of maximally sized offspring, and suffering no consequences to its probability of surviving from one year to the next, and so would live to the maximum time span that is biologically possible for its species.

A trade-off, then, is a negative association or correlation between one trait and another, such as:

- postreproductive survival of an adult declining with increased reproductive effort;
- future individual growth rate declining with increased investment in the care of offspring; and
- the size of individual eggs produced by a female declining with increases in the number of eggs she produces.

Trade-offs may be purely phenotypic in origin. It is, for example, a negative phenotypic correlation that is quantified in experiments in which the numbers of eggs are manipulated (this is a method used to investigate the energetic costs associated with parental care) in order to explore how changes in clutch size might affect parental survival. Although phenotypic correlations are not necessarily indicative of genetic correlations, they can still be relevant from an evolutionary perspective if the traits involved are indeed heritable.

Among species that have indeterminate growth, one widely acknowledged trade-off is the reduction in future growth that is caused by the diversion of energy from somatic biomass to the demands of reproduction—to behaviour, physiology, and tissues associated with reproductive effort. This reduction of growth rate produces an associated decrease in future fecundity, because of the strong relationship that exists between seed/egg number per individual and body size in most plants, fish, amphibians, and reptiles. This cost is illustrated graphically in several ways: (1) by depicting possible growth trajectories that are associated with different ages at maturity, (2) by noting the body sizes that are associated with ages subsequent to maturity, and (3) by estimating the fecundity associated with each of the resultant body sizes **(Figure 8.17)**.

In addition, to determine whether a trade-off is genetic in origin, one or more metrics of reproductive effort can be manipulated and the consequences measured for individuals of known genotype and degree of relatedness. Studies on genetically different individuals can be carried out using a "common-garden" experimental design, in which all experience the same environmental conditions so that nongenetic sources of trait variability are controlled.

An especially powerful way to detect negative genetic correlations between life-history traits is to perform a

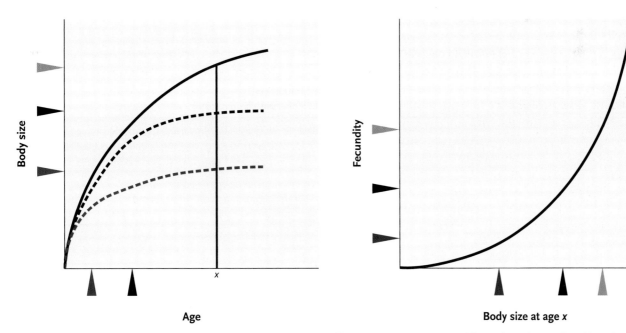

FIGURE 8.17 Age at Maturity and Future Fecundity There is a trade-off between age at maturity and future fecundity, mediated by reductions in growth rate and subsequent sizes at future ages. In the absence of reproduction, the growth trajectory increases with age and would follow the uppermost (solid black) curve in the left panel. At ages at maturity indicated by the black and red triangles on the age axes, the associated growth trajectories (black and red-dashed curves) would decline in both slope and asymptote because of the diversion of energy from somatic growth to tissues needed for reproduction (e.g., gonads). The body size at age x will differ under these three scenarios, as indicated by the green (no reproduction), black (reproduction), and red triangles (earlier reproduction) on the vertical axis of the left panel. The fecundity cost of reproduction can be illustrated in the right panel as the difference (decrease) in egg number at sizes at age x that are associated with the green and black triangles. The earlier age at maturity (red triangle) is associated with an even greater fecundity cost.

selection experiment. It might involve selection for increases in a trait, such as female reproductive gonadal volume (a product of egg number and egg size) and monitoring the correlated selection response in terms of postreproductive survival. If positive directional selection in one trait is associated with negative directional selection in another, then the traits are negatively genetically correlated and that the trade-off has a genetic basis. These types of experiments have consistently revealed moderate levels of heritable variability in life-history traits, meaning that the value of a trait expressed by a parent will often be expressed in a similar manner by its offspring (Roff, 2002).

Reproductive Constraints Impose Reproductive Costs

Predominant among the trade-offs that characterize life histories are those that lead to a **cost of reproduction**. Seminal work in this area began with inductive arguments for why reproductive costs should exist and theoretical assessments of their life-history consequences. Examples are the pioneering studies of Fisher (1930), Cole (1954), Williams (1966), Gadgil and Bossert (1970), and Bell (1980).

The central tenet that emerged from this early work is that behavioural, physiological, and anatomic correlates of reproduction demand some sort of cost to future reproductive success in terms of reduced survival, fecundity, and/or growth. First, compared with a non-reproductive individual of age x, reproduction at age x, or even breeding activities immediately prior to reproduction, can reduce the probability of survival to age $x + t$, where t might represent any unit of time, such as days or years—this is termed a survival cost of reproduction.

Second, reproduction can directly reduce an individual's future ability to produce offspring; high energetic or physiological costs expended at age x might, for example, leave an organism with insufficient energy reserves to produce the same number of offspring at age $x + t$—this is a fecundity cost of reproduction. Another fecundity cost is a consequence of the energy allocated to the behavioural and physiological demands of reproduction at the expense of energy that would otherwise have been allocated to somatic growth. Reduced future size-at-age associated with a reduction in growth rate, coupled with the positive relationship that is typically observed between fecundity and body size in many indeterminately growing species, results in a reduction in potential fecundity. In this sense, an individual reproducing at age x will produce fewer eggs at age $x + t$ than another that did not reproduce at age x (**Figure 8.17**).

There are a number of proximate **constraints of reproduction**, which may be energetic, ecological, or genetic in origin, that can generate reproductive costs that may be manifested in the short term (acute costs) or long term (chronic costs) (**Table 8.1**). Many reproductive costs can be attributed to the metabolic appropriation of carbohydrates, lipids, and proteins associated with various

TABLE 8.1	**Constraints and Resulting Costs of Reproduction**
	A chronic cost is paid over a longer time, and an acute one is more immediate.
Constraint on Reproduction ENERGETIC losses leading to:	Cost of Reproduction EXAMPLES of acute/chronic cost:
• Reduced ability to maintain basal metabolic rate because of allocations of resources to such factors as gonad production, mate competition, and/or parental care	• Reduced survival during or immediately following breeding (acute); reduced future fecundity or fertility (chronic); reduced future growth (chronic)
• Increased risk of infection or parasitism due to weakened immune system	• Reduced survival during or immediately following breeding (acute) or later in life (chronic); reduced future fecundity or fertility (chronic); reduced future growth (chronic)
• Increased risk of predation because of factors such as reduced locomotion, impaired vigilance, increased feeding rate	• Reduced survival during or immediately following breeding (acute)
ECOLOGICAL risks resulting from:	EXAMPLES of acute/chronic costs:
• Physical injuries incurred during mate competition	• Reduced survival prior to breeding (acute) or later in life (chronic)
• Increased vulnerability to predators because of factors such as mate searching, mate attraction, parental care	• Reduced survival prior to, during, or immediately following breeding (acute)
GENETIC trade-offs resulting in:	EXAMPLE of acute/chronic costs:
• Antagonistic pleiotropy, i.e., a negative genetic correlation between traits associated with present and future survival and/or fecundity	Reduced survival and/or fecundity in longer term (chronic)

physiological (e.g., gonad production) and behavioural (e.g., mating) correlates of reproduction. These energetic and biochemical demands may be considerable, as can be demonstrated by comparing the weight losses of reproductive individuals compared with those of non-reproductive ones during a time interval. For example, Jean-Denis Dutil (1986) of Fisheries and Oceans Canada found that postreproductive Arctic char (*Salvelinus alpinus*) had 35–46 percent smaller fat reserves than non-reproductive individuals. Moreover, France Dufresne and colleagues (1990) of Université Laval concluded that depleted energy reserves were the primary cause of the doubling in mortality rate that is experienced by postreproductive three-spine sticklebacks (*Gasterosteus aculeatus*) breeding in tide pools along the St. Lawrence River, when compared to their nonbreeding counterparts. Similarly, Brokordt et al. (2003) of Université Laval found that reproduction negatively affected the escape response of the common whelk (*Buccinum undatum*) in the Gulf of St. Lawrence by reducing their overall energetic status and the metabolic capacity of their foot muscle. Finally, based on a 25-year data set for a population of bighorn sheep (*Ovis canadensis*) inhabiting Ram Mountain, Alberta, Marco Festa-Bianchet of Université de Sherbrooke and colleagues (1998) reported that heavier females experienced smaller reproductive costs (i.e., reduced energetic losses) than lighter ones, particularly at high population densities.

Ecological constraints of reproduction can also reduce the probability of future survival, notably in the short term. For instance, mating can elevate the risk of predation. Locke Rowe (1994) of the University of Toronto found that greater movements by female water striders (*Gerris buenoi*) increase their vulnerability to predation by backswimmers (order Heteroptera) **(Figure 8.18)**. Bright colouration, which is a secondary sexual characteristic in males guppies (*Poecilia reticulata*) and an attractant to females, can at the same time increase risk of predation to the male (Houde and Endler, 1990) (see Section 6.4, as well). Physical injuries may be caused by competition for mates in male ungulates and many other animals, and in salmon mate competition has been shown to negatively affect short- and long-term survival probabilities (Fleming, 1996). Breeding activity in some arthropods has proven costly to future breeding opportunities because it can result in an increased risk of parasitism, reduced foraging success, and genital damage (see Arnqvist and Rowe, 2005, for a review).

Although reductions in individual growth rate provide one obvious means by which the environment can reduce future fecundity **(Figure 8.17)**, there are also more subtle means by which such changes can occur. For example, changes in biotic aspects of the environment can have physiological consequences that might affect

dabijola/Shutterstock.com

Marek R. Swadzba/Shutterstock.com

FIGURE 8.18 Risk of Predation Reproduction can increase the probability of being detected by a predator. Greater movements by female water striders (*Gerris buenoi*; upper photo) increases their vulnerability to predation by backswimmers (e.g., *Notonecta undulata*; lower photo).

reproductive output. Michael Sheriff and Charles Krebs of the University of British Columbia and Rudy Boonstra of the University of Toronto (2009), for example, found that predator-induced increases in the concentration of glucocorticoids (steroid hormones related to physiological stress) reduce the reproductive output of snowshoe hares (*Lepus americanus*), as reflected by decreases in their litter size and in the birth weight and length of offspring **(Figure 8.19)**.

In addition to the negative genetic correlations identified in the section above on trade-offs, reproductive costs have been hypothesized to originate from the actions of a single gene acting on more than one fitness-related trait, a phenomenon called **pleiotropy** (a single gene influencing multiple phenotypic traits). As such, particular genes may have a positive influence on a trait in early life (e.g., fecundity) but a negative effect on another trait (e.g., survival) later on. This is known as

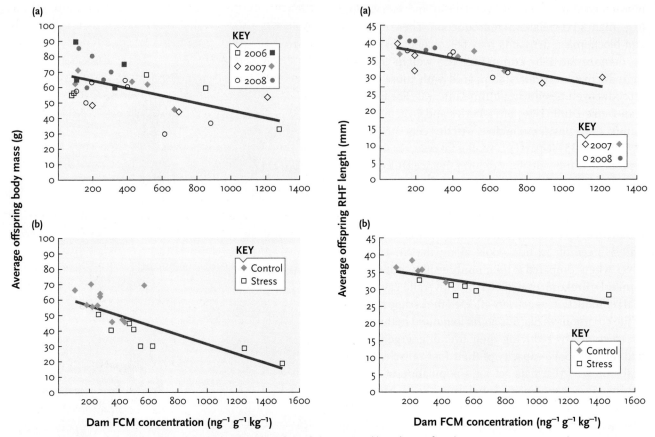

FIGURE 8.19 Physiological Stress and Reproduction Physiological stress caused by a threat of predation can generate reproductive costs. Elevated, predator-induced levels of fecal cortisol metabolite (FCM) in female snowshoe hares (*Lepus americanus*) is associated with reductions in offspring body mass (left panel) and offspring length, as reflected by the right hind foot (RHF) length (right panel).

SOURCE: Sheriff, M.J., C.J. Krebs, and R. Boonstra. 2009. "The sensitive hare: Sublethal effects of predator stress on reproduction in snowshoe hares," *Journal of Animal Ecology*, 78: 1249-1258. Reprinted by permission from John Wiley and Sons, Inc.

antagonistic pleiotropy, and it was first proposed by Williams (1957) as a possible explanation for the evolution of aging, or senescence.

Finally, to accurately quantify reproductive costs, we must be able to estimate the future survival and/or growth of a specific individual at age $x + t$ depending on whether it had reproduced at age x or not. This is an important point that is not always reflected in life-history studies. Although we can get a sense of the magnitude of reproductive costs by comparing reproductive with nonreproductive individuals in the same population (while controlling for variables such as age and size), differences in *quality* between individuals (e.g., physiological condition, learning abilities, foraging behaviour) can, and often do, obscure the true magnitude of costs.

For example, we might undertake a study and find that the average future survival of postreproductive animals is the same as that of nonreproductive individuals of the same population. However, we cannot conclude from such a study that a survival cost of reproduction does not exist in this population. The postreproductive individuals may have been in better physical condition prior to the breeding period, and so better able to survive afterward, than nonreproductive individuals in poorer condition.

To accurately quantify the reproductive costs experienced by a given individual, we need to be able to compare the future conditions (at age $x + t$) experienced by that individual (in terms of survival, fecundity/fertility, and/or growth) depending on whether it had reproduced in the past (at age x) or not. This is not an easy task to undertake, which is why the estimation of reproductive costs is very challenging, despite the logical basis for their existence.

8.3 Natural Selection on Life Histories

A life history is based on the two most fundamental components of life, which are also the two most important metrics of fitness: survival and reproduction. If an individual (i.e., a genotype) is to be evolutionarily successful, it must contribute its genes to succeeding generations at least at the same rate as other genotypes in the population. To do this the individual must survive to an age at which it can reproduce, and contribute to the production of offspring that themselves survive to reproduce and produce viable offspring, and so on.

The central premise of life-history theory is that natural selection favours genotypes whose age-specific schedules of survival (l_x) and fecundity (m_x) result in the highest per capita rate of increase (r), or fitness, relative to other genotypes in the population (see Chapter 5 to review population growth models). This is a fundamental component to the meaning of life, and the reason that the evolution of life histories is among the core areas of research in ecology.

Life-history research also plays a vital role in the applied fields of bioresource management and conservation (see Chapter 14). This is because of the fundamental link that exists between individual life histories and the per capita rate of population growth. As we examined in Chapter 5, the per capita rate of increase (r) is inextricably linked to the ability of a population to sustain various levels of exploitation, to recover after being reduced to a low abundance, and to persist in the face of introductions of non-native species with which it might interact as competitor, predator, or prey.

Life-history theory can also be used to predict how changes to abiotic and biotic environments might influence the fundamental "decisions" that genotypes face concerning reproduction. Consider, for example, the alteration or outright destruction of some area of habitat that is critical for the persistence of a population or species. If such habitat damage were to increase the mortality of adults, there are several questions that might arise:

- Would the increased mortality brought about by habitat damage affect the average age at maturity, or the level of reproductive effort, in the population?
- If reproductive effort is affected, what are the potential consequences for survival, growth, and reproductive success?
- If changes in life-history traits are favoured by natural selection, what consequences might they have on per capita population growth rate, and thus on the likelihood of persistence of the population or species?

Age at Maturity and Reproductive Effort

Age at maturity reflects an evolutionary compromise between the benefits and costs to fitness of reproducing early or late in life. Benefits associated with early maturity, which results in a reduced generation time, include an increased probability of surviving to reproduce and a greater rate of gene input into the population. However, for many species, particularly those with indeterminate growth, early maturity can also reduce in fecundity/ fertility and postreproductive survival because of the smaller body size typically associated with earlier

maturity. A major cost of delaying maturity is the increased risk that an individual will die before it actually gets a chance to reproduce. By contrast, the primary fitness advantage to delaying maturity (although not necessarily for those with determinant growth) is the larger initial body size attained by individuals when they first reproduce. In general, the larger an organism is, the greater are its chances of surviving to later years, the higher the number of offspring that can be produced (if female), the higher the probability of securing a mate and/or fertilizing eggs (if male), and the greater the ability to provide parental care.

Assuming that natural selection acts on age-specific expectations of producing future offspring (Fisher, 1930), the optimal age at which an individual matures can be predicted from the mean and variance of the probability of surviving through the juvenile and adult stages, that is, of survival preceding and following the age at maturity, respectively. The life stages are as follows:

Birth--------------------Maturity------Senescence or Death
|----juvenile stage (j)----| |---------adult stage (a)----------|

Under natural selection, reductions in the ratio of adult to juvenile survival (s_a/s_j), or increases in the variance in adult survival relative to that of juveniles [$\sigma^2(s_a)/\alpha^2(s_j)$], are predicted to favour younger age of maturity and increased reproductive effort (Cole, 1954; Gadgil and Bossert, 1970; Schaffer, 1974). These predictions make intuitive sense. As external mortality (i.e., that *not* associated with reproduction) at potentially reproductive ages increases, selection would be expected to favour those individuals (genotypes) that reproduce prior to those vulnerable ages, thereby increasing their probability of contributing genes to future generations. A similar argument can be made for environmental perturbations that increase the variance in survival at potentially reproductive ages, because increased variance in survival is associated with increased uncertainty of an individual's continued longevity.

When considering the influence of survival on life-history evolution, it is vitally important that mortality attributable to external sources be distinguished from that caused by internal ones resulting from reproductive costs. External sources of mortality are those upon which natural selection will primarily act, potentially leading to changes in the expression of life-history traits of individuals. Internal sources of mortality are those resulting from "decisions" pertaining to reproduction, such as the amount of energetic or biochemical resources allocated to gonadal development or to parental care, and age and size at maturity. In other words, when thinking about how selection affects life history by acting on age-specific survival (l_x; and ultimately changes in r), it is the age-specific survival driven by external sources of mortality

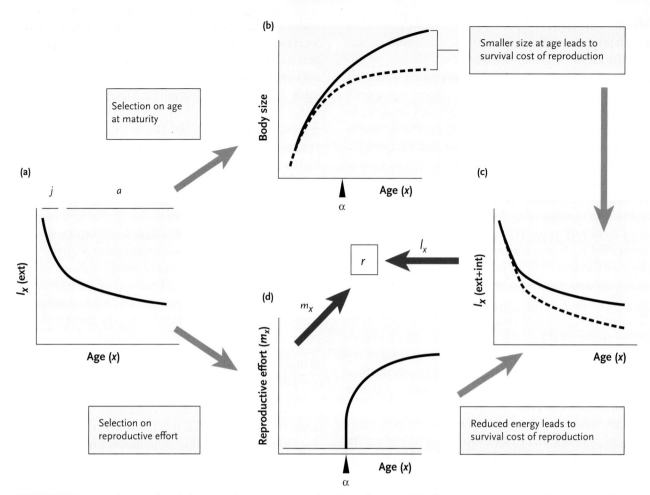

FIGURE 8.20 Survival, Fecundity, and Fitness This diagram provides a basic framework for illustrating how age-specific schedules of survival and fecundity determine the fitness associated with the life history of an indeterminately growing organism. The pattern of survival due to external causes ($l_{x(ext)}$) experienced during the juvenile (*j*) and adult (*a*) stages (panel a) is a primary determinant of how selection acts on age at maturity (α). Maturity results in a diversion of energy from somatic tissue (which increases body size) to gonadal tissue, resulting in a decline in the growth trajectory (panel b). The survival cost associated with reproduction leads to a downward shift in the curve that relates age-specific survival caused by both external and internal (reproductive decisions) sources of mortality ($l_{x(ext + int)}$) (panel c). The age at maturity also influences the amount of effort that is expended at reproduction, a pattern that can be represented by the number of eggs produced by a female (m_x) (panel d). The resulting fitness (represented by *r*) associated with the life history in question is, then, a consequence of both age-specific rates of survival and fecundity.

($l_{x(ext)}$) that initiates or drives selection. But it is the age-specific survival, which incorporates both external and internal sources ($l_{x(ext + int)}$) that is included in life tables (Chapter 5) and in formulas such as the Euler–Lotka equation when we seek to estimate *r*.

The process of natural selection on age and reproductive effort at maturity can be illustrated in a graphical form. **Figure 8.20a** shows the age-specific survival schedule that is experienced by an individual in a particular environment (it is reminiscent of the Type III Survivorship Curve illustrated in Chapter 5). The ages encompassed by the juvenile (*j*) and adult (*a*) stages are shown. Predicated by this survivorship schedule (which we designate $l_{x(ext)}$ because it is driven by external factors in the environment), natural selection has favoured a particular age at maturity, α_{black} (indicated by the black triangle on the horizontal axis in **Figure 8.20b**). This in turn affects individual growth (for an indeterminately growing

organism) by slowing the rate of increase in body size with increasing age (dashed line in **Figure 8.20b**) relative to what growth would have been if the individual had not matured at α_{black}. Because of the positive correlation that typically exists between body size and survival, the smaller size at age resulting from maturity (represented by **Figure 8.20b**) contributes to reduced survival postmaturity. This is depicted by the dashed line in **Figure 8.20c**, which identifies the age-specific schedule of survival resulting from both external sources and internal allocation decisions associated with reproduction, that is, $l_{x(ext + int)}$. [Note that the solid line in **Figure 8.20c** is the same as the curve in **Figure 8.20a**; the cost of reproduction can be thought of as the *difference* in the survival functions in the absence (solid line) and presence (dashed line) of reproduction.]

The survivorship schedule given in **Figure 8.20a** will also favour, via natural selection, a particular reproductive effort at maturity (and pattern with subsequent ages). At

α_{black}, the reproductive effort (represented in **Figure 8.20d** by m_x) will be higher (curved line) relative to what it would be in the absence of reproduction (essentially nil, as reflected by the horizontal solid line). Given that effort expended toward reproduction will necessitate the diversion of resources that might have enhanced survival in other ways, the reduced energy available to individuals after maturity can be expected to contribute to the survival cost of reproduction (**Figure 8.20c**). The resultant fitness associated with this life history is given by r, and it is a function of both l_x and m_x, as described by the Euler–Lotka equation.

Now, assume that some factor external to the organism results in increased mortality, which is realized primarily during the adult stage; this is reflected by the red survivorship function shown in **Figure 8.21a**. This change would result in a reduction in adult survival (s_a) relative to that experienced during the juvenile stage (s_j), leading to a

decrease in the ratio of adult to juvenile survival (s_a/s_j). As illustrated in **Figure 8.21b**, life-history theory would predict that this would favour earlier maturity at α_{red} (represented by the red-coloured a) and a concomitant change in growth rate (red curve). The smaller sizes at subsequent ages would then result in further reductions in postreproductive survival, resulting in lower values of $l_{x(ext + int)}$ (**Figure 8.21c**). Theory also predicts that the change in survivorship depicted in **Figure 8.21a** would lead to increased reproductive effort at (and beyond) α_{red} (red line in **Figure 8.21d**) as well as increased survival costs. The new age-specific schedules of survival (red l_x) and fecundity (red m_x) can ultimately be expected to lead to a change in fitness, which is represented by the red-coloured r.

A long-term study of guppies inhabiting streams in Trinidad provides one of the best empirical tests in a wild population of the prediction that reductions in the ratio

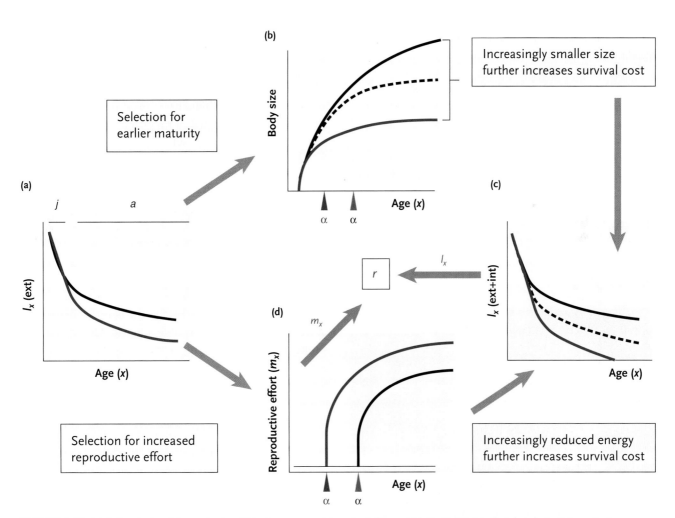

FIGURE 8.21 Adult Survival and Reproduction This diagram provides a basic framework for illustrating how reduced adult survival can select for earlier age and increased reproductive effort at maturity. Decreased age-specific survival, notably among adults, results in selection for earlier maturity and increased reproductive effort, both of which are associated with increased reproductive costs that ultimately have an impact on fitness. Compared to the original (black) survivorship schedule in panel a, the new age-specific schedule of survival (red) reflects a decline in the ratio of adult (a) to juvenile (j) survival which, in turn, is predicted to favour a reduction in age at maturity (red α, compared to the original age at maturity represented by the black α) (panel b). This reduction in α is associated with smaller size at maturity, which, in turn, leads to further reductions in age-specific survival (red curve) after reproduction (panel c). Higher reproductive costs, coupled with higher reproductive effort (panel d), will lead to a life-history induced change in fitness (r).

of adult to juvenile survival should favour earlier maturity and increased effort (Reznick et al., 1990). Guppies were transplanted from an area in which predation on adults was high, compared to that on juveniles, to another habitat where predation on adults was greatly reduced. This would have meant that the ratio of adult to juvenile survival (s_a/s_j) would have increased. After 30 to 60 generations following this shift in predator-induced mortality from adults to juveniles, guppies with the presumed increase in (s_a/s_j) had lower a reproductive allotment (weight of eggs per unit of female body weight) and higher age at maturity, exactly as theory would predict.

In another study, Michael Fox and Allen Keast (1991) of Queen's University compared the life histories of pumpkinseed sunfish (*Lepomis macrochirus*) from five populations in eastern Ontario that experienced either high or low levels of overwinter mortality (**Figures 8.22** and **8.23**). They found that males and females that inhabited high adult-mortality environments matured earlier and allocated a greater proportion of their body tissue to their gonads than did populations in low adult-mortality habitats.

Hutchings (1993), who estimated (s_a/s_j) directly for brook trout populations in southeastern Newfoundland, noted that reductions in the ratio of adult to juvenile survival were associated with earlier maturity and increased reproductive effort. Similarly, Wolfgang Jansen (1996) of the University of Alberta found a negative association between age at maturity and reproductive effort (the latter indicated by the proportion of gonadal tissue to total body weight, and by size-specific fecundity) for populations of yellow perch (*Perca flavescens*) in central Alberta.

Fish have also proven amenable to tests of predicted changes in life history that are associated with differences in the variance of adult survival relative to that of juveniles. Bill Leggett and Jim Carscadden (1978) of McGill University examined population differences in age at maturity among five populations of American shad (*Alosa sapidissima*) ranging from Florida to New Brunswick. In accordance with life-history theory, they found that males and females in the northern populations, for which they presumed juvenile mortality is more variable than in southern populations because of climatic influences, matured up to 11 percent and 14 percent older, respectively, than did southern ones. They also found that northern populations of shad produced fewer eggs per unit body size, and had a higher incidence of repeat spawning than southern ones, which again was presumed to be due to differences in variation in juvenile mortality.

Influence of Growth Rate on Life History

Growth rate is of major importance to life-history evolution, particularly in organisms that continue to grow after attaining maturity. This is because of the relationship of growth rate to the body size at any age, and the positive associations that can exist between body size and various metrics of fitness. Once the minimum body size has been attained at which reproduction can occur, the maturation strategy of an individual is predicted to depend on the consequences to its present and future survival and fecundity of reproducing at various ages.

A trade-off between present and future fecundity, caused by declines in growth rate once maturity has been attained, formed the basis of initial predictions of how growth rate might influence life history (Gadgil and Bossert, 1970; Bell, 1980). For example, Schaffer (1974) predicted that environments that allowed for increased growth during potentially reproductive ages should favour delayed maturity and increased reproductive effort. Hutchings (1993) introduced a theoretical framework similar to that of the ratio of adult to juvenile survival. He argued that studies of the effects of growth rate on life histories should partition the growth experienced during the juvenile stage from that experienced by adults (with effects of individual reproductive decisions excluded from the estimates). He predicted that increases in juvenile growth rate relative to that of adults should favour increases in reproductive effort and reductions in age at maturity. These predictions were subsequently borne out by empirical data on populations of brook trout in Newfoundland, pumpkinseed sunfish in Ontario (Fox, 1994), and brown trout in Sweden (*Salmo trutta*; Näslund et al., 1998).

r- and K-Selection

It has long been assumed that life histories have evolved to form highly generalized patterns of coadapted life-history traits, and that these should be broadly

FIGURE 8.22 A Pumpkinseed Sunfish (*Lepomis gibbosus*) This colourful fish inhabits warm, still waters with abundant vegetation in southern and eastern Ontario and in southeastern Quebec, as well as much of the eastern United States. Its mortality rates were studied by Fox and Keast (1991); see Figure 8.23.

Mirage3/Dreamstime.com

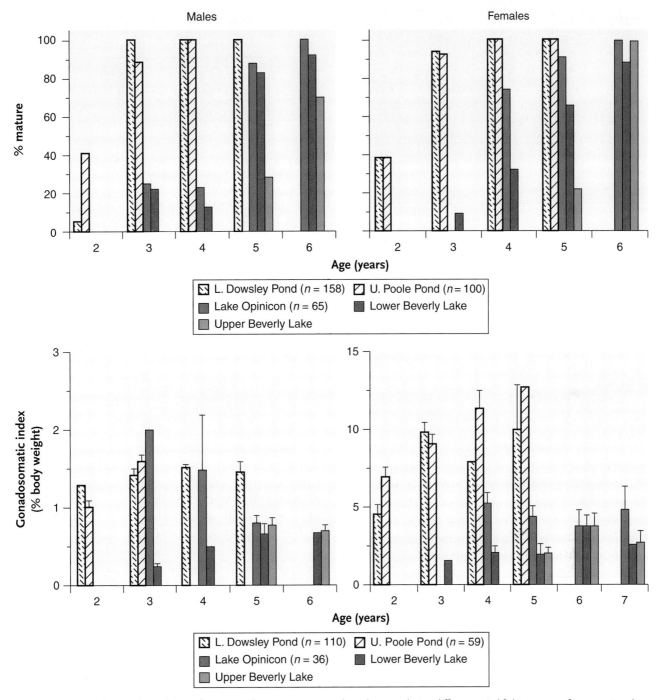

FIGURE 8.23 Adult Mortality Affects Life History These comparisons show that population differences in life history are often associated with population differences in adult mortality. Pumpkinseed sunfish (*Lepomis gibbosus*) from populations in which adult overwinter mortality is high (Lower Dowsley Pond, Upper Poole Pond) mature earlier in life (upper panel) and allocate greater reproductive effort (lower panel) than those from populations in which adult overwinter mortality is low.

SOURCE: Fox, M.G. and A. Keast. 1991. "Effect of overwinter mortality on reproductive life history characteristics of pumpkinseed (*Lepomis gibbosus*) populations," *Canadian Journal of Fisheries and Aquatic Sciences*, 48: 1792-1799. © 2008 Canadian Science Publishing or its licensors. Reproduced with permission.

evident among various groups of organisms. In the 1960s, population density was thought to be a key selective influence on life-history evolution (see Chapter 5). The idea is as follows. When density is low, and intraspecific competition is also low, organisms should be favoured to invest higher amounts of energy and other resources into reproduction, and so to produce many small offspring, each of which should have a reasonable opportunity to survive within the low-competitive environment presumed to exist at low densities (Pianka, 1978). By contrast, in an environment with a high-density population, where competitive interactions are presumed to be intense, the optimal life-history strategy should be one in which resources are more likely to be allocated to competition and body maintenance than to reproduction, a situation that would favour strategies that result in the production of fewer but larger offspring.

TABLE 8.2 | Patterns of Life-History Traits

This table shows typical patterns of life-history traits characteristic of species under r and K-selection, according to Pianka (1970).

Trait	r-Selected	K-Selected
Age at first reproduction	Young	Old
Size at first reproduction	Small	Large
Breeding events per lifetime	Few	Many
Number of offspring	Many	Few
Size of offspring	Small	Large

TABLE 8.3 | Traits of Fast and Slow Life Histories

Trait	Fast	Slow
Fecundity	High	Low
Life expectancy	Short	Long
Age at maturity	Young	Old

Therefore, life histories are expected to depend on whether density-independent or density-dependent competitive interactions are likely to dominate. The selective forces under each of these contrasting scenarios were termed r-selection and K-selection by MacArthur and Wilson (1967). Pianka (1970) then described patterns of covariation of life-history traits that he hypothesized might be characteristic of species under r- and K-selection **(Table 8.2)**.

Although the life histories of some groups of organisms may fall along an r – K continuum of trait covariation (e.g., mammals; Stearns, 1983), a limitation noted by Pianka (1978) and others is that many (and perhaps most) do not (e.g., salmonid fish; Hutchings and Morris, 1985) (see Ecology in Depth 8.1). An additional point that has troubled many researchers of life-history evolution is the fact that *all* organisms are r-selected, insofar as natural selection will always favour a life history that maximizes r in any particular environment. Natural selection cannot act on the carrying capacity of a population, a circumstance that renders the term "K-selection" confusing. Despite these limitations, and perhaps driven by a human penchant for categorization, the terms "r-selection" and "K-selection" and the suites of life-history traits with which they are thought to be associated, are frequently used by ecologists.

An analogous and arguably similarly ambiguous set of terms is that of *fast* and *slow* life histories (Gaillard et al., 1989; Dobson and Oli, 2008). There is evidence within birds and mammals that species can be arranged along a continuum of life-history trait covariation that distinguishes species **(Table 8.3)**. However, these are essentially the same suites of traits that are characteristic of r and K-selection, but they are given the "new" names of fast and slow life histories, respectively.

A Plant-Focused Classification

There are also life-history classifications that focus on plants. One proposed by Philip Grime (1977, 2002) has classified plants into three groups—competitors, ruderals, and stress tolerators—based on their life-history

traits and adaptedness to habitat conditions, particularly to the influences of disturbance and stress **(Figure 8.24)**. According to Grime, disturbance is the partial or total destruction of vegetation and it can be mild or severe in intensity, and uncommon or frequent. Stress is any condition that reduces the rate of productivity, and it can be mild if moisture, nutrients, and light are freely available, or intense if any of them are deficient. Any environment can be characterized in terms of the influence of these two factors, resulting in four major kinds of habitat conditions:

- low stress, rare disturbance;
- low stress, frequent disturbance;
- intense stress, rare disturbance; and
- intense stress, frequent disturbance.

Because plants cannot cope with an environment that is both highly stressful and frequently disturbed, Grime describes only three major life-history strategies of plants, competitors, ruderals and stress tolerators, with most species falling somewhere in the middle of the C_S_R triangle **(Figure 8.24)**. **Competitors** (C-type) dominate in habitats in which environmental stress is relatively benign and disturbance is rare, so that competition is the major agent of natural selection on plant evolution and on the organization of their communities. Competitive plants are effective at acquiring resources and in achieving a dominant position in their community. Typical adaptations are tall growth, a broad canopy, and a spreading root system, all of which occupy space and appropriate resources. Seedlings of competitive plants can usually establish beneath a closed canopy. Most tree species are competitors.

Ruderals (R-type) are adapted to living in recently disturbed habitats with abundant resources, so that stress is not intense. Ruderals are typically short-lived and intolerant of competition and stress. They grow rapidly and produce large numbers of seeds that usually have an ability to widely disperse so that newly disturbed habitats can be colonized. Many agricultural weeds are ruderals.

Stress tolerators (S-type) are adapted to difficult environments in terms of climate, moisture, and nutrient supply, but that are stable because they are infrequently disturbed. Stress-tolerant plants are typical of arctic, desert, and other severe environments, and they are

ECOLOGY IN DEPTH 8.1
The Fallacy of Fecundity and Extinction Risk in Marine Fish

Unprecedented reductions in the abundance of a variety of species have hastened efforts to identify factors related to the risks of extinction. Several life-history traits are potentially useful in this regard, as correlates of maximum per capita population growth rate (r_{max}, a proxy for extinction; see Chapter 5). The traits include large body size, slow individual growth, long life span, delayed age at maturity, and fecundity (e.g., Gaston and Blackburn, 1995; Reynolds et al., 2005).

Among the potential life-history correlates of r_{max}, arguably none has had a longer history of investigation than fecundity. Many have thought it obvious that fitness should increase with the numbers of offspring produced. Prominent among them are scientists who have studied marine fish. Thomas Huxley (1825–1895), famously described as Charles Darwin's "bulldog" because of the tenacity with which he supported the theory of evolution by natural selection, proffered the following opinion about the sustainability of marine fisheries at the Great International Fisheries Exhibition in London in 1883: "... the cod fishery, the herring fishery, the pilchard fishery, the mackerel fishery, and probably all the great sea-fisheries, are inexhaustible; that is to say that nothing we do seriously affects the number of fish."

Obviously, in view of the many observations of depleted fish stocks in recent times, Huxley was wrong in his belief about limitless marine bioresources. However, his opinion was based partly on the knowledge that most marine fish of commercial importance produce vast numbers of eggs, a trait which he thought would prevent fishing from having any significant impact on their populations.

Remarkably, a similar argument is often heard today, albeit in a modified form. For example, the Food and Agricultural Organization of the United Nations has suggested that "greater potential fecundity tends to make aquatic species more resilient to depletion and results in a lower risk of extinction" (FAO, 2002). The American Fisheries Society concurred with this view, identifying fecundity as a positive correlate of r_{max} (Musick et al., 2000) and a negative one of extinction risk.

However, to a life-history researcher this refrain is deeply flawed because it obfuscates the importance of fecundity to reproductive fitness. This fallacy was, in a sense, recognized at the same Fisheries Exhibition of 1883 by the English biologist, Sir Ray Lankester (1847–1929), who argued, in effect, that the millions of young produced by marine fish are not superfluous. He posited that animal populations are in an equilibrium, such that "those that survive to maturity in the struggle for existence merely replace those which have gone before" (Smith, 1994).

If this is reworded using the terminology of today, it states that when an animal population is at or near equilibrium, for example, at its carrying capacity, natural selection will favour those individuals whose reproductive strategy allows them to produce enough offspring to replace themselves. However, phylogenetic constraints, coupled with the varying challenges that different environments pose to organisms, have conspired to produce a wide variety of reproductive strategies. For example, a porbeagle shark (*Lamna nasus*) is a *K*-selected species producing only one to five large offspring every one to two years, for perhaps 10 to 15 years of reproductive activity; this is the porbeagle's strategy for replacement. In contrast, an Atlantic cod (*Gadus morhua*) is an *r*-selected species producing several hundred thousand to a few million eggs every year for perhaps 5 to 10 years of reproductive activity; this is the cod's strategy for replacement. In an evolutionary sense, however, the two strategies are equivalent in terms of their result—replacement at equilibrium.

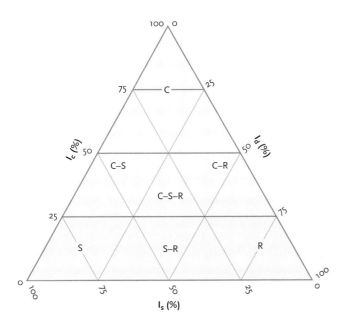

FIGURE 8.24 Plant Life Histories The life histories of plants can be classified into three groups. These are competitors, ruderals, and stress tolerators, and are based on the plant's life-history traits and adaptedness to habitat conditions.

SOURCE: Grime, J.P., "Evidence for the existence of three primary strategies in plants and its relevance to ecological and evolutionary theory," *The American Naturalist*, 111: 1169-1194. Copyright © 1977, The University of Chicago.

generally short of stature, slow-growing, long-lived, and intolerant of competition.

These classification schemes have been of some use to ecologists as a means of organizing life histories and of exploring their adaptive basis. However, rather than continuing to create new terms to describe patterns of life-history traits that are evident in some species but not in others, there may be merit in dispensing with such terminology. Instead, simply describing the observed patterns of covariation, whatever they may be for particular groups of organisms, along a continuum ranging from low to high maximum rates of per capita population growth, r_{max} may be more useful.

Life-History Invariants

The objective of most life-history research is to account for the extraordinary variation in life histories that exists within and among species. An alternative approach has been to focus on the constancy, or invariance, in the associations between certain life-history traits because that phenomenon may reflect adaptive processes of a broad and universal nature across species. Charnov (1993) provides an overview of studies of such **life-history invariants** for a variety of species, and Beverton (1992) for fish, which have been particularly examined in this regard.

Work on life-history invariants reflects a search for constancy amidst a prevailing diversity of relationships among traits. This was evident in quantitative studies of patterns of growth, maturation, and longevity in the late 1950s. For example, Alm (1959) conducted experiments on populations of brown trout in Sweden and sought patterns among their growth rate and age and size at maturity. Similarly, Beverton and Holt (1959) used data primarily from commercially exploited marine fish to investigate general associations among the growth pattern. They used the von Bertalanffy growth coefficient, k, which is based on a model of growth as a function of age (it expresses the rate at which an asymptote is approached) and asymptotic length, L_∞; age (α) and length at maturity (L_α); natural mortality (M); and lifespan (proportional to M^{-1}). Life-history invariants, therefore, are ratios of parameters that are expressed in the same units of measure, so that their ratios are dimensionless. Among the most commonly examined life-history invariants are those between mortality and growth rate (M/k), and length at maturity and asymptotic length (L_α/L_∞).

The practical objective underlying much of the early research to discover life-history invariants was to identify generalizations that could then be used to estimate the natural mortality rate in commercially exploited fish. The value of natural mortality is a parameter that is fundamentally important to fisheries resource management models, but it can be extremely difficult to measure. Daniel Pauly (1980), now of the University of British Columbia, analyzed 175 stocks of teleost (bony) fish and found that the invariant M/k had a value of about 1.7. [In later research, Charnov (1993) suggested a range of possible values of 1.6–2.1.] If an estimate is available of the von Bertalanffy growth coefficient, k, for a given population, which is a relatively easy metric to approximate, then the invariant $M/k = 1.7$ could be used to estimate the natural mortality for that population.

In addition to their practical utility, invariants have the potential to provide insight into the evolution of life histories. For example, the invariant M/k implies that fast-growing species experience higher natural mortality rates than slow-growing ones. Another invariant that appears to have some consistency among taxa is L_α/L_∞, which Jensen (1997) estimated to be 0.66 for fish, implying that maturity occurs at a length that is approximately two-thirds of the maximum.

Although life-history invariants have been studied for about five decades, our understanding and applications of the concept are still in an infancy. Much of the research undertaken to date has searched for constant patterns among combinations of life-history metrics. While this has been a useful approach, the greater challenge is to formulate and test hypotheses that would identify the processes responsible for the observed patterns. It must also be borne in mind that life-history invariants may be more evident in some kinds of organisms, such as fish and mammals (Charnov, 1993), than in others, such as birds (Bennett and Owens, 2002).

8.4 Offspring Size and Number

Why do some species produce many small offspring, while others produce only a few large offspring? This is the central question that has driven ecologists to try to understand the observed variations that exist in what are referred to as offspring-size/offspring-number strategies.

Among plants, for example, the smallest seeds are produced by orchids, only 0.2–1.7 µm long and 1/5 as wide and each weighing about 1 µg, while the largest seeds are those of the coco de mer, up to 30 cm long and weighing as much as 18 kg (Westoby et al., 1992). Among fish, the size of egg released by a female can range from those of the surfperch (*Cymatogaster aggregata*) of the Pacific coast, at only 0.3 mm diameter (Kamler, 1992), to the 14 mm eggs produced by tropical mouth-breeding catfish (Coates, 1988). Among mammals, the smallest newborns are those of the Etruscan shrew (*Suncus etruscus*), only 4–5 mm long, and the largest are the massive calves of the blue whale at up to 6.5 m and 7.3 tonnes (Whitehead and Mann, 2000).

Assuming that only limited resources can be allocated to the production of gonadal tissue, or to seeds, eggs, or embryos, then the number of offspring produced by an individual female during a breeding event cannot increase unless the size of each one decreases. This apparent trade-off between offspring number and their size was first considered in detail by David Lack, a British ornithologist, in the late 1940s. In species of birds in which the young are fed by their parents at the nest (these are known as altricial birds), and for which food resources are limited, the number of young produced cannot increase without a reduction in the amount of nutrition provided to each offspring. Lack (1947) reasoned that the clutch size in these altricial birds was primarily influenced by the number of offspring that parents can feed and raise to the fledgling stage, at which time they become substantially independent of their parents.

The evolutionary implications of the trade-off between the number and size of offspring was initially considered by Gunnar Svärdson (1949), a Swedish fish biologist. He suggested that there must be an upper limit to fecundity, which depends on the influence of egg size on offspring survival and parental reproductive success. Otherwise, he argued, directional selection—or as he put it, a tendency to increase egg number every generation—would favour continual increases in the numbers of eggs per female.

Svärdson (1949) remarked that "from a theoretical point of view it is rather easy to conclude that there must be a selection pressure for decreasing egg numbers, but it is not so extremely evident how this selection works" (p. 115).

The theoretical underpinning of most research investigating the adaptive significance of variability in offspring size/number is a graphical model proposed by Smith and Fretwell (1974), who asked how a parent should distribute a fixed amount of resources to an indeterminate number of young. In their model, optimal offspring size is defined graphically by the point on the fitness function at which a straight line drawn from the origin (the dashed line in **Figure 8.26**) is tangential to the offspring survival curve (the solid curve). In other words, the optimum corresponds to the offspring size at which the instantaneous rate of gain in fitness per unit increase in offspring size is at its maximum. Smith and Fretwell's model has proven to be extremely influential, as evidenced by their 1974 paper being cited more than 1200 times in the scientific literature (ISI Web of Knowledge).

Optimal Egg Size

It has been argued that natural selection acts primarily on the size of offspring, and that their numbers are mainly a by-product of this selective process, given the trade-off described above. In a sense, this is what underlies the thesis of Smith and Fretwell (1974). One might then be tempted to interpret population differences in offspring size as being a proxy for adaptive variation. But for selection to favour particular offspring sizes in different populations or environments, the relationship between their size and survival must also differ in those situations.

FIGURE 8.25 The Size of Offspring Organisms vary enormously in the size of their progeny. Among plants, the largest seed in the world is that of the coco de mer (*Lodoicea maldivica*) of the Seychelles Islands, which has a double-seed that can weigh up to 18 kg.

Courtesy of Brenda Kostiuk

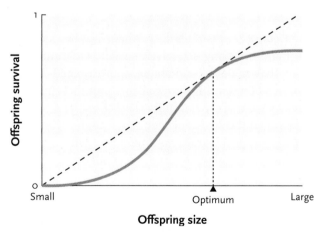

FIGURE 8.26 The Smith–Fretwell Model This model relates offspring survival to offspring size. The optimal offspring size is defined by the point on the fitness function (curved solid line) at which a straight line drawn from the origin (the dashed line) is tangential to the fitness curve.

SOURCE: Based on Smith and Fretwell (1974).

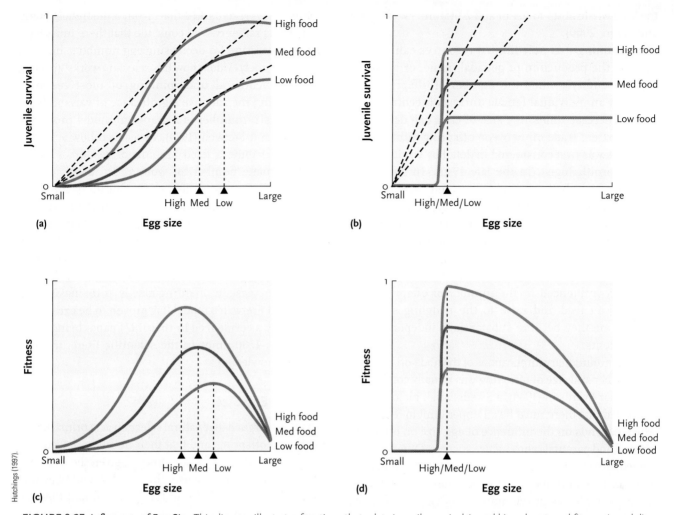

FIGURE 8.27 Influences of Egg Size This diagram illustrates functions that relate juvenile survival (a and b) and maternal fitness (c and d) to egg size. Solid triangles below each x-axis indicate optimal egg sizes. (a) Size-dependent survival: optimum egg size declines with increased food abundance. (b) Size-independent survival: optimum egg size does not vary with food abundance. (c) Size-dependent survival: high-food and low-food environments favour the production of small and large eggs, respectively. (d) Size-independent survival: the egg size at which parental fitness is maximized is independent of food abundance.

SOURCE: Hutchings, JA. (1997). "Life history responses to environmental variability in early life," *Early Life History and Recruitment in Fish Populations* (ed. R.C. Chambers & E.A. Trippel), pp. 139–168. Chapman & Hall, London, with kind permission from Springer Science+Business Media B.V.

Figure 8.27 illustrates the relationships between survival and offspring size given specific environments. Note that maternal fitness is approximated by the product of offspring survival and number (holding gonadal volume constant). Two basic functions are considered: (1) the size-dependent survival, for which offspring survival varies continuously with egg size (**Figure 8.27a**), and (2) the size-independent survival, for which survival above and below a narrow range of egg sizes is constant (**Figure 8.27b**). For the former, any factor that is expected to increase offspring survival across all egg sizes, such as food supply, is predicted to result in a reduction in optimal egg size (**Figure 8.27a**), thus favouring females that produce relatively numerous but smaller offspring (**Figure 8.27c**). In contrast, if offspring survival is independent of their size, the optimal egg size is predicted to unaffected by changes in a factor that increases offspring survival (**Figure 8.27d**).

The evolutionarily stable strategy of investment per offspring in these species would be to maximize the numbers of offspring, each of which approaches the physiological minimum size below which survival probability declines to zero. This may be the basis of the strategy employed by most wind-dispersing plants, most marine invertebrates, and fish that are broadcast spawners (i.e., that disperse their eggs and sperm into the aqueous environment, where fertilization occurs). These exhibit the classic life-history responses of organisms that provide no parental care and disperse large numbers of offspring into the physical and biological vagaries of the environment.

The assumption that resources are allocated evenly among offspring is common to the Smith–Fretwell model (and many others). However, this pattern is not generally observed in nature. The size of eggs, for example, often varies considerably among females within the same population, and even within the gonad, or seed pod, of the same individual. Among-female variability (i.e., within a population) has been attributed in particular studies to such factors as habitat variation in parasitic trematodes (Poulin and Hamilton, 2000), female condition in common eiders (*Somateria mollissima*; Hanssen et al., 2002), and a host of variables in arthropods (e.g., female diet and size, the oviposition host, competition among females, environmental factors such as temperature, and risk of predation; Fox and Czesak, 2000). Within particular females, variability in egg size has been attributed to age in arthropods (Fox and Czesak, 2000), pond type in Hyla tree-frogs (temporary versus permanent sites for egg deposition; Crump, 1981), male attractiveness in mallards (*Anas platyrhynchos*; Cunningham and Russell, 2000; **Figure 8.28**), and risk of egg predation in shield bugs (Acanthosomatidae; Kudo, 2001).

Variability per se has been explained as an adaptation to unpredictable environments (Capinera, 1979). Where the environment is stable from year to year, natural selection might favour a relatively consistent offspring size, whereas a variable environment might favour the production of a range of offspring sizes (assuming, of course, that offspring survival varies with their size). Marten Koops of Dalhousie University and colleagues (2003) tested this prediction within and among female brook trout from 10 populations in Newfoundland. They found support for the hypothesis that females adjust the allocation of resources among eggs in response to unpredictable environmental conditions, as a way of offsetting the cost of imperfect information (**Figure 8.29**). However, they noted that care should be taken to not overly interpret the potential adaptive significance of egg size variability within clutches.

In summary, for natural selection to favour an increase in egg size, the resulting survival benefits to offspring must exceed the fitness costs to the parents of producing fewer eggs. Furthermore, the evolution of strategies for selecting offspring size, or their numbers, depends primarily upon the shape of the function that relates egg size to offspring survival.

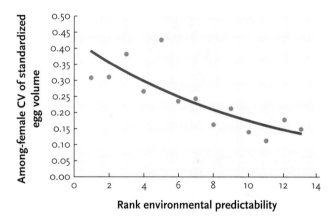

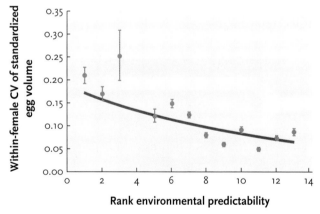

FIGURE 8.29 The Existence of Variable Egg Sizes within Females May Be Adaptive As the year-to-year predictability in the environment declines, variability in egg size increases in brook trout in Newfoundland, whether egg-size variation is measured among females (upper panel) or within females (lower panel). Each point represents a different population; error bars in the lower panel represent 1 standard error.

SOURCE: Koops, M.A., J.A. Hutchings, and B.K. Adams. 2003. "Environmental predictability and the cost of imperfect information: Influences on offspring size variability," *Evolutionary Ecology Research*, 5: 29–42.

Marcelo Saavedra/Shutterstock.com

FIGURE 8.28 Influences on Egg Size Individual female mallards (*Anas platyrhynchos*) lay larger eggs after copulating with preferred males and smaller eggs after copulating with less preferred males (Cunningham and Russell, 2000).

8.5 Alternative Life Histories

Alternative life histories represent combinations of anatomical, physiological, and behavioural traits (polymorphisms) that are correlated to distinctive reproductive alternatives occurring within the same sex, in a single population, at a point in time. These reproductive polymorphisms are common in both invertebrate and vertebrate animals (Taborsky, 2001; Tomkins and Hazel, 2007). One reproductive polymorphism occurs when there are large and small reproductive males in a population. Males that mature relatively early in life, usually at a comparatively small size, attempt to obtain access to females by "sneaking" fertilizations. They compete with later-maturing, larger males. The larger males are behaviourally dominant to the smaller ones, and they have primary access to females through various territorial or mate-defence behaviours (they are sometimes called "fighter males").

The dung beetle (*Onthophagus taurus*) is a widely studied example of alternative reproductive behaviours and associated dimorphisms. The larger males are armed with horns on their head, which help when they fight for access to females, whereas smaller hornless males attempt to sneak copulations (Hunt and Simmons, 2001). Another example is male Pacific salmon (*Oncorhynchus* spp.) typically mature either as smaller "jacks," following a relatively short time at sea, or as larger "hooknose" males (so-called because of the hook-like shape of the jaws), which often spend one or more years at sea (Gross, 1985).

Another excellent of a life-history polymorphism is that exhibited by male bluegill sunfish **(Figure 8.30)**. Field research on bluegills has been undertaken in Lake Opinicon, Ontario, by Mart Gross (1979, 1982) of the University of Toronto and continued by Bryan Neff and Rosemary Knapp (2009) of the University of Western Ontario. In Lake Opinicon bluegills, "parental" males mature at about seven years of age, construct nests, court and spawn with females, and eventually provide sole parental care for their developing young. In contrast, smaller "cuckolder" males become sexually mature earlier in life at a smaller size, but do not construct nests or provide parental care. Cuckolders initially obtain some degree of reproductive success at two to three years of age as so-called "sneaker" males, which dart out from behind a cover of plants and woody debris into nests just when a female is releasing her eggs while spawning with a territory-holding parental male. As the sneakers become older (four to five years) and larger, they become "satellite males" that obtain fertilizations by mimicking a female. By mimicking the colour and behaviour of a female, the satellite misleads a parental male, and manages to fertilize some of the clutch laid by a true female. See Ecology in Depth 8.2 for another example of a life-history polymorphism.

Within populations, the alternative maturation phenotypes can be maintained by several means. As with many characters, the origins of alternative phenotypes may be purely genetic, or a phenotypically plastic combination of genetic and environmental influences. From a semantic perspective, the genetic basis (or lack thereof) of alternative life histories is of some importance as is reflected by a considerable literature on terminology in the field (e.g., Gross, 1996; Taborsky, 2001). The emerging consensus is that alternative life histories should be considered to be different "strategies" only if the differences have an underlying genetic basis. However, if the differences are entirely a function of an individual's status (perhaps reflected by its condition or size) relative to that of others with whom it might compete for mates, then the differences are termed "tactics" (a strategy may comprise multiple tactics).

Environmentally Determined Tactics and "The Best of a Bad Situation"

Within-population variation in reproductive strategies may not be under direct genetic control. Instead, reproductive strategies may reflect a range of mating behaviours and ages/sizes at maturity that are phenotypically plastic, and therefore partly a consequence of variability in environmental conditions. Under these circumstances, the existence of alternative life histories is usually predicated by a difference in dominance rank or status. For a variety of reasons (such as poor feeding opportunities or young age), individuals that are relatively small in size or poor in condition may be subordinate to others that are

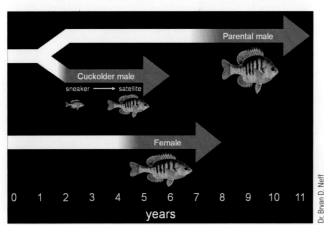

FIGURE 8.30 Alternative Life-History Strategies Male bluegill sunfish (*Lepomis macrochirus*) have two alternative life-history strategies: parental and cuckholder. Cuckholder males exhibit two tactics, as either sneaker or satellite males. Females exhibit a single strategy. The blue portions of the arrows represent sexual maturity.

ECOLOGY IN DEPTH 8.2
Extreme Alternative Life Histories

One of the more phenotypically extreme examples of an alternative life history in vertebrates is that of the Atlantic salmon (Jones, 1959; Myers, 1984; Myers et al., 1986; Fleming, 1996; Hutchings and Jones, 1998). Males can become sexually mature as **anadromous** males, which breed following a migration to the ocean, where they may spend one to three years before they return to their natal river at a weight of >1 kg and age of four to eight years. Alternatively, males may mature early as parr, and thereby reproduce at sizes that are two to three orders of magnitude smaller than anadromous males (only 10–150 g) and at a much younger age (only one to two years). Prior to spawning, mature parr compete physically among themselves for access to a spawning female and her unfertilized eggs, and there may also be stiff competition with one or more much larger anadromous males. As a group, the success that parr achieve in fertilizing eggs may vary between 15 and 60 percent; at the individual level, however, parr fertilization success tends to be low (usually less than 5 percent) and highly variable (for many parr the fertilization success is nil).

The adoption of either of the maturation phenotypes is associated with important life-history trade-offs. The fitness benefits gained by parr that mature at an earlier age include a greater likelihood of surviving to reproduce and an increased rate of gene input into the population, but those benefits are offset by reduced postreproductive survival and reduced fertilization success. In contrast, the higher fertilization success of anadromous males is offset by the low probability of surviving the arduous migration to and from the ocean.

The expression of alternative reproductive strategies in Atlantic salmon depends on both the environment experienced by an individual and on that individual's genetic background. In general, the fastest-growing males in a population are those most likely to mature as parr, and there is evidence that the male progeny of mature male parr are more likely to adopt that strategy than those fathered by anadromous males. To incorporate both the environmental and genetic determinants of alternative reproductive strategies in this species, parr maturation is modelled as a threshold trait such that adoption of either the parr or the anadromous strategy depends on whether an individual's growth rate in early life exceeds that specified by a genetically determined growth-rate threshold.

The existence of alternative strategies in salmon has implications from a management and a conservation perspective. The fact that more than 75 percent of the males in some populations mature as parr (Myers et al., 1986) means that, in some rivers, the number of male salmon returning from the ocean is very small because of the higher mortality experienced by males that mature as parr relative to those that do not. Fewer returning salmon translates into fewer angling opportunities for recreational fisheries. However, the existence of high numbers of mature male parr may provide increased population resilience because of the high genetic variability that they can potentially contribute during spawning. Laura Weir of Dalhousie University (2008), for example, found that as many as 16 males—most of which are parr—could contribute to the fertilization of a single female's egg batch in a tributary of the Miramichi River, New Brunswick. However, despite the ecological, management, socioeconomic, and conservation implications of alternative strategies in Atlantic salmon, there are no monitoring programs for mature male parr in Canada (although these do exist for Pacific salmon jacks in some rivers in British Columbia).

larger and/or healthier. The fitness of individuals exhibiting such suboptimal maturation phenotypes (which may be fixed for a breeding season or for life) is likely lower than the fitness of optimal maturation phenotypes. However, rather than foregoing potential breeding opportunities, the subordinates may be making the "best of a bad situation."

Julian Mainguy and colleagues (2008) of Université Laval studied a population of mountain goats (*Oreamnos americanus*) at Caw Ridge, Alberta, and found that subordinate males adopted an alternative mating tactic of "coursing" (i.e., disruption of a mating pair, often by pursuit of the female). They did this because of their inability to directly compete in jousts with dominant males. Male grey seals breeding on Sable Island, Nova Scotia, also exhibit two mating tactics. The primary one involves prolonged and vigorous defence of a harem of females. The alternative tactic, which results in a fertilization success three to four times less than the primary one, involves mating with females that have weaned their offspring and are leaving the colony (Lidgard et al., 2004).

Derek Roff: Life Histories and Genetics—From Fish to Crickets

FIGURE 1 Derek Roff

Derek Roff is a quantitative evolutionary geneticist whose research papers and multiple books have had a profound influence on the study of life histories (**Figure 1**). After completing his B.Sc. at Sydney University, Australia, Roff moved to Canada where he undertook his Ph.D. at the University of British Columbia under the auspices of C. S. (Buzz)

Holling (whose formulation of functional and numerical responses in predator–prey relationships were examined in Chapter 5). In 1978, Roff took up a position with the Department of Fisheries and Oceans in St. John's, Newfoundland, where he researched the life history and population dynamics of marine fish. In 1980, he accepted a faculty position in the Biology Department at McGill University and then, in 2001, he moved to the University of California at Riverside.

During his time at McGill Roff wrote four of his six books (to date), two of which have been particular landmarks in the study of life-history evolution: *The Evolution of Life Histories* (1992) and *Life History Evolution* (2002). His research on flatfish in Newfoundland led him to explore how correlations among age at maturity, individual growth, and mortality in fish might be a function of evolutionary changes in life-history trade-offs (Roff, 1984). He followed this work with an examination of how life-history models can be used to predict body size, based on the premise that "survival and fecundity, two parameters at the core of Darwinian fitness, are both functions of body size" (Roff, 1986).

While at McGill, Roff began to question how life-history trade-offs might evolve. This collaborative research with Daphne Fairbairn tested hypotheses examining the evolution of trade-offs that exist between flight capability and reproductive traits; these exchanges are evident in many insects, notably the sand cricket, *Gryllus firmus*. Based on his ever-increasing research on the genetics of wing dimorphism in insects, Roff subsequently focused on the evolution of threshold traits (such as alternative reproductive strategies), whereby individuals whose trait exceeds a genetically determined "switch-point" develop into one morph, or life history, while individuals below the threshold develop into the alternative.

Swimming against the academic tide of increasing narrowness in research interests, Roff's intellectual breadth has made him one of few individuals who are knowledgeable about life-history evolution, the trade-offs that constrain the expression of traits, the reproductive costs that affect fitness, and the underlying genetics that govern how natural selection moulds life histories given the ecological and evolutionary vagaries of existence. Roff is a Fellow of the Royal Society of Canada and of the American Association for the Advancement of Science, and his sixth book, entitled *Modelling Evolution*, was published in 2010.

The potential for fishing to cause evolutionary change in life-history traits is not appreciably different from that of other forms of predator-induced mortality—the key is the propensity of exploitation to result in consistently different rates of mortality among genotypes. Nevertheless, many fishery scientists have been reluctant to acknowledge that fishing has the potential to elicit genetic change, or they are doubtful that such an effect would be harmful. The latter point is important because it raises questions as to whether human-induced evolution caused by exploitation is likely to significantly affect population attributes, such as the maximum sustainable yield (Section 5.4), a population's resistance to natural environmental change, or the likelihood of recovery following depletion.

Fishing has long been associated with reductions in two key life-history traits: the age and size at maturity (Hutchings and Fraser, 2008). However, changes in these traits are not necessarily based on direct genetic influences; they could also be caused by phenotypic plasticity in life-history responses to reductions in population density due to harvesting. As density decreases, competition for food and space is relaxed and this should lead to individuals growing at a faster rate. Fish generally respond to an increased growth rate by maturing earlier in life (Wootton, 1998; Roff, 2002). Therefore, fishing could lead to earlier maturity solely as a consequence of density or environment-driven changes to individual growth rates. Alternatively, by selecting against individuals whose genes predispose them to breed at older ages

TABLE 8.4 Fishing and Evolution

These are examples of fish species for which commercial or recreational fishing has been hypothesized to have generated an evolutionary response in one or more traits.

Species	Hypothesized Selection Response	Reference
Northern pike (*Esox lucius*)	Increased fecundity	Law (1979)
Lake whitefish (*Coregonus clupeaformis*)	Smaller body size; slower growth	Handford et al. (1977)
Atlantic salmon (*Salmo salar*)	Smaller size at maturity	Bielak and Power (1986); Consuegra et al. (2005); Quinn et al. (2006)
Pink salmon (*Oncorhynchus gorbuscha*)	Smaller size at maturity	Ricker (1981)
Chinook salmon (*Oncorhynchus tshawytscha*)	Smaller size at maturity	Ricker (1981)
Sockeye salmon (*Oncorhynchus nerka*)	Earlier run-timing	Quinn et al. (2007)
	Smaller girth	Hamon et al. (2000)
	Smaller size at maturity	Kendall et al. (2009)
European grayling (*Thymallus thymallus*)	Earlier age at maturity	Haugen (2000); Haugen and Vøllestad (2000)
Atlantic cod (*Gadus morhua*)	Earlier age at maturity	Hutchings (1999, 2005); Heino et al. (2002); Barot et al. (2004); Olsen et al. (2004, 2005)
	Smaller size at maturity	Barot et al. (2004); Hutchings (2005)
	Smaller body size	Law and Rowell (1993)
	Slower growth	Sinclair et al. (2002); Swain et al. (2007)
Smallmouth bass (*Micropterus dolomieui*)	Earlier age at maturity	Dunlop et al. (2005)
Orange roughy (*Hoplostethus atlanticus*)	Increased fecundity	Koslow et al. (1995)
European plaice (*Pleuronectes platessa*)	Earlier age at maturity	Rijnsdorp (1993); Grift et al. (2003)
	Increased reproductive investment	Rijnsdorp et al. (2005)
American plaice (*Hippoglossoides platessoides*)	Earlier age at maturity	Barot et al. (2005)

and larger sizes, fishing might favour genotypes that mature at a relatively young age, or a small body size, or that grow at a slower rate.

Long-term changes in life-history traits have been interpreted as representing genetic responses to the size-selectivity of fishing gear in a number of fish **(Table 8.4)**. Although it seems logical to hypothesize that harvesting can generate evolutionary change in exploited populations, it should also be acknowledged that there is no unequivocal empirical evidence of genetic change that has resulted from fishing.

There is, however, strong evidence of harvest-induced evolution in a terrestrial mammal. Male bighorn sheep in Alberta are sport-hunted for their impressive horns **(Figure 8.33)**. The longer and more curved the horns, the more desirable they are to trophy hunters, some of whom will pay handsomely for the opportunity to fell a prized ram (one hunter reportedly paid over $1 million for special permits to hunt trophy rams in Alberta in 1998 and 1999; Coltman et al. 2003). Not surprisingly, the largest horns are found on the biggest sheep. David Coltman of the University of Alberta

and colleagues (2003) examined changes in horn size and body weight of bighorn sheep on Ram Mountain, Alberta, where trophy hunters had for several decades been targeting rams with large horns. Within that population, the body weight and horn size of rams declined significantly between 1975 and 2002 **(Figure 8.34)**, and quantitative genetic analyses demonstrated that the reductions in those heritable traits represented an evolutionary response to hunting.

Consequences of Harvest-Induced Changes in Life History

Harvest-induced evolution shifts traits from their naturally selected optimal values. Within that context, it is unlikely that anthropogenic selection for earlier maturity would have positive consequences for an exploited population. Rather, it has the potential to reduce both individual fitness and the maximum per capita population growth rate. Changes such as these can be expected to eventually lead to reduced harvests and diminished ability of exploited populations to recover from decline. Given the

Mars Evis/Shutterstock.com

FIGURE 8.33 A Bighorn Sheep (*Ovis canadensis*) The size and weight of the horns of male bighorn sheep on ram mountain, alberta, have declined as an evolutionary response to hunting; see Figure 8.34.

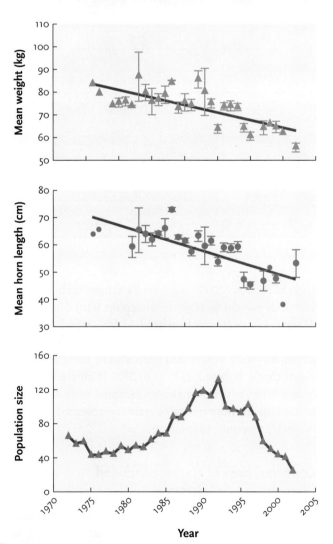

FIGURE 8.34 Hunting and Evolution This graph shows evolutionary change in a terrestrial mammal caused by hunting. Reductions in horn length and body weight of male bighorn sheep on Ram Mountain, Alberta, caused by evolutionary responses to hunting pressure.

SOURCE: Reprinted by permission from Macmillan Publishers Ltd: NATURE, 426, Coltman, D.W., P. O'Donoghue, J.T. Jorgenson, J.T. Hogg, C. Strobeck, and M. Festa-Bianchet. 2003. "Undesirable evolutionary consequences of trophy hunting," copyright 2003.

links between life-history traits and maximum population growth rate, it is surprising that relatively little research has examined the demographic consequences of harvest-induced changes in life history, including harvest-induced evolution.

The potential demographic consequences of life-history change have been examined in northern cod, a marine species that was once commercially important in Atlantic Canada. Between the early 1960s and the early 1990s, northern cod declined by about 99 percent in the region between southeastern Labrador and the northern Grand Banks off Newfoundland, at which point a fishing moratorium was enacted that is still largely in place (in 2013; see Chapter 15).

Between the mid-1950s and the early 1990s, the age at 50 percent maturity of cod (i.e., the point at which half of the population is sexually mature) is estimated to have declined from 6.5–7.0 years to 5.0–5.5 years. Such reductions in the age at maturity might be interpreted as a genetic response to intensive fishing (Olsen et al., 2004). Based on the empirically supported premise that the probability of surviving reproduction declines with reductions in age and size at maturity, Hutchings (2005) reported that a shift in age at maturity from six to four years for cod could potentially reduce the population growth rate by 25–30 percent, while doubling the likelihood of population decreases occurring in subsequent generations. More recent work, however, suggests that fisheries-induced evolution might not negatively affect cod recovery (Kuparinen and Hutchings, 2012).

One prediction that is common to studies of harvest-induced evolution is that the genetic changes will be slow to reverse themselves. An example of this may be provided by the work of Doug Swain and colleagues

(2007) of the Department of Fisheries and Oceans on cod in the southern Gulf of St. Lawrence. They concluded that the observed decline in individual growth rate of cod can be attributed to fisheries-induced selection against individuals that are genetically predisposed to grow fast (more rapid growth leads to individuals more quickly achieving a size that is vulnerable to fishing, while also extending that period of exposure). An important observation is that slow growth has persisted in this over-exploited cod population, despite large reductions in fishing pressure and seemingly favourable environmental conditions for individual growth over the past two decades. The persistence of small sizes is consistent with the hypothesis that the strength of selection for rapid growth when fishing pressure is low is unlikely to be as large as that against fast growth when the harvesting intensity is high (Law, 2000).

There is a simple mitigation of the problem of harvest-induced life-history evolution—reduce the intensity of harvesting. There are good reasons to believe that management strategies that are designed to minimize deleterious evolutionary change are consistent with traditional objectives, such as the maximization of yield, establishment of mortality reference points, and minimization of the likelihood of population decline (Hutchings, 2009). As such, adherence to conventional management reference points may be sufficient to safeguard against undesirable evolutionary change in exploited populations. For that to work, however, the intensity and size selectivity of the fishing pressure must be set at appropriate levels.

CHAPTER SUMMARY

(LO 8.1)

- There are extraordinary differences in the ways in which organisms attempt to propagate genes to future generations. These differences in life-history traits are reflected by variability in age and size at maturity, offspring size and number, and lifespan. An individual's life history ultimately affects its fitness.

(LO 8.2)

- A trade-off is a negative association between traits; for example, the size of offspring is negatively correlated with offspring size. Reproduction has a cost to future reproductive success in terms of reduced survival, fecundity, and/or growth.

(LO 8.3)

- Comparisons of the likelihood of survival before and after maturity can be used to predict the age at which individuals should reproduce and the level of reproductive effort that they should expend.

(LO 8.4)

- The size and number of offspring produced by an organism depends on how an organism's size in early life affects its survival. This can, in turn, be influenced by factors such as food availability and environmental predictability.

(LO 8.5)

- The differences in life history observed among species can often be observed among individuals in the same population. One prevalent example is the existence of small, young and larger, older males that compete against each other for access to females. This can be explained by frequency-dependent selection.

(LO 8.6)

- As with any predator–prey relationship, human activities such as fishing and hunting can create genetic change. By altering the selection pressures to which individuals are exposed, human-induced evolution can select for life histories in harvested populations (e.g., younger age and size at maturity) that differ from those in unharvested populations.

(LO 8.7)

- The life history of an individual determines its fitness which in turn can be measured by that individual's genotypic rate of increase, r. This is the same parameter that is used to describe population growth rate (Chapter 5). Given that r determines things such as sustainable rates of harvesting and ability to recover following depletion, life histories provide a fundamental link between individual fitness, population growth, resource management, and conservation biology.

QUESTIONS FOR REVIEW AND DISCUSSION

1. Age and size at maturity often differ between males and females in the same population. In most birds and mammals, males usually mature at an older age, and larger size, than females. Natural selection may favour increased age in males because of the positive influence that larger size can have on male competitive attempts to secure a territory or to gain access to one or more females. In fish, however, it is usually the female that matures at an older age. Why might this be so?

2a. The data below are a life table for a fish of moderate fecundity, such as a salmon. For each of four potential ages at maturity (2 through 5 years), the two right-hand columns indicate the age-specific schedules of survival (l_x) and fecundity (m_x) at each age x. (No individuals live beyond six years.) Regarding age-specific survival, note that this value is the product of three factors: (a) the exploitation rate; (b) the survival cost of reproduction; and (c) annual survival probabilities from age x to age $x + 1$. Regarding age-specific fecundity, these data include a fecundity cost of repro-duction. [For example, note that the m_4 value for individuals maturing at age 4 (1600 eggs) is greater than the m_4 value for individuals maturing at age 2 (400 eggs).] The baseline table presented below represents a population that is not fished (exploitation rate = 0 at each age) and that does not experience a survival cost of reproduction. Using the Euler–Lotka equation to calculate the fitness (r), determine the optimal age at maturity for this unfished population for which survival reproductive costs are absent. (The optimal age at maturity is the one that yields the highest fitness.)

Age at Maturity (years)	Age (x)	(1—Exploitation Rate) (A)	(1—Survival Cost of Reproduction) (B)	Annual Survival (C)	Age-Specific Survival, l_x (=l_{x-1}*A* B*C)	Age-Specific Fecundity, m_x
2	0	1	1	1	1	0
	1	1	1	0.2	0.2	0
	2	1	1	0.1	0.02	100
	3	1	1	0.5	0.01	200
	4	1	1	0.5	0.005	400
	5	1	1	0.5	0.0025	800
	6	1	1	0.5	0.00125	1600
3	0	1	1	1	1	0
	1	1	1	0.2	0.2	0
	2	1	1	0.1	0.02	0
	3	1	1	0.5	0.01	400
	4	1	1	0.5	0.005	800
	5	1	1	0.5	0.0025	1600
	6	1	1	0.5	0.00125	3200
4	0	1	1	1	1	0
	1	1	1	0.2	0.2	0
	2	1	1	0.1	0.02	0
	3	1	1	0.5	0.01	0
	4	1	1	0.5	0.005	1600
	5	1	1	0.5	0.0025	3200
	6	1	1	0.5	0.00125	6400
5	0	1	1	1	1	0
	1	1	1	0.2	0.2	0
	2	1	1	0.1	0.02	0
	3	1	1	0.5	0.01	0
	4	1	1	0.5	0.005	0
	5	1	1	0.5	0.0025	6400
	6	1	1	0.5	0.00125	12800

b. Part (a) of this question required the determination of the optimal age at maturity for an unfished population for which survival reproductive costs were absent. To determine how a survival cost might influence this optimum, let the survival cost of reproduction (which can vary from 0 to 1) be 0.2. This can be interpreted as meaning that the probability of surviving from one age to the next after maturity has been attained is reduced by 20 percent [represented by $(1 - 0.2)$] in column 4 of the life table). How has the optimal age at maturity for this population changed once a survival cost of reproduction has been incorporated?

c. Part (b) of this question required the determination of the optimal age at maturity for an unfished population for which reproduction reduced annual survival probabilities by 80 percent. To determine how fishing mortality might influence this optimum, let the exploitation rate (which can vary from 0 to 1) be 0.4 for fish older than 2 years of age (meaning that 40 percent of the 3-, 4-, 5-, and 6-year-olds are removed annually by fishing). What is the optimal age at maturity for this population when it is subjected to a 40 percent exploitation rate?

Community Ecology

LEARNING OBJECTIVES

After studying this chapter you should be able to:

1. Distinguish between Clements' organismal concept of community organization and Gleason's individualistic concept, and explain the differences of equilibrium and non-equilibrium views of community organization.

2. Understand various levels of the functional organization of communities.

3. Distinguish between an organism's fundamental niche and its realized niche.

4. Explain how various processes contribute to structuring natural communities, such as competition, facilitation, herbivory, predation, and disturbances, in addition to the effects of rare and unpredictable events of disturbance.

5. Distinguish between dominant species and keystone species, and understand their influences on a community.

6. Describe circumstances under which a community may exist in more than one stable state.

7. Discuss the various models of community structure, such as top–down versus bottom–up regulation, trophic cascades, and those proposed by Connell and by Menge and Sutherland.

9.1 The Nature of the Community

An ecological **community** is a group of organisms that live together at the same place and time and interact directly or indirectly. A community includes all of the organisms present—plants, animals, fungi, and bacteria—and their interactions may involve competition for scarce resources (such as light, nutrients, food, or water), herbivory, predation, disease, or cooperative relations such as **facilitation.**

But how do we define "a group of organisms"? Pioneers to North America would have recognized the "forest community" in the east, which gave way abruptly to a vast "grassland community" that stretched to the Rocky Mountains. The vegetation of the Rockies provided yet another type of "forest community." But any hiker, trapper, photographer, or naturalist will be quick to point out that there are many different types of habitats within

each of those ecological regions. For example, if you were to travel eastward from coastal British Columbia, you would pass through a series of noticeably different vegetation zones **(Figure 9.1)** (Pojar and Meidinger, 1991; B.C. Ministry of Forests, 1996–1999):

- a coastal low-elevation zone dominated by western hemlock (*Tsuga heterophylla*) **(Figure 9.2)**;
- a zone in the southern interior with open forests of Douglas fir (*Pseudotsuga menziesii*) and interspersed dry grasslands;
- a cedar (*Thuja plicata*) and hemlock zone;
- a region dominated by ponderosa pine (*Pinus ponderosa*);
- different types at higher elevation, such as forests dominated by Engelmann spruce (*Picea engelmanii*) and subalpine fir (*Abies lasiocarpa*); and
- above these there are alpine tundra and non-vegetated rockfields.

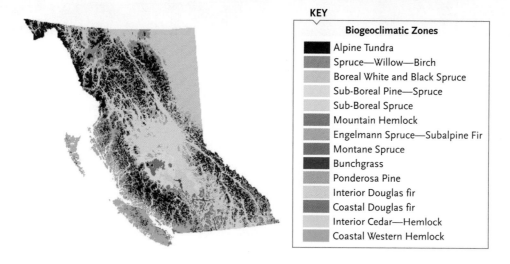

KEY

Biogeoclimatic Zones

- Alpine Tundra
- Spruce—Willow—Birch
- Boreal White and Black Spruce
- Sub-Boreal Pine—Spruce
- Sub-Boreal Spruce
- Mountain Hemlock
- Engelmann Spruce—Subalpine Fir
- Montane Spruce
- Bunchgrass
- Ponderosa Pine
- Interior Douglas fir
- Coastal Douglas fir
- Interior Cedar—Hemlock
- Coastal Western Hemlock

FIGURE 9.1 The Biogeoclimatic Zones of British Columbia The distinctive geological and climatic environments of each zone result in the development of a characteristic vegetation type mostly dominated and characterized by the trees after which the zones are named.

SOURCE: Ministry of Forests and Range. 2009. *Biogeoclimatic Zones of British Columbia*. http://www.for.gov .bc.ca/hfd/library/documents/ treebook/biogeo/biogeo.htm. Copyright © Province of British Columbia. All rights reserved. Reproduced with permission of the Province of British Columbia. www.ipp.gov.bc.ca

Moreover, a variety of community types are embedded in all of these major biogeoclimatic zones, including distinctive forests of various ages and species composition, other kinds of terrestrial communities, and various sorts of wetlands, ponds, lakes, and streams. As the plant composition changes, so too will the kinds of animals, fungi, bacteria, and functional groups such as pollinators and decomposers.

Community Organization

Discrete versus Continuous Organization

Change in one or more environmental factors across space is called an **environmental gradient**. That kind of change can be rapid, or more gradual. For example, as we travel across a landscape, there are places when one ecological community ends relatively abruptly and is immediately replaced by a different one. This typically

FIGURE 9.2 A Coastal Western Hemlock Forest The coastal Western Hemlock zone occurs from sea level to mid-elevations (up to 900 m in British Columbia), mostly west of the coastal mountains and stretching from northern Oregon and Washington, along the entire BC coast and into Alaska. The zone covers much of Vancouver Island and Haida Gwaii (formerly the Queen Charlotte Islands).

occurs in conjunction with a sudden change in soil type or in elevation **(Figure 9.3a)**. It is more usual, however, for communities to gradually transition from one type to the next **(Figure 9.3b)**.

In either case, rapid or gradual, the zone of transition is called an **ecotone**. In part, the disparity of these changes reflects a fundamental difference of opinion about the nature of communities. The most extreme positions are represented by two American ecologists: Frederic Clements (1874–1945), who emphasized the nature of the community as a holistic entity (Clements, 1916, 1936), and Henry A. Gleason (1882–1975), who focused on the individualistic responses of species within a community (Gleason, 1926, 1939).

Clements, along with British ecologist Arthur G. Tansley (1871–1955), proposed the **organismal (or community unit) hypothesis** of the community. They argued that a community acts like a "superorganism"—a highly organized and closely integrated entity that is composed of mutually interdependent species that are to varying degrees co-adapted (see Section 9.3 for more details about symbioses). Stephen A. Forbes (1844–1930) expressed a similar opinion about species living together in lakes (Forbes, 1887). This view assumes that the species comprising a community have overlapping habitat requirements, and therefore we would predict that fairly narrow boundaries would be observed between community types, with few species in common **(Figure 9.4a)**. This view argues that groups of species function in concert toward some predictable end-point of succession, such as a stable and predictable ecosystem that is referred to as the climax (or **climax community**; see also Chapter 10).

In contrast, Gleason's **individualistic (or continuum) hypothesis** views the community as a coincidental assemblage of species that have similar environmental requirements. While the species of a community interact, there is no predictable or repeatable end-point **(Figure 9.4b)**.

riekephotos/Shutterstock.com

FIGURE 9.3 Abrupt and Gradual Gradients Natural grassland is abruptly replaced by trees along this elevation gradient in Central Mongolia (left). White spruce forest above the Slims River, Yukon, more gradually gives way to dwarf shrubs and then alpine vegetation (right).

Each community is viewed as being unique because it is the product of the specific environmental conditions that occur at any particular place and time. Because all species are distributed independently, they have overlapping distributions along physical environmental gradients, and so there is continuous variation in community composition, rather than the discrete boundaries of the Clementsian organismic model. In Section 10.3, you will learn more about Clements and Gleason and how their theories relate to successional changes in community structure over time.

Although many ecologists agreed with Gleason's arguments, the ideas of Clements had a stronger following at the time (about the 1920s through the 1940s). Indeed, it was not until the mid-1950s to 1960s that Robert Whittaker (1920–1980) seriously challenged Clements' view of a community. Whittaker (1956, 1975) surveyed vegetation along elevation gradients in the Great Smoky Mountains of Tennessee, the Siskiyou Mountains of Oregon, and the Santa Catalina Mountains in Arizona. In all of those disparate places, he demonstrated that forest communities changed gradually in species composition

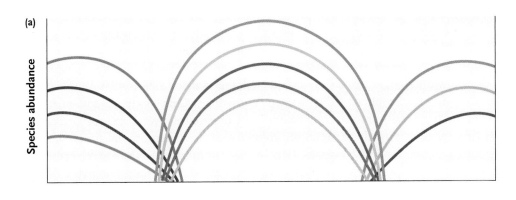

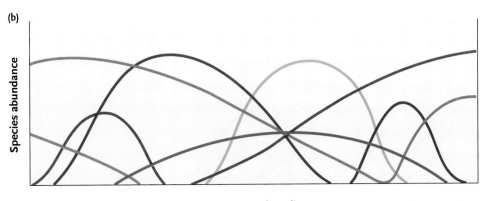

Environmental gradient

FIGURE 9.4 Comparison of Two Models of the Structure of Communities (a) Clements predicts discrete community types with sharp ecotones between them, while (b) Gleason suggests there is continuous variation. The distributions of plant species (each coloured line represents a different plant species) are shown along a continuous gradient of environmental change.

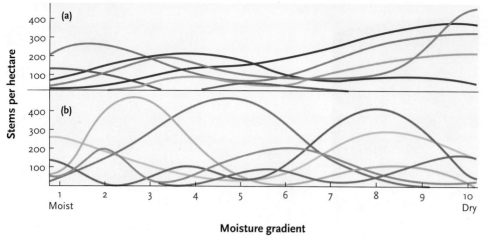

FIGURE 9.5 Whittaker's Distribution of Vegetation in Mountains in Oregon and Arizona The distributions of tree species (each coloured line represents a different species) are shown along a continuous gradient of environmental change (moisture) associated with increasing altitude.

SOURCE: R. H. Whittaker and W. A. Niering, "Vegetation of the Santa Catalina Mountains, Arizona III. Species Distribution and Floristic Relations on the North Slope," *Journal of the Arizona Academy of Science*, Vol. 5, No. 1 (Mar., 1968), pp. 3-21. Used with permission.

(a) Siskiyou Mountains, Oregon

(b) Santa Catalina Mountains, Arizona

and without sharp boundaries along elevation gradients **(Figure 9.5)**, and in so doing he showed that Gleason's view on boundaries was correct. Discrete boundaries do unquestionably occur in some cases, but they are usually related to underlying abrupt changes in environmental conditions, such as a rapid change in moisture between a lake and an adjacent upland, or in places where the soil type suddenly varies because of the local geology.

A conceptual development of important topics is central to any field of science, including ecology. The historical dichotomy of communities as superorganisms (sensu Clements), or as more random assemblages of species due primarily to a varying environment (sensu Gleason), is still being challenged. Today, most ecologists recognize that some elements of both arguments are valid, but most hold to a view more similar to that of Gleason than of Clements. Nevertheless, like so many topics in ecology, wide variations of opinion are driven by differences in observations and analyses. For example, Christopher Lortie and colleagues (2004, 2006) of York University proposed an integrated community concept as a more all-encompassing method of accounting for the species composition of communities; this includes competition and facilitation, but also stochastic processes (involving chance or probability), abiotic tolerances, and indirect interactions with other trophic levels.

In fact, an insufficiently critical interpretation of Gleason's arguments might lead us to believe that the distributions of species are determined solely by their individualistic tolerances of environmental factors, such as moisture, temperature, or light. However, species do interact, sometimes quite closely, and so we must consider the ways that competition, symbioses, and other biotic processes might influence the distribution of organisms. We will deal with this key topic in more detail in Section 9.3, but for now we can imagine a situation in which competition between certain species may produce relatively discrete boundaries, so that we might observe some Clementsian-like ecotones embedded within an otherwise Gleason-like continuum **(Figure 9.6)**. Moreover, maps force us to pigeon-hole community distributions in a Clementsian fashion, although this is also a useful and practical way of displaying their extent (see Chapter 13). In addition, many communities are composed of several layers of species, for example, ground vegetation, shrubs, and trees within a forest. If these layers act independently, it may be possible to observe continuous change in the composition of the ground layer, but discrete changes in the trees.

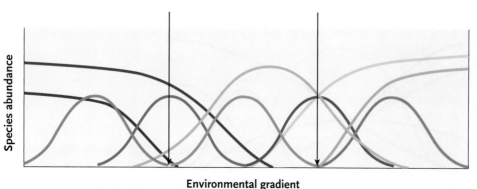

FIGURE 9.6 Combination of the Models of Clements and Gleason Discrete, Clementsian boundaries may be embedded within an otherwise Gleason-like continuum.

Most of what we have considered so far applies to terrestrial systems; aquatic systems have somewhat different, although often overlapping, patterns of organization. In particular, the primary determinant of the distribution of organisms is their physiological tolerance of factors in the abiotic environment (e.g., light intensity, temperature, nutrients, and pH). Those abiotic factors may be modified by the influences of neighbours and also by variability in the physical environment. In aquatic systems water is often moving (e.g., rivers, marine currents, tides, and waves) and this physical dynamic provides a structuring process that is not common in terrestrial systems. Of course, aquatic organisms are adapted to these conditions and may even be dependent on them.

Functional Organization

Communities are also organized in terms of the functional roles that species may play. We previously noted in Chapter 3 that species can be organized into *food webs*, in which functional relationships within a community are organized by their feeding relationships. Within that context, communities can be studied in their entirety—including the various species that are *autotrophs, herbivores, carnivores,* or *detritivores* (Figure 3.19). Often, however, to reduce the complexity, these trophic levels are considered separately. For example a researcher may study a specific plant community, or a detrital food web.

An additional way of looking at community organization is on the basis of similarities in the ways that species use resources. Species that use a similar resource base are referred to as a **guild**. For example, all of the seed-eating animals (e.g., many rodents and birds) in a desert could be considered a guild, even though they are not necessarily taxonomically related. Likewise, birds, bats, and insects that feed on nectar and pollen can be grouped as a floral-visiting guild **(Figure 9.7)**. Structurally comparable groups of plants are also guilds, such as trees, shrubs, forbs (herbaceous dicotyledonous plants), graminoids (grass-like monocots), and epiphytes (plants that live on other plants, such as many orchids and bromeliads).

Although most researchers use the terms "guild" and "functional group" more or less synonymously, these two concepts actually have different meanings. A guild primarily refers to the mechanisms of resource sharing by species, whereas a **functional group** defines how a resource is processed by different species to provide a specific ecosystem service or function. For example, legumes, alders, and other plants that have the capacity to fix atmospheric nitrogen into ammonia (Chapter 4) constitute a functional group based on that attribute.

Ernst Haeckel, Kunstformen der Natur (1904), plate 99: Trochilidae

FIGURE 9.7 A Floral Guild Birds, bats, and insects that feed on nectar and pollen can be grouped as a floral-visiting guild. This colour plate from Ernst Haeckel's "Kunstformen der Natur" (1899, plate 99) shows a variety of hummingbirds (Trochilidae).

Equilibrium versus Non-Equilibrium Organization

Much of the thinking in ecology, and many of its concepts and theories, have been structured within an **equilibrium framework**—in the context of a relative constancy of conditions because competing influences are balanced. For instance:

- Many of the population models developed in Chapter 5 are based on an equilibrium view.
- The end-point of Clementsian succession is a stable, or equilibrium, condition called the climax community (Section 10.3).
- The theory of island biogeography of MacArthur and Wilson (1967) is an equilibrium model (Section 14.4).

Of course, local environments vary over time and space, and they respond to changes in climate and many other environmental factors. In addition, the populations of all organisms change in unpredictable ways. Communities are dynamic entities because of these real-world variations, and as a consequence much of our thinking about them occurs within a **non-equilibrium framework**. This context also underlies much of what is sometimes called **new ecology** (Section 13.1), a viewpoint that emphasizes complexity and change.

However, the distinction between equilibrium and non-equilibrium theories is only a matter of degree. Equilibrium theories are based on a balance of properties and processes that operate within a community at some point of stability, and they focus attention on how the system returns to that condition after a disturbance. In contrast, non-equilibrium theories focus on dynamic environmental conditions that shift a community away from any apparent equilibrium, with particular attention on the processes that caused the shift and the time for the changes to occur. Expressed in simple terms, non-equilibrium theories focus on the shift away from an apparent equilibrium, and equilibrium theories focus on the return to a stable condition.

It is simplistic to think of a community stabilizing at an equilibrium point for more than a short period of time, but this does not negate the usefulness of equilibrium models. Disturbance and predation are the major non-equilibrium processes that we will later consider in more detail in Section 9.3. These influences can mediate the availability of resources and therefore have the potential to influence the outcome of species interactions, and thereby the structure of communities. Some of the issues raised in this paragraph will be clarified and expanded later on in this chapter, in the section on the intermediate disturbance hypothesis.

Centrifugal Organization

A general model of community organization, called **centrifugal organization**, was proposed by Paul Keddy (1990) of the University of Ottawa, building on earlier models by Rosenzweig and Abramsky (1986). Centrifugal organization is based on the notion of core (or preferred) and peripheral (or marginal) habitats. All species in a community have a shared preference for the core habitat, but each may also be the best competitor in some habitat that is peripheral to the core **(Figure 9.8)**. This means that the diversity of marginal habitats will largely determine the richness of plant species in the community.

Keddy has extended this model to more complex communities and has specifically applied it to those of wetland plants. For example, in marsh wetlands that are dominated by tall graminoids (see Chapter 11), he proposes that a core habitat is characterized by low disturbance, high productivity (>1000 gm^{-2}; **Figure 9.8**), and dominance by taller competitive species such as cattail (*Typha latifolia*; **Figure 9.9**) that can form a dense canopy (its life-history strategy is in the Competitive type group of Grime, described in Chapter 8). In other marsh communities, a core area may be occupied by different competitive species having a similar morphology, such s the reed *Phragmites communis*, or the

blue-joint grass *Calamagrostis canadensis*. Radiating out from these core habitats are various environmental axes that are defined by levels of disturbance or nutrient availability, so that productivity and biomass of the vegetation decreases toward the periphery. Different groups of wetland species and community types occupy specific regions along these radiating axes, with competitively inferior species occurring in the most peripheral habitats.

Community Composition

Naturalists (and ecologists) have long been fascinated by the observation that species may be common or rare. Terms such as "diversity," "species diversity," and "biodiversity" all relate to several key aspects of species occurring in a community:

- the **species richness**, which is the number of species that is present;
- the evenness, or the relative abundance of species; and
- and the **species diversity**, which is an integrated measure of both richness and evenness, and is often calculated by a measure called the Shannon index (or Shannon-Wiener).

These terms and ways to measure them are described in Chapter 12 in the broader context of biodiversity and its conservation. Although we refer to these terms in the present chapter, we are more concerned with the patterns of occurrence of species within ecological communities.

Rank Abundance

If the complexity of species within a community is described using only one indicator, such as the Shannon index of diversity, a lot of valuable information may be lost. This loss can include the ranking of species, which is related to the fact that some are common, others moderately abundant, and many rare. A more complete picture of the diversity of a community can be gained by plotting the relative abundances of species against their rank in abundance—this is called a **rank–abundance** curve **(Figure 9.10)**. Abundance may be measured in various ways, such as the number of individuals, their biomass, or their productivity, although counting "individuals" is not always easy in plant species that spread vegetatively, such as those connected by underground rhizomes.

There are several ways of presenting rank–abundance data. The two most widely used are (1) the logarithmic series, and (2) the log-normal distribution. The **logarithmic series** is characteristic of communities that have a large number of rare species and only a few common ones. If the species in such a community are

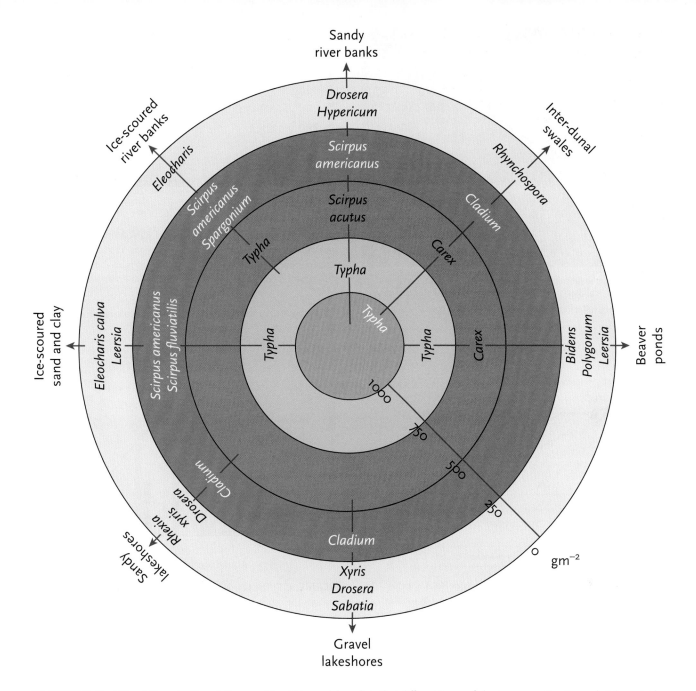

FIGURE 9.8 Centrifugal Organization of Communities This model predicts that different types of plant communities (named at the outside edge of the circle) are organized along gradients of environmental factors that radiate outward from a core habitat, with species and communities sorting out according to their competitive abilities and tolerance of environmental stresses. The best competitors occur at the centre of the diagram where productivity is relatively high, while inferior competitors are at the periphery.

SOURCE: Keddy, P.A. 1990. "Competitive hierarchies and centrifugal organization in plant communities," pp. 265-289. (Figure 5, p. 284). In: *Perspectives on Plant Competition* (J. Grace and D. Tilman, eds.). Academic Press, New York, NY. Reprinted by permission of the author.

divided into abundance classes (i.e., the numbers of species that are represented by a single individual, the number represented by two, by three, and so on), then the logarithmic series predicts that the single-individual species will be the largest class (i.e., it will contain the largest number of species). This pattern was first detected in a classic four-year study of the abundance of moths and butterflies in Britain **(Figure 9.11)**.

When the abundance classes are plotted on a logarithmic scale on the *x*-axis, rather than on an arithmetic one, the numbers of species in the classes are usually normally distributed (i.e., the distribution looks like a bell-shaped curve). This log-normal distribution is illustrated in **Figure 9.12** for the British moth data, and it has also been successfully applied to numerous other communities. Such a log-normal distribution infers that species with an

FIGURE 9.9 Cattail (*Typha latifolia*) This emergent aquatic plant can grow densely and is a strong competitor that appears at the centre of Keddy's model of centrifugal organization of plant communities; see Figure 9.8.

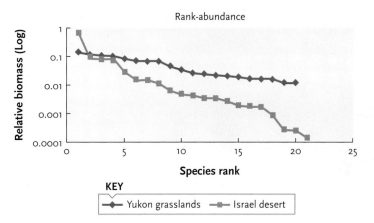

FIGURE 9.10 Comparisons of the Rank–Abundances of Plant Species These data are from perennial grasslands in the Kluane region of southern Yukon and from annual grasslands in the Negev desert of Israel. Both plots form approximately straight lines on a logarithmic plot, which indicates that the abundance of any species is a constant proportion of the next-most abundant species in their community. The slope of the Negev grassland is steeper, which indicates that species evenness is much lower than for the Yukon community. Note that the most abundant Negev species accounts for almost 90 percent of the total biomass of its community, and that most of the other species are rare. In contrast, the most abundant Yukon species accounts for only about 10 percent of the community biomass.

SOURCE: Unpublished data of J. McLaren and R. Turkington.

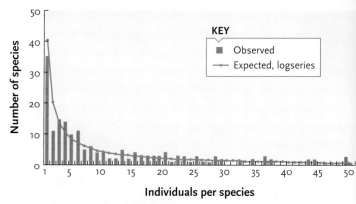

FIGURE 9.11 The Logarithmic Series of Rank Abundance Species of moths were collected over a four-year period at a light-trap at the Rothamsted Field Station in the United Kingdom. The observed rank-abundance series is shown by the bars, and the logarithmic prediction as a solid line.

SOURCE: HUBBELL, Stephen P.; THE UNIFIED THEORY OF BIODIVERSITY AND BIOGEOGRAPHY. © 2001 by Princeton University Press. Reprinted by permission of Princeton University Press.

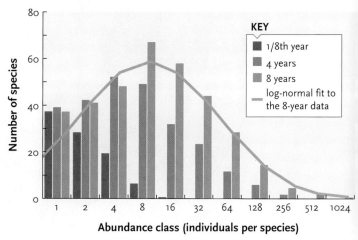

FIGURE 9.12 The Log-Normal Distribution of Rank Abundance In this analysis the moth data from the Rothamsted study were analyzed using progressively larger data sets, and they developed an increasingly better fit to the log-normal distribution.

SOURCE: HUBBELL, Stephen P.; THE UNIFIED THEORY OF BIODIVERSITY AND BIOGEOGRAPHY. © 2001 by Princeton University Press. Reprinted by permission of Princeton University Press.

intermediate abundance are more frequent than rare ones. The log-normal distribution is especially prominent with larger sample sizes, which are more effective at sampling rarer species. Indeed, as the British moth surveys were extended over many years, the observed distribution became increasingly log-normal (Williams, 1964).

The relative abundances of species can also be usefully presented using dominance-diversity curves. These are plots of the logarithm of the abundance plotted against the rank of their abundance, with the most common species on the left of the graph. On such a plot, the logarithmic series is a straight line and the log-normal one is curvilinear (**Figure 9.13**). These types of plots have been applied to many communities. **Figure 9.14** shows the very large number of species of trees in tropical forests (**Figure 9.15**; more than 260) compared to forests at higher latitudes, especially to boreal types (only about 10 species). Note also that the vast majority of species in the tropical forest are infrequent with no dominant species, whereas the boreal forest typically has one or two locally dominant tree species.

Neutral Models

Hubbell (2001) proposed an additional distribution of relative species abundance called the zero-sum multinomial, which he describes as being "log-normal-like."

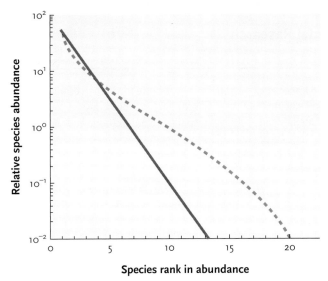

FIGURE 9.13 Dominance-Diversity Curves The logarithmic series is plotted as a straight line, indicating that the abundance of any species is a constant proportion of the next most abundant species in the community; communities with a steeper slope have lower evenness. The log-normal plot is curvilinear and is the more usual distribution with larger sample sizes; this plot shows that the vast majority of species in a community are infrequent.

SOURCE: R. H. Whittaker and W. A. Niering, "Vegetation of the Santa Catalina Mountains, Arizona III. Species Distribution and Floristic Relations on the North Slope," *Journal of the Arizona Academy of Science*, Vol. 5, No. 1 (Mar., 1968), pp. 3-21. Used with permission.

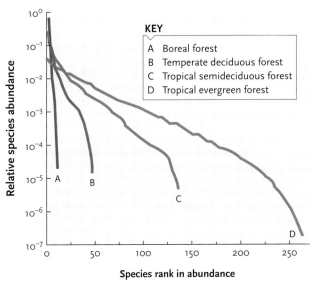

KEY

A Boreal forest
B Temperate deciduous forest
C Tropical semideciduous forest
D Tropical evergreen forest

FIGURE 9.14 Dominance-Diversity Curves These are comparisons of dominance-diversity curves for several kinds of mature forest communities. See the text for a discussion of differences among the forest types.

SOURCE: HUBBELL, Stephen P.; THE UNIFIED THEORY OF BIODIVERSITY AND BIOGEOGRAPHY. © 2001 by Princeton University Press. Reprinted by permission of Princeton University Press.

As data sets on the relative abundance of species get even larger, the distributions frequently have long tails of very rare species; even the log-normal distribution underestimates these scarce organisms. Hubbell's zero-sum multinomial distribution is based on a *neutral model,* and it

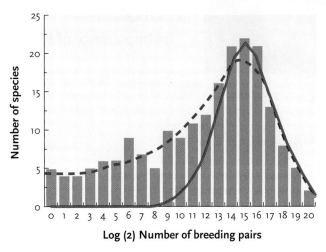

FIGURE 9.15 The Zero-Sum Multinomial Both the log-normal (dashed line) and the zero-sum multinomial (solid line) accurately predict the observed (bars) number of abundant species. However, the zero-sum multinomial distribution more accurately predicts the large numbers of rare species, within a trophic level, that occur in some communities.

SOURCE: HUBBELL, Stephen P.; The UNIFIED THEORY OF BIODIVERSITY AND BIOGEOGRAPHY. © 2001 by Princeton University Press. Reprinted by permission of Princeton University Press.

more accurately predicts the large numbers of rare species, within a trophic level (i.e. all forest trees, or all birds), that occur in some communities.

The zero-sum multinomial distribution works well for British birds (Gregory, 1994) and for trees in closed-canopy tropical forests (Hubbell, 2001). Nevertheless, this model is controversial, in part because it assumes that differences among members of a community are irrelevant, or neutral, to their ecological success. Hubbell treats individual organisms within the community as being essentially identical, in the sense that individuals of any species obey the same rules of ecological behaviour and traits, such as birth rates and death rates. Complex interactions are permitted among individuals of the community, such as competition, provided that all individuals follow the same rules.

The model also assumes that the community is saturated with species, so that new individuals can enter only when existing ones die or leave. When an individual dies, it will be replaced by another individual, chosen at random, regardless of species, and having the same ecological influence on the community—hence the label "zero-sum" for the model (**Figure 9.15**).

Hubbell's original model was based largely on the abundances of tree species in a tropical rainforest in Panama. Such forests are extremely diverse (**Figure 9.16**) and typically have many rare species but few common ones. While Hubbell's model closely predicts the rank-abundance curve, so do some non-neutral models (McGill, 2003).

Fundamental research is inquiry that is driven by curiosity about how the natural world is organized. It is often compared to **applied research**, which is driven by the desire to solve ecological problems. Fundamental research is pursued by many scientists who are inquisitive about nature and its existence, and who are willing to devote their professional lives to improving our understanding of those great questions.

Remarkably, many people hold the view that curiosity-driven research is not as worthwhile as applied work because they cannot understand how non-applied work may be useful. In part, these critics are in error because they are unwilling to acknowledge the many cases in which insights gained from fundamental research have resulted in important applied advances in fields ranging from genetics, to improved materials and energy sources, to technology in general. For example, Gregor Mendel (1822–1884) and Thomas Hunt Morgan (1866–1945) laid the foundation of much of modern genetics by conducting fundamental research on peas and fruit flies, respectively, and Charles Darwin's (1809–1882) fundamental research on the distribution of species opened the door to the theory of evolution by natural selection.

There is a more important reason that critics of fundamental research are short-sighted in their view of the role that kind of basic inquiry plays in our society. The scope of science is not merely to serve the human economy by discovering improved ways of harvesting resources, manufacturing and transporting commodities and products, and handling information. These are obviously important applications of scientific knowledge, but they are not its sole or even its primary rationale. Rather, science is engaged in helping society to understand how and why the natural world exists and functions, and to provide context for the position of humans within that grand realm. Fundamental research helps us understand these big questions in ways that the narrow results of applied work cannot. This is the key reason fundamental research is important, and why it should continue to be well supported.

Roy Turkington

FIGURE 9.16 Species-Rich Subtropical Forest This is an extremely species-rich subtropical forest in Southwestern China in which more than 500 species of trees were present in a study plot of only 0.5 km².

A conceptual development of important topics is central to any field of science, including ecology (Ecology in Depth 9.1).

9.2 Community Structure

A **dominant species** is typically the most conspicuous and abundant one in a community and in most cases it has the greatest influence on community structure and functioning. Nevertheless, in some communities, relatively uncommon species exert a disproportionately strong influence, and these are known as **keystone species** (see also Chapter 14).

Often, a dominant species is defined separately for each trophic level; for example, in the pre-agricultural prairies of western Canada, the dominant plants were grasses and forbs, the dominant herbivores were bison (*Bison bison*) and pronghorn (*Antilocapra americana*), and the dominant predators were the wolf (*Canis lupus*) and grizzly bear (*Ursus arctos*). This natural prairie no longer exists at a geographical scale necessary to support all of those species, but a comparable one survives in the savanna of the Serengeti in east Africa. There, the dominant plants are grasses, the dominant herbivore is the wildebeest (*Connochaetes taurinus*), and the dominant predators are lion (*Panthera leo*) and spotted hyena (*Crocuta crocuta*).

Plant ecologists have generally assumed that dominant species are also the most competitive members of their community. In recently disturbed habitats, however, this may not be the case, and initial colonists may have a large influence on the composition of the community, sometimes even over the long term (see Chapter 10). For example, if most of the early invaders of a recently disturbed site are similar in their dispersal ability, tolerance of local conditions, growth rate, and competitive ability, then their community is likely to be quite diverse. This model is called a **founder-controlled community**, and it may apply to some fish communities on tropical reefs (Sale and Douglas, 1984).

If these assumptions about the equivalence of founder species are not met, then as succession proceeds the communities will become progressively more dominated by competitively superior species—this is referred to as a **dominance-controlled community**. It is interesting that animal ecologists tend not to think of dominant species as being the best competitors, especially among herbivores. For insight into why this may be, refer to the section on "top–down versus bottom–up" control later in this chapter.

Patterns and Processes

The first stage in the growth of any scientific discipline is to describe the subject area being investigated. For ecologists, this is broadly considered to be the structure and function of the natural world, but specifically those parts related to organisms and ecosystems. As we noted in Chapter 1, key considerations are:

- the documentation of species;
- description of the habitats in which they are found; and
- identification of abiotic (e.g., temperature and nutrients) and biotic (e.g., competitors and predators) factors that influence their distribution and abundance.

Consequently, much effort in ecology consists in making such descriptive "natural history" observations, but in a quantitative manner. In fact, almost everything presented so far in this chapter has been a description of patterns of distribution and abundance, with little attempt to provide causal explanations (i.e., related to processes) of how these relationships came to be. In some cases, interpretations were provided of what might be occurring, but usually alternative explanations of the observed phenomena are also available.

A vital aspect of ecological science is to identify important questions for research by making astute observations in the field. For ecology to truly develop as a science, however, we must seek explanations, make predictions, and rigorously test them in two ways:

1. by observing patterns of biological and environmental change (including gradients), and developing statistical and mathematical models of the potential causal relationships; and
2. by conducting controlled experiments (in a laboratory, greenhouse, or in the field), in which factors are carefully manipulated in ways that test the predictions of hypotheses.

Experiments provide powerful tests of hypotheses. In ecology, the best experiments are done in the field, although work done in laboratories is also helpful. Much of the material in the remainder of this chapter examines the design and results of field experiments that have been conducted to investigate carefully framed questions related to ecological processes that influence the patterns of communities that we observe in nature.

Let us begin by imagining ourselves travelling through any natural ecosystem. This could be a tract of boreal forest in northern Canada **(Figure 9.17)**, an eastern deciduous forest, a prairie grassland, a marshy wetland or treed swamp, alpine or arctic tundra, a rocky intertidal zone, a lake, or a subtidal kelp forest. These biomes (Chapter 11) and their embedded communities are typically named after their dominant organisms, which in terrestrial habitats are usually plants. Aquatic systems are typically defined on the basis of abiotic properties such as salinity (freshwater vs. marine), nutrient levels, or water flow. The primary reason for the bias in naming terrestrial systems is evident—it reflects obvious differences in the abundances of the constituent species.

FIGURE 9.17 Biomes in Canada Examples of many of the world's major biomes are found in Canada, ranging from the boreal forest and alpine tundra to prairie grasslands and desert. This portion of the boreal forest in Yukon (top) is dominated by white spruce (*Picea glauca*), with various species of willow (*Salix*) and birch (*Betula*) in the understorey. The Saskatchewan mixedgrass prairie (bottom) is characterized by various species of grass and forbs.

In most terrestrial landscapes, the vast majority of organisms that are seen are plants. Usually they are tightly packed and living in close proximity, often with leaves and branches of nearby individuals intermingling. And although we cannot directly see it, there is a comparable mélange and interaction occurring belowground among the roots and rhizomes of the plants. Knowing this, it is obvious that the plants are competing for space and other resources, and this interaction is a structuring or organizing force within their community.

In contrast, animals are not so apparent in many landscapes because their biomass is much smaller and their frequency of encounter is less (but see Section 3.7 for aquatic food webs). This is particularly true of larger animals—smaller ones, such as insects, may actually be quite abundant but not so easy to visualize. In the case of animals, it is less obvious that competition among them is structuring their community, although the possibility cannot be ruled out. Indeed, with so much plant biomass seemingly available, it has been suggested that herbivores are seldom food-limited and are therefore unlikely to compete for this vital resource (although this may only be true during the growing season—in the wintertime, competition for scarce food may be an important constraint on herbivores that do not hibernate or migrate to avoid the stresses of that difficult season).

Because of these initial ideas by ecologists, the prevalent view, up to the 1970s, was that competition was the major factor influencing the structure of communities. More recently, however, increasing prominence has been given to additional factors, such as disturbance (this includes wildfires and windstorms but also herbivory and other effects of animals on plants) and changing environmental conditions, such as in climate. In Section 9.3, we will examine the influences of competition, herbivory, predation, and disturbance on the structure of ecological communities. But first we will examine an important concept that pervades all of ecology—that of the niche.

The Niche

The **niche** of a species is defined by all of the environmental factors that limit its distribution, growth, and reproduction. The **fundamental niche** is the full range of environmental tolerances of a species, under circumstances in which it is free from interference from other species. In the reality of the natural world, however, species are pressured by competitors and other influences, and so they occupy a **realized niche**, which is a restricted range within the fundamental niche.

Conceptualization of the niche has had a long and sometimes controversial history. The term was first used in an ecological context in 1917 by the American natur-alist Joseph Grinnell to describe the habitat relationships of a bird he was studying, the California thrasher (*Toxostoma redivivum*). It was then more broadly defined by British ecologist Charles Elton (1927) as an animal's "place in the biotic environment, its relations to food and enemies … and the status of an organism in its community." More loosely, Elton considered an organism's niche as its "profession" or "occupation" within a community. However it was Anglo-American ecologist G. Evelyn Hutchinson (1957) and his students who constructed a formal definition of the niche as a multidimensional space, or hypervolume, of environmental factors that a species can tolerate (the fundamental niche), within which it lives (the realized niche), and to which it is well adapted.

Although the concept of the niche as just explained is attractive, it can be difficult to apply to the real world of plants and animals. This is because most niche theory is explained in terms of a single or few dimensions of particularly great influence, such as moisture, temperature, light availability, water depth, size of food items, or others. In nature, however, additional environmental factors are also important, even though a particular influence may indeed have a disproportionate effect on a species. Therefore, species do not often sort themselves on a single environmental axis.

In most diagrams illustrating niche relationships, each species has only two neighbours along a one-dimensional axis. However, there can be many more neighbours in a two-dimensional niche area, and even more in a three-or-more-dimensional volume. It is difficult to conceive of a "space" defined by multiple niche axes, but we can begin to visualize a multidimensional volume by building a three-dimensional one **(Figure 9.18)**.

Consider, for example, a hypothetical species that can establish, grow, and reproduce in a range of moisture conditions. **Figure 9.18a** is a one-dimensional representation (i.e., a line) that assumes no other factors are limiting. In actual fact, however, the species is influenced by more than one factor, so when we add a second factor, temperature, the niche diagram changes to a two-dimensional area. If a third axis is also added, a three-dimensional volume is created. There are also fourth, fifth, and subsequent axes, which unfortunately cannot be depicted on a flat page. Nevertheless, try to understand that this sort of hyperdimensionality is the reality of all species living in nature.

Because all species have unique biological qualities and environmental tolerances, no two of them can have exactly the same niche dimensions. If they did (theoretically) then they could not coexist indefinitely and one species, randomly, would eventually emerge the winner and the other would become extinct. Although species may overlap closely along certain niche axes, they are

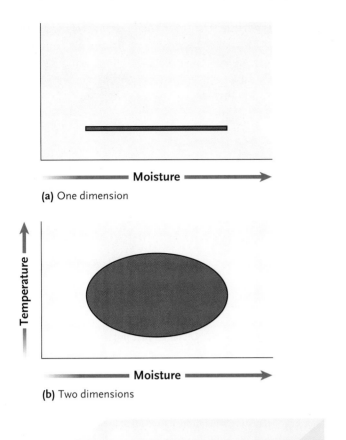

(a) One dimension

(b) Two dimensions

(c) Three dimensions

FIGURE 9.18 A Conceptual Visualization of Niche Dimensions Diagram (a) illustrates a one-dimensional niche axis that is associated with only a single environmental factor, such as moisture; (b) is two-dimensional, perhaps involving soil moisture and temperature; and (c) is a three-dimensional volume that is defined by three factors. If additional niche axes are added, the space is referred to as a hypervolume.

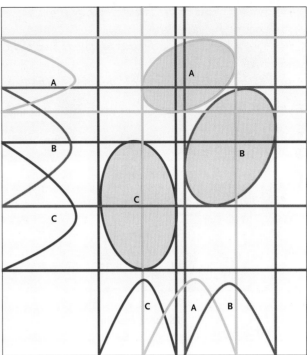

FIGURE 9.19 Overlap of Niches The diagram shows how three species may occupy different but overlapping regions along two niche axes, and how that is further differentiated in a two-dimensional space.

separated along others (**Figure 9.19**). Note that species A and B overlap along each axis in **Figure 9.19**, but when they are put together as a two-dimensional space, there is no overlap. Species C overlaps with species A on the *x*-axis and with species B on the *y*-axis, but in the two-dimensional space, there is no overlap. These basic concepts of niche theory serve as a framework to help understand the effects of competition and other ecological interactions on the distribution and abundance of species.

We will begin to develop the niche framework by assuming that most species in nature exist at some position along an environmental gradient. Such a gradient may take one of two forms. First, there may be a continuous (or actual) gradient of an environmental factor or resource, such as variation of water depth from a pond on to the adjacent land, or changing altitude up a hillside. Alternatively, the gradient may be more abstract, in which the full range of an environmental factor (e.g., soil moisture) is present but in a discontinuous or patchy manner (**Figures 9.20** and **9.21**). For example, a grassland may be quite flat and homogeneous with respect to moisture availability, or it may have a more complex microtopography that includes mounds on top of which the soil is dry, lower dips that are moist or wet, and positions on the slopes with intermediate moisture conditions. The distributions of plant species will reflect the variations of moisture availability, but in either a continuous manner or in a patchy way (**Figure 9.21**). These patterns could be demonstrated by plotting the abundances of plant species on a graph of variations of soil moisture.

The above discussion refers to continuous or patchy gradients occurring at a local scale, but they also exist over greater distances. For example, there are continuous gradients of temperature change along large-scale transects extending from tropical to polar regions. Likewise, large-scale abstract gradients are represented by the wide range

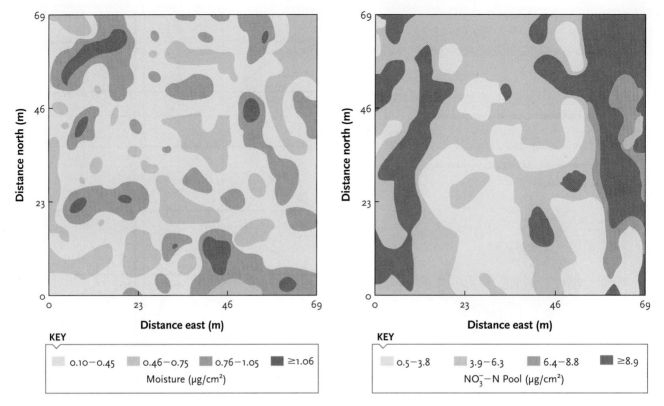

FIGURE 9.20 **Patchy Distributions of Soil Moisture and Nitrogen** This study of soil moisture and nitrogen found that both occurred in a highly patchy distribution, rather than as gradually continuous over space.

SOURCE: Used with permission of the Ecological Society of America, from "Spatial variability in a successional plant community: Patterns of nitrogen availability," *Ecology*, 69 (5): 1517-1524, Robertson, G.P., Huston, M.A., Evans, F.C. & J.M. Tiedje. © 1988. Permission conveyed through Copyright Clearance Center, Inc.

of soil nutrients and moisture levels that occur across the vastness of the boreal forest that stretches from western Alaska to eastern Canada.

Next, we must try to consider the environment from the "view" of a plant or an animal. An organism living in a particular environment is probably not directly influenced by changes in altitude, but rather by variations of a resource that is affected by altitude, such as temperature or moisture. Likewise, changes of water depth in a lake or ocean might not be directly important to organisms, but rather some covarying factor such as the availability of light. The ecologically important aspect of environmental gradients is the fact that important resources and abiotic factors can vary among them. It is these direct, or proximate, factors that affect the distribution and abundance of species along environmental gradients.

We will now apply niche theory to gradients, and show how species richness and coexistence within a community depend on how species compete for resources and so are positioned along gradients. In **Figure 9.22** the *x*-axes represent a changing availability of resources along an environmental gradient (it may be actual or abstract, or small or large-scale). The *y*-axes represent some measure of success of the species, such as fitness, growth rate, or biomass, and are a reflection of the ability

to access resources. Each curve represents a particular species in a community. A species may be a specialist that occupies a narrow portion of the gradient, or a generalist that occurs in a broader portion, and their relative success is indicated by the height of the curve. The overlap of species indicates the degree of competition between them. Complete overlap (not shown) would lead to competitive exclusion, while partial overlap may result in displacement. We will return to these ideas when we consider the effects of competition on the distribution of species.

One of the common phrases uttered by ecologists is "it depends on the circumstances," and this conditionality is part of what makes ecology so excitingly unpredictable. The answers to seemingly uncomplicated questions about pattern, structure, and processes in the natural ecological world are not always obvious. And into this world of founder-influenced and dominance-controlled communities we can introduce the further complexity of species interactions, such as competition, herbivory, and predation. We must also consider the agents of disturbance—wildfire, windstorm, irruptions of destructive animals or diseases, and also anthropogenic influences. In the remaining section of this chapter, we will consider some theory and examples related to each of these vital influences.

(a) 23-yr-old field

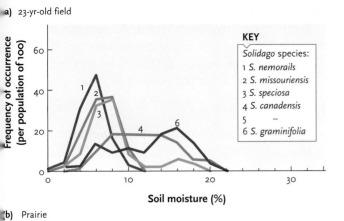

(b) Prairie

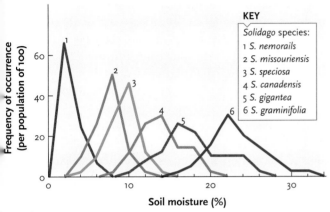

FIGURE 9.21 Distribution of Goldenrod Species along a Moisture Gradient Goldenrod species along a moisture gradient (a) in a field abandoned 23 years before the study, and (b) in a mature prairie habitat that has never been plowed and could be centuries old. Five of the six species of goldenrod occur in the younger abandoned field and the species have broadly overlapping distributions along a soil moisture gradient. In the older prairie, the six species of goldenrod have spread along the gradient resulting in much less-overlapping distributions. In both fields, each species utilized a different range of moisture availability and there were patchy distributions of both soil moisture and goldenrods. However, when species abundance is plotted against soil moisture it "appears" as a gradient, especially in the older prairie.

SOURCE: Modified from: Werner, P.A. and W.J. Platt . 1976. Ecological relationships of co-occurring goldenrods (Solidago: Compositae). *American Naturalist*, 110: 959–971. The University of Chicago Press.

Interactions among Species

The interactions that occur among species are a key subject area in community ecology. The interactions include herbivory, predation, competition, disease, and symbiosis, the latter including mutualism, commensalism, and parasitism. These interactions all influence the presence and abundance of species within communities, and their effects may be direct or indirect.

Herbivory

Herbivory is the consumption of plant tissue by animals. It can occur at various rates and intensities. For example, larvae of the spruce budworm (*Choristoneura fumiferana*) eat the foliage of fir and spruce trees, and they are always

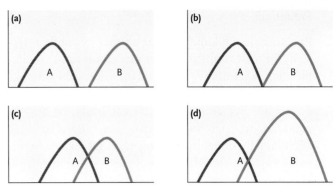

FIGURE 9.22 Resource Partitioning and Niche Overlap There are various ways by which resources may be partitioned among species A and B in a community: (a) there is no overlap and no competition; (b) the niches do not overlap and so there is no competition, although the proximity suggests that there may have been overlap in the past; (c) both species have similar but overlapping niche breadths and are similarly competitive; (d) the species have overlapping but asymmetric niche breadths, and B is a superior competitor to A.

present in a low density in mature stands. Sometimes, however, environmental conditions promote a rapid proliferation of budworm, known as an irruption, and when this happens their voracious feeding can kill almost all mature food trees in affected stands, as periodically occurs in eastern Canada. The destruction of the forest canopy results in many environmental effects, including a high availability of light for previously shaded understorey plants, which respond by growing vigorously. The resulting changes in vegetation affect the habitat of birds and other animals, and microorganisms and other detritivores are affected because large amounts of dead tree biomass are available to be decomposed.

Similarly, when elk (*Cervus canadensis*) are abundant, their feeding can interfere with the regeneration of their favoured species of woody browse, such as aspen and willows, and this has an enormous impact on many of the other species in their community—including plants, herbivores, and carnivores.

Some insects have mouth parts that allow them to puncture plant cell walls and feed on the sugary sap produced in foliage and transported in the phloem tissue. The majority of sap-sucking insects are in the orders Hemiptera (true bugs) and Homoptera (aphids, leaf- and plant-hoppers, and scales). Most of these sap-sucking insects are small but their feeding can affect plant hormones, causing enlarged growths or galls, leaf curling, bleaching, or yellowing of foliage. These abnormal tissues may injure the plant directly by producing necrotic (dead) spots in host tissue and otherwise reducing their productivity. Sap-sucking insects may also affect plants indirectly by introducing lethal diseases. Most sap-sucking insects reduce growth rates and weaken their host plants, but a few are able to kill their food species.

Predation

Predation is the killing of one animal by another, typically for food. Some predators may significantly reduce the abundance of their prey, and in so doing they change the structure of their community. For example, during their breeding season most forest birds eat insects and other invertebrates, which are nutritious for both adults and their rapidly growing nestlings. Experimental studies have enclosed individual plants or small areas of vegetation in netting whose mesh size excludes the avian predators of insects and spiders but allows the invertebrates to freely move about. These studies have observed much higher densities of invertebrates inside the bird exclosures, but slower growth of plants because of defoliation suffered from herbivorous insects (Marquis and Whelan, 1994).

Competition

Competition is an interaction that occurs when two or more organisms require a common resource that is in short supply compared with the biological demand. It occurs when an organism uses more energy to obtain, or maintain, a unit of resource because of interference from other individuals, of the same or different species, than it would otherwise do.

Plants typically compete for access to sunlight, nutrients, and water, while animals compete for food, nesting sites, or mates. If there is great asymmetry in the competitive abilities of species, then the stronger competitors may reduce others within the community, or occasionally may totally exclude some of them. Conversely, if an effective competitor is removed from a community, the previously suppressed species may increase in abundance. For instance, American chestnut (*Castanea dentata*) is a highly competitive tree that was once abundant and widespread in eastern hardwood forests, but it suffered a deadly blight from an introduced fungal pathogen (*Cryphonectria parasitica*) and was rapidly eliminated from essentially all of its original range. When that happened, less-competitive species experienced a degree of ecological release and quickly filled in the gaps left by the dead chestnuts.

Disease

Disease is a biological relationship that involves a pathogenic microorganism infecting a plant or animal, making the host ill and sometimes killing it. Other diseases may be caused by abiotic factors, such as toxic substances. Individuals that are healthy, meaning they have a relative absence of disease, are more competitive, productive, and fecund, and populations of such organisms may be prominent in their community. In contrast, a population affected by a virulent pathogen may be eliminated from its community, and other species will increase in abundance to fill any gaps that were created. For example, the green sea urchin (*Strongylocentrotus droebachiensis*) sometimes irrupts in abundances and severely overgrazes kelps in its intertidal habitat (Scheibling and Stephenson, 1984). However, unusually warm water induces a potent disease of the urchins, which causes their population to collapse and allows the kelp-dominated community to re-establish.

Symbiosis

Symbiosis refers to intimate relationships occurring among species, some of which are obligate so that the symbionts cannot live apart, but more commonly the association is flexible. Symbioses may affect the performance of species by improving their competitive ability and decreasing their vulnerability to predation, disease, or other stresses. There are several kinds of symbioses: mutualisms, parasitism, and commensalism.

Mutualism is a relationship in which both of the partners benefit. Lichens are a familiar example—these are an obligate association of a fungus and either an alga or a cyanobacterium. The fungus benefits from food provided by its photosynthetic symbiont, and the latter from improved access to nutrients and a relatively moist microhabitat. A mycorrhiza is another mutualism; it is an intimate association between plant roots and soil fungi, with the plant gaining enhanced access to nutrients, especially phosphate, and the fungus receiving organic exudates from the roots. Many species of legumes (family Fabaceae) live in mutualisms with nitrogen-fixing *Rhizobium* bacteria, which provide ammonia, an important nutrient, while benefiting from microhabitat provided in specialized root nodules. Pollination is yet another mutualism—the pollinator has access to nectar and pollen as food, and the plant is able to have its ova cross-fertilized with pollen from another individual. Finally, the diverse communities of microorganisms that live in the guts of essentially all herbivorous vertebrate animals are another example of mutualisms. The microorganisms secrete enzymes that help to digest cellulose and lignin so they can contribute to the nutrition of the host. Deer, bison, and other ungulates have a fore-pouch of their stomach known as the rumen that provides specialized habitat for this beneficial community of microbes.

Parasitism is a symbiotic relationship in which one organism benefits but the other is harmed, an influence that may affect its competitive ability and thereby influence its relative abundance within its community. Extreme levels of parasitism may be lethal for the host and can directly reduce the population of the affected species.

Commensalism is a symbiotic relationship in which one organism benefits without harming the other. An example is the community of epiphytic lichens, mosses, and plants that often grows on the surface of trees. The epiphytes obviously benefit from this relationship because they get to grow in a relatively sunny place high in the canopy, but the host trees are not affected to a significant degree.

Effects of Competition on Community Structure

Chapter 5 introduced interspecific competition and the Lotka–Volterra competition model. The Lotka–Volterra model predicts that for two-species mixtures, the outcome of competition may result in an outright winner or loser (Figures 5.25 and 5.26), a coexistence of both species in a stable equilibrium (Figure 5.28), or competitive exclusion in an unstable equilibrium (Figure 5.27).

Clearly then, competition between species can have an important influence on the distribution and abundance of species. Some 65 years before Lotka or Volterra, Charles Darwin remarked on this relationship in his *On the Origin of Species* (Darwin, 1859):

> *We have reason to believe that species in a state of nature are closely limited in their ranges by the competition of other organic beings quite as much as, or more than, by adaptation to particular climates. ... the deeply-seated error of considering the physical conditions of a country [i.e., the soil conditions] as the most important; whereas it cannot be disputed that the nature of the other species with which each has to compete, is at least as important, and generally a far more important element of success.*

In a famous series of laboratory experiments, Georgii Gause (1932, 1934, 1935) grew mixed cultures of protozoans in the genus *Paramecium* to see whether they would co-habit, or if any would become eliminated (see Section 5.5; Figure 5.23). Essentially, yeast was provided as food for the *Paramecium* species, but it was a limiting resource for which the protozoans were competing. Gause observed that species of *Paramecium* were unable to cohabit for long, and that one or the other species would die out in the mixed culture, although he could not always predict which species would be the "winner." Gause interpreted his observations as suggesting that species with very similar ecological needs, that is, with closely comparable or "identical" niches, could not coexist. He called this the **competitive exclusion** principle. However, the work of Gause and many subsequent studies have demonstrated that if the niches of species are not too similar, coexistence is possible.

It is widely accepted that competition has a large influence on the distribution and abundance of species, on their evolution, and on the structure of communities. It is usual to think of short-term responses to competi-

tion, such as the exclusion of a species, as being ecological, and longer-term ones as being evolutionary. For example, if the realized niche of a species is restricted by competition, but the species still retains the ability to occupy its fundamental niche, this is an ecological response. However, if competitive stressors are prolonged and multigenerational, and their associated selective influence results in population-level genetic changes such that an affected species occupies a different range of conditions than before, then the fundamental niche has been altered and an evolutionary response has occurred.

Competition in the Field

As mentioned above, in Chapter 5 you were introduced to interspecific competition and the Lotka–Volterra competition model. Like many topics in ecology, general field observations give rise to questions, and subsequent predictions, that are often framed in terms of mathematical models. The predictions of these models are often first tested under simple laboratory, or highly modified natural, conditions. Then, as theory and knowledge advance, attention often turns to testing theories in less simplified, more natural field conditions; here we will focus our attention on the demonstration of competition in field studies.

A classic study on plant competition was conducted by Arthur Tansley almost 100 years ago (Tansley, 1917). He observed that the bedstraw *Galium saxatile* grows on acidic (low pH) sites in Britain, while *Galium sylvestre* occurs on basic (high pH) limestone soils. He conducted experiments that demonstrated that either species could grow well in both acidic and basic soil, provided they were grown alone. However, when the species were grown together, *G. sylvestre* eliminated *G. saxatile* on limestone soil in about one year, while on acidic soil, *G. saxatile* dominated after six years. These experiments suggest that competitive exclusion is the explanation of the distribution of the two *Galium* species in nature, and not any physiological requirement or tolerance of the special conditions of acidic or basic soils.

The expansion of the distribution of a species in the absence of a competitor is called **competitive release**. It occurs when the fundamental niches of two species have considerable overlap, and when one of them is removed, the other increases its realized niche and thereby occupies a greater portion of its fundamental niche. In the example provided by Tansley, the competitors are closely related, but competition and competitive release can also be demonstrated among unrelated species.

Much of the earliest research on competition was done by zoologists working in laboratories with simple experimental systems that involved species of flour beetles (*Tribolium*) and *Paramecium*. Since then, there have been many field studies of interspecific competition (i.e., occurring between different species). For instance, Koplin and Hoffman (1968) observed that in the Rocky Mountains the meadow vole (*Microtus pennsylvanicus*) lives in both dry and wet habitats, but usually close to a pond or another water source, while the montane vole (*Microtus montanus*) lives only in dry habitats. When meadow voles were trapped and removed from wet habitats, the montane voles immediately began to occupy the vacated areas. Stoecker (1972) performed the opposite test by removing montane voles, and found that meadow voles increased their use of dry habitats. These results show that both of the voles are restricted in their realized niche by the presence of the other species. Many comparable experiments with similar results have been done with other species in various kinds of habitats.

The influence of competition among species in lakes can be easily demonstrated by the addition of nutrients. Schindler (1974) added nutrients to a lake in the Experimental Lakes Area in northwestern Ontario (see Environmental Applications 2.1). They divided an hourglass-shaped lake with a curtain, and fertilized one half with carbon and nitrogen, and the other with phosphorus, carbon, and nitrogen. Only the half receiving phosphorus developed an algal bloom, with cell populations up to 100 times greater than in control lakes, indicating that P was the limiting nutrient for productivity. Moreover, these newly fertile conditions led to strong competitive interactions among lake organisms. Phosphorus addition also caused a rapid increase in other plants in the lake and the algal community changed from dominance by green algae to cyanobacteria.

Competition and Physical Conditions

In previous examples, each species limited the distribution of the other. However, species may also be limited by their tolerance of physical conditions (as well as by competition). This was demonstrated by Grace and Wetzel (1981), who studied the distributions of two species of cattails growing at the edges of ponds. *Typha latifolia* grows primarily in shallow water, while *Typha angustifolia* is more abundant in somewhat deeper habitats farther from the shore. The researchers did field experiments in which each species was grown in isolation along the entire depth gradient. They found that when grown alone, *T. angustifolia* could extend its distribution into shallow water, but *T. latifolia* was not able to grow in deeper water. They interpreted these results as showing that *T. angustifolia* is excluded from shallow-water sites by competition from *T. latifolia*, but *T. latifolia* is excluded from deeper waters by its intolerance of that habitat **(Figure 9.23)**. This situation is known as **asymmetric competition**, which in niche terms means that *T. latifolia* restricts the realized niche of *T. angustifolia*, but not vice versa.

A final example of the interaction between competition and tolerance of physical conditions is provided by a

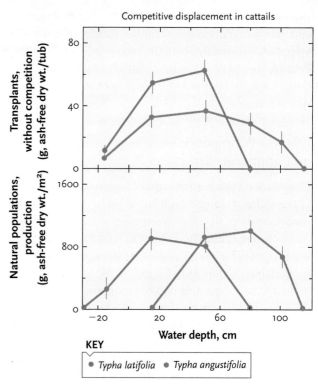

Competitive displacement in cattails

FIGURE 9.23 Distributions of Cattails along a Gradient of Water Depth This field experiment involved growing *Typha latifolia* and *Typha angustifolia* at various depths to determine the importance of competition and environmental tolerance as influences on their distributions in nature.

SOURCE: Modified from: GRACE J., B., and R. G. WETZEL. 1981. "Habitat partitioning and competitive displacement in cattails (Typha): experimental field studies," *The American Naturalist*, 118: 463-474. The University of Chicago Press.

classic series of experiments by Connell (1961a, b) in a rocky intertidal habitat on the Pacific coast. At low tide, the height distributions of many species of invertebrates and macro-algae are clearly delimited as a series of horizontal bands, or zones **(Figure 9.24)**. The stellate barnacle (*Chthamalus stellatus*) occupies the upper intertidal zone, while the rock barnacle (*Balanus balanoides*) inhabits the middle intertidal. Connell performed a series of experimental manipulations that involved transplants and removal of one species or another. These demonstrated that *Chthamalus* could extend its lower distribution downward in the absence of *Balanus*, showing that its lower limit was influenced by competition from *Balanus*. However, the upper limit of *Chthamalus* is set by desiccation, because the animals dry out during the relatively prolonged exposure that occurs during the low part of the tidal cycle, which is most intense in the upper zone. The upper limit of *Balanus* is also set by physical conditions, but because it is even more sensitive to desiccation and high temperatures than *Chthamalus*, it inhabits a lower zone, from which it is able to exclude *Chthamalus*. This study has comparable results and interpretation to that described above for the two species of *Typha*, but it involves animals, albeit sessile ones that mimic some aspects of the ecology of plants.

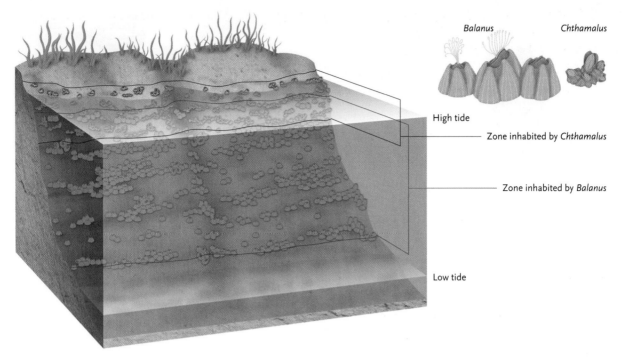

FIGURE 9.24 Distributions of Barnacles along a Rocky Intertidal Gradient

Resource Partitioning

Resource partitioning occurs when species in a community use limiting factors in different ways because they occupy dissimilar realized niches. When species partition resources along a particular gradient, this allows more species to coexist. For example, in the Werner and Platt (1976) study, only five species of goldenrod coexisted along the soil moisture axes in a relatively young field (**Figure 9.21a**). However, in an old prairie, as the degree of overlap of the five species is reduced, an additional species occurs in the community (**Figure 9.21b**).

The *competitive exclusion principle* states that in a stable environment, no two species can occupy the same niche—one will be eliminated. If this is true, then the greater the degree to which species can partition available resources, the more of them can be packed into a community. One of the earliest and most important contributions to this research field was made by Robert H. MacArthur (1930–1972), who was born in Toronto and was a graduate student of G. Evelyn Hutchinson at Yale.

In a classic study, MacArthur (1958) examined the niches of five warbler species (genus *Dendroica*) in eastern spruce forest. All of the warblers are about the same size, feed on insects that they glean from tree foliage and bark, and live in the same kind of forest. In fact, some ecologists at the time believed that these birds might be cohabiting—an exception to the principle of competitive exclusion. However, the meticulously detailed observations of MacArthur showed that the various warblers foraged in and otherwise used different parts of the trees, and thus they do conform to the principle (**Figure 9.25**).

For example, the Cape May warbler (*Dendroica tigrina*) (**Figure 9.25a**) was observed almost exclusively near the tops of the trees. The distribution of the blackburnian warbler (*Dendroica fusca*) (**Figure 9.25b**) overlapped with that of the Cape May but extended farther down the tree. Note that overlap in distribution does not necessarily lead to exclusion—in zones of overlap there may be competition, but if two species do not completely overlap they can coexist. The bay-breasted warbler (*Dendroica castanea*) (**Figure 9.25c**) and black-throated green warbler (*Dendroica virens*) (**Figure 9.25d**) concentrated on the middle branches, while the yellow-rumped warbler (*Dendroica coronata*) (**Figure 9.25e**) spent most of its time in the lower parts of the trees and on the ground. MacArthur also documented that the nesting heights and breeding territories of the five warblers varied, further differentiating their niches. This famous study demonstrated that although the five closely related birds lived in the same habitat and fed on similar foods, they were able to coexist by partitioning the resources.

Root and Shoot Competition

By this stage you may be thinking that competition is the primary structuring factor in communities, and that we have a good understanding of its effects. However, Welden and Slauson (1986) made an important distinction between the **intensity of competition** and the **importance of competition** in studies of plant communities. In this context, "intensity" is the degree to which competition for a limited resource reduces plant performance below the physiological maximum that is otherwise achievable in a given environment. "Importance" is the effect of competition relative to that of other environmental constraints.

FIGURE 9.25 Niche Partitioning by Warblers in a Conifer Forest The five species of warblers forage in different portions of the forest canopy, and this allows them to coexist. The trees are approximately 15 m tall and MacArthur divided each branch into three zones, one of bare or lichen-covered base (B), a middle zone of old needles (M), and a terminal zone of new needles and buds (T). The study area is in coastal Maine.

SOURCE: Used with permission of the Ecological Society of America, from "Population ecology of some warblers of northeastern coniferous forests," *Ecology*, 39(4): 599-619, MacArthur, R.H. © 1958. Permission conveyed through Copyright Clearance Center, Inc.

Competition for light plays an obvious role in structuring plant communities, because larger plants cast shade and so may competitively stress or exclude smaller ones; this is asymmetric competition based on size. In some communities, however, roots make up the majority of the plant biomass and most of the competition occurs belowground. Again, we might expect that plants with a larger root system would have greater access to water and nutrients than those with a smaller one; this would be asymmetric competition based on root biomass.

Eric Lamb and James Cahill (2008) of the University of Alberta examined how competition influenced the structure of a rough-fescue (*Festuca campestris*) grassland community (**Figure 9.26**). There was intense root competition, but it was seemingly unrelated to species richness or community composition, and only slightly related to a small decrease in species diversity. These results raise questions about the role of competition in structuring low-statured communities, such as grassland, desert, and tundra, in which much of the biomass is belowground. Root competition is intense in those habitats, but it may not be so important if it has few measurable consequences for the structure of the plant community (horizontal line on **Figure 9.26a**).

Lamb et al. (2009) further investigated this enigma using experimental "communities" that were planted with nine grassland plants growing under various levels of soil fertility. They measured root and shoot competition. Just as before, they found that increases in the intensity of root competition had no direct effect on species diversity. However, increasing the intensity of shoot competition did cause a reduction of diversity. They also found that increased root-competition intensity resulted in higher shoot-competition intensity. Therefore, while root competition does not *directly* influence diversity in the plant community, it may affect shoot competition, which in turn influences community structure.

Effects of Facilitation on Community Structure

We have been emphasizing the role of competition in structuring communities, but plants in particular may also interact in positive ways. This is referred to as **facilitation**, or a beneficial effect on one species by the influence of another one. The role of facilitative interactions in plant communities was long neglected as a research area, but it has received considerable attention since the publications of Bertness and Callaway (1994), Callaway (1995), and, more recently, Brooker et al. (2008). They pointed out that facilitation not only occurs as one of the processes driving succession, but also influences plant success and community composition in stable, non-successional communities. Christopher Lortie (2010) at York University in Toronto has done extensive research on the value of facilitation as a mechanism to explain changes in

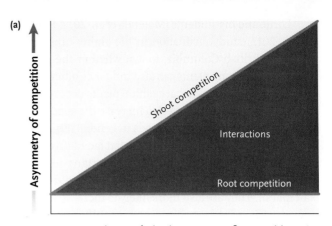

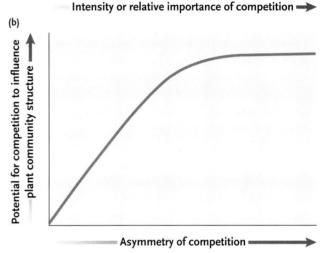

FIGURE 9.26 Root and Shoot Competition This is a conceptual model of competition between roots and shoots in a fescue grassland in Alberta. (a) An increase in the intensity of root competition has no influence on the overall asymmetry of plant competition (horizontal line), and therefore (b) the low asymmetry has little impact on plant community structure (bottom left portion of (b)). In contrast, as the intensity of shoot competition increases (a) it has a strong influence on the overall asymmetry of plant competition, and therefore (b) the higher asymmetry has a large impact on plant community structure.

SOURCE: Lamb, E.G., S.W. Kembel, and J. F. Cahill. 2009. "Shoot, but not root, competition reduces community diversity in experimental mesocosms," *Journal of Ecology*, 97: 155-163. Reprinted by permission of John Wiley and Sons, Inc.

plant community composition along environmental gradients and under varying intensities of environmental stress.

There has been a particular interest in positive, nontrophic interactions that occur between plants, and that are mediated through changes in the abiotic environment or through other organisms. Some researchers have described the classic "nurse-habitat" effects in which rotting logs provide a substrate for the establishment of seedlings, such as those of hemlock trees (*Tsuga species*). Other well-recognized positive interactions include the improved attraction of pollinators by the simultaneous flowering of several plant species, the effects of nitrogen-fixing shrubs such as alders (*Alnus* species) on soil fertility, and the capacity for individuals of the same or different species to share resources through mycorrhizal connections (this is especially important for phosphorus nutrition).

Lortie and his students (Molenda et al., 2012; Reid and Lortie, 2012) study facilitation in the alpine tundra, primarily in British Columbia, to test whether the positive interactions among plants can also influence other trophic levels. They have shown that cushion plants not only facilitate other plant species, but also increase the species richness of pollinators and arthropods in general **(Figure 9.27)**.

One of the common themes is that facilitative effects among plants tend to be most important in severe environments, such as desert, arctic or alpine tundra, and salt marsh. They are also more likely to increase in prominence with increasing altitude, over a shift from warmer to colder environments, and from damper to arid conditions (Bruno et al., 2003). However, plants may be simultaneously competing with their neighbours while also facilitating those same nearby individuals. For example, a larger, more competitive individual may be exploiting limited nutrients such as nitrogen or phosphorus, yet at the same time may provide shelter for a smaller individual, or protection from herbivory.

Brittany Cranston and Luise Hermanutz (2009) of Memorial University of Newfoundland have been investigating whether shrubs of dwarf birch (*Betula glandulosa*) might facilitate the recruitment of tree seedlings (black and white spruce, *Picea mariana* and *Picea glauca*). Their study was conducted in an area of tree-line in the Mealy Mountains of Labrador, an ecotone where boreal forest is transitioning to alpine tundra **(Figure 9.28)**. The tundra experiences colder temperatures, stronger winds, and a shorter growing season than forests at lower altitudes. The hypothesized mechanisms of facilitation involve the birches serving as "nurse shrubs" that enhance the growth and survival of tree seedlings during the critical first growing seasons following germination.

However, as the tree-line and alpine climate warms due to anthropogenic climate change, the relationship between nurse shrubs and tree seedlings could shift from facilitation to competition, which might help the tree-line to advance into currently alpine habitats. In their fieldwork, Cranston and Hermanutz found that the germination and initial survival of spruce seedlings is higher beneath nurse shrubs than in the open tundra. Additional facilitation is associated with the calcium-rich leaf litter of the birch shrubs, which essentially doubles the content of that crucial nutrient in the surface organic mat. Calcium is important because it enhances tolerance to cold, drought, and shade in spruces.

The observation that spruce seedlings have improved emergence and survival within the moderated microenvironment provided by birch shrubs suggests that this facilitative interaction could help the boreal forest invade the tundra as the regional climate warms. As the boreal forest advances, there will be a corresponding decline in the vegetation of the alpine tundra. If the mountains are not high enough to allow tundra plant communities to persist in the region, there will be a decline in the biodiversity of plants and other organisms that are dependent on tundra habitats.

Effects of Herbivory, Predation, and Disturbance on Community Structure

In addition to competition, other biological interactions such as herbivory and predation, as well as disturbances, have an influence on the structure and dynamics of communities. Consider these remarks by Charles Darwin (1859) in *On the Origin of Species*:

> *Seedlings, also, are destroyed in vast numbers by various enemies; for instance, on a piece of ground three feet long and two wide, dug and cleared, and where*

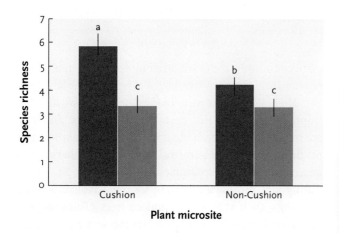

FIGURE 9.27 Effects of Microsite The number of different species (mean ± 1se) of arthropods and pollinators is higher on cushion plants than on non-cushion plants at high-altitude alpine sites on Whistler Mountain, British Columbia. The changes in numbers from non-cushion to cushion plants are statistically significant.

SOURCE: Based on Reid, A. M. and Lortie, C. J. 2012. "Cushion plants are foundation species with positive effects extending to higher trophic levels," *Ecospheres*, 3(11): 96. http://dx.doi.org/10.1890/ES12-00106.1.

FIGURE 9.28 An Ecotone This ecotone is between the boreal forest and alpine tundra near Postville, Labrador. This landscape is similar to that in which Cranston and Hermanutz did their research.

there could be no choking from other plants, I marked all the seedlings of our native weeds as they came up, and out of 357 no less than 295 were destroyed, chiefly by slugs and insects. If turf which has long been mown, and the case would be the same with turf closely browsed by quadrupeds, be let to grow, the more vigorous plants gradually kill the less vigorous, though fully grown plants; thus out of twenty species grown on a little plot of mown turf (three feet by four) nine species perished, from the other species being allowed to grow up freely.

A theme that we have developed in this chapter, and in other places in this book, is that biological interactions have effects on individuals and on populations, and thus on the structure of communities. Farmers have long made practical use of this sort of knowledge, for instance, by adjusting the numbers and species of grazing livestock, such as cattle, sheep, and goats, to manage the species composition and productivity of managed grasslands. In fact, this is essentially what Darwin was speaking to in the second sentence of the quotation above.

However, the effects of herbivores and predators are not always easy to separate from those of other types of disturbances. For example, in his theory of three primary plant strategies, Grime (1977) defines a **disturbance** as "the total or partial removal of vegetation," which of course is what herbivores do when they are eating plant biomass. Some authors limit the use of the word "disturbance" to abiotic events that kill or damage organisms, such as wildfire, flooding, or crashing waves on a shore. However, it may be argued that whatever the agent of damage, whether biotic or abiotic, a space is opened in a community that may be advantageous to certain species. This is the reason that, here and in Chapter 10, we note that disturbances can be caused by both abiotic and biotic agents.

The effects of herbivores or predators on community structure are often the result of them causing a diminished abundance of competitively dominant species. The resulting biological disturbance may be devastating, such as the damaging effects of overgrazing by abundant snow goose (*Chen caerulescens*) on the coastal marshes on La Pérouse Bay in northern Manitoba, the spruce bark beetle (*Dendroctonus rufipennis*) in Yukon **(Figure 9.29)**, the mountain pine beetle (*Dendroctonus ponderosae*) in central British Columbia, or the spruce budworm (*Choristoneura fumiferana*) in eastern Canada. These are all native herbivores, and they can cause stand-replacing disturbances when they are abundant and widespread (see also Chapter 10).

More commonly, however, herbivores cause less-severe disturbances that result in damage, but not of an intensity that is catastrophic to the entire community—these are microdisturbances. For example, grazing animals frequently scratch and leave holes in pastures, in addition to trampling and urinating on them. Of course, herbivores also eat plants in that pasture, but some may do so in a selective manner—they find some species to be tasty, and others to be unpalatable or they may eat only certain plants that grow low to the ground, while leaving taller ones alone. Grazers, for example, feed on graminoids (mostly grasses and sedges) and forbs (herbaceous dicots), while browsers eat leaves and twigs of woody plants, granivores consume seeds and grains, and frugivores eat entire soft fruits. By feeding differentially on plants according to their distinct preferences, herbivores have a great influence on their communities.

The topic of disturbance is examined in more detail in chapters 10 and 11. However, the various causes of disturbances, including anthropogenic ones, are nicely summed up by Townsend et al. (2002, p. 331):

Disturbances that open up gaps (patches) are common in all kinds of communities. In forests, they may be caused by high winds, lightning, earthquakes, elephants, lumberjacks, or simply death of a tree through disease or old age. Agents of disturbance in grassland include frost, burrowing animals, and teeth, feet, and dung of grazers. On rocky shores or coral reefs, gaps in algal or sessile animal communities can be formed as a result of severe wave action during hurricanes, tidal waves, battering by logs or moored boats, fins of careless scuba divers, or action of predators.

Because the effects of disturbances and predation can lead to so many different outcomes, we will focus on a few examples that highlight key ecological principles. Nevertheless, continue to remember that biological interactions and disturbances can have an enormous range of effects in ecological systems.

The Intermediate Disturbance Hypothesis

The great richness of species in tropical rain forests and coral reefs is legendary (see Chapter 12). Such observations force us to question how such high levels of diversity

(a)

Jennie McLaren

Roy Turkington

(b)

FIGURE 9.29 Extreme Herbivory The effect of herbivores and predators on plant communities can sometimes be devastating. (a) A small area on the shores of La Perouse Bay, Manitoba, protected from grazing and grubbing by Snow geese. Without protection, much of the area is reduced to a mud flat. (b) Dead trees caused by spruce bark beetle in Kluane, Yukon.

are maintained. Joseph Connell (1978) argued that in the absence of disturbances, these communities would progress toward lower levels of diversity—to communities dominated by the most competitive species. However, it appears that tropical forests and coral reefs are subject to disturbances frequently enough that this longer-term equilibrium may never be attained. This is a clear illustration of the difference between equilibrium and non-equilibrium models that we referred to earlier in this chapter. In tropical forests, trees or groups of them may be killed or damaged by windstorms, landslides, lightning strikes, or biotic agents, and coral reefs by storms, freshwater incursions, sedimentation, or predators.

Connell's **intermediate disturbance hypothesis** suggests that the highest levels of diversity are maintained at intermediate scales of disturbance **(Figure 9.30)**. It predicts that if the frequency of disturbances is high, then diversity will be low because the times for establishment and

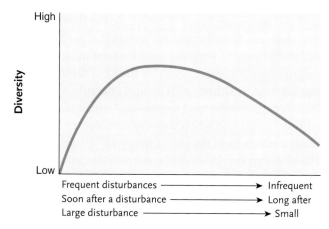

FIGURE 9.30 The Intermediate Disturbance Hypothesis The highest levels of species diversity occur at an intermediate frequency of disturbance.

SOURCE: From Connell, J.H. 1978. "Diversity in tropical rain forests and coral reefs," *Science*, 199: 1302-1310. Reprinted with permission from AAAS.

regeneration are short and only those few species that are producing seed and are within dispersal range will colonize. Such communities will consist of a repeating cycle of species that are capable of quickly reaching maturity. If the interval between disturbances increases, diversity will increase. The additional time permits species that may have poorer dispersal or slower productivity to invade, grow, and mature. These species would have been excluded by more frequent disturbances. If the interval between major disturbances increases further, diversity will decline because the most competitive species will manage to exert their dominance over the system. At a certain intermediate frequency, disturbances will interrupt and prevent the process of competitive exclusion by damaging the most competitive species.

One of the first experimental tests of the intermediate disturbance hypothesis was carried out by Wayne Sousa (1979a, b), a graduate student of Connell. He classified intertidal boulders into groups of small, intermediate, or large, depending on the force of a wave that would be required to move them—smaller boulders are tumbled more frequently and larger ones much less so, allowing more time for organisms to colonize. Sousa then monitored species richness on the various boulders every month for two years. He found that the small boulders supported only barnacles and a green alga (*Ulva*), that rapidly colonized bare rock surfaces, but were poor competitors. Intermediate-sized boulders had a more diverse community that comprised middle successional algal species **(Figure 9.31)**. The largest, infrequently moving

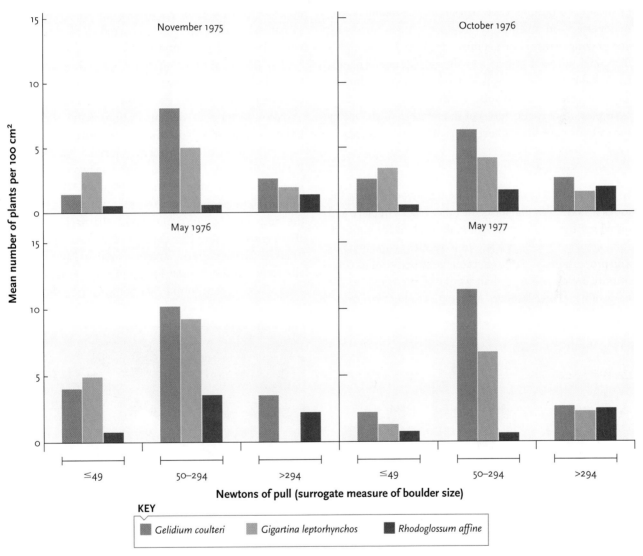

FIGURE 9.31 **The Intermediate Disturbance Hypothesis** Here of the intermediate disturbance hypothesis is illustrated using three species of middle-successional algae growing on intertidal boulders. Because of their lighter mass, small boulders are frequently moved and tumbled by wave action, which prevents many intertidal species from colonizing their surface. In contrast, the largest boulders tumble less frequently and provide a relatively stable environment, which becomes dominated by the most competitive species. This figure shows how the abundance of three species of middle-successional algae changes with degree of disturbance. The highest species diversity occurs on middle-sized boulders, on which species can colonize but the most competitive ones do not have time to become strongly dominant.

SOURCE: Used with permission of the Ecological Society of America, from "Disturbance in marine intertidal boulder fields: the nonequilibrium maintenance of species diversity," *Ecology*, 60(6): 1225-1239, Sousa, W.P. © 1979. Permission conveyed through Copyright Clearance Center, Inc.

boulders were covered with a single red alga, *Gigartina canaliculata*. These results demonstrate that there are more species on the intermediate-sized boulders than on either the smaller or larger ones, which supports the intermediate disturbance hypothesis.

We will now consider an example in which the intensity of grazing by an herbivore is imposing the disturbance. This study by Zeevalking and Fresco (1977) examined the relationship between the intensity of grazing by rabbits (*Oryctolagus cuniculus*) and the diversity of plants in coastal sand-dune vegetation in Western Europe. The outcome is consistent with the intermediate disturbance hypothesis because plant species richness was highest under moderate grazing pressure **(Figure 9.32)**.

A similar pattern was shown by studies of the activities of prairie dogs (*Cynomys* sp.) in shortgrass prairie (Whicker and Detling, 1988). These colonial rodents cause major effects on community structure by their burrowing and grazing. Areas close to prairie-dog burrows are highly disturbed and are dominated by short-lived ruderal plants, while habitat farther away is less disturbed and is dominated by competitive plants. However, as in previous examples, in-between zones of moderate disturbance by the rodents have the highest levels of species diversity.

Keystone Species

In architecture, a keystone is the wedge-shaped piece at the top of a stone arch that locks the other blocks in place and on which the entire structure is dependent for support. Analogously, in ecology a **keystone species** is one that has a disproportionately large effect on the structure of its community, much more so than would be predicted on the basis of its relative biomass or frequency of occurrence.

One of the first examples was reported by Tansley and Adamson (1925) who showed that grazing by rabbits has a major influence on the species composition of grasslands in Britain. The researchers demonstrated this by building small fenced plots that excluded rabbits. Within six years the initially species-rich plant community had degenerated to one dominated by only a few tall species. At one of the study sites, a plot with rabbits had 8000 plants/m² with 21 species, and the vegetation was only 4–5 cm tall and dominated by short *Festuca ovina*. In contrast, a plot without rabbits was also dominated by *Festuca ovina*, but it was 18–20 cm tall and the dense shade it cast limited the other vegetation to 11 species and 320 plants/m². Eventually, the exclusion plots were colonized by woody species, which are otherwise eliminated by the rabbits (Hope-Simpson, 1940). Further evidence of the keystone action of rabbits is provided by a "natural experiment" that occurred in the mid-1950s, when the viral disease myxomatosis killed about 95 percent of those animals in the United Kingdom. The resulting large-scale changes of vegetation were similar to those observed in the exclusion experiments.

Another famous demonstration of the effects of a keystone animal on community structure was done by Robert Paine (1966) in a rocky intertidal habitat in the Pacific Northwest. That ecosystem has two major predators, a sea star *Pisaster ochraceus* **(Figure 9.33)**, and a gastropod *Thais emarginata*. *Pisaster* is a major predator of the mussel *Mytilus californianus*, barnacles such as *Balanus glandula*, and the chiton *Katharina tunicata*, while *Thais* feeds primarily on *Balanus glandula*. Paine continually removed the *Pisaster* for up to three years from an area of 16 m², and found that without the influence of

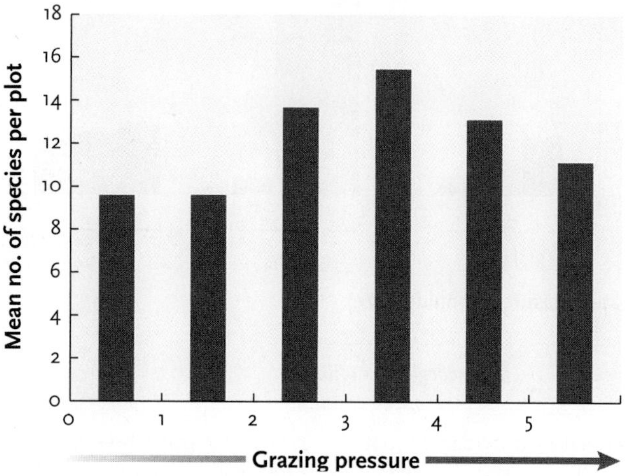

FIGURE 9.32 Another Illustration of the Intermediate Disturbance Hypothesis In this case, an intermediate intensity of grazing by rabbits results in the highest level of species diversity in a coastal sand-dune plant community.

SOURCE: Based on Begon, M., Harper, J.L. & C.R. Townsend. 1990. *Ecology* (2nd ed.). Blackwell.

Fergus Spowart

FIGURE 9.33 The Sea Star (*Pisaster ochraceus*) This predator is a classic illustration of a keystone species. When it is removed from rocky intertidal habitats in the Pacific Northwest, the result is a decline in the species richness of their community. Here, a researcher tests this effect by removing sea stars from plots in Howe Sound, near Vancouver, British Columbia.

this predator the previously rich community of 15 species was reduced to only 8. The key influence of the sea star was to limit the dominance of *Mytilus californianus*, the competitively superior member of the community, which crowded out other species when the *Pisaster* was removed **(Figure 9.34)**.

Predation is also one of the primary determinants of community structure in lakes and ponds. Fish in particular have often been shown to have strong effects on the numbers of their prey. A particularly striking example of this is provided by Lake Victoria in east Africa, the world's second largest freshwater lake by area (Kaufman, 1992; Lake Superior is the largest). In the early 1960s, the large predatory Nile perch (*Lates niloticus*) was introduced to the lake, slowly increasing in population and then exploding in abundance in the late 1970s **(Figure 9.35)**. As a result of this irruption at least 200 species of cichlid fish, all of them endemic to the lake, were eliminated or reduced to endangered levels because of unsustainable predation by the alien *Lates*. The lake had formerly supported about 200 kg ha^{-1} of fish biomass, of which about 80 percent was cichlids. By the late 1980s the fish biomass had declined to only 100 g ha^{-1}, 90 percent of which was Nile perch. Many other changes occurred to community structure of this lake, mostly related to the direct and indirect effects of exotic fish introductions, especially the Nile perch.

Alternative Stable States

Succession is the process by which communities change over time, as they recover from a disturbance (Chapter 10). In the absence of another intervening disturbance, succession may eventually achieve a climax community—a stable end-point under the prevailing environmental conditions. However, there is ongoing discussion among ecologists as to whether such a stable end-point is ever achieved, highlighting the difference between equilibrium and non-equilibrium views of how ecosystems work.

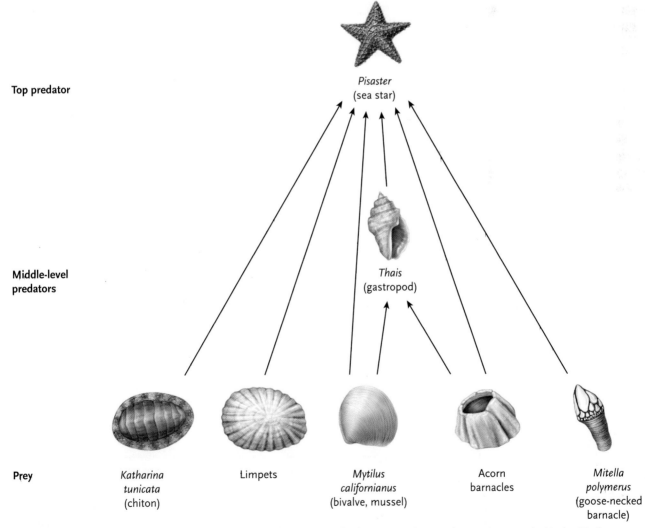

Top predator

Pisaster
(sea star)

Middle-level predators

Thais
(gastropod)

Prey

| *Katharina tunicata* (chiton) | Limpets | *Mytilus californianus* (bivalve, mussel) | Acorn barnacles | *Mitella polymerus* (goose-necked barnacle) |

FIGURE 9.34 Keystone Predator in a Rocky Intertidal Habitat Predation by the sea star *Pisaster ochraceus* prevents the bivalve *Mytilus californianus* and the goose-necked barnacle *Mitella* from competitively excluding other species from the habitat.

SOURCE: Based on Paine, R.T. 1966. "Food web complexity and species diversity," *American Naturalist*, 100: 65-75.

FIGURE 9.35 The Nile Perch and Lake Victoria Cichlids When population levels of the introduced Nile perch (*Lates niloticus*) irrupted in the late 1970s, this large predatory fish had a major impact on the community structure of fish in Lake Victoria, drastically reducing the number of species of cichlids.

Consider, for example, the case of an old pasture that was abandoned from agricultural use in the springtime—would it have different initial colonists than if it had been forsaken in the autumn, and, if so, how would that affect the ensuing successions? Or, if after glacial meltback the exposed rocky till was colonized by species of bryophytes, or alternatively by vascular plants, would the different colonists lead to varying successions and to dissimilar end-points? Or would there be a convergent and inevitable climax that is determined by the prevailing environmental conditions, regardless of the initial colonists? The variable-climax view is one form of the concept of **alternative stable states** (or **multiple stable states** if there are more than two states)—the occurrence of more than one possible stable community, even under similar environmental conditions.

There is yet another way of considering this concept of alternative stable states, if only two such end-of-succession communities are proposed. The question here revolves around the issue of whether an existing community can be perturbed to such a degree that it changes to an entirely different but stable community, and does not subsequently return to its initial state after the stressor has been relaxed. This principle is graphically illustrated in **Figure 9.36** in which an initial community is represented by a ball located in a depression, one of many such basins across a landscape. If the ball is given a strong enough push, such as by a strong disturbance, then the inherent **resistance** of the community to substantial change can be overcome and it may move into a different valley, where it again stabilizes in an alternative state. An essential aspect of this conceptual model is that the ball is stable in either basin, and in the absence of a disturbance it does not spontaneously move between them. It is also understood that in either of the alternative stable states, the communities may be subjected to relatively minor intensities of disturbance or other stres-

Moreover, we can raise an intriguing question: If succession occurs along a fairly predictable trajectory to an expected and stable end-point, are the initial and intermediate stages of the process also predictable?

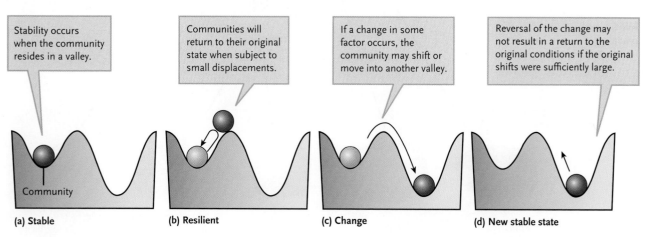

FIGURE 9.36 Multiple Stable States In this diagrammatic model, the balls represent different kinds of communities, and the basins are forces that retain them in a stable state. It takes a relatively large intensity of disturbance or another environmental stressor to overcome the inherent resistance of the community to substantial change in its structure and function. This resistance is illustrated by the force required to move a ball from one basin to another. If the applied force is not sufficient to move a ball out of its basin, then when the stressor is alleviated, the community will return to its original condition—this is a demonstration of resilience.

SOURCE: Based on Beisner, B.E., D.T. Haydon and K. Cuddington. 2003. "Alternative stable states in ecology," *Frontiers in Ecology and the Environment*, 1:376-382. (Fig 16.18, p. 358).

sors without being propelled out of the valley—in these cases, the community is **resilient** and returns to its original condition (see Chapter 10 for a more detailed consideration of the terms "resistance" and "resilience").

The existence of such alternative states is still debated, largely because of disagreement among ecologists concerning the weight of evidence that is required to demonstrate their reality. To illustrate this difficulty we will examine a classic study titled "Aleuts, Sea Otters, and Alternate Stable-State Communities" by Simenstad et al. (1978). These researchers investigated the contents of middens (heaps of discarded shells, bones, and other garbage) of prehistoric Aleut settlements in the Aleutian Islands of Alaska. Their observations led them to suggest that these Aboriginal peoples had affected the local nearshore ecosystem by overharvesting sea otters (*Enhydra lutris*) in some areas, driving them close to extirpation. They also compared the flora and fauna of two subtidal habitats in the area, with and without otters, and demonstrated that predation by otters profoundly influences the organization of the communities **(Table 9.1)**. The otters do this by greatly reducing the abundance of herbivorous sea urchins, limpets, and chitons, which then allows an abundant community of macroalgae to flourish (known as a kelp "forest") which then attracts fish typical of nearshore habitats. In contrast, habitats without otters support large populations of the herbivorous invertebrates that over-graze the macroalgae, so that bare rocky substrate is abundant and there are fewer fish (and mostly pelagic ones).

Interestingly, the sea otter was almost rendered extinct by overhunting for its dense and lustrous fur. In 1911, it was protected from further hunting and it has since made a population recovery in some regions, including places on the west coast of Vancouver Island. During the period when the otters were scarce, the subtidal habitats were predominantly open rocky expanses maintained by the voracious feeding of abundant large-invertebrate herbivores (such as urchins). In contrast, in areas where otters have recovered in abundance, their predation has reduced the herbivore populations, which has allowed large kelp species to again flourish **(Figure 9.37)**. In other words, there are apparently two stable communities, with one or the other occurring depending on the presence of sea otters, which are a keystone predator in the ecosystem. However, these are not alternative stable states because the "apparent alternative state" persists only as long as there is hunting of sea otters. Once the hunting of otters is stopped, there is a slow but continual return to the former state. In the strict definition of an alternative stable state, there would be no recovery of the community after the hunting of otters was stopped.

Remarkably, this famous ecological case has recently developed a new wrinkle. In the early 1990s, groups of killer whales (*Orcinus orca*) began to hunt sea otters in

TABLE 9.1	Effects of Sea Otters (*Enhydra lutris*)	
	This table compares the status of nearshore communities on Aleutian Islands with sea otters (Amchitka) and without them (Shemya and Attu).	
Species	**Community with Sea Otters**	**Communities without Sea Otters**
Sea otter (*Enhydra lutris*)	Abundant for several decades; population at time of the study >6000	None or sparse
Macroalgae	Abundant, principally four species of Laminaria, Agarum cribosum, Rhodophyta, and Alaria fistulosa	Rare and restricted to sublittoral fringe and patches
Sea urchins (*Strongylocentrotus polyacanthus*)	Rare; maximum size <32 mm; increasing size and density with depth	Dense; maximum size >100 mm; highest density and size in sublittoral fringe
Limpets (*Collisela pelta*)	Density 8/m² and maximum size 52 mm	Density 82–356/m² and maximum size 67 mm
Chitons (*Katharina tunicata* and *Cryptochiton stelleri*)	Rare; density <1/m²	Common; density 32/m²
Mussels (*Mytilus edulis* and *Modiolus* spp.)	Rare and small; density <4/m²	Common and large; density 711/m²
Barnacles (*Balanus glandula* and *Balanus cariosus*)	Rare and small; density <5/m²	Common and large; density 1215/m²; dominating upper littoral zone
Nearshore fish	Abundant and diverse community; supported by algal detritus food web	Sparse fauna except for deepwater forms; associated with sparse deepwater patches of macroalgae
Harbour seal (*Phoca vitulina*)	Density 8/km of coastline; frequently observed in groups of >50 individuals	Density 2/km of coastline; seldom in groups of >10 individuals

SOURCE: From Simenstad, C.A., J.A. Estes, and K.W. Kenyon. 1978. "Aleuts, sea otters, and alternate stable-state communities," *Science*, 200: 403-411. Reprinted with permission from AAAS.

(a)

Ian McAllister/All Canada Photos

(b)

Chris Cheadle/All Canada Photos

FIGURE 9.37 Alternative Stable States in Subtidal Habitats The nearshore habitats may exist (a) as rocky urchin-dominated barrens, or (b) as lush kelp "forests," depending on the predatory relationships occurring among a complex of species, including humans. These photographs were taken on British Columbia shorelines.

An actual demonstration of alternative stable states has emerged from the work of Bob Jefferies and his students at the University of Toronto (see A Canadian Ecologist 4.1). This research was done at La Pérouse Bay near Churchill, Manitoba, where vegetated areas of intertidal marshes are dominated by the grass *Puccinellia phryganodes* and the sedge *Carex subspathacea*. In 1976, there were about 3300 breeding pairs of snow geese using about 10 km² of salt-marsh habitat in the study area, but by 1997 the population had increased to 44 500 over 175 km² (Abraham et al., 2005). The enormous increase in geese has been attributed to less hunting during their autumn migration, the creation of wildlife refuges in the United States, and improved wintering habitat in the southern United States because of changes in agricultural practices that left grain in fields that the geese could eat.

At La Pérouse Bay, the intense foraging by increasing numbers of snow geese has severely altered plant communities and soil in intertidal and supratidal marshes. The damage begins when overgrazing of intertidal salt-marshes converts the preferred forage of *P. phryganodes* to a short "grazing lawn," and then to an unvegetated mudflat (**Figure 9.29a**). The unvegetated areas initially developed as isolated patches, which grew larger as the overgrazing continued and eventually coalesced into expansive muddy barrens. As the intertidal vegetation deteriorated, the geese moved to secondary feeding habitats in supratidal and brackish marshes, which also became converted to grazing lawns and then to mudflats.

McLaren and Jefferies (2004) investigated the ability of transplants of *P. phryganodes* to grow in bare soil and in intact grassy lawns. The transplants survived in the lawns but not in the bare soil. Analyses of the soil found that the unvegetated areas had higher salinity and lower nitrogen, and were relatively compacted and dry, with the degradation being most acute in larger patches. It was these difficult soil conditions that prevented the transplants from surviving, and that interfered with

some areas (Estes et al., 1998). This caused the abundance of otters to rapidly decline. As a result, sea urchins and other herbivores increased, and the kelp forests were destroyed. It is thought that declines of fish stocks in the North Pacific, caused by commercial overfishing, have resulted in a decline in fur seals (*Callorhinus ursinus*) and sea lions (*Eumetopias jubatus*), which are the usual food for killer whales in the region. As a consequence, the killer whales may have turned to sea otters as an alternative prey.

revegetation of the damaged mudflats, along with continued grazing by the geese. Handa and Jefferies (2000) were able to mitigate the soil conditions by adding nutrients to increase fertility and peat to decrease the bulk density, and this allowed transplants of *P. phryganodes* to survive, but only if they were inside goose exclosures.

An additional example of an ecosystem with alternative stable states comes from the work of Tony Sinclair of the University of British Columbia, who has been working in Serengeti National Park, Tanzania, for almost 50 years (see A Canadian Ecologist 9.1). He has documented the decline of riverine forests over several decades, and recently, along with graduate student Gregory Sharam and colleague Roy Turkington (Sharam et al., 2009), has uncovered the reason for that decline **(Figure 9.38)**. The process begins when the closed forest canopy becomes partially opened, perhaps by fire or damage caused by the feeding of elephants. This leads to an emigration of many of the fruit-eating birds from the forest, which are important because they scarify the seeds within the fruits and so enhance their germination, and later disseminate them by defecation. When there are not enough fruit-eating birds to perform this service, the seeds decay or are attacked by beetles so that the recruitment of seedlings

decreases. Over decades, this leads to further opening of the forest canopy, which is replaced by grassland. Once this process has begun, even if the initial stressors are alleviated, there is an inexorable fragmentation of the forest and unravelling of its community. The beetles are the main factor determining the germination rate of seeds. A function of the birds is to counter seed predation by beetles and so to contribute to the stability in the ecosystem. Therefore, disturbances that lead to the opening of the canopy initiate a series of interactions that contribute to a reduction in tree recruitment and the disappearance of forest patches. The forest, and the grasslands that replace them, are alternative stable states.

Cryptic Herbivores

Andrew MacDougall of the University of Guelph and Scott Wilson of the University of Regina (2007) studied the diversity and structure of old-field pasture communities in southern Saskatchewan. The ability of plant species to persist in these communities depended on whether they could recover their abundance after periodic declines caused by drought and other stressors. Normally, recovery occurs when conditions improve in a stressed ecosystem, but

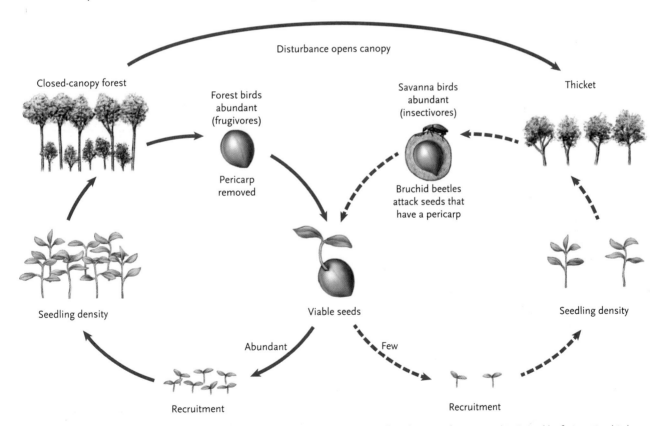

FIGURE 9.38 Fruit-Eating Birds Maintain Closed-Canopy Forests in Serengeti Closed-canopy forests are dominated by fruit-eating birds. When the canopy is opened (by fire, for example), these frugivorous birds are gradually replaced by insect-eating birds. Seeds that are consumed by fruit-eating birds, and subsequently regurgitated or defecated, are not attacked by beetles and can germinate and contribute to the recruitment of tree seedlings and continuation of the forest. However, seeds not consumed by frugivorous birds are instead attacked by bruchid beetles and few survive to germinate. Therefore, the opening of a forest canopy initiates a series of processes that inexorably lead to its conversion to grassland, which is an alternative stable state of the ecosystem (Sharam et al., 2009).

recently this had not been occurring in the pastures. MacDougall and Wilson showed that the failure of species to recuperate was caused by the grazing of seedlings by unapparent (or **cryptic**) small native herbivores, such as rodents and hares **(Figure 9.39)**. These effects occurred despite the fact that the herbivores are not obviously abundant and had been assumed to be of minor importance. There was no evidence that herbivory was substantially affecting mature plants. Further research will be needed to determine whether effects of cryptic consumers are unusual.

Although a definitive answer is beyond their data, MacDougall and Wilson (2007) proposed the occurrence of an "ecological meltdown" in which small native consumers become an agent of ecosystem transformation. Several interacting factors may be influencing the dynamics of the small herbivores, including a decline of their natural predators, the high palatability of an abundant alien grass (*Bromus inermis*), and altered grazing impacts of large ungulates (involving the elimination of cattle grazing in some areas, and a switch from native to alien ungulates in others). While speculative, these scenarios suggest that the transformation of the prairies of Canada by invasive aliens, loss of native species, and shifting relative abundances, may especially be influenced by the loss of keystone predators and large native grazers.

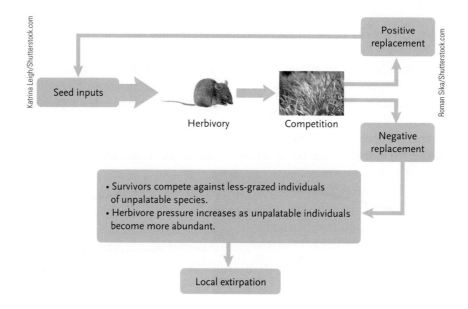

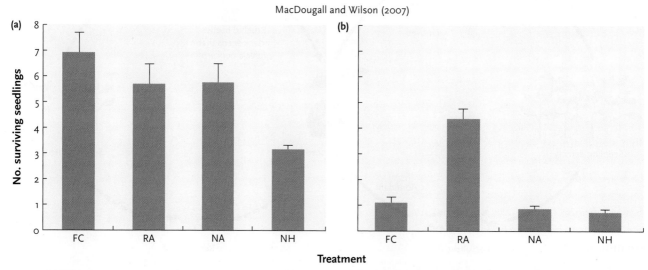

FIGURE 9.39 Cryptic Herbivores The numbers of surviving seedlings are affected by various experimental treatments. The data in (a) are for conditions at the beginning of the experiment, and (b) is at the end. The treatments are FC = full competition, RA = reduced aboveground competition, NA = no aboveground competition, and NH = herbivores excluded by fencing. These data are mean values, and the bars are one standard error.

SOURCES: Panel a: Courtesy of Andrew MacDougall. Panel b: Used with permission of the Ecological Society of America, modified from "Herbivory limits recruitment in an old-field seed addition experiment," *Ecology*, 88(5): 1105–1111, MacDougall, A.S. and S.D. Wilson © 2007. Permission conveyed through Copyright Clearance Center, Inc.

Tony Sinclair: A Champion of Biodiversity

FIGURE 1 Tony Sinclair

Anthony (Tony) Sinclair was born in Zambia but did his Ph.D. training at Oxford University **(Figure 1)**. He then worked in the Serengeti of Tanzania and in tropical Australia until 1974 when he took up a position as a professor in the Department of Zoology at the University of British Columbia, where he helped found the Biodiversity Research Centre. His work has led to a deeper understanding of the processes that regulate animal populations, and of the ecological consequences of natural and anthropogenic perturbations to those regulatory influences.

Sinclair has made abundant contributions to ecology, having supervised the research of many graduate students and postdoctoral researchers and contributed to more than 200 articles, including 7 books and more than 30 book chapters, His work has led to a deeper understanding of processes that regulate animal populations, and of the ecological consequences of natural and anthropogenic perturbations to those regulatory influences. Among his fundamental contributions to conservation and sustainability are:

- his development of theory for the regulation of animal populations and ecosystems, and demonstration how it can be used for the purposes of biological conservation;
- his demonstration that ecological knowledge is necessary to understanding how environmental crises affect people in the less-developed world, particularly with respect to famines in northern Africa; and
- his advocacy for the vital role that biodiversity plays in maintaining ecosystems and the awful consequences of losing that biological richness.

Sinclair's ecological research has had a remarkable geographic scope. He has worked in the Serengeti since 1965, mostly on the mechanisms of regulation of large-animal populations, as well as on whole-ecosystem research, all with a view to providing advice for conservation. In Canada, he played a central role in the Kluane Boreal Forest Ecosystem Project in Yukon, which examined the workings of a northern forest, including influences on the famous 10-year cycle of snowshoe hare populations (see Section 5.7). He has also worked in Australia on the conservation of endangered marsupial species and their alien predators, the red fox and feral cats.

Tony Sinclair and the many researchers who have worked with him have influenced the development of ecological theory. However, their contribution goes beyond that because of its intersection with the needs of society for advice on the conservation of biodiversity. Sinclair has shown how basic research into the dynamics of natural populations can be applied to understanding anthropogenic impacts on ecosystems, and how to avoid or repair the resulting damage. This work shines helpful ecological light on appropriate pathways to sustainable development in Canada and in other countries.

Effects of Chance, Rare, and Uncontrollable Events

In some of the previous sections we examined the ways that well-designed field and laboratory experiments can yield insights into factors that influence the structure of communities. However, there are also examples that suggest that mere chance and random events may also have an important influence. This has been shown by a series of experiments that were initially designed to examine the effects of competition on community structure (Goldberg et al., 1995, 2001; Shilo-Volin et al., 2005; Rajaniemi et al., 2009). The method involved manipulating the density of an entire community in a way similar to how a single species might be modified.

For example, most of the time in the blazing heat of summer in the Negev desert, not even a single annual plant appears to be present. However, there is a population of viable seeds in the dry sand. When the first rains come in late November, a sparse grassland develops from this *in situ* seed bank. The seedlings grow quickly and develop into mature plants that flower and produce and disperse their own seeds, which will provide a seed bank for the next growing season. In essence, during the summer drought the plant community exists as a population of quiescent but viable seeds that is mostly located in the surface 2 cm of the desert sand.

To study this phenomenon, Shilo-Volin et al. (2005) ran experiments in which 1 m² of sand was scraped to a depth of 2 cm, and the material then mixed to evenly distribute the seeds that were present. That material was then spread over other areas that had previously been devegetated by scraping the surface sand away, thus removing any seed bank that had been present. To investigate the role of seed density in possible creating "new" communities, they spread the 1 m² of sand with its seeds bank over several experimental areas: 0.5 m², 1 m², 2 m², or 4 m². Each would initially have the same species composition and relative abundances as the natural one, but the density would be four, one, one-half, or one-quarter times as large. Such multispecies mixtures that vary in density are called a community density series (CDS). This novel experimental procedure allowed the researchers to obtain densities below and above the natural condition of the community of annual plants. The lowest-density plots represent a "null" community, in which density is low enough to preclude interactions among the plants, such as competition. This is compared to higher-density plots, in which biotic interactions have a greater effect on the plant community. The researchers ran a variety of multiyear studies in which natural regeneration was allowed to occur in subsequent years. One of the questions they examined was whether low-density and high-density plots would eventually converge in their species composition, or in biomass, to a condition similar to that of the natural (or reference) community. However, their results showed that the initial density had significant effects on species composition, which remained discernible over three years, even as the total abundance of vegetation in the communities became progressively more similar among the treatments. After three growing seasons, the differences in biomass among the density treatments diminished, but they had not converged to a common biomass. In addition, plots sown at different densities did not show a convergence of species composition or even in functional groups over time **(Figure 9.40)**.

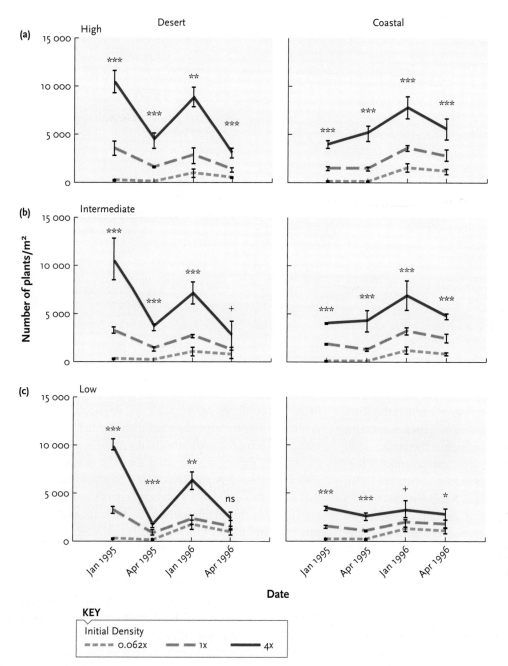

FIGURE 9.40 Effects of Initial Seed Density on Community Trajectory in Annual Grassland Communities Seeds were collected from annual plants occurring at two semi-stabilized areas of sand dunes sites (source communities) in Israel. The less productive community was in the Negev desert and the more productive one was a site near the Mediterranean coast. The three seed-density treatments were × 0.06 (1/16), × 1, and × 4 the natural seed-bank density, and plots in the three irrigation treatments mimicked aspects of the precipitation regimes of the two source sites, plus an intermediate regime. These data are averages (±1 standard error) at various times during two growing seasons. Asterisks indicate a statistically significant difference between the 4 × treatments and the others. Note the convergence toward a similar seedling density as the experiment proceeds over two growing seasons.

SOURCE: Modified from: Shilo-Volin, H., A. Novoplansky, D.E. Goldberg D.E. and R. Turkington. 2005. "Density regulation in annual plant communities under different resource levels," *Oikos*, 108: 241-252. Reprinted by permission of John Wiley and Sons, Inc.

In nature, of course, there is no such thing as 1 × density, and this circumstance is captured by the range of the experimental community density series. Rather, across the desert landscape there are variations of seed bank density that range from low to high, with all values in between, and the species composition of the seed bank also varies. The spatial variations are influenced by factors such as the specific locations and sizes of adult plants that are dispersing seeds, the nature of the terrain, the wind speed and direction when seeds are being scattered, the abundance of seed predators, and other variable effects. Therefore, the species composition and structure of these desert communities of annual plants, although heavily influenced by competition and herbivory, are seemingly indeterminate at the local scale and may be substantially due to chance and the relative influence of different and unpredictable events.

Interactive Effects

So far in this chapter we have examined studies that suggest that patterns of community structure can be influenced by single factors, such as competition, herbivory, or disturbance. While these factors may work alone, and in some cases have a dominant influence on particular communities, there can also be interactions among them. In this section we will consider a few examples of these kinds of interactions and present models that attempt to explain the complexity.

Brown and his colleagues (1977, 1979) studied interspecific competition between two seed-eating guilds in deserts of the southwestern United States: ants and rodents (a feeding guild is a group of species that eat similar foods, in this case, the seeds of desert grasses). In that arid habitat the annual rainfall is a good indicator of the potential primary productivity, including seed production, and this has a positive influence on the numbers of species in each of the seed-eating guilds (**Figure 9.41**). A careful examination of the diets of the ants and rodents showed significant overlap, which is an indication that there likely is competition for a limited food resource (**Figure 9.42**). To test this idea, eight experimental plots were established: in two of them, ants were removed; in two, rodents were removed; in two others, both were removed; and the final two were unmanipulated controls. When either the ants or rodents were removed, the remaining group increased in abundance and consumed about as many seeds as occurred when both were present (**Table 9.2**). Only when both ants and rodents were removed did the numbers of uneaten seeds dramatically increase.

Further studies by Davidson (1977a, b) showed that there was also resource partitioning among the ant species, such that larger ones ate bigger seeds. This also has an influence on community structure. When rodents were

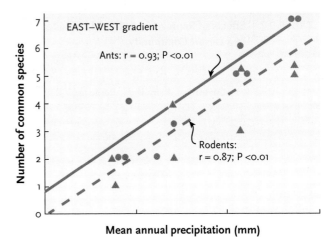

FIGURE 9.41 Species Richness of Seed-Eating Guilds along a Rainfall Gradient The study area is desert in the southwestern United States. These data are species richness of two seed-eating guilds: ants (●) and rodents (▲).

SOURCE: Modified from Brown, J.H. and D.W. Davidson. 1977. "Competition between seed-eating rodents and ants in desert ecosystems," *Science*, 196: 880-882. Reprinted with permission from AAAS.

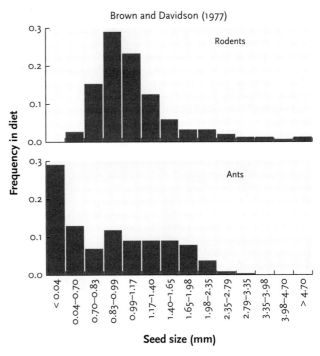

FIGURE 9.42 Comparison of the Diets of Seed-Eating Guilds of Ants and Rodents The two guilds have an overlapping diet of variously sized seeds.

SOURCE: From Brown, J.H. and D.W. Davidson. 1977. "Competition between seed-eating rodents and ants in desert ecosystems," *Science*, 196: 880-882. Reprinted with permission from AAAS.

removed, ants increased in abundance, and larger seeds had a lower probability of being eaten (even though there is broad overlap in the diet of the two guilds, ants tend to eat smaller seeds; **Figure 9.42**). Eventually, this treatment resulted in larger-seeded grasses, such as *Aristida adscensionis* and *Eragrostis lehmannianna*, outcompeting

TABLE 9.2	Effects of Removal of Ants and/or Rodents in a Desert Community			
	Control	Rodents Removed	Ants Removed	Rodents and Ants Removed
Number of ant colonies	318	543	0	0
Number of rodents	122	0	144	0
Seed density relative to control	1.0	1.0	1.0	5.5

SOURCE: From Brown, J.H. and D.W. Davidson. 1977. "Competition between seed-eating rodents and ants in desert ecosystems," *Science*, 196: 880-882. Reprinted with permission from AAAS.

smaller-seeded ones **(Figure 9.43)**. This reduced the seed output of smaller-seeded plants, but also the primary diet of the ants, so by the tenth year of the study the ants in this treatment had declined almost to extirpation. In contrast, removing the ants caused an increase in smaller-seeded grasses, but had no effect on larger-seeded ones.

In summary: larger-seeded grasses are taller, so they are superior competitors to smaller-seeded ones in these habitats. This is true to such a degree that even when rodents are removed and ants increase their consumption of smaller seeds, the reduction in smaller grasses has

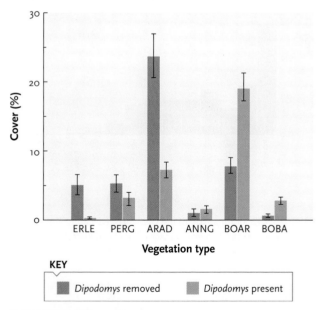

FIGURE 9.43 Effects of Kangaroo Rats (*Dipodomys* sp.) on a Plant Community These data show the cover of various grass species with and without the rats. ERLE = *Eragrostis lehmannianna*; PERG = various tall perennial grasses; ARAD = *Aristida adscensionis*; ANNG = various tall annual grasses; BOAR = *Bouteloua aristidoides*; BOBA = *Bouteloua barbata*.

SOURCE: From Brown, J.H. and E.J. Heske. 1990. "Control of a desert-grassland transition by a keystone rodent guild," *Science*, 250: 1705-1707. Reprinted with permission from AAAS.

no noticeable effect on the abundance of larger-seeded plants. However, selective predation by rodents on larger seeds reduced the competitive superiority of the taller, larger-seeded grasses, and this maintained the diversity of the shorter, smaller-seeded ones.

Rocky intertidal shorelines have been the subject of much experimental research in community ecology. One of the earliest manipulative field studies in the intertidal zone was done by Jane Lubchenco (1978), who evaluated the effects of generalist herbivores on the diversity of seaweeds. The most abundant and important herbivore in this community is the periwinkle snail *Littorina*. Its preferred foods are primarily ephemeral algae, such as the green alga *Enteromorpha*, which is also the dominant competitor for space on rocky substrates; other algae, such as the red *Chondrus*, are rarely eaten by *Littorina*. Contrary to expectations, however, tidal pools dominated by *Enteromorpha* have a low density of *Littorina* (only 4 per m²), while those dominated by *Chondrus* have more of these snails (>230/m²). Lubchenco hypothesized that intense grazing by *Littorina* might be eliminating the competitive *Enteromorpha*, and thus allowing the less-edible, less-competitive *Chondrus* to be abundant. She further suggested that gulls were indirectly affecting the diversity and abundance of algae in tide pools by eating crabs, which are an important predator of *Littorina* **(Figure 9.44)**. This series of effects of one species upon others at a lower trophic level is called a **trophic cascade**, and we will examine it in more detail in the next section. However, this four-level cascade was never tested experimentally by Lubchenco.

More recent research in this subject area by Ellis et al. (2007) has helped to clarify relationships among various trophic levels in rocky intertidal habitats. During the past several decades, predatory gulls, chiefly the great black-backed gull (*Larus marinus*) and herring gull (*Larus argentatus*), have dramatically increased in abundance along the northwestern Atlantic coast, and both of them prey heavily on crabs, sea urchins, and mussels. Gull predation on the Jonah crab (*Cancer borealis*), itself a generalist predator, reduces its abundance in intertidal habitats, which affects the densities of other invertebrates. The Jonah crab feeds on a wide variety of prey, including other crabs, mussels, polychaetes, sea urchins, and snails, including *Littorina*, which Lubchenco (1978) showed to be an important intertidal herbivore that is capable of affecting macroalgal cover on rocky shores **(Figure 9.44)**. Although Ellis et al. found strong evidence for a three-level trophic cascade (gulls, crabs, snails) that was precipitated by the abundance of gulls, they were not able to demonstrate a four-level cascade from gulls down to macroalgae.

Another trophic cascade occurred in the 1990s as a result of the overfishing of cod (*Gadus morhua*) stocks off the east coast of Canada (Scheffer et al., 2005; see also

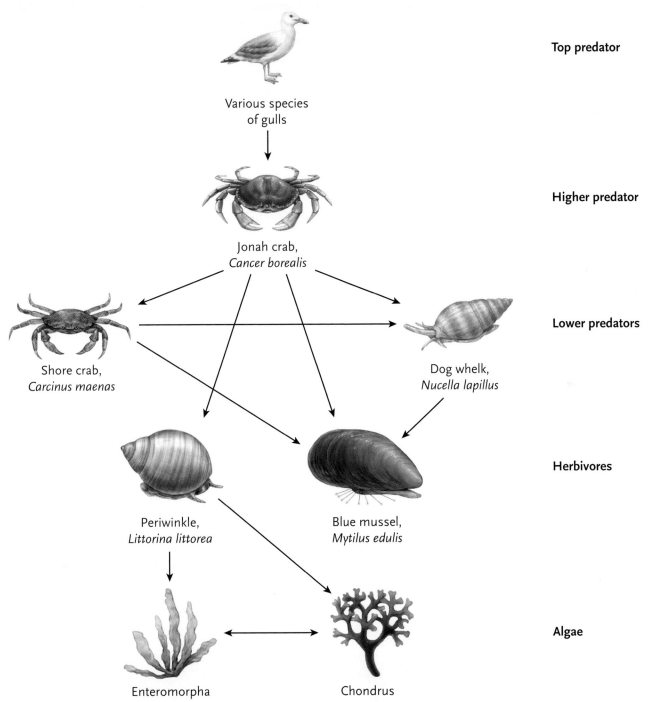

Top predator

Various species
of gulls

Higher predator

Jonah crab,
Cancer borealis

Lower predators

Shore crab,
Carcinus maenas

Dog whelk,
Nucella lapillus

Herbivores

Periwinkle,
Littorina littorea

Blue mussel,
Mytilus edulis

Algae

Enteromorpha

Chondrus

FIGURE 9.44 Summary Model of Interactions in the Rocky Intertidal Arrows indicate interactions in the community. Predation by gulls prevents the Jonah crab (*Cancer borealis*) from maintaining a large population. Smaller invertebrate predators and herbivores are then released from intense predation by the crab. It is important to note the contrasting effects on community diversity depending on whether predation is selective on the dominant competitor or not.

SOURCES: Compiled and adapted from Lubchenco (1978) and Ellis et al. (2007)

chapters 5, 8, and 15). With the great reduction of cod, a higher-level predator within its community, the biomass of smaller prey fish increased in some areas, as did that of various benthic invertebrates. As a consequence of the increased abundance of small fish, their zooplankton prey declined, which allowed their food of phytoplankton to become more abundant. Moreover, at the time that the cod stocks were collapsing, the populations of two species of seals were increasing (harp seal, *Pagophilus groenlandicus*, and grey seal, *Halichoerus grypus*). Some people concluded that these marine predators must be eating the cod and so preventing their recovery, and suggested that large numbers of seals be culled in order to help the fishery regenerate. However, studies of the stomach contents of seals have shown that cod are not important prey for them, which suggests that a mass cull would not be effectual (Bowen and Lidgard, 2011).

9.3 Conceptual Models of Community Structure

To this point we have examined a number of examples that illustrate the influences of competition, herbivory, predation, and disturbance on the structure of communities. In some cases, we have used these relationships to illustrate ecological principles, such as the niche, dominance, the intermediate disturbance hypothesis, keystone species, and alternative stable states. Ultimately, the distribution and abundance of species are determined by their tolerance to the abiotic conditions of their environment, but they are usually limited to a narrower range because of interactions with other organisms. We will now examine some overview models that attempt to tie many of these ideas together. The models also illustrate the circumstances and kinds of habitats in which the various influences are more, or less, important.

Top–Down versus Bottom–Up Regulation and Trophic Cascades

In a famous paper, Hairston, Smith, and Slobodkin (1960) proposed one of the first models of community regulation. They asked a provocative question about the processes that may be limiting ecological communities: "Why is the world green?" or "Why don't herbivores increase in numbers to such levels as to deplete or devastate the vegetation that they eat?" At the time, there were

two main arguments about the role of herbivores in ecosystems: the bottom–up (resource-control) hypothesis and the top–down (consumer-control) hypothesis.

The **bottom–up** or **resource-control hypothesis** states that the abundance of a population (or of populations) is limited by nutrients or by the availability of food. In other words, systems are regulated by resource flows from below, and higher trophic levels have no regulating effect on the productivity or biomass of trophic levels below them. It is important to note that, especially for the vegetation level, it is not the amount of biomass available that is important, rather it is the availability of food that can be accessed. Frequently, there is lots of vegetation but it may be heavily defended or unpalatable to herbivores **(Figure 9.45)**.

The **top–down** or **consumer-control hypothesis** states that the abundance of a population is limited by the consumers it supports—top predators are self-regulating, and they also regulate the trophic level below, and so on down the food web, so that plants are limited by their herbivores rather than by the availability of the inorganic nutrients and other resources that they need to grow.

Hairston et al. (1960) argued that predators limit the abundance of herbivores, and therefore prevent them from competing much among themselves and also from over-exploiting their food source of plants (and that is one reason the world remains "green"). In the real world of ecology, however, both kinds of controls usually operate simultaneously, although their relative strengths may vary depending on the circumstances. For this reason, other models have been proposed that involve variations of the top–down and/or bottom–up hypotheses.

This is an important subject area, because understanding whether a community is primarily structured from the top–down or the bottom–up has key implications for conservation and wildlife management. This

FIGURE 9.45 Protection from Herbivores Stiff, sharp spines between 5–7 cm long defend various species of cactus (left) and acacia (right) from mammalian herbivores

is an important consideration on larger landscapes, and also in protected areas, such as national parks. Moreover, the relative effects of these influences are being increasingly affected by anthropogenic stressors, such as:

- the culling of large carnivores (recall the seal example above, and see the wolf example below, and **Figure 9.46**), sometimes resulting in their eradication, which releases their prey from top–down control;
- excessive harvesting of large herbivorous animals, such as deer and elephants, whose choices during feeding exert top–down influences on plant communities;
- nutrient loading to terrestrial and aquatic ecoscapes (Environmental Applications 2.1), which has a bottom–up influence by increasing primary productivity; and
- area-harvesting of ecosystems, such as by clear-cutting in forestry and trawling in a fishery, which has a large bottom–up effect by diminishing the food base of higher trophic levels.

In their aggregate, these anthropogenic influences are changing the relative strengths of top–down and bottom–up forces in ecosystems throughout much of Canada and worldwide. Consider, for example, the eco-logical consequences of hunters eradicating wolves from montane landscapes consisting of a mosaic of conifer and aspen forests and grasslands. Examples of such ecosystems include the Rocky Mountain parks of Canada (e.g., Banff and Jasper National Parks) and comparable ones in the United States (such as Yellowstone National Park). In the absence of predation by wolves, large ungulate herbivores such as elk (*Cervus canadensis*) become unusually abundant and overbrowse some of their preferred foods, such as shoots and seedlings of trembling aspen (*Populus tremuloides*) and willows (*Salix* species) (**Figure 9.46**). These and other changes in vegetation caused by excessive populations of herbivores can result in habitat degradation, including an impairment of forest regeneration. When wolves were reintroduced to Yellowstone National Park, their influence on elk and other large herbivores resulted in a general improvement of the "health" of the ecosystem, including the first observations of aspen regeneration in many decades (Ripple et al., 2001).

These kinds of serial changes in species abundances and distributions at lower trophic levels, occurring in response to changes at a higher level, are referred to as a trophic cascade (Carpenter et al., 1985; see also **Figure 9.47**).

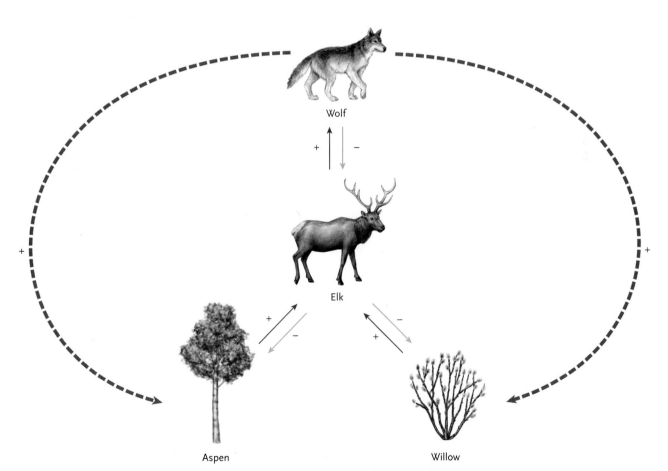

FIGURE 9.46 Trophic Interactions This is a simplified illustration of trophic interactions in Banff National Park. Areas with higher wolf populations have lower elk populations, which in turn reduce herbivore pressure and allow aspen and willow to increase in abundance. Arrows show the direction of an effect, with + being a positive effect of one trophic level on another, and − having a negative effect (modified from Hebblewhite et al., 2005).

Source: Republished with permission of Ecological Society of America, from Hebblewhite et al. 2005, "Human Activity Mediates a Trophic Cascade Caused by Wolves," *Ecology*, 86(8) p. 2138; permission conveyed through Copyright Clearance Center, Inc.

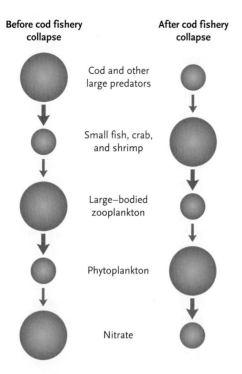

Before cod fishery collapse   **After cod fishery collapse**

Cod and other large predators

Small fish, crab, and shrimp

Large–bodied zooplankton

Phytoplankton

Nitrate

FIGURE 9.47 A Trophic Cascade The collapse of the cod fishery off the east coast of Canada led to a series of effects at lower trophic levels; this sequence is called a trophic cascade. The sizes of the circles represent the relative abundance of a trophic level and the size and direction of the arrows depict the intensity and direction of the top–down cascading effects (modified from Scheffer et al., 2005).

SOURCE: Based on Scheffer et al. 2005. *Trends in Ecology and Evolution*, 25(11), p. 580.

In some boreal regions, the populations of woodland caribou (*Rangifer tarandus caribou*), a large ungulate herbivore, are declining. The cause appears to be a complex of factors, including excessive hunting, damages to forest habitat by timber harvesting and by mining (particularly the loss of critical wintering habitat that is rich in lichen biomass), in some areas high predation by natural predators, and perhaps climate-related ecological changes (Bergerud, 1974; Bergerud et al., 2007). Because of a contracting range, declining abundance, and increasing population fragmentation, woodland caribou are now considered to be threatened over large areas of their range in Canada (COSEWIC, 2002). Wittmer et al. (2005) analyzed data for woodland caribou in British Columbia and suggested that they are declining as a consequence of increased predation, mostly by wolves. This was similar to a conclusion by Bergerud (1974), who hypothesized that caribou had declined due to wolf predation and overhunting rather than from a shortage of their winter forage of lichens. To test these hypotheses, for 30 years until 2003, Bergerud and his colleagues monitored caribou populations on islands in Lake Superior, where wolves were absent, and on the nearby mainland, which has wolves

(Bergerud et al., 2007). The results concurred with the prediction that the caribou decline is being driven by predation rather than by a food shortage. These studies support the idea that ecosystems without predators are limited bottom–up by food, while those with predators are structured top–down by predation.

Another study monitored an area of the northern Serengeti for more than 30 years in which poaching had removed most of the large mammalian carnivores, and compared it with an adjacent area where their populations remained intact (Sinclair et al., 2003). In the area with reduced predators, five species of medium-sized mammalian herbivores increased markedly in abundance, but not in the other areas with high predation **(Figure 9.48)**. Once poaching stopped and the predators returned to the area, the herbivores declined in abundance. In contrast, the abundance of giraffe, one of the largest herbivores, did not increase in the area where predators had been removed, or change after the poaching stopped, apparently because they are too big to be hunted by carnivores. It was concluded that in this savannah community with diverse herbivores, carnivores were imposing intense predation pressure in a manner related to their choice of prey according to body size. This and related factors resulted in top–down pressure that was somewhat focused on smaller prey species, and resource limitation (bottom–up influence) for larger ones. The researchers suggested that there is a threshold of prey body size of about 150 kg, above which the dominant influence on herbivores switches to bottom–up control.

It is a difficult task to test all of these predictions simultaneously in any one community. Ideally, an entire community or ecoscape would be studied as a whole, but in most terrestrial ecosystems this poses great challenges in terms of experimental design, statistical analysis, logistics, and funding. Nevertheless, there have been a few such ambitious attempts to study and understand an entire ecosystem. One is the Kluane Boreal Forest Ecosystem Project in southern Yukon, led by ecologists from several Canadian universities (see Ecology in Depth 9.2). Although the observations of this boreal ecosystem are best explained by a mixture of top–down and bottom-up influences, in other systems one or the other model may be predominant.

Sinclair et al. (2000) suggested that top–down effects are of primary importance in aquatic ecosystems. Indirect effects are well known in freshwater and marine communities, and it is possible that they attenuate less rapidly than they often do in many terrestrial ecosystems. In tropical savannah and temperate grassland, where herbivores dominate the large-animal community, there is likely to be a top–down effect of herbivores on vegetation, and a bottom–up effect of herbivores on carnivores. Both the Serengeti

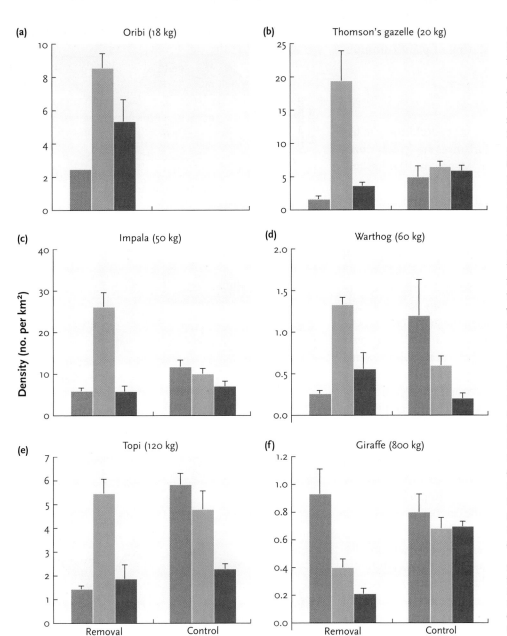

(a) Oribi (18 kg)

(b) Thomson's gazelle (20 kg)

(c) Impala (50 kg)

(d) Warthog (60 kg)

(e) Topi (120 kg)

(f) Giraffe (800 kg)

Density (no. per km²)

Removal   Control

Removal   Control

FIGURE 9.48 Control of Herbivore Abundance These figures compared top–down and bottom–up controls of the abundance of herbivores in a Savannah community. One study area in the northern Serengeti had a relatively small population of large predators because they were being poached, while in the adjacent Mara Reserve they had a normal abundance. The orange bars are for the period 1967–1980 prior to the reduction of predators; the brown bars are for 1981–1987 during which time predators were removed; the blue bars are for 1988–2001 when the predator removal stopped and their populations increased. The prey species are (a) oribi (*Ourebia ourebi*; 18 kg); (b) Thomson's gazelle (*Eudorcas thomsoni*; 20 kg), (c) impala (*Aepyceros melampus*; 50 kg), (d) warthog (*Phacochoerus africanus*; 50 kg), (e) topi (*Damaliscus korrigum*; 120 kg); and (f) giraffe (*Giraffa camelopardalis*; 800 kg). In northern Serengeti with reduced predators, five smaller species of herbivores increased in abundance, but this did not occur in the Mara Reserve.

SOURCE: Reprinted by permission from Macmillan Publishers Ltd: NATURE, 425, Sinclair, A.R.E, S.A,R. Mduma, and J.S. Brashares. "Patterns of predation in a diverse predator-prey system," copyright 2003.

ecosystem and the Kluane Boreal Forest ecosystem demonstrate strong effects of predators on herbivores.

Connell's Model

Joseph Connell (1975) also made an early attempt to provide a conceptual model of community structure under diverse influences. His emphasis was on marine subtidal and intertidal communities, but the principles may be applied to other habitats dominated by sessile organisms, such as plants in terrestrial ecosystems. Connell's model proposes that few species reach a high enough density to compete for resources. This is because of either harsh physical conditions or the loss of most of their recruits and juveniles to herbivores or predators. On occasion,

however, the harsh conditions may be ameliorated, or the herbivores or predators reduced in abundance. When this happens the recruits may "escape" from their controls and reach sufficient abundance and size to colonize open patches of habitat. Connell further suggested that predation is more intense under relatively benign physical conditions, and that fortuitous "escapes" are more likely in harsher ones, leaving competition as the dominant influence in intermediate physical conditions. His conceptual model was especially important because he was challenging the prevailing scientific viewpoint at the time—that competition was the principal influence on the structure of natural communities. When developing his model, Connell presented convincing evidence about the relative influences of physical factors, natural enemies (predators, herbivores, parasites, or pathogens), and competition as key mechanisms in the structuring of plant communities.

Menge and Sutherland's Model

The Hairston et al. (1960) model is applicable only to terrestrial ecosystems where disturbances are typically only of local importance. However, Menge and Sutherland (1987) recognized that many aquatic communities are strongly influenced by physical disturbances and these are more likely to be the primary determinants of structure than they are in terrestrial systems. To this end they developed an alternative model that incorporates parts of the Hairston et al. (1960) model, and expands the Connell (1975) model. They did this by adding a variable recruitment rate, and by applying it not only to the sessile organisms in a habitat, but also to the herbivore and carnivore components **(Figure 9.49)**. Their model suggests that (1) the relative importance of physical environmental factors, competition, herbivory, and predation varies in a predictable way depending upon trophic level, amount of recruitment, and environmental conditions, and that (2) the relative importance of predation and competition are modified by the intensity of physical stress. At the highest levels of stress no species can establish, but as the stress is reduced the community becomes more diverse and predation and competition become important. At the lowest intensities of stress, the model is essentially equivalent to the Hairston et al. model.

The Menge–Sutherland model makes three predictions for plant communities that have high recruitment rates. First, in a physically harsh environment, consumers will have little effect because they are rare, and plants are limited by the difficult conditions, so neither herbivory nor competition has much influence on the structure of the community. Second, in intermediate conditions, herbivores are more abundant but are still ineffective at regulating plant populations, which allows plants to attain high densities, leading to competition. Third, in relatively benign physical environments, predators are numerous and are able to keep herbivore densities low enough to lessen or prevent competition among them. This leads to greater plant production and strong competition among the plants.

In addition, a reduction in the numbers of plant recruits reduces the influence of competition at any given stress level. Among herbivores, and especially predators, low recruitment will slow their rate of population increase, meaning that competition will be less important even in benign conditions. In communities in harsh environments, the severe conditions will keep the density of consumers low regardless of their recruitment rates.

Despite the considerable progress that has been made in understanding the factors that affect the

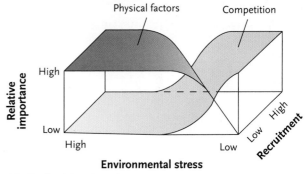

(a) Top level (carnivores)

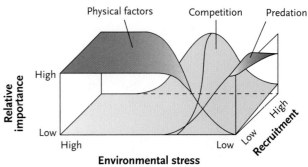

(b) Intermediate level (herbivores)

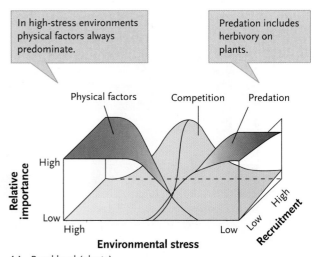

(c) Basal level (plants)

FIGURE 9.49 The Model of Menge and Sutherland Three factors are viewed as driving community organization—competition among species, predation, and physical factors. The relative importance of the three influences varies with trophic level, overall harshness of the environment, and amount of recruitment into the population.

SOURCE: Modified from: Menge, B.A. and J.P. Sutherland. 1987. "Community regulation: Variation in disturbance, competition, and predation in relation to environmental stress and recruitment," *American Naturalist*, 130: 730-757. The University of Chicago Press.

distribution and abundance of organisms within ecological communities, ecologists have not yet achieved unanimity as to general models of the controlling influences. This does not represent any sort of failure among community ecologists—rather, it is a reflection of the importance and excitement of this field of study.

ECOLOGY IN DEPTH 9.2
The Kluane Boreal Forest Ecosystem Project

FIGURE 1 Snowshoe Hare (*Lepus americanus*)

FIGURE 2 Red Squirrel (*Tamiasciurus hudsonicus*)

FIGURE 3 Lynx (*Lynx canadensis*)

The Kluane Boreal Forest Ecosystem Project was an ambitious attempt to understand the major links in an entire ecosystem—an area of boreal forest in southern Yukon (Krebs et al., 2001). The project was financed by the Natural Sciences and Engineering Research Council of Canada (NSERC), a federal agency that provides most funding for Canadian ecological research. The project was carried out between 1986 and 1996, and was led by Charles Krebs, Tony Sinclair, and Stan Boutin. Overall it involved nine professors from three Canadian universities (University of British Columbia, University of Alberta, and University of Toronto). The primary objective of the project was to address two questions:

1. What factors regulate the dynamics of species within the boreal forest around Kluane?

2. Are the species regulated from below (bottom–up control through primary productivity) or from above (top–down control through predators and herbivores), or by a combination of these mechanisms?

The main plants in the ecosystem are white spruce (*Picea glauca*), shrub-sized willow (*Salix*) and birch (*Betula*), and various grasses and herbaceous dicots **(Figure 9.17)**. The dominant herbivores are snowshoe hare (*Lepus americanus*) **(Figure 1)**, which exhibits an approximately 10-year population cycle, Arctic ground squirrel (*Spermophilus parryii*), red squirrel (*Tamiasciurus hudsonicus*) **(Figure 2)**, and various species of voles (*Clethrionomys* and *Microtus*). The major carnivores are lynx (Lynx canadensis) **(Figure 3)**, coyote (*Canis*

latrans), and various raptors, notably the great horned owl (*Bubo virginianus*).

Field experiments were used to explore these questions. Typically, a trophic level was systematically removed, or in some cases supplemented, and subsequent effects on the productivity, biomass, or activity of other levels were monitored. The experimental manipulations included:

- an aerial broadcast application of fertilizer to two areas of 100 ha;
- food supplementation for hares by the addition of commercial rabbit chow, year-round to satiation in two areas of 35 ha;
- reduction of carnivores from a 100-ha area using electrified wire fencing that was permeable to hares and squirrels (a central 10-ha portion of this area was covered with an overhead monofilament screen to deter great horned owls);
- addition of commercial rabbit chow to a 35-ha area inside a 100-ha carnivore exclusion (reduction) electrified fence;
- exclusion of hares from a 4 ha area;
- exclusion of hares and addition of fertilizer to a 4-ha area; and
- removal of vegetation from 50 plots, each of 1 m^2.

The direct effects of each manipulation produced strong top–down and bottom–up changes in biomass (Boutin

(Continued)

et al., 1995; Krebs et al., 1995; Turkington et al., 1998; Sinclair et al., 2000). Fertilizer increased the growth rate of plants, but it increased the intensity of herbivory during the winter to an even greater degree so that biomass declined. Therefore, top–down effects outweighed bottom–up ones on the plant community in winter. In contrast, during the summer growing season, herbivory had virtually no effect on plant biomass, in comparison to the stimulation from fertilizer addition.

Top–down effects dominated bottom–up ones at the herbivore level. In fact, much of the vertebrate community is regulated by top–down influences. A number of the predator species act as a guild, and their populations were influenced by that of snowshoe hare, the major prey species. In addition, the dramatic population cycle of hares was tracked by that of lynx.

No bottom–up influences of nutrients on vegetation were observed in populations of carnivores.

Overall, the experiments produced results that are consistent with two-way (reciprocal) interactions at each level. Indirect effects on species one or two levels removed from the experimental manipulation were either weak or undetectable. Top–down effects were strong when direct, but attenuated quickly through the food web. Bottom–up effects were less strong but persisted as indirect effects on herbivores.

This project has given us a detailed description of the food web of a boreal forest. Just as importantly, it provides a crucial database that will serve as a marvellous platform against which ecologists can compare their future research on questions related to, for example, global climate change.

Nils Stenseth (2002), an ecologist who reviewed the summary book about the Kluane Boreal Forest Ecosystem Project, stated the following:

This type of project is also exactly what is needed to enable ecologists to help politicians manage the biological diversity of the Earth when faced with a growing population, and the resulting increase in demand for resources. All such demands must ultimately be met from our natural resources. Research-funding agencies, and hence politicians, must realize that it is not enough to have had one Kluane project. We need many, so that we can compare the dynamics of ecosystems under different settings. Before the Kluane Project we had no role model—now we have one.

CHAPTER SUMMARY

(LO 9.1)

- An ecological community consists of all the organisms living together at the same place and time and that interact directly or indirectly. A community may be a discrete entity (Clements' organismal concept), but more often it is gradually replaced by another along some environmental gradient (Gleason's individualistic concept). Equilibrium models of community organization focus on the relative stability of the species composition, and resistance and resilience to disturbances. In contrast, non-equilibrium models posit that communities are not steady in composition, and never reach a stable condition because they are always recovering from disturbances.

(LO 9.2)

- Communities may be organized in terms of the functional roles that their component species may play, such as autotrophs, herbivores, carnivores, or detritivores. Centrifugal organization is based on the notion of core and peripheral habitats. All species in a community have a shared preference for the core habitat, but each is also the best competitor in some habitat that is peripheral to the core. Thus the diversity of peripheral habitats will largely determine the richness of plant species in the community.

(LO 9.3)

- The niche of a species is defined by all the environmental factors limiting its distribution, growth, and reproduction. The fundamental niche is the full range of environmental tolerances of a species, under circumstances in which it is free from interference from other species. In nature, however, species occupy a restricted range, referred to as the realized niche, which is constrained within the fundamental one by the influences of competitors, predators, diseases, and other factors.

(LO 9.4)

- The major factors contributing to community structure are the physical conditions of the environment, biological influences such as competition, facilitation, herbivory, and predation, and unpredictable events of disturbance. Physical conditions typically provide the limits of the distributions of species, and within those constraints biotic factors often determine their relative abundances. The influence of competition varies along environmental gradients. Herbivores, predators, and disturbances often have similar effects on community composition, with intermediate levels typically promoting higher species diversity.

- There are two ways to consider the concept of alternative stable states—the occurrence of more than one possible stable community, even under similar environmental conditions. First, succession is the process by which communities change over time, as they recover from a disturbance. Depending upon initial conditions, the recovery process may follow different trajectories and finish at different stable end-points. Second, an existing community can be perturbed to such a degree that it changes to an entirely different but stable community, and does not subsequently return to its initial state after the stressor has been relaxed.

(LO 9.6)

- A dominant species is typically the most conspicuous and abundant one in a community and in most cases it has the greatest influence on community structure and functioning.

Nevertheless, in some communities, relatively uncommon species exert a disproportionately strong influence, and these are known as keystone species; the loss of keystone species typically results in a major decline in species diversity.

(LO 9.7)

- The bottom–up model of community organization states that the abundance of a population is limited by nutrients or by the availability of food—in this sense, communities are regulated by resource flows from below. The top–down model states that the abundance of a population is limited by the consumers it supports. The models of Connell, and Menge and Sutherland, propose that the relative importance of physical factors, competition, and herbivory and predation varies in a predictable way depending upon trophic level, recruitment, and environmental conditions.

QUESTIONS FOR REVIEW AND DISCUSSION

1. What is an ecological community? Provide examples of its structural characteristics, and of functional ones.

2. Consider the following argument: "The reason that the Atlantic coast of Canada supports so few species of intertidal barnacles, mussels, snails, and other sedentary or slow-moving herbivores compared to the Pacific coast is that predators (such as sea star) are rare on the Atlantic coast, thereby permitting only a few dominant herbivores to succeed." Describe an experiment that you would perform to test this idea about controlling factors in these intertidal communities.

3. Five grassland areas in the Negev Desert have been used by Bedouin herdsmen to graze their sheep and goats for nearly 90 years. Sheep and goat densities have been fairly consistent over that period. The table below shows data that were collected recently in the grasslands.

   a. What ecological principle is illustrated by this data set?

   b. Why do areas with either low or high numbers of grazing animals have fewer plant species than those with intermediate levels of grazing?

4. Consider a case in which two species of birds coexist in a forest. They appear to overlap completely in all environmental factors related to resources (e.g., food, nest sites) and inorganic conditions (e.g., climatic factors) that you can measure. Do these species have the same niche? Explain your answer.

5. It is sometimes claimed that species in one community are ecological "equivalents" of those in another community. For example, kangaroos of Australian grassland are sometimes likened to be equivalents of antelope in Africa or of bison in the original prairie of Canada. Does this imply that these large herbivores have the same niche?

6. Chance plays an important role in the success of dispersal. Isolated places like oceanic islands, or recently disturbed patches of land, are likely to be colonized mostly by such chance dispersal events. Does this mean that community structure in such places is determined *only* by chance? Explain your answer.

7. Two species of salamander are distributed in a broadly overlapping manner in hilly terrain. Three distributional zones are observed: one with only salamander A, one with both species, and another with only B. Outline a field experiment that you would use to determine if these species of salamander are competing with each other.

8. Explain the ecological principle that is illustrated by the studies that were described of sea otters in near-shore habitats of the Aleutian Islands.

9. In the Kluane Boreal Forest Ecosystem Project in southern Yukon, some plots in the understorey were treated with fertilizer for 20 years, others were fenced to eliminate or reduce herbivores for 20 years, others received both fencing and fertilizer, and others were the control. In the table below, indicate what biomass responses you would predict to occur in the

Grasslands	Number of Animals/ha	Number of Plant Species
1	2	7
2	8	22
3	15	36
4	22	43
5	30	18

understorey plant community in the three treatment plots (these data are corrected for changes in the control plots), if they are (a) under strict bottom–up regulation, and (b) under strict top–down regulation. Note that the question is not asking about *both* bottom–up and top–down acting simultaneously. In plots where you predict a change in biomass, explain what might be happening to the species composition of those plots.

Treatment	Bottom–Up Predictions	Top–Down Predictions
Fertilized	Increase	No change
Fenced	No change	Increase
Fertilized and fenced	Increase	Increase

Disturbance and Succession

LEARNING OBJECTIVES

After studying this chapter you should be able to:

1. Explain the differences between gap-phase disturbances and stand-replacing ones, and their varying influences on the structure and function of ecosystems.

2. Describe how disturbance is followed by a successional recovery, but not necessarily back to the original kind of ecosystem.

3. Explain the broad patterns and mechanisms of successional recoveries after disturbance.

4. Discuss the key differences between primary and secondary successions.

5. Explain how life-history strategies are adaptive to the participation of species in various stages of succession.

6. Describe typical examples of disturbance and succession in Canada, including natural and anthropogenic cases.

7. Explain how the patterns and processes of natural disturbances can be emulated to soften the environmental impacts of anthropogenic systems of harvesting and management.

10.1 Disturbance and Succession

A **disturbance** is an event that causes the destruction of some part of a community or of a larger ecoscape. Disturbance is followed by a process of community-level recovery, called **succession**. Disturbances and their associated successions have always been caused by natural environmental agents, such as wildfires, windstorms, and epidemics of disease or insects. Increasingly, however, disturbances are being caused by human activities, often in novel ways that organisms and their communities have not previously experienced.

Disturbance and succession are important processes that impinge on almost all aspects of ecology, which is why they were briefly examined in other chapters of this book. In the present chapter we examine the causes and ecological consequences of disturbance and succession

in much more detail, using examples caused by natural and anthropogenic agents.

For several reasons, it is important to study a diversity of examples of disturbance and succession. First, knowledge of them is important to ecological literacy—all ecologists need to have a basic understanding of the effects of major kinds of disturbances, both natural and anthropogenic ones. At the same time, it is important to identify commonalities of the pattern and process among various agents of disturbance and pathways of succession, so that models can be developed and used to predict the likely consequences of future events.

Resistance and Resilience

By its very nature, a disturbance imposes shorter-term instability onto an affected ecosystem, which is immediately followed by the beginning of a recovery. If the resulting succession restores a community or landscape that is similar to that existing prior to a disturbance, then the ecological dynamics might be considered to have a degree of longer-term constancy or **stability**. In a relative sense, the stability is greater if the succession quickly restores the pre-existing conditions, and it is less if it takes a longer time for that to happen.

Resilience and resistance are additional concepts that are important to succession and stability (see also Chapter 9). **Resilience** refers to the ability of a perturbed ecosystem to recover to its original condition. For example, if a boreal stand of white spruce (*Picea glauca*) and its associated species in northern Saskatchewan were burned in a wildfire, and the site then recovered to a similar community through succession, then the ecosystem would be judged to be resilient to that kind of disturbance. However, if that initial spruce-dominated community were clear-cut and the early succession became diverted to a persistent fen wetland dominated by a dense growth of blue-joint (*Calamagrostis canadensis*, a species of grass), then the ecosystem would not be considered resilient in its longer-term dynamics and stability. This circumstance was demonstrated by field studies by Vic Lieffers and others (1993) from the University of Alberta, who found that the blue-joint is highly competitive in post-clear-cutting succession, and that spruce seedlings cannot easily invade or be productive in that regenerating community.

Resistance (sometimes known as **tolerance**) refers to the ability of an ecosystem to avoid a displacement from its present stage of ecological development as a result of either a disturbance or another agent of intensified stress. For example, a lightning strike occurring during a prolonged rain event might not result in a wildfire—in that circumstance an otherwise vulnerable forest might resist that potential cause of disturbance, whereas in drier conditions it might not. Similarly, a slope with a well-established forest might be better able to resist a devastating landslide, compared with a lightly vegetated community on a comparable site that is more vulnerable to that kind of disturbance.

In general, communities with a higher species richness are thought to be more resistant because their species composition might not change much if one of its species were to be devastated by a pathogen. Consider, for example, the case of the American chestnut (*Castanea dentata*), a once abundant tree that was decimated in the first third of the 20th century by an introduced fungal blight (caused by *Cryphonectria parasitica*) in mixed-species hardwood forest in southern Ontario and elsewhere in eastern North America. Although the chestnuts were wiped out, the space they had occupied in their forest community was quickly occupied by other species of trees. This might be considered to represent an

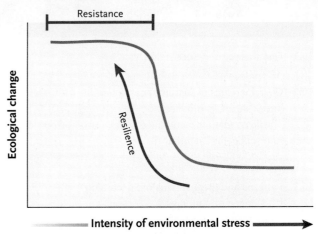

FIGURE 10.1 Resistance and Resilience Communities have a certain ability to resist an intensification of environmental stressors, including those associated with disturbance, without undergoing a substantial change in their structure or function. However, once this *resistance* (or *tolerance*) is overcome, large and rapid changes occur until a new ecological condition is established. When the disturbance event is finished, an ecological recovery by succession begins. If the succession regenerates an ecosystem that is similar to the original one, then a high degree of *resilience* has been demonstrated. However, if the succession ends with an ecosystem that is markedly different from the original, the resilience is low.

example of species redundancy in the structural and functional characteristics of this mature temperate forest. This community-level interpretation of the effects of chestnut blight does not diminish the importance of that devastating alien pathogen—it has, in fact, caused terrible damage to the global population of American chestnut, a highly valued component of native biodiversity. Nevertheless, the community of which the chestnut was formerly a member has shown a high degree of resistance to suffering an ecological collapse initiated by the removal of one of its prominent members by a species-specific disease.

Whatever the cause, when resistance is exceeded, an obvious result is a large change in communities and ecosystems **(Figure 10.1)**. Once a disturbance event has ended, a period of ecological recovery begins, known as succession.

10.2 Characteristics of Disturbance

A disturbance may cause mild to severe damage to the structure and function of a pre-existing ecosystem and may vary spatially from less than a square metre to thousands of square kilometres. The frequency of repeated disturbances also varies, from less than a day to centuries. In this section we examine how disturbances are characterized by their scale and frequency, including both natural and anthropogenic examples.

The Scale of Disturbance

Smaller-Scale Disturbances

At the smaller end of the spatial spectrum, **microdisturbances** occur at a local scale within an otherwise intact community. In such cases the disturbed area is a gap within which resources are relatively abundant and competition less severe. A **microsuccession** occurs within that opening as plants vie to take advantage of the ecological opportunity and fill it with their own **biomass** and propagules.

The death of a large tree within an older forest is an example of a microdisturbance **(Figure 10.2)**. Such disturbances may be the result of a lightning strike or a disease, which causes local damage but within a context where the surrounding forest remains otherwise undamaged. At the stand level, the dynamics of the subsequent **gap-phase microsuccession** result in the development of the highly complex, multispecies, variously aged structure that is typical of trees growing in an old-growth forest.

Microdisturbances may also occur as a result of a landslide in steep mountainous terrain, which results in a locally affected patch within an otherwise intact expanse of older communities. It is followed by a successional recovery whose rate and plant composition will vary depending on whether naked bedrock has been exposed as well as other terrain features.

Biotic factors, such as animal activity, can also trigger a microsuccession. For example, local diggings associated with a colony of black-tailed prairie dogs (*Cynomys ludovicianus*) in otherwise unbroken mixedgrass prairie in southern Saskatchewan will result in patches of loose

Bill Freedman

FIGURE 10.3 Microdisturbances Can Also Be Caused by Animals In southern Saskatchewan, these black-tailed prairie dogs' (*Cynomys ludovicianus*) burrows and associated earthen mounds create patches of early successional habitat within an expanse of otherwise unbroken mixedgrass prairie.

dirt **(Figure 10.3)**. Those patches offer local habitat for early-successional (or ruderal) plant species that might not otherwise be present within the grassland community. Selective grazing by cattle on the most-palatable species of plants in their pasture also causes microsuccession. The cattle leave the distasteful or well-armed spiny plant species uneaten, thereby changing the relative abundance of species in the habitat.

Microsuccession also occurs in aquatic habitats. For example, the death of individual colonies of brain-coral (*Diploria labyrinthiformis*) or of other large coral species, as a result of a disease or a warm-water bleaching event, creates a gap in the community within which early-successional species can occur and contribute to the recovery. Similarly, ice-scoured patches are caused when current-borne icebergs drift through shallow continental-shelf waters off Newfoundland and Labrador, occasionally scraping the seabed. This creates locally eroded areas that are initially devoid of life but then regenerate to develop communities typical of the local kind of benthic substrate.

Larger-Scale Disturbances

Toward the larger end of the spatial spectrum, **stand-replacing disturbances** affect entire communities. At the even grander scale of a landscape or seascape, the diverse community patches of various postdisturbance ages represent an ecological dynamic that is referred to as a **shifting mosaic** (see Section 13.3). These larger-scale disturbances are caused by various agents, which may be natural or anthropogenic in origin.

Wildfire is a common agent of disturbance in some natural communities, including tallgrass prairie and

Bill Freedman

FIGURE 10.2 Microdisturbance These smaller-scale disturbances occur within an otherwise intact community, creating gaps within which there is a local recovery. This scene from a hardwood forest in southern Ontario shows a tree that has been snapped by wind, creating a gap in the overhead canopy below which a microsuccessional recovery is occurring.

FIGURE 10.4 Stand-Replacing Disturbance These larger-scale disturbances affect extensive areas and are followed by a community-level successional recovery. This fire took place in Yukon.

Digital Vision/Jupiter Images

various kinds of forest, particularly those that experience seasonal dryness and are dominated by conifers **(Figure 10.4)**. Examples of fire-prone communities include boreal stands of black and white spruce (*Picea mariana* and *Picea glauca*) and jack pine (*Pinus banksiana*), montane forests of ponderosa and lodgepole pine (*Pinus ponderosa* and *Pinus contorta*), and east-temperate stands of white and red pine (*Pinus strobus* and *Pinus resinosa*). The species found in these fire-prone communities are well adapted to periodic wildfires and may even require this disturbance for their regeneration and persistence on the landscape.

The area and configuration of a wildfire are highly contextual, being affected by community and site influences on the vulnerability to burning, such as stand age, fuel loading, species composition, and site moisture. Also important are the weather conditions at the time of ignition, especially the wind speed and whether there has been a recent drought. Because of these variable influences, the area of a particular wildfire may range from only a few hectares to tens of thousands of them. Moreover, the boundaries are typically ragged and complex and there are many unburned "skips," often of moist or wet habitat. These variations contribute to the spatial complexity of both wildfires and the regenerating postfire communities that exist on any fire-prone landscape.

The average area burned in Canada every year is about 2.5 million ha, but in some years it may exceed 10 million ha (Freedman, 2010). There are about 8000 wildfires each year, of which 45 percent are ignited by lightning strikes. However, this natural cause of ignition is responsible for 80 percent of the burned area because it often occurs in remote regions where wildfires may not be quenched by fire-fighting. Fires started by people account for the other 55 percent of ignitions, but they mostly occur in more settled regions and an effort is usually made to extinguish them as quickly as possible.

Windstorms are another natural disturbance that may operate at a large scale. Forests are particularly

affected by this cause of disturbance. A stand is especially vulnerable if it occurs in an exposed location, if the trees are large, and if a windstorm occurs when the soil is moist (which makes the roots more slippery within the ground). Wind-damaged trees may have their main stem or large branches broken, or they may be uprooted, which results in the development of a pit-and-mound topography within an affected forest.

Windstorms may occur as relatively small cyclonic phenomena that are embedded within thunderstorms and tropical storms, but they may also be massive events occurring during a rare hurricane-force gale (defined as having peak wind speeds >120 km/hr) that can blow down thousands of hectares of forest. For example, Hurricane Juan, which made landfall near Halifax in September 2003, caused about 231 km^2 of stand-level forest damage (this is the sum of affected patches larger than 1 ha) along a broad swath, plus an additional 780 km^2 of windthrow at smaller scales (Bruce, 2009).

Biological agents may also cause extensive damage to natural ecosystems, sometimes affecting millions of hectares. In terrestrial ecosystems, the damage is typically done to a dominant component of the plant community, such as an abundant species of tree in a specific kind of forest. The biological agent may be a defoliating or stemboring insect that rapidly irrupts to an extremely high population level, or a microbial pathogen (usually a fungus). In cases where only a particular species is damaged, we might think of such an event as being a **population-replacing disturbance** (as we earlier examined with respect to chestnut blight). This may cause serious ecological damage, but because much of the community survives, it is different than a full community-replacing disturbance.

Biological disturbances may be protracted, sometimes lasting for several years during which time there is a progressive build-up of damage until the affected population or community is devastated; at that point the biological agent itself collapses in abundance. In Canada, a number of native insects cause extensive ecological damage (Freedman, 2010) **(Figure 10.5)**. The mountain pine beetle (*Dendroctonus ponderosae*), for example, has caused extensive damage to montane forests of lodgepole pine in British Columbia (>16 million ha were affected in 2013). In eastern Canada the spruce budworm (*Choristoneura fumiferana*) feeds on balsam fir (*Abies balsamea*) and white spruce (*P. glauca*). About 60 million ha of forest were affected during a budworm irruption that occurred between the early 1970s and early 1990s.

Nonforested ecosystems may also be affected by irruptions of native herbivores. The migratory grasshopper (*Melanoplus sanguinipes*) and other locusts periodically irrupt and cause damage to millions of hectares of agricultural cropland and pastures, especially in the Prairie Provinces. Introduced species are also agents of biotic disturbances (see Environmental Applications 10.1)

In coastal waters off Nova Scotia, the green sea urchin (*Strongylocentrotus droebachiensis*) sometimes reaches a great abundance in coastal kelp "forests" dominated by the large seaweeds *Laminaria* and *Agarum*. When this happens the abundant urchins overgraze these macroalgae and convert the ecosystem to a rocky "barren ground." This community persists until a year with unusually warm water causes a bacterial disease to kill the urchins, after which their collapse allows the kelp to regenerate (Scheibling, 1986; Lauzon-Guay et al., 2009).

Glaciation

The development of persistent sheets of ice over extensive terrestrial regions, or **glaciation**, may also be considered to represent a kind of disturbance. However, glaciation is a distinct kind of disturbance because it causes a highly protracted effect. The development of sheets of massive ice will smother, grind, and obliterate prior ecosystems for centuries or millennia, until the glaciers eventually melt and expose the landscape and allow a successional recovery to begin.

The most recent continental-scale glaciation in North America was the Wisconsinan event (it has different names in other regions and continents). The most recent expansive phase of that glaciation began about 30 000 years ago and reached a maximal extent 21 000 years ago. The great ice sheets then melted back due to climate warming and the continental-scale glaciation substantially ended 10 000 to 13 000 years ago, depending on the location. In fact, remnant glaciers still exist on Greenland and on several arctic islands in Canada, particularly on Baffin, Axel Heiberg, and Ellesmere Islands, and also at high altitudes in the Rockies and other western mountains. Of course, the largest glaciers in the world are in Antarctica. All of these surviving glaciers are now melting quite rapidly because of global warming during the past century or more.

At the peak of the Wisconsinan ice age, glaciers covered virtually all of Canada, in some regions with ice as thick as several kilometres. In fact, so much of the water of Earth was tied up on land in glacial ice that sea level was as much as 120 m lower than at present. This resulted in extensive areas of the currently suboceanic continental shelf being exposed as terrestrial habitats—during glacial times the "land" extended up to 100 km farther east off eastern Canada than it does today, onto what are now shallow marine waters. This also occurred off British

FIGURE 10.5 Biological Agents May Be Causes of Disturbances The pale-winged grey moth (*Iridopsis ephyraria*) irrupted in and around Kejimkujik National Park, Nova Scotia, in 2002. Severe defoliation over several years killed mature trees of eastern hemlock (*Tsuga canadensis*). Because only mature hemlock trees are affected by the moth, this might be considered a population-replacing disturbance.

Bill Freedman

Columbia, but not to the same extent because the continental shelf is much narrower on the Pacific coast.

When the massive continental-scale glaciers eventually melted, the freed-up terrestrial substrates became available for colonization by organisms that were capable of dispersing to the newly freed-up habitats. This resulted in an extended successional recovery on deglaciated landscapes. In fact, almost all of the terrestrial and freshwater ecosystems of Canada have developed since the melting of the continental-scale glaciers. The only exceptions are small regions that were not glaciated, particularly in northwestern Canada, which were **refugia** from this massive disturbance. Those nonglaciated areas of northern Yukon and the adjacent coastal Northwest Territories supported plants and animals throughout the most recent glacial epoch, and today they are relatively rich in endemic species (see Chapters 12 and 16).

The Frequency of Disturbance

Disturbances vary in how often they are reoccur. They may be common, rare, or periodic. The length of time between successive disturbance events is referred to as the **return frequency** (or **rotation**), which may be a predictably regular occurrence, or more unpredictable and sporadic.

Estuaries and salt marshes experience both regular and sporadic disturbances. They are naturally exposed to predictable disturbances by flooding and salinity associated with their twice-per-day tidal inundation **(Figure 10.6)**. The tidal oscillations can be quite accurately predicted from knowledge of the timing of the rotation of Earth, and the likely heights of tides can be calculated according to the cycle of the Moon and its positioning with respect to the Sun and Earth. For instance, the so-called "spring tides" are relatively high because the Sun, Earth, and Moon are lined up and produce a larger gravitational influence, whereas "neap tides" are lower, and the two kinds occur over a rotation of about seven days (the higher tides are "springing" in elevation; this is not a seasonal reference). In addition, whenever a full moon coincides with a time when that satellite is in the perigee (least distance) of its elliptical orbit around Earth, there are especially high tides (this occurs every 7.5 lunar cycles). There are also highly predictable locational effects of tides, such as those associated with gently sloping embayments that cause incoming tidal flows to build up, sometimes to a remarkable height. The global average tidal range is about 0.8 m, but the largest ones are 16 m and they occur in the upper Bay of Fundy and in Ungava Bay (during low tide at Parrsboro, Nova Scotia, more than three kilometres of mudflats are exposed). These various influences on tides are so predictable that their occurrences are known years in advance. However, there are also unpredictable influences on tidal heights, caused by severe weather such as powerful following winds associated with a hurricane, or by an earthquake that causes a tsunami (seismic sea wave) to occur.

Another natural disturbance with a predictable timing is the flush of streamflow that occurs during the springtime in most regions of Canada. This phenomenon is related to the accumulation of a snowpack during the cold of winter, which then quickly melts when the atmosphere warms in the spring. The sudden flush of meltwater causes a spate of waterflow to occur in streams, which

Bill Freedman

FIGURE 10.6 Tides In general, the timing and height of tides are extremely predictable because they are affected by measureable periodic influences such as the phase of the Moon and its distance from Earth, as well as local topography. However, there are also highly unpredictable influences on tides, such as windstorms and tsunamis. The highest tides in the world occur predictably at several places in Canada—in the upper Bay of Fundy and Ungava Bay, where they can reach 16 m. This image suggests the extreme tidal range of the upper Bay of Fundy near Scots Bay, Nova Scotia.

disturbs communities of benthic invertebrates as a result of the tumbling of rocks and the shearing force of rapidly moving water. The exact timing and magnitude of the annual peak flow cannot be accurately predicted, but its seasonal occurrence is a regular event. Rivers in such regions also have their annual peak flow at this time, but it is more protracted than in streams because of the integrating effect of the much larger watersheds of rivers.

Such high-flow events can cause rivers to spill over their banks, often causing extensive flooding that can be a natural disaster for people living in low-lying areas. These events occur regularly in Canada. For example, in June 2013, the alpine snowmelt coincided with several days of extremely heavy precipitation, which caused extensive flooding of several rivers in southern Alberta. Floodplains along a number of rivers were affected, including the Bow and Elbow Rivers that run through Calgary. A total of 100 000 people were forced out of their homes by emergency evacuation orders, the total economic damage could amount to $5 billion, and it will take years to repair the damage to public infrastructure and private property. Another such disaster occurred in the spring of 1997, when the Red River received an unusually large volume of meltwater and the resulting flooding affected more than 2000 km^2 of terrain in southern Manitoba and North Dakota. In addition to the economic and ecological damage, about 74 000 people had to be evacuated from their homes and farms. In regions where the terrain is vulnerable to flooding damage, almost every spring is worrisome because of the recurring potential for damage.

In addition, unpredictable spates of massive flow in streams and rivers may be caused by big rain events associated with cyclonic weather systems, such as a tropical storm or hurricane. One such event affected the Saguenay region of Quebec in 1996, when 15.5 cm of precipitation fell during a 50-hour period and caused massive riverflow and flooding that displaced 16 000 people and destroyed 1350 homes.

Another example of a predictable physical disturbance is the scouring of shoreline habitats by drifting rafts of sea or lake ice. Typically, this local disturbance occurs each spring, after the surface ice breaks up into chunks that move about in response to wind, currents, and tides. The occurrence of ice scouring is predictable in a seasonal context, although the actual heights of the annual disturbance events will vary depending on the uncertain environmental influences just noted.

Wildfire is also a disturbance with a somewhat predictable return frequency. For example, once boreal forest dominated by jack pine reaches a mature condition, the high loading of flammable biomass makes the habitat vulnerable to a stand-replacing wildfire; all that is required is an ignition event by lightning (or by an anthropogenic source, such as an arsonist). Of course, it cannot be accurately known when a local thunderstorm will provide an ignition event by lightning, but once the jack-pine community becomes mature and develops a high fuel-loading, the likelihood of a catastrophic wildfire becomes increasingly higher. That provides a degree of predictability for the occurrence of the next wildfire, and a probabilistic estimate of the typical fire rotation. The wildfire rotation is important to some highly adapted species, such as the Kirtland's warbler (*Setophaga kirtlandii*) and black-backed woodpecker (*Picoides arcticus*), and also to the jack pine itself, which requires that kind of disturbance for regeneration (see Section 1.3 for a discussion of group selection relevant to wildfire).

Of course, some kinds of natural communities are rarely disturbed and so they are relatively stable and predictable over time. One example is some types of old-growth forest, which rarely experience large-scale disturbances. In fact, their very existence is predicated on the rarity of stand-replacing disturbances—otherwise the old-growth condition would never be reached because the forest succession would be truncated. Similarly, ecological communities of the abyssal depths of the oceans are highly stable because disturbances are rare in those regions. Nevertheless, if stands of old-growth forest or deep benthic communities were to be closely monitored for a long time, they would be found to be subjected to some degree of microdisturbance dynamics, associated perhaps with the deaths of individual organisms because of senescence or disease. At the very least, these and all other ecosystems are influenced by changes in regional climate and by other long-term and pervasive dynamics, such as evolution.

Anthropogenic Disturbances

Many types of disturbances are caused by human activities, and they are increasingly important causes of ecological change. Sometimes the anthropogenic agents of disturbance have broad parallels to natural ones, but they are always novel to some degree and are affecting native species and natural communities in ways that have not previously been experienced.

The selective harvesting of trees from a forest that is otherwise left intact is an example of an anthropogenic microdisturbance. This has obvious similarities to certain natural small-scale disturbances, such as when individual trees are killed by a lightning strike or disease. However, there are also important differences—the natural death of a tree leaves a standing dead snag behind. In an old-growth forest a large dead tree may stand for more than a century until it eventually falls, and it may then exist for additional centuries as a decaying log lying on the forest floor. Both snags and big logs are important habitat elements for many birds and other wild life of the forest, and these qualities are not emulated when trees are harvested and removed from the site.

Sometimes native species become unusually abundant, and may cause severe damage to their community. In addition to natural population cycles, there may be an anthropogenic influence on irruptions of native species. For example, when populations of top predators, such as wolf (*Canis lupus*) or cougar (*Puma concolor*), are reduced by excessive trapping or deliberate extirpations, their top–down control of prey species is eliminated (see Chapter 9). This can allow species such as the white-tailed deer (*Odocoileus virginianus*) and elk (*Cervus canadensis*) to increase in abundance to the degree that they impede the regeneration of trees and shrubs and even endanger rare plants.

Increasingly, however, non-native (also referred to as alien or exotic) species are becoming invasive in natural habitats and are causing a great deal of ecological damage. Sometimes, invasive aliens dominate habitats to the degree that native species are displaced. In addition, introduced disease pathogens may be so virulent that they eliminate vulnerable native species throughout their range. The problem of alien invaders is extremely important—they are the second-most important cause of damage to global biodiversity, after the outright destruction of natural habitats (Chapter 12).

Introduced fungal pathogens of trees have caused some of the worst damage to ecosystems. Examples relevant to Canadian ecosystems are noted below; all of these diseases were likely introduced by importing alien trees for horticultural use:

- The chestnut blight fungus (*Cryphonectria parasitica*) was introduced around 1900–1908 and it attacked American chestnut (*Castanea dentata*), which was a prominent tree in eastern hardwood forests. By 1940 that once abundant tree was extirpated throughout almost all of its range.
- Dutch elm disease (*Ceratocystis ulmi*) was introduced in 1928 and it is extensively killing white elm (*Ulmus americana*) and other native elms.
- The beech-bark disease fungus (*Neonectria faginata*) was introduced in Halifax around 1890 and it damages American beech (*Fagus grandifolia*).
- Butternut canker (*Sirococcus clavigignenti*) was first reported in 1967 and it is killing butternut (*Juglans cinerea*).

Some alien invertebrates are also causing population-replacing disturbances in Canadian ecosystems. The following tree-killing beetles were likely introduced through imported lumber and wooden cargo pallets:

- The brown spruce longhorn beetle (*Tetropium fuscum*) was introduced in Halifax in the 1980s. It is killing red spruce (*Picea rubens*) and other species of spruces.
- Emerald ash borer (*Agrilus planipennis*) was introduced near Detroit around 2001 and is spreading rapidly in the American midwest as well as southern Ontario and Quebec. It kills all native ashes (*Fraxinus* species).
- Asian long-horned beetle (*Anoplophora glabripennis*) was introduced in the 1990s in several places, including Toronto, and is killing many species of native hardwood trees.

Other alien invertebrates were introduced via the ballast waters of ocean-traversing cargo ships:

- European green crab (*Carcinus maenas*) damages estuarine beds of eel-grass (*Zostera marina*) on both the east and west coasts, while also aggressively predating native invertebrates, such as soft-shell clam (*Mya arenaria*).
- Zebra mussel (*Dreissena polymorpha*) displaces native bivalve mollusks by competing for hard-rock substrates in lakes, and it causes economic damage by fouling municipal and industrial water-intake pipes and other built structures.

Some alien plants are so invasive that they can exclude native species from affected habitats. They exert their effect mostly by aggressive competition that allows them to appropriate habitat. This results in a conversion of original communities into other kinds of habitat that are unsuitable for native species, and so might be regarded as a kind of biotic disturbance. Here are some examples relevant to Canadian habitats:

- Japanese knotweed (*Fallopia japonica*) is a tall perennial herb from eastern Asia that was introduced through horticulture. It is invasive in terrestrial habitats and can almost totally exclude native plants (**Figure 1**).
- Himalayan blackberry (*Rubus discolor*) is a semi-shrubby Eurasian plant that can dominate moist habitats in southern British Columbia.
- Garlic mustard (*Alliaria petiolata*) invades lowland temperate forests in eastern Canada and dominates the

Additional examples of anthropogenic microdisturbances include the scouring of coral reefs by boat anchors, and preferential hunting of larger and older deer from a multiaged population, or of big fish from a comparable aquatic population. Paths used by hikers, bikers, or users of all-terrain motor vehicles are another cause of smaller-scale disturbances.

Anthropogenic stand-replacing disturbances may be caused by clear-cutting, explosions, the ploughing of agricultural land, and bottom trawling in a fishery. These larger-scale disturbances result in heavy damage or even obliteration of the original community, and are then followed by a successional recovery (although not necessarily to the original condition). The conversion of natural ecosystems into a longer-term anthropogenic use, such as for residential or agricultural purposes, may be viewed as a protracted disturbance that is analogous to glaciation. If the converted lands are eventually abandoned from

understorey, greatly reducing or eliminating native plants.

Additional examples of invasive aliens are provided in Chapter 14. It is clear that they represent an extremely important ecological problem because of the damage they cause to ecosystems and native species. In fact, deliberate and accidental movements of species around the globe have become so prevalent that some ecologists refer to the present era as the **Homogecene**—a time during which the ancient and coevolved biotas of Earth's biogeographic realms have become severely mixed up and otherwise damaged by alien species.

The cure for this ecological pathology is well known, but it is not yet being widely implemented by governments. The necessary actions include:

- stringent control on the importing of non-native plants for use in horticulture and agriculture, and of animals as pets;
- effective measures to kill organisms that are transported in the ballast waters of ships, or in the goods that are being transported;
- diligent efforts to eradicate newly established invasive aliens as soon as they are noticed—if this action is delayed, it may no longer be feasible to control them; and
- changes in horticultural aesthetics to favour the cultivation of native species—this has the great benefit of providing seminatural habitats for use by native species, while also disfavouring the growing of aliens, any of which may turn out to be invasive of natural or economic habitats.

FIGURE 1 **The Japanese Knotweed (*Fallopia japonica*) Is an Invasive Species** It dominates habitats to the degree that native species are not able to cohabit with it.

those uses, an ecological recovery will occur, but again, not necessarily back to the original ecosystem.

Biological agents of disturbance may also be anthropogenic, such as when introduced species become invasive of natural or anthropogenic habitats and cause severe and extensive damage to them (see also Chapter 14). Examples of introduced species that have damaged vulnerable communities in Canada and elsewhere in North America are provided in Environmental Applications 10.1.

10.3 Patterns and Mechanisms of Succession

Whatever the spatial scale of a disturbance or its return frequency, once the event ceases, it is followed by a period of community-level recovery known as succession. Recovery usually proceeds as a relay of sequential community types (or **seral stages**), which in its entirety is known as a **sere**.

A succession will progress as long as there is no intervening disturbance that sets conditions back again. Eventually, a relatively stable community may develop that represents the final stage of the sere, and whose characteristics are determined by a number of interacting factors, including:

- *enduring site features,* such as topography, climate, the type of bedrock and soil in terrestrial environments, and the water depth, currents, nutrient supply, and kind of sediment in aquatic systems;
- *the species present,* which is related to their ability to survive the disturbance or to colonize afterward, as well as biological interactions occurring among them, such as competition, predation, and disease; and
- *stochastic factors* that cannot be predicted, such as weather conditions at the time of the disturbance and afterward, and the local availability of potentially colonizing species.

Late-Stage Communities

In Section 9.1, we examined how Frederic Clements and Henry Gleason viewed influences on the structure of communities. They also extended their ideas to how communities change over time during succession.

Clements suggested that successions have a predictable end-point community that he named the **climax**, which in terrestrial ecosystems is largely dependent on the local climate (Clements, 1916, 1936). He believed that the climax represents the "potential vegetation" of a site, which would always be attained if successions were able to run their full course without an intervening disturbance that truncates the sere. Clements initially believed that there are only a few dominant kinds of climax communities, which he called **climatic climaxes** (because they are determined mostly by climate). According to this **monoclimax** idea, the longer-term influence of climate trumps other effects on community development during succession, such as differences in topography and the kind of soil.

Further work expanded the monoclimax concept to allow for different sorts of climaxes that depend on environmental influences beyond that of climate. Clements suggested that:

- **Edaphic climaxes** are related to local soil conditions, such as infertile, nickel-rich serpentine soil that causes physiological stress and toxicity to nonadapted plants and so may sustain only low tundra-like vegetation, even though the climate is suitable for boreal forest; these soil conditions occur in areas of Gros Morne National Park in western Newfoundland and in parts of Quebec (see also Chapter 13).
- **Disclimaxes** occur in situations that have an unusual disturbance regime, such as grassland that is naturally maintained by frequent wildfires that kill invading shrubs and trees. Without those frequent burns an open forest would establish. This disclimax is typical of tallgrass prairie in southeastern Manitoba and southwestern Ontario (in situations where the natural fire regime has been disrupted, these prairies must be managed using prescribed burns).
- **Polyclimaxes** are a more complex idea that suggests that multiple end-states of succession are possible depending on variations of key factors such as topography, slope, exposure, the local regime of moisture and nutrients in soil, and the kinds of disturbances that affect the community.

In contrast to Clements, Gleason believed that communities are highly complex entities that are largely structured by the diverse population-level interactions occurring among their species, by the physical environment, and also by the disturbance regime (Gleason, 1926, 1939). According to Gleason's equilibrium view, communities are individualistic and the abundances and distributions of their component species are unpredictable. This contrasts with the Clementsian idea of more sharply defined and bounded types of communities.

These differing views of succession were hot topics of discussion among ecologists for much of the first half of the 20th century. Eventually, field research showed that there can be broad continua among the late-stage communities that develop through succession. Ecologists have observed that many species occur in their own idiosyncratic niche-spaces along continuous gradients of environmental change, and so there may be unbroken variation among communities.

The work of Robert Whittaker (1920–1980) and John Curtis (1913–1961) was influential in this emerging consensus—they showed that species of trees have characteristic distributions along altitudinal gradients in mountainous terrain, and the transitions between their community types (or **ecotones**) are not necessarily distinct or rapid (except in places where there are large changes in environmental conditions over a short distance, such as between a wetland and a forest, or where dissimilar soil types conjoin; these zones of rapid change are known as **step-clines**) **(Figure 10.7)**.

Moreover, it is now better understood that environmental conditions are endlessly changing, and this makes it impossible for a stable climax-type community to be maintained over the longer term. The most prominent environmental contingencies include climate change, intervening disturbances (including gap-phase microdisturbances), immigration of new species and extirpation of others, as well as anthropogenic influences. As a result, most ecologists today are comfortable with the idea of nonequilibrium models of the functioning of ecosystems—these paradigms acknowledge that change is normal, continuous, and often unpredictable.

FIGURE 10.7 An Ecotone Is a Zone of Transition between Different Communities The altitudinal tree-line is a transition between montane forest and alpine tundra. Within the ecotone, there may also be transitional edges at a more local level, as is shown in this image of tree-line near Whitehorse, Yukon.

Nevertheless, under some environmental conditions, older ecosystems may develop and remain rather stable for a long time, and within that ecological context they may be viewed as representing a kind of climax community **(Figure 10.8)**. Old-growth forest is one example of such a climax community. It typically develops within an environmental regime that is characterized by abundant rainfall throughout the year, so that stand-replacing wildfires are rare. Although old-growth forest has microdisturbance-related dynamics that are associated with the death of individual trees, the community as a whole may persist for millennia in some environments, such as in high-rainfall regions of coastal British Columbia. Comparable examples in marine systems include the benthic communities of deepwater habitats, which may also be stable over millennia, and on shorter time scales, temperate kelp "forests" dominated by large species of seaweeds, and tropical coral-reef habitats. Because resources needed by the biota are relatively constrained in all of these environments, competition is the major influence on the structure and dynamics of their late-successional communities.

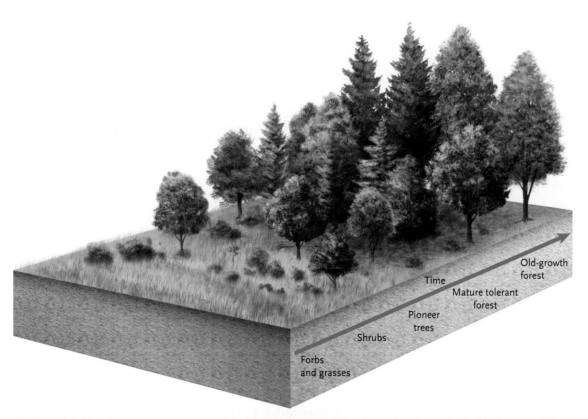

FIGURE 10.8 Plant Succession in a Temperate Forest The initiating stand-replacing disturbance might have been a wildfire, clear-cut, or abandonment of an agricultural field. The initial seral stages are dominated by ruderal plants plus regenerating individuals that survived the disturbance. As time passes, the community becomes increasingly dominated by woody species that are tolerant of biotic stressors associated with competition. Eventually, in the absence of another stand-replacing disturbance, an old-growth forest develops. That late-stage community has its own dynamics that are related to gap-phase disturbances associated with the deaths of individual trees, as well as with pervasive environmental changes (such as in climate). Nevertheless, old-growth forest is relatively persistent and stable and could be viewed as the climax of the sere.

SOURCE: Based on http://mff.dsisd.net/Environment/PICS/Succession.jpg.

Environmental Conditions

Environmental conditions have a large influence on the sequence of recovering communities—the sere—that occurs after a disturbance. As we previously noted, the most favourable climatic and site conditions in a terrestrial environment may allow old-growth forest to develop. Old-growth forest represents a high level of ecosystem development, in the sense that abundant biodiversity is supported by the community, gross productivity is high, biomass storage is exceptionally large, and nutrient retention by the ecosystem is efficient (see also Chapters 4 and 12). Old-growth forests in the humid tropics support especially high levels of biodiversity in terms of species per hectare—in fact, more so than any other kind of ecosystem.

Under more constraining environmental conditions on land, the late-stage community of succession might be a prairie, tundra, or sparsely vegetated desert. In the coastal realm, environmental stress associated with twice-daily tidal inundations may limit community development to a grassy salt marsh or mangrove forest, while in the abyssal depths of the oceans it might be constrained to a low-biomass muddy-bottom assemblage. These communities are stable and might be considered to represent a climax state, but they develop under stressful environmental circumstances associated with difficult climate, insufficient water, utter darkness, or frequent disturbance.

In any event, predictable suites of environmental conditions do exist, and they may result in the occurrence of particular seres, in terms of the communities that make up the successional sequence. Specific types of seres are named after the type of substrate on which they develop

For instance, a **hydrosere** typically begins with a "young" lake, such as one that has recently begun its ecological life as a water-filled depression in the bedrock after a glacier melted back, as was typical of much of Canada **(Figure 10.9)**. Initially, the lake may be oligotrophic,

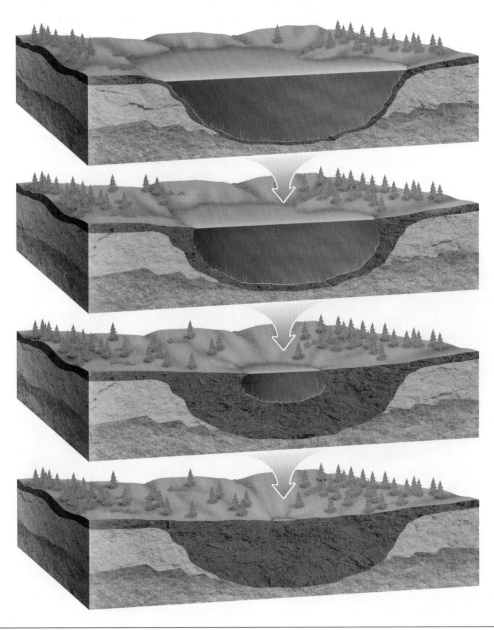

FIGURE 10.9 A Hydrosere Succession The sere begins with a lake, which gradually infills with mineral sediment eroded from its terrestrial watershed, along with autochthonous organic matter that originates with its own local productivity. As the lake becomes increasingly shallow, the littoral fringe of marshy vegetation expands and covers an increasingly large fraction of the surface area. Eventually the lake is completely infilled and it may then develop into a humid forest growing on peaty substrate, or perhaps become a permanent wetland as a raised bog.

SOURCE: Based on http://kidfish.bc.ca/ images/lake%20succession.gif.

meaning its productivity is sparse because of a low supply of nutrients, especially phosphorus and nitrogen. At that stage most of the primary production is associated with phytoplankton (microscopic algae that occur in the water column), with some additionally contributed by a fringe of macrophytes (larger aquatic plants) growing in shallow water of the littoral zone along the shore. During this young stage of the hydrosere, the rate of sediment accumulation is typically slow, occurring as inorganic particulates eroded from terrestrial parts of the watershed settle to the lake bottom as clay, silt, and sand. There is also a slow accumulation of organic matter in the sediment, mostly derived of the undecomposed biomass of phytoplankton and macrophytes, as well as inputs of litter from the terrestrial watershed.

As time passes, the accumulation of inorganic and organic sediment causes the lake basin to become increasingly shallow. Its productivity also may increase because of the accumulation and more rapid cycling of nutrients. As the lake becomes shallower, highly productivity communities of emergent and floating-leaved macrophytes become more prominent. Eventually, the lake may completely infill with sediment and organic matter, and, depending on its fertility and other factors, it may become a shallow-water wetland such as a marsh, fen, or bog (see Section 11.2 for explanations of these different kinds of wetlands). Finally, the hydrosere may culminate in the development of a swamp or another kind of moist forest growing on organic-rich soil, or alternatively it may become a raised bog that remains wet enough to resist invasion by trees.

The time taken to complete a hydrosere can vary enormously, depending on the initial depth of the lake, the rate at which inorganic materials erode into it and then settle as sediment, the primary productivity and rate of accumulation of dead organic matter, and other factors. Most lakes in Canada are younger than 8000 to 12 000 years, so the speed of their hydroseres is extremely slow. However, when shallow basins experience rapid sedimentation, the full sere may take only a few centuries to complete.

A **lithosere** begins on an exposed rocky surface, such as the scoured bedrock and boulders that emerged after glaciers melted back, or lava that cooled after a volcanic eruption **(Figure 10.10)**. Typically, the sere begins with colonization of the bare substrate by crusts of algae and blue-green bacteria, which slowly accumulate biomass and nutrients. Those pioneers help to prepare the surface for other early colonists, such as crustose lichens, then foliose lichens and certain mosses, which are then succeeded by grasses and forbs, then shrubs, and eventually trees.

A **psammosere** is a terrestrial succession that occurs on a sandy substrate, typically along the shore of a large

Bill Freedman

FIGURE 10.10 A Lithosere Succession A lithosere is a primary succession that occurs on a bare-rock surface. This kind of succession is common after deglaciation and other severe disturbances in northern Canada, especially in regions of Precambrian bedrock. Among the first colonists are algae, lichens, and mosses, whose accumulating organic matter makes it possible for plants to establish. This image shows various species of lichens growing on bare granite, and a bed of the moss *Rhacomitrium lanuginosum*, whose biomass provides a microhabitat in which several kinds of vascular plants are establishing. In essence, the moss facilitates the invasion of the site by the vascular plants. The location is near Deception Bay, in the Nunavik region of northern Quebec.

lake or ocean, or on an inland dune system. At a coastal situation, the youngest seral stages are closest to the water, and they become progressively older and more mature farther inland (see the case study of primary succession at Grand Bend, in Section 10.4).

Alternative Stable States

As was previously noted, if succession restores a community similar to the one that was initially present, the ecosystem is said to be resilient to the disturbance in question. However, this does not always happen—after some disturbances the end-point of succession may be a community that is dissimilar to the original one. In such cases, the ecosystem and its dynamics may be said to have multiple (or alternative) stable states (Lewontin, 1969; Holling, 1973, May 1977; see also Chapter 9).

The varying stable states may be due to differences in several factors: (1) interactions occurring among species, such as competition or predation, (2) the species that are available to colonize newly disturbed habitats, and (3) changes in the abiotic environment, such as in climate. Any of these factors may contribute to a successional trajectory that results in the development of alternative communities. The different states may be persistent, lasting perhaps until another disturbance reboots a new successional process and direction.

Examples of multiple successional trajectories that have been observed in Canada include the following:

- A combination of natural disturbances by spruce budworm and frequent wildfires appears to maintain extreme southern outliers of open spruce-lichen woodland in Quebec, in a region more typically covered by a closed spruce-fir-bryophyte forest (Jasinski and Payette, 2005).

- After fire or clear-cutting of black spruce forest and some mixedwood types on shallow soil in much of eastern Canada, the ecosystem may regenerate to a forest of the same trees that were originally present, or to a persistent community dominated by shrubs in the heath family (Ericaceae), such as lambkill (*Kalmia angustifolia*) and huckleberry (*Gaylussacia baccata*), which create conditions that are hostile to tree regeneration (Damman, 1971; Mallik, 1993; we previously examined a similar case involving spruce and blue-joint in northern Alberta). Given enough time, a spruce forest may eventually develop, but the heathland is so slow to do this that it is reasonable to conclude that it represents a persistent condition.

- Subtidal communities of the coastal Pacific may be characterized by abundant "forests" of the giant seaweeds *Macrocystis* and *Nereocystis*. But this is only if sea otters (*Enhydra lutris*) are present, because they are predators of invertebrate herbivores of the seaweeds. If the otters are absent, perhaps because they have been overhunted for their fur, the grazing by abundant herbivores may convert the habitat into a rocky "barren ground" with little algal biomass (Simenstad et al., 1978; see also Chapter 9). We earlier examined a similar case from the Atlantic coast, in which kelp forests are one persistent state, but irruptions of sea urchins can convert it to a "barren ground" **(Figure 10.11)**.

- Benthic and near-benthic communities off Newfoundland were formerly dominated by abundant cod (*Gadus morhua*). However, the cod were severely depleted by overfishing, and the ecosystem has changed to a persistent community dominated by herring (*Clupea harengus*), northern shrimp (*Pandalus borealis*), and queen crab (*Chionoecetes opilio*) (see also Chapter 15).

FIGURE 10.11 Irruptions of Urchins The Green Sea Urchin (*strongylocentrotus droebachiensis*) sometimes increases enormously in abundance in coastal waters off Nova Scotia. When this happens the urchin overgrazes large kelps and other seaweeds and converts the ecosystem into a "barren ground" with little algal biomass or productivity. This condition is stable and lasts until unusually warm water induces a disease in the urchins, whose population then collapses, allowing the kelp beds to re-establish. The image on the left shows a subtidal community dominated by the large kelps *Laminaria digitata* and *Laminaria lonicruris*, and the one on the right shows urchins in a defoliated barren ground. These early-summer scenes were photographed at a water depth of about 10 m near Ketch Harbour, Nova Scotia.

Mechanisms of Succession

In natural ecosystems, succession occurs as a spontaneous process that involves the growth and reproduction of species that managed to survive an initiating disturbance, plus others that invaded afterward. Some of the species are present only at the beginning of the succession, some only later, and others throughout. The trajectory of a sere, in terms of the composition and relative abundance of species in the progression of communities, is influenced by a variety of factors. These include the initial and later site conditions, the complex of interactions that occur among species, as well as unpredictable (or stochastic) influences, such as weather during critical times and the local presence of colonizing species.

Humans may also affect the trajectory and speed of succession, through the application of various kinds of management interventions. For instance, if an old pasture is abandoned for agricultural purposes, the succession to a forest may be sped up by planting trees at an optimal spacing and then tending them to enhance their survival and growth. These actions can greatly accelerate the recovery of trees on an abandoned pasture, compared with the alternative of a spontaneous invasion of the pasture and eventual development of a forest. The management also makes it more likely that the species composition of the forest will be one that is considered desirable by the landowner.

Ecologists often think of succession as being a "self-organizing" (or spontaneous) process, but for this to occur there must be mechanisms that drive the process. Much of the current thinking about the means of succession was stimulated by a study by Connell and Slatyer (1977), who proposed the existence of three basic models: facilitation, tolerance and inhibition.

The **facilitation model** suggests that early species in a sere are important because they change the abiotic conditions in ways that enhance the environmental setting for later-invading species. For example, lichens and mosses invading a newly deglaciated site help to accumulate organic matter and nutrients, making the conditions less hostile for plants that invade later. According to this model, the replacement of pioneer species by later ones is largely driven by their relative abilities to cope with the stresses of competition for scarce resources, which in terrestrial environments is usually for light, moisture, and nutrients.

The **tolerance model** suggests that a predictable sequence of species occurs during succession because they differ in their abilities to use the available resources at various times. In general, earlier species need a relatively unfettered access to resources such as light, moisture, and nutrients. However, as the abundance of organisms increases during succession, so does the

intensity of competition, which reduces the availability of vital resources. When this happens, the early species, which are intolerant of competition, become replaced by others that are more tolerant of resource constraints associated with increasing competitive interactions. The tolerant species can establish, grow, and reproduce under competitive conditions, but the intolerant ones cannot do this and so they die out.

The **inhibition model** suggests that early-establishing species resist invasions of later ones. Consequently, later species can penetrate the community only when early ones die, usually because of the effects of a local microdisturbance or some biological influence (such as a predator, herbivore, or disease). The replacement series during succession is affected by the longevity of the early species, and the ability of later ones to disperse to and occupy sites as they become available. Ultimately, however, species with a longer life span are favoured and they dominate later stages of the sere.

Field studies done at many places suggests that all three of Connell and Slatyer's models are relevant to at least some seres, or to certain stages of succession. In general, however, the facilitation model is most frequently invoked as a key mechanism operating early in succession, while the tolerance and inhibition ones are considered more important in later stages.

David Tilman (1982, 1990) has provided an additional model of changes in communities during succession. Its simplest expression is based on a scenario in which two species are competing for the same limiting resource. The winner (or best competitor) is the species that can deplete the resource to the smallest availability that still allows it to survive, a circumstance that would eliminate the other one from the community. The dynamics of the system are also affected by variations in the availability of resources during succession, a change that affects which species will be the best competitor at a particular time.

Tilman also identifies circumstances that allow species to coexist because they have varying competitive abilities for different key resources. For instance, if species A is a better competitor for resource A, and species B for resource B, and both need some degree of access to both resources, then coexistence is a likely outcome. Eventually, if the availability of resources stabilizes at a certain level at a late stage of succession, then the community will also stabilize and be dominated by the best competitors under that circumstance.

Tilman's models are mostly applied to changes in plant communities, and the predictions are partly supported by the results of field experiments in which key resources, such as nutrients, have been manipulated and the outcomes monitored in terms of changes in the abundances of plant species.

Life History and Succession

In general, communities that occur early in succession are dominated by opportunistic species with an *r*-type life history (see Chapters 8 and 9). The British ecologist Philip Grime (2002) uses the term "ruderal" to refer to many of the plants that are typical of, and often dominant in, younger successional ecosystems. As was explained in Section 9.3, ruderal plants are relatively short lived but fast growing and are well adapted to the environmental conditions of recently disturbed habitats, which include a relatively low intensity of competition and a high availability of site resources. Ruderals produce large numbers of seeds that have an ability to disperse widely so that other recently disturbed habitats can be colonized. Typically, ruderal species are prominent in the earlier years of a postdisturbance sere, along with plants of the original community that managed to survive the disturbance and then regenerate.

As time passes and succession progresses, the biomass of vegetation becomes more abundant, the intensity of competition increases markedly, and resources become more limiting. This causes the early-successional and intolerant ruderal plants to be replaced by others that are more tolerant of these increasingly stressful conditions—these are referred to as competitors. Competitors are comparable to Grime's C-type species (Section 8.1)—they are effective at acquiring resources and in achieving a dominant position in their community. Competitor plants are typically tall, develop a broad and shading canopy, and have a spreading root system, all of which help to occupy space and appropriate resources. Seedlings of competitive plants can usually establish beneath a closed canopy, while those of ruderals are intolerant of shaded conditions.

However, the end point of ecological development may be constrained by an environmental regime that is stressful in terms of its climate, soil, nutrients, light availability, or frequency and intensity of disturbances. Under such conditions the climax community might be limited to a grassland, tundra, desert, or hard-rock intertidal community. These ecosystems have a low productivity compared with what is possible under less stressful conditions. Stress-tolerant species typically dominate these difficult habitats. These species are adapted to habitats that are highly stressed but stable, in the sense that they are not often disturbed. Stress-tolerant plants are typical of arctic, alpine, desert, and other severe environments, and they are generally low growing, unproductive, long lived, and intolerant of competition.

Means of Regeneration

Regardless of its scale, disturbance creates a chance for organisms to colonize or regenerate in a habitat in which competition is not intense. The recovery may occur by the regrowth of individuals that survived the disturbance, or by the recruitment of new individuals into the community. We can illustrate the means of regeneration by examining the kinds of plants that participate in the recovery of a forest that has been disturbed by a wildfire, windstorm, or clear-cut. These disturbances kill or damage many of the plants that are initially present, and are then followed by a spontaneous regeneration involving a range of tactics.

Depending on the intensity of a disturbance, many individuals may survive it and contribute to the regeneration in the aftermath conditions. Surviving but damaged plants will regrow through **vegetative regeneration**. For example, burnt or cut trees and shrubs of many species will resprout from still-living roots or rhizomes. Species of ash, aspen, maple, and other hardwood trees are proficient at this, and their vigorous sprouting contributes to the rapid establishment of another forest. For example, if a mature red maple (*Acer rubrum*) tree is cut, up to several hundred woody shoots will sprout from the stump **(Figure 10.12)**. The shoots are genetically identical (the group is known as a clone, and each stem is a ramet) and they eventually self-thin to only a few stems after several decades (Prager and Goldsmith, 1977). Lees (1981) excavated the belowground parts of a large red maple tree in New Brunswick and found that there were at least three stump-sprout generations of that individual plant, each of which had been initiated by a separate disturbance event.

In a mature forest, there is often an abundant population of small individuals of tree or shrub species, which

Bill Freedman

FIGURE 10.12 Vegetative Regeneration Some plants that survive a disturbance then regenerate by vegetative growth that issues from perennating tissues. In this case, cut trees of red maple (*Acer rubrum*) are regenerating by prolific sprouting from the surviving root system, which produces numerous shoots that are genetically identical (each is a ramet, and the grouping is a type of clone). Each of the three shrub-like groupings behind the observer consists of hundreds of sprouts, which over the ensuing decades self-thin to the degree that only one to three survive as mature tree-sized plants.

collectively is referred to as an **advanced regeneration** population ("advanced" in the sense that they are pre-established before the disturbance occurs). After a disturbance opens up the mature stand, surviving individuals of the advanced regeneration are "released" from competitive stresses previously exerted by the dominant trees, which allows them to grow rapidly and be prominent in the next stand. For example, mature fir-spruce forest that develops on the highlands of Cape Breton typically supports about 45 000 small individuals of balsam fir per hectare and more than 3000 of white spruce (MacLean, 1984). Most of these small plants will survive an irruption of spruce budworm, which preferentially kills the larger fir and spruce. The advanced regeneration then grows rapidly and helps to restore another forest that is similar in community structure to the original one.

It is typical that a major disturbance of a forest creates a mosaic of affected patches on the ground surface. The local damage ranges in intensity from places where the organic layer has been removed and the mineral soil exposed, to others where little damage has been caused to the forest floor. The removal of the overhead canopy and disruption of the organic layer result in surface conditions that favour the establishment of seedlings of various plant species. The seedlings may originate through an immigration of seeds or from those produced on-site.

Some of the new seedlings will originate from seeds that have undergone a long-distance dispersal into the disturbed site. Typically, their parents are growing in some other place, but they produce large numbers of seeds that are widely dispersed and well adapted to colonizing suitable habitat elsewhere. For example, fireweed (*Chamaenerion angustifolium*) produces tiny seeds with fluffy plumes that allow them to waft a long distance on the wind, in anticipation of finding a recent burn where they may germinate, establish, grow, and themselves reproduce. The seeds of many other plants, such as conifers and birches, are also small and wind dispersed, although not over such long distances as those with plumed seeds. Other seeds are dispersed by animals, such as the shadbush or saskatoon (*Amerlanchier alnifolia*), whose pips are embedded within a tasty fruit that is eaten by birds, are resistant to digestion, and survive passage through the avian gut to eventually be defecated somewhere else. Another animal-dispersed plant is the beggar-tick (*Bidens frondosa*), whose seeds adhere to the fur of mammals and become widely dispersed in that way.

Any mature plants that survive the disturbance may produce seeds that disperse locally and may establish new seedlings. Although jack pine trees are often killed by a wildfire, soon after a burn their seeds may become locally dispersed from their persistent cones. This is known as **serotiny**, and it is an adaptation of several pine species in which the cones and their content of viable seeds are held persistently aloft on the branches for several years **(Figure 10.13)**. The cone scales are sealed closed by a wax, which prevents their enclosed seeds from dispersing. However, if the serotinous cones are subjected to heat of more than about 80°C, as can happen during a wildfire, the wax will melt, allowing the scales to spread apart, and the seeds to then scatter locally to produce seedlings that participate in the regeneration of another stand of jack pines.

Most stands of forest also have an enduring population of viable seeds in the forest floor that is referred to as a **seed bank**. When these dormant seeds are exposed

Bill Freedman

FIGURE 10.13 A View of Serotinous Cones of Jack Pine (*Pinus banksiana*) The cones are persistent on the tree and their scales are sealed shut, but high temperatures during a wildfire cause them to open up, allowing their seeds to be locally scattered. This establishes a cohort of seedlings that eventually regenerates another stand of jack pine.

to environmental cues associated with a disturbance, such as an increased availability of light (due to disruption of the forest canopy) or a high concentration of nitrate (from stimulation of nitrification; see Chapter 4), they are stimulated to germinate and so can participate in the regeneration. Seeds of *pin cherry (Prunus pensylvanica) and red raspberry (Rubus idaeus)* can survive for more than a century in the forest floor, in patient anticipation of a disturbance that will stimulate them to germinate (Marks, 1974; Grignon, 1992). Many other species also have dormant seeds in the seed bank, but they are not necessarily as long lived as those of pin cherry and red raspberry.

These various sources of natural regeneration help to quickly re-establish a new plant community on disturbed sites. As the vegetation develops through a relay of successional stages, the habitat becomes suitable for various species of animals that invade and take advantage of the opportunities that are newly available for them.

Changes in Structural and Functional Properties during Succession

The structural and functional properties of communities and ecosystems change markedly during succession. The particulars of the changes vary greatly, depending on the circumstances, but some of the broader trends include the following.

Organic Matter and Carbon Storage

Disturbance typically results in a decreased amount of organic matter in an affected ecosystem, followed by a progressive reaccumulation during the recovery process of succession. Note that as used here, the term **organic matter** includes biomass, or the living and recently dead tissues of organisms, as well as longer-dead and more humified organic materials that occur on and in the soil (see Section 4.3). Biomass and other forms of organic matter are commonly measured in units of dry weight, and often also in units of carbon (about half of their dry weight is carbon).

The model of organic-matter dynamics presented in **Figure 10.14** begins with an old-growth forest, which maintains large and steady amounts of organic matter in the form of living biomass, dead litter, and humus in the soil. The forest is then affected by a stand-replacing disturbance (such as a windstorm, wildfire, or clear-cut) that immediately diminishes the amount of organic matter present. There is a further loss for several additional years, during the **reorganization phase** of succession, when the rate of decomposition of dead biomass (D) exceeds the gross ecosystem production (GEP), so that the net ecosystem production (NEP) is negative. Eventually, however, NEP becomes positive again and biomass steadily accumulates—this represents the

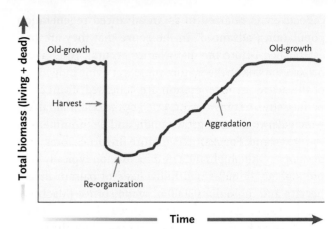

FIGURE 10.14 General Model of Organic Matter during Succession The model begins with a community in an old-growth condition. It is then affected by a stand-replacing disturbance, which quickly reduces the amount of biomass that is present. However, not all of the organic matter of the forest is lost—some remains in the form of organisms that survived the disturbance, or as dead biomass present as woody debris, or as humus in the soil. During the initial reorganization period of succession, the rate of decomposition of dead biomass (D) may exceed that of gross ecosystem production (GEP), so the net ecosystem production (NEP) is less than zero and there is a further decline in the total organic matter present. Eventually, however, NEP again becomes positive and organic matter accumulates steadily, until the old-growth condition is again reached (assuming there is no intervening disturbance). This model is modified from one proposed by Bormann and Likens (1979).

SOURCE: Modified from: Bormann, F.H. and G.E. Likens. 1979. *Pattern and Process in a Forested Ecosystem.* Springer-Verlag, New York, NY, with kind permission from Springer Science+Business Media B.V.

aggradation phase of succession. The process of biomass accumulation continues unless there is another intervening disturbance, or until the old-growth condition is again reached. In general, biomass accumulation is zero or relatively small in old-growth ecosystems—although living organisms continue to grow their biomass, others who die lose theirs through decomposition, so at the stand level the net change is about zero. However, unlike the aftermath conditions of the reorganization phase of succession, when the amount of organic matter present is at its lowest, it is at a peak during the old-growth phase.

Although this general model of organic-matter change during succession is based on a scenario involving old-growth forest, it is also applicable to other kinds of ecosystems, albeit at different scales of time and biomass. For instance, an area of tallgrass prairie that is affected by a wildfire would also lose some of its existing stocks of organic matter, although compared with a burnt forest the successional recovery would be much faster.

Nutrient Capital

Many studies have shown that disturbance can cause a disruption of biological "control" over functions such as decomposition and nutrient cycling, which can result in a loss of some of the accumulated nutrient capital from the ecosystem. This is especially important for nitrate (NO_3^-) and potassium (K^+), which are highly water soluble and therefore mobile in soil and vulnerable to leaching out of the system.

One of the most impressive demonstrations of this effect occurred in a large-scale experiment at Hubbard Brook in New Hampshire in which all trees in a 16-ha watershed were felled (Likens et al., 1978). The trees were left lying on the ground rather than being harvested from the site, and the area was then treated with a herbicide for three growing seasons to inhibit the regeneration of plants. The intent of this work was to examine the effects of **devegetation**, an extremely severe disturbance, on nutrient cycling and other ecosystem functions. During a 10-year period following this intense disturbance, the devegetated watershed lost 499 kg/ha of NO_3^--N (this is nitrate expressed as its nitrogen content), along with 450 kg/ha of calcium and 166 kg/ha of potassium. Those losses were measured in streamflow—the nutrients leached through the soil with percolating rainwater, until bedrock was reached, after which the flow was lateral and eventually reached the stream that was draining the watershed. The nutrient losses were much larger than from a nearby watershed that was an undisturbed reference (or "control") treatment for the experiment (43 kg/ha of NO_3^--N, 131 kg/ha of Ca, and 22 kg/ha of K).

This nutrient-leaching effect is also often seen after the industrial clear-cutting of tracts of forest. However, the intensity of the leaching is much less because vegetation regenerates vigorously after timber harvesting, and this helps to absorb some of the soluble nutrients and prevent them from leaching away. When they have this absorptive effect, plants are sometimes referred to as a biological "sponge." A study in New Brunswick that involved clear-cutting a 391-ha watershed reported a moderate loss of nitrate of only 19 kg NO_3^--N/ha over a three-year period (this was a commercial timber harvest—the logs were removed and herbicide was not applied to the land to inhibit the regeneration; Krause, 1982).

Evapotranspiration

Well-vegetated communities evaporate a lot of water to the atmosphere, mostly through foliage in a process referred to as transpiration (this, combined with evaporation from nonbiological surfaces, is referred to as evapotranspiration) (Section 3.4). For example, the annual loss of water by evapotranspiration from four watersheds in forested terrain in Nova Scotia was equivalent to 15–29 percent of the total input by precipitation (Freedman et al., 1985). During the summer, however, the relative effect of evapotranspiration is much larger—in fact, so much water may be pumped to the atmosphere that soils become parched and pools of standing water and small brooks may dry up.

A disturbance usually results in a large but temporary decrease in the amount of plant foliage that is present on the affected site. This results in correspondingly less transpiration, which in turn may cause a larger amount of streamflow to occur from a disturbed watershed. This phenomenon was observed in the Hubbard Brook devegetation experiment that we just examined—the disruption of transpiration resulted in a 31 percent increase in streamflow during the three years that herbicide was applied (Likens et al., 1978). However, when the herbicide spraying ended and the vegetation recovered, this effect on evapotranspiration and streamflow rapidly disappeared.

Physical Structure and Complexity

The physical structure of a community or larger ecosystem refers to the patterns in which its biomass is distributed over space. This includes its distribution over vertical space, both above- and belowground, as well as over horizontal space. Complexity refers to the variability of those structural attributes.

Shortgrass prairie is an example of a community with a relatively low level of vertical complexity, because the living biomass occurs close to the soil surface in both the above- and belowground dimensions. In contrast, an older forest has a much greater amount of vertical complexity, having layers of aboveground biomass distributed in intricate patterns that extend from the ground surface to the high canopy, and with a similarly complicated dispersal belowground.

Complexity may also be expressed on a horizontal plane, being relatively high in habitats that are patchy in nature. An example is an old-growth forest that has some areas dominated by large trees, and others where gap-phase disturbance dynamics have resulted in patches of younger vegetation, as well as types intermediate to those extremes.

In general, stand-replacing disturbances reduce the complexity of the physical structure of affected communities or ecosystems, followed by a progressive recovery during succession. In contrast, smaller-scale gap-phase disturbance dynamics occurring within older ecosystems will increase the complexity of the physical structure.

Biodiversity

Biodiversity refers to biological richness and it may be expressed at three broad levels: (1) genes within populations, (2) species within communities, and (3) communities on landscapes and seascapes (see Chapter 12). Some disturbances are so severe that they can temporarily obliterate biodiversity on the affected habitat—by removing all of the pre-existing organisms. This may occur as a result of glaciation, a mass-flow of mud or lava, an explosion, or when an area is paved with asphalt or concrete. Such extreme disturbances eliminate the biodiversity that was initially present, although an ensuing succession will recover it to some degree.

Consider another example—one that involves a landscape uniformly covered with mature communities of a particular type, such as conifer-dominated boreal forest. Within that context of initial ecological homogeneity, if some patches on the landscape were to be affected by stand-replacing disturbances (perhaps by wildfire, windstorm, or clear-cutting), the terrain would be converted into a more complex mosaic that is composed of a variety of community types in various stages of succession, ranging from young to mature. Because each of the communities supports a distinctive assembly of species, only some of which were present in the original forest, the patch-disturbed landscape mosaic would support a higher overall level of biodiversity than the original one **(Figure 10.15)**.

Higher levels of biodiversity should not necessarily be viewed as representing an "improvement" in the ecological "quality" of an affected landscape. Such a judgment of ecological integrity (see Section 17.2 for a

discussion of this concept) is partly subjective and would involve consideration of factors such as:

- the rarity of the original community types (e.g., old-growth forest and extensive wilderness are becoming increasingly scarce in Canada);
- whether the gain of "additional" species characteristic of early-successional habitats is occurring at the expense of rarer ones of older community types; and
- whether the additional species are native or alien.

It is remarkably difficult to generalize about the changes in biodiversity that occur as a result of disturbance and succession. Many studies have been made in a wide range of places, and their results are variable and dependent on the ecological circumstances. While severe disturbances can obliterate biodiversity from affected areas, less-intense ones do not do this—many species survive the disturbance, and others invade afterward.

This phenomenon is illustrated in **Figure 10.16**, which shows changes in biodiversity in a series of communities of various ages following clear-cutting in an area of hardwood-dominated forest. These communities form a **chronosequence**—a series of communities of various ages that have regenerated from a similar kind of disturbance, which allows them to be studied as a group to infer patterns of ecological change during a succession. Species diversity is measured as the Shannon-Weiner index (H'), which is based on both the number of species and their relative abundances (see Section 12.3 for details on this and other biodiversity indices). Species richness is the number of species present, but standardized to the sampling area (per m² for plants, and per 10 ha for birds). Basal area (m²/ha) is an indicator of the biomass of all the trees and shrubs in the community, which progressively increases during succession, and it is presented for purposes of comparison to the biodiversity data. The plots of the biodiversity of both vegetation and birds suggest that, although they change during this post-clear-cutting succession, they do so much less than the steady increase in stand biomass.

It is important to understand, however, that species diversity and richness are community-level indicators of biodiversity, and so they do not identify the particular species that are present. For example, in the chronosequence illustrated in **Figure 10.16b**, the avian communities of younger and older stands are composed of different species of birds, even though they do not differ much in their levels of biodiversity. In that study, the younger clear-cuts were dominated by alder flycatcher (*Empidonax alnorum*), chestnut-sided warbler (*Dendroica pensylvanica*), common yellowthroat (*Geothlypis trichas*), dark-eyed junco (*Junco hyemalis*), white-throated sparrow (*Zonotrichia albicollis*), and song sparrow (*Melospiza melodia*). In contrast, the dominant birds of the mature forest were least flycatcher (*Empidonax minimus*), hermit

Bill Freedman

FIGURE 10.15 Patches of Various Postdisturbance Ages Contribute to Landscape-Scale Diversity This aerial view of central Labrador shows several age-classes of forest after wildfire. The oldest forest is dark green, while younger stands are lighter green, and the most recently burnt areas are whitish because of abundant reindeer lichens.

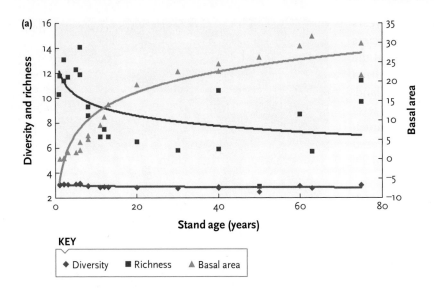

(a)

KEY

◆ Diversity   ■ Richness   ▲ Basal area

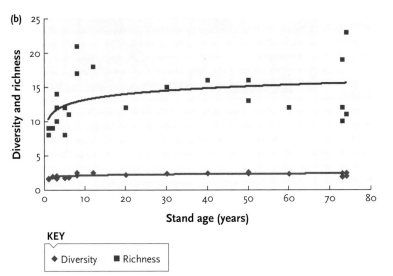

(b)

KEY

◆ Diversity   ■ Richness

FIGURE 10.16 Changes in Biodiversity during Post-Clear-Cutting Succession The data are based on studies of a chronosequence of stands of various ages following the clear-cutting of hardwood-dominated forest in Nova Scotia. Species diversity is measured as the Shannon-Weiner index (H'), while species richness is the number of species present (see text for additional explanation). Basal area (m²/ha) is an indicator of the increasing plant biomass of the stands. Plot (a) shows data for the ground vegetation, which involves all vascular plants growing within 2 m of the ground surface, including young individuals of shrubs and tree species, while (b) is birds that are breeding in many of the same stands. Logarithmic trend lines are included.

SOURCES: Based on data from Crowell and Freedman (1994) and Morgan and Freedman (1986). Panel (a): Crowell, M. and B. Freedman. 1994. "Vegetation development during a post-clearcutting chronosequence of hardwood forest in Nova Scotia, Canada," *Canadian Journal of Forest Research*, 24: 260–271.

thrush (*Catharus guttatus*), red-eyed vireo (*Vireo olivaceus*), northern parula (*Parula americana*), black-throated green warbler (*Dendroica virens*), American redstart (*Setophaga ruticilla*), and ovenbird (*Seiurus aurocapillus*). These are all native species, and none of them are rare or endangered in the study region, so any judgment of the "quality" of the change in avian biodiversity as a result of the timber harvesting might be somewhat ambivalent.

10.4 Primary Succession

Some disturbances are so intense that they destroy all organisms and wreck the inherent ability of the ecosystem to regenerate. In such cases, succession can occur only if the affected terrain is invaded by organisms that disperse from intact habitats somewhere else. This kind of ecological recovery from severe disturbances, on what is initially abiotic habitat, is referred to as a **primary succession**.

Natural disturbances that are destructive enough to initiate a primary succession include lava flows, mudslides, and glaciation. Anthropogenic disturbances that initiate

primary successions include the abandonment of old buildings or paved sites, the dumping of thick layers of dirt or sludge, bulldozing of vegetated terrain, and massive explosions. In all of these cases, the damage is so complete that succession cannot begin until colonizing organisms disperse into the freed-up space and establish new populations.

One of the early studies of primary succession in North America was by Henry Cowles (1899), who examined the process on sand dunes exposed along the shore of Lake Michigan. His study was based on the premise that the plant communities on dunes of a particular age represented a distinct seral stage of the succession. He reasoned that if a time-series of sites and communities of various ages were identified, the entire succession might be examined—this is now referred to as the chronosequence method.

Deglaciation

Virtually all of the Canadian landmass has been affected by glaciation. This is readily apparent from a map of the maximal extent of the great continental ice masses during the most recent glaciation, which ended 10–12 000 years ago (see Figure 16.1 in Chapter 16). In fact, glaciers extended out to sea a considerable distance beyond the present terrestrial boundaries of Canada. This occurred because so much global water was tied up as ice on land, in glaciers up to several kilometres thick, that sea level was about 120 m lower than it is today. As a result, much of the now-submerged continental shelf was exposed land, although much of that terrain was covered by glaciers.

In any event, virtually all of the present-day ecosystems of Canada, both terrestrial and coastal marine, have developed since the most recent glacial epoch. The only exceptions were a few refugia of nonglaciated terrain, mostly occurring in northwest Canada and nearby Alaska, and likely also on exposed mountaintops in some regions.

Ecological recovery after **deglaciation** (the meltback of glacial ice) occurs through a primary succession. This is because there is typically no residue of previous ecosystem development on deglaciated sites—there are no living plants or propagules and no soil development. The devastation is due to the glaciers persisting for thousands of years so organisms could not survive beneath them, plus the fact that they scoured the ground surface bare of traces of previous ecosystems. When the glaciers melted back, they left an expansive topography of naked bedrock, mixed or homogenous tills, and water-filled basins. These abiotic substrates were soon colonized by opportunistic species that had the ability to disperse to newly deglaciated places **(Figure 10.17)**. Sometimes the colonists originated in vegetated habitats that survived to the south of the glaciers, or from nearby mountaintops that had not been glaciated (known as nunataks) or other refugia. Many of the colonists arrived after a long-distance dispersal, involving spores or seeds blown from afar (even tiny invertebrates can do this—small spiders and mites disperse widely by "ballooning" in a windy atmosphere, using threads of silk as a flotation device).

The first immigrants would have been microbes such as blue-green algae (cyanobacteria), soon followed by lichens and bryophytes, and then vascular plants. As the vegetated habitat developed, animals immigrated. Eventually, late-successional communities developed, of a type suitable to the local environmental conditions.

Almost all of the natural communities of Canada have developed during 10–12 000 thousand (or fewer) years of postglacial succession. Depending on climate and other environmental factors, this has resulted in landscapes being extensively covered by forests of various kinds, or grasslands, tundra, wetland, or desert. In some cases of extreme environmental conditions there are still extensive sparsely developed "barrens" with almost no organisms present, despite the considerable time that has passed since deglaciation. Examples occur at high altitude

Bill Freedman

FIGURE 10.17 Ecological Recovery After Deglaciation Is by a Primary Succession The melting of the ice exposes a surface that is devoid of life and with no inherent capacity to regenerate, so it must be invaded by organisms from elsewhere. This photo shows a person sitting beside the melting front of a glacier on Ellesmere Island, Nunavut, as well as terrain that has recently been released by melting and is now available for primary succession.

on mountain tops, at high latitude in the Arctic, and in the driest desert.

However, natural environmental conditions are constantly changing, particularly with respect to climatic factors. Moreover, many species of limited migratory ability have not yet managed to colonize all of the suitable deglaciated terrain that is potentially available and suitable for them. As a result of these factors, the postglacial ecosystems of Canada and other countries are still in a dynamic, nonequilibrium condition (see Chapter 9 for a discussion of nonequilibrium influences on ecological communities).

For instance, it appears that native earthworms (family Lumbricidae) never managed to recolonize postglacial Canada, likely because of their limited ability to move over long distances (Reynolds, 1977). Virtually all of the lumbricids that are currently abundant in Canada are aliens that were deliberately or accidentally introduced by European settlers, who recognized the natural absence of these animals and understood the benefits that could be gained by introducing earthworms to pastures and other agricultural settings.

Similarly, many species of plants appear to have not reached their full potential range in postglacial Canada. One example is white cedar (*Thuja occidentalis*), which in

Nova Scotia has an extremely limited natural distribution, but performs well beyond that range if planted in suitable habitat. Similarly, numerous species of plants are native to the United States, but their natural distribution does not include Canada, yet they do well if planted here in suitable habitat. Those species may also have been limited in their northern distribution by the relatively short period of time that has passed since deglaciation. A few examples of such plants that are often used in horticulture include bald cypress (*Taxodium distichum*), black locust (*Robinia pseudoacacia*), catalpa (*Catalpa speciosa*), Kentucky coffee tree (*Gymnocladus dioica*), sweet gum (*Liquidambar straciflua*), yellow buckeye (*Aesculus flava*), and varieties of large-leaf rhododendron (*Rhododendron catawbiense*).

Much can be learned about primary succession from studies of postglacial recovery, as we examine in the following sections.

Postglacial Succession on Ellesmere Island

There are exceedingly rare cases in which cover by persistent glacial ice did not eradicate all traces of the previous ecosystem. One such example was studied at Alexandra Fiord on Ellesmere Island, where a modern glacier is melting back and, as it does so, patches of dead but remarkably intact vegetation are being exposed (Bergsma et al., 1984; Jones and Henry, 2003). Some of the patches are large enough for their dead plant "community" to be sampled, and when this was done they were found to be similar to those occurring today in the area (Figure 10.18). Radiocarbon dating of the emerged plants showed that they were about 400 years old when first entombed. This suggests that the vegetation had been covered by snow at the beginning of the Little Ice Age, a

period of climatic deterioration that lasted from about 1450 to 1850. Because of cooling of the climate, the snow did not melt completely during the brief arctic summer, and in fact it accumulated during subsequent winters and eventually became compacted into glacial ice. However, the glacier has been melting recently due to global warming since the mid-19th century. The reason that the entombed vegetation was not obliterated by the ice is because it is beneath a glacier that is apparently frozen to the ground. This means that the ice movement is by internal deformation and does not involve sliding along the ground, as occurs in most other glaciers.

Some of the plant biomass recovered from beneath the glacier at Alexandra Fiord was studied for signs of life in the field and laboratory, for example, by looking for an emission of carbon dioxide, which would have indicated that respiration was occurring. None was found. However, later studies of intact moss biomass being released from a different glacier at Sverdrup Pass on Ellesmere Island did find an indication of survival. That astonishing observation was made by Catherine La Farge and colleagues (2013) of the University of Alberta, who collected samples of mosses being released by glacial meltback and found they could regenerate in a laboratory setting, demonstrating that the plants had survived an entombment of about four centuries.

Soon after the local terrain is released from glacial ice at the Alexandra Fiord study site, the exposed dead biomass decomposes or is washed away and a primary succession begins on the fresh substrate of bedrock and loose sand and gravel. The succession involves an initial colonization by plants originating in the nearby vegetated tundra, which typically establish by wind-dispersed propagules.

Bill Freedman

FIGURE 10.18 Plants Released from a Glacier At a few places on Central Ellesmere Island, Nunavut, the melting of glaciers is exposing dead vegetation that became covered by persistent snow and ice about year 1450. Remarkably, the dead biomass is now being released physically intact and easily identifiable to species, as in the case of this dwarf shrub, arctic white heather (*Cassiope tetragona*). The green plant is the living moss *Psilopilum cavifolium*, which is one of the earliest species in this primary succession.

An analysis of data collected from sites of various ages in a 44-year chronosequence suggested that four main stages form a replacement series of communities:

1. an initial ephemeral community of colonizing (or perhaps, surviving) mosses, dominated by *Psilopilum cavifolium*;

2. a woodrush-grass-forb community, with northern woodrush (*Luzula confusa*), arctic bluegrass (*Poa arctica*), and arctic poppy (*Papaver radicatum*);

3. a deciduous shrub-moss community, dominated by arctic willow (*Salix arctica*) and the mosses *Polytrichum* and *Pogonatum*; and

4. an evergreen dwarf shrub-moss community, with mountain avens (*Dryas integrifolia*), arctic white heather (*Cassiope tetragona*), three-toothed saxifrage (*Saxifraga tricuspidata*), purple saxifrage (*Saxifraga oppositifolia*), and the moss *Rhacomitrium* being prominent (species of stages 2–3 are also present in stage 4, but they are not dominant).

The last stage is persistent and develops into the old-growth community that is typical of mesic sites in that part of the High Arctic. The fact that most of the vascular plants are present throughout the succession, except for the first several years, is a reflection of the broad ecological tolerances of the species involved, as well as the prevailing environmental conditions, which are suited to stress-tolerant plants but not to competitive ones.

Postglacial Succession at Glacier Bay

Another place where primary succession has been examined after deglaciation is at Glacier Bay, located near the border of Yukon and southern Alaska. This region has a cool-temperate climate, and the end-point of the succession is a high-biomass coniferous forest, as opposed to the dwarf-shrub tundra of Ellesmere Island. The glacier within Glacier Bay advanced a remarkably long distance (more than 100 km) during the Little Ice Age and achieved a thickness of up to 800 m (Crocker and Major, 1955; Reiners et al., 1971). However, the glacial front has retreated quickly during the warming that began around 1850, and its known locations at certain times have been used to assemble a chronosequence of sites and communities of various postrelease ages. Although there is a continuous variation of community change along the chronosequence, several broad types have been distinguished:

1. a pioneer stage that lasts for 5–20 years and is dominated by *Rhacomitrium* mosses and the vascular plants willow-herb (*Epilobium latifolium*), variegated horsetail (*Equisetum variegatum*), mountain-avens (*Dryas drummondii*), and arctic willow (*Salix arctica*);

2. alder-willow tall-shrub thicket that is dominant at 20–40 years, and whose most prominent species are willows (*Salix alaxensis, Salix barclayi*, and *Salix sitchensis*) and green alder (*Alnus crispa*);

3. mature forest, which at 50–70 years is dominated by cottonwood (*Populus trichocarpa*) and then by Sitka spruce (*Picea sitchensis*)—these species are eventually joined and then outcompeted by western hemlock (*Tsuga heterophylla*) and mountain hemlock (*Tsuga mertensiana*); and

4. old-growth conifer forest is the stable type of community on well-drained sites on slopes, which are prevalent in the deglaciated terrain, but on flatter sites where drainage is impeded a process known as **paludification** occurs because the organic forest floor retains so much water that trees die from the waterlogging, so that a peat-rich, boggy wetland known as muskeg develops.

Crocker and Major (1955) studied soil development in the chronosequence at Glacier Bay. The initial postglacial parent material was a fine rocky till derived from a mixture of granite, gneiss, schist, and 7–10 percent carbonate minerals, with a pH of 8.0–8.4. Over time this substrate became leached by percolating water and modified by the developing vegetation, and its acidity increased. The soil reached a pH of 5.0 after 70 years of succession, when a mature coniferous forest was present. The acidity of the forest floor eventually stabilized at pH 4.4 in the oldest forest communities, and the underlying mineral soil at pH 4.6–4.8. The acidification was partly due to a large decrease of the amount of calcium in the mineral soil, from an initial concentration of 5–9 percent to less than 1 percent. The decrease of calcium was caused by its being leached by abundant rainfall to below the rooting depth of the trees, as well as its uptake by trees and other plants and storage in their biomass.

Other changes in soil properties during succession included large accumulations of organic matter and nitrogen, due to the biological fixation of atmospheric CO_2 and N_2 into biomass. The fixation of nitrogen is carried out by a relay of species during the succession, beginning with lichens of the pioneer stage, then mountain-avens with N_2-fixing *Frankia* actinobacteria living in root nodules, and later at especially high rates by alder, which also has a *Frankia* mutualism.

Postglacial Succession Inferred from Palynology

Much longer records of postglacial succession have been studied using the paleoecological technique of palynology (see Section 16.3). This involves the reconstruction of past communities through the study of fossil pollen grains extracted from dated layers of lake sediment. If a long-enough sediment core can be recovered, insight can be gained about the kinds of vegetation that were in place in early postglacial times, and then to the present.

Les Cwynar and colleagues from the University of New Brunswick have been doing palynology research in various places in Canada and in other countries. In central Yukon, cores were collected from ponds in a region where the present vegetation is shrubby tundra (Cwynar and Spear, 1991; **Figure 10.19** shows a pollen diagram). The record indicates that 10 000–8000 years BP (before present) the site was a shrub-tundra with forested groves of balsam poplar (*Populus balsamifera*). White spruce (*Picea glauca*) colonized around 9400 BP, and its population increased to form an open woodland that persisted until 6500 BP, when black spruce (*Picea mariana*) and green alder (*Alnus crispa*) became prominent. Then until about 5000 BP there was an open boreal forest of a species composition similar to what occurs today to the south of the study area, which, depending on site conditions and local climate, is (a) stands dominated by white spruce on drier south-facing slopes and alluvial sites, or (b) balsam poplar and black spruce on colder, wetter, north-facing sites and bottoms of wide valleys. At 5000 BP the climate deteriorated again and the forest reverted to a shrub-tundra, comparable to what is today predominant on the local terrain. There are still groves of spruce present, mostly of white spruce, but these are considered to be persistent relicts occurring on favourable sites with a warmer and drier microclimate. The overall conclusion of the study is that this region of northwestern Canada and adjacent Alaska experienced a relatively warm postglacial growing season from 10 000 BP to 5000–6000 BP, followed by a cooling that resulted in an extensive decline in tree populations and a reversion to shrub-tundra vegetation.

Sand Dunes

Sand dunes at various places along the Great Lakes are being slowly uplifted from extended submergence due to the phenomenon of **isostasy**. In essence, isostasy is an elastic rebound of Earth's crust following its release from the immense weight of as much as several kilometres of overlying ice during the height of the continental glaciation. That ice had been so heavy that it pressed the underlying bedrock hundreds of metres into the slightly plastic mantle. When the glaciers retreated, the bedrock was released from that colossal weight and began to slowly uplift, and is still doing so in many regions.

In certain places on the Great Lakes with a gently sloping coastal terrain, isostasy has resulted in the

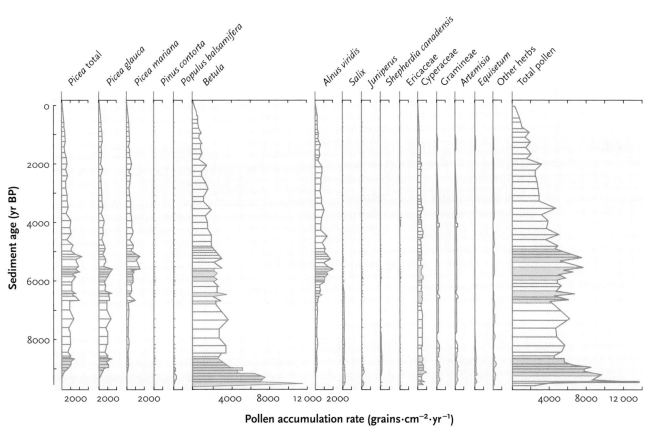

FIGURE 10.19 Pollen Diagram for Honeymoon Pond in Central Yukon The vertical axis is years before present, and the individual graphs are the pollen accumulation rates for particular species or groups of them. See the text for an interpretation of changes in the absolute and relative rates of pollen deposition in terms of vegetational changes in the region.

SOURCE: Used with permission of the Ecological Society of America, from Cwynar, L.C. and R.W. Spear. 1991. "Reversion of forest to tundra in the central Yukon," *Ecology*, 72(1): 202-212; permission conveyed through Copyright Clearance Center, Inc.

FIGURE 10.20 Primary Succession on Sand Dunes This kind of coastal habitat occurs on the shores of rivers, lakes, and oceans across Canada. The initial stage of primary succession on sand dunes is the establishment of specialized grass species that are early invaders. They help to stabilize the substrate, encourage additional sand to accumulate, and facilitate the invasion of other species as the succession proceeds. This image shows sparse clumps of marram grass (*Ammophila breviligulata*), which is the primary invader of exposed sand on coastal beaches in eastern Canada. The image is from Sable Island, Nova Scotia.

Bill Freedman

occurrence of young, recently emerged dunes close to the lake, and progressively older ones farther inland. The age of the dunes can be estimated in several ways, such as their height above the present lake surface, coupled with knowledge of the rate of uplift of the terrain. This spatial progression of dunes of various ages, and the communities they support, can be studied as a chronosequence to reconstruct changes that occurred during primary succession **(Figure 10.20)**. In fact, this was the basis of the early work of Cowles (1899) on succession on sand dunes along the shore of Lake Michigan.

A series of dunes at Grand Bend on Lake Huron was also studied by Morrison and Yarranton (1973, 1974) of the University of Toronto. They divided the plants of the sand-dune succession into colonizing species and persistent species **(Figure 10.21)**. The colonizing species stabilize the sandy matrix and help to accumulate organic matter and nutrients. They are abundant in the initial communities, in which the intensity of competition is relatively low. The persistent species are prominent in the more stable communities of late-successional forest, in which competition is a major factor affecting the vegetation.

Morrison and Yarranton also divided the overall succession into three major periods:

A. First, there is a colonizing stage that begins on recently emerged sand and lasts about 1600 years. It is dominated by type I species with a sparse cover of annual and biennial colonizing plants, such as sea rocket (*Cakile edentula*) and seaside spurge (*Euphorbia polygonifolia*). These colonizing plants soon give way to a higher-biomass cover of the perennial dune-grasses *Calamovilfa longifolia* and *Ammophila breviligulata* and various forbs, such as wormwood *Artemisia biennis*. This community is replaced by a prairie-like one of more-competitive

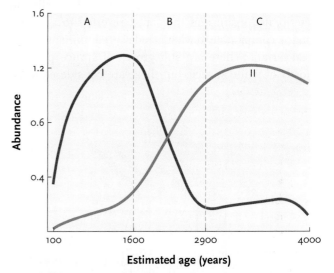

FIGURE 10.21 Model of Plant Succession on Sand Dunes at Grand Bend, Ontario The plants are divided into two classes: (I) colonizing species, which are important in stabilizing the substrate and are prominent in the initial communities, and (II) persistent species, which occur in the more stable communities of late-successional forest. The primary succession is divided into three stages: (A) colonizing, (B) transitional, and (C) persistent.

SOURCE: Modified from: Morrison, R.G. and G.A. Yarranton. 1974. "Vegetational heterogeneity during a primary sand dune succession," *Canadian Journal of Botany*, 52: 397–410. © 2008 Canadian Science Publishing or its licensors. Reproduced with permission.

herbaceous plants, such as little bluestem (*Andropogon scoparius*), big bluestem (*Andropogon gerardii*), indian-grass (*Sorghastrum nutans*), and dense blazing-star (*Liatris spicata*). The older communities within the colonizing stage are dominated by shrubs and trees that are relatively intolerant of competition, such as common juniper (*Juniperus communis*), eastern red-cedar (*Juniperus virginiana*), and dwarf chinkapin oak (*Quercus prinoides*).

B. A second, transitional phase lasts from 1600 to 2900 years, during which type II species with more intermediate tolerance become dominant, including a red-black oak hybrid (*Quercus velutina x rubra*), fragrant sumac (*Rhus aromatica*), and choke cherry (*Prunus virginiana*). The communities in this stage begin as small patches, which grow increasingly larger until they eventually coalesce, a dynamic successional process that is referred to as **nucleation**.

C. Finally, a persistent climax-like stage occurs from 2900 to >4800 years. This involves an extensive consolidation of a forest dominated by type II species that are relatively tolerant of competition. The most prominent trees in the late-stage communities are red oak (*Quercus rubra*), black oak (*Quercus velutina*), white oak (*Quercus alba*), and white pine (*Pinus strobus*), which are tolerant of an environment characterized by periodic summer dryness, because the sandy soil is so well draining.

Morrison and Yarranton also studied community-level changes in the vegetation, using summative indicators that are not related to the particular species that are present **(Figure 10.22)**. They found that species diversity (the Shannon-Weiner index), evenness (a measure of how similarly abundant the various species are), and species richness (the number of species present in sampling plots) all increased rapidly during the early succession, and then levelled off.

Morrison (1973) also studied soil changes during succession on sand dunes at Grand Bend. The initial parent material is a fine-grained sand with a pH of 6.9, almost devoid of organic matter (only 0.4 percent) and water-holding capacity (0.3 percent), and lacking in nutrients (soluble K of 5 ppm). As succession proceeds,

there is a general accumulation of biomass, which reached a level of 16 to 20 percent in the upper mineral soil after 1000 years. The accompanying improvement of tilth enhanced water-holding capacity to 5 to 10 percent and K to 100 ppm. At the same time, the soil became more acidic, reaching pH 5.5–5.9 under mature forest. The acidification was caused by the combined influences of the leaching of calcium and other bases by percolating rainwater and the uptake of those nutrient cations by vegetation, which reduces the amount left in the soil. Furthermore, the uptake of base cations is offset by the release of an equivalent amount of positive charges associated with H^+ to the soil, to maintain its electrochemical neutrality—this also contributed to acidification of the soil.

Ice-Scouring

During the winter, coastal areas of lakes and rivers in much of Canada freeze over, and even oceanic waters also do this in cold regions. When the weather warms up in the spring, the continuous surface ice breaks up into large chunks that are driven by the wind, currents, or tides. When the ice impacts a shoreline, it scours the rocks, sediment, and vegetation. The scraping often leaves a bare surface that is devoid of organisms, and this is followed by a local primary succession within a linear environment along the shoreline.

The width of the ice-scour zones varies according to local circumstance as well as the strength of windstorms, currents, and tides, and can range from a few metres to hundreds of them. These ice-scoured zones are readily apparent along the coast of any waterbodies that are affected in this manner. Along rivers and lakes, the scour-zones are typically dominated by ruderal plants during

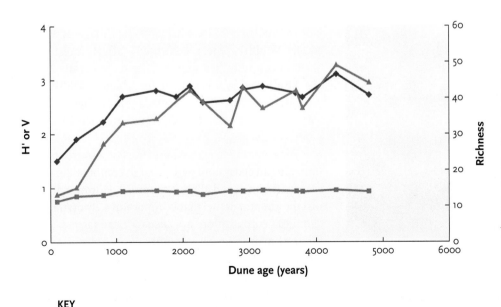

FIGURE 10.22 Changes in Community Indicators during Plant Succession on Sand Dunes at Grand Bend, Ontario Species diversity, evenness, and richness all increase quickly in the early stages of succession, and then level off in the older communities.

SOURCE: Based on data from Morrison, R.G. and G.A. Yarranton. 1973. "Diversity, richness, and evenness during a primary sand dune succession at Grand Bend, Ontario," *Canadian Journal of Botany*, 51: 2401-2411. (Page 2404)

KEY
— Diversity   — Evenness   — Richness

the growing season, with annuals prominent in the most heavily scraped places, and short-lived perennials in situations that are relatively protected, such as on the lee side of large boulders.

On marine shores that are routinely affected by ice-scouring, the local habitats are dominated by annual seaweeds and *r*-type invertebrates. Bergeron and Bourget (1986) of Université Laval studied heavily ice-scoured shores of the northern Gulf of St. Lawrence. They found that the summer community of sessile organisms was sparse on exposed smooth-rock surfaces in the intertidal zone, but more abundant where there was structural heterogeneity in the form of crevices in the bedrock, which provide refugia from the ice-scouring. Seaweed (*Fucus vesiculosus*), mussels (*Mytilus edulis*), and barnacles (*Semibalanus balanoides*) were much more abundant in crevices. These species partitioned the refuge habitat, with *Mytilus* dominating the bottom of crevices and the other two the zone above (but beneath the scoured surface). Macpherson et al. (2008) of St. Francis Xavier University studied the settlement of larvae of *S. balanoides* on ice-scoured intertidal habitat in the southern Gulf of St. Lawrence. They found extensive recruitment of larval barnacles throughout the area during the growing season, but development to the adult stage was limited to microsites that were protected from ice-scouring.

Minchinton et al. (1997) of Dalhousie University studied a rare ice-scouring event on a rocky shore of western Nova Scotia **(Figure 10.23)**. This is a region where sea ice does not form, but occasionally in the springtime pack ice from the Gulf of St. Lawrence is blown southward and it affects normally ice-free coastal areas. In this case,

the ecologists had been studying intertidal habitats for another purpose before the rare ice-scouring event, but when the disturbance obliterated the existing community of their study site they switched their focus to examining its immediate effects and then the primary succession. Minchinton et al. observed that ephemeral algae such as *Cladophora* and *Ulva lactuca* were the initial colonists, and they dominated the ice-scoured habitats for the first growing season. However, they were soon replaced by perennial algae, such as *Fucus evanescens*, *Fucus vesiculosus*, *Fucus spiralis*, and *Chondrus crispus*. The mussels *Mytilus edulis* and *Mytilus trossulus* originally covered more than half of the intertidal habitat, and they were devastated by the ice-scouring. The rate of recovery of the mussels was inversely related to height in the intertidal zone: in the low- and mid-elevation zones, their cover was similar to the original after four years, but in the high zone it had not recovered even after six postscouring years.

10.5 Secondary Succession

If a disturbance is not so severe that it wipes out all organisms from an affected area, then some local regenerative capacity will survive. In such cases, the ecological recovery will involve a **secondary succession**, which is based on the regeneration of organisms that survived the disturbance as well as growth by others that invaded the disturbed area afterward. Because secondary succession begins with an inherent capacity to regenerate that is associated with survivors, the recovery is considerably more rapid than occurs by a primary succession.

Wildfire

A wildfire is an uncontrolled burn, often affecting unmanaged areas or wilderness, although they may also occur close to rural or suburban habitations (see **Figures 10.4** and **10.24**). Wildfires most commonly affect forests, but shrubby communities, grassland, and even peatland may also be affected by this kind of disturbance. Wildfires are a common occurrence in Canada, on average affecting about 2.5 million ha annually, but more than 10 million ha in some years.

For a wildfire to occur there must be a source of ignition, plus an ecosystem with enough combustible fuel to maintain a burn and allow it to spread. However, it is not just the amount of fuel that is important—its dryness and chemical composition are also critical factors. Some kinds of plant biomass contain a high concentration of combustible oils or resins, which will burn explosively if ignited. Here is a camping tip—even on a wet day you can start a fire for cooking and warmth if you have some bark of white birch (*Betula papyrifera*) to use as kindling; because of the oils it contains, this material ignites easily

Bob Scheibling

FIGURE 10.23 Severe Ice-Scouring Can Initiate a Primary Succession
In this case, a rare ice-scour event in 1995 devastated the intertidal zone of the Atlantic coast of western Nova Scotia. This habitat is normally well vegetated with a high biomass of several kinds of fucoid seaweeds and mussels, but the ice-scouring entirely removed them so the recovery was by a primary succession.

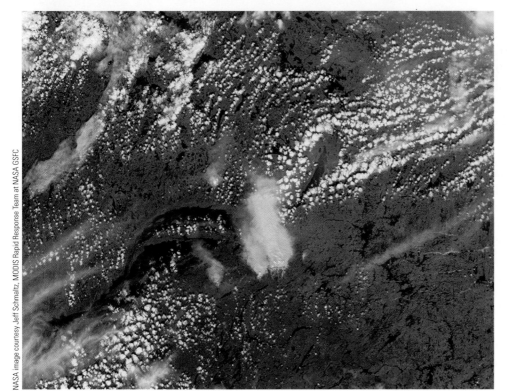

FIGURE 10.24 Satellite Photo of Wildfires in the Boreal Forest The image shows several clusters of wildfires that were burning in July 2011, in a vast region of boreal forest located just east of the northeastern tip of Great Slave Lake, Northwest Territories. The wildfires were ignited by lightning strikes during a period of dry conditions in the summertime. Because they were in a remote region with no settlements or commercial development, the fires were monitored by the territorial government but no effort was made to try to quench them. Large areas of the boreal forest burn every year in northern Canada, each of which is followed by a recovery by secondary succession.

NASA image courtesy Jeff Schmaltz, MODIS Rapid Response Team at NASA GSFC

and is a good material for starting a fire. Other extremely flammable kinds of biomass include conifer foliage and dry grasses.

Once a wildfire is ignited, its rate of spread is greatly affected by the recent occurrence of drought (which dries the fuel), the weather at the time, and sometimes the topography (low areas are often wet and resistant to burning). Key weather-related factors are the windiness, relative humidity, and air temperature. The windspeed, however, is particularly important because strong winds will fan the flames and may cause an uncontrollable conflagration to occur. Wind-driven wildfires can jump natural firebreaks, such as wetlands and rivers, as well as constructed ones, such as roads and bulldozed gaps.

The largest wildfires typically occur during a windstorm, and they may cover tens of thousands of square kilometres. Some of the most devastating burns that have occurred in Canada include the following (Wikipedia, 2012):

- the Miramichi fire of 1825 in New Brunswick, which affected 12 000 km²;
- the Saguenay fire of 1870 in Quebec; 3900 km²;
- the Mississagi-Chapleau fire of 1948 in Ontario; 2600 km²;
- the Chinchaga fire of 1950 in British Columbia and Alberta; 35 000 km²;
- the Okanagan Mountain fire of 2003 in British Columbia; 2000 km²;
- the West Kelowna wildfires of 2009 in British Columbia; 98 km²; and
- the Slave Lake fire of 2011 in Alberta; 4700 km².

These and other particularly big wildfires are famous because they affected great areas, caused huge economic damage, and sometimes resulted in a loss of human life. Even more expansive wildfires occur in more remote regions of Canada, but they have not been "named" because they did not pose great risks to homes or businesses.

Many natural ecosystems are viewed as being fire-dependent because this kind of disturbance is necessary for their periodic regeneration. Over the longer term, such ecosystems are influenced by a cyclic succession that involves repeated iterations of wildfire → successional recovery to a vulnerable condition → wildfire → recovery, and so on. Examples of fire-dependent ecosystems in Canada include forests dominated by pines, such as jack pine (**Figure 10.13**) and lodgepole pine, as well as tallgrass prairie.

In some regions, past management policies often tried to quench wildfires that became ignited in these fire-prone ecosystems. However, this management practice resulted in landscapes becoming increasingly vulnerable to severe fires because of the large amounts of flammable biomass that accumulated. In contrast, recent management policies are more sympathetic to the role of fire in dependent ecosystems, and not all ignitions are necessarily quenched unless there is an obvious risk to homes or to other economic infrastructure. In some cases, deliberate **prescribed fires** are ignited to reduce the risk of an uncontrollable conflagration, or to improve the habitat of rare species or endangered kinds of natural communities (such as tallgrass or mixedgrass prairie and forest with Garry oak, *Quercus garryi*; see Chapter 14).

Alternatively, natural ecosystems may become degraded if wildfires occur too frequently. Often this occurs in communities that have been penetrated by invasive alien plants whose biomass is extremely flammable, so that the fire rotation becomes un-naturally shortened and a positive feedback loop is established that results in a degradation of the ecosystem. For instance, this has become a problem in chaparral and semi-desert in the western United States, particularly in regions affected by the annual cheatgrass (*Bromus tectorum*) (Brooks and Lusk, 2008). This alien grass accumulates a highly combustible biomass, and when it becomes dominant in an invaded community there can be frequent and intense burns that favour the cheatgrass but inhibit most native plants.

A wildfire generally causes severe damage to an affected community: biomass is combusted, many plants are killed by scorching, the forest floor may be partly consumed, erosion may be caused, and animals may die from heat or asphyxiation. Usually, however, the damage is not so severe that it precludes some capacity for regeneration by surviving organisms. Because of this characteristic ability to regenerate, the postfire recovery is an example of a secondary succession. And because wildfire is such an important disturbance of natural ecosystems in Canada, it has been widely studied, particularly in regions of boreal and montane forest.

A number of generalizations can be made about the ecological effects of forest fires in Canada:

- *A shifting mosaic:* In regions where wildfire is the predominant agent of disturbance, the landscape becomes structured as a shifting mosaic composed of an assortment of stands in various stages of postfire regeneration (see also Chapter 13). The age spectrum of the stands ranges from recently burnt to older growth, the latter typically occurring in habitats that are low and moist because they occur in the vicinity of wetlands or lakes.
- *Within-stand heterogeneity:* When a stand burns, there are often local embedded "skips" where the damage is less or negligible, a dynamic that creates within-stand heterogeneity. These unburned patches tend to occur in microhabitats that are low and wet, but the intensity of the burn also has a great influence on this feature—a severe fire has fewer nonburnt areas than a less-severe one.
- *How much is burnt:* Wildfires vary in their intensity, and this greatly affects the amount of the stand biomass that they consume. A ground-fire is a relatively light burn that mostly consumes low-growing vegetation and litter, and because it does not "ladder" into the foliated crown of the stand, trees will typically survive the event. In contrast, a crown-fire is a much more intensive burn that kills many trees, typically

leaving charred snags behind. The most severe wildfires may consume much of the biomass of the dead trees, and even that of the forest floor, so that only an ashy mineral substrate is left and the recovery is by a primary succession.

- *Some plants survive—others do not:* Species of plants differ greatly in their ability to survive a wildfire, and this affects how they regenerate and contribute to the postfire succession. Among trees, for example, most conifer species are vulnerable to being killed by scorching, particularly by a crown-fire in which the foliage is burnt; however, conifers with relatively thick bark, such as red pine, often survive ground-fires that do not spread into their canopy. In contrast, the aboveground biomass of trembling aspen (*Populus tremuloides*) may be killed by a wildfire, but the underground rhizomes commonly survive and then prolifically regenerate by issuing large numbers of sprouts. Of course, species whose local population is killed by a wildfire must recolonize the aftermath site to participate in the ensuing succession, but they are generally well adapted to doing this. In contrast, species that survive the disturbance are well positioned to quickly regenerate afterward, and they are often prominent in the early years of succession.
- *Community change may be complex:* Successional changes in postfire stands may represent a linear relay of species and community replacements that eventually results in the development of another fire-prone ecosystem. However, local species mixes and environmental conditions may result in quite complex changes. Taylor et al. (1987) of the University of Toronto studied these patterns in a postfire chronosequence of black-spruce stands up to 120 years old in northern Ontario (**Figure 10.25**). The younger stands were dominated by reindeer-lichens (*Cladonia gracilis* and *Cladonia rangiferina*), bryophytes (mosses and liverworts), low-growing vascular plants, and a dense regeneration of spruce seedlings. As the canopy cover increased during succession, the ground vegetation changed to stronger dominance by mosses, eventually resulting in a thick mat of the feather-mosses *Pleurozium scheberi*, *Hylocomium splendens*, and *Ptilium crista-castrensis*. However, on sites that were relatively flat and low, the succession advanced to a wetter stage that was dominated by peat-mosses (*Sphagnum* species), while under more mesic (better drained) conditions there was greater prominence of alder (*Alnus rugosa*) and herbaceous plants.
- *Effects on animals:* Many animals suffer directly from a wildfire, particularly in severe burns where they may be killed by heat, scorching, or toxic gases. Larger animals that are relatively mobile can often flee from a less-intensive wildfire, assuming the burn

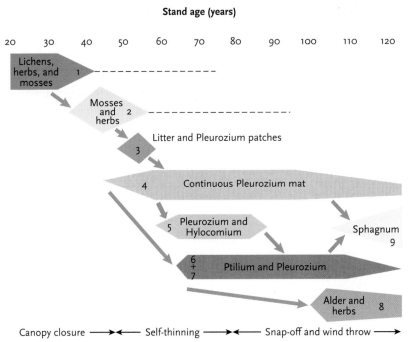

Stand age (years)

20　30　40　50　60　70　80　90　100　110　120

Lichens, herbs, and mosses　1

Mosses and herbs　2

Litter and Pleurozium patches　3

Continuous Pleurozium mat　4

Pleurozium and Hylocomium　5

Ptilium and Pleurozium　6 + 7

Sphagnum　9

Alder and herbs　8

Canopy closure ⟶ ⟵ Self-thinning ⟶ ⟵ Snap-off and wind throw ⟶

FIGURE 10.25 Changes in Communities of Ground Vegetation during Succession in Postfire Stands of Black Spruce in Northern Ontario The younger stands are dominated by lichens, bryophytes, and low-growing vascular plants, but this changes to a stronger dominance by mosses, and depending on site conditions, may result in a wet community of peat mosses, or a more mesic one of alder and herbs.

SOURCE: Modified from Taylor, S.J., T.J. Carleton, and P. Adams. 1987. "Understorey vegetation change in a Picea mariana chronosequence," *Vegetatio*, 73: 63-72, with kind permission from Springer Science+Business Media B.V.

is not moving so fast that it prevents their escape. In general, however, the indirect effects of a wildfire are more consequential than the direct ones for animals living in a burnt habitat. By changing the species composition and physical structure of the plant community, a wildfire indirectly affects the animals that can use the regenerating habitat. For example, some larger animals, such as white-tailed deer (*Odocoileus virginiana*) and elk (*Cervus canadensis*), may benefit from the abundant and nutritious forage of young woody shoots and herbaceous plants that occur on regenerating burns, so long as there is also nearby mature forest that provides refuge for the animals at night and during the winter. In contrast, woodland caribou (*Rangifer tarandus*) need an extensive cover of older forest in their range, because this is where they obtain their essential winter food of lichens, and so they tend to become less abundant after a wildfire.

- *Pollution:* Wildfires are an important source of emission of pollutants to the atmosphere. One of the key air pollutants is carbon dioxide (CO_2), an important greenhouse gas that originates from the combustion of biomass. Also important are oxides of nitrogen (NO and NO_2, collectively these are known as NO_x), which are involved in the photochemical production of ozone as well as acid rain. There are also abundant emissions of smoke, or particulates in the form of ash and carbonized materials (soot) that are small enough to be wafted over great distances, where it may interfere with visibility and affect people by odour and respiratory irritation. In hilly terrain, wildfires may also greatly increase erosion, and thereby damage aquatic ecosystems by increasing turbidity, siltation, and nutrient loading.

Wildfire also interacts with other natural agents of disturbance, such as windstorms, insect irruptions, and diseases. For example, the presence of large numbers of dead trees because of a recent infestation of insects or a severe windstorm can set the stage for a catastrophic wildfire. This is a present danger in much of the interior of British Columbia, where millions of hectares of lodgepole-pine forest have been killed by the mountain pine beetle. But the opposite is also relevant—in the absence of a natural disturbance rotation of periodic wildfires, the forest may become increasingly vulnerable to insect attack. For instance, in the absence of wildfire, conifer forest in northwestern Quebec becomes more susceptible to suffering intense mortality from an infestation of spruce budworm. This is because balsam fir, the preferred food of the budworm, steadily increases in prominence the longer that a stand had not been affected by a wildfire (Bergeron and Leduc, 1999).

Irruptive Animals and Diseases

Earlier in this chapter we learned that biological agents can irrupt in abundance and cause a stand-replacing disturbance to occur, which is followed by a secondary succession. Examples of native invertebrates that cause this sort of "natural" damage include the mountain pine beetle in pine forests in British Columbia, spruce budworm in fir-spruce forests in eastern Canada, and the green sea urchin in kelp "forests" off Nova Scotia. Some introduced insects can also cause this intensity of damage to occur, including the emerald ash borer

A CANADIAN ECOLOGIST 10.1
Yves Bergeron: Succession in the Eastern Boreal Forest

FIGURE 1 Yves Bergeron

Yves Bergeron of the Université du Québec à Montréal is a plant ecologist who is engaged in basic research on the distribution and dynamics of boreal-forest ecosystems **(Figure 1)**. His research involves field studies of species and communities, supplemented by laboratory work in dendroecology. His approach is to examine the relationships among key environmental influences and the distributions and dynamics of species and communities, particularly disturbances in conjunction with abiotic factors such as climate, geomorphology, and soil.

His work on natural disturbance regimes has included historical reconstructions of the occurrence and effects of wildfires, windstorms, and insect irruptions.

However, Bergeron is also committed to seeing that his research on natural ecosystems results in improved management of forest resources. His approach is to assess how the harvesting and management of particular kinds of boreal-forest communities and landscapes can be undertaken in ways that emulate the effects of natural disturbances. If that is successfully done, then the ecological influences of forestry will be more "natural" in their effect.

Much of the research is done out of a field-station at Lake Duparquet near Rouyn-Noranda. This well-equipped research facility was constructed and is jointly run by the Université du Québec à Montréal and the Université du Québec en Abitibi-Temiscamingue, with financial support from federal and provincial governmental agencies and several industrial partners.

Bergeron and his colleagues are running a large program that encompasses both basic and applied research. Its success can be judged as successful in several ways:

- Large numbers of undergraduate and graduate students are being provided with excellent opportunities to engage in ecological research, with a focus of fieldwork in real-world situations.

- There is a constant output of publications in scientific journals and other reputable outlets—this is a clear demonstration of a contribution to the development of ecological science.

- There is a commitment to integrating the outcomes of basic ecological research with improved ways of managing one of Canada's most important renewable resources— forests and their biomass. This is a helpful contribution to the sustainable development of our country.

(*Agrilus planipennis*) in southern Ontario, as can introduced pathogens (usually fungi) such as the ones that cause chestnut blight (*Cryphonectria parasitica*), beech-bark disease (*Cryptococcus fagisuga*), and Dutch elm disease (*Ophiostoma ulmi*).

Once these irruptions or diseases have caused their damage, the ecosystem regenerates by a secondary succession. If the ecosystem is resilient, a similar community may regenerate, so there is a longer-term stability to the cyclic phenomenon of biological disturbance and recovery. However, if alien pathogens establish, different communities regenerate because the vulnerable native species have been eliminated from or are greatly reduced in the affected ecosystem.

Numerous studies have examined the effects of spruce budworm on conifer forest, and of the subsequent recovery **(Figure 10.26)**. The budworm is a native moth, but it is the larvae that cause the forest damage. Their preferred foods are young cones and foliage of balsam fir, followed by those of white and then red spruce. The

FIGURE 10.26 Spruce Budworm (*Choristoneura fumiferana*) This pest is a native moth that sometimes irrupts in abundance and damages mature forest dominated by balsam fir (*Abies balsamea*) and white spruce (*Picea glauca*). This image shows a fir-spruce forest on Cape Breton Island that was damaged by several years of defoliation during an irruption in the 1970s and 1980s. The surviving trees around the wetland are black spruce (*Picea mariana*), which is relatively resistant to defoliation by the budworm.

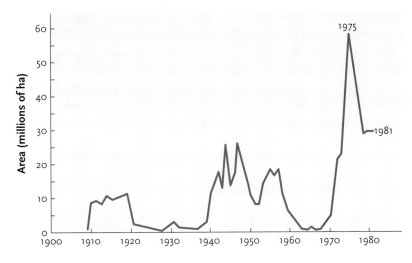

FIGURE 10.27 Area of Forest Affected by Spruce Budworm during the 20th Century The data are for stands suffering moderate-to-severe levels of defoliation, and their pattern suggests that the irruptions became more extensive and prolonged over time. The most recent irruption collapsed in the early 1990s.

SOURCE: *A Cartographic History of Spruce Budworm Defoliation from 1967 to 1981 in Eastern North America: Information Report*, Environment Canada, 1983. Reproduced with the permission of the Minister of Public Works and Government Services Canada, 2013.

budworm is always present in a low density (referred to as an endemic population level) in mature forest within its range, but occasionally its populations increase rapidly and cause extensive damage to trees. Periodic irruptions of spruce budworm have long occurred in vulnerable boreal landscapes. J. R. Blais (1965) of the Canadian Forest Service studied the ring-width patterns of old host trees and established an outbreak chronology extending to the 18th century in Laurentide Park, Quebec. He found that budworm infestations had occurred at fairly regular intervals, with a mean periodicity of about 35 years (**Figures 10.27** and **10.28**).

David MacLean (1984) of the University of New Brunswick found that spruce budworm causes a progressive tree mortality. In stands examined in Cape Breton, about 4 percent of fir trees were dead after 2 years of heavy defoliation, 9 percent after 4 years, 22 percent after 5 years, 48 percent after 8 years, 75 percent after 10 years, and 95 percent after 12 years. Much of the mortality

occurred after the budworm population had collapsed, as weakened trees succumbed to environmental stresses that might be tolerated by healthier ones, especially winter stresses. Blais (1981) studied forest in the Ottawa Valley in which a budworm outbreak had collapsed in 1975, at which time the mortality of balsam fir averaged 44 percent, but that increased to 91 percent after four additional years following the collapse of the irruption. During the same period, the mortality of spruce increased from 17 percent to 52 percent.

Although mature fir and spruce trees are heavily defoliated and often killed by budworm, smaller individuals of these species are only slightly affected and they form an abundant pre-established "advanced" regeneration in the understorey of affected stands. For example, severely damaged stands on Cape Breton had an average of 45 000 small balsam fir per ha and 3250 spruce/ha (MacLean, 1988). Most of these individuals survived the budworm irruption and then grew quickly in the aftermath habitat to establish the next fir-spruce forest.

Other low-growing plants of the ground vegetation also responded favourably to opening of the forest canopy by budworm-caused mortality. Large increases of abundance occurred in the shield fern (*Dryopteris carthusiana*), large-leaved goldenrod (*Solidago macrophylla*), wild sarsaparilla (*Aralia nudicaulis*), wood sorrel (*Oxalis montana*), and red raspberry (*Rubus strigosus*). Eventually, the secondary succession results in the development of another mature fir-spruce forest, which will again be vulnerable to supporting another budworm irruption.

The dynamic budworm–conifer system is a cyclic succession with a long-term ecological stability, and it has likely recurred on the landscape for thousands of years. Evidence supporting the hypothesis of longer-term stability includes (1) the presence of large areas of relatively even-aged forest dominated by balsam fir and white spruce; (2) the observed successional trajectory following stand-replacing disturbance by the budworm; and (3) paleoecological data showing that budworm outbreaks are ancient and periodic.

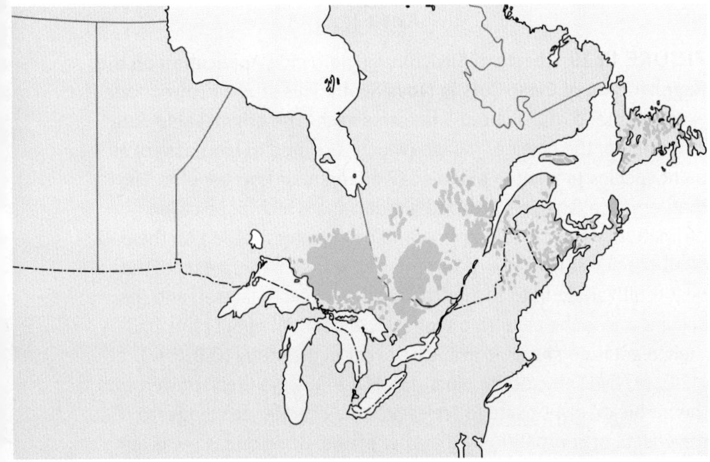

FIGURE 10.28 Regions Suffering Forest Damage Caused by the Most Recent Irruption of Spruce Budworm The data are for stands suffering moderate-to-severe levels of defoliation.

SOURCE: *A Cartographic History of Spruce Budworm Defoliation from 1967 to 1981 in Eastern North America: Information Report*, Environment Canada, 1983. Reproduced with the permission of the Minister of Public Works and Government Services Canada, 2013.

In contrast to this apparent longer-term ecological stability, the budworm causes economic instability by damaging a forest resource that is needed for the production of paper and lumber. In a sense, this native insect and the forest industry are in competition for a limited resource—the fir-spruce forest. To try to manage the economic damage from budworm-caused resource depletion, huge areas of conifer forest in eastern Canada were sprayed with various insecticides from the 1960s to 1993 (this was a major environmental controversy at the time). A cumulative area of more than 118 million ha was treated with insecticide (this total includes stands that were repeatedly sprayed in various years; Freedman, 2010; see also Chapter 15). The insecticide spraying was not intended to eradicate the budworm, but to reduce its abundance enough that it would not kill fir and spruce trees, so they would be available to be harvested by the forest industry.

Timber Harvesting and Management

Timber harvesting is an important economic activity in Canada: in 2011, about 688 000 ha of forest were harvested, 90 percent by clear-cutting (CFS, 2012; see also Chapter 15). Tree seedlings were planted on about half of the harvested area to establish plantations, and the rest regenerated naturally.

In some respects, natural regeneration after timber harvesting resembles the secondary succession that occurs following a wildfire in the comparable kind of forest (see Environmental Applications 10.2). Of course, this is not exactly the case, particularly in situations where foresters have managed the postharvest regeneration through some kind of silvicultural prescription (**silvicultu**re refers to management practices in forestry; see Section 15.3). This might involve the planting of conifer seedlings, the use of herbicide to reduce the effects on crop trees of competition from weeds, and thinning of overly dense regeneration (usually done using motorized saws).

Successional changes after various kinds of disturbances related to forestry are examined in several places in this book. In Chapter 15, Figure 15.11 shows the successional recovery of biomass after the clear-cutting of hardwood forest, and Table 15.4 examines some effects on birds. In this chapter, **Figure 10.14** provides a general model of biomass recovery, while **Figure 10.16** examines changes in indicators of biodiversity.

The indicators in **Figure 10.29** are related to changes in plant communities in a study of herbicide spraying in forestry in Nova Scotia. The research involved four plots of 5 ha each that were studied over a four-year period. The raw data are based on the amount of foliage cover of all plants that were present, which represents a huge database of many species, treatments, and years. This great complexity of information was mathematically reduced using an analysis known as ordination. This method allows the plant

"communities" occurring in the various plots and study years to be represented by relatively simple multivariate vectors that integrate data for many plant species, so that overall patterns of change can be interpreted relatively easily.

The plots had their vegetation sampled in the first year of the study, and then three of them received a silvicultural treatment of the herbicide glyphosate to reduce the abundance of "weeds" that were competing with economically desired conifer seedlings. The fourth plot was left unsprayed as a control. The analysis shows that all four plots had similar communities before the herbicide spraying (these are the plot-years C-0, H1-0, H2-0, and H3-0 in **Figure 10.30**). Over the subsequent years of the study, the vegetation of the control did not change much, reflecting the normal course of secondary succession after clear-cutting (C-0, C-1, C-2, and C-4). In contrast, the herbicide-treated plots had much larger changes in vegetation. Initially, the herbicide caused large decreases to occur in the amount of foliage, as well as big changes in the relative abundances of species, but this was followed by a strong postspray recovery. After four postspray years, the herbicided plots had almost the same plant cover as the control. None of the initial species

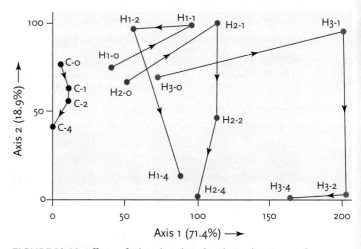

FIGURE 10.29 Effects of Silvicultural Herbicide Application on the Regeneration of Clear-Cuts in Nova Scotia This study involved four experimental plots of about 5 hectares each. The original field data consisted of the cover of foliage (which is related to biomass) of all plant species present in a grid of 32 quadrats of 1 m² per plot. The mathematical analysis involved a multivariate technique called ordination, which develops single values (vectors) based on the data of all species at the time of sampling. The first axis represents the best multivariate fit to the initial variation of each dataset, and the second axis is the best fit to the residual data. All of the plots had their vegetation sampled in the first year of the study (C-0, H1-0, H2-0, H3-0). Three of the plots (H1, H2, H3) were then sprayed with the herbicide glyphosate to "release" small conifer seedlings from the effects of competition with other plants, while one (C) was left unsprayed as a control treatment. The vegetation of all of the plots was re-sampled in the first, second, and fourth post-spray years.

SOURCE: Modified from: Freedman, B., R. Morash, and D.S. MacKinnon. 1993. "Short-term changes in vegetation after the silvicultural spraying of glyphosate herbicide onto regenerating clearcuts in central Nova Scotia," *Canadian Journal of Forest Research*, 23(10): 2300–2311. © 2008 NRC Canada or its licensors. Reproduced with permission.

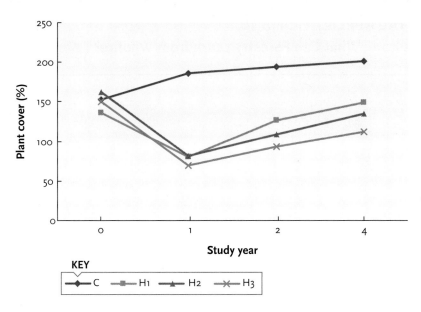

FIGURE 10.30 Changes in Plant Cover as a Result of Herbicide Treatment of Regenerating Clear-Cuts in Nova Scotia The data show the initial plant cover in four of the research plots (year 0), followed by the ensuing four years after being treated with the herbicide glyphosate (H1, H2, and H3), plus a nonsprayed control (C). See text for further explanation.

SOURCE: Based on data from Freedman, B., R. Morash, and D.S. MacKinnon. 1993. "Short-term changes in vegetation after the silvicultural spraying of glyphosate herbicide onto regenerating clearcuts in central Nova Scotia," *Canadian Journal of Forest Research*, 23: 2300–2311. (Page 2303)

were lost from the herbicide-treated plots, although lingering changes in their relative abundances were reflected in the results of the ordination analysis.

Of course, there are also successional dynamics in animal communities after timber harvesting. In general, animals are not much affected by the direct effects of timber harvesting—they are not usually killed or injured by falling trees. Rather, their response is indirect and caused by profound alterations of habitat conditions due to changes in the species composition, abundance, and physical structure of the vegetation. For example, when a stand of forest is clear-cut, the bird community dependent on mature habitat becomes totally replaced by a different one that prefers younger vegetation. This effect is illustrated in Table 15.4 (Chapter 15), which compares bird communities among mature hardwood forest and recent clear-cuts. The forest and clear-cuts both supported rich avian communities, but the species were almost completely different (see also **Figure 10.16** in this chapter).

In contrast, herbicide spraying has much less of an effect on the breeding birds of treated clear-cuts. In a study of herbicide-treated sites in Nova Scotia, there were large initial changes in the vegetation, but the responses of birds were not as great **(Table 10.1)**. The abundance of

TABLE 10.1 | **Populations of Birds on Clear-Cuts Treated with Glyphosate Herbicide in Nova Scotia**
The data are pairs of breeding birds per km², surveyed before the herbicide treatment (year 0) and then for four postspray years. The data for sprayed plots are the average of four replicates; only abundant species are listed.

Species		Sprayed Plots				Control Plot			
	Year:	0	1	2	4	0	1	2	4
Alder flycatcher (*Empidonax alnorum*)		36	7	17	63	20	40	41	102
American robin (*Turdus migratorius*)		14	21	30	31	10	10	20	10
Red-eyed vireo (*Vireo olivaceous*)		0	0	0	4	0	10	31	41
Magnolia warbler (*Dendroica magnolia*)		5	5	5	102	0	20	20	143
Palm warbler (*Dendroica palmarum*)		0	4	18	53	0	10	51	31
Mourning warbler (*Oporornis philadelphia*)		50	13	12	19	71	41	20	31
Common yellowthroat (*Geothlypis trichas*)		151	140	90	136	122	112	122	163
White-throated sparrow (*Zonotrichia albicollis*)		203	118	89	155	143	71	93	163
Dark-eyed junco (*Junco hyemalis*)		42	62	61	69	31	41	61	102
Lincoln's sparrow (*Melospiza lincolnii*)		23	20	41	44	20	+	+	0
Song sparrow (*Melospiza melodia*)		43	28	60	86	41	20	10	10
American goldfinch (*Carduelis tristis*)		52	24	15	13	61	41	20	20
Total birds		623	447	444	805	539	396	528	836

SOURCE: Based on data from MacKinnon and Freedman (1993).

Emulation Silviculture: What Can Forestry Learn from Wildfire?

Some kinds of forest communities are naturally adapted to wildfire as a natural disturbance. In such ecosystems there may be broad similarities in the ecological effects associated with wildfires and clear-cutting. Both are usually stand-replacing disturbances in which the dominant organisms are all killed either by burning or by harvesting. This is followed by a period of regeneration of the ecosystem to another mature forest, then another wildfire or clear-cut, then regeneration, and so on **(Figure 1)**.

Because of these broad resemblances, foresters and ecologists have considered whether some aspects of timber harvesting and silvicultural management might be undertaken in ways that more closely mimic the effects of wildfire, so that commercial forestry could be done on a more "natural" basis. This field is known as **emulation silviculture**. It is becoming increasingly popular in Canada and elsewhere because of its potential to alleviate some high-profile environmental issues that are associated with intensive forestry practices—especially with clear-cutting followed by the establishment of tree plantations.

But is the comparison between wildfire and silviculture apt? When evaluating these disturbances, it becomes clear that there are some compelling differences in their effects on biodiversity, productivity, carbon storage, nutrient cycling, and other aspects of the structure and function of ecosystems (McRae et al., 2001). If these ecological differences cannot be satisfactorily resolved by the modification of forestry practices, then they cannot be said to be emulating the natural disturbance regime of wildfire.

For example, wildfire and timber harvesting influence biodiversity in different ways, depending on the type of forest community being affected, the harvesting method, the postharvest management, and the scale of disturbance. Here are some key differences:

- The patch sizes created by logging are generally much larger than those resulting from wildfire. The latter results in many small disturbances, but also a small number of extremely large ones, whereas timber harvesting creates patches that are generally larger and much more uniform in size and distribution on the landscape.
- The rotation of timber harvesting is usually different from the return interval of natural wildfire. In Canada, wildfires recur over a wide range of intervals, from a decade to centuries, whereas in forestry the harvest frequency is dictated by the stand age at merchantable size (when the trees are big enough to be profitably harvested), which is typically 40 to 80 years. The generally shorter rotation in forestry means that the species composition of the community does not fully recover before the next harvest occurs—this is particularly the true of older-growth forest.
- Wildfire commonly allows older-growth stands to occur as a component of the shifting mosaic of stand-age distributions on a landscape. However, forestry does not necessarily do this—all accessible stands are harvested, except for any that have been specifically set aside within protected tracts such as parks or wilderness areas.
- Wildfires leave large numbers of standing dead trees and abundant woody debris, while clear-cutting typically does not leave much of these features. This is an important distinction between the disturbances, because woody debris and dead trees, especially if they have cavities, are critical aspects of habitat for many kinds of wildlife.
- If logging is followed by natural regeneration in some regions of Canada, the successional pathway commonly favours a greater dominance by angiosperm trees and less dominance by conifers, although this may be overcome by planting and tending conifer seedlings. In contrast, after a wildfire the previous conifer-dominated stand type usually regenerates.
- Unlike wildfires, forestry requires the development of an extensive network of woodland roads, which often cause erosion on slopes and at stream crossings, reduce the net amount of vegetated habitat, fragment the landscape for wide-ranging species, and allow easier access by people, including hunters and fishers. There is no such analogue of roads after typical wildfires.

Clearly, there are similarities and differences between wildfire and silviculture as disturbances of forest ecosystems. To some degree, the effects of wildfires can be emulated by forestry, but the mimicry is highly imperfect. For this reason, it is important to identify the residual ecological impacts of forestry, and to mitigate them to whatever degree is possible.

Moreover, it must be recognized that wildfire is not an important influence on the development of some kinds of natural forest, particularly old-growth forests growing in high-rainfall regions of coastal British Columbia and elsewhere in Canada, including some regions of the eastern provinces. Because those old-growth ecosystems are not well adapted to stand-replacing disturbances, clear-cutting might not be an ecologically appropriate way to harvest their timber. For old-growth forests whose disturbance regime typically involves gap-phase disturbance dynamics, an emulation system would involve selection-harvesting, in which only some of the trees are taken at any time, leaving the physical and ecological integrity of the stand substantially intact.

Bill Freedman

Bill Freedman

FIGURE 1 Clear-Cutting of a Forest Is Followed by Regeneration by a Secondary Succession The image on top is a 3-year-old clear-cut of a mature stand of mixed-hardwood (angiosperm) tree species in Nova Scotia. The bottom image is a 20-year-old naturally regenerated clear-cut in the same area.

which could help to increase the populations of some rare and endangered species. It is important to note, however, that those benefits would be offset by any ongoing destruction of natural alvars to develop new quarries for their limestone rock—the alvars can never be fully restored from that kind of destructive use.

These examples show that land that is abandoned from anthropogenic uses can regenerate to a semi-natural condition, to the degree that useful ecological values are supported. This is a good thing. Nevertheless it is important to recognize that such developments do not represent adequate or even substantive offsets against the ecological damages that are caused by the reverse process—that of ongoing destruction of natural ecosystems and their conversion into anthropogenic ones. The ecological damage caused by those kinds of losses of natural habitats are the leading cause of the ongoing biodiversity crisis, as we examine in Chapter 14.

CHAPTER SUMMARY

(LO10.1)

- A disturbance is an event that destroys part of a community or a larger ecoscape. The damage can range from mild to severe, and the spatial scale affected from small (gap-phase or microdisturbance) to large (stand-replacing disturbance).

(LO10.2)

- Following a disturbance, successional recovery begins. Succession may eventually restore an ecosystem that is similar to the original condition, or it may result in one that is fundamentally different and represents an alternative stable state.

(LO10.3)

- Succession begins with the regeneration of surviving organisms as well as invasion of the disturbed habitat. Initially resources are abundant and competition is weak, but as succession proceeds, the intensity of competition increases progressively. These changes greatly affect the kinds of species that are present at various stages of succession.

(LO10.4)

- Primary succession occurs after severe disturbances that remove any in situ capacity for regeneration, so species must invade the site in order to participate in the ecological recovery. In contrast, secondary succession occurs after less-extreme disturbances, which allows some species to survive the event and contribute to the regeneration, along with others that invade afterward.

(LO10.5)

- Ruderal species that are adapted to habitats with abundant resources and a low intensity of competition are prominent early in succession. As succession proceeds, resources become increasingly limited and species that are strong competitors become increasingly dominant in communities.

(LO10.6)

- Primary successions in Canada are initiated by severe natural disturbances such as glaciation and mudflows, and by anthropogenic ones such as the abandonment of built-up land and old quarries. Examples of natural disturbances that initiate secondary successions include windstorms, wildfires, and irruptions of herbivorous insects, while anthropogenic ones include clear-cutting and the abandonment of cultivated land and pastures.

(LO10.7)

- The patterns and processes of natural disturbances can be emulated by forestry and other resource-harvesting industries in order to reduce their environmental impacts. In forestry, for example, the natural microdisturbance dynamics of old-growth forest can to some degree be emulated by selection-harvesting systems. In contrast, clear-cut harvesting does not emulate the natural disturbance regime of old-growth forests.

QUESTIONS FOR REVIEW AND DISCUSSION

1. What is a stand-replacing disturbance? Provide two examples of their natural causes, and two that are anthropogenic.

2. Define resistance and resilience, and give examples of each. What factors result in decreasing levels of resistance and resilience in ecosystems?

3. What are the key differences between primary and secondary successions? Provide examples of each.

4. Why is wildfire such a common and extensive agent of disturbance in Canada? Is it a natural force, or an anthropogenic one? What factors should be considered when making a decision about whether to fight a forest fire?

5. What are key similarities and differences between wildfire and clear-cutting?

6. Find a plot of land that has been abandoned from an anthropogenic use in the area where you live, and describe how managed and/or spontaneous successional processes are restoring an improved habitat condition. Make a list of the most prominent species that are now present on the disused land, note whether they are native or alien, and comment on the implications for ecological integrity.

Biomes and Ecozones

LEARNING OBJECTIVES

After studying this chapter you should be able to:

1. Describe the major biomes, including their distribution and major biotic characteristics.

2. Characterize the ecological qualities of urban, agricultural, and industrial habitats.

3. Explain the differences and similarities of natural and anthropogenic ecosystems.

4. Identify the terrestrial and marine ecozones of Canada, and describe their distributions and prominent physical and biotic characteristics.

11.1 Ecosystems at a Global Scale

Order Out of Complexity

Complexity is a vital attribute of ecosystems. In this sense, all ecological communities and habitats are unique in their structural and functional attributes—at every scale they vary in their natural characteristics and influences, and in the ways they have been affected by humans. Such complexity is a key reason that the science of ecology is so complicated, and many of its predictions are fraught with potential errors.

Consider, for instance, the characteristics of patches of habitat in the boreal forest, a sprawling ecosystem that covers 35 percent of the land area of Canada (about 3.6 million km²). Ecologists who study vegetation in the boreal forest work at a scale that is appropriate to the questions of interest, such as the size of the plants and the spatial patterns of their distribution, the areas of various kinds of communities, or the landscapes used by wide-ranging species such as caribou and wolves. For example, mosses and lichens growing on the forest floor might be examined using plots of only 1 m² or less in area. Nevertheless, ecologists studying them at that scale would observe that no two patches are exactly alike in terms of the presence and abundance of the various species, or in environmental conditions related to microclimate, moisture, or nutrients. This would also be the case if ecologists were studying shrubs in larger plots of 25 m², or trees in parcels of 400 m². If carefully measured, any

of these commonly sampled areas would be found to have unique characteristics. That would also be the case at larger scales, up to thousands of square kilometres of boreal terrain. Over space and time, all ecosystems are matchless.

Despite this impressive and genuine complexity of ecosystems, it is possible to discover commonalities within their variations. Ecologists do this by classifying areas in terms of their biota, productivity, and environmental conditions, including any anthropogenic influences. There are practical reasons for doing this. First, we can only begin to understand the structure and functioning of the biosphere if we can discover some degree of order within its complexity. Second, ecological research is doable only if the complexity of the natural world is aggregated into units that can be studied—into clusters that reflect common attributes among species and their environmental circumstances. This is especially true of basic research in ecology, which is motivated by curiosity about the natural world. It is also relevant to applied work that is driven by the need to develop practical solutions to problems, such as how to properly manage a forest or fishery, or to avoid or repair damages caused by pollution.

Working to these ends, ecologists have developed classification schemes that allow them to investigate the natural world by dividing its complexity into groups that represent reasonably distinct assemblies. In essence, ecologists have aggregated ecological variation into clusters that have a general similarity of structure and function. This is similar to how climatologists have grouped factors related to longer-term weather conditions into broad climatic zones, and have portrayed them on geographic maps that provide valuable information to architects, ecologists, engineers, and gardeners. The ecological clusters are referred to by various names, such as biomes and ecozones, and they are the topic of this chapter.

Biomes

At the global level, the largest kinds of ecosystem clusters are known as **biomes**. Each biome exists over an extensive geographic range, and it occurs anywhere in the world that the environmental conditions support its development **(Figure 11.1)**. The morphological and physiological traits of the dominant organisms, or their **life form**, provide the defining characteristics of a biome. This means that the particular complement of species that is present is not the distinguishing feature—rather, it is their life form.

Terrestrial biomes are usually characterized by their late-successional natural vegetation. The most influential environmental factors that affect the development of terrestrial biomes are the prevailing climatic conditions, with soil, bedrock, and other factors playing a lesser role. In marine biomes, the dominant animals are the distinguishing feature, and physical oceanography and nutrient supply are the key environmental influences.

Although biomes are characterized by their existing qualities, they can also be viewed as a result of the evolution of species and the spontaneous organization of their communities under prevailing environmental regimes occurring over long periods of time—even millions of years. During those extended times, the biodiversity within biomes changed and reorganized in response to the influences of evolution, extinction, and changes in environmental conditions. In Canada, for example, almost all biomes that exist today have spontaneously reorganized since the time of deglaciation some 10–12 000 years ago. Some of the original species of immediate postglacial times are now extinct, such as the mastodon, mammoths, giant bison, sabre-toothed tiger, and other elements of a lost megafauna of the Pleistocene era (see Chapter 14).

The global distribution of the major terrestrial biomes is shown in **Figure 11.2**, and their range in North America is shown in **Figure 11.3**. The location and boundaries of the biomes are influenced by the distribution of environmental conditions that support the species that are their dominant life forms. The range of terrestrial biomes is mostly affected by soil moisture and the temperature regime **(Figure 11.4)**. However, within a terrestrial biome, distinct communities may occur; for example, an environmental gradient may be associated with moisture or elevation, which will affect the local habitats and the kinds of communities that are present (see Chapter 9). In a region of temperate forest, this can result in different communities of forest. If there is surface water there may also be various communities occurring within streams, rivers, lakes, and wetlands such as swamps and marshes.

FIGURE 11.1 Biomes All situations are unique, but some ecosystems are similar enough to be grouped according to their commonalities of species and environmental conditions. In ecology, the largest such groupings are known as biomes. This landscape in southwestern Alberta is in the montane forest biome and also in the montane cordillera ecozone. Ecological communities that are visible include alpine tundra, open montane forest of lodgepole pine (*Pinus contorta*) at tree-line, and lower-altitude closed montane forest.

Bill Freedman

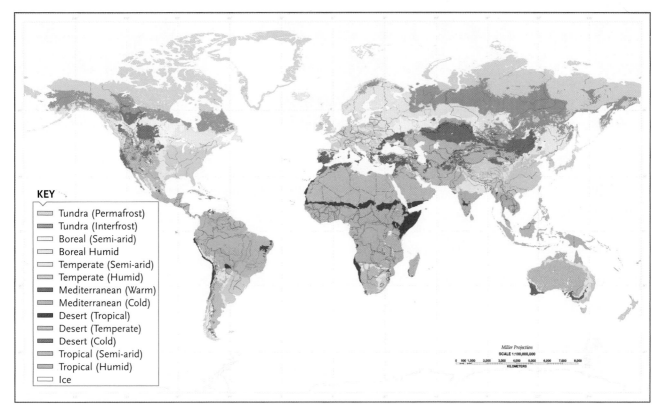

FIGURE 11.2 **Global Distribution of the Terrestrial Biomes** Biomes are wide-ranging ecosystems that are similar in their structure and function and occur wherever environmental conditions are suitable for their development. Typically, however, the same biome on different continents is dominated by different species.

SOURCE: Modified from USDA. 2009. *Major Biomes Map.* United States Department of Agriculture, Natural Resources Conservation Service. Washington, DC. http://soils.usda.gov/use/worldsoils/mapindex/biomes.html.

In freshwater habitats, the local occurrence of surface water and the nutrient supply are key influences on the communities that develop. In the marine realm, open-water biomes are largely affected by water depth and its relation to the availability of light for autotrophs, as well as the distribution of upwellings of nutrient-rich deeper water to the surface. Benthic marine biomes are influenced by water currents and the physical characteristics of the substrate, and coastal ones by those factors along with the intensity of wave action.

Same Play but Different Actors

Biomes, which are defined by their similarity of structure and classified by their dominant life forms, may develop in varying geographical regions and even on different continents if the right environmental conditions are present **(Figure 11.2)**. Nevertheless, different species may dominate in widely separated regions of the same biome. In a metaphorical sense, this is comparable to the Shakespearian play, *Hamlet*, being staged in widely separated places in the world, by different casts of actors and using varying sets, but nevertheless having strong commonalities because all are using the same script from about 1601.

Although the dominant species of far-flung reaches of a biome may not be closely related in a phylogenetic sense, their life forms are convergent, which means they are similar in anatomy, physiology, and other key attributes. Their **convergent evolution** has occurred because although they inhabit widely spaced places, the environmental conditions are similar and so therefore are the regimes of natural selection. This results in parallel (or convergent) evolutionary responses of different species occurring in far-flung reaches of a biome.

To illustrate the results of convergent evolution in a terrestrial context, we can examine the dominant life forms of the boreal forest that exists in northern tracts of Canada, Alaska, and Eurasia. This high-latitude biome is positioned south of the Arctic tundra and north of the temperate forest and prairie/steppe grasslands. Its environment involves long and cold winters, short but warm summers, extended daylight during the growing season and much less in winter, moist soil conditions, and a stand-replacing disturbance regime associated with wildfires, windstorms, and insect epidemics. Coniferous trees usually dominate the boreal forest, but the particular species differ among far-flung regions of the biome.

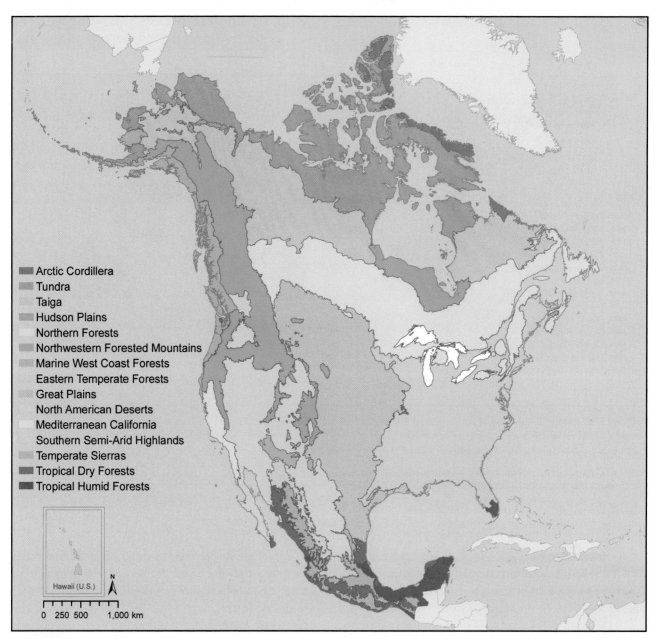

FIGURE 11.3 Distribution of the 15 Terrestrial Ecoregions (Level 1) Designated for North America These are North American representatives of global biomes, such as tundra and boreal forest.

Arctic Cordillera
Tundra
Taiga
Hudson Plains
Northern Forests
Northwestern Forested Mountains
Marine West Coast Forests
Eastern Temperate Forests
Great Plains
North American Deserts
Mediterranean California
Southern Semi-Arid Highlands
Temperate Sierras
Tropical Dry Forests
Tropical Humid Forests

Hawaii (U.S.)
N
0   250 500   1,000 km

SOURCE: Commission for Environmental Cooperation. 1997. *Ecological Regions of North America: Toward a Common Perspective.*

In Canada, most of the boreal forest is covered by stands of black spruce (*Picea mariana*) **(Figure 11.5)**. In some areas, however, balsam fir (*Abies balsamea*), jack pine (*Pinus banksiana*), tamarack (*Larix laricina*), or white spruce (*Picea glauca*) may be the prevailing species. In northern Eurasia, however, the boreal forest is dominated by other species of the same genera. In Scandinavia there are Norway spruce (*Picea abies*) and Scotch pine (*Pinus sylvestris*). Northern Russia has yet other species, such as *Abies sibirica*, *Larix sibirica*, *Picea obovata*, and *Pinus sibirica*. In northern Japan, Korea, and far-eastern Russia, the boreal climate is relatively moderate because of the proximity of the Pacific Ocean, and these regions have yet

other species of coniferous trees. Nevertheless, these various kinds of conifer-dominated boreal forests are similar ecosystems within the same biome—their component species are convergent entities in an evolutionary and ecological sense.

Even though their ecosystems are structurally and functionally similar, biomes are not homogeneous across long distances. Biomes are characterized by their most extensive mature communities, but they also contain other kinds of habitats. For instance, although coniferous trees dominate the boreal forest of Canada, there are also large areas of mature angiosperm (broad-leaved or hardwood) trees, such as trembling aspen (*Populus tremuloides*)

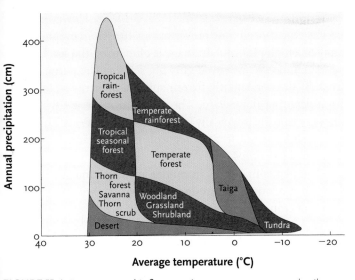

FIGURE 11.4 Environmental Influences Average temperature and soil moisture are key factors influencing the distribution of terrestrial biomes.

SOURCE: From Odum/Barrett, *Fundamentals of Ecology*, 5E. © 2005 Cengage Learning.

Bill Freedman

FIGURE 11.5 The Boreal Forest Is Characterized by Its Dominant Life Forms These are usually conifer trees occurring in mature stands, or younger ones recovering from a stand-replacing disturbance such as wildfire. This is an aerial view of open boreal forest in Labrador in which black spruce (*Picea mariana*) and light-coloured reindeer lichens (*Cladina* species) are the dominant organisms. However, different species of conifers and lichens may be predominant in other regions of boreal forest.

and paper birch (*Betula papyrifera*). Moreover, persistently wet sites within the boreal forest will support communities typical of rivers and lakes, or wetlands such as fens and bogs.

Disturbances also affect the communities in a biome. They do this by killing the dominant organisms or otherwise disrupting the ecosystem (Chapter 10). Following such disturbances, an ecological succession occurs, which initially results in new, younger communities that include many species that were not prominent in the original mature forest. The pervasive influence of natural disturbances means that many landscapes consist of a complex and dynamic mosaic of stands of various ages and stages of succession (Chapter 13).

Natural and Anthropogenic

Any biomes that support a large human population, and/or their economic activities, will have embedded within them habitats that are essentially anthropogenic in origin. In essence, the character of those habitats is most strongly determined by the ways they are managed or otherwise influenced by human activities. Such anthropogenic habitats include urban areas and lands that are used for agricultural or industrial purposes. Although they are embedded within the larger **natural biomes**, collectively they might be considered to represent **anthropogenic biomes** whose key attributes are determined by the kinds of human activities that occur within and help to define them.

In fact, anthropogenic influences have affected all of the biomes of modern times to some degree. For example, all living organisms, even those in the most remote places, now contain trace residues of manufactured organochlorine chemicals in their tissues (such as DDT, dieldrin, PCBs, dioxins, and furans). These organochlorines have become widely dispersed in the environment, where they are persistent, almost insoluble in water, but highly soluble in fats (lipids). Within ecosystems, organochlorines preferentially sequester (become isolated) in the fat tissues of organisms. In addition, they biomagnify to particularly high concentrations in the fatty tissues of top predators (see Environmental Applications 2.2). Of course, there are additional reasons that there are no longer any truly pristine habitats in the biosphere, including the pervasive influences of anthropogenic climate change (see Chapter 3).

11.2 The Major Biomes

In this section, the distribution and characteristics of the major biomes of the world are examined. Note, however, that the emphasis is on the natural communities that dominate the various biomes. In actual fact, much of the original extent of some biomes has been extensively **converted** into anthropogenic ecosystems, such as agricultural and urban areas. We will also briefly examine the qualities of these anthropogenic habitats. An important consequence of widespread conversions is the endangerment of many natural communities and their species. This important conservation issue is examined in Section 11.3 and in Chapter 14.

Regardless of such widespread human influences, there remain extensive tracts of wild, self-organizing ecosystems that are dominated by species indigenous (i.e., native) to the local bioregion. These can be reasonably thought of as being "natural ecosystems," even if they are no longer absolutely pristine. The biomes mapped in **Figures 11.2** and **11.3** are "natural" because their communities of plants, animals, and microorganisms have spontaneously organized under the influence of the prevailing environmental conditions.

Terrestrial Biomes

Tundra

The tundra occurs in environments in which the growing season is cool and short and the winter is cold and long. It is a treeless biome dominated by plants of short stature. The Arctic tundra exists in high-latitude regions, particularly in far northern expanses of the Northern Hemisphere and the far south of the Southern Hemisphere. In comparison, alpine tundra may exist at any latitude, even at high elevations on tropical mountains, such as the equatorial island of New Guinea. However, alpine tundra occurs at lower elevations at higher latitudes, sometimes even merging with Arctic tundra, as occurs near the coast of the Beaufort Sea in northern Yukon.

Meteorologically, most tundra exists in a "desert" condition, because the amount of water input with rain and snow is usually less than 25 cm/year. However, because the cool climate prevents moisture from evaporating at a high rate, and drainage is often poor, the soil is generally moist during the growing season. The **permafrost**, or the persistently frozen subsoil, prevents water from draining downward. The **active layer** of soil that thaws seasonally is typically less than 50–70 cm deep. The soil itself, referred to as a regosol, is young and little developed (Section 4.8).

The plants that grow in tundra are short and small, and it is a relatively unproductive ecosystem with a low standing crop of biomass **(Figure 11.6)**. In the polar desert and semi-desert of the most northerly tundra of the High-Arctic islands, the plants are diminutive but long lived and grow no taller than 5–10 cm above the surface. In the mid-Arctic, where the climate is somewhat less severe and there is more moisture, the characteristic vegetation is low shrub-heath and graminoid (sedges, cottongrass, and grasses) meadows. In the Low Arctic, shrubs can grow up to 1–3 m tall in well-drained habitats, and in wetter places there are relatively productive meadows of graminoids.

Boreal Forest

The boreal forest is also known as taiga, a Siberian word for "little sticks." It is widespread in the Northern Hemisphere, especially in great northern expanses of Canada,

FIGURE 11.6 Tundra The Arctic tundra is a northern biome dominated by plants of short stature. This is a view of Arctic tundra in coastal NWT near Cape Bathurst. The dominant large herbivore in the region is migratory caribou (*Rangifer tarandus*).

Bill Freedman

Alaska, Russia, and Scandinavia. In those regions the winter is cold and lengthy, the growing season is warm but brief (although the sunlit days are long during the summer), and the soil has abundant moisture. Most of the northernmost regions of boreal forest are underlain by permafrost, with a seasonally thawed active layer up to 1 m deep. The ground is subject to intense frost-heaving because of freeze–thaw action, and, because the trees are shallow rooted in the active layer, their trunks may lean in all directions, giving the name "drunken forest" to these boreal stands. The soils are mostly acidic podsols, and the dominant plants are coniferous trees, notably species of spruce, pine, and larch **(Figure 11.7)**. However, some hardwood trees also occur, such as aspen, birch, and poplar. In most regions of boreal forest, natural disturbances periodically result in stand-replacing catastrophes, followed by successional recovery. The most frequent causes are lightning-ignited wildfires, severe windstorms, and irruptions of insects that kill trees after several years of infestation. Because of this disturbance regime, boreal landscapes are a dynamic mosaic consisting of forest communities of various ages of successional recovery.

Montane Forest

Montane forest exists below the tree-line that marks the beginning of alpine tundra in mountainous regions. In temperate latitudes, this biome is similar in structure to the boreal forest of higher latitudes and coniferous trees are also the dominant vegetation **(Figure 11.1)**. The montane forest experiences a cold winter, but the growing season is relatively long and warm compared with the boreal zone.

FIGURE 11.7 Boreal Forest The boreal forest is a northern biome that is usually dominated by coniferous trees. This is a view of boreal forest in Labrador, with the tree cover mostly black spruce (*Picea mariana*) and the ground vegetation several species of feather-mosses. The mound of dirt has been excavated in order to investigate the soil profile in the site, whose plant species composition was also being studied.

Climate-related influences are strongly affected by changes in altitude, so montane forest at lower elevations is more productive and supports larger and taller trees than does that higher up, and some sites may have large amounts of orographic precipitation. Near the tree-line the conifer trees may develop a distinctively stunted, gnarled, slow-growing form referred to as krummholtz (or "twisted-wood"; in Atlantic Canada, this growth form is called tuckamoor, and elsewhere it may be called elfin-wood). The montane forests of Canada occur in mountainous regions in the western provinces and territories. Montane forest is periodically disturbed by lightning-ignited wild-fires, windstorms, and insect outbreaks, and so its landscape is a dynamic mosaic of stands of various ages.

Temperate Deciduous Forest

Temperate deciduous forest exists in regions where the winter is short and moderately cold and snowy, and the growing season is long, hot, and humid. In Canada, this biome occurs mostly in southern Ontario, southern Quebec, and parts of the Maritime provinces. The soils, known as a brunisol or brown forest soil, are relatively fertile. Temperate deciduous forest generally supports a diverse mixture of species of broadleaved trees, particularly in relatively southern regions, which in Canada are known as Carolinian forest.

Deciduous trees and shrubs characterize this biome; their leaves are grown in the spring and summer and then senesce in the autumn, in some species turning brilliant colours of yellow, red, orange, or brown before they are shed **(Figure 11.8)**. The colours are due to the oxidation of green chlorophyll pigments during senescence, which destroys their normally dominant influence and unmasks other pigments that are present in the foliage, such as anthocyanins and carotenoids. The seasonal loss of foliage is an adaptation to surviving the severe drought and cold stresses that occur during the winter. Forest communities in this biome are variable in species composition, as they respond in complex ways to gradients of soil moisture and fertility, soil and air temperature, disturbance regime, and other key factors.

Temperate Rainforest

Temperate rainforest flourishes in regions where there is ample precipitation throughout the year, the winter is brief and mild, and the growing season is warm. Wild-fires are rare under such humid conditions, and the lack of catastrophic disturbances allows old-growth coniferous forest to be widespread. The old-growth rainforest is richer in conifer species than any other biome, with some individual trees being hundreds of years old and of enormous girth and height. The most productive stands of temperate rainforest, with the tallest trees and greatest

Michael Sewell/Photolibrary/Getty Images

FIGURE 1 The Northern Spotted Owl (*Strix occidentalis caurina*) Depends on Old-Growth Forest

biomass, occur in lower-elevation riparian habitats and valley bottoms. At higher elevations the forest is less productive, but it still contains impressively large conifer trees of various species.

In Canada, the temperate rainforest biome mostly occurs along the Pacific coast of British Columbia (see Ecology in Depth 11.1). The tallest trees in the world occur in this biome. The tallest in Canada is a 95 m Sitka spruce (*Picea sitchensis*) known as the "Carmanah Giant," which grows in a stand of bottomland old-growth rainforest on Vancouver Island. The tallest trees in the world are a 116 m coast redwood (*Sequoia sempervirens*) in northern California, followed by a 100 m Australian mountain-ash (*Eucalyptus regnans*) in Tasmania, Australia; these are also growing in temperate rainforest.

Old-growth ecosystems occur late in succession. The term is usually used in reference to older kinds of forest, but it could also apply to other kinds of ecosystems. **Old-growth forest** has a number of key characteristics:

- There is an all-aged population structure of the trees, meaning all age classes are present, including some old, large ones.
- The physical structure is complex in both vertical and horizontal dimensions, with multiple layers of the canopy and some gaps where old trees have died and younger ones are filling the freed-up space.
- There are large logs lying on the forest floor and standing dead trees (or snags) are present.

Because old-growth forest has these particular attributes, certain species of wildlife require it as a critical habitat. This is particularly true of old-growth forest in tropical regions (also known as **primary forest**). This biome sustains many dependent species that occur nowhere else, including numerous **endemics** that have only a small geographic distribution. In contrast, boreal and temperate old-growth forests have relatively few dependent species, although there are some.

Examples of animals that require old-growth forest as a component of their range in Canada are the northern spotted owl (*Strix occidentalis caurina*) **(Figure 1)**, marbled murrelet (*Brachyramphus marmoratus*), and American marten (*Martes americana*). Some plants are more abundant in old-growth forest, such as Pacific yew (*Taxus brevifolia*) and lungwort lichen (*Lobaria pulmonaria*). However, species

in Canadian old-growth forest are not yet fully researched, and additional work will discover more cases, particularly of less-prominent elements of biodiversity such as invertebrates, fungi, lichens, mosses, and microorganisms.

Because old-growth forest is a natural ecosystem with unique values, conservationists and ecologists consider it to have great intrinsic value and to be a precious element of natural heritage. Moreover, old-growth forest provides important ecosystem services, such as the provision of clean air and water and carbon storage in biomass.

At one time, tracts of old-growth forest were extensive in Canada. Today, however, they are much rarer, particularly in the eastern provinces, where most old-growth has been converted into agricultural or urbanized land uses. Timber harvesting is also important, because it converts old-growth into second-growth forest, which is itself harvested before the old-growth condition is reattained. Depending on the region, the remaining old-growth in eastern Canada covers only from <1 percent to a few percent of the total forested area.

However, old-growth forest is still fairly extensive in parts of western Canada, particularly in more remote regions of the Pacific coast, where a wet climate promotes the development of this ecosystem because wildfires are uncommon. Even in coastal British Columbia, however, most accessible tracts of old-growth forest have been logged or converted to urbanized land use. And because old-growth logs are so valuable, much of the remaining old-growth is threatened by timber harvesting. Except for areas that are set aside in protected areas, such as parks and wilderness reserves,

almost all of the surviving old-growth forest will be logged in the next few decades and converted into second-growth stands. These will in turn be harvested long before they reattain an old-growth condition.

Because the conservation of old-growth forest has become a high environmental priority, there is controversy over the continued logging of its remaining tracts. So-called "new forestry" practices can retain some of the characteristics of old-growth forest—these harvesting systems do not involve clear-cutting and so they result in less-intensive changes to the ecosystem. One example is selection-cutting with snag and cavity-tree retention, which removes only some of the economically valuable trees from the stand and so leaves the physical and ecological integrity substantially intact, although inevitably some damage is done.

Ultimately, if society decides that we should conserve old-growth forest as a special natural ecosystem, the goal can be realistically achieved only by establishing landscape-scale protected areas. The protected areas must be big enough to sustain the ecological dynamics that permit old-growth forest to develop and endure over the longer term; in particular, the natural disturbance regime must be accommodated. This sort of landscape perspective is crucial, because no stand of old-growth forest can be preserved forever—it will unavoidably become damaged by environmental change and/or a natural disturbance. Only landscape-scale protected areas are capable of conserving the ecological influences that are necessary to sustain old-growth forest and its intrinsic values, including its dependent biodiversity.

Temperate Grassland

The temperate grassland is an intermediate biome between forest and desert. It develops in regions with cold winters, long hot summers, and an annual precipitation of 20–60 cm. Because the annual precipitation is usually less than the potential evapotranspiration, there are often soil moisture deficits and even drought during the growing season. As a result, there is not enough soil moisture to support a forest, but there is an adequate amount to prevent the formation of a desert.

Temperate grasslands, known as prairie in North America and as steppe in Eurasia, cover extensive regions of those continents, as well as Africa and Australia. The characteristic soil is chernozem, which is fertile, but in drier regions it can build up high concentrations of soluble minerals (salts) that degrade its quality. In Canada, prairie ecosystems are classified according to the height

Bill Freedman

FIGURE 11.8 Temperate **Forest** Trees of the temperate forest biome may have brilliantly coloured foliage in the autumn. This occurs because their chlorophyll degrades during senescence and unmasks other pigments that are present in the leaves. This area of hardwood-dominated forest in Nova Scotia is visually enhanced by the scarlet autumn foliage of red maple (*Acer rubrum*).

and species composition of their vegetation: shortgrass, mixedgrass, and tallgrass **(Figure 11.9)**. The shortgrass prairie receives little precipitation and experiences periodic severe drought. The mixedgrass prairie usually has somewhat more rainfall and can support taller species of grasses and forbs (the latter is a term used to describe perennial but herbaceous, broadleaved, angiosperm plants). The tallgrass prairie occurs in a more humid climate, and species of grasses and forbs may grow as tall as 1–2 m. In fact, the climatic regime of tallgrass prairie could support the growth of shrubs or even an open forest, but the occurrence of frequent wildfires holds this woody vegetation back.

Bill Freedman

FIGURE 11.9 **Temperate Grassland** The temperate grassland biomes are dominated by graminoids and forbs. This is a view of shortgrass prairie in the early summer in Grasslands National Park in southern Saskatchewan.

Chaparral

The so-called Mediterranean climate regime occurs in southern temperate environments in which there is abundant rain and moderate temperatures during the winter, and heat and drought during the summer. These conditions promote the development of chaparral, whose vegetation is dominated by shrubs and well-spaced short trees, with herbaceous plants forming the matrix and being especially abundant in open areas. In part, the structure of this ecosystem is maintained by periodic wildfires. Chaparral does not occur in Canada, and in North America it is prevalent in coastal regions of southern California and Mexico.

Desert

The desert is a dry ecosystem, and it can exist in either a temperate or tropical climate **(Figure 11.10)**. It usually occurs in the interior of a continent or in a rain-shadow region of mountainous terrain. The amount of moisture in the soil is the key factor in the distribution of deserts: in temperate latitudes a desert occurs where there is less than about 25 cm/year of precipitation, but it may occur under a higher rainfall regime in tropical latitudes because of the much larger potential for evapotranspiration. The most xeric (dry) desert may not support any vegetation at all, but desert habitats that have a little moisture, particularly in the late winter and spring, may support abundant succulent and herbaceous plants, including annuals and perennials. Within a desert, a perennial spring of water, known as an oasis, will provide a rare habitat with enough soil moisture to support relatively lush vegetation, sometimes including shrubs and

FIGURE 11.10 Desert This an extremely dry biome that does not support much plant productivity. This is a view of desert near Abancay on the western side of the Andes of Peru. The climate is extremely dry, but occasional years of relatively high precipitation sustain a low density of perennial plants, and also support an exuberant flowering of annuals on rare occasions when the rains come.

Bill Freedman

trees. The most extreme forms of desert do not occur in Canada, although there is a small area of semi-desert in the southernmost Okanagan Valley of British Columbia. That habitat is an extension of a much greater expanse of the desert biome in the western United States and Mexico.

Tropical Grassland and Savanna

Tropical grassland and savanna are a low-latitude (subtropical and tropical; therefore not occurring in Canada) biome that receives a moderate amount of rainfall, up to 120 cm/yr, but with a pronounced dry season. The savanna ecosystem is characterized by an extensive matrix of diverse grasses and forbs, within which scattered trees and shrubs provide an open woodland canopy (Figure 11.11).

Large populations of big animals may live in tropical grassland and savanna, especially during the annual migrations of some animal species, and when the vegetation is lush and productive during the rainy season. The African savanna sustains a particularly high diversity of large mammals, including antelopes, elephant, giraffe, hippopotamus, rhinoceros, and water buffalo, as well as their predators, such as cheetah, hyena, lion, and wild dog.

Semi-Evergreen Tropical Forest

An equatorial biome, the semi-evergreen tropical forest is a closed forest, meaning the canopy of tree foliage is continuous. This ecosystem develops in tropical regions where the climate is consistently warm and there are

FIGURE 11.11 Tropical Savanna This biome has an extensive matrix of grasses and forbs, with scattered shrubs and trees, and it may support a high density of large mammals. This tropical savanna and African elephant (*Loxodonta africana*) are in Amboseli National Park, Kenya.

Evelyn Turkington

distinct wet and dry seasons. The deciduous trees and shrubs that dominate this biome shed their foliage at the beginning of the dry season. The semi-evergreen forest supports a rich biodiversity, although somewhat less than occurs in the evergreen tropical rainforest.

Evergreen Tropical Rainforest

The evergreen tropical rainforest occurs in equatorial regions that have a warm and wet climate throughout the year. This biome sustains an exceptionally rich biodiversity of plants, animals, and microorganisms, more so than any other kind of ecosystem. Because precipitation is abundant throughout the year, catastrophic disturbances such as wildfire are rare and so large areas of the biome support old-growth forest **(Figure 11.12)**. The distinguishing characteristics of this primary rainforest are its exceedingly rich biodiversity, the great range of ages and sizes of the many tree species present, and the persistence of foliage on its evergreen trees, which has evolved because soil moisture is always sufficient. Because evergreen tropical forest supports so much biodiversity, has high productivity and rapid nutrient cycling, and maintains great stocks of biomass, it might be considered to represent the peak of terrestrial ecological development.

Freshwater Ecosystems

The aquatic ecosystems described in this section are not large or extensive enough to be referred to as true biomes—rather, they are distinctive habitats and communities that are embedded in wet places within the terrestrial biomes. Nevertheless, it is important for ecologists to be familiar with the basic kinds of aquatic systems, and so we examine them here.

Lentic

Lakes and ponds, which contain standing (nonflowing) water, are known as **lentic ecosystems**. Their shape and volume (bathymetry), nutrient concentration, water transparency, and local climate are key influences on the kind of ecological development that occurs in them. Lentic ecosystems contain distinct habitats: the **littoral zone** occurs along the shore; the **pelagic zone** is in deeper open waters, and the **benthic zone** is in and just above the bottom sediment. Horizontal zonation is related to changes in water depth, and is influenced by the slope and physical characteristics of the bottom and length of the shoreline. Vertical zonation occurs in deeper waters, and it is related to the amount of light that is present, the water temperature, and concentrations of oxygen and nutrients. A deep lake is typically much less productive than a shallow one of a comparable surface area.

Nutrient supply is a key factor in the productivity of lentic ecosystems: **eutrophic** bodies of water have a high rate of primary productivity due to a large supply of nutrients; **oligotrophic** waterbodies are unproductive because they lack nutrients; and **mesotrophic** ones are intermediate. Phosphorus (as phosphate) is the most frequent limiting nutrient to primary productivity, followed by nitrogen (usually as nitrate; see also Environmental Applications 2.1 in Chapter 2).

Water transparency influences the aquatic ecosystem by affecting how deeply sunlight can penetrate. At some water depth in any lake, depending on the water transparency and intensity of sunlight, the amount of light

FIGURE 11.12 Evergreen Tropical Rainforest This biome supports higher levels of biodiversity than any other kind of ecosystem. This primary forest supports trees of many sizes and ages, and the extremely heterogenous structure of the ecosystem provides niche space for a wide variety of plants and animals. This is a view of a large *Ficus* tree with its immense supporting buttresses in an area of primary lowland rainforest in Tambopata National Park in Amazonian Peru.

Bill Freedman

available is not sufficient to allow phytoplankton to maintain a positive net productivity (i.e., their gross photosynthesis is less than their respiration). The region above that depth is called the **euphotic zone**, while the trophic system below is reliant on organic matter sinking from above. Low transparency can be caused by high concentrations of fine suspended particulates in the water (or **turbidity**), or by dissolved humic substances (large molecular-weight organic compounds) that make the water tea-coloured. Waterbodies with poor transparency due to these influences are less productive than would be predicted by their nutrient concentration. However, in eutrophic waterbodies, low transparency can also be caused by the seasonal occurrence of a large abundance of phytoplankton cells, known as an algal "bloom."

Lotic

Flowing water is the distinguishing feature of **lotic ecosystems** such as rivers and streams **(Figure 11.13)**. The amount of water flow as well as its speed and seasonal variation are particularly important environmental influences. Turbidity is also influential because it reduces the amount of light that can penetrate into the water and thereby the primary productivity. In places with slowly flowing water, fine suspended particles are deposited and

FIGURE 11.13 Lotic Ecosystems Are Characterized by Flowing Water This is an aerial view of the Churchill River in Labrador.

a muddy bottom develops. In contrast, turbidity may be high when water flows are strong, and places with vigorous currents have a rocky bottom because fine particles are washed away. Lotic ecosystems support aquatic plants and algae, but the productivity of higher trophic levels, such as aquatic invertebrates and fish, is mostly sustained by biomass that has entered the system from upstream lakes and the terrestrial watershed.

Wetlands

Freshwater wetlands, also called mires, occur in soggy places on land. There are four major kinds of wetlands: bogs, fen, swamps, and marshes.

Bogs are wetlands with relatively low productivity that develop under a cool and wet climate regime. Their water and nutrient supplies are referred to as **ombrotrophic** (or "fed from the sky"), because their surface hydrology is cut off from direct flows of groundwater. This means that their water is derived from precipitation falling directly on the bog, and the sparse nutrient supply comes only from chemicals dissolved in precipitation and atmospheric gases and dust. Bogs are acidic habitats because they have a meagre supply of calcium yet organic acids are abundant products of anaerobic decomposition in their wet substrate. Typically, bogs are dominated by species of *Sphagnum* moss (also known as peat moss), and they can accumulate organic peat to a depth of several metres or more **(Figure 11.14a)**.

Fens are **minerotrophic** ecosystems, meaning they are fed partially by groundwater (as are the other wetland types examined below). Fens develop in a cool and wet climate. Because the nutrient supply of fens is better than in bogs, they are less acidic and more productive. Low-growing sedges and rushes are relatively abundant in the vegetation of fens, and there are different kinds of *Sphagnum* mosses than occur in bogs. Fens also accumulate peat, but to a much lesser depth than bogs.

Swamps are productive wetlands that are dominated by tall shrubs or trees and are flooded either seasonally or permanently **(Figure 11.14b)**. Treed swamps are uncommon in Canada, and are usually associated with flats of **riparian** (riverside or lakeside) forest that become flooded during the high water flows of the springtime. Water-tolerant tree species, such as ash, elm, and silver or red maple, are predominant in forested swamps in Canada. Shrub swamps are more widespread, and are typically dominated by species of alder and willow.

Marshes have an abundant growth of tall graminoid (grass-like) plants, such as species of bulrush, cattail, and reed **(Figure 11.14c)**. The graminoids are rooted in the sediment and may grow as tall as several metres above the water surface. Marshes may also have areas of open water with submerged plants and floating-leaved ones such as

FIGURE 11.14 Several Kinds of Wetlands (a) A raised bog in western Nova Scotia, with vegetation dominated by *Sphagnum* mosses and shrubs in the heath family (Ericaceae). (b) A swamp is a wetland whose vegetation is dominated by shrubs or trees, as is this silver maple (*Acer saccharinum*) swamp in southern Ontario. (c) A marsh is dominated by tall graminoids, this one being almost entirely narrow-leaved cattail (*Typha angustifolia*); note the photo was taken in the springtime before the cattails had grown much, so the standing biomass is from the previous year.

water lily and lotus. Marshes occur in relatively fertile habitat and are the most productive kind of wetland.

Marine Biomes

The Open Ocean

The open-ocean realm is not strongly affected by physical or chemical influences originating on the continents. It can be divided into a number of distinctive ecological regions.

Pelagic (open-water) regions are complex ecosystems where variations of physical and chemical factors determine the local ecological characteristics. The most important influences are currents and upwellings, nutrient concentration, salinity, temperature, and light intensity. The rate of primary productivity of the pelagic ecosystem is low and comparable to that of terrestrial desert. However, the biome has an immense size and so its total amount of production is extremely large (see **Table 3.2**). The primary productivity is associated with phytoplankton that range in size from miniscule photosynthetic bacteria to larger (but still microscopic) unicellular and colonial algae. Small zooplankton (most are crustaceans) graze the phytoplankton and are in turn eaten by larger zooplankton and small fish. At the top of the pelagic food web are large-bodied predators, such as tuna, sharks, squid, and whales.

Benthic ecosystems of the open ocean are a deep-water biome—the average depth of the Atlantic Ocean is about 3900 m, that of the Pacific Ocean is 4600 m, and the deepest place in the world is in the Mariana Trench of the south Pacific at 11 000 m. Pelagic benthic ecosystems are essentially heterotrophic because their energetic foundation is a sparse rain of dead biomass that sinks from surface waters. Although the benthic regions of the open oceans are not well studied, they are stable ecosystems, have a low productivity, and are rich in animal species.

Regions with persistent upwelling occur where the local oceanographic conditions force deep-water currents to rise to the surface, where their improved nutrient availability sustains a high rate of primary productivity. This vigorous energetic foundation supports a high productivity of filter-feeding zooplankton, which in turn provides for an abundance of fish, seabirds, and marine mammals. The largest and most productive areas of upwelling occur off the west coast of South America and in great regions of the Antarctic Ocean **(Figure 11.15)**.

Gyres are enormous rotating surface currents. They are caused by persistent strong winds that are affected by the Coriolis effect that is associated with the rotation of Earth. In the Northern Hemisphere, gyres rotate in a clockwise direction, and in the Southern Hemisphere they rotate counter-clockwise. A gyre may accumulate large amounts of floating material in its central region, including floating seaweeds such as *Sargassum*, as well as anthropogenic

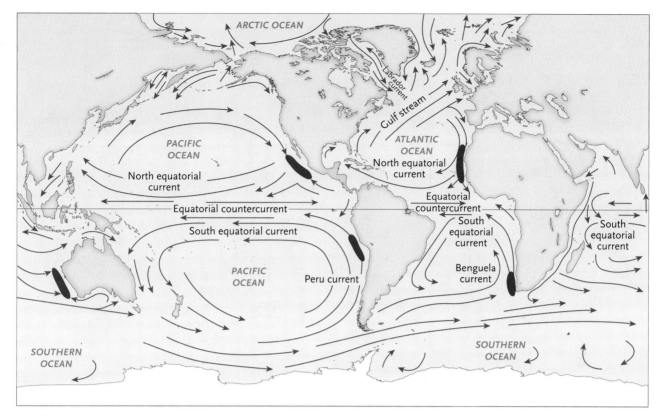

FIGURE 11.15 Major Oceanic Currents and Upwellings The currents (indicated by vectors) are driven by prevailing winds as well as by the Coriolis force associated with the direction of Earth's rotation. Coastal upwellings (dark shading) are determined by persistent strong winds, deep currents, and undersea topography and are naturally fertile regions that support high ecological productivity.

SOURCE: From Odum/Barrett, *Fundamentals of Ecology*, 5E. © 2005 Cengage Learning.

garbage from coastal dumping and debris from fishing fleets. One example is the North Atlantic gyre, also known as the Sargasso Sea, and another is the North Pacific gyre (these are obvious in the Northern Hemisphere of **Figure 11.15**).

Seamounts are uncommon oceanographic features that occur where oceanic mountains, usually volcanoes, rise from abyssal depths toward the surface, but do not necessarily emerge above it. When a seamount obstructs a deepwater current, it may cause a local upwelling to occur. The resulting fertility of local surface waters may support a high rate of productivity, which, along with the complex physical structure of seamounts, results in them being rich "hot spots" of marine biodiversity.

Deep-sea hydrothermal vents are hotspots of another kind—they are rare places in geothermally active regions where seawater is heated by near-surface magma, establishing a convective current that is exhausted through vents on the sea bottom (**Figures 11.16** and **11.17**). The hot water contains sulphide minerals that are oxidized by specialized chemosynthetic bacteria at the vents, which is the basis of their primary productivity (Chapter 3). Hydrothermal vents are locally productive ecosystems that support unusual communities of specialized tubeworms, clams, crustaceans, and fish.

Continental-Shelf Waters

Oceanic waters occurring above a continental shelf (an underwater projection of the emergent landmass) are relatively shallow, typically less than 100–200 m in depth. In Canada, the most expansive continental-shelf waters are in the Arctic and Atlantic regions. They extend offshore as far as 320 km from Newfoundland and 180 km from parts of Nova Scotia. British Columbia has narrower shelf waters, typically no more than 50 km beyond the landmass or major islands, such as Vancouver Island and Haida Gwaii (the Queen Charlotte Islands). Within this extensive biome in Atlantic Canada, shallow waters less than about 100 m deep are known as banks. These shallow coastal waters are relatively warm and fertile compared to the deeper open ocean. The banks are more fertile because they receive nutrients from riverine inputs and from deeper waters that are lifted to the surface by turbulence during windstorms. The relatively abundant nutrient supply allows these coastal waters to be productive and to support a much larger biomass of fish and other animals than occurs in the deeper ocean (**Figure 11.18**).

In addition to their prevailing shallow pelagic areas, continental-shelf waters support a number of spatially restricted coastal ecosystems that are important, such as seashores, estuaries, and coral reefs.

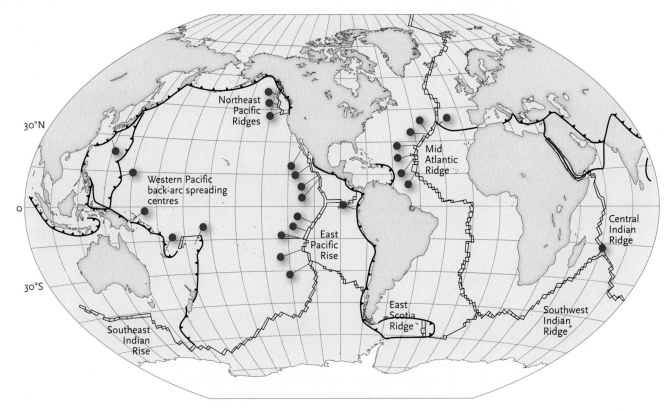

FIGURE 11.16 Locations of Major Deep-Sea Hydrothermal Vents These rare features (red dots) are associated with places where magma occurring close to the surface heats seawater that has been drawn into a hydrothermal system within the ocean floor. The hot seawater exhausts from the vent, supporting an unusual chemosynthetic ecosystem whose primary productivity is dependent on the oxidation of sulphide minerals rather than on sunlight. The jagged lines represent the edges of tectonic plates, where sea-floor spreading and subduction are occurring.

SOURCE: From Odum/Barrett, *Fundamentals of Ecology*, 5E. © 2005 Cengage Learning.

FIGURE 11.17 Hydrothermal Vents These are rare places at the bottom of the ocean where currents of geothermally heated water emerge. This vent is associated with a gigantic undersea volcanic seamount called Kawio Barat in Indonesia.

SOURCE: NOAA Okeanos Explorer Program, INDEX-SATAL 2010, NOAA/OER.

Seashores are a complex of distinctive ecosystems that connect the oceanic and terrestrial realms. Their specific character is influenced by local environmental factors, such as the characteristics of the bottom, the local strength of wave action, and the frequency of disturbances such as violent storms. In temperate regions, hard-rock and cobble bottoms support productive communities dominated by the biomass of large seaweeds (kelps). In areas with a softer bottom of silt or sand, the local communities are supported by inputs of organic detritus from elsewhere as well as the relatively small local productivity of a benthic film of microscopic algae.

FIGURE 11.18 Continental-Shelf Waters Are Relatively Fertile and Productive The relatively high rates of ecosystem productivity support large populations of marine life as well as commercially important fisheries. This image shows greater shearwaters (*Puffinus gravis*) feeding on fish guts being discarded by a coastal fishing boat off western Nova Scotia.

Bill Freedman

Invertebrates, especially crustaceans, echinoderms, marine worms, and mollusks, dominate these soft-bottom benthic communities.

Estuaries are semi-enclosed coastal ecosystems that are transitional between marine and freshwater habitats. They typically occur as a coastal embayment or semi-enclosed river mouth. An important characteristic of estuaries is their regular fluctuations of salinity due to the twice-daily tidal cycle, along with inflows of freshwater from the nearby land, usually from a river, and occasional storm-surges of saltwater intrusion. Because estuaries have a semi-enclosed geomorphology that retains much of the water-borne input of terrestrial nutrients, they are highly productive ecosystems. In the temperate and boreal climates of Canada, estuaries may support extensive mudflats, beds of eel-grass, and grass-dominated salt-marshes. In tropical regions, estuaries often sustain mangrove forest. The high productivity of estuaries nourishes many species of fish, including the juvenile stages of some economically important pelagic species, as well as abundant shellfish, crustaceans, and coastal birds and mammals.

Coral reefs occur in tropical regions in shallow infertile water close to land. The physical structure of a coral reef consists of the calcium carbonate shells of dead and living corals and mollusks. Corals are cnidarian animals that dominate the reef structure. They live in a mutualism with unicellular algae, and because their symbiosis is efficient in absorbing nutrients they can be highly productive in spite of living in infertile water. Coral reefs support a veneer of many species of crustose algae, corals, other invertebrates, and fish, making this the most biodiverse of marine ecosystems **(Figure 11.19)**.

Anthropogenic Ecosystems

Immense areas that were formerly occupied by natural habitats have been converted into ecosystems that directly serve the human economy in various ways. Human-dominated ecosystems are anthropogenic, in the sense that their characteristics have developed as a consequence of environmental conditions that are heavily influenced by the activities of people. Anthropogenic ecosystems have a distinctive character that, like natural biomes, can be aggregated on the basis of broadly shared characteristics.

The character of anthropogenic ecosystems is often an intended result of management practices, such as occurs in agricultural and urbanized land uses. However, other kinds of disturbances and pollution also affect the character of these ecosystems. Anthropogenic ecosystems are dominant wherever people live in dense populations, and also in rural areas where agriculture or resource-extraction industries are prominent, such as forestry and mining. The great diversity of types of anthropogenic ecosystems can be aggregated into three broad clusters: urban ecosystems, rural techno-ecosystems, and agroecosystems.

Urban Ecosystems

The urban ecosystem is characterized by buildings, roads, parking lots, and other physical infrastructure that occurs wherever the human population is large and dense in towns and cities. Urban habitats support other species in addition to people, but most of them have been introduced from distant places. Most alien species cannot survive without the assistance of humans (for instance, in cultivated gardens), but some have become feral and they now invade wild ecosystems, where they damage the habitat of native species.

A variety of community types can be identified within most urban areas, which vary in their degree of naturalness (or ecological integrity; see Section 17.2), largely based on how strongly their communities are dominated by alien species. The least natural habitats are mostly concrete or asphalt, with few organisms present. Horticultural green spaces associated with residential and institutional areas, such as lawns and aesthetic gardens, are intermediate in natural condition because they support a high cover of plants and some animals, although they are dominated by alien species. The most natural communities occur in parks that have been set aside as protected areas to both conserve regional biodiversity and provide people with recreational opportunities.

Rural Techno-Ecosystems

Technological development includes an extensive rural infrastructure that consists of extensive networks of highways, railroads, and electricity transmission lines, as well as

FIGURE 11.19 **Coral Reefs** This biome supports higher levels of biodiversity than any other marine ecosystem. This image shows a coral-reef community near Puerto Morelos, Mexico.

more localized industrial facilities and towns that exist to harvest and process natural resources. These rural techno-ecosystems support a mixture of native and alien species that are tolerant of disturbances and other stressors that are associated with anthropogenic activities in rural habitats.

Agroecosystems

Agricultural ecosystems, or **agroecosystems**, are a vital part of the human economy because they are used to grow plants and animals for use as foods, medicines, materials, and energy **(Figure 11.20)**. **Monocultures** are intensively managed agroecosystems, consisting of single-crop communities of plants or animals (usually aliens) that are cultivated in agriculture, forestry, or aquaculture (see Chapter 15). The cultivation system is designed to manage environmental conditions to favour the productivity of the crop. Intensive management practices may include ploughing, fertilizer application, and the use of herbicide, insecticide, and other pesticides. Some less-intensively managed agroecosystems use organic practices, which avoid the use of synthetic fertilizer and pesticides, and **polycultures**, in which mixtures of crops are grown in the same fields. The management of agroecosystems for grazing by livestock may involve "tame pasture" in which native grassland has been converted to a mixture of alien grasses and legumes that provide good forage. Native prairie may also be used for grazing by livestock, while at the same time maintaining much of the original biodiversity (this is by far the most "natural" of the agroecosystems of Canada). Intensive management of livestock also includes "factory-farms," which are indoor environments where animals are reared in dense conditions and are fed to satiation.

FIGURE 11.20 **An Agroecosystem** This is an anthropogenic ecosystem that is manage to grow crops for use as food or for other purposes. This field of potatoes (*Solanum tuberosum*) is in Prince Edward Island.

11.3 Ecozones and Ecological Regions

Ecozones are similar to biomes in that they are extensive regions that are distinguished and mapped largely on the basis of ecological similarities. What distinguishes ecozones, however, is that they are categorized not only on their dominant late-successional communities, but also on their prominent species and "enduring" attributes related to bedrock, soil types, climate, and topography. The kinds of human activities, and their environmental influences, are also a feature of ecozones. As such, ecozones integrate natural features and influences with human socioeconomic ones. The resulting classification and mapping system is useful for conservation planning and other aspects of land use.

Ecozones are at the summit of a hierarchical classification of the distinctive ecological regions of Canada (Ecological Stratification Working Group, 1995; Scott, 1995; Wiken et al., 1996; Wilkinson et al., 2009). Canada has 15 terrestrial ecozones and five marine ones **(Figure 11.21** and **Tables 11.1** and **11.2).**

Ecoregions are the level below ecozones—they are characterized at a smaller geographic scale by their distinctive climatic conditions and landforms, and to a lesser degree by their soil, vegetation, fauna, and land use.

A total of 194 terrestrial ecoregions has been mapped in Canada. Ecodistricts occur at an even smaller scale, and there are 1020 of them in Canada. The marine ecozones of Canada have not yet been divided into ecoregions or ecodistricts. However, when learning about the science of ecology at an introductory level, the focus is on ecozones—on how ecological attributes vary over extremely large regions.

The Commission for Environmental Cooperation (CEC) is a trinational body that was established under the terms of the *North American Free Trade Agreement* (NAFTA). The mission of the CEC is to foster cooperation among Canada, Mexico, and the United States on transboundary environmental issues. The CEC has undertaken a collaborative study among the three countries to develop a common map of the larger ecological zones of North America. Their designated units are referred to as **ecoregions** (or as **ecological regions**; these are not the same as the ecoregions in the Canadian system of ecozones), and these have been mapped for both terrestrial and marine environments. The terrestrial CEC ecoregions are extensive areas of general similarity in terms of their physiography, climate, and biological characteristics. The marine ones share similarities in terms of physiography, oceanography, and biological

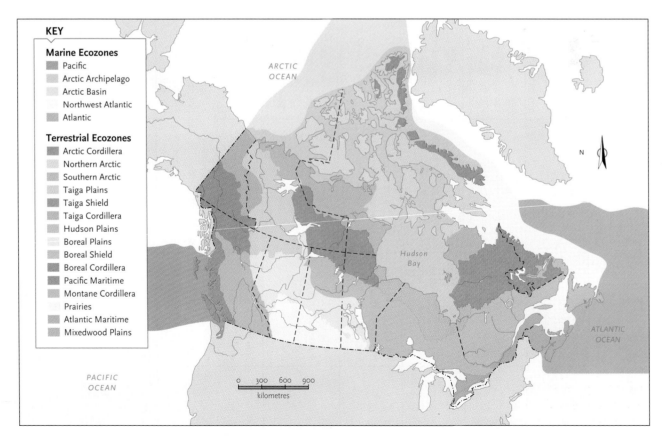

FIGURE 11.21 Distribution of the 15 Terrestrial and 5 Marine Ecozones of Canada

SOURCE: *State of Canada's Environment, 1996*, Environment Canada, 1996. Reproduced with the permission of the Minister of Public Works and Government Services Canada, 2013.

TABLE 11.1

Characteristics of the Terrestrial Ecozones of Canada

Each of the 15 terrestrial ecozones is distinct in terms of its geomorphology, climate, and prevailing ecological communities. MAT is the mean annual temperature; MST is the mean summer temperature.

Ecozone	Region	Geomorphology	Climate	Soil	Prevailing Vegetation
Northern Arctic	Northern QC, mainland & eastern islands of NU	Rocky lowlands; much exposed bedrock & glacial debris	High-Arctic; long, cold winters; short, cool summers; MAT –17 to –11°C; MST –2 to 4°C; precipitation 10–20 cm/yr	Regosol; permafrost throughout; active layer 30–50 cm; generally moist soil	High-Arctic tundra (Arctic desert or semi-desert); dominant cover is lichens, mosses, & low-growing vascular plants
Arctic Cordillera	Northern Labrador of NL, eastern Arctic islands of NU	Mountains & rocky uplands; glacial ice fields; much exposed bedrock & glacial debris	High-Arctic; long, cold winters; short, cool summers; MAT –20 to –6°C; MST –2 to 6°C; precipitation 10–60 cm/yr	Regosol; permafrost throughout; active layer 20–40 cm; generally moist soil	75% of terrain is rocks or ice; elsewhere High-Arctic tundra of lichens, mosses, & low-growing vascular plants
Southern Arctic	Northern QC & across mainland NU & northern NT	Extensive rolling terrain & lowlands; much exposed bedrock & glacial debris	Low-Arctic; long, cold winters; short cool–warm summers; MAT –11 to –7°C; MST 4 to 6°C; precipitation 20–40 cm/yr	Regosol; permafrost through-out (except under large lakes & rivers); active layer 50–70 cm; generally moist soil	Low-Arctic tundra, with more continuous cover than in High-Arctic; low-shrub heath & graminoid meadows
Taiga Plains	Western NT, northern BC, northwestern AB; taiga watershed of Mackenzie River	Rolling plains & uplands; postglacial sediment & debris abundant; lakes & wetlands common	Subarctic; long, cold winters; short, warm summers; MAT –10 to –1°C; MST 7 to 14°C; precipitation 20–50 cm/yr	Podsol; permafrost discontinuous; active layer > 80 cm; generally moist soil	Open boreal forest (taiga) of relatively short, well-spaced, slow-growing trees, mostly spruce & pine with aspen, poplar, & birch; periodic wildfires
Taiga Shield	Central QC, Labrador, southeastern NT, northern SK & MB	Rolling terrain on quartzitic shield bedrock; much exposed bedrock & glacial debris; lakes & wetlands common	Boreal continental; long, cold winters; short, warm summers; MAT –8 to 0°C; MST 6 to 11°C; precipitation 20–50 cm/yr	Thin podsol, permafrost discontinuous; active layer > 80 cm; generally moist soil	Open boreal forest (taiga) of relatively short, well-spaced, slow-growing trees, mostly spruce & pine with aspen, poplar, & birch; also open tundra-like areas of low shrubs; periodic wildfires
Boreal Shield	Newfoundland & southern Labrador of NL, southern QC, northern ON, central MB, northern SK	Rolling terrain on quartzitic shield bedrock; much exposed bedrock & glacial debris; lakes & wetlands common	Boreal continental; long, cold winters; short, warm summers; MAT –4°C in continental areas to 5.5°C in maritime NL; MST 11 to 15°C; precipitation 10–50 cm/yr in continental & 90–160 cm/yr in maritime	Podsol; generally moist soil	Closed boreal forest, mostly of spruce, pine, fir with aspen, poplar, & birch; periodic wildfires
Atlantic Maritime	NB, NS, PE, adjacent Gaspé of QC	Rolling terrain on various bedrock, from quartzitic to sedimentary; abundant glacial debris; lakes & wetlands common	Temperate coastal to continental; cold winters; long, warm summers; MAT 4 to 7°C; MST 13 to 16°C; precipitation 90–150 cm/yr	Complex soils, from podsol to brunisol; generally moist soil	Mixed-species forests of temperate trees, ranging from angiosperm-dominated to coniferous-dominated
Mixedwood Plains	Southern QC & ON within Great Lakes–St. Lawrence valley	Gently rolling terrain over sedimentary, often limestone bedrock	Temperate continental; cold winters; long, hot summers; MAT 5 to 8°C; MST 16 to 18°C; precipitation 70–100 cm/yr	Deep, base-rich (high-calcium) brunisol, especially on postglacial lakebed parent materials; generally moist soil	Mixedwood forest, mostly angiosperm-dominated; most of the natural cover is converted to agriculture & urban uses

Ecozone	Location	Terrain	Climate	Soil	Vegetation
Boreal Plains	Central MB & SK to northern AB & northeastern BC	Rolling terrain over moraine & flatter areas of postglacial lake sediment; abundant wetlands	Boreal continental; long, cold winters; short, hot summers; MAT −2 to 2°C; MST 13 to 16°C; precipitation 30–63 cm/yr	Deep podsol to brunisol; generally moist soil	Mostly conifer-dominated forest, with angiosperm-dominated in the south
Prairies	Southern & central MB, SK, AB	Rolling terrain over moraine & flatter areas of postglacial lake sediment; abundant ponds & wetlands	Temperate continental; cold winters; long, hot summers; MAT 2 to 4°C; MST 14 to 16°C; precipitation 25–70 cm/yr	Chernozem; soil dry to moist	Prairie dominated by grasses & forbs, ranging from tallgrass to mixedgrass to shortgrass types; most of the natural cover is converted to agriculture & urban uses
Taiga Cordillera	Western NT & northern YK	Steep to rolling terrain of northern Rocky Mountains & foothills; streams & rivers, fewer lakes	Subarctic coastal to continental; long, cold winters; short, warm summers; MAT −10 to −5°C; MST 7 to 10°C; precipitation 30–70 cm/yr	Podsol; generally moist soil	Because of altitudinal range, vegetation ranges from alpine tundra to subarctic boreal forest of spruce & birch
Boreal Cordillera	Northern BC & southern YK	Rugged mountainous terrain with foothills & deep wide valleys; streams & rivers, fewer lakes	Boreal continental; long, cold winters; short, warm summers; MAT 1 to 6°C; MST 10 to 12°C; precipitation <30 cm/yr in rain shadow to >150 cm/yr of orographic precipitation (i.e., increased by mountainous terrain that forces moist air masses to rise in altitude, cool, & precipitate their water content)	Podsol; permafrost discontinuous in north, with active layer >80 cm; generally moist soil	Because of altitudinal range, vegetation ranges from alpine tundra to montane forest of spruce & aspen; open forest & grasslands in southern areas
Pacific Maritime	Coastal BC	Rugged mountainous terrain with foothills & narrow coastal lowlands; streams & rivers, fewer lakes	Temperate coastal; short, cool winters; long, warm summers; MAT 5 to 9°C; MST 10 to 16°C; precipitation 60 cm/yr in dry Gulf islands to 400 cm/yr if orographic precipitation; generally 150–300 cm/yr	Podsol; moist soil	Because of altitudinal range & variable rainfall, vegetation ranges from alpine tundra to open dry forest to old-growth mixed-species conifer rainforest
Montane Cordillera	Southwestern AB & southern BC	Rugged mountainous terrain with foothills; streams & rivers, fewer lakes	Temperate continental; short, cold winters; long, warm summers; MAT 1 to 8°C; MST 11 to 17°C; precipitation 30 cm/yr in rain shadow to 120 cm/yr if orographic precipitation	Podsol; drier soil	Because of altitudinal range & variable rainfall, vegetation ranges from alpine tundra to open grassland-forest to closed mesic forest
Hudson Plains	Northwestern QC, northern ON, northeastern MB	Lowlands of postglacial James & Hudson Bays; surface waters abundant	Boreal coastal to continental; long, cold winters; short, cool summers; MAT −4 to −2°C; MST 11 to 12°C; precipitation 40–80 cm/yr	Regosol & podsol; permafrost discontinuous, with active layer >80 cm; generally moist soil	Coastal areas have salt marsh, then tundra farther inland, & then open boreal coniferous forest

SOURCES: Based on data from Ecological Stratification Working Group (1995) and Freedman (2010).

TABLE 11.2

Characteristics of the Marine Ecozones of Canada
Each of the five marine ecozones is distinct in terms of its geomorphology, climate, and prevailing biota.

Ecozone	Region	Geomorphology	Climate	Indicator Biota
Northwest Atlantic	Atlantic waters off Baffin Island, northern QC, Labrador & Newfoundland, Gulf of St. Lawrence	Coastal shelf waters, flows of Labrador Current & St. Lawrence River are dominant features	Subarctic to boreal marine; cold, long winters; cool, short summers; sea ice is abundant in the north, with pack ice everywhere in early summer	Subtidal kelp beds in coastal waters; cod, herring, capelin, harp seal, diverse cetaceans
Atlantic Marine	Atlantic waters off eastern NL, NS, NB in Bay of Fundy	Coastal shelf waters erratically influenced by both Labrador Current & Gulf Stream; extensive shallows < 150 m deep are known as banks	Temperate marine; cold, short winters; cool-warm summers; no sea ice, but drifting icebergs off eastern Newfoundland in summer	Intertidal & subtidal kelp beds, abundant animals include cod, haddock, redfish, hake, turbot, herring, lobster, queen crab, diverse seals & cetaceans
Pacific Ecozone	Coastal waters off BC	Narrow continental shelf, then deep waters beyond	Temperate marine; cool, short winters; warm, long summers; no sea ice	Kelp forest in shallow coastal waters; Pacific salmon, herring, crab, sea lions, orca, grey whales
Arctic Archipelago	Waters between Arctic islands, Beaufort Sea, Hudson & James Bays, bordering QC, ON, MB, NT, NU	Continental shelf waters, Mackenzie delta; occasional polynya above seamounts	Arctic marine; cold, long winters; cold, short summers; abundant sea ice	Polar cod, Arctic char, Greenland turbot, ringed seal, bowhead whale, walrus, polar bear
Arctic Basin	Polar waters north of Arctic islands of NU	Deep polar waters beyond continental shelf	High-Arctic marine; cold, long winters; cold, brief summers; continuous sea ice & pack ice widespread	Sparse animal populations, including ringed & bearded seal, narwhal, polar bear, ivory gull

SOURCES: Based on data from Ecological Stratification Working Group (1995) and Freedman (2010).

attributes. The CEC ecoregions have three nested levels, of which the highest is Level 1.

Figure 11.3 shows the distribution of the 15 terrestrial ecoregions that are designated for North America; these are the Level 1 ecoregions and are roughly equivalent to biomes. **Figure 11.22** shows the distribution of the next level of designation, in which there are 52 Level 2 ecoregions for the terrestrial landmass; these are roughly comparable to the ecozones of Canada. **Figure 11.23** shows the distribution of the 24 marine ecoregions (Level 2), which are comparable to the marine ecozones of Canada.

Terrestrial Ecozones of Canada

Arctic Cordillera

The Arctic cordillera is a remote and mountainous region in the eastern High-Arctic islands, especially Baffin, Devon, and Ellesmere, as well as northern Labrador. This ecozone contains the highest mountains and the largest extant glaciers in Canada. The climate is cold and dry, and the growing season is short and cool but with continuous daylight. Permafrost occurs throughout, with an active layer of up to 50 cm. The landscape is mostly exposed bedrock, rock fields, and glacial ice, and only a small area supports sparsely vegetated tundra. The most productive habitats occur in moist sites at lower elevation, and this is also where animal wildlife is more abundant. The ecozone is almost unpopulated, and there is little economic activity.

Northern Arctic

The northern Arctic is a remote ecozone of High-Arctic tundra occurring at low-to-moderate elevations in Nunavik (northern Quebec), the northeastern Northwest Territories, and the Arctic islands of Nunavut **(Figure 11.24)**. The climate is cold and dry, with a long, frigid winter and a brief, cool growing season. However, the growing

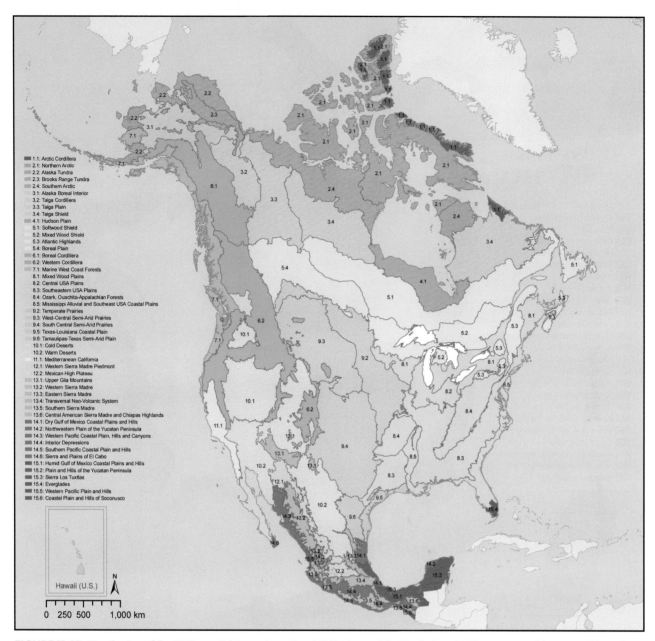

FIGURE 11.22 Distribution of the 52 Terrestrial Ecoregions (Level 2) Designated for North America These are roughly comparable to the ecozones of Canada.

SOURCE: Commission for Environmental Cooperation. 1997. *Ecological Regions of North America: Toward a Common Perspective.*

conditions are somewhat enhanced by the continuous sunlight of the summer at high latitudes. Throughout the ecozone there is permafrost, or perennially frozen ground, up to 600 m deep. However, a seasonally thawed active layer at the surface provides a substrate in which plants can grow. Although there is little precipitation, typically <10–20 cm/year, moist habitat occurs because of limited drainage and low evaporation rates. Because of the harsh climate most of the terrain is sparsely vegetated, and the vegetation is referred to as Arctic desert or semi-desert. In lowlands and river valleys that are protected by the surrounding terrain from strong winds, more productive vegetation develops in the relatively warm and moist conditions. Although such places cover

only a small percentage of the terrain, these Arctic "oases" provide critical habitat that supports denser populations of animals. Few people live in the Northern Arctic ecozone and there is little industrial or other commercial activity.

Southern Arctic

The southern Arctic is a remote Low-Arctic tundra of rolling hills and lowlands that ranges over northern Quebec, continental regions of Nunavut, much of the Northwest Territories, and northern Yukon. The climate is cold but less dry than in the High Arctic, with a long, cold winter and a short, cool summer. Permafrost is distributed throughout this ecozone,

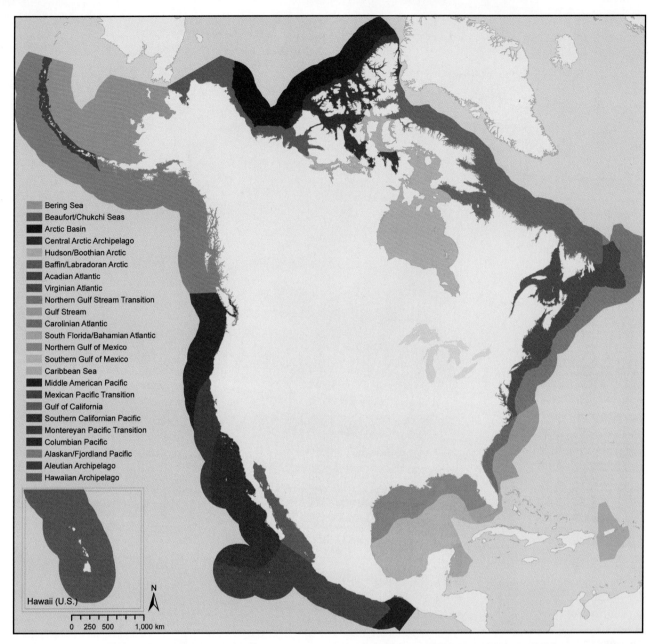

FIGURE 11.23 Distribution of the 24 Marine Ecological Regions (Level 1) Designated for North America These are roughly comparable to the marine ecozones of Canada. The seaward boundaries of the marine ecoregions are inexact—they actually extend further into the open ocean.

Legend:
- Bering Sea
- Beaufort/Chukchi Seas
- Arctic Basin
- Central Arctic Archipelago
- Hudson/Boothian Arctic
- Baffin/Labradoran Arctic
- Acadian Atlantic
- Virginian Atlantic
- Northern Gulf Stream Transition
- Gulf Stream
- Carolinian Atlantic
- South Florida/Bahamian Atlantic
- Northern Gulf of Mexico
- Southern Gulf of Mexico
- Caribbean Sea
- Middle American Pacific
- Mexican Pacific Transition
- Gulf of California
- Southern Californian Pacific
- Montereyan Pacific Transition
- Columbian Pacific
- Alaskan/Fjordland Pacific
- Aleutian Archipelago
- Hawaiian Archipelago

Hawaii (U.S.)

N

0 250 500 1,000 km

SOURCE: Wilkinson T., E. Wiken, J. Bezaury-Creel, T. Hourigan, T. Agardi, H. Herrmann, L. Janishevski, C. Madden, L. Morgan, M. Padilla. 2009. *Marine Ecoregions of North America*. Commission for Environmental Cooperation.

except below large lakes and rivers, and the active layer thaws up to 80 cm. Abundant glacial deposits include sinuous mounds of till, known as eskers, which were deposited by rivers of meltwater running beneath glaciers. Unusual surface features develop as a result of pressure exerted by formations of solid ice within the ground, including geometric-patterned ground caused by linear ice wedges, and ice-cored hills known as pingos that rise up to 70 m in height. This ecozone also has many lakes, ponds, rivers, streams, and wetlands. The region is well vegetated, mostly of plants less than 1 m in height, but in relatively protected habitats there may be shrubs up to several metres tall. This ecozone is sparsely populated, with little economic activity.

Taiga Plains

The taiga plains is a remote region of undulating uplands and flats, encompassing the northern watershed of the Mackenzie River in the western Northwest Territories, Yukon, northern British Columbia, and northwestern Alberta. The winter is cold and long, but the growing season is moderately warm and improved by relatively long days. The distribution of permafrost is extensive but discontinuous. The amounts of precipitation are low, but the soil is usually moist because permafrost impedes drainage and the evaporation rate is low. There are widespread deposits of glacial debris and riverine outwash,

FIGURE 11.24 The Northern Arctic Ecozone This a remote ecozone of High-Arctic tundra. This artist is painting the Arctic landscape near Pangnirtung, on Baffin Island, Nunavut.

and surface waters and wetlands are common features. The vegetation is primarily an open and slowly growing boreal forest, dominated by species of spruce, pine, and aspen. Most of the human population and economic activity occurs in the vicinity of the Mackenzie River.

Taiga Shield

The taiga shield is a vast, remote region of open boreal forest growing on hard quartzitic bedrock and thin glacial soils of the Precambrian Shield of central Quebec, Labrador, southern Nunavut, the southeastern Northwest Territories, and northern Manitoba and Saskatchewan. The winter is extremely cold, but the growing season is moderately warm with long days. Permafrost is widespread, but not throughout. Deposits of glacial debris are prevalent and wetlands are abundant, mostly in impermeable basins in the rolling bedrock. The forest consists of open stands of short and unproductive conifer trees, mostly of spruce and pine. The ecozone is sparsely populated and supports little economic activity.

Taiga Cordillera

The taiga cordillera is a mostly forested subarctic region of northern Yukon and parts of the adjacent Northwest Territories. It covers the northernmost region of the Rocky Mountains, so much of the terrain is steep, with wild rivers in deep valleys, and more gently sloping foothills at lower elevation. The climate is continental arctic and subarctic, with a long, cold winter and a short, cool summer with long days. Permafrost is extensively distributed. Surface waters are mostly rivers and streams, with

ponds and lakes more frequent on the northern coastal plain and in lowlands of the Old Crow River. The landscape is a complex mosaic of vegetation that ranges from alpine tundra at high elevation, to Low-Arctic tundra on the coastal plain, to taiga forest of spruce and birch at lower elevations in the south. This is a remote ecozone, with few people and little economic activity.

Hudson Plains

The Hudson plains ecozone covers the extensive lowlands of postglacial Hudson and James Bays, extending from northern Quebec and adjacent Ontario to northeastern Manitoba. The cold waters of Hudson and James Bays help to create a climate that is more subarctic than might be expected from the latitude, with a long, cold winter and a short, warm summer. Permafrost is discontinuous and there are abundant streams, rivers, ponds, lakes, and wetlands. Tidal flats develop extensive areas of salt marsh. Shrubby Low-Arctic tundra occurs near the coast, but the habitat changes inland to an open and short-treed taiga, and eventually to a closed-canopy boreal forest. This is a remote ecozone, with few people and little economic activity.

Boreal Plains

The boreal plains ecozone is a broad forested belt that extends from central Manitoba and Saskatchewan, across northern Alberta, to northeastern British Columbia. The hilly landscape consists of deposits of glacial moraine and flat areas with deep soil derived from postglacial lake sediment. The climate is continental, with a cold winter and warm summer. Surface waters and wetlands are abundant.

The forest consists mostly of conifer-dominated stands of spruce and pine, with aspen and poplar more abundant in southern regions. Forestry and fossil-fuel mining are major economic activities in this ecozone.

Boreal Shield

The boreal shield is a vast ecozone that occurs on thin soil and hard quartzitic bedrock of more southern reaches of the Precambrian Shield. It extends through Newfoundland and Labrador, much of southern Quebec, most of northern Ontario, central Manitoba, and northern Saskatchewan. The climate is cold in the winter and warm in the summer. Glacial debris is widespread, and waters and wetlands are common in perched basins (i.e., located in a natural basin within the surface of bedrock). The dominant vegetation is a closed boreal forest dominated by conifers, particularly species of spruce, fir, and pine. Logging and mining are major economic activities in this ecozone.

Boreal Cordillera

The boreal cordillera is a region of mountainous topography in southern Yukon and northern British Columbia. The ecozone has diverse terrain, with many steep slopes, deep and wide valleys, high plateaus, and sloping foothills and lowlands. The climate is continental boreal, with a long, cold winter and a warm summer. Surface waters are mostly streams and rivers, and northern regions have discontinuous permafrost. Local climatic conditions in areas of mountainous terrain are influenced by the inclination (degrees of slope) and aspect (direction faced) of the land. In southern regions, south-facing slopes are relatively warm and dry and support grassland and open forest, while northerly exposures have a more closed montane forest. Alpine tundra occurs at higher elevations. This is a sparsely populated ecozone, with forestry and mining the principal economic activities.

Pacific Maritime

The Pacific maritime ecozone is situated in mountainous terrain of the islands and coastal mainland of British Columbia (**Figure 11.25**). The climate is moderated by proximity to the Pacific Ocean, and it is humid temperate, with a short, cool winter and a long, warm summer. However, altitude and aspect have a large influence on the local climate. Surface waters are mostly streams and rivers. A diverse mix of conifer species is the predominant vegetation of the extensive temperate rainforest. The wet climate favours the development of old-growth forest because wildfire is uncommon. Higher-altitude sites develop a conifer-dominated montane forest, or alpine tundra closer to the summit of mountains. Forestry and mining are the main economic activities in sparsely populated rural regions, but areas in the extreme south are urbanized.

FIGURE 11.25 The Pacific Maritime Ecozone This ecozone sustains extensive tracts of temperate old-growth rainforest, although that ecosystem is greatly diminished because of logging. This is an old-growth tree of western red cedar (*Thuja plicata*) on Meares Island, near Tofino on western Vancouver Island.

Montane Cordillera

The montane cordillera is a mountainous ecozone of southern British Columbia and southwestern Alberta. The climate is temperate continental, with a cold winter and hot summer, but altitude and aspect greatly affect local conditions. Moisture is highly variable, ranging from dry valleys and plateaus in the rain shadow of mountains (where mountainous terrain has caused moist air masses originating over an ocean to rise in altitude and cool, so the water content of the atmosphere condenses and precipitates out as abundant rain and snow, to the degree that when the mountains are traversed the moisture content is greatly depleted, resulting in a region of "rain shadow" with a drier climate), to wetter at higher elevations in southeastern areas with orographic precipitation (this is the seaward side of the mountains with abundant precipitation). Surface waters are mostly streams and rivers, with some large lakes occurring behind natural impoundments of rivers. The ecozone is dominated by coniferous forest, but community types vary according to the terrain and environmental conditions. Alpine tundra occurs at higher altitude, with coniferous montane forest below, and temperate stands in lower valleys. Some areas with relatively high rates of precipitation support inland temperate rainforest. This is a sparsely populated ecozone, with forestry the principal economic activity, except in the extreme south where there is agricultural and urbanized activity.

Prairies

The prairies ecozone is a nonforested region that covers southern Alberta, Saskatchewan, and Manitoba. The landscape is a rolling moraine with flatter areas of fertile postglacial lake sediment. The climate is continental, with a cold winter and hot summer, but soil moisture deficits often limit plant growth because of sparse precipitation and a hot windy summer that promotes evaporation. Lakes and ponds with fringing wetlands, known as potholes and sloughs, are common, especially in years with abundant precipitation. Three kinds of prairie are identified by the height and species composition of their vegetation, which is mostly species of grasses and forbs. Tallgrass prairie has plants 1–2 m tall, while mixedgrass prairie has medium and short grasses and forbs, and shortgrass prairie has species less than about 25 cm tall. Southernmost parts of the ecozone are drier and have areas of semi-desert habitat. Agriculture and fossil-fuel mining are major economic activities along with those associated with urbanization.

Atlantic Maritime

The Atlantic maritime is an eastern ecozone that occurs throughout the Maritime Provinces and in adjacent Gaspé and southeastern Quebec. The terrain is rolling and the bedrock is a complex mosaic of granites and sedimentary rocks. The ecozone has moderately abundant precipitation and is cold in winter and warm in summer, but the climate is more moderate closer to the Atlantic coast. Surface waters and wetlands are abundant and the temperate forest is made up of productive mixed-species communities of various coniferous and hardwood species. The ecozone is widely settled and supports diverse economic activities, including those associated with resource extraction, agriculture, manufacturing, and urbanization.

Mixedwood Plains

The mixedwood plains ecozone is located in the valley of the St. Lawrence River and the postglacial floodplain of Lakes Erie and Ontario, in the most southerly regions of Ontario and Quebec. The terrain is gently rolling, bedrock is mostly limestone and other sedimentary rocks, and soils are relatively deep and fertile. The climate is continental temperate, with a cold winter and a hot summer. The natural forest is much richer in species than anywhere else in Canada, supporting many species of hardwood trees of a relatively southern distribution. This is particularly the case in extreme southern Ontario, where the Carolinian forest supports species that are rare in Canada but widespread in the eastern United States. This is Canada's most densely populated and intensively used ecozone, where the main economic activities include agriculture, manufacturing, and urban-associated sectors.

Marine Ecozones of Canada

Pacific

The Pacific ecozone occurs in waters off the islands and mainland of British Columbia. The climate is marine temperate, with a short cool winter, a long warm summer, and no sea ice. Shallow areas have extensive beds (or "forests") of giant kelps, while deeper regions have pelagic ecosystems. Species of Pacific salmon are prominent in the ecoregion—these fish spend their adult life at sea, but migrate up their birth river to spawn, after which they die. Some islands provide nesting habitat for large populations of marine birds. This ecozone supports commercial fishing and much shipping traffic.

Arctic Archipelago

The Arctic archipelago ecozone occurs in the waters of Hudson Bay and James Bay, the Beaufort Sea, and among the High-Arctic islands. The climate is marine arctic, with a long, cold winter and a short, cool summer. For most of the year the ocean surface is covered with ice up to several metres thick, and the ice-free summer is only 1–2 months long. Most of the primary productivity occurs during the ice-free season, but some takes place beneath the sea ice during the Arctic springtime. In a few places, the bottom topography forces deepwater currents toward the surface, where the turbulence creates **polynya**—these are ice-free areas that provide critical habitat for marine birds and mammals **(Figure 11.26)**. This is a remote ecozone, but southern regions support some commercial fishing and shipping.

Arctic Basin

The Arctic basin is a deep-water ecozone that is situated to the north and west of the High-Arctic islands. The climate is marine High-Arctic, with a long, cold winter and a brief, cold summer. Sea ice has a complete cover in the northernmost regions, and nearly so in the south. Large areas of sea ice break up during the summer into a drifting pack that moves in an immense clockwise loop, rafting on a current known as the Arctic (or Beaufort) gyre that is roughly centred on the North Pole. This ecozone

Dr. Rob Wright

FIGURE 1 Stan Rowe Standing in a Clear-Cut of Boreal Forest

Stan Rowe (1918–2004) **(Figure 1)** was an ecologist, educated at the University of Manitoba and University of Nebraska, with a background in botany, forestry, and

landscape ecology. He worked for 19 years as a research forester with the federal government, and then in 1967 became a professor at the University of Saskatchewan. Rowe and his students studied the distribution of the biomes and ecozones of Canada, including the effects of natural disturbances such as wildfire and windstorms on the dynamics of their communities. In 1959, Rowe wrote the first edition of the book *Forest Regions of Canada*, which has greatly influenced our knowledge of the distribution, biodiversity, and environmental factors affecting the natural regions of Canada. He also wrote a well-regarded paper with a more theoretical outlook, titled "The Level-of-Integration Concept in Ecology," which explored the unity of ecological context, which ranges across all echelons of life, as well as the environmental factors that allow and influence the existence of the biota.

In addition to his work on biomes and landscape ecology, Rowe was profoundly concerned about

environmental issues and their intersection with conservation. His own ethics and worldview were ecocentric, meaning he regarded humans as being a component of ecosystems and as having an inherent responsibility to conduct their economy in a manner that does not threaten other species and natural habitats. Rowe showcased his love for species and the biosphere in the book *Home Place* (1990), a collection of essays that explored those themes and influenced the rapidly developing conservation movement. A second book of essays, *Earth Alive*, was published posthumously in 2006. Rowe also gave many public addresses, particularly about the damaging effects of clear-cutting, the degradation of water resources, and the conservation of wilderness. He was also a key advisor to conservation NGOs, including the World Wildlife Fund (Canada). Rowe won numerous awards, including in 1994 the Harkin Conservation Award for his advocacy related to the conservation of parks and wilderness areas in Canada.

Bill Freedman

FIGURE 11.26 A Polynya Within the Arctic archipelago marine ecozone, polynyas are areas that are permanently ice-free or become open unusually early in the summer. Because these open-water places support a high productivity of marine invertebrates and fish, they are critical habitat for polar bears, cetaceans, seals, and seabirds. This polynya occurs on the east coast of central Ellesmere Island, Nunavut.

has a sparse marine productivity and it supports only small populations of fish and marine mammals. This is a remote ecozone, with no economic activity.

Northwest Atlantic

The northwest Atlantic ecozone is located in the Gulf of St. Lawrence and the continental-shelf waters off western and northern Newfoundland, Quebec, Labrador, and Baffin Island. The hydrology of the St. Lawrence River has a powerful effect in the Gulf of St. Lawrence, and the southeast-flowing Labrador Current is a major influence elsewhere in the ecozone. The climate ranges from marine subarctic to boreal, with a cold winter and cool-to-warm summer. In winter the northern regions are covered by sea ice, which breaks up and melts completely in the springtime. Fish populations are abundant and widespread, as are seabirds and marine mammals. This ecozone supports commercial fishing and much shipping traffic, especially in the Gulf of St. Lawrence region.

Atlantic

The Atlantic marine ecozone covers continental-shelf waters off eastern Newfoundland and Nova Scotia, as well as the Bay of Fundy. Extensive regions shallower than about 150 m are known as banks, but there are also postglacial riverine trenches and other deep habitats. The climate is marine temperate, with a cold winter and warm summer. Surface waters are particularly balmy in areas that are temporarily affected by eddies of the Gulf Stream, a warm-water current that flows from the Caribbean Sea toward no... Europe. Sea ice does not form during the ... icebergs carried by the Labrador Current re... into the northern banks, and riverine pack... imported from the Gulf of St. Lawrence in ... time. Populations of fish are plentiful and ... in both inshore waters and the offshore banks, and seabirds and marine mammals are abundant. This ecozone supports commercial fishing, fossil-fuel mining, and much shipping traffic.

CHAPTER SUMMARY

(LO11.1)

- The disparate ecosystems of Earth can be aggregated at various scales, the largest of which are biomes. These are characterized by the life forms of their dominant biota, but not necessarily the particular species. The biomes of Canada range from low temperate to High-Arctic in character.

(LO11.2)

- There are also anthropogenic biomes, which are strongly influenced by human activities and management practices.

(LO11.3)

- Natural and anthropogenic ecosystems may have many similarities in their structure and function, but in general the human-dominated systems support relatively low levels of biodiversity, much of which is alien, and the levels of stress associated with pollution and disturbances are high.

(LO11.4)

- Ecozones are categorized by their dominant late-successional communities, as well as their prominent species and their "enduring" attributes related to bedrock, soil, climate, and topography. A total of 15 terrestrial ecozones and 5 marine ones have been designated in Canada.

QUESTIONS FOR REVIEW AND DISCUSSION

1. Describe the essential characteristics of five biomes that occur in Canada, and two tropical ones.

2. Identify an ecozone that occurs in your province or territory and describe its characteristics. What are the most important environmental influences on the species and ecological communities of the ecozone? How do you think these factors have changed during the past decade? Over the past century? How did the species and ecological communities respond?

3. Ecozones are characterized in part by their dominant native species, but they may also contain many alien ones. Why do the aliens not play more of a role in the description of ecozones? Does this somehow reflect the higher "value" that ecologists may place on native species?

4. You have been given the job of mapping and describing the kinds of ecological communities that occur in a park or some other kind of protected area (choose one that you are familiar with, perhaps close to where you live). What methods would you use to map the various terrestrial, wetland, and aquatic communities in the park, and to determine their characteristics?

12 Biodiversity

LEARNING OBJECTIVES

After studying this chapter you should be able to:

1. Define biodiversity and describe its hierarchical elements.

2. Explain why biodiversity is so much richer in humid tropical biomes than in those at higher latitudes.

3. Discuss why biodiversity is important and should be preserved.

4. Explain how ecologists measure the various elements of biodiversity.

5. Discuss differences in the values of alien and native biodiversity.

12.1 Biodiversity

Biodiversity refers to the richness of biological variation, occurring at all levels of ecological organization **(Figure 12.1)**. The word "biodiversity" is an amalgam of **biological diversity** and it is a recent entry in the ecological lexicon, having first been published as the title of a book by E. O. Wilson (1988) that summarized a meeting about the conservation of natural values.

According to the Convention on Biological Diversity (CBD, 2012), biodiversity is "the variability among living organisms from all sources, including, *inter alia* [among other things], terrestrial, marine, and other aquatic ecosystems and the ecological complexes of which they are part: this includes diversity within species, between species, and of ecosystems." This definition has a kind of legal standing because it was used in Article 2 of the Convention on Biological Diversity (CBD), an international treaty adopted in 1992 under the auspices of the United Nations Environment Program that is intended to sustain the diversity of life on Earth. Canada was the first developed country to ratify this treaty. Although the United States has signed on to its provisions and implemented many of them more effectively than most countries, its government has not ratified the CBD.

The CBD definition indicates that biodiversity includes the totality of biological variation occurring at three levels of organization:

- genetic variation occurring within populations and species;
- the number of species (species richness) present in an ecological community or in some other defined area; and
- the assortment of communities occurring on any **ecoscape**, that is, the landscapes of terrestrial environments and the seascapes of marine ones.

Sometimes, larger-scale attributes of ecosystems are also considered as aspects of biodiversity. Within this context, ecologists acknowledge the important environmental functions that ecosystems perform, such as the provision of oxygen, storage of carbon, and regulation and purification of water flows. However, these functional properties are best considered to be attributes of biodiversity, rather than as its integral components.

Ultimately, biodiversity comprises all biological variation in the biosphere. However, any of its elements can be examined in smaller areas defined for the purposes of a study, such as a biome, a particular ecological community, a park or protected area, or a university campus, or in a political region such as a province or country.

(a)

(b)

(c)

(d)

FIGURE 12.1 Biodiversity Is the Richness of Biological Variation This photo montage shows: (a) a layer of purple sulphur bacteria (order Chromatiales) growing on the surface mud of a salt marsh in Nova Scotia; these photosynthetic proteobacteria use hydrogen sulphide (H_2S) as their reducing agent instead of water (H_2O), and instead of producing oxygen (O_2) as a waste product of photosynthesis they produce elemental sulphur (S); (b) the fruiting body (mushroom) of a dryad saddle (*Polyporus squamosus*) growing on a heart-rotted tree in southern Ontario; this fungus is a saprophyte that feeds on rotting tree biomass; (c) bunchberry (*Cornus canadensis*) and its namesake fruit clusters growing on the floor of a boreal spruce forest in Labrador; (d) a black colour-phase parasitic jaeger (*Stercorarius parasiticus*) sitting on its nest on Ellesmere Island, Nunavut.

Genetic Variation

Arguably, all biodiversity is ultimately based on genetic variation—on differences among the genomes of individuals within populations and species, as well as among different species, and beyond that among higher phylogenetic groups such as genera and families. Every individual organism has a unique **genome**, which is ultimately encoded in the specific base sequences of its DNA (deoxyribonucleic acid). The genetic variation occurring among individuals is manifest in various ways, such as in the numbers of alleles that exist for particular genes. It is ultimately expressed through individual **phenotypes**—the biochemical, developmental, morphological, and behavioural attributes that organisms display.

IGURE 12.2 Genetic Variation Is an Element of the Hierarchical Concept f Biodiversity Both the various kinds of dogs and the humans differ because f variations of their genotypes. However, the expression of their genetic otential has also been affected by environmental circumstances encountered uring life, a phenomenon called phenotypic plasticity.

Within a population, differences among the phenotypes of individuals are based on two kinds of influences **(Figure 12.2)**:

- An underlying pool of genetic variation that has developed through a balance among the mixing of genotypes during sexual reproduction and the rates of mutation, genetic drift, gene flow, and natural selection; and
- The variable expression of the genetic potential, known as **phenotypic plasticity**, which occurs in response to the vagaries of environmental conditions (although the degree of phenotypic plasticity that is possible is itself controlled by the genotype).

The genetic mixing that occurs during sexual reproduction has a powerful influence on the unique character of genomes. In brief, the biology of this process is as follows: During sexual reproduction, organisms produce "sex" cells (or gametes) by meiosis, a process of reductional division during which the paired (diploid) chromosomes of the parent separate, with one of each homologous pair (meaning they are complementary in the sequence of their nucleotide bases) randomly going to a daughter sex cell (which is haploid, having only one copy of each chromosome). However, just before the paired strands separate, a phenomenon known as crossing-over may occur, involving an exchange of genetic material between them that somewhat increases the genetic variability of the sex cells. A diploid progeny results when haploid gametes (one from each parent) combine during fertilization to begin the life of a "new" individual organism. The number of chromosomes of the progeny is the same as in the parent, but its genetic information is unique, although profoundly influenced by that of each parent. This is, essentially, the way in which sexually breeding parent organisms pass along their genetic information to their progeny, and it results in genetic variation among the individuals within a population.

However, in some populations or species there is little variation among the genomes of individuals. In such cases, organisms are propagating by vegetative (non-sexual) means to form **clones** of genetically uniform organisms. Many plants, for example, form clones because their vegetative propagation does not involve genetic exchange among parent organisms. Consequently, the clones represent one and the same genetic "individual," even though they may be physically discrete plants (or not—they may be connected by underground stems known as rhizomes).

Although clonal propagation is common in plants and microorganisms (but much less so in animals), most populations and species contain a great deal of genetic variation. Still, it is interesting to examine several examples of clonal populations. One familiar case is the common duckweed (*Lemna minor*), a tiny aquatic plant that floats on the surface of fertile ponds. It has an oval-shaped frond about 8 mm in diameter and tiny root-like rhizoids that extend a few millimetres into the water. When it flowers, which is rare, the plant is self-fertilizing. It usually propagates by developing small buds at the edge of its frond, which grow and eventually detach to form "new" plants, which are genetically identical to the parent. Liette Vasseur and her colleagues (1991) of Queen's University studied clones of duckweed that were collected from 28 widely spaced locations on four continents, and then were grown for several years under controlled laboratory conditions. The clones remained genetically uniform, but there was a high degree of variability among them, as indicated by differences within selected groups of allozymes (these are variant forms of a particular enzyme that are coded for by different alleles of the same gene). Because the clones had been grown for many generations under identical conditions, and the allozyme variation had no obvious relationship to their geographic origin, Vasseur et al. concluded that the variation was neutral in character (i.e., random) and not a result of differential natural selection in their original habitats.

The trembling aspen (*Populus tremuloides*) provides another example of clones, some of which are remarkably extensive. The largest one known covers more than 43 ha, consists of about 47 000 stems, has an estimated weight of 6 million kg, may be thousands of years old, and in terms of biomass, may be the weightiest organism in the world (Mitton and Grant, 1996). This species is dioecious (an individual tree is either female or male, but not both), and the clone is male and apparently genetically uniform (apart from minor accumulated variation due to somatic mutations). Although aspen trees also reproduce by

An **endemic species** has a restricted distribution—it occurs in a local area and is not geographically widespread. Endemics are most frequent in tropical biomes, and nowhere more so than on remote, low-latitude islands that have been evolutionarily isolated for a long time (Vitousek, 1988; Eldredge and Evenhuis, 2003; Goodman and Benstead, 2004). For instance, the Hawaiian Islands are the most remote archipelago in the world, located 1600 km from the closest island group in the Pacific and 4000 km from the nearest continent. The archipelago is also ancient, with the oldest islands being about 70 million years old. Prior to its discovery by Polynesian seafarers about 1500 years ago, the native Hawaiian flora included about 2000 species of angiosperm plants, of which 98 percent occurred nowhere else. The archipelago also supported at least 71 endemic land birds (species or subspecies) out of a total richness of 86 native taxa.

Another case is the island of Madagascar, which also has many endemics. It is located about 500 km from the coast of Africa, having been isolated from that continent for at least 160 million years, and it has an original flora of more than 12 000 species, of which 90 percent are endemics. In addition, 95 percent of the reptiles and amphibians and all of the native mammals of Madagascar

are endemics (including 40 lemurs, an endemic family of primates).

Unfortunately, the extreme endemism of the native biota of ancient islands makes them extremely vulnerable to suffering extinctions when colonizing humans destroy their habitat. Less than 5 percent of the primary ecosystems of Madagascar now survive, and most of its original species are extinct or endangered. Of the original 68 endemic birds of Hawaii, 23 are now extinct and 30 of the surviving 38 are at risk.

In North America, endemics are most abundant in "older" ecosystems south of the region that was iced over during the most recent glacial epoch, which, depending on the region, typically began to end 11 500 to 17 000 years ago. However, in many regions the continental ice sheets were more persistent than this. In fact, much of Canada was still covered in glacial ice 7000 years ago, including parts of Labrador, northern Quebec, and Keewatin, and glaciers still persist today in mountainous regions of western Canada and Nunavut. Although most of Canada has supported postglacial vegetation since then, this is a relatively short period on an evolutionary timescale and, consequently, few Canadian species have undergone the extreme adaptations to local conditions that result in the evolution of distinct endemics. In this sense,

the postglacial recolonization of Canada has involved widespread species that spread into vast areas of newly available habitat.

Nevertheless, there *are* a number of Canadian endemics, and they are a highly valued and unique part of the natural heritage of our country. Among plants, there are a few places that support local concentrations of endemics for one or several reasons: (1) they were nonglaciated refugia where plants survived for much longer than was possible in most of Canada; (2) there are local environmental regimes that resulted in steep gradients of natural selection that may have accelerated the evolutionary process; and (3) in several cases, they are isolated oceanic islands. The "hot spot" of Canadian endemism is in a region known as Beringia, which includes nonglaciated valleys of central Yukon, parts of the Mackenzie Mountains, the Mackenzie delta, western Banks Island, and the western coastal plain of Yukon and the Northwest Territories. Areas of more modest endemism are the Athabasca sand dunes of northern Alberta, the freshwater estuary of the St. Lawrence River in Quebec, the mountains of Gaspé, the limestone barrens of western Newfoundland, Sable Island off Nova Scotia, shorelines of the Great Lakes, and the Queen Charlotte Islands of British Columbia.

sexual means and routinely produce large numbers of highly dispersive seeds, they typically regenerate profusely by vegetative regeneration after a natural wildfire or following a clear-cut. After such a disturbance, an aspen produces many genetically identical shoots called ramets from its extensive system of underground stems (rhizomes) and roots. There can be as many as 2.5 million of these adventitious shoots per hectare. They grow quickly, up to 1 m in height per year, and then self-thin (meaning that intra-individual competition causes some shoots to die) to an eventual density of several hundred stems per hectare. Each "tree" may live for a century or more until the next disturbance again begins the process of clonal regeneration. The aboveground appearance of a mature stand of trembling aspen is that of numerous apparently individual trees, but in actuality there is

usually a mosaic of a number of clones, each of which is genetically uniform. Although each clone is genetically uniform, there may be considerable variation among them, possibly due to the cumulative influence of the occasional establishment of "new" individuals by seedlings (Cheliak and Dancik, 1982; Yeh et al., 1995).

According to conservation biologists, it is generally better for populations to have a large amount of genetic diversity. Within limits, such diversity allows for adaptive evolutionary responses to changes in environmental conditions, such as climate warming or exposure to new diseases or predators. In contrast, small populations with low levels of genetic diversity may be at greater risk from those kinds of environmental challenges. This is particularly the case of **endemic** (locally distributed) species that maintain small populations and are vulnerable to extinction

Where plant endemics occur, they typically represent a number of families. For example, in Haida Gwaii (the Queen Charlotte Islands) and nearby parts of British Columbia, there are five endemic plants representing five families: the Queen Charlotte false rue-anemone (*Enemion savilei*), Queen Charlotte avens (*Geum schofieldii*), alp lily (*Lloydia serotina var. flava*), Taylor's saxifrage (*Saxifraga taylori*), and Newcombe's butterweed (*Senecio newcombei*) (Centre for Applied Conservation Research, 2007).

There are also a few endemic animals in Canada. Among the endemic fish are the Acadian whitefish (*Coregonus huntsmani*) of southwestern Nova Scotia, Aurora trout (*Salvelinus fontinalis timagamiensis*) of south-central Ontario, and the Cowichan Lake lamprey (*Lampetra macrostoma*) of southern Vancouver Island. Endemic species of mammals include the Vancouver Island marmot (*Marmota vancouverensis*), the Gaspé shrew (*Sorex gaspensis*), and the maritime shrew (*Sorex maritimus*), but there are more endemic subspecies, including the wood bison (*Bison bison athabascae*; **Figure 1**), Peary caribou (*Rangifer tarandus pearyi*), Vancouver Island wolverine (*Gulo gulo vancouverensis*), and Newfoundland marten (*Martes erminea atrata*). Endemic birds in Canada include the Ipswich sparrow (*Passerculus sandwichensis princeps*) that breeds only on Sable Island, the Harris's sparrow (*Zonotrichia querula*) that nests only in the Canadian taiga and tundra west of Hudson Bay, and the Peale's peregrine falcon (*Falco peregrinus pealei*), which breeds only on Haida Gwaii and the Aleutian Islands.

FIGURE 1 The Wood Bison (*Bison bison athabascae*) This is an endemic subspecies of the American bison *(Bison bison)*. It occurs in northern Alberta and the southwestern Northwest Territories.

© Michael DeFreitas North America/Alamy

caused by ecological changes after their isolated habitats become colonized and used by people (see Ecology in Depth 12.1 and Chapter 14). This can also be a problem for remnant populations of previously widespread species, whose genetic variation, heterozygosity, and fitness have become greatly reduced through inbreeding (a phenomenon known as inbreeding depression).

For example, the population of several hundred beluga whales (*Delphinapterus leucas*) living in the estuary of the St. Lawrence River has been greatly reduced from its historical abundance of about 5000 animals. Samples collected from these whales suggest that they have lower levels of genetic variation compared with animals from larger populations in other parts of the range of the species, particularly in the Arctic (Patenaude et al., 1994; Murray et al., 1995; de March et al., 2002). Along with pollution and other causes of habitat degradation, reduced genetic variability may heighten the conservation risk faced by the St. Lawrence belugas.

The Florida panther (*Felis concolor coryi*) is another example of a remnant population whose survival is at risk partly because of inbreeding depression and low genetic diversity. In the mid-1990s, this highly endangered population consisted of only about 30 individuals, which were relatively vulnerable to diseases and congenital maladies and had low survival rates of cubs. Conservationists have increased the genetic variation of the population by introducing eight female animals from a Texas population of a different subspecies (Pimm et al., 2006). This action has helped to increase the abundance, health, and sustainability of panthers in Florida, but it also degraded the genetic integrity of the *coryi* subspecies.

Another important consideration with respect to biodiversity at the level of genetics is that of **population diversity** (sometimes referred to as **ecotypic variation** or **provenance**), which is related to the variations of genetic and phenotypic characters that exist among populations of a species (Hughes et al., 1997). Each population consists of a group of individuals that share aspects of their genetics and phenotypic attributes, more so than they do with other populations of their species. Obviously, an endemic species that lives only in one location is likely to have low population diversity. However, a species with a widespread geographic range and that uses a wide variety of habitats would have a great deal of population diversity, especially in places near the periphery of its range where the habitat is relatively marginal for its survival. Although the rate of extinction of populations is much greater than that of species, populations also evolve more quickly in response to changes in local environmental conditions. A high level of population diversity is generally viewed as a desirable attribute from a conservation perspective, because it might allow a species to better cope with and adapt to large-scale changes in environmental conditions, such as climate warming or new disturbance regimes.

Richness of Species

The term **species richness** refers to the number of species occurring in a specific area. It can be measured in a particular ecological community, or in a property, such as a park or a protected area, or in any politically defined area, such as a county, province, or country **(Figure 12.3)**. Species richness is also the level of biodiversity that most people can easily understand and relate to.

As previously defined in Chapter 1, a **species** is an aggregation of individuals that are capable of

interbreeding and producing fertile offspring. The species is a core unit of biological classification and nomenclature, an aspect of biology known as taxonomy. Species are identified using a "proper" common name as well as a Latinized binomial that consists of two words. For example, the large rodent whose fur stimulated much of the exploration of vast regions of present-day Canada and the United States is the American beaver, or *Castor canadensis*.

Some species also have distinct subspecies. For example, the brown bear (*Ursus arctos*) has about 20 subspecies, each of which is assigned a trinomial. The natural range of this animal includes almost all of North America and much of Eurasia. In North America, the subspecies are the relatively widespread grizzly bear (*Ursus arctos horribilis*), the endemic Kodiak bear (*Ursus arctos middendorffi*) of several Alaskan islands, and the extinct California golden bear (*Ursus arctos californicus*) and Mexican grizzly (*Ursus arctos nelsoni*). Similarly, there are several subspecies of caribou (*Rangifer tarandus*) in Canada, and even more in northern Eurasia, where the animal is known as reindeer.

In addition to their scientific binomial, many species have a recognized common name and sometimes additional informal ones, particularly in different languages if they occur in various countries. One example is the trembling aspen, which ranges over much of North America and whose common names include the following:

English: American aspen, golden aspen, mountain aspen, poplar, quaking aspen, trembling poplar, and this author's particular favourites: popple, quakers, and quakies.

French: *peuplier faux-tremble, tremble*

Spanish: *alamo blanco, alamo temblón*

Because there are often ambiguities with the use of common names, it is the Latinized binomial that biologists use and refer to in their research.

Ultimately, species richness comprises all of the plants, animals, and microorganisms that are present in a designated study area. However, ecological studies that involve species richness are usually restricted to a narrower range of organisms, such as certain plants, birds, or another selected group in which an ecologist may be interested. Sometimes only functional groups might be examined; for example, the tree-sized plants of a forest, or the various birds that use cavities for nesting. In general, the kinds of species that ecologists enumerate depend on the research questions that are being investigated.

The ways that species richness is studied also depend on the taxonomic competence of the researchers—one cannot investigate birds without knowing how to identify them, and the same is true of insects, plants, fungi, and any other groups of organisms. Many ecologists achieve

Bill Freedman

FIGURE 12.3 Species Richness The number of species in a community or another defined area, such as a country, is an element of biodiversity. This image shows various kinds of invertebrates in an intertidal community on the Pacific coast of Vancouver Island.

their taxonomic proficiency by being naturalists—they take an interest in the species that occur in the region where they themselves live or where they are doing research, and they learn how to identify them. Ecologists who are good naturalists are the ones most capable of doing field studies related to species richness, as well as in other fields that require an ability to identify species.

Species Richness of the Biosphere

Taxonomists have studied and given a scientific binomial to about 1.8 million species **(Table 12.1)**. However, it is estimated that the biosphere might actually support 30–50 million or more species. The best-known groups of organisms are those that are relatively large or abundant, especially vertebrate animals, of which only a few species are being discovered and named each year. In contrast, there are millions of as yet "undiscovered" species of small animals (particularly invertebrates) and microscopic organisms (such as bacteria, fungi, and protists) that inhabit ecosystems which are not yet thoroughly explored, particularly in the humid tropics. The oceanic realm is also not well known, especially in its abyssal depths (see Ecology in Depth 12.2).

Of the total number of species identified and assigned a name by taxonomists, about 35 percent occur in tropical habitats and 65 percent are in temperate and boreal climes (WRI, 2009). In contrast, an estimated 90 percent of the as yet undiscovered species live in tropical rainforests, in which the smaller biota, particularly invertebrates and microorganisms, is not yet well studied. The largest part of this "hidden biodiversity" is likely to be undescribed small insects of tropical forests, particularly beetles (order Coleoptera). Evolutionary biologist J. B. S. Haldane (1892–1964) was once asked by a group of theologians to tell what he could infer of God's purpose and thinking, based on his knowledge of "His Creation" (meaning biodiversity as it was known in the 1950s). Haldane allegedly replied that God has "an inordinate fondness of beetles." In fact, more than 350 000 species of beetles have already been named, amounting to 37 percent of all insects and 20 percent of all named species. However, entomologists have estimated that there are millions of additional species of beetles yet to be discovered.

The species richness of major groups of organisms in Canada is summarized in **Table 12.2**. Other than microorganisms, the numbers of species within these major groups are rather well known, a fact that reflects the relatively large numbers of biologists who have lived and worked in this country.

In comparison with many other countries, the ecosystems of Canada support a relatively low species richness **(Table 12.3)**. Although Canada is the world's second-largest country (after Russia), it harbours many fewer species than

TABLE 12.1 Global Biodiversity

The numbers of identified species are based on recent tallies, while the estimated totals (where available) are based on the opinions of expert biologists about how many species may eventually be discovered.

Group	Identified	Estimated
Viruses	5 000	500 000
Bacteria	4 000	3 000 000
Fungi	72 000	1 500 000
Mushroom fungi	30 000	—
Protozoans	40 000	100 000
Algae	40 000	350 000
Green algae	3 962	—
Red algae	6 076	—
Brown algae	3 040	—
Others	26 922	—
Lichens	17 000	21 000
Bryophytes and liverworts	16 000	20 000
Vascular plants	272 468	300 000
Ferns and allies	12 838	—
Conifers	980	—
Dicotyledons	199 350	—
Monocotyledons	59 300	—
Mollusks	81 000	200 000
Corals	2 175	—
Crustaceans	40 000	150 000
Other invertebrates	61 209	—
Arachnids	98 000	750 000
Insects	950 000	8 000 000*
Fish	30 700	32 000
Amphibians	6 347	6 800
Reptiles	8 734	9 000
Birds	9 990	10 200
Mammals	5 488	5 800
TOTAL	**1 760 000**	**15 000 000***

*Some recent estimates suggest that there could be more than 30 million species of insects, largely in tropical forests, and more than a million species of bacteria, fungi, and mites (Arachnids).

SOURCES: Based on data from Groombridge (1992), Heywood (1995), World Resources Institute (2009), IUCN (2009).

the United States and enormously less than many tropical countries. The relatively low species richness of Canada is substantially due to almost all of its landmass being covered by glacial ice as recently as 10–12 000 years ago, so that present-day ecosystems have not had much time (on an

It is remarkable that we know so little about the biodiversity of Earth—the only planet where life is known to exist. To try to deal with this deficiency of knowledge, a number of collaborative projects have developed with the intent of exploring relatively poorly known regions and cataloguing their novel and hidden biodiversity. One of the most ambitious of these projects was the Census of Marine Life (CoML, 2010).

The CoML was an international network of specialists in marine biodiversity that began its work in 2000 and released a comprehensive report in 2010. That report documented what is known about the diversity, distribution, and abundance of oceanic species, including the historical, present, and likely future conditions. The CoML was a global effort, and Canadians played key roles. This included Ron O'Dor of Dalhousie University, who was the senior scientist of the CoML, and Paul Snelgrove of Memorial University, who led the effort to synthesize the massive scientific collaboration, which involved about 2000 scientists from 82 countries who studied global marine biodiversity from microbes to whales.

A major goal of the CoML was to develop a comprehensive encyclopedia of marine life forms, in collaboration with the online *Encyclopedia of Life*. This was done by collating existing data on oceanic biodiversity, while adding to what is known by undertaking fieldwork in less-explored regions (14 major field projects were undertaken, each using an array of methodologies and employing many specialists to document the species). For instance, at the beginning of the CoML in 2000, there were about 230 000 described species of marine animals **(Figure 1)**. By 2010, thousands of "new" species had been discovered and were in the queue to formal taxonomic description and naming. In 2010, the CoML database held more than 16 million records, and that tally continues to grow.

The CoML has reported on what is known, not yet known, and perhaps unknowable about biodiversity in the global oceans (CoML, 2010). That information will serve as a baseline for marine research for decades to come. An online encyclopedia with a Web page for each species, including distribution maps and estimates of abundance, is being developed to supplement the written report. "Hot spots" of marine biodiversity—places with unusually dense foci of species, including endemics—and cold spots—areas with little marine biodiversity—are being identified and mapped.

Interestingly, there has not yet been a comparable survey of terrestrial life that seeks to develop an encyclopedic information base for that important part of the biosphere (although there are excellent databases for larger organisms, such as vertebrate animals). The closest to such an initiative is the work of the World Conservation Monitoring Center, a division of the United Nations Environment Program (WCMC, 2012). This organization has a focus on data related to the status, distribution, and trade of species- and ecosystems-at-risk, rather than on the assembly of a comprehensive database about biodiversity.

Because so little is known of the smaller elements of life—tiny invertebrates and microorganisms—it is important for initiatives like the CoML to understand not only what is known, but also what is not yet known. Even when its first 10-year cycle was completed and known marine biodiversity was catalogued, there were still an estimated million or more oceanic species yet to be described. Many of these are fish and larger invertebrates. However, the great majority of as yet undiscovered marine species are tiny animals, protists, and microbes, and particularly those of poorly explored, abyssal habitats (deeper than 1 km). There is much more yet to be done.

---

ecological scale) to recover from that cataclysmic disturbance. Just as important, there has not been enough time for many endemics to evolve in Canada—almost all of the species that occur in Canada also have a broad distribution in other countries.

In contrast, regions where there have been longer periods of continuous ecological development generally support much higher levels of biodiversity. This is particularly true of low-latitude, tropical regions, but it is also the case of nonglaciated temperate regions, such as much of the southern United States. These trends are evident from consideration of data on the species richness of selected countries in **Table 12.3**. Note the especially rich biodiversity of Brazil, Mexico, and Peru in comparison to Canada. Those countries sustain a great variety of natural ecosystems and a huge richness of species in all groups of organisms, including numerous endemics.

In fact, humid tropical forests support more species than any other habitats in the world. For this reason, ecologists consider the tropical rain forest to represent the pinnacle of ecosystem development on land. Unfortunately, the destruction of tropical rain forest is occurring at a rapid rate, mostly because the terrain is being converted to agricultural, industrial, and urbanized land uses (see Chapter 14). As a result of this irretrievable loss of tropical forests, many species have become extinct or endangered. This is the leading cause of the biodiversity crisis of the modern era. This crisis is less pronounced in Canada. Nevertheless, a

FIGURE 1 An *Enypniastes* This transparent species of sea cucumber, photographed at a depth of about 2750 m in the northern gulf of mexico, is an example of a discovery made in the course of a CoML project.

Photo by Laurence Madin, Woods Hole Oceanographic Institution.

number of indigenous species have become extinct or extirpated in Canada because of habitat destruction or excessive harvesting—and hundreds more are at risk of disappearing.

Estimates of the hidden biodiversity of Earth suggest that it may amount to several tens of millions of as yet unidentified species, compared to the 1.8 million that have already been named. One of the first researchers to arrive at this conclusion was the entomologist T. L. Erwin, whose research involved fogging small areas of tropical-forest canopy in South America with an insecticide. This method killed arboreal invertebrates, which fell as a "rain" of dead specimens that were collected in arrays of sampling devices laid on the ground. Erwin and his colleagues spent years laboriously sorting through and identifying their many specimens, and as their work progressed they realized that many of the insects they had collected (especially small beetles) were new to science. Moreover, many of them were endemics, having a local distribution and often restricted to only one kind of forest, or even to a particular species of tree. In a study of four kinds of Amazonian forest in Brazil, Erwin (1983) identified 24 000 beetles and found 1080 species among them; 83 percent of the species occurred only in a particular kind of forest, with 58–78 percent being endemics. In fact, the tree *Luehea seemannii* had more than 1100 species of beetles in its canopy, 15 percent of which were not found on other species of trees. Because this kind of work is difficult and expensive to undertake, there have not been many comparable

TABLE 12.2 | Biodiversity of Canada

The estimated totals are based on the opinions of expert biologists about how many species may eventually be discovered.

Group	Identified	Estimated
Viruses	200	150 000
Bacteria	2 400	23 200
Fungi	11 310	16 500
Protozoans	1 000	2 000
Algae	5 303	7 300
Lichens	2 500	2 800
Mosses & liverworts	1 500	1 800
Vascular plants	4 153	4 400
Mollusks	1 500	1 635
Crustaceans	3 139	4 550
Arachnids	3 272	11 006
Insects	29 913	54 566
Fish	1 100	1 600
Amphibians	42	44
Reptiles	42	42
Birds	430	430
Mammals	194	194
TOTAL	68 000	282 000

SOURCES: Based on data from Environment Canada (1997), World Resources Institute (2009), IUCN (2009).

TABLE 12.3 | Species Richness in Selected Countries

	Canada	USA	Mexico	Brazil	Peru
Vascular plants	4 153	19 473	26 071	56 215	17 144
Freshwater fish	128	1 101	674	471	166
Amphibians	42	285	358	695	361
Reptiles	42	360	837	651	354
Birds	430	888	1 026	1 712	1 781
Mammals	194	468	544	578	441
Country area (10^6 ha)	998.5	963.2	196.4	851.5	128.5

SOURCES: Based on data from Environment Canada (1997) and World Resources Institute (2009).

studies. It is remarkable that so little is known of the "smaller-sized" biodiversity of Earth.

In comparison with tiny arthropods, the species richness is better known for larger organisms that inhabit tropical forest. This is particularly true for vegetation, because plants are relatively easy to sample inside plots

(although specialized taxonomic knowledge is needed to identify the many species that occur in tropical communities). Consider the following data for primary lowland tropical forest in various regions (primary forest has not been logged or used for agriculture):

- 365 species of vascular plants occurred in a plot of only 0.1 ha in a lowland tropical forest in Ecuador (Gentry, 1986).
- 742 species of tree with diameter at breast height (DBH) greater than 10 cm occurred in a 3-ha plot of moist forest in Sarawak, Malaysia, with 50 percent occurring as single individuals (Primack and Hall, 1992).
- 240 tree species >10 cm DBH occurred in a 1-ha plot in lowland Kalimantan forest (Indonesian Borneo; MacKinnon et al., 1996).
- a range of 83–113 tree species >10 cm DBH occurred among ten 1-ha plots of lowland forest in Cameroon (Comiskey et al., 2003).
- 90 tree species >20 cm DBH occurred in 0.8 ha of lowland forest in Papua New Guinea (Paijmans, 1970).
- 44–61 tree species >20 cm DBH occurred among five 1-ha plots of lowland forest on Barro Colorado Island, Panama (112 species were observed among the five plots; Thorington et al., 1982).
- More than 300 species of woody plants occurred in a 50-ha forest plot on Barro Colorado Island (Hubbell and Foster, 1983).
- 283 tree species occurred in a 1-ha plot in Amazonian Peru, with 63 percent represented by only one individual and 15 percent by two (Gentry, 1988).

However, not all tropical forests are so rich in species. In Sumatra and Borneo, for example, lowland stands dominated by ironwood (*Eusideroxylon zwageri*) are almost monospecific, with up to 96 percent of trees being that species, occurring in all size and age categories (Whitten et al., 1987). Similarly, stands of coastal mangrove forest may have only a few species of tree present. As in all of ecology, we have to be careful about making broad generalizations, including about the rich biodiversity of all tropical forests.

In contrast, temperate forests in North America typically have only 9–12 or even fewer tree species in plots of comparable size to those noted above for rich tropical forest. The Great Smoky Mountains of the eastern United States have the richest temperate forests in the world. That region supports at least 131 species of native trees and 30–35 species in a typical stand (Stupka, 1964; Leigh, 1982), far fewer than occurs in most tropical forests. Boreal forests, which cover much of Canada, have only 1–4 species of trees present in a stand.

There have been a number of studies of the species richness of birds in lowland tropical forest. For example,

Terborgh et al. (1990) found 245 resident species plus 74 transient ones in a 97-ha plot of Amazonian forest in Peru. Thiollay (1992) recorded 239 bird species in a primary Amazonian rain forest in French Guiana. Whitten et al. (1987) reported 151 species in a 15-ha plot of lowland forest in Sumatra. These levels of avian richness are much greater than occurs in temperate forests in North America or elsewhere. For example, Cindy Staicer and colleagues (2001) of Dalhousie University studied two stands of temperate forest in Nova Scotia for three years and found 32 species breeding on a 35-ha hardwood-dominated plot, and 31 species on a 20-ha hemlock-dominated plot. In New Hampshire, a 15-year study of birds in a 10-ha plot of hardwood forest found that the number of breeding species ranged from 17 to 28 (Holmes et al., 1986).

A few more-comprehensive biodiversity assessments of tropical ecosystems have involved the study of numerous groups of biota at the same time and place. In one case, a dry tropical savannah in Costa Rica was studied for several years in a 108 km² protected area (Janzen, 1987). That site supported about 700 species of plants, 400 vertebrate animals, and a remarkable 13 000 insects, including 3140 moths and butterflies. Another study of a 676 km² protected area of tropical forest in Cameroon found 950 species of plants (including 351 trees), 111 butterflies, 67 dragonflies, 81 reptiles, 313 birds, and 15 larger mammals, including 8 primates (Comiskey et al., 2003).

Richness of Communities

A third level of biodiversity is the variety of ecological communities that occurs on a landscape or seascape. Research on biodiversity at this level involves studying the communities within a designated area, including how many distinct types there are and their relative abundances, variations of size and shape, and connectedness. An ecoscape has low community-level biodiversity if it is consistently occupied by only one or a few kinds of communities. In contrast, an ecoscape with a dynamic mosaic of many kinds of communities is richer in this level of biodiversity. These topics are examined in more detail in the context of landscape ecology (Chapter 13); the following provides only an overview, mostly in the context of terrestrial landscapes.

Most landscapes support a spatial mosaic that consists of various kinds of ecological communities (Figure 12.4). For example, wet places on a landscape may support ponds or marshes, and upland habitats will have forest or grassland. The communities will also vary according to other site factors, such as the fertility and depth of soil. They may also reflect stands of differing seral (i.e., successional) age after a disturbance, including natural ones such as a wildfire, windstorm, or insect irruption, or an anthropogenic one such as clear-cutting or abandonment of agricultural land. This dynamic aspect of ecological communities is reflected in the model of patch-scale community dynamics referred to as a shifting mosaic (Chapters 10 and 13).

Coevolved species and their self-organizing communities within a natural landscape mosaic have intrinsic value, and that alone is a reason to conserve them (see Section 12.2). In addition, however, these larger-scale ecosystems provide environmental services that support the human economy and its sustainability, such as carbon storage in biomass, regulation of water flows, and the production of biological resources that are valuable as materials, energy, or food. From the perspective of human

FIGURE 12.4 The Richness of Communities Occurring on a Landscape Is an Element of Biodiversity This complex landscape on the Tuktoyaktuk Peninsula of the northwestern Northwest Territories has various upland and wetland tundra communities as well as a winding river and its cutoff (oxbow) lakes.

Bill Freedman

needs and interests, these are important reasons to conserve biodiversity at the levels of community and landscape, and they are as significant as protecting genetic variation and species richness. Nevertheless, throughout the world, natural communities and landscapes are being degraded and lost (Chapter 15).

There are many examples of such losses occurring in Canada (Freedman, 2010). For example, older forests are becoming increasingly rare. This is especially the case in eastern Canada, such as in Nova Scotia, where less than 1 percent of the forest estate is now older than 100 years. Even in coastal British Columbia, where the humid climate is generally favourable to the development of old-growth forest (because wildfire is uncommon), this ecosystem is rapidly becoming less extensive. The rarest type is dry coastal forest dominated by Douglas-fir (*Pseudotsuga menziesii*), of which only 2 percent of the old growth remains. Timber harvesting is primarily responsible for the depletion of old-growth forest and its subsequent conversion into a younger, second-growth forest.

Furthermore, only <2 percent of the original Carolinian forest of southern Ontario survives, because the rest was destroyed when its land base was converted into agricultural and urbanized uses. Similarly, only 5 percent of the original extent of the Garry-oak (*Quercus garryana*) forest of southern Vancouver Island has avoided being converted into urbanized and agricultural land uses.

During the past century, almost all the original tall-grass prairie in Canada was converted to agricultural use, so that only about 0.2 percent survives. Much of the original area of wetlands of southern Canada has been extensively destroyed or degraded by pollution, in-filling, and other disturbances. Natural fish populations have also been widely decimated, including mixed-species communities in the Great Lakes, salmonid species (salmon and trout) in western Canada, and groundfish off the Atlantic Provinces.

These and other natural communities, landscapes, and seascapes of Canada are now endangered. They survive only in remnant patches rather than as integral parts of vast, robust, self-organizing, natural ecosystems. Furthermore, even the remaining vestiges are at risk of being converted or suffering other damages from human use.

12.2 The Importance of Biodiversity

Biodiversity is important for many reasons. They range from the intrinsic value of unique and irreplaceable components of the natural world, to the provision of ecological goods and services that are essential to the human economy **(Figure 12.5)**. The following section describes the ways that biodiversity is important and valuable, and that provide credence for its conservation.

FIGURE 12.5 Biodiversity Is Important to Human Welfare These domestic cows (*Bos taurus*) on Prince Edward Island are being cultivated for their meat.

Instrumental Value

Certain elements of biodiversity have **instrumental or utilitarian value** because they are useful to people and the economy as sources of food, medicine, materials, or energy. These necessary uses of biodiversity represent a vital connection between people and the rest of the biosphere.

All foods that people consume are derived from biodiversity, being edible biomass of various sorts. Plant tissues or foods processed from them provide us with grains, fruits, tubers, vegetables, sugars, and starches. Animal products include meat of cows, pigs, chickens, and fish, or other foods such as milk and eggs. Most foodstuffs are derived from plants and livestock that are cultivated to provide commercial foods, but there is also considerable hunting of wild stocks of animals for a market economy or for subsistence, such as fish, waterfowl, and deer.

Prior to the 20th century, almost all medicines were derived from products of biodiversity (a few others were inorganic compounds of such elements as arsenic and mercury). Classical examples are the anti-inflammatory drug acetylsalicylic acid (aspirin) derived from willows (*Salix* spp.), heartbeat-regulating digitoxin from foxglove (*Digitalis purpurea*), pain-killing alkaloids from the opium poppy (*Papaver somniferum*), and antimicrobial drugs from *Penicillium* and *Streptomyces* fungi. Although many newer medicines are based on synthetic active ingredients, most are still derived from biochemicals found in plants and other organisms. For instance, between 1981 and 2006, 63 percent of 974 new small-chemical entities that were examined as potential medicines were derived from natural compounds or inspired by them (the latter includes synthetic analogues of natural chemicals; Neuman and Cragg, 2007). For drugs used to treat microbial infections, cancer, hypertension, and inflammation, the figure is even higher, at 75 percent.

Trees provide lumber that is used to construct buildings and homes, to manufacture furniture, and for many other purposes. Paper is another commercial product derived from tree biomass, as are methanol, turpentine, and plastic-like celluloid. Various plants supply fibres that are woven into textiles, including coconut (coir), cotton, flax, and hemp. Textiles are also woven from the wool of sheep, goats, and alpaca. Clothing is also made of furs and leather made from the skins of both livestock and wild animals.

Biomass is a renewable source of energy that can be burned as a fuel for space heating and to produce steam-driven electricity. Trees are the most commonly used source of commercial-scale biomass energy. In addition, oils derived from the seeds of certain plants (such as oil-seed canola and oil-palm) can be used as a fuel in diesel engines, and starch and sugars can be fermented to produce ethanol or methanol, which can be used as fuels in internal-combustion engines and for other purposes.

Many animals are kept by people as pets, and in that capacity they provide important services as companions, sources of amusement, and even health benefits associated with walking and stress reduction. In Canada, there are about 8 million pet cats and 6 million dogs, living in about 70 percent of households (CAHI, 2008).

Remarkably, only a small proportion of known species has been examined for potential usefulness to humans. Consequently, there is a great wealth of as-yet undiscovered products of biodiversity that may prove to be valuable. Much field and laboratory research is being undertaken to find novel uses for the products of wild plants, animals, and microorganisms. This can be illustrated by the case of the rosy periwinkle (*Catharanthus roseus*), a small wildflower native to Madagascar (Myers, 1983; Miller and Tangley, 1991). The rosy periwinkle was long used in traditional medicine as a remedy for various diseases, and it caught the attention of health scientists when screening tests found it to be pharmacologically active in suppressing the growth of tumour cells. Further research showed that the active property is due to several alkaloid compounds that the periwinkle synthesizes to deter herbivores. These chemicals, vincristine and vinblastine, are now extracted from periwinkles grown for the purpose and are used in chemotherapy to treat leukemia, lymphomas, and several other malignancies. Prior to the discovery of these drugs, children with leukemia had only a 5 percent likelihood of remission, but this was increased to 94 percent by treatment with periwinkle-based medicine; similarly, persons with Hodgkin's lymphoma had almost no chance of survival, but this was increased to 70 percent.

A comparable example is taxol (paclitaxel) derived from various yews (*Taxus* species), which has been proven effective against lung, breast, and ovarian cancers **(Figure 12.6)**. Wild stocks of two native species, the Pacific

FIGURE 12.6 Biodiversity Can Provide Crucial Sources of Medicine The foliage of Canada yew (*Taxus canadensis*) yields a chemical known as taxol that is effective in chemotherapy against several kinds of cancers.

Bill Freedman

yew (*Taxus brevifolia*) and Canada yew (*Taxus canadensis*), are being harvested to provide this medicine. These are only two examples of recently discovered medicinal benefits that are provided by chemicals found in wild organisms, and there are many additional ones that have not yet been found. These future prospects are a good reason to prevent the extinction of elements of natural biodiversity.

In general, organisms or their populations are capable of regenerating after they or their products are harvested as sources of foods, medicines, materials, or energy. Because of this regeneration, biodiversity is a potentially renewable source of these natural goods. However, a sustainable system of harvesting and management is possible only if the harvest rate does not exceed the capacity of the stocks to regenerate (Chapter 15). Unfortunately, many biodiversity resources have been "mined" to such a degree that they have become depleted. This syndrome is known as **overharvesting** or **overexploitation**, and it is usually caused by an excessive harvesting rate and inadequate fostering of the regeneration, which results in bioresources becoming diminished in quantity and degraded in quality.

There are even cases of overexploited species becoming **extinct** or locally **extirpated** (extinct in a place or region, but surviving elsewhere), so their unique resource values are no longer available to be used to benefit people. Examples of Canadian species that became extinct primarily because of commercial overharvesting include the great auk (*Pinguinus impennis*), passenger pigeon (*Ectopistes migratorius*), Eskimo curlew (*Numenius borealis*), and sea mink (*Neovison macrodon*). Regional extirpations have been much more frequent in areas where the human economy is dominant, and include those of bison (*Bison bison*), cougar (*Puma concolor*), grizzly bear (*Ursus arctos*), timber wolf (*Canis lupus*), wolverine (*Gulo gulo*), and wild ginseng (*Panax quinquefolius*) over most of their original ranges.

Provision of Ecological Services

Ecosystem functions are important both to the human economy and to the maintenance of wild biodiversity itself. There are two general types of ecosystem (or ecological) services: (1) *provisioning services* that involve the production of food, biomaterials, flows of water, and other renewable resources; and (2) *regulating services* that help to moderate environmental conditions, such as carbon storage in biomass and other influences on climate, and controls on pests and diseases. Examples of ecological services include the following:

- *Biological productivity* is vital to all species, because it is the foundation of all ecosystems, and it is also obviously important to the human economy because it provides crucial sources of foods, materials, and energy **(Figure 12.7)**.
- *Nutrient cycling* refers to processes by which specific microorganisms or the broader microbial community act to transform nonavailable forms of nutrients into compounds that can be taken up by autotrophs and used to generate new biomass. Chapter 4 explains key processes in nutrient cycling, such as the decomposition of dead biomass, nitrogen fixation, and nitrification.
- *Clean-environment services* (or *waste-regulating services*) include the cleansing of soil, water, and atmosphere of pollutants, such as carbon dioxide, sulphur dioxide, and ozone, as well as the provision of gaseous oxygen by photosynthesis, the control of erosion, and the hydrologic regulation of watersheds.
- *Stability of communities and larger ecosystems* refers to their constancy over time. It integrates both resistance to environmental change and the degree of resilience after a perturbation (chapters 2, 9, and 10). Stability is an overarching quality that is relevant to all structural and functional attributes of ecosystems. Stability is generally considered a desirable attribute

of economically important ecosystems, because it allows for predictable harvests of natural resources.

The idea that ecosystems with greater levels of biodiversity are more stable began with the musings of MacArthur (1955) and Elton (1958) about community-level buffering and species redundancy in the face of biotic and abiotic perturbations. These ideas have been the subject of a great deal of theoretical and empirical research, some of which (including the modelling work of May, 1973) has resulted in contrary ideas, including the suggestion that higher levels of diversity do not always result in greater stability. Although the subject area remains controversial and is not yet resolved (McCann, 2000), the notion of biodiversity promoting stability is a commonly expressed idea in support of the need for conservation action. For example, it is widely believed that ecosystems with higher levels of biodiversity are more resistant to being penetrated by **alien** (or **non-native**) species, or that they have greater resilience to such damages and so can recover more quickly. In fact, stability may be associated not only with the richness of biodiversity, but also with the kinds of species that are present and the particular roles they play within their communities.

Regardless of the controversy, it is clear that ecological services are crucial to maintaining the stability and integrity of natural ecosystems, including those managed to directly serve the human economy. Peter Raven (1990, p. 770), an advocate of biodiversity conservation, once said: "In the aggregate, biodiversity keeps the planet habitable and ecosystems functional."

Despite the obvious importance of ecosystem services, most people assume those functions are provided by biodiversity for "free" (at no cost). For this reason,

FIGURE 12.7 Biodiversity Feeds Us Elements of biodiversity provide us with all of our food, most of which is cultivated; however, some is obtained by harvesting wild animals and plants. This image shows a field of canola (*Brassica napus*), a cultivated variety (or cultivar) of rapeseed that has a high yield of oil and a low concentration of distasteful erucic acid. Canola was developed at the University of Manitoba by Keith Downey and Baldur Stefansson in the early 1970s, and it has become a globally important crop, as well as in Canada. The oil is used as a food for people and as a biodiesel fuel for vehicles.

Bill Freedman

society has not attributed an appropriate economic value to ecological services. This is because few economists or leaders of society understand and appreciate the important role that well-functioning ecosystems play in sustaining the human economy and the natural world, and the vital role of biodiversity in providing those functions.

Some ecological services are dependent on the presence of specialized organisms, such as the nitrogen-fixing mutualism that involves *Rhizobium* bacteria living in root nodules of leguminous plants (Section 4.4) and the top predators that help to regulate the abundance of organisms at lower trophic levels of their communities (Section 9.2). For instance, in 1995, wolves were reintroduced to Yellowstone National Park and its surrounding ecosystem, a region where they had been extirpated for about a century (Hamlin and Cunningham, 2009). In the absence of wolves and other abundant predators (such as grizzly bear), an overpopulation of elk (*Cervus elaphus*) had developed and these large herbivores were degrading their food resource. In particular, they were preventing the regeneration of aspen and willows by excessive feeding on shoots and saplings. The introduced wolves quickly increased in abundance in the greater Yellowstone region, reducing the elk population, which in turn allowed the woody species to regenerate and improved the overall health of the ecosystem.

In other cases, vital ecological services are driven by an entire community, such as the decomposition of dead organic matter, which in a terrestrial habitat is accomplished by the microbes, animals, and other members of the soil ecosystem. Landscape-level biodiversity is also relevant to functional ecology in, for example, modifying the flows and water quality of streams and rivers that drain a watershed. See Ecology in Depth 12.3 to read more about the relationships of biodiversity and ecosystem functioning.

Aesthetic Value

Aesthetic value is associated with sensory and emotional perceptions. Aesthetic value involves critical thought on cultural expressions (such as literature, art, music, and video) and also on aspects of the natural world, including judgments about sentiment and tastefulness. Perceptions of aesthetic values are conditioned by social influences, which may be associated with religion, group culture, and other collective views.

Aesthetic value is highly relevant to biodiversity because many people find certain of its elements to be charismatic and alluring. For example, many people are attracted to baby animals, and to iconic species such as the giant panda (*Ailuropoda melanoleuca*), harp seal (*Phoca groenlandica*), orca (*Orcinus orca*), and polar bear (*Ursus maritimus*). Many people also find certain natural ecosystems to be appealing and even to have a spiritual quality, such as old-growth forest with gigantic trees, free-flowing rivers, and other sorts of wilderness. Because so many people hold affectionate feelings about wild creatures and wild places, they are increasingly influencing politicians and other decision makers to conserve natural biodiversity.

Moreover, people in many countries believe that biodiversity and its aesthetics are important to their national cultural identify. In Canada, for example, images of biodiversity figure prominently on many of our symbols, starting with the flag (with a maple leaf) and extending to coinage, paper currency, and stamps, as well as different forms of artistic and literary expression (**Figures 12.8** and **12.9**). The native species and wild places of Canada are iconic in the minds of Canadians, and this indicates a great affection for those natural values.

Aesthetic values of biodiversity can become instrumental, if people are willing to pay for access to these appealing "resources." Many people like to spend time in wild places to directly experience biodiversity, and they may spend a lot of money in order to travel long distances to do so. They may also engage biodiversity indirectly, by spending time and money to read about it, by watching its coverage on television and other visual media, and by purchasing themed art. They may also donate funds to environmental charities whose focus is the conservation of biodiversity.

Intrinsic Value

Intrinsic value (or **inherent value**) is associated with unique, irreplaceable, and aesthetic qualities that are assigned to biodiversity and other components of the natural world, and also to human cultural expressions, such as art, literature, and music. Intrinsic value exists "within itself" and "for its own sake," and it is separate from utilitarian valuation because it is not based on what people need, either directly or indirectly.

Because biodiversity has intrinsic value, ethical questions arise concerning human actions that might threaten any of its levels: genetics, species, communities, and ecoscapes. Even though humans can survive only by harvesting and using the products of biodiversity, do we have the right to degrade or even exterminate any of its unique and irretrievable elements?

In fact, the modern human enterprise is physically able to achieve that sort of destruction because of our advanced technological and socioeconomic systems. Moreover, this damage is occurring widely in the form of extinctions of species and the endangerment of certain natural communities. But is it the ethical thing to do, in view of the losses of irreplaceable entities having their own intrinsic value? Is human existence itself degraded by extinctions and endangerment caused by our wanton practices?

Biodiversity has always been involved in processes that regulate the amounts and fluxes of energy and materials in ecosystems, and ultimately in the biosphere as a whole. These biological and ecological functions are highly varied, but they include photosynthesis and other means of primary production, the cycling of nutrients, and the storage and decomposition of organic matter.

It is well known that these natural functions are essential to supporting the human economy. In spite of their importance, the actions of people are causing widespread damage to biodiversity, ranging from the diminishment of genetic variation within species, to losses of species through extinction, and the endangerment of entire communities and even ecoscapes. In view of these facts, there is apprehension about the risks associated with a substantial degradation of environmental functions that are needed to sustain both the natural world and the human economy. To investigate these issues, a new field of research has emerged within ecology—the study of biodiversity and ecosystem functioning (or BEF).

A study published by Cardinale and others (2012) has provided a comprehensive assessment of the potential consequences of degraded biodiversity for the delivery of goods and services needed by humanity. This study reviewed the BEF research that has investigated relationships between the rates of ecosystem functions (such as productivity, decomposition, and nutrient cycling) and the level of biodiversity (as indicated by the diversity of genes, species, or functional traits at higher ecological levels, such as within communities). Cardinale et al. found that higher levels of biodiversity often promoted desirable levels of ecosystem functioning, and the reverse when biodiversity had been degraded by anthropogenic influences.

Based on their wide-ranging review of BEF research, Cardinale et al. came to the following conclusions about the impacts of biodiversity loss on ecosystem functioning. In essence, losses of biodiversity result in:

- a reduction in the efficiency by which communities fix energy, maintain stocks of biomass and nutrients, and support decomposition and nutrient cycling;
- a decrease in the stability of ecosystem functions;
- nonlinear damages to ecosystem functions, in the sense that as losses of biodiversity accumulate, there are accelerating damages;
- losses of certain species that have a disproportionately large influence on ecosystem functions (such as keystone species);
- risks to the total assimilation of resources by communities, because the diversity of functional traits among species results in a larger overall functioning than would otherwise occur; and
- a large loss of ecosystem functions if all trophic levels are affected, compared with losses that are restricted to a particular trophic level.

Notwithstanding these conclusions, Cardinale et al. (2012) acknowledge that much more work must be done to further clarify the relationships between biodiversity and the rates of ecological functions needed to support both people and the biosphere. In fact, this knowledge is vital to understanding how the human economy can be sustained over the longer term, while also accommodating other species at viable levels of abundance.

These are, of course, philosophical issues that cannot be resolved by the cool logic of ecological or any other kind of science. However, truly enlightened people and societies would not facilitate irreparable damage caused to biodiversity. This is an ethic and opinion that many, if not all ecologists recognize.

Biodiversity Is Viewed as Important

Those who understand the issues about biodiversity believe that it is worthwhile and must be conserved. This broadly held public view is increasingly being shared by politicians and other decision makers, who are beginning to take coordinated actions to help conserve biodiversity.

At the international level, this fact is evidenced by the CBD, an international treaty under the auspices of the United Nations Environment Program that has been ratified by Canada and an additional 190 countries. Under the terms of the CBD, Canada is obliged to assess the adequacy of its efforts to conserve biodiversity, to use its biological resources in a sustainable manner, and to identify and fill gaps in its relevant policies and actions. One obligation is to develop a national strategy for implementation of the CBD. This has led to the development of important policies and actions, including:

- a Canadian biodiversity strategy to guide the implementation of provisions of the CBD (Environment Canada, 1995);
- assessments of biodiversity and its conservation needs in Canada; and
- a national *Species at Risk Act* (2002) and comparable legislation in the provinces and territories.

These initiatives and others by environmental organizations in Canada (including non-governmental ones)

FIGURE 12.8 Biodiversity and Culture The fame of artists such as Emily Carr and the Group of Seven reflects the value Canadians attach to natural landscapes. This 1920 painting, *Algoma Bush, September*, is by Group of Seven artist J. E. H. MacDonald.

SOURCE: J.E.H. MacDonald, "Algoma Bush, September," 1920, McMichael Canadian Art Collection, Gift of Mr. R.A. Laidlaw, Object number 1966.15.3.

Bill Freedman

FIGURE 12.9 Biodiversity and Aboriginal Art Elements of biodiversity are also a commonly expressed aesthetic of Aboriginal artists throughout Canada, and even globally. This soapstone carving of a walrus by Simeonie Uppik of the Belcher Islands in eastern Hudson Bay, Nunavut, shows a commonly expressed theme of Inuit art, which often features animals that are important as food and in spirituality.

are examined in detail in Chapter 14. For now, it is sufficient to acknowledge that issues related to the conservation of biodiversity and the sustainable use of its products are now widely recognized as being important to society, and actions to achieve these goals are beginning to be undertaken. However, the global biodiversity crisis is proceeding apace, much more must yet be done, and ecologists have a key role to play in these initiatives.

12.3 Measuring Biodiversity

Biodiversity is a broad and hierarchical concept, and ecologists need standard measures that are relevant at its various levels. Measuring the various aspects of biodiversity, and the factors affecting them, are not simple tasks—although the notion of diversity is intuitively easy to understand, its elements can be difficult to quantify.

John Macoun and Paul Hebert: Two Cataloguers of Canadian Biodiversity—The Old and the New

Topley Studio/Library and Archives Canada/PA-033784

FIGURE 1 John Macoun

Paul Hebert

FIGURE 2 Paul Hebert

The first people to seriously begin the systematic cataloguing of the biodiversity of Canada were field-naturalists. Those 17th to early 20th century biologists were interested in the kinds of organisms that occurred in unexplored or otherwise poorly known regions. Some of them were brave and intrepid explorers of enormous tracts of Canadian wilderness, spending long, uncomfortable months in wild places collecting specimens during the growing season, and then using the winter to prepare, identify, and classify their many specimens.

One of the best known of the early field-naturalists to work in Canada was John Macoun (1831–1920) **(Figure 1)**, the first Dominion Botanist of the Geological Survey of Canada. He was a tireless and insightful biologist who worked all across our country, from coast to coast and also in the Arctic. Macoun identified many new species and clarified the ranges of untold others, catalogued thousands of

botanical specimens (these are deposited in the National Herbarium at the Canadian Museum of Nature in Ottawa), and wrote the epic tomes *Catalogue of Canadian Plants* (in seven parts, published between 1883 and 1902) and *Catalogue of Canadian Birds* (in three parts, 1900–1902; coauthored with James Macoun, his son).

The taxonomic work of Macoun and other earlier biologists was largely based on the anatomical characteristics of specimens, often of whole organisms. Today their valuable collections, together with those of many other collectors and taxonomists, fill voluminous shelves and drawers in museums and herbaria (plant collections), and these great compendia of biodiversity are still being added to. These repositories provide vital support to biologists working on biodiversity using the relatively traditional methodologies of classification, taxonomy, and phylogenetics of the 20th century, such

as careful measurements of the bones of vertebrates or the exoskeleton of invertebrates, or of the floral and foliar organs of plants, followed by statistical and mathematical analyses to establish differences and relationships among groups of organisms.

The classical methods of systematic research still have great value, but they are being augmented by new developments such as techniques in molecular biology. For example, the identity and relatedness of species is being studied using molecular techniques to analyze the nucleotide sequences of nucleic acids, particularly DNA. Molecular biologists are also developing innovative methods to identify unknown specimens.

One of the leaders in this approach is Paul Hebert **(Figure 2)** of the University of Guelph. He has undertaken work on the molecular biology and evolutionary relationships of various groups of organisms, particularly insects. Perhaps more importantly he is the champion of the International Barcode of Life Project, a collaborative initiative that collects diverse biological specimens from around the world, analyzes their DNA, and catalogues the data on high-capacity computer systems for easy retrieval and comparison with new specimens as they arrive.

One goal of that program is to develop a practical facility that would allow ecologists to easily identify large numbers of specimens collected during fieldwork. Another goal is loftier—to analyze the large accumulated database in ways that will allow for novel insights into the evolutionary relationships of biodiversity, ranging from those of closely related groups to others more distantly connected on the diverse tree of life.

Nevertheless, these measures provide useful indicators that enable comparisons to be made of biodiversity among different environmental situations. This makes it possible to evaluate the outcomes of human activities that have the potential to damage biodiversity (such as mining, forestry, and urbanization), as well as actions that may be undertaken to conserve biodiversity. The following indicators are frequently used in ecological studies to measure and report on biodiversity.

Genetic-Level Biodiversity

Genetic variability within populations, or among them, may be studied by examining various kinds of **markers**— a genetic element (allele, gene, DNA sequence, or chromosome feature) of an individual that can be detected by cytological, molecular, or phenotypic methods. Frequently reported indicators at the molecular level include heterozygosity and the numbers of different alleles that exist for a selection of genes in a population. Heterozygosity is the frequency of occurrence of heterozygotes (pairs of different alleles) for a particular gene. Genetic variation may be studied by a variety of methods, including the sequencing of genes or selected regions of DNA, or other analyses such as "DNA fingerprinting" that examine particularly variable regions of a genome.

An additional method involves studying the phenotypic variations that occur when organisms are grown under identical environmental conditions (for plants this is known as a "common-garden" experiment). Such experiments presume that observed differences in morphology or biochemistry are due to genetic differences among individuals; this is because the common-environment research design reduces the influence of phenotypic plasticity.

Differences in any of these indicators might be examined among populations occurring in different environmental regimes, along geographical or environmental gradients, or under varying management regimes.

Diversity of Species

The following sections present some commonly used indicators related to the diversity of species. They are especially used in studies relevant to the composition and biodiversity of ecological communities (Chapter 9).

Species Richness

Species richness is the simplest indicator. It is usually expressed as the number of species encountered after a search of an ecological community, or in some other geographical area, such as a park, university campus, or a province or country. Occasionally, species richness within a community is expressed as a density function, such as species/m^2 or species/ha.

In many studies, community-level biodiversity is considered separately for groups of organisms, either on a phylogenetic basis (such as bryophytes, vascular plants, arthropods, fish, birds, or mammals) or as groups with a functional similarity (or **guilds**, such as ground vegetation, trees, epiphytes, or birds that share foraging or nesting habits). The particular choices of groups are usually made to suit the needs of the research project (for instance, there may be an interest in studying only birds).

An important problem with species richness is that it is a rather simplistic measure. For one thing, it does not take the relative abundances of species into account— the fact that some are common and others rare **(Figure 12.10)**. This idea can be illustrated by a comparison of two imaginary communities, each with 100 individuals divided among a richness of four species. However, in one of the communities 97 individuals are of one species, and there are only one each of the other three species. In the other community, there is a more even 25 individuals of each of the four species. These two communities have the same species richness but vastly different **evenness** (sometimes called equitability), which is a measure of the similarity of the relative abundances of species within a community.

Evenness is important as an indicator of the likelihood of encountering species within a community. Imagine that you are in the field sampling plants, small

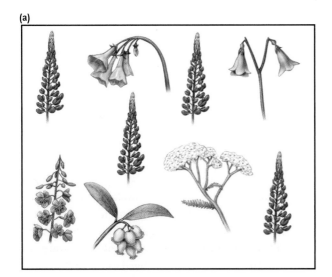

(a)

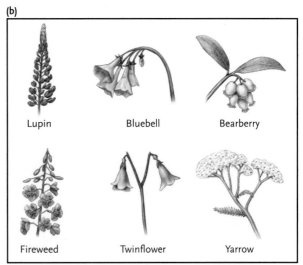

(b)

Lupin Bluebell Bearberry

Fireweed Twinflower Yarrow

FIGURE 12.10 Richness and Evenness Both communities have the same richness of six species, but (b) has greater evenness because the relative abundances of the species are more similar than in (a).

mammals, or other kinds of organisms within a community. If you ask the question "What is the probability of correctly predicting the species of the next individual that I randomly sample?", then you are asking a question about the both the species richness and the evenness of the community. These two indicators are combined in a third measure used by ecologists: the species diversity (see below). In general, a community in which the answer to the above question is highly predictable has relatively low species diversity, and diversity is higher in one with a lower predictability.

Another problem with species richness is that it does not account for the actual identity of species, including whether they are native or alien to the local biogeography (note that this is also true of other biodiversity indicators examined in this section, such as species diversity). For habitats that have been invaded by non-native species, this is an important consideration because the presence and/or dominance by aliens represent a degradation of habitat quality (and of ecological integrity; see Chapter 17) **(Figure 12.11)**. For this reason, in spite of some ecological benefits that may be associated with higher levels of community-level biodiversity, conservation managers would not seek to maximize that objective if it were accomplished by adding non-native species (see Chapter 14 for a more detailed examination of invasive aliens).

These are important issues with the use of species richness as an indicator of biodiversity, but they can be accommodated by using additional measures, such as those described below, and also by discussing the identity of species, such as any that are aliens. Consequently, species richness is still a commonly used indicator in ecological studies.

In communities with a small area, and in those with few species, measuring species richness may be a straightforward task and the estimate can be quite accurate. However, in larger or diverse communities it is difficult to get a complete tally of all of the species present. Moreover, this task may be confounded by taxonomic difficulties, because it requires specialized biological expertise to properly identify species of plants, animals, and microorganisms.

In any event, the amount of sampling effort has a large influence on the number of species that is detected, and therefore on the accuracy of a measurement of species richness. In general, the larger the area searched, the longer the time spent doing so, and the more observers that are working will all affect how many species are discovered. Of course, the most common species in a community are likely to be sampled in the first few plots that are randomly examined within a large study area. Then, as more and more plots are added to the sample, many of the infrequent species will also be captured. However, the sampling cannot proceed indefinitely. At some point, few or no species are added to the list and the measure of richness becomes asymptotic despite increasing sampling effort **(Figure 12.12)**.

This is an example of the use of **rarefaction** in ecology, a technique for assessing species richness based on the results of cumulative sampling. This is usually done using a rarefaction curve, which is a plot of the number of species as a function of the sampling effort, measured as either the number of samples, their collective area or volume, or the amount of time spent sampling. Closer to the left-hand side of **Figure 12.12**, where the number of samples is small, the slope of the curve is steep, which indicates that many species are yet to be encountered. With additional sampling the curve eventually levels off, and the point where that happens is an indicator of the total species richness in the area being investigated.

Species Diversity Indices

Species diversity is a commonly reported indicator that accommodates both the number of species present (species richness) and their relative abundances (evenness). For this purpose, evenness may be estimated as the relative population size (i.e., the abundance of a particular species divided by the total of all species) or the relative biomass. There are many indices to estimate these aspects of biodiversity, but in the section we examine only several of the most commonly used ones.

The Shannon-Weiner Diversity Index (H'; sometimes known as the Shannon Index) is a commonly used

FIGURE 12.11 Identity Is Also Important Species richness and diversity are useful indicators, but they do not account for the identity of species in a community. This can be an important problem with non-native species, which may become abundant in natural habitats and cause serious ecological problems. The dominant plant in the ground vegetation of this lowland hardwood forest in southern Ontario is garlic mustard (*Alliaria petiolata*), an invasive plant that damages native species by crowding them out of understory habitat.

Bill Freedman

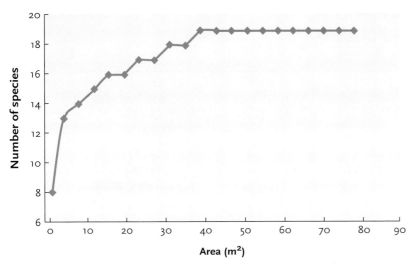

FIGURE 12.12 A Species-Area Curve These data show that within a community or other study area (such as a large park), the observed species richness increases as the sampled area becomes larger, eventually reaching an asymptote where no additional species are added. These data are for an alpine meadow community in Kluane National Park, Yukon.

SOURCE: Unpublished data of J. McLaren and R. Turkington.

indicator of species diversity. It is calculated using the following equation:

(12.1)
$$H' = -\sum_{i=1}^{s} p_i \log_e p_i$$

where p_i, often estimated as relative abundance, is an estimate of the probability that any randomly encountered individual will be of a designated, ith species. The value of H' is greatest if evenness is maximized—if all species have the same relative abundance, and it is least when a particular species is strongly dominant. See Ecology in Depth 12.4 for an example of how to calculate this commonly reported index.

Simpson's index (D) is another indicator of diversity. It estimates the probability that two randomly sampled individuals will be of the same species, and is calculated using the following equation:

(12.2)
$$D = 1 - \frac{\Sigma n(n-1)}{N(N-1)}$$

where n = the number of individuals of a particular species and N = the total individuals of all species. The value of D may range from 0 (no diversity) to 1 (high diversity).

Values of these various indices of biodiversity are compared in **Table 12.4**, which shows two theoretical communities, each composed of five species and 100 individuals. Both communities have the same species richness, but their diversity as measured by the Shannon and Simpson's functions are different on the basis of the equitability of distribution of individuals among species. In general, the Shannon and Simpson's indices are better indicators because they accommodate differences among species in their rarity and commonness, whereas species richness does not do this.

Note that the species richness and diversity *within* an ecological community is referred to as **alpha (α) diversity**.

TABLE 12.4	Species Richness and Diversity for Two Sample Populations	
	Abundance (Number of Individuals)	
Species	Community A	Community B
A	96	20
B	1	20
C	1	20
D	1	20
E	1	20
Species richness	5	5
Shannon-Wiener (H')	0.2	1.3
Simpson's (D)	0.079	0.808

However, ecologists may also compare the differences in species composition *among* communities—this is called **beta (β) diversity**. Beta diversity is low when the species composition is similar among communities and highest when they have no species in common.

Richness of Communities

At the level of an ecoscape, biodiversity is related to the variety of distinct ecological communities, as well as the heterogeneity of their spatial distribution and dynamics over time. A landscape or seascape that is blanketed with a single community has little biodiversity at this level, compared with one that supports a rich and dynamic mosaic of types. This is called **gamma diversity (γ)**, or the richness of different communities within a larger study region. This kind of diversity is especially low in landscapes that have been converted into uses primarily for agriculture or plantation forestry, whereas previously they had been naturally occupied by a rich mixture of terrestrial and wetland communities.

ECOLOGY IN DEPTH 12.4
Calculating Species Diversity

The Shannon Index is one of the most common ways of expressing species diversity, particularly in studies of community ecology. Although the index and its calculation are not very complicated, they can be a bit tricky, so we have provided a worked example to illustrate their use.

Table 1 is based on real-world data for two understorey communities in boreal forest in the southern Yukon (Turkington et al., 2002). The plots were initially surveyed in 1990, and then for 10 years were treated annually with fertilizer, while also being enclosed by fences to reduce herbivory by mammals. Note that 10 years of these treatments only slightly increased the cover of vegetation, from 200 percent to 214 percent, but there was a marked decline in species richness from 23 to 12, and in diversity from 2.00 to 1.56. Cover can exceed 100 percent because of overlapping layers of foliage. Only the abundant species are listed here.

TABLE 1	Calculating Species Diversity in Two Sample Populations							
	Abundance (%)		Proportion (p_i)		$\log_e p_i$		$p_i \log_e p_i$	
Species	1990	1999	1990	1999	1990	1999	1990	1999
Festuca altaica (Altai fescue)	82.4	87.1	0.412	0.406	−0.886	−0.900	−0.365	−0.366
Lupinus arcticus (lupine)	28.4	1.8	0.142	0.008	−1.952	−4.808	−0.277	−0.039
Linnaea borealis (twinflower)	24.0	1.4	0.120	0.006	−2.119	−5.049	−0.255	−0.032
Arctostaphylos uva-ursi (bearberry)	20.8	1.3	0.104	0.006	−2.265	−5.145	−0.235	−0.030
Mosses & liverworts	13.9	0.0	0.069	0.000	−2.667	−	−0.185	0.000
Salix glauca (grayleaf willow)	6.1	6.3	0.031	0.029	−3.485	−3.535	−0.107	−0.103
Achillea millefolium (yarrow)	5.9	28.9	0.029	0.135	−3.526	−2.005	−0.104	−0.270
Mertensia paniculata (bluebell)	3.0	30.5	0.015	0.142	−4.198	−1.950	−0.063	−0.277
Epilobium angustifolium (fireweed)	1.4	53.3	0.007	0.248	−4.979	−1.393	−0.034	−0.346
14 additional species (in 1990) and 4 (in 1999), with a total abundance of 1%	1.0	1.0	0.005	0.005	−25.297	−5.368	−0.027	−0.025
Species Richness	23	12						
Total % cover	199.8	214.4	$H' = -\sum\limits_{i=1}^{s} p_i \log_e p_i = 1.997 - 1.564$					

SOURCE: Turkington, R., E. John, S. Watson, and P. Seccombe-Hett. 2002. "The effects of fertilization and herbivory on the herbaceous vegetation of the boreal forest in northwestern Canada: A ten-year study," *Journal of Ecology*, 90: 325–227.

Indicators of biodiversity at the landscape level might be examined over a large area that has been designated for the purposes of management (such as a park), or for an ecological study (such as an ecozone or ecoregion; Chapter 11), or for a political purpose (such as a country or province). The indicators typically involve measures that parallel those used for ecological communities:

- *Richness*: This involves the number of distinctive community types (patches) occurring within a large designated area.

- *Shannon-Wiener and Simpson's diversity*: These are computed from community richness and the relative area of the types, calculated using the same equations as noted above.

- *Other criteria*: These relate to the spatial complexity of ecoscapes and are discussed in Chapter 13, such as the shape, size, connectedness, age-class adjacency, and ratios of edge to area of patches.

CHAPTER SUMMARY

(LO12.1)

- Biodiversity is the very fabric of life, comprising all of the variation of genes, organisms, and ecosystems. It represents the richness of all life in the biosphere. Biodiversity is a long-term result of the genesis of life on this planet, and of its evolutionary modification over time in response to environmental changes.

(LO12.2)

- In general, biodiversity is much richer in tropical biomes than in those at higher latitudes. This is especially the case of tropical forests, which support more biodiversity than any other kinds of ecosystem. A key reason for the lower amounts of biodiversity in higher latitudes, such as anywhere in Canada, compared to the tropics, is the fact that most of the existing temperate, boreal, and arctic regions were released from glaciation no more than 10–12 000 years ago. Consequently, the habitats are relatively young and have not had time to evolve many endemic species or to develop the extreme complexity of ecological relationships that exist in older tropical ecosystems.

(LO12.3)

- Biodiversity is important because it is useful in many ways to people and their economy. In addition, all elements of biodiversity are unique and that gives them intrinsic value, which is in itself a good reason for their conservation.

(LO12.4)

- Ecologists have a variety of indicators to measure biodiversity at the levels of genetics, within communities, or at larger levels of landscapes and seascapes. The most basic indicators are the numbers of species that are present (species richness), their richness coupled with relative abundances (species diversity), and whether communities have species in common (Simpson index).

(LO12.5)

- Ecologists believe that higher levels of biodiversity generally represent a desirable condition. A higher level of genetic diversity may allow for adaptive responses to environmental change. High levels of species richness and diversity in communities and on ecoscapes may provide a degree of functional redundancy that allow for stability even when environmental change eliminates some of the species. However, alien elements of biodiversity are not as highly valued as indigenous ones, and when abundant they are considered to detract from ecological integrity.

QUESTIONS FOR REVIEW AND DISCUSSION

1. What is biodiversity? Explain how it exists at several hierarchical levels.
2. What is an endemic species? Why are they uncommon in Canada, compared with tropical places?
3. Why is biodiversity important? Provide examples of how it affects your own life.
4. Explain the notion of intrinsic value, and why it is relevant to biodiversity.
5. The data in the table below relate to the cover (an estimate of abundance, measured in percentage) of the plant species in two tundra communities on Baffin Island. For each community, calculate the species richness, Shannon-Wiener diversity, and Simpson's index.

Species	Community 1	Community 2
Arctagrostis latifolia (a grass)	1	1
Carex bigelowii (a sedge)	2	0
Cassiope tetragona (arctic heather)	5	25
Dryas integrifolia (arctic avens)	40	25
Empretrum nigrum (black crowberry)	17	5
Pedicularis capitata (capitate lousewort)	3	0
Salix arctica (arctic willow)	25	10
Saxifraga tricuspidata (prickly saxifrage)	2	0
Saxifraga oppositifolia (purple saxifrage)	3	5
Silene acaule (moss phlox)	1	1

Landscape Ecology

LEARNING OBJECTIVES

After studying this chapter you should be able to:

1. Define landscape ecology and describe how it uses hierarchical scales in space and time.

2. Discuss how European and North American approaches to landscape ecology can apply to Canadian urban, rural, and wildland settings.

3. Explain the importance of landscape elements (patch, corridor, and matrix).

4. Understand the purpose of basic landscape metrics.

5. Use spatial and graphical approaches to understand how landscapes have changed historically and will do so in the future.

6. Describe landscape-scale functions (processes), with particular attention to the water cycle and disturbances.

7. Understand the importance of remote sensing, geographic information systems (*GIS*), and computer modelling as tools for working in landscape ecology.

8. Explain the importance of landscape ecology in pure ecology and in practical applications.

13.1 Introduction to Landscape Ecology

A **landscape** may be defined as a heterogeneous land area with repeated forms at any scale. Within that context, **landscape ecology** is the integrative, scale-related investigation of the structure, function, and dynamics of ecosystems (see Section 1.2). There are five core themes of landscape ecology (McGarigal, 2009b): (1) detecting and quantifying the spatial **patterns** of ecosystems (spatially repeated landscape elements); (2) characterizing abiotic and biotic influences on the development of patterns, including landforms, species and their interactions, and anthropogenic factors; (3) understanding the implications of patterns for populations, communities, and landscape-scale ecosystems; (4) characterizing and quantifying the dynamics of patterns and processes (such as disturbances and movements of materials) over space and time; and (5) managing landscapes and their dynamics to achieve conservation and economic objectives.

Definitions of landscape vary greatly. However, an organism-orientated approach allows us to conceptualize a landscape at any scale that is relevant to a particular problem being examined. In this sense, a landscape may be only a square metre from the perspective of an insect, or hundreds of square kilometres for a wide-ranging mammal.

Clearly, because we examine landscapes in a scale context, we must clarify what is meant by "large" and "small" dimensions. However, the meaning of these terms is confused in ordinary parlance, and so ecologists use the term **coarse scale** to refer to a large area (which typically is examined in relatively little detail) and **fine scale** to denote the opposite. This is illustrated in **Figure 13.1** for an area of farms, woodlots, and cities of southern Ontario. The system is hierarchical and so landscape mosaics cascade downward from coarse land-use scales to finer patterns such as those of plants growing in seams of dirt among paving stones in a driveway.

Landscapes are exceedingly complex ecosystems whose components interact in an intriguing, nonlinear, and sometimes unpredictable fashion (Holling, 1992). The ecology of streams that support Pacific salmon in western Canada illustrates this principle. In this system,

avalanches and debris flows cause trees to topple into streams. These disturbances increase the abundance of woody debris that provides nutrients and physical structure that are important to many aquatic species, including salmon (Nakamura et al., 2000). A moderate accumulation of woody materials may improve salmon habitat, but if the debris is too abundant the fish cannot migrate upstream and potential breeding habitat becomes unavailable. Thus, erosion and other local factors can mediate the ability of salmon to spawn and of their young to survive.

In addition, there are cascading effects of these influences on nursery streams. For instance, if breeding is successful, juvenile salmon migrate to the ocean, where they feed and grow to adulthood. Oceanic salmon are food for large predators, such as orcas and seals, and are an important fishery for humans. When mature salmon eventually migrate back to their natal river to

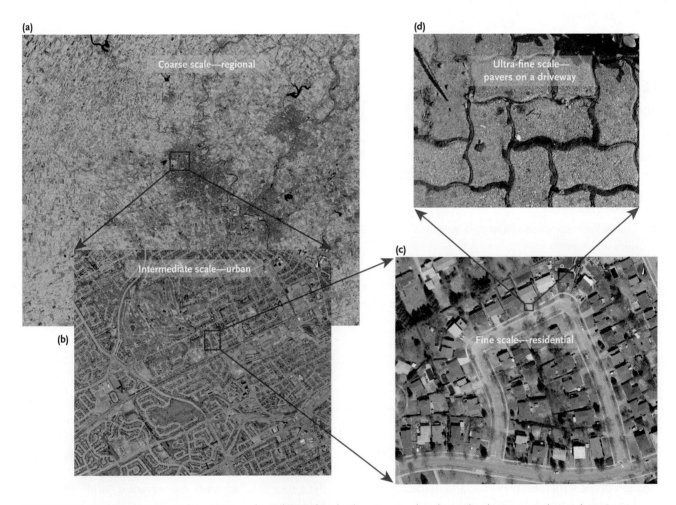

FIGURE 13.1 Landscape Ecology Relates to Hierarchy and Spatial Scale These images show hierarchical patterns in the southern Ontario region that encompasses Guelph, Kitchener-Waterloo, and Cambridge. (a) At the coarsest scale, in a false-colour image, a rectangular pattern exists as a dominant matrix of agricultural land (light green and pink), with remnant woodlots (dark green) and urbanized patches (purple and grey). (b) At an intermediate scale, a suburban mosaic is structured artificially by a grid of streets. (c) At a fine scale, the pattern of the urban ecosystem is influenced by house-lots and patterns of landscaping. (d) At an ultra-fine scale, a micro-ecosystem of small plants and mosses exists as a network among paving stones in a driveway.

SOURCE: (a) Landsat.org, Global Observatory for Ecosystem Services, Michigan State University (http://landsat.org); (b) and (c) Geographic Information Systems (GIS), The City of Kitchener. http://www.kitchener.ca/en/businessinkitchener/gis_interactive_mapping.asp; (d) Roger Suffling.

spawn, they act as a "conveyor belt" that takes packages of nutrients inland from the ocean, helping to sustain the productivity of streams (Schindler et al., 2003). Moreover, bears drag salmon carcasses into streamside forest, thereby enhancing the nutrient supply in that terrestrial part of the watershed (Quinn et al., 2009) (See cover illustration). Clearly, all parts of this large-scale system are interconnected, and ecological properties emerge in a landscape that cannot easily be predicted from its component ecosystems. Note that there are also aquatic "landscapes." They include seascapes and riverscapes, as well as an integration of these with terrestrial areas, as in watersheds. The term **ecoscape** is useful in this context—it refers to coarse-scale ("large-scale") patterns and ecological processes occurring in the contexts of terrestrial and/or aquatic environments.

The Importance of Landscape Ecology

Landscape ecology can help us understand ecosystems because it allows for novel insights into ecological problems. This can be illustrated by the work of Jens Roland (1993) of the University of Alberta, who investigated forest tent caterpillars (*Malacosoma disstria*) in Ontario forests **(Figure 13.2)**. This native moth periodically irrupts in huge numbers. Its larvae feed on aspen trees (*Populus tremuloides*), which are defoliated at a regional scale, with important ecological and economic consequences. Rather surprisingly, Roland found that the abundance of the aspen host on the landscape had little influence on the persistence of the outbreak. He then hypothesized that regions in which the forest had become fragmented would have longer-lasting irruptions. Theoretical studies

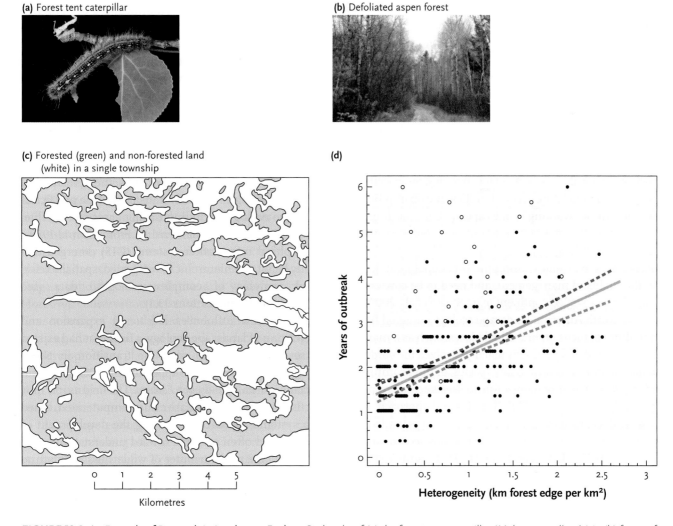

(a) Forest tent caterpillar

(b) Defoliated aspen forest

(c) Forested (green) and non-forested land (white) in a single township

(d)

Years of outbreak

Heterogeneity (km forest edge per km²)

FIGURE 13.2 An Example of Research in Landscape Ecology Outbreaks of (a) the forest tent caterpillar (*Malacosoma disstria*) in (b) forest of trembling aspen (*Populus tremuloides*) will (c) last longer where there has been extensive fragmentation of the original forest by land clearance and conversion. Each dot on the graph (d) represents one township. Although there are more aspen trees in the disturbed townships, the length of the outbreak is not related to the amount of aspen, but rather to the degree of fragmentation of its forest.

SOURCES: (a) Thérèse Arcand, Natural Resources Canada, Canadian Forestry Service; (b) Doug Collicutt/Nature North Zine; (c) With kind permission from Springer Science+Business Media: Roland, J. 1993. "Large-scale forest fragmentation increases the duration of tent caterpillar outbreak," *Oecologia*, 93: 25–30. Map 1C, p. 26; (d) With kind permission from Springer Science+Business Media: Roland, J. 1993. "Large-scale forest fragmentation increases the duration of tent caterpillar outbreak," *Oecologia*, 93: 25–30. Figure 2, page 27.

Geographical Information Systems (GIS) are used to model spatial systems using computer-manipulated maps. A GIS system is a software program and hardware that enables a user to capture, store, manipulate, analyze, manage, and present geographical data. A computer holds and analyzes the data, a scanner and plotting table are used to input new information to the computer, and a plotter, printer, or video screen are used to display results.

Each set of information is either imported from a standard source (e.g., topographic information), or the user makes new *layers* to represent that information **(Figure 1)**. An example of a GIS layer would be a map of the locations of all the known turtle nesting sites in a study area. All the layers are represented in a standard format so that they can be overlaid in useful combinations. GIS systems normally have a *relational database*,

which is a set of high-level spreadsheets that relates all of the layers to each other in a tabular format. The layers can be represented by raster/grid information or, more efficiently, by polygons. The information assists in studies and guides planning **(Figure 2)**.

GIS systems are widely used in fields of study, such as ecology, forestry, and soil science that use mapped data. They are also used in nonscience disciplines such as archaeology and land-use planning, as well as in technological applications ranging from where tanks should be positioned on a battlefield to where to establish fast-food outlets. GIS technology not only displays data but also, increasingly, influences how we perceive our spatial world.

GIS input layers can include original research data or, in many cases, standardized regional information built up over many years by governments,

companies, or NGOs. Geocoding is the process of converting locational data (e.g., a concession and lot number as the location of an organism) to latitude and longitude that can be entered into a GIS system.

Note, however, that a *GIS is not a GPS!* A GPS (Global Positioning System). GPS enables users to locate their position on Earth's surface, and in some cases, their altitude. It does this by referencing stationary satellites that send signals to GPS units. One can now buy relatively inexpensive and accurate GPS units, but even more sophisticated units with submeter precision are used when needed. GPS units are also integrated into other technology, being included in smart phones, land survey equipment, marine buoys, and radio-tagging units used to track research animals. GPS users commonly upload their georeferenced data to a GIS database.

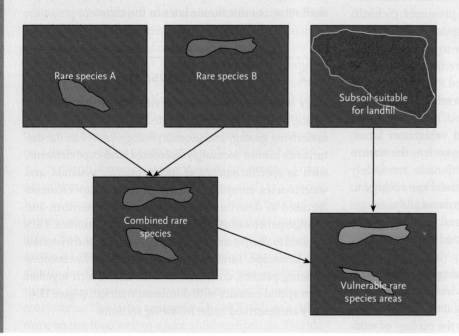

FIGURE 1 GIS A geographical information system integrates computer hardware and software to analyze spatial information in "layers."

environmental influences that affect the distribution and abundance of species and thus produce spatially distinct ecological communities.

Patches can arise because of the underlying structure of the landscape, such as its topography, moisture, or geochemistry **(Figure 13.5)**, or they may be created by disturbances such as wildfire, flooding, or clear-cutting.

Although Forman and Godron (1986) defined five kinds of patches created by disturbances, patch formation often has multiple causes **(Figure 13.6)**. For example, the three, round volcanic hills shown in **Figure 13.6e** retain much of their natural forest today because their rugged topography made their areas unsuitable for the agricultural conversions that

Data accumulation in layers
(in relational databases)

Output—plotter/printer, etc.

Software analysis in computer

Operator directs GIS system/
interprets output

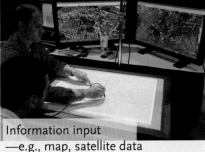

Information input
—e.g., map, satellite data

Digitizing or scanning map/airphoto information

Field data input

Collecting field information; here using GPS

FIGURE 2 Using GIS to Develop New Information for Ecological Studies and to Guide Planning When the layers concerning rare species and areas whose soils are safe for a landfill are overlain, spatial information is available to integrate land-use planning and biological conservation.

SOURCES: Photographs: centre, top, bottom left, Scott Prokop/Shutterstock.com; middle right, tmcphotos/Shutterstock,com; bottom right, photograph by Andrew Stevens, USGS; top left, Federal Geographic Data Committee.

occurred on nearby sedimentary lowlands. However, even before the European settlement the forest of these volcanic hills would have differed from that of the surrounding lowlands and would have constituted distinct patches on the landscape.

Patches have transitions where they abut other kinds of patches. Examples are a transition from forest to grass-land, or where terrestrial vegetation meets a lake. Where the change is spatially abrupt it can be called an **edge** or step cline. Alternatively there may be a relatively gradual transition from one patch to another that exhibits characteristics of both types and is known as an **ecotone** (see also Section 10.3). A coastal salt marsh is an ecosystem with distinct zonation—at the lower (seaward) edge is a

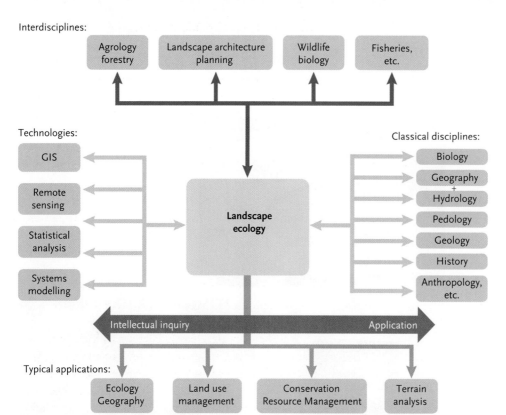

FIGURE 13.3 Professional **Cultures** This conceptual model of landscape ecology shows the kinds of disciplinary and interdisciplinary fields that are engaged, the tools that are used, and the sorts of fundamental and applied investigations that are pursued.

Interdisciplines:

Agrology forestry

Landscape architecture planning

Wildlife biology

Fisheries, etc.

Technologies:

GIS

Remote sensing

Statistical analysis

Systems modelling

Landscape ecology

Classical disciplines:

Biology

Geography + Hydrology

Pedology

Geology

History

Anthropology, etc.

Intellectual inquiry   Application

Typical applications:

Ecology Geography

Land use management

Conservation Resource Management

Terrain analysis

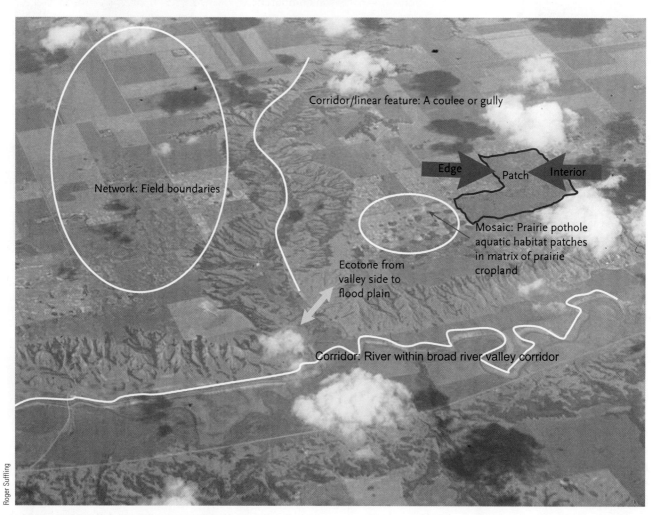

Corridor/linear feature: A coulee or gully

Edge   Patch   Interior

Network: Field boundaries

Mosaic: Prairie pothole aquatic habitat patches in matrix of prairie cropland

Ecotone from valley side to flood plain

Corridor: River within broad river valley corridor

Roger Suffling

FIGURE 13.4 Landscape Elements This example is from the Qu'appelle Valley, Saskatchewan. The elements include mosaics, linear features, matrices, and patches, some occurring at various scales.

FIGURE 13.5 An Example of a Landscape Structure This image, from Gros Morne National Park in western Newfoundland, shows the visible boundary between two kinds of ecological communities. In this case, an inherent edge is determined by a rapid spatial change in the local geology and soil type. The lower community is influenced by naturally occurring serpentine minerals, which are stressful to plants because they contain toxic nickel and cobalt and are highly deficient in the nutrients calcium, phosphorus, and nitrogen. Plants growing in serpentine-influenced soils are typically stunted in growth form, and they include species that are more usually found in arctic-alpine habitats. The higher community in the image is a stand of mature boreal forest growing on a less-stressful nonserpentine site, and it is more typical of the region.

an abrupt edge or a gradual ecotone. For example, at relatively fine scales, a salt marsh can be studied as a number of distinct communities and patch types. At a coarser scale, however, salt marshes are a land–ocean ecotone whose width depends on the steepness of the coastal gradient and height of the local tides **(Figure 13.7)**. At an even coarser scale, the transition will be represented as an edge.

Patch shape is also an important consideration, because it affects the configuration and length of edges **(Figure 13.9)**. A circular patch has the smallest ratio of edge to area, and so will have the largest proportion of interior habitat for any given patch size. Conversely a patch with a highly irregular shape will have a large amount of edge in relation to its area. Patch shape is potentially influenced by inherent factors in the landscape as well as the history and kinds of disturbances.

A sufficiently large patch will have an **interior habitat** within which there are distinct environmental conditions and a particular community. The patch interior is surrounded by an ecotonal zone that is influenced by adjacent patches. Small patches may have only an ecotonal zone, without a distinct interior that is uninfluenced by edge conditions.

Certain species may be primarily restricted to interiors or to ecotones of patches. For example, ruderal plants are prominent in fragmented landscapes with abundant edge habitat, but are rare in extensively forested areas. This is also true of some animals, such as the red-tailed hawk (*Buteo jamaicensis*), which in southern Ontario is found mainly in regions with fragmented forest occurring in small patches, and even in suburbs. In contrast, the red-shouldered hawk (*Buteo linearis*) requires a more extensively forested landscape with bigger treed patches having interior zones (Bosakowski and Smith, 1997).

Many people associate interiors and ecotonal zones with forested landscapes, but the concept is broader than that. In fact, any patch in any ecoscape type, including grassland and coral reefs, may have ecotonal and interior zones.

Corridors

A **corridor** is a linear feature that differs from the **matrix** on either side. A corridor may be natural in origin, such as a stream, river, or avalanche track through mountain forest. It may also be anthropogenic, such as a right-of-way for a road or transmission line, or a treed hedgerow between agricultural fields.

A corridor can provide a passage through which animals and plants can move between patches. This **connectivity** may allow a landscape with only limited areas of suitable habitat patches, such as older forest,

community dominated by marine species, and at the upper margin by ones tolerant of a wide range of salinity because the higher terrain is only infrequently flooded by tides **(Figure 13.7)**.

Because species experience an ecotone differently, their individual reactions to the environmental transitions will vary. Some species, such as moose (*Alces alces*), take advantage of ecotones and edges by using resources from both of the adjacent patches. The example in **Figure 13.8** shows one classification of edges.

Whether a spatial change in physical environment is gradual or sudden can control the development of either

Kinds of Patches

(a)

(b)

(c)

(d)

(e)

FIGURE 13.6 The Kinds of Patches Identified by Forman and Godron (1986) and Forman (1995) (a) A spot patch: this disturbance-caused patch is being created by a prescribed burn in a tract of boreal forest. (b) A regenerated patch: an aspen (*Populus tremuloides*) clone is spreading onto grazing land in the Rocky Mountains, with more success to the right of the fence where there is less pressure from browsing by livestock. (c) Remnant patches: eucalypt groves among dairy pastures developed from converted forest in Victoria, Australia. (d) An ephemeral patch/introduced patch: corn and soybean cropland on a karst hillside in Guangxi, China. (e) An environmental patch created by a sharp environmental discontinuity: in this case, three plugs of ancient volcanic rocks in the St. Lawrence Valley of Quebec (circular, speckled patches) have retained their forest cover because their steep and rugged terrain was unsuitable for agricultural conversion, in contrast to the surrounding fields on low-lying sedimentary materials.

SOURCES: (a) Spot patch photo (fire): Terry Curran; (b) Charles E. Kay; (c) Roger Suffling; (d) Yuqing Huang; (e) Image Science and Analysis Laboratory, NASA-Johnson Space Center. "The Gateway to Astronaut Photography of Earth." <http://eol.jsc.nasa.gov/scripts/sseop/LargeImageAccess.pl?directory=EFS/highres/ISS014&filename=ISS014-E-19807.JPG&filesize=982258>.

FIGURE 13.7 The Width of an Ecotone May Depend on the Sharpness of an Environmental Gradient On flat, sheltered, coastal areas a gradual transition from land to sea allows the development of salt marshes that flood and drain twice daily with the tides: this is a classic ecotonal community between marine and terrestrial habitats. However, where the land rises steeply from the sea the transition is spatially abrupt, as on the far shore of this image, which shows coastal ecosystems on Cape Breton, Nova Scotia.

to support extensive but viable **metapopulations** of various species. Metapopulations are spatially discrete subpopulations that are linked by dispersal, so there is gene flow among them. This is illustrated by a study by Bennett and colleagues (1994) of Carleton University, who found that chipmunks (*Tamias striata*) used shrubby fencerows to move between patches of forested habitat in a landscape dominated by agricultural fields **(Figure 13.10)**.

A corridor that facilitates the movement of one species between patches may not function well for others with different habitat needs. In fact, what is a corridor for one species may be a barrier to others—for example, a road may serve as a corridor to spread ruderal plants, but it can be a barrier for many animals. The quality of the habitat between patches in which a species lives is important. If this matrix is not so different from the primary habitat of a species, or if it can be crossed quickly, then it is **permeable** to movements even if it cannot be lived in on a long-term basis.

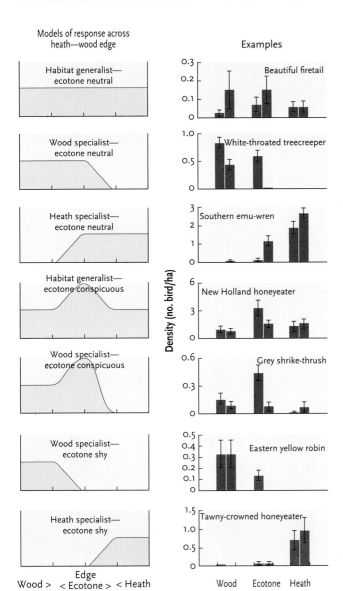

Models of response across heath–wood edge

- Habitat generalist— ecotone neutral
- Wood specialist— ecotone neutral
- Heath specialist— ecotone neutral
- Habitat generalist— ecotone conspicuous
- Wood specialist— ecotone conspicuous
- Wood specialist— ecotone shy
- Heath specialist— ecotone shy

Edge
Wood > < Ecotone > < Heath

Examples

Density (no. bird/ha)

- Beautiful firetail
- White-throated treecreeper
- Southern emu-wren
- New Holland honeyeater
- Grey shrike-thrush
- Eastern yellow robin
- Tawny-crowned honeyeater

Wood   Ecotone   Heath

FIGURE 13.8 Various Species Experience an Ecotone Differently In this Australian case, different birds use the resources in the patches on either side of an ecotone in varying ways. The types identified here follow the typology of Odum and Odum (1959).

SOURCE: Used with permission of the Ecological Society of America, from Baker, J., K. French, and R.J. Whelan, 2002. "The edge effect and ecotonal species: Bird communities across a natural edge in southeastern Australia," *Ecology*, 83 (11): 3048–3059. Figure 7, p. 3054; permission conveyed through Copyright Clearance Center, Inc.

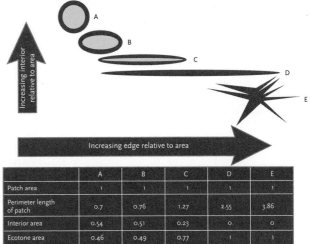

Increasing interior relative to area

Increasing edge relative to area

	A	B	C	D	E
Patch area	1	1	1	1	1
Perimeter length of patch	0.7	0.76	1.27	2.55	3.86
Interior area	0.54	0.51	0.23	0	0
Ecotone area	0.46	0.49	0.77	1	1

FIGURE 13.9 The Influence of Patch Shape on Its Ecological Characteristics Each of the hypothetical patches has the same area. Patch interiors are indicated by yellow, and edge/ecotones by blue. The effective width of the edge habitat is influenced by the requirements of species under study.

routinely used by animals such as elk (*Cervus canadensis*), wolf (*Canis lupus*), and black bear (*Ursus americanus*) (Clevenger et al., 2002). However, in the absence of such evidence, one should not assume that a corridor provides a useful conservation function. A more conservative approach is to regard untested landscape corridors as being linear habitat features that may benefit some species.

Networks

A **network** is a series of interconnected linear elements, often surrounding patches of another type. A natural example is the network of aquatic connections that exist among lotic (streams and rivers) and lentic (ponds and lakes) waterbodies within a watershed. In the sub-arctic, freeze–thaw action makes for intricate networks based on soil characteristics **(Figure 13.12)**. An anthropogenic example is the system of hedgerows that is often seen in agricultural regions.

Mosaic and Matrix

In most landscapes, the mix of elements forms a **mosaic**— a spatially integrated complex of patches, corridors, and networks that gives a landscape its ecological character. A mosaic usually consists of a predominant cover type that is known as a matrix community, in which are embedded island-like patches of other kinds of ecosystems. Two main groups of factors that affect the character of mosaics are (1) the inherent characteristics of the climate, geology, and topography and (2) dynamic influences based on disturbance and succession. Most mosaics are influenced by both of these factors.

The functioning of corridors has been widely discussed on a theoretical basis. However, to some degree the empirical testing of hypotheses has been outpaced by an enthusiastic real-world implementation of corridors by planners, foresters, and resource managers. Indeed, some recent publications are critical of the strong emphasis that has been placed on connectivity (e.g., Hodgson et al., 2011). However, other studies have found that connections can function well as, for instance, with wildlife "underpasses" and "overpasses" that have been installed across the Trans-Canada Highway in Banff National Park **(Figure 13.11)**. They are being

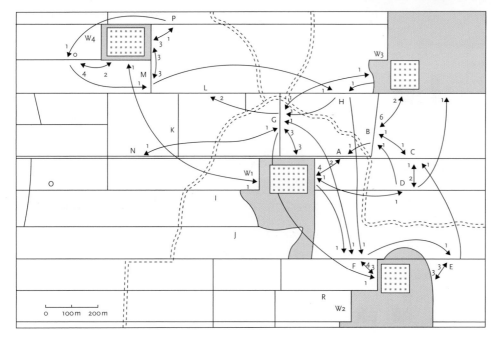

FIGURE 13.10 Interpatch Movements and Corridors This map depicts the numbers and recorded movements of chipmunks (*Tamias striata*) between patches of woodland (W1–W4) in a largely agricultural landscape with fencerows (A–R). Most interpatch movements involve animals travelling along shrubby fencerows at the margins of the open fields. Arrows indicate the direction of movement, but not the pathway. Fencerows are represented as thin solid lines and streams are dashed lines.

SOURCE: Modified from: Bennett, A.F., K. Henein, and G. Merriam. 1994. "Corridor use and the elements of corridor quality: Chipmunks and fencerows in a farmland mosaic," *Biological Conservation*, 68: 155–165. Figure 1, p. 159, with permission from Elsevier.

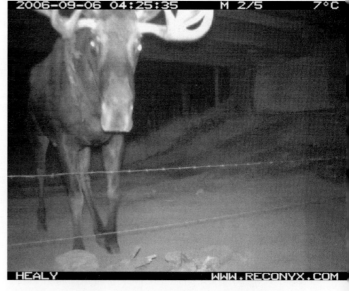

FIGURE 13.11 Fragmentation of Habitats The Trans-Canada Highway that runs through Banff National Park fragments critical habitats and is a barrier to wildlife movement. To facilitate the movements of large, wide-ranging animals such as grizzly bear, wolverine, elk, and moose, overpasses and underpasses were constructed. The rest of the highway was fenced in a way that directs animals to the underpasses or overpasses, which are now providing connections between fragmented habitats and allow for gene flow between subpopulations.

The processes that generate and maintain mosaic patterns are a key topic in landscape ecology. Mosaics can arise from underlying physiography and from ecological and other influences. For example, many of the numerous wetland complexes of the prairie region **(Figure 3.13)** occur in depressions created in former times by heavy blocks of glacial ice. The water that now fills these wetlands, which are known as "potholes," is primarily maintained by snow-melt and rainfall, so that fluctuations of weather affect the wetlands' hydrology. However, the vitality of the pothole ecosystem for breeding waterfowl is also tied to human activities. Farmers tend to plough farther into the pothole depressions in dry years, thereby damaging the marsh habitat. The cultivation pressure is also affected by the profitability of the farm, which in turn relates to commodity prices and other economic influences. Therefore, the pothole mosaic arises from inherent geological factors, and is also affected by

(a)

Roger Suffling

FIGURE 13.12 Networks in Landscape Ecology
(a) A network of hedgerows in a cultural landscape in Worcestershire, United Kingdom.
(b) Ice-wedge polygons dictate a vegetation network in peatland of the Hudson Bay lowlands of Manitoba.

(b)

Reproduced with the permission of Natural Resources Canada 2013, courtesy of the Geological Survey of Canada (Photo 2001–120 by Lynda Dredge).

U.S. Fish and Wildlife Services: http://www.fws.gov/Contaminants/images/ aerialpotholewetlands.jpg

FIGURE 13.13 An Aerial View of Pothole Ponds and Lakes in a Region of Prairie in Saskatchewan

13.2 STRUCTURE OF LANDSCAPES

Lenore Fahrig: Landscapes for Sustainable Populations

FIGURE 1 Lenore Fahrig

Lenore Fahrig of Carleton University studies the effects of landscape structure on the distribution, abundance, and persistence of populations. In this large-scale meaning, the structural attributes of landscapes include the amounts and spatial arrangement of land-cover types, such as tracts of various kinds of forest, wetlands, or anthropogenic patches, as well as linear features such as rivers and roads. Landscape structure is important because it affects populations by exerting influences on factors such as reproduction, mortality, and movement. This work is of inherent interest, but it is also of great applied value because of the ways that humans are changing the structure of landscapes, such as by activities related to forestry, agriculture, and urbanization. Consequently, the research of Fahrig and her colleagues is highly relevant to land-use decisions and their environmental impacts **(Figure 1)**.

Fahrig and her research group use a combination of field studies and spatial simulation modelling to examine questions relevant to maintaining populations of particular species of animals or about biodiversity more generally. Their research questions include the minimum amounts of habitat on a landscape that allow viable populations to be sustained (known as **minimum viable area**), effects of roads on the distribution and persistence of populations, ways of structuring agricultural landscapes to reduce the abundance of pests while also maintaining high levels of biodiversity, and the importance of habitat heterogeneity and habitat fragmentation and connectivity on populations of certain animals and on species richness more generally.

A special aspect of this research program is that Fahrig and her colleagues do not just work to identify problems; they also focus on finding landscape-scale solutions to issues related to anthropogenic alterations of habitats at a large scale. Those solutions are important because they help to guide large-scale economic activities along sustainable pathways.

TABLE 13.2	**Commonly Reported Metrics in Landscape Ecology That Are Often Calculated Using the FRAGSTATS Statistical Package**	
Class of Metric	**Metric**	**Explanation**
Composition (does not consider spatial characteristics of the landscape)	Richness	The number of patch types that are present
	Evenness	The proportional abundance of each cover class
	Diversity	Composite indices of richness and evenness, e.g., Shannon-Wiener or Simpson's indices
Spatial Configuration (considers the character and spatial arrangement of patches)	Patch size	Average patch size, number of patches per unit area, etc.
	Patch shape complexity	Simple or convoluted patch shapes represented, for instance, by length of edge per unit area of patches
	Core area	Relative amounts of interior and edge habitat
	Patch isolation	Distance to next patch of the same type
	Contrast	How different are various patch types?
	Dispersion and Contagion	Are similar patches regularly distributed, or clumped?
	Subdivision	Does a patch type occur in only one patch, or broken into numerous patches?
	Connectivity	For each species, is the landscape connected by permeable patches and corridors, or broken into discontinuous pieces?

SOURCE: Based on data from Mcgarigal, K. 2009. FRAGSTATS Spatial Pattern Analysis Program for Categorical Maps. Computer software program produced by the authors at the University of Massachusetts, Amherst. Available at the following web site: www.umass.edu/landeco/research/fragstats/fragstats.html.

TABLE 13.3 | **Examples of Landscape-Scale Ecological Functions**

Function	Relationship to Other Topics	Example	Reference for a Landscape-Scale Study
Movement (flux) of materials between ecosystem elements	Biogeochemical cycling	Movement of phosphate and nitrate from terrestrial to aquatic parts of a watershed	Schindler et al. (2008)
Ecosystem development affected by the movement of air, water, or sediment	Limiting factors, physiological ecology	Development of patches of stunted tree growth (krummholz or tuckamor) on exposed mountain and coastal habitats; water currents in rivers and salt marshes	Fonseca and Bell (1998), Alftine and Malanson (2004)
Retention of materials within landscape elements and ecosystem components	Biogeochemical cycling	Retention and export of biomass and other materials from beaver ponds	Naiman et al. (1994)
Movement of organisms between landscape elements	Metapopulation analysis	Populations and ranges of large carnivores in relation to human influences	Weaver et al. (1996), Broadfoot et al. (2001)
Influence of landscape patterns on distribution and abundance of animals and plants	Conservation biology, road safety	Spatial aspects of conservation planning; effects of roads on animals and plants	Trombulak and Frissell (2000)
Mediation of physical conditions	Limiting factors, physiological ecology	Effects of toxic SO_2 and metals on vegetation in zones around smelters	Freedman and Hutchinson (1980)
Patch-level disturbance	Succession	Fire, windthrow, clear-cutting	Van Wagner (1978)
Self-organization of patches through succession	Succession	Forest development	Turner et al. (1997)

SOURCE: Based on Forman, R.T.T. and M. Godron. 1986. *Landscape Ecology*. John Wiley and Sons, New York, NY.

Moreover, in humid maritime regions where the ratio of precipitation to evapotranspiration is high, raised bogs may develop. The middle parts of these domed wetlands are higher than their margins, but they remain wet because their peat functions like a giant sponge that retains water. Therefore, when a raised bog develops, the landscape-scale hydrology changes from drainage into a wet basin, to the reverse condition of water flowing radially outward from the wetland.

The movement of water and dissolved substances from the terrestrial landscape through riparian habitats and into streams is another important hydrological function of landscapes. Streams erode their banks, particularly during times of high flow, and the mobilized sediment eventually becomes deposited in places where the current slows. These sedimentary deposits are the substrates upon which flood-plain ecosystems develop, which in turn are landscape elements that filter sediment, nutrients, and pollutants from water as it drains from uplands to the adjacent aquatic system. Therefore, stream processes are affected by their adjacent terrestrial ecosystems, but they also influence the land **(Figure 13.16)**.

Water also works on the landscape as ice. In cold regions the tundra vegetation can mediate the development of permafrost (permanently frozen ground) by insulating the soil and its water from the warmer atmosphere during the growing season. In areas where the soil is insulated by a well-developed organic mat and vegetation, the underlying active layer of annually thawed ground is relatively thin, and so the permafrost occurs closer to the surface. In the sub-arctic, mature taiga forest shades the ground surface. This fosters the development of permafrost at relatively low latitudes, which in turn influences succession and community development. These are all reciprocal interactions because permafrost and vegetation greatly affect each other. See also **Figure 13.12**, where the distribution of water as ice wedges has determined vegetation patterns.

Disturbance as a Landscape Function

The agents of disturbance are diverse and pervasive (Suffling and Perera, 2004). Examples of abiotic disturbances include wildfire (naturally ignited by lightning, or otherwise by people), windstorms, ice storms, avalanche,

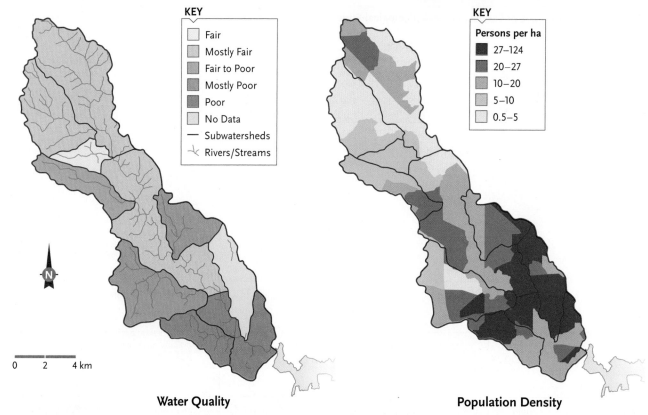

KEY

- ☐ Fair
- ☐ Mostly Fair
- ☐ Fair to Poor
- ☐ Mostly Poor
- ☐ Poor
- ☐ No Data
- — Subwatersheds
- ⊀ Rivers/Streams

KEY

Persons per ha
- ■ 27–124
- ■ 20–27
- ☐ 10–20
- ☐ 5–10
- ☐ 0.5–5

N

0   2   4 km

Water Quality

Population Density

FIGURE 13.16 Stream Processes Are Affected by Adjacent Upland Areas In this heavily urbanized small watershed in the Baltimore (Maryland) area, water quality relates to the amount of human pressure on the adjacent upland areas, as indicated by population density.

SOURCE: Based on data from http://www.beslter.org/gfatlasr/gfatlaslr.pdf pp. 26, 34; S.E Brun,L.E Band, "Simulating runoff behavior in an urbanizing watershed," *Computers, Environment and Urban Systems*, 2000, Elsevier.

flooding, drought, events of severe heat or cold, occurrences of intense pollution, volcanic eruptions and resulting flows of lava or mud, tsunamis (seismic sea waves), and meteorite impact (Chapter 10). Biological agents of disturbance include irruptions of defoliating insects or other herbivores and epidemics of fungal pathogens or other diseases. To these one may add many kinds of anthropogenic disturbances associated with agriculture, forestry, urbanization, and other activities.

On a particular landscape, communities are typically affected by only a few kinds of disturbances, and this has a major influence on ecological development. To illustrate, we can examine the influence of wildfire on certain kinds of forests. The ecological effects of wildfire are complex, partly because these disturbances vary greatly in **intensity** (indicated, in the case of fire, by the rate of energy release per unit of burnt area), and **severity** (the degree to which the ecosystem is disrupted by mortality of its organisms):

- A **crown fire** burns the forest canopy, and in Canadian forests, generally kills the trees, so this kind of disturbance is usually stand-replacing **(Figure 13.17)**. These are high-intensity fires, often with high severity effects.
- A **surface fire** combusts shrubs and ground vegetation but does not spread into the canopy, so most trees survive the disturbance. These burns tend to be of low intensity and severity.

Terry Curran

FIGURE 13.17 An Intense Crown Fire in Northern Ontario Fires of this kind in boreal forest usually kill most or all trees and regenerate to patches of even-aged forest.

- A **ground fire** is limited to burning the organic matter of the forest floor and soil, which kills trees by consuming, scorching, or steaming their roots. Ground fires tend to be of low intensity and high severity **(Figure 13.18)**.

Most wildfires in the boreal regions of Canada are crown fires that kill a large proportion of the mature trees

FIGURE 13.18 A Wildfire in the Burns Bog in the Fraser River Delta, British Columbia This ground fire cooks the tree roots. The intensity is low, but the severity is high and causes much tree mortality. The relationship between fire intensity and severity is complex and depends on the frequency of burning, the weather, fuel loading, soil moisture, and the degree of adaptation of organisms. Contrast this fire with the severe and intense crown fire in Figure 13.17.

AP Photo/Alexander Zemlianichenko Jr.

Petra Suffling

FIGURE 13.19 Even an Intense Fire May Not Be Stand-Replacing in Some Types of Forest These red tingle (*Eucalyptus jacksonii*) trees in western Australia live up to 400 years and are adapted to surviving relatively frequent high-intensity crown fires. The red and white circles show char from previous nonlethal fires that reached high above the canopy.

so that new communities regenerate by secondary succession (Chapter 10). However, forest communities vary greatly in their responses to fire. For example, in the interior of British Columbia, montane stands of ponderosa pine historically had mostly low-intensity wildfires. This was because of a relatively small loading of shrubby fuel so that wildfires often did not reach the crown and most of the trees survived. However, long-term fire suppression has resulted in a higher fuel loading in that region, which set the stage for intense crown fires (See Figure 13.17 for an example of crown fire).

In Australia, intense crown fires in certain *Eucalyptus* forests may not be stand- replacing, because the trees are adapted to and survive this kind of frequent disturbance **(Figure 13.19)**. In contrast, even a low-intensity ground fire in wetland forest growing on peat may kill all trees by burning or steaming their roots **(Figure 13.18)**. Therefore, it is useful to characterize the ecological effects of disturbances in terms of the severity of the damage that is caused **(Table 13.4)**.

13.5 Landscape Change

Disturbance and its consequent succession are functions that bring about changes in landscapes (Chapter 10), as do longer-term variations of conditions such as those of climate. Changes like these are a major theme of landscape ecology, because landscapes are always in flux, as are their elements, such as patches. What happens at one place—in a particular abandoned pasture or a burn that is returning to forest—is often typical of a dominant change occurring on the greater landscape. Therefore, landscape change can be expressed in terms of **patch dynamics**, or the process of changes in the extent and character of patches.

Change may also be understood in terms of the function of landscape elements, which may, for example, become more or less permeable to the movements of organisms, water, or nutrients. Change may also be manifest through dynamics in the patch structure of a landscape—an overall pattern that is characterized as a **shifting mosaic**.

Landscape functions are also affected by net changes in the mosaic. For instance, Ludwig et al. (2005) described how vegetated patches in semi-arid Australian woodlands affect the broader landscape by absorbing runoff more efficiently than interpatch areas with less plant cover. To understand the implications of the mosaic, it is often necessary to characterize what is happening in the various patch types, and to then extrapolate to the entire landscape.

Understanding Temporal Change: The Historical Landscape

Ecological change occurs at various time scales, including those longer than most research projects, careers of ecologists, and even human lives and collective memory. This

TABLE 13.4	The Major Components of Natural Disturbance Regimes That Affect Forested Landscapes	
Component of the Disturbance Regime	Definition	Example
Frequency (return interval or rotation)	Number of events caused by a given disturbance agent per unit of time at a given point in the landscape; Return interval = 1/frequency	In boreal stands of black spruce (*Picea mariana*), if 1.3% of area is burned per year, the return interval is 75 years.
Intensity	Amount of energy released by a disturbance per unit area per unit time	Megajoules of energy released per ha per minute during a wildfire, amount of snow released in an avalanche, or windspeed in a tornado
Severity	Effects of the disturbance on individual organisms, populations, communities, and landscapes	Numbers of trees that are killed per area by a wildfire event, area of avalanche or tornado track
Patch size	The sizes of individual disturbed patches as well as their size-frequency on the landscape	In a particular region, the average wildfire might affect 1000 ha, and the modal size is 50 ha (i.e., the most frequent fire size)
Residual structure or "legacy"	The complex of physical and biological materials remaining after a disturbance event	Shapes of patches, density of surviving trees, density of snags, amount of large woody debris
Causal agent	The kinds of disturbance agents in a study region, and their frequency of occurrence	Wildfire, windstorm, flooding, avalanche, ice storm, insect irruptions
Relative influence of agents of disturbance	How often each agent occurs and the magnitude of the impact relative to those of other agents	Fire annually affecting 0.5% of the study region, compared with windstorms affecting 0.2% of the area
Interactions, synergisms, and antagonisms among agents of disturbance	The ways that disturbance agents influence one another	An irruption of bark beetles may kill many trees, resulting in a high loading of dry fuel that makes affected stands vulnerable to severe wildfire

SOURCES: Modified from: Pickett, S.T. and P.S. White. 1985. *The Ecology of Natural Disturbance and Patch Dynamics*. Academic Press, New York, NY; Suffling, R. and A. Perera. 2004. "Characterizing natural forest disturbance regimes," pp. 43–54 in: *Emulating Natural Forest Landscape Disturbances: Concepts and Applications*. (A. Perera, L.J. Buse, and M.G. Weber, eds.). Columbia University Press, New York, NY.

makes longer-term **longitudinal studies** (or continuous studies) difficult to carry out and therefore rare. (One exception is the Broadbalk experiment in the United Kingdom, a managed field ecosystem that has been continuously studied since 1843; Rothamsted Research, 2009.) Because of the difficulty or impossibility of running continuous long-term studies in one place, ecologists have developed alternative methodologies, such as the chronosequence technique (Chapter 10) and those used in paleoecology, such as dendrochronology and analyses of pollen and diatoms in dated layers of lake sediment (Chapter 16).

Ecologists can also use certain kinds of historical information for longitudinal studies. For example, the Hudson's Bay Company kept remarkably detailed records of the numbers and kinds of furs and other commodities that were purchased by its trading posts in Canada from 1670 to the 1940s. Roger Suffling and colleagues of the University of Waterloo used those fur-trade data to track ecological change (Fritz et al., 1993). For example, they observed that financial accounts of skins and meat traded, as well as correspondence of the traders, all indicated that

woodland caribou disappeared at Osnaburgh House in northwestern Ontario in the early 19th century. The caribou did not reappear for several decades. Their disappearance corresponded with a multiyear outbreak of forest fires that was also noted in reports and could be further verified by tracking the days when smoke was observed in weather records of the trading post. Suffling and Wilson (1994) have summarized numerous ways in which ecologists have used the records of the Hudson's Bay Company.

Early land surveyors also recorded "witness trees" and they noted changes in vegetation along survey lines as these workers demarcated future roads and properties through the then-wilderness of Canada. When witness trees were used, a surveyor typically recorded its species and girth. The trees were selected on the basis of being the closest to a survey point, so they constitute a randomized and semi-quantitative sample of the kinds and sizes of trees in their historical forest communities. One example of a landscape reconstruction using this kind of data is presented in **Figure 13.20**, based on work by students at the University of Waterloo.

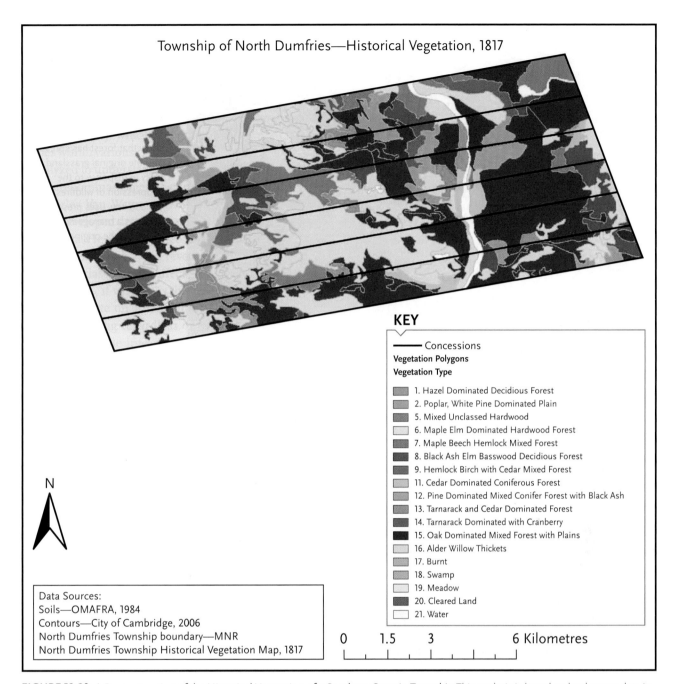

Township of North Dumfries—Historical Vegetation, 1817

N

Data Sources:
Soils—OMAFRA, 1984
Contours—City of Cambridge, 2006
North Dumfries Township boundary—MNR
North Dumfries Township Historical Vegetation Map, 1817

KEY

—— Concessions
Vegetation Polygons
Vegetation Type

1. Hazel Dominated Deciduous Forest
2. Poplar, White Pine Dominated Plain
5. Mixed Unclassed Hardwood
6. Maple Elm Dominated Hardwood Forest
7. Maple Beech Hemlock Mixed Forest
8. Black Ash Elm Basswood Deciduous Forest
9. Hemlock Birch with Cedar Mixed Forest
11. Cedar Dominated Coniferous Forest
12. Pine Dominated Mixed Conifer Forest with Black Ash
13. Tarnarack and Cedar Dominated Forest
14. Tarnarack Dominated with Cranberry
15. Oak Dominated Mixed Forest with Plains
16. Alder Willow Thickets
17. Burnt
18. Swamp
19. Meadow
20. Cleared Land
21. Water

0   1.5   3   6 Kilometres

FIGURE 13.20 A Reconstruction of the Historical Vegetation of a Southern Ontario Township This analysis is based on land survey data in the 1817 field notes of a land surveyor. The kinds of vegetation are colour-coded. The study was done by undergraduate students at the University of Waterloo.

SOURCE: Students in EnvS 469, *Landscape Ecology and Restoration*, University of Waterloo 2008 and 2009.

Another was developed by Serge Lutz (1997) of the University of New Brunswick, who used early survey data to describe the character of the Acadian forest of the 19th century in a region of southern New Brunswick. The original forests were dominated by large old trees of species that are relatively tolerant of competition, such as beech (*Fagus grandifolia*), red spruce (*Picea rubens*), sugar maple (*Acer saccharum*), and white pine (*Pinus strobus*). Such old-growth forest is rare today in that region, where the woodland is now typically dominated by younger, smaller, less shade-tolerant trees such as balsam fir (*Abies bal-*

samea), red maple (*Acer rubrum*), white birch (*Betula papyrifera*), and white spruce (*Picea glauca*).

Historical photographs, paintings, and drawings can also be useful for indicating how landscapes have changed. Jeanine Rhemtulla, Eric Higgs, and colleagues (2002) of the University of Victoria used this method with a land surveyor's 1915 panoramic photographs in what is now Jasper National Park **(Figure 13.21)**. From that information it is evident that trees have been spreading into former grasslands in response to the suppression of wildfires. This source of historical information has influenced recent

Jim Broadfoot, and others associated with the Ontario Ministry of Natural Resources, analyzed population data on raccoon (*Procyon lotor*) and striped skunk (*Mephitis mephitis*) from an urban area in Toronto (Broadfoot et al., 2001). They developed spatially explicit population models for use in disease control, especially for rabies management. (Raccoons and skunks are rabies vectors, and so are a potential threat of transmission to people and domestic animals.) Because the spread of rabies correlates positively with raccoon and skunk densities, the team developed a standard method to identify areas of high-density populations within urban areas, including subpopulations likely to function as sources of dispersal. Those areas could be targeted in disease control programs.

The team combined data from a LANDSAT satellite, mapped by GIS, with a stochastic, age-structured population model. The model incorporated habitat-specific demographic data and functions relating to animal dispersal. They modelled the urban raccoons and skunks as metapopulations with spatially discrete subpopulations that were linked by dispersal, mostly of subadults **(Figure 1)**. Broadfoot et al. predicted that five raccoon subpopulations and one skunk subpopulation would accumulate high relative densities of dispersing animals (>125 percent of the carrying capacity of their habitats). Because of their high density, those subpopulations were also at higher risk of supporting a rabies outbreak than surrounding subpopulations.

In contrast, one raccoon subpopulation stabilized at a relatively low population density by exporting dispersing youngsters.

Using culling, sterilization, or vaccination, animal control authorities can try to prevent the spread of rabies. This research showed how those efforts could be best concentrated in target areas with high raccoon and skunk populations, while also predicting where those vector populations would be located. The GIS landscape data can allow this to be done without having to develop a vector population model for each city. Work of this kind requires transdisciplinary input—in this case, from the fields of wildlife ecology, remote sensing, epidemiology, statistics, and landscape ecology.

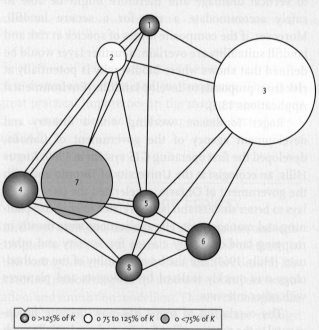

o >125% of K ○ o 75 to 125% of K ○ o <75% of K

FIGURE 1 Transdisciplinary Approaches Complex problems may be better understood using a transdisciplinary approach, as in this case, where the demonstration of raccoon metapopulations provided valuable insights for the management of rabies. The diagram is a schematic representation of the patch structure of the Scarborough raccoon metapopulation showing relative size, location, density at which each subpopulation stabilizes (as % of carrying capacity, K), and resultiig animal dispersal linkages of subpopulations.

SOURCE: Republished with permission of Ecological Society of America, from Broadfoot, JD, Rosatte, RC, O'Leary, DT. 2001. "Raccoon and skunk population models for urban disease control planning in Ontario, Canada," *Ecological Applications*, 11:295–303; permission conveyed through Copyright Clearance Center, Inc.

Relational databases are a key to this analytical process. They are similar to spreadsheets, but allow each piece of data to be linked to others of relevance. For instance, when plotting the locations of all known occurrences of a plant species on a landscape, one might also be able to specify which individuals are growing beneath a forest canopy or in the open, which have been flooded (and when), and how old each individual is. GIS analyses use relational databases to link tabular information and map layers, and this allows the layers to be summarized and examined using statistical methods. Thus, the numbers of distinctive patches can be defined (e.g., all forest patches containing individuals of the plant that are older than the most recent flood), and their individual and collective areas can then be determined using FRAGSTATS or another statistical analysis software (see **Table 13.2**). An example of this approach is provided in Environmental Applications 13.2.

Modelling

Landscape ecologists use an array of conceptual and mathematical models. Most models allow simulations to be run of structural and functional changes over large areas. Commonly used simulation models include FARSITE, LANDIS, and BFOLDS, which can be used to investigate theory and also to explore natural change or management scenarios for real landscapes.

Earlier raster simulation models were based on a grid of cells, and were **deterministic models**, meaning that a specific input gave a particular and reproducible output. These simple approaches have been supplanted by more complex and detailed models based on polygons that are integrated with GIS systems. When using these models, ecologists may run a scenario many times using randomly timed or spaced inputs that match a predetermined statistical pattern. Simulation "experiments" are done in this manner because neither the exact timing nor the locations of future disturbances are known. The methodology allows the most likely outcomes of scenarios and their statistical variation to be computed, a process known as **stochastic modelling**.

13.8 Who Uses Landscape Ecology?

Landscape ecology is a relatively young field that is distinguished by its spatial emphasis. In part, the vitality and utility of landscape ecology arises from its fusion of several disciplines and approaches in spatial analysis (see Environmental Applications 13.2). Many successful projects in landscape ecology could never have been conceived and brought to fruition by individual researchers working in classical disciplines and without consulting other disciplines. Rather, an interdisciplinary methodology was needed—one that brought together the insights and methodologies of several disciplines.

Most landscape ecologists work in developed countries such as Canada, but also increasingly in developing ones. The field is being applied in terrestrial and marine ecosystems, and from the tropics to the Arctic. The methods of landscape ecology are used in fundamental research, with the intent of improving our understanding of factors that affect the structure and function of the natural world. However, most practitioners address

ecological problems of applied importance, often in the contexts of agriculture, forestry, fisheries, conservation biology, protected-areas management, global change studies, environmental planning, or urban design. The applied studies are vital and necessary to guiding economic development along ecologically sustainable pathways (see Environmental Applications 13.3).

Given the diversity of its applications, landscape ecologists have a wide range of philosophies that raise intense debates (see Dessler and Parson, 2006). On one side are those who see landscape ecology as being driven by the classical approaches of hypothesis generation and objective testing through observation and experiment. Conversely, a minority sees the field as a manifestation of "postnormal science," and perceive science as a societal activity with its own assumptions, biases, and culture. They argue that landscape ecology, as a land-management tool and as a way of understanding and dealing with the global ecological crisis, is inherently value based and therefore, in a sense, political. This variety of philosophies is reflected in the wide range of places where landscape ecologists publish their ideas and findings.

Achievements, Problems, and the Way Forward

Landscape ecology is contributing to advances in pure and theoretical ecology, but it is particularly successful in providing models and ideas for conservation biology and environmental planning. Landscape ecology has been empowered by its adoption of trans- and interdisciplinary approaches, and by the development of technologies such as remote sensing, GIS, and modelling. Synthesis has been a great strength of this field, and it continues to develop rapidly (Rapport, 1997).

However, the grand scale of inquiry in landscape ecology is unwieldy in space and time, and this has hampered experimental testing in real-world situations. Despite the lack of field testing, some of the concepts proposed by landscape ecologists are being enthusiastically adopted by foresters, landscape architects, and planners. Examples include the implementation of measures to establish corridors and to decrease fragmentation, without much prior field-testing of their efficacy. In such cases, it is essential that these conservation actions be studied after their implementation to see whether they actually deliver their intended benefits. An example of this approach is a large-scale field experiment in Brazil to test the effects of Amazonian rain forest clearance. Blocks of uncleared forest ranging from a few hectares to tens of thousands of hectares are being set aside from deforestation and monitored for their surviving ecological values (Laurence, 2007).

As Turner (2005) has stressed, the integration of ecosystem and landscape ecology remains challenging but is necessary to the understanding of landscape function.

The methods and tools of landscape ecology are routinely used by conservation organizations in both government and the private sector to plan large-scale activities. One such organization is the Nature Conservancy of Canada (NCC), an environmental non-governmental organization (NGO) that acquires important tracts of land and manages them as protected areas for native biodiversity. To guide its work and use its limited funding effectively, ecologists at NCC undertake landscape-scale planning exercises to identify areas and properties where its actions would make the greatest difference to conserving the biodiversity of Canada.

The first step in NCC's system planning is to develop a conservation blueprint (or ecoregional assessment) of a particular ecoregion (see Section 11.3). This is a large-scale exercise that characterizes and maps the environmental conditions and communities. By 2013, NCC had completed 16 blueprints, covering much of southern Canada, where conservation risk is greatest and NCC does most of its work. An important aspect of a blueprint is that its boundaries are determined by the mapped distributions of the distinctive landforms, climate, and communities that define the ecoregion, rather than by political boundaries. This is illustrated in **Figure 1**, for the Northern Appalachian–Acadian Ecoregion that encompasses New Brunswick, Nova Scotia, Prince Edward Island, part of southeastern Quebec, and adjacent New England. A key purpose of a blueprint is to identify focal areas for potential conservation action. These are either large matrix blocks of representative habitat of high ecological integrity, or areas where there is important biodiversity-at-risk, either species or communities.

NCC then evaluates those focal areas for three broad attributes: (1) their biodiversity values and ecological integrity; (2) the degree of risk posed by anthropogenic stressors; and (3) whether there is opportunity for conservation. If all the criteria are met, NCC may undertake the next stage in its planning process—the development of a Natural Area Conservation Plan (NACP) for an area where it intends to focus its conservation actions. An NACP identifies places that should be protected to conserve important biodiversity in the natural area—ultimately, this involves the selection of individual properties. The NACP also evaluates threats to the biodiversity in the natural area, proposes an action plan to conserve key properties, describes stewardship actions that must be undertaken once properties are secured, and outlines a budget for those integrated activities, including a business plan to raise the necessary funds. As of 2013, NCC had plans to develop and implement 94 NACPs across southern Canada.

An example of a mapped output is presented in **Figure 2** for Pelee Island, a vital area in the Western Lake Erie Lake NACP. This natural area is in extreme southwestern Ontario, a region that supports a disproportionately large number of Canadian at-risk species and ecosystems. Many native species and ecological communities reach the northern limits of their distribution in this region; however, most of the landscape has been converted to economic uses, such as agriculture and urban areas, so that natural habitats are now rare. Within this context, Pelee Island provides extremely important habitat for endangered biodiversity. More than 30 federally designated species at risk and 200 provincially rare species occur there, along with rare communities, including stands of Carolinian forest dominated by southern plant species, and alvar habitat, where

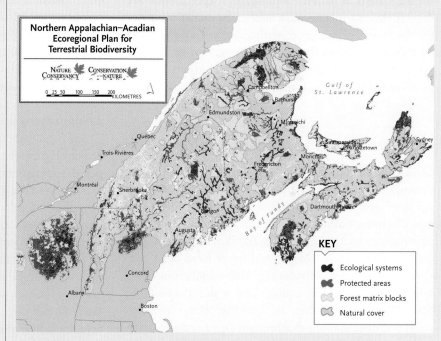

FIGURE 1 The Northern Appalachian–Acadian Ecoregion The boundary of the ecoregion is based on the defining ranges of its landforms, climate, and ecological communities, rather than on political boundaries.

SOURCE: Nature Conservancy of Canada.

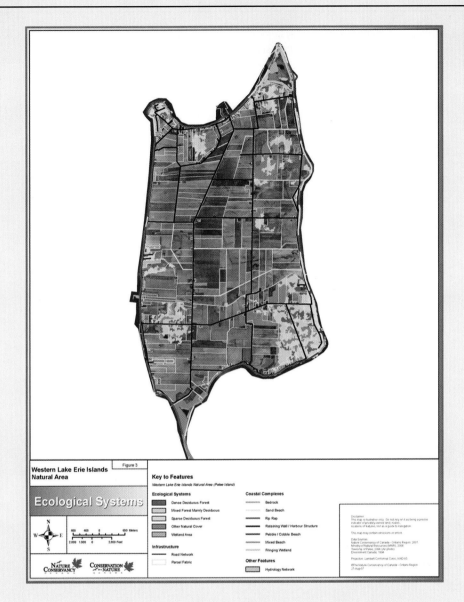

Figure 3

Western Lake Erie Islands Natural Area

Ecological Systems

Key to Features

Western Lake Erie Islands Natural Area (Pelee Island)

Ecological Systems
- Dense Deciduous Forest
- Mixed Forest Mainly Deciduous
- Sparse Deciduous Forest
- Other Natural Cover
- Wetland Area

Infrastructure
- Road Network
- Parcel Fabric

Coastal Complexes
- Bedrock
- Sand Beach
- Rip Rap
- Retaining Wall / Harbour Structure
- Pebble / Cobble Beach
- Mixed Beach
- Fringing Wetland

Other Features
- Hydrology Network

FIGURE 2 Conservation Plan for Pelee Island The map shows properties and ecological systems that support species at risk and rare communities, such as alvar and stands of Carolinian forest.

SOURCE: Nature Conservancy of Canada.

limestone pavement is exposed at the surface and sustains unusual vegetation. The map shows the remaining natural habitats and the existing protected areas, and identifies specific properties that must be acquired to complete a viable network of protected areas on Pelee Island.

In spite of the great importance of Pelee Island to endangered biodiversity, most of its area had already been converted into agricultural and residential land uses in the late 19th century. Moreover, some of the remaining privately owned natural habitats were also threatened. The tension between anthropogenic land uses, natural values (species, ecological communities, ecosystem processes, resources, services, etc.), and legislation to protect endangered species led to long-standing controversy between local proponents of economic "development" and conservation interests. However, by engaging key stakeholders in the process of developing the NACP and vetting its recommendations, the Nature Conservancy of Canada was able to achieve wide consensual support for its proposed conservation actions. This has allowed NCC to secure the most important natural properties on Pelee Island and to manage them for its biodiversity targets. This NACP and its implementation are an incipient "success story" of conservation in Canada.

FIGURE 1 Marie-Josée Fortin

Marie-Josée Fortin studied biology at the University of Montréal **(Figure 1)**. She then did graduate research on spatial statistics in ecology and went on to do postdoctoral research at Université Laval with Serge Payette on the spatial dynamics of wildfires in the boreal forest. During that research she developed improved tests for autocorrelation among ecological factors at a landscape scale.

Fortin then taught at several Canadian universities (Sherbrooke, Simon Fraser, Montreal) and now heads the Landscape Ecology Laboratory at the University of Toronto. Her group of postdoctoral fellows and graduate students focuses on spatial ecology and the development and use of landscape and spatial statistics. Their major research themes include the dynamics and modelling of ecosystem changes caused by wildfire and timber harvesting, and effects of climate change on species, with a broader objective of conserving species and natural ecosystems.

One of Fortin's widely cited papers, prepared with Serge Payette and Isabel Gamache (Payette et al., 2001), is illustrative of her work and its application to global-change issues. They studied the climate-sensitive forest-tundra transition, which extends across Canada from the limits of the continuous boreal forest in the south to the arctic tree line. This landscape has been likened to a "Swiss cheese full of holes," reflecting how fire-prone forest with isolated treeless patches, transitions northward to tundra with isolated patches of forest, and then to wholly treeless tundra. In the southern regions of that ecological gradient, the tundra-like "holes" occupy rocky hilltops with a relatively harsh microclimate, and the surrounding upland forest burns relatively easily.

In their paper, Payette et al. showed how the proportions of upland tundra and forest varied over space, so that the continental-scale forest-tundra ecotone is actually a "constellation of treelines" **(Figure 2)**. The various controlling factors on this latitudinally varying spatial mosaic include macroclimate, microclimate, site drainage, permafrost, and the propensity of wildfires to spread (which is greater in the more continuous forest of the south, and also where muskeg wetlands are less frequent).

Payette et al. showed that the forest cover in the northern part of the transition can be up to several thousand years old, and does not regenerate well after a wildfire. This observation suggests that the tree line marks the northern limit of forest expansion during the warm Hypsothermal Period that occurred about 3000 years ago. Because the colonization of tundra patches by tree seedlings is sluggish, the reaction of the forest landscape to climatic warming in the region may also be slow.

Fortin and Mark Dale (University of Northern British Columbia) have written a book, *Spatial Analysis: A Guide for Ecologists* (2005), which is greatly influencing the approaches and methodologies used by ecologists to analyze spatial patterns on landscapes. Fortin has become widely recognized for her deep expertise in this field, and is frequently consulted by ecologists about ways to approach and analyze difficult problems using spatial statistical analyses.

Landscape ecology should continue to refine knowledge of when spatial heterogeneity is fundamentally important, rigorously test the generality of its concepts, and develop a more mechanistic understanding of the relationships between pattern and process.

Landscape ecology has largely progressed through the early stage of development, common to most disciplines, of defining the field and preparing a terminology. Its practitioners are now busy formulating ideas, but they have more questions to examine than resources to evaluate them. This is an imbalance, but it is also a great opportunity because the approaches and methodologies of landscape ecology are some of the most powerful tools that ecology can offer to society as it strives to develop ecologically sustainable ways of developing the human economy.

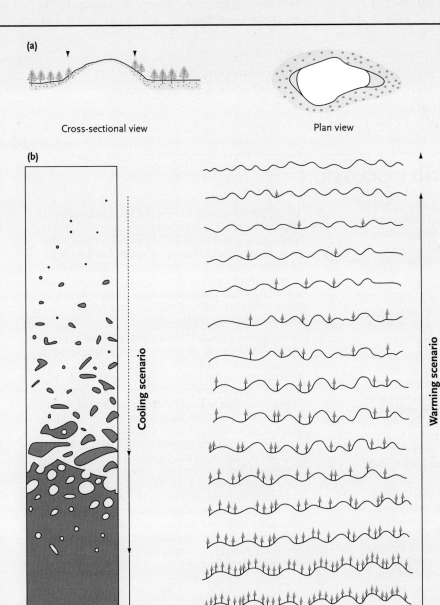

(a)

Cross-sectional view

Plan view

(b)

Cooling scenario

Warming scenario

FIGURE 2 A Constellation of Treelines

Panel (a) shows cross-sectional (left) and overhead (right) views of a typical granitic hill supporting a fire-induced vegetation mosaic. A treeline exists at the junction of the forest with the treeless tundra-like vegetation on the hilltop (arrows). The overhead view shows the trees (dots) and subarctic treeline (solid line). Panel (b) shows overhead (left) and cross-sectional (right) views of the whole forest-tundra transition. It can be seen that the initially patchy distribution of tundra (white) increases in more northerly regions. The cross-sections show the distribution of forest from the continuous boreal forest limit, through the patchy subarctic treeline, to the continuous Arctic tundra.

SOURCE: Used with permission of the American Institute of Biological Sciences, from Payette, S., M.J. Fortin, and I. Gamache. 2001. "The subarctic forest-tundra: The structure of a biome in a changing climate," *BioScience*, 51(9): 709–718, fig. 3; permission conveyed through Copyright Clearance Center, Inc.

CHAPTER SUMMARY

(LO13.1)

- Landscape ecology examines spatial elements ecology by using hierarchical scales in space and time.

(LO13.2)

- European and North American approaches to landscape ecology have developed separately but they are now coming together. Both have been applied in Canadian urban, rural, and wilderness settings.

(LO13.3)

- Landscape elements describe the type, size, shape, number, and arrangement of distinct communities within a landscape. They may be patches, corridors, or networks that together form spatial mosaics with dominant matrices.

(LO13.4)

- Landscape metrics are widely applied to quantify measurements of landscape elements, and thus to allow inferential statistics to be applied.

(LO13.5)

(LO13.5)

- Spatial and graphical approaches are used to understand how landscapes have changed historically, and how they will do so in the future.

(LO13.6)

- Landscape-scale functions (processes), such as disturbance by wildfire and the water cycle, can be better understood using the spatial approaches of landscape ecology.

(LO13.7)

- Landscape ecology employs advanced technologies of remote sensing, geographic information systems (GIS), and computer modelling.

(LO13.8)

- Landscape ecology is proving invaluable both in pure ecology and in "real-world" applications.

QUESTIONS FOR REVIEW AND DISCUSSION

1. Describe a landscape that you can see from a local hill or tall building in terms of the structural elements described in the chapter. Alternatively, do this using a local air photo or remote-sensing imagery, such as from Google Earth. Speculate on how the elements of the landscape might interact in terms of biogeochemical cycling, drainage, the spatial distribution of disturbances, and the movements of plants and animals. Compare your observations with those of a classmate, and explain any differences in terms of your differing assumptions and knowledge of the system.

2. Geographer J. P. Jackson once wrote that "Landscape is history made visible." Using a landscape ecology approach, choose a favourite place (an area less than 100 m in diameter) in a landscape that you know well. It might be a home or cottage, a farm or woodlot, a place on a shore, or a park. Describe, in ecological terms, how this place affects the area around it, and how it has been affected by other parts of its surrounding landscape. How has the place changed over time, and why?

3. Examine Figure 13.21, which shows an area in Jasper National Park. The photographs show how dramatically the landscape has changed, but can we assume that the 1915 situation was "natural"? What landscape-ecological or other approaches might help to answer this question? If we want to restore this system, what condition or date should be used as a reference benchmark, and why? Is it even possible to find an appropriate benchmark for the natural condition?

4. Using the information in Figure 1 in Environmental Applications 13.3, summarize how the structure of landscapes can change, and provide examples to fit each category from the region where you live. For example, a forested landscape may be dissected by roads, railways, power lines, and pipelines, or be disturbed by wildfire or clear-cutting. Explain which of these sorts of influences are most ecologically important in your landscape.

5. Use a spreadsheet to build a graph of stand-age (x-axis) versus stand-area (y-axis) for a forested landscape, as in Figure 13.22. To do this, assume a constant rate of disturbance and an equal chance of stand-replacing fire in each age-class (use age-classes of 20 years). Each spreadsheet line will represent a time period, and each column will be an age-class. A row of cells will be graphed as a stand age-class distribution for a particular era. Once you get the model working, use the "fill down" command to add extra lines until the system reaches equilibrium. Now imagine that a company wants to log the area, harvesting stands that are older than 80 years. Follow the graphs through time to see how they change. What are the conservation implications for a species that requires older forests, such as pileated woodpecker or woodland caribou? How might species of younger habitats, such as snowshoe hare and ruffed grouse, fare?

Conservation of the Natural World

CHAPTER OUTLINE

LEARNING OBJECTIVES

After studying this chapter you should be able to:

1. Explain how extinctions have always provided a context for the evolution of life and the development of ecosystems.

2. Outline how anthropogenic influences are causing the modern global crisis of extinction and endangerment.

3. Provide Canadian and international examples of species that have become extinct or endangered as a result of human activities, as well as "success stories" of species recoveries.

4. Describe examples of species and ecological communities that are at risk in Canada.

5. Explain how protected areas are helpful for the preservation of indigenous biodiversity, but that conservation actions are also necessary on "working" ecoscapes.

6. Outline the key roles played by governments, non-governmental organizations, private interests, and ecologists in conserving biodiversity.

14.1 Conservation of the Natural World

A key message of conservation is that the rapidly growing human economy is degrading the resources it is utterly dependent on, while also diminishing natural habitats and endangering many elements of biodiversity. The economy is growing because of increases in the human population as well as an excessive use of renewable and nonrenewable natural resources (see Chapter 15). Although severe damage has been caused to many natural ecosystems and the numerous species they sustain, conservation biologists are developing practical ways of mitigating that degradation. There are two major approaches to doing this: (1) prudently managing the landscapes and seascapes from which resources are harvested, while (2) also ensuring that protected areas are designated. This is the subject matter of the present chapter: conserving the natural world.

The Meaning of Conservation

In the context of ecology and environmental studies, the word **conservation** has two meanings:

-   sustainable use of renewable natural resources, and
-   stewardship of the natural world.

The first was the initial sense of conservation—the "wise use" of natural resources in ways that do not deplete their stocks and that benefit large numbers of people. Of course, this is possible only for renewable resources, which have the ability to regenerate after they are harvested. Renewable resources include all bioresources as well as others that are associated with solar energy. These include the direct use of sunlight (such as passive solar energy for heating), as well as indirect applications, such as electricity generated by flowing water (hydroelectricity), wind and tidal turbines, and photovoltaics.

If potentially renewable resources are used wisely, meaning the rate at which they are harvested is less than that of their regeneration, then their stocks will not be diminished. This is why a sustainable human economy must ultimately be based on renewable resources. Nonrenewable resources, such as fossil fuels and metals, also have a role to play, but it is limited by the fact that their stocks are inexorably diminished by their use (see Chapter 15 for a more detailed examination of these important issues).

These ideas about **resource conservation** are intuitive and well known. They were embraced by early leaders of the conservation movement in North America, such as George Perkins Marsh (1801–1882), Gifford Pinchot (1865–1946), and Theodore Roosevelt (1858–1919). These early conservationists were alarmed by observations of the extensive destruction of forests and wild game such as bison and waterfowl, and they worked to bring a measure of control over that awful damage **(Figure 14.1)**.

That kind of destruction was also happening over much of southern Canada, and many Canadians were similarly apprehensive about those widespread damages to natural resources. This led to the formation in 1909 of the Commission of Conservation, under the leadership of Wilfrid Laurier (1841–1919) and Clifford Sifton (1861–1929). Its goal was to provide scientific advice about better ways to use and manage the natural resources of Canada. James Harkin (1875–1955), who was the first commissioner of the new Dominion Parks Branch in 1911, was also highly influential, particularly in the early development of national parks. The initiatives of these and other Canadians who were deeply concerned about conservation issues, as they were understood at the time, resulted in a number of helpful governmental initiatives. They included the designation of the first large parks in the country (Banff National Park in 1885 and Algonquin Provincial Park in 1893) and legislative actions such as the *Migratory Birds Convention Act* of 1917, which controlled the previously wanton hunting of waterfowl and other birds.

The attitude of the early resource conservationists is encapsulated by a famous quote of Gifford Pinchot: "Conservation means the greatest good to the greatest number for the longest time." However, this sense of the word "conservation"—the wise use of natural resources to benefit people—is not the subject area of the present chapter. Rather, the topic of resource conservation is covered in Chapter 15, where we examine the application of ecological knowledge to the management of biological resources. In the present chapter, we explore the conservation of the **natural world**—a subject area also known as **biological conservation (Figure 14.2)**.

The Natural World

What is the natural world? In the context of ecology, its major attribute is biodiversity, which we defined in Chapter 12 as the richness of biological variation, at scales

FIGURE 14.1 Conservation The first meaning of the word "conservation" was in reference to the "wise use" of natural resources. This use of the word was in reaction to the irresponsible and destructive use of natural resources that was remarkably common into the early 20th century, and in some cases continues today. This image shows a pile of bison skulls that were gathered from the prairies in the mid-1870s after the mass commercial slaughter of the enormous bison herds, mostly for their hides and meat. The skulls were to be ground up for use as an agricultural fertilizer (bones are rich in phosphorus and calcium, which are important plant nutrients).

Burton Historical Collection, Detroit Public Library

In the next section of this chapter, we examine the dimensions of the modern biodiversity crisis, which is characterized by a spate of extinctions and endangerment of species and even of entire natural communities. This damage is being caused by anthropogenic influences, principally by the widespread destruction of natural habitats. Some of this ecological damage, such as extinctions, is not reversible. Nevertheless, many useful things can be done to mitigate the biodiversity crisis. If prudent actions are quickly taken, it is still possible to avoid much destruction of biodiversity, and some of the damages already caused can be repaired.

Once we characterize the dimensions of the biodiversity crisis, we then examine the ways that ecological science can help society to resolve that global problem. We will examine the aspects of ecological knowledge that are most crucial to understanding the causes and consequences of the biodiversity crisis, and to avoiding or repairing those damages so that all elements of biodiversity can continue to survive.

FIGURE 14.2 Conservation Today, the word "conservation" also refers to actions taken to protect the natural world and its biodiversity. This image shows a humpback whale (*Megaptera novaeangliae*) in a "spy-hopping" manoeuvre to curiously observe ecotourists in a small boat as they observed it off Brier Island in the Bay of Fundy. Like all large whales, humpbacks were badly depleted by excessive hunting, but they are now protected and their abundance is recovering.

ranging from genetics, to species richness, and the shifting mosaic of landscapes and seascapes. We also examined the reasons that biodiversity is important—it has intrinsic value, and also sustains the human economy because it provides vital resources as well as ecosystem functions.

Wilderness is another aspect of the natural world that is relevant to biological conservation. This term refers to wild and uninhabited tracts that are little used by modern industrial people, especially not for resource extraction or other intensive activities. However, low-impact activities such as hiking and even subsistence hunting may occur in wilderness areas. Areas of wilderness usually have high levels of **ecological integrity** in the sense of being little affected by anthropogenic stressors and characterized by native species, self-organized communities, and ecoscapes characteristic for the natural environmental regimes that are present (ecological integrity is examined in more detail in Section 17.2).

14.2 The Biodiversity Crisis

The biodiversity crisis is a global phenomenon that is characterized by high rates of extinction and endangerment of species, and even losses of entire natural communities. This destruction has been particularly acute for the past century or so, but today it is happening faster than ever and will likely further intensify in the near future. This modern biodiversity crisis is anthropogenic—it is mostly being caused by economic activities that result in the destruction of natural ecosystems. However, extinctions have always been part of natural biological change, a fact that provides a context against which the human-caused biodiversity crisis can be compared.

Natural Extinctions

The great majority of species that have ever evolved and lived on Earth, more than 99 percent of them, are now extinct—the only survivors are the relatively few that are currently extant (still living). Almost all of the extinctions were prehistoric, and even prehuman, and in that sense they were "natural" events.

Some causes of natural extinction were extraordinarily rare and singular events, such as Earth being struck by a meteorite. Those occurrences resulted in catastrophic damage of epic proportions, known as a **mass extinction**, which wiped out most of the species that existed at the time. Natural extinctions have also occurred at pervasive, much slower rates, as species individually disappeared because they could not cope with longer-term changes in biotic and abiotic conditions.

The greatest events of natural mass extinction are used to mark the passage from one geological (and evolutionary) era to another. For example, as we noted in Chapter 1, the evolution of the first photosynthetic organisms about 2.5 billion years ago resulted in an accumulation of oxygen in the atmosphere (because O_2 is a by-product of photosynthesis). As the oxygen concentration increased, environmental conditions became increasingly toxic for almost all of the original (prephotosynthesis) organisms, which then suffered a mass extinction. The few surviving O_2-tolerant microbes then proliferated in habitable parts of the planet and underwent an **evolutionary radiation** that resulted in a proliferation of new species. This is a likely scenario for what happened, but in practice the fossil record is sparse and extraordinarily difficult to interpret for those primeval changes in microbial biodiversity.

However, much more is known about subsequent geological transitions that are marked by mass-extinction events. There have been about 10 mass extinctions that have left reliable fossil traces. Five of the transitions are particularly famous because of the large proportions of the existing biota that were lost (Raup and Seposki, 1982; Erwin, 1990; Bamback et al., 2004; Eldredge, 2005). The greatest of the natural mass extinctions were the following:

- *end of the Ordovician*: this event occurred about 440 million years ago (MYA), likely because of a sudden global cooling of unknown causation, and resulted in the loss of about 25 percent of marine families, each consisting of several to thousands of species;
- *end of the Devonian*: occurred 370 MYA, possibly caused by global climate change, with 19 percent of marine families being lost;
- *end of the Permian*: occurred 245 MYA, possibly because of global climate change somehow associated with

plate tectonics, or perhaps a meteorite impact, with 54 percent of families being lost, along with 84 percent of genera and 96 percent of species (this is the most intensive mass extinction in the geological record);
- *end of the Triassic*: occurred 210 MYA, of unknown causation, with 23 percent of families lost;
- *end of the Cretaceous*: occurred 65 MYA, likely caused by blast and climatic deterioration from a meteorite impact in the region of Yucatan, Mexico, which resulted in 17 percent of families, 57 percent of genera, and 76 percent of species being lost across the phylogenetic spectrum, including the last of the dinosaurs, pterosaurs, and marine ammonites (**Figure 14.3**).

Each of the natural mass extinctions was followed by an evolutionary radiation and proliferation, as vacant niches became reoccupied by newly evolved species. The first of the radiations to be relatively well documented occurred at the beginning of the Cambrian era about 542 MYA, when there was a rapid proliferation of larger-bodied animals (Metazoa). This proliferation is best known from the study of fossil deposits in Yoho National Park, British Columbia. A famous bed of stratified rocks known as the Burgess Shale (from about 505 MYA) has yielded 15–20 phyla of now-extinct metazoans, some of which were soft-bodied forms such as sponges (which rarely preserve well in the fossil record) as well as many kinds of arthropods with exoskeletons of chitin (a hard polysaccharide) (Conway Morris, 1998; Gould, 1998).

Comparable evolutionary radiations of surviving biodiversity occurred after all of the mass extinction events in the geological record. For example, following the end-of-Cretaceous mass extinction, which wiped out most of the large reptiles, there was a diverse radiation of birds and mammals.

Although almost all species that have ever existed have become extinct as a result of natural forces, no

FIGURE 14.3 Dinosaurs The last of the dinosaurs (order Dinosauria) became extinct in a mass-extinction event at the end of the cretaceous period about 65 million years ago. This model of a *Troodon formosus*, a bird-like coelurosaurid dinosaur, is in the National Museum of Natural History in Ottawa. This medium-sized predator was about 1 m tall, weighed up to 45 kg, and lived in western North America between 75 and 65 million years ago. Its fossils have been found in southern Alberta.

Bill Freedman

biologist has ever directly observed a natural extinction of a full species. In other words, during historical times all observed extinctions of species have been anthropogenic.

However, there have been a few observations of the natural **extirpation** of local populations of wide-ranging species on oceanic islands, or in isolated habitats on continents (Diamond, 1984). These events were stochastic—caused to a small population by an unpredictable catastrophe such as an episode of severe weather. For instance, Ehrlich et al. (1972) had been studying an isolated subalpine population of the butterfly *Glaucopsyche lygdamus* for several years in Colorado, when a late snowstorm killed the flower primordia of the lupine *Lupinus amplus*, which is the only food plant of the butterfly larvae. This unpredictable weather-caused calamity resulted in extirpation of the local population of the *Glaucopsyche*, although it recolonized the site several years later.

Small butterfly populations have also been observed to become extirpated in Canada, such as the Karner blue (*Lycaeides melissa samuelis*) and frosted elfin (*Incisalia irus*) that were studied in southern Ontario by Laurence Packer (1994) of York University. However, those losses were anthropogenic—the butterflies occurred only in savanna dominated by black oak (*Quercus velutina*) and containing their obligate food plant, another species of lupine (*Lupinus perennis*), but this natural habitat has mostly been destroyed and now persists in only <1 percent of its original range in Canada.

Local extirpations of some bird species were documented after the rising waters of Lake Gatun, created by flooding associated with construction of the Panama Canal in 1914, isolated Barro Colorado Island from previously continuous tropical lowland forest (Karr, 1982). Initially, the island supported at least 218 species of resident birds, but by 1981 at least 56 species or 26 percent of the avifauna were extirpated. However, 26 of the extirpated species inhabit younger, disturbed habitats, which disappeared from the island as its forest underwent successional development. In addition, eight aquatic birds disappeared because their prey of small fish was reduced by the introduction of a large, alien, piscivorous fish to the lake. The other 22 known extirpations were of birds that inhabit mature forest (the actual losses may have been up to 50–60 species, because the birds of this habitat had not been completely documented in 1921, when the survey began). The reasons for their extirpations are not clear, especially since the area of mature forest actually increased between 1921 and 1981 because of succession. Presumably, those mature-forest species disappeared because of insufficient areas of suitable habitat to support a long-term breeding population, coupled with stochastic extirpation events caused by severe weather. Although the extirpated species are abundant and widespread in larger areas of continuous forest in the region, their limited dispersal ability has apparently prevented them from recolonizing Barro Colorado Island (i.e., they do not fly across long stretches of water).

And so, extinctions have always been a context for life and evolution. In rare cases they occurred as mass events, sometimes triggered by cataclysmic environmental changes associated with tectonic activity or a meteorite strike. These natural events of mass extinction were then followed by a biotic recovery through the evolutionary radiation of new species that took advantage of ecological opportunities presented by the vacant niches of extinct taxa. Moreover, even during the protracted intervals between mass-extinction catastrophes, there was a pervasive background of extinctions occurring at much slower rates, as species disappeared because they were unable to cope with moderate changes in environmental circumstances. These various natural extinctions provide an ecological context for the mass extinction that is currently ongoing, and is being caused by anthropogenic influences.

Anthropogenic Extinctions and Endangerment

There is a sixth mass extinction of a scale comparable to the ones previously noted, but this one is anthropogenic and ongoing and will likely become even more intense in the near future. This is the **modern biodiversity crisis**, sometimes referred to as the **Holocene biodiversity event**.

Anthropogenic extinctions may occur directly, as when species are harvested so intensively that their global population is wiped out. They may also occur indirectly, as when forest is extensively cleared and converted into agricultural land uses, to the degree that no habitat survives for dependent species. Indirect effects may also involve the introduction of alien species that become invasive of natural habitats and severely damage them. These kinds of stressors cause originally continuous and large populations of many vulnerable species to become smaller and fragmented, so they suffer from the deleterious effects of additional disturbances and inbreeding, and eventually become locally extirpated or globally extinct **(Figure 14.4)**.

Although the current anthropogenic mass extinction began about 10–12 000 years ago, it has been rapidly intensifying since then into present times, and has been particularly accelerating during the past several centuries. In fact, this biodiversity crisis is mostly being caused by the activities and influences of people who are alive today.

The modern biodiversity crisis is characterized by three main elements:

- First, species are becoming extinct at rates far higher than the natural background attrition. This is occurring in all biomes and ecosystems, but the damage is especially severe in tropical climes. Some biologists, such as E. O. Wilson, one of the best-known specialists in biodiversity, believe that half of existing species could be lost within the next century.

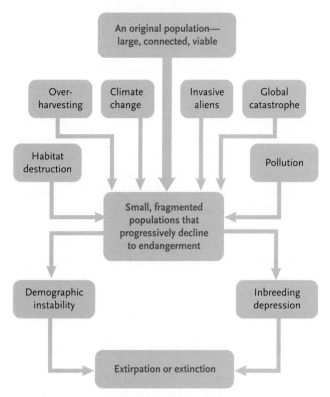

FIGURE 14.4 **The Extinction Vortex** Extinction may be caused by natural or anthropogenic stressors, such as the destruction of natural habitats, climate change, excessive harvesting, and alien diseases. These stressors cause populations that are initially large and viable to become fragmented into increasingly smaller and isolated units that are vulnerable to the effects of inbreeding and population instability caused by disturbances and other environmental changes. These cumulative stressors may cause endangered populations to further decline, and may ultimately result in their extirpation or extinction. This accelerating spiral of endangerment is sometimes called the "extinction vortex."

SOURCE: Caption, Gilpin and Soulé, 1986.

- Second, the number of species at risk is rapidly increasing. Species are at conservation risk (i.e., at risk of becoming extinct) if their population is much smaller than it used to be, and/or their necessary habitat has become greatly reduced in area or quality. The numbers of species that are endangered in this way are rapidly increasing in all countries, including Canada (see Section 14.3).

- Third, natural communities are being endangered. This is because some kinds of communities have been extensively destroyed, mostly by conversion to anthropogenic land uses. This diminishment means that the affected communities may no longer be able to maintain their dependent species and functional qualities. In such cases, the communities are endangered in their entirety, as are the many species of plants, animals, and microorganisms that depend on their habitats.

The most important cause of the modern biodiversity crisis is the destruction of natural habitats (**Figure 14.5**). On land, this has primarily occurred through the conversion of natural ecosystems into various kinds of agricultural, urbanized, or industrial land uses whose habitats are not suitable for native species. This problem is acute everywhere, but particularly in countries with tropical forest, because those primary habitats support more biodiversity than any other kind of ecosystem.

In the oceans, the destruction of natural ecosystems has primarily occurred through the overharvesting of commercially important species and associated collateral damage (such as by-catch; see Chapter 15).

In some of the worst cases, species have been rendered extinct or endangered because they were excessively

FIGURE 14.5 **Habitat Destruction** The leading cause of the modern biodiversity crisis is the destruction of natural habitats and their conversion into anthropogenic land uses. In this case, a lowland tropical forest in West Kalimantan in Indonesian Borneo has been logged for its highest-value trees. The logging road allows people and businesses interested in agricultural development to invade, and they clear and burn the remaining forest so that crops can be grown.

Bill Freedman

harvested as economic commodities or as wild game. This is the nastiest possible way to harvest a potentially renewable biological resource—so intensively that its populations collapse, even to the point of extinction. This is akin to the unsustainable mining of a nonrenewable resource, such as a metal or fossil fuel. Later in this chapter, we will examine some examples of these sorts of damages.

Another important cause of the biodiversity crisis is the introduction of **invasive aliens** (or **exotics**; see also Chapter 2). These are non-native species that become **naturalized** (or **feral**, meaning they are able to persist and regenerate in native habitats), and if they also become abundant they cause ecological changes that result in declines of native species. Invasive aliens include species of plants and animals, as well as introduced diseases that can be devastating to indigenous species. Later in this section we will examine cases of invasive aliens that are causing important ecological damage in Canada.

Because various kinds of anthropogenic stressors have been affecting biodiversity in all parts of the world, the past several centuries have witnessed huge increases in the rate of extinction and in the numbers of species threatened with this catastrophe. Moreover, during this period the problem has become increasingly worse. It is now a more severe problem than it has ever been, and will likely become even more ruinous in the foreseeable future. This deteriorating situation is caused by the ongoing destruction and diminishment of natural ecosystems,

particularly in the tropics, coupled with the cumulative effects of alien introductions and excessive harvesting of certain bioresources.

The Species Survival Commission (SSC) of the International Union for the Conservation of Nature and Natural Resources (IUCN) has the mandate to compile and analyze global data about species at risk. According to its database **(Table 14.1)**, there are 737 known cases of extinct animals plus another 10 840 that are threatened (this includes species that are critically endangered, endangered, or vulnerable; we examine these categories of risk in Section 14.3). There are also 121 extinct plants and 9390 that are threatened.

However, these data should be regarded as gross underestimates of the actual numbers of anthropogenic extinctions and of species at risk. In actual fact, many extinctions occurred prior to the affected species being "discovered" by biologists, especially in tropical regions and on remote islands. Even today there is little information about the conservation status of smaller organisms that occur in poorly explored ecosystems, such as many regions of tropical rain forest or large expanses of the deep oceans. Because of this ignorance, there have undoubtedly been many thousands of "hidden" extinctions of species that were never documented by biologists. Therefore, although there is relatively good knowledge of extinct and vulnerable species for large and conspicuous animals, especially those of higher-latitude countries where most

TABLE 14.1 | **Global Data on Species at Risk**

These data are compiled by the International Union for the Conservation of Nature and Natural Resources (IUCN).

Group of Organisms	Extinct	Critically Endangered	Endangered	Vulnerable
Mammals	79	196	446	497
Birds	134	197	389	727
Reptiles	22	144	296	367
Amphibians	36	509	767	657
Fish	66	413	494	1148
Crustaceans	12	116	145	335
Insects	61	119	207	503
Mollusks	324	5498	480	828
Others	3	18	33	235
Total animals	737	2261	3282	5297
Bryophytes	3	23	27	21
Ferns	3	44	48	74
Conifers	4	83	127	169
Flowering plants	111	1671	2350	4643
Total plants	121	1821	2655	4914

SOURCE: Based on data from International Union for the Conservation of Nature and Natural Resources (IUCN). 2008. *The IUCN Red List of Threatened Species*. IUCN, Gland, Switzerland. http://www.iucnredlist.org.

greatly intensified when Europeans moved in. The damage continues today as the indigenous biodiversity of islands is wracked by the destruction of natural habitats to develop the land for agriculture, industry, tourism, and towns. At the same time, remnants of natural habitat are damaged by invasive aliens, and small lingering populations of native species are affected by introduced predators and diseases.

For instance, smaller Pacific islands and archipelagos supported long-isolated biotas that were highly vulnerable to extinction and quickly declined after the islands were colonized by prehistoric Polynesian cultures (Steadman, 2006). Most of the 800 or so Polynesian islands likely had several endemic species of rails (family Rallidae) plus other unique birds, possibly totalling thousands of species, most of which became extinct from overhunting, predation by introduced rats, and habitat changes. An excavation of bird bones from an archaeological site on the island of Ua Huka, in the Marquesas of the equatorial Pacific, revealed that 14 of the 16 original species of birds are now extinct or extirpated from the island, including 10 endemics.

In fact, most of the known extinctions of species since 1500 have occurred on islands (Baillie et al., 2004). A total of 88 percent of bird extinctions have involved island endemics, as have 86 percent of those of reptiles, 68 percent of mollusks, 62 percent of mammals, and 54 percent of amphibians. These data are, however, only for the known extinctions—undoubtedly, there have also been many unrecorded extinctions of endemic species on both islands and in continental tropical regions where the original fauna was not well documented.

More Recent Extinctions

Clearly, people have been causing extinctions for a long time. During the past century, however, the ability of the human economy to cause damage to biodiversity has increased tremendously. This is primarily due to the enormous growth in our technological capability to destroy natural ecosystems and convert them into anthropogenic land uses. In the rest of this section we will consider recent cases of extinction and endangerment and their causes. Then in following sections we will examine the role of ecology in helping to avoid those damages through the planning and implementation of conservation measures.

The first documented extinction during historical times was that of the dodo (*Raphus cucullatus*), a flightless, turkey-sized relative of pigeons (order Columbiformes) that was last seen alive in 1662 (Staub, 1996; IUCN, 2008). The dodo lived on Mauritius, an island in the Indian Ocean that was discovered by the Portuguese in 1507 and colonized by the Dutch in 1598. Sailors and colonists hunted the dodo and gathered its eggs as food, while

clearing its lowland habitat for agricultural use and introducing cats, monkeys, and pigs that killed and ate the birds or their eggs in ground-level nests. These stressors caused the dodo to rapidly decline and become extinct, and today not even a complete skeleton exists. The closely related solitaire (*Pezophaps solitaria*), another flightless pigeon from the nearby island of Rodrigues, also became extinct, around 1715, for similar reasons as the dodo.

The extinction of the dodo was largely caused by excessive hunting as food, in combination with other stressors. Overexploitation has also caused other extinctions, including several in North America. We will illustrate this point with two famous examples of grossly nonsustainable harvesting: the great auk and the passenger pigeon.

The great auk (*Pinguinus impennis*), a large seabird, was the first anthropogenic extinction in historical times of a North American species (it had an amphi-Atlantic distribution, occurring in both European and North American waters; Nettleship and Evans, 1985; Fuller, 2003) **(Figure 14.8)**. The great auk was the first bird to be named a penguin (or pennegoin) by early mariners and naturalists, but it was from the auk family (Alcidae) rather than that of the true penguins (Spheniscidae) of the southern hemisphere. The physical similarity of birds in these two families is due to their convergent evolution, occurring in response to comparable regimes of natural selection.

The great auk was a flightless seabird that ate small fish, nested on rocky islands that lacked mammalian predators, laid only a single egg, and likely bred only every few years. It was also extremely vulnerable to being hunted by people, because it was flightless and could be rounded up on its nesting islands and killed in large numbers by clubbing. The species had long been eaten by Aboriginal people and European fishers, but it quickly declined in abundance when it became the target of a rapacious commercial hunt for its skin and feathers in the mid-1700s. The great auk was rendered extinct by 1852.

Funk Island off eastern Newfoundland supported the largest breeding colony of great auks in the northwestern Atlantic, and also the largest commercial harvest of them. This profitable but short-lived operation was described in 1785 (from Nettleship and Evans, 1985, p. 79):

> It has been customary of late years, for several crews of men to live all summer on that island, for the sole purpose of killing birds for the sake of their feathers, the destruction of which they have made is incredible. If a stop is not soon put to that practice, the whole breed will be diminished to almost nothing, particularly the penguins.

The slaughter of great auks and other seabirds on Funk Island was so enormous that much of the soil that currently occurs there is formed from their composted bodies. Bill Montevecchi of Memorial University studies seabirds breeding on Funk Island, and has observed common puffins (*Fratercula arctica*) carrying auk bones

FIGURE 14.8 The Great Auk (*Pinguinus impennis*) This was a large, flightless seabird of the North Atlantic Ocean, and was the first historically documented anthropogenic extinction of a species that occurred in North America. (a) This folk-art carving was made by E. Learning of Mount Pearl, Newfoundland, based on a painting in a field guide. (b) These bones of great auks were excavated by Bill Montevecchi of Memorial University on Funk Island off northeastern Newfoundland. They were used to assemble skeletal specimens of this extinct seabird.

out of the organic substrate as they dig their nesting burrows (Kirkham and Montevecchi, 1982). The great auk was extirpated on Funk Island by the early 1800s, and the last sighting anywhere was on the Grand Banks in 1852.

The passenger pigeon (*Ectopistes migratorius*) is another example of a species that was rendered extinct by relentless market hunting. It may have been the most abundant terrestrial bird in the world, numbering some 3–5 billion individuals, or one-quarter of all birds in North America (Schorger, 1955; Eckert, 1965; Blockstein and Tordoff, 1985). It was a highly social animal that migrated in immense flocks, which were said to "blacken the sky." It nested in large colonies, with up to a hundred nests occurring in an individual tree and hundreds of millions in a colony. In 1810, naturalist Alexander Wilson estimated that a migrating flock he observed was 0.6 km wide and 144 km long, and contained two billion pigeons. The breeding range was the northeastern United States and southern Canada, including southern regions of the Maritimes, Quebec, Ontario, Manitoba, Saskatchewan, and possibly Alberta. The breeding habitat was mature hardwood forest that produced

abundant nuts of beech, chestnut, and oak (*Fagus grandifolia*, *Castanea dentata*, *Quercus rubra*, and other *Quercus species*), and it wintered in similarly nut-rich forests of the southeastern United States.

The irresistible abundance and communal habits of passenger pigeons combined to make it easy to harvest them in huge numbers, and they were subjected to a rapacious market hunt, mostly for meat to sell to the urban poor. The birds were killed in astonishing numbers by clubbing, shooting, and netting. According to Alexander Wilson in 1829 (Feduccia, 1985): "Wagon loads of them are poured into the market ... and pigeons became the order of the day at dinner, breakfast, and supper, until the very name became sickening."

Some of the annual harvests were staggering in their quantity. In 1869, an estimated one billion pigeons were taken in Michigan alone. In 1874, netters took 700 000 pigeons over a 28-day period.

The relentless overhunting was an obvious cause of the precipitous decline of the passenger pigeon, but other stressors were also at work (Blockstein and Tordoff, 1985). They included the destruction of much of the birds' breeding habitat by timber harvesting and clearing for agriculture. Also important was the precipitous decline of the American chestnut because of the ravages of chestnut blight (*Cryphonectria parasitica*), an introduced fungal pathogen that virtually wiped out this once abundant and widespread tree. Moreover, the pigeon was such a communal animal that once its abundance decreased below some level, perhaps still in the millions, there may have been insufficient social facilitation for the birds to breed successfully, particularly in view of the intense interference associated with the hunting. The last observed attempt at nesting was in 1894, and the last individual, a captive named Martha in the Cincinnati Zoo, died a solitary death in 1914. The hunting of this pigeon had been so intense that within only a few decades, the world's most abundant bird had been rendered extinct.

Commercial overhunting as food was not the only reason for causing species to become extinct. The Carolina parakeet (*Conuropsis carolinensis*) was exterminated because it was perceived to be an agricultural pest, owing to damage it caused when feeding in fruit orchards and grain fields. This native parrot was a common, brightly plumaged bird that foraged and roosted in social groups in mature hardwood forest in the southeastern United States. The Carolina parakeet was easy to eradicate because it lived in communal groups, and would assemble around a wounded colleague so that an entire flock could be killed by a hunter. The last known individual died in the Cincinnati zoo in 1918 (in the very cage that Martha had vacated in 1914).

Some other species were made extinct largely because most of their natural habitat was destroyed. An example of this is the ivory-billed woodpecker (*Campephilus principalis principalis*), which inhabited extensive mature hardwood forests and cypress swamps in the southeastern United States. Most of that habitat was heavily logged or converted to agriculture by the early 1900s, driving the ivory-billed woodpecker into a rapid decline and eventually to extinction (notwithstanding claims of sightings in 2004–2005).

Tropical Deforestation and Extinctions

The few selected cases of famous losses of species that we just examined are representative of the tragedy of extinction. The animals we considered were beautiful creatures that had evolved over millions of years, only to be rendered extinct in a few decades by the actions of avaricious humans. Those people valued their immediate profit over the sustainability of their enterprise, and they paid no heed to the continued survival of the species they were harvesting, or whose habitat they were destroying.

It would be nice to know that these sorts of appalling mistakes are only things of the past, but unfortunately,

FIGURE 14.9 The Destruction of Tropical Forest Is the Leading Cause of Extinction and Endangerment This is a view of moist tropical forest in Manu National Park, in lowland Amazonian Peru.

that is not the case. Extinctions are still being caused, and at an accelerating rate. The worst damage is occurring in the biome that supports more of Earth's biodiversity than any other—primary tropical forest (**primary** or **frontier forest** occurs in large blocks of self-organizing ecosystems, often in an old-growth condition, and it sustains all of the appropriate dependent species, including wide-ranging animals) **(Figure 14.9)**. These natural ecosystems are packed with a great richness of species, many of which are endemics, so when their habitat is destroyed they have no alternative refuges and become extinct. The extinction of smaller species typically happens before they have been "discovered" and named by biologists.

The rate of deforestation in poorer countries has increased alarmingly during the present century, and particularly in the past several decades. On a global level, there is a net annual **deforestation**, or a permanent loss of forest area, of more than 5 million ha per year (FAO, 2012; **Table 14.2**). Most of the deforestation in less-developed countries comes from the clearing of natural forest for timber, followed by conversion of the land use to agriculture **(Figure 14.5)**. The amount and rate of deforestation varies enormously among countries. China, for example, retains only 22 percent of its original forest cover, and only 2 percent of that is primary forest. However, its net forest cover has been increasing in recent years, by 3 million ha or 1.6 percent annually between 2001 and 2010. This is because of a massive effort to establish tree plantations as timber crops and to control soil erosion in hilly terrain.

However, most less-developed countries that support tropical forest are rapidly losing that natural ecosystem. Nigeria, for example, retains only 11 percent of its original forest cover and it is suffering an ongoing deforestation rate of 3.7 percent per year (**Table 14.2**; if maintained, this rate of deforestation would decrease the remaining forest cover by half in only 19 years). Burundi is even worse—it

TABLE 14.2

Deforestation in Selected Countries

Original forest is the estimated cover about 8000 years ago. Frontier forest refers to extensive blocks of natural forest, dominated by native species and able to sustain large wide-ranging animals. Change in forest area is between 2001 and 2010, expressed in thousands of ha per year and as annual percentage change.

Region or Country	Existing Forest Area as Percentage of Original	Existing Frontier Forest as Percentage of Original	Change in Forest Area (10^3 ha/yr)	Change in Forest Area (%/yr)
WORLD	53.4	21.7	−5211	−0.2
North America	77.3	34.1	+188	+0.0
South America	69.1	45.6	−3997	−0.5
Central America	54.5	9.7	−248	−1.2
Europe	58.4	21.3	+676	+0.1
Africa			−3414	−0.5
Asia			+2235	+0.4
Less-developed countries				
Bangladesh	7.9	3.8	−0.3	−0.2
Brazil	66.4	42.2	−2642	−0.5
Burundi	3.5	0.0	−3	−1.4
Cambodia	65.1	7.3	−145	−1.3
China	21.6	1.8	+2986	+1.6
Colombia	53.5	36.4	−101	-0.2
Cuba	28.8	0.0	+44	+1.7
Haiti	0.8	0.0	−1	−0.8
Honduras	51.6	16.4	−120	−2.1
India	20.5	1.3	+304	+0.5
Indonesia	64.6	28.5	−498	−0.5
Madagascar	13.1	0.0	−57	−0.4
Malaysia	63.8	14.5	−114	−0.5
Mexico	63.4	8.1	−195	−0.3
Nigeria	10.7	0.6	−410	−3.7
Peru	86.6	56.7	−122	−0.2
Venezuela	83.6	59.3	−288	−0.6
Developed countries				
Canada	91.2	56.5	+0	+0.0
France	16.5	0.0	+60	+0.4
Germany	26.3	0.0	+0	+0.0
Japan	58.2	0.0	+10	+0.0
Russia	68.7	29.3	−18	+0.0
United Kingdom	6.0	0.0	+9	+0.3
United States	60.2	6.3	+383	+0.1

SOURCES: Based on data from World Resources Institute (WRI). 2010. EarthTrends database, http://earthtrends.wri.org/.

has lost 96 percent of its original forest and is still deforesting at 5.5 percent per year.

The situation is different in wealthier countries, where forest cover has recently been fairly stable. In fact, Europe had an annual net gain of 0.7 million ha of forest between 2001 and 2010 **(Table 14.2)**. In North America, there was little net change (0.0 percent) in forest cover between 2001 and 2010, and 77 percent of the original forest area is still intact, although only 34 percent of the primary forest has survived. In Canada, 91 percent of the original forest remains, including 57 percent of the primary forest, and there has been no net deforestation in recent years. Of course, these national data hide a great deal of variation across Canada—there has been extensive deforestation in southern parts of our country, where most people live and most agriculture occurs.

Feral Cats: Natural Born Killers

The domestic cat (*Felis catus*) makes a wonderful pet, and for this reason millions of them live with people as companion animals. Some of them are "working" pets that help to keep the populations of mice and rats from becoming too abundant, especially on farms. However, many other cats live as feral animals in the wild, where they make their living by killing and eating small mammals and birds **(Figure 1)**. Feral cats are causing some native animals to be much less abundant than formerly, even to the point of being endangered.

This problem is especially acute on isolated islands and other places where cats or other placental predators did not originally occur, such as Australia and New Zealand. Even in Europe and North America, however, free-ranging pet and feral cats are among the most important predators of small native animals. A recent study in the United States estimated that these abundant predators were killing 1.4–3.7 billion birds and 6.9–20.7 billion mammals annually (Loss et al., 2013). Most of the mortality was caused by un-owned feral cats, as opposed to pets that were allowed to spend some time

outdoors. Overall, the cat-related deaths are thought to be the largest anthropogenic cause of mortality of birds and small mammals in North America.

The authors of this study, and those of comparable research elsewhere, strongly recommend that the numbers of feral cats be greatly reduced as a necessary measure to conserve native animals.

However, many people love cats and as a result there is intense opposition to proposed culls of these animals in the wild. This is an example of an ethical dilemma associated with affection for animals—in this case, a love of domestic cats is pitted against a love of native birds and mammals that are being severely affected by these alien natural-born killers.

FIGURE 1 An Alien Predator Domestic cats are extremely effective predators, and they are responsible for killing large numbers of native birds and other small animals.

Flip De Nooyer/Foto Natura/Minden Pictures/Getty Images

sanguinalis), common plantain (*Plantago major*), dandelion (*Taraxacum officinale*), and goutweed (*Aegopodium podagraria*). Other alien plants are invasive of semi-natural urban habitats, such as parks and ravines, and include English ivy (*Hedera helix*), European white birch (*Betula pendula*), Japanese knotweed (*Fallopia japonica*), Norway maple, and Scots pine (*Pinus sylvestris*).

AGRICULTURAL HABITATS Alien weeds in cultivated agricultural lands cause economic damage by competing with crop plants, thereby reducing their yield. This is an important problem, worth billions of dollars annually, and it is typically dealt with by management practices such as tilling (or ploughing) the soil and/or spraying herbicide to reduce the abundance of weeds. Many species of alien plants are important weeds in cultivated agriculture, including barnyard grass (*Echinochloa crusgalli*), common burdock (*Arctium minus*), quack grass (*Agropyron repens*), spotted knapweed (*Centaurea maculosa*), and wild mustard (*Sinanpsis arvensis*).

Pastures grazed by livestock can also be degraded by invasions of alien plants. So-called tame pasture is established by converting natural habitat, including native prairie, into communities dominated by alien forage plants, such as alfalfa (*Medicago sativa*), bluegrass (*Poa pratensis*), and timothy (*Phleum pratense*). Both tame pasture and native prairie, which may also be used for grazing livestock, are degraded for that use if they are abundantly invaded by alien species that are poisonous or otherwise damage the habitat. Some of the worst invasive aliens of pastures and prairie in Canada include blue weed (*Echium vulgare*), creeping thistle (*Cirsium arvense*), drooping brome (*Bromus tectorum*), European buckthorn (*Rhamnus cathartica*), leafy spurge (*Euphorbia esula*), mouse-eared hawkweed (*Hieracium pilosella*), and smooth brome (*Bromus inermis*).

NATURAL HABITATS From an ecological perspective, the most important kinds of damage caused by invasive aliens are to natural habitats, because it is in those places that native species are affected **(Figure 14.13)**. Native prairie may be damaged by various aliens, including those noted

FIGURE 14.13 Alien Invasive Species Are an Important Cause of Ecological Damage This image shows dead man's fingers (*Codium fragile*), a green alga native to the eastern Pacific Ocean that was accidentally introduced to the Atlantic, where it has become abundant in subtidal habitats, displacing native seaweeds and otherwise damaging communities on rocky bottoms.

just above. Wetlands are also degraded by invasive aliens, such as Eurasian reed (*Phragmites australis*), Eurasian water-milfoil (*Myriophyllum spicatum*), European frog-bit (*Hydrocharis morsus-ranae*), and purple loosestrife (*Lythrum salicaria*). Forested habitats may be damaged by invasions of garlic mustard (*Alliaria petiolata*), gorse (*Ulex europaea*), and thistles (*Cirsium* species).

However, the worst ecological damage to native forests has been caused by alien tree-killing pathogens and insects. Prominent among the pathogens are the beech-bark disease (*Neonectria faginata*) that kills American beech (*Fagus grandifolia*), Dutch elm disease (*Ceratocystis ulmi*) that affects white elm (*Ulmus americana*) and other native elms, chestnut blight (*Endothia parasitica*) that kills American chestnut (*Castanea dentata*), and butternut canker (*Sirococcus clavigignenti*) that kills butternut (*Juglans cinerea*). Examples of alien tree-killing insects include the Asian long-horned beetle (*Anoplophora glabripennis*) that destroys many species of native hardwood trees, brown spruce longhorn beetle (*Tetropium fuscum*; **Figure 14.14**) that kills red spruce (*Picea rubens*) and other spruces, and emerald ash borer (*Agrilus planipennis*) that kills all species of ashes (*Fraxinus* species).

These and other alien invaders of natural ecosystems cause enormous damage to the biodiversity of Canada. Their effects on native species and communities are second in importance only to the outright destruction of natural habitats by their conversion into anthropogenic land uses.

14.3 Canadian Biodiversity at Risk

Much of the indigenous biodiversity of Canada, and around the world, is at risk of extirpation or extinction. The major issues are the survival of many rare and endangered species whose abundance has become greatly depleted, and of certain natural communities whose extent has become so diminished that their persistence is jeopardized.

FIGURE 14.14 Mature Red Spruce (*Picea rubens*) Killed by the Brown Spruce Longhorn Beetle (*Tetropium fuscum*) This alien beetle attacks and kills mature spruce trees of various species. It first invaded North America in Halifax in the 1980s, likely having hitch-hiked in wooden materials used to secure or pack cargoes in container ships. Although it is spreading relatively slowly, this alien beetle is a threat to the spruce-dominated boreal forest across Canada.

Canadian Species at Risk

Species at risk in Canada are studied and designated by an organization known as the Committee on the Status of Endangered Wildlife in Canada (COSEWIC). Its role is mandated by the federal Government of Canada, and its 31-member committee is composed of biodiversity specialists and other representatives from governments (federal, provinces, territories), the Aboriginal community, and the non-governmental sector, including universities and environmental organizations.

COSEWIC has 10 specialist subcommittees that deal with particular groups of organisms, plus one on Aboriginal traditional ecological knowledge (TEK). The subcommittees use a broad-reaching consultative process to develop lists of candidates for designation of at-risk status. COSEWIC mostly considers the status of native species of wildlife, but it may also examine subspecies, varieties, and other taxonomic units (collectively, these are referred to as **taxa**, or singular, **taxon**). COSEWIC may also consider "evolutionarily significant populations" that are discrete and linked through evolution to some particular ecoscape (such as a genetically unique population of salmon that breeds only in a particular river system).

The COSEWIC subcommittees contract experts to prepare a status report for each candidate species, based on an analysis of the best-available scientific information and TEK relevant to Canada, but in the context of the global distribution of the taxon. If there is a lack of knowledge about a candidate species, then a precautionary approach is taken that is mindful of the potential conservation risks. The subcommittee considers the advice offered by the status report and then recommends to the main body of COSEWIC whether the species should be listed. That committee then makes its own decision about the designation of conservation status and communicates it to governments and the Canadian public. In addition, most provinces and territories have established a comparable process to designate species at risk within their own jurisdictions.

COSEWIC recognizes six categories of conservation risk, each of which has a particular meaning in terms of imminent threats to the survival of species (COSEWIC, 2010). The categories are:

- **Extinct** refers to a species (or taxon) that once occurred in Canada but no longer exists anywhere in the world. Seven species whose range included Canada are extinct: the Labrador duck (*Camptorhynchus labradorium*), passenger pigeon (*Ectopistes migratorius*), great auk (*Pinguinus impennis*), sea mink (*Mustela macrodon*), deepwater cisco (*Coregonus johannae*), eelgrass limpet (*Lottia alveus*), and Macoun's shining moss (*Neomacounia nitida*). Extinct subspecies include the blue pike (*Stizostedion vitreum glaucum*) and Queen Charlottes caribou (*Rangifer tarandus dawsoni*).
- **Extirpated** refers to a species that formerly occurred in Canada but now survives only elsewhere, usually in the United States **(Figure 14.15)**. The 22 extirpated taxa of Canada include the Atlantic grey whale (*Eschrichtius robustus*), greater prairie chicken (*Tympanuchus cupido*), timber rattlesnake (*Crotalus horridus*), paddlefish (*Polyodon spathula*), dwarf wedge-mussel (*Alsamidonta heterodon*), and Oregon lupine (*Lupinus oreganus*).

- **Endangered** refers to a species that is at imminent risk of extinction or extirpation in all or an important portion of its range in Canada. As of 2013, 298 taxa were listed as endangered in Canada. Examples include the swift fox (*Vulpes velox*), right whale (*Balaena glacialis*), northern bobwhite (*Colinus virginianus*), whooping crane (*Grus americana;* **Figure 14.16**), piping plover (*Charadrius melodus*), burrowing owl (*Speotyto cunicularia*), leatherback seaturtle (*Dermochelys coriacea*), greater short-horned lizard (*Phrynosoma hernandesi*), eastern prickly pear cactus (*Opuntia humifusa*), Rocky Mountain tailed frog (*Ascaphus montanus*), Atlantic whitefish (*Coregonus huntsmani*), yucca moth (*Tegeticula yuccasella*), eastern mountain-avens (*Geum peckii*), American chestnut (*Castanea dentata*), and Atlantic boreal felt lichen (*Erioderma pedicillatum*).
- **Threatened** refers to a species that is likely to become endangered unless factors affecting its risk are mitigated. As of 2013, 164 taxa were listed as threatened in Canada. Examples are the grey fox (*Urocyon cinereoargenteus*), northern fur seal (*Callorhinus ursinus*), least bittern (*Ixobrychus exilis*), Ross's gull (*Rhodostethia rosea*), hooded warbler (*Wilsonia citrina*), Butler's gartersnake (*Thamnophis butleri*), northern abalone (*Haliotis kamtschatkana*), Fowler's toad (*Bufo fowleri*), phantom orchid (*Cephalanthera austiniae*), and lakeside daisy (*Hymenoxys herbacea*).
- **Special concern** (formerly referred to as **vulnerable**) refers to a species that is at risk of becoming threatened because of small or declining numbers or occurrence in a limited range. As of 2013, 192 taxa were of special concern.

FIGURE 14.15 The Black-Footed Ferret (*Mustela nigripes*) Was Extirpated in Canada It survives only as an endangered species in drier prairie regions of the United States. In 2009, however, a small number of these rare animals was released to Grasslands National Park in southern Saskatchewan, in an attempt to re-establish a breeding population in Canada.

FIGURE 14.16 The Whooping Crane (*Grus americana*) This large bird is endangered in Canada and throughout its natural range in North America. It breeds in and around Wood Buffalo National Park in northern Alberta (shown here) and the southwestern Northwest Territories, and migrates to spend the winter on the coast of the Gulf of Mexico in Texas.

Ryan Hagerty, courtesy of US Fish & Wildlife Service

- **Data deficient** applies when the available information is not sufficient to resolve an assessment of conservation status of a species. As of 2013, 56 of the taxa that had been examined in the COSEWIC process were designated as data deficient, and another 172 as not being at risk.

Each year, the number of species listed by COSEWIC as being at risk grows longer. This occurs because the committee is diligently performing the work expected of it—considering the conservation status of a backlog of rare Canadian species, and in the process of doing so, finding additional ones that are at risk. Moreover, any designation of status is ephemeral, because situations are continuously changing for better or worse. This is why COSEWIC periodically reconsiders designated species, typically on a five-year rotation, to determine if a change of status is warranted.

The speed with which COSEWIC and its specialty subcommittees can work is limited by the funding and other forms of support that they receive and also by their own energy and time—the members are specialists who are volunteering their support to the work of assessing the conservation status of the native species of Canada. In some cases there has also been difficulty in moving forward with COSEWIC recommendations to an actual designation of certain species as being at risk under the federal *Species at Risk Act* (SARA). This sort of politicization has been especially prominent in the final listing of marine species of importance in commercial fisheries.

Of course, it is not sufficient merely to designate species as being at risk of extirpation or extinction—the responsible follow-up requires that recovery plans for the listed species be developed and implemented. In Canada, all taxa listed by COSEWIC as endangered or threatened must also have a **recovery strategy** developed that would promote an increase of their population to a viable level. This work is done by an organization known as RENEW

(REcovery of Nationally Endangered Wildlife). As of 2013, 149 recovery strategies had been finalized and 23 others were in various stages of development (Environment Canada, 2013). This means that recovery plans have been completed for only about one-third of the taxa for which they are required, and another 5 percent are in progress. However, action has not yet begun on the remaining taxa designated by COSEWIC as endangered or threatened.

Communities at Risk

Some kinds of natural communities now occur only as small remnants of their former extent in Canada, usually because most of their original distribution has been converted into agricultural or urbanized land uses. In such cases, the sustainability of entire natural ecosystem types is at risk. The most endangered indigenous communities of Canada are:

- tallgrass prairie of southeastern Manitoba and southwestern Ontario, which survives at less than 1 percent of its original extent;
- mixedgrass and shortgrass prairie of western Canada, which are also greatly depleted through conversion into agriculture, although not to the same degree as tallgrass prairie;
- Carolinian forest of southern Ontario, of which <2 percent survives;
- dry coastal forest dominated by Douglas fir (*Pseudotsuga menziesii*), of which only 2 percent remains;
- Garry oak (*Quercus garryi*) forest of southern Vancouver Island, of which <5 percent survives;
- semi-desert of southeastern British Columbia, which is diminished to <5 percent of its original extent;
- various kinds of old-growth forest communities in all parts of forested Canada, but especially in the east—for instance, less than 1 percent of the forest estate in Nova Scotia is now older than 100 years;

even in coastal British Columbia, where the humid climate is particularly favourable to the development of old-growth forest, these communities are rapidly becoming less extensive, mostly because of timber harvesting that converts the primary ecosystem into a younger, second-growth forest; and

- natural fish communities, which have also been widely decimated, including mixed-species ones in the Great Lakes, salmonids (salmon and trout) in western Canada, and groundfish and deepwater sponge and coral habitats off the Atlantic provinces.

Some of the natural communities at risk are habitats for numerous species at risk. This is particularly true of tallgrass prairie, semi-desert, Carolinian forest, and Garry oak forest, all of which provide critical habitat for many rare plants and animals. As we examine in more detail in Section 14.5, it is crucial that the remaining tracts of these endangered communities are conserved in protected areas, such as ecological reserves and parks.

14.4 Conservation Biology

Conservation biology applies scientific knowledge to help elements of biodiversity survive threats posed by anthropogenic stressors. It is a highly interdisciplinary field, with ecology and biology at its core, and economics, sociology, geography, and other subjects also being important to the management of some problems. Conservation biology is a relatively recent subject area—the first book by that title was published in 1980 by Soulé and Wilcox, at about the same time as the word and concept of biodiversity emerged into general use.

The mission of conservation biology is to discover effective ways of preventing losses of biodiversity at any of its levels—genetics, populations, species, communities, or ecoscapes. This is an urgent mission, because grievous damage to biodiversity is proceeding apace and may even be accelerating. Actions to sustain biodiversity must be undertaken in two major ways:

1. *By conserving biodiversity in areas that are "working" to provide the economy with natural resources,* such as agricultural products, the biomass of trees and fish, and other commodities. Even in these sorts of "working" ecoscapes there are many opportunities to provide habitat for elements of native biodiversity. This is particularly the case in areas that are not intensively harvested and managed, but much less so where the management systems are intensive and intended primarily to serve the needs of the economy. Nevertheless, even in urban and agricultural areas there are ways of managing habitats to provide conditions suitable for many native species and other elements of biodiversity. The knowledge

of conservation biology provides invaluable advice about the helpful mitigations that favour these sorts of improved ecological conditions.

2. *By preserving biodiversity in protected areas that are set aside from intensive economic use,* such as parks, ecological reserves, and wilderness areas. Protected areas are intended to sustain biodiversity values that are not compatible with the economic activities that occur on "working" ecoscapes. For example, the special values of old-growth forests and their dependent species are generally irreconcilable with environmental changes that occur when timber is harvested. This may also be the case of certain wide-ranging animals, such as grizzly bear, timber wolf, and orca; their needs may be incompatible with certain kinds of economic activities in the ecoscapes where they live. By ensuring that a sufficient network of protected areas is established to accommodate the special needs of these vulnerable natural ecosystems and species, we can increase the likelihood that they will continue to survive at viable levels of abundance, even while the human economy is supported in other ecoscapes. Again, conservation biology provides crucial advice about the design and stewardship of systems of protected areas.

Moreover, the mission of conservation biology also recognizes that local people must support actions that sustain biodiversity and the ecological services that it provides. In general, conservation actions are less likely to be successful if the needs and aspirations of local human communities are not integrated into management plans.

Fields within Conservation Biology

Because biodiversity is a hierarchical concept, so are the fields of investigation of conservation biology. The major subject areas are:

- *Conservation genetics,* which focuses on questions such as the amount of genetic diversity that is necessary to prevent small and isolated populations from suffering deleterious consequences from breeding among closely related individuals (this is known as inbreeding depression) (see Chapter 12);
- *Population biology,* which examines the demographic parameters of species at risk, such as fecundity, mortality, immigration, and emigration, as well as biological and environmental factors that influence those parameters, while also estimating the minimum viable population that must be maintained to prevent species from spiralling into extinction (see chapters 2 and 5);
- *Behavioural ecology,* which investigates activities and related traits that influence population size and viability, such as habitat and food choices, seasonal migrations, and factors that affect long-distance

movements and hence the ability to colonize isolated patches of suitable habitat (see Chapter 6);

- *Landscape ecology,* which provides insight into the patch dynamics of natural ecoscapes and how they are affected by disturbances and other environmental influences (see chapters 10 and 13). This knowledge is essential to the design and management of networks of protected areas, as well as appropriate management systems for "working" ecoscapes;
- *Functional ecology,* which is essential to understanding the magnitude of ecosystem services that are provided by ecoscapes that are conserved or protected, and that are essential to sustaining both the human economy and the natural world (see Chapter 4). Examples include the storage of carbon in biomass (and so keeping it out of the atmosphere as CO_2, an important greenhouse gas), regulation of hydrological conditions, prevention of erosion, and cleansing the environment of anthropogenic pollutants such as sulphur dioxide, ozone, and pesticides;
- *Ecological economics,* which provides an objective method of assigning value to biodiversity and ecological services that goes beyond their intrinsic worth (see Chapter 15). This valuation (measuring worth in dollars) is crucial because it allows economists to subtract the "cost" of ecological damage from the "revenues" of economic activities that are causing them to occur, so that an ecologically appropriate measure of "profit" can be made. If the value of ecological damage is greater than the revenue from resource extraction, then no true profit is being made—in fact, there is an accumulation of "natural debt." According to Costanza et al. (1997), the aggregate value of ecological services provided by the biosphere is almost double that of the global gross domestic product (the researchers estimated global ecosystem services to have a value of about \$US33 trillion in 1997, a year when the annual GDP was about \$US18 trillion);
- *Environmental sociology,* which helps us to understand and integrate the needs and concerns of local communities, including Aboriginal nations, into conservation actions in the regions where they live and may have long-standing occupancy or ownership claims.

Important Concepts in Conservation Biology

Within these major areas of knowledge, a number of concepts are particularly important and relevant to conservation biology. We explore these in the following sections.

Minimum Viable Population

The **minimum viable population (MVP)** is the least abundance that would allow a population to persist in the wild (Shaffer, 1981). Populations less than the MVP are expected to dwindle to extirpation or extinction. MVPs are estimated using computer simulation models known as a population viability analysis (PVA), which accounts for biological factors such as fecundity, mortality, longevity, immigration, and inbreeding depression, as well as environmental influences such as the likelihood of unpredictable disturbances, climate change, and other agents of stress or mortality. The PVA simulations are typically run thousands of times to estimate a likelihood of survival under particular biological and ecological scenarios of a species being investigated. Typical MVPs for terrestrial vertebrates are in the low thousands of individuals (Traill et al., 2007).

Minimum Viable Area

Minimum viable area (MVA) is a similar concept to the MVP, and it refers either to the least area of suitable habitat that would allow a population at risk to persist in the wild, or for an imperilled community type to survive. The latter kind of MVA must account for the natural patch-scale dynamics of the ecoscape in which the community is embedded. For instance, if the objective is to conserve a particular kind of old-growth forest, then the viability analysis would have to account for the return frequency and typical area of stand-replacing disturbances, as well as the length of successional time that is required to regenerate an old-growth forest on a disturbed patch. The ability of species to disperse among old-growth patches is also a key consideration.

Rarity

Rarity is related to a low likelihood of encountering a particular species. It could be due to a very low population density or to a species occurring only in small and isolated populations, and sometimes the double jeopardy of both of those characteristics. There are several important aspects to rarity that must be considered when evaluating the viability and conservation status of a species at risk. These considerations include the number of populations, the size and viability of each one, and their connectedness—is it likely that individuals or propagules can disperse among isolated patches of suitable habitat, or is the surrounding matrix too inhospitable to allow this to occur?

Estimating Extinction Rates

Estimating extinction rates is a relatively simple task for species whose range and abundance are well known, and for groups of organisms for which most species have been identified and named, such as vertebrate animals. However, other groups of organisms have not yet been well studied and little is known about their levels of biodiversity. Because we do not yet understand how many species of small invertebrates there are, or of bacteria and other microorganisms, we cannot accurately measure or predict their rates of extinction.

As we learned earlier in this chapter, conservation biologists believe that the present rate of extinction is exceedingly high, and that millions of species could become extinct within the next century—in aggregate, this would be equivalent to about half of the existing biodiversity of the planet. However, the great majority of the losses will be "hidden" extinctions of species that biologists have not yet "discovered." This lack of knowledge about extinctions is an important issue, because it allows environmental skeptics to minimize the importance of the biodiversity crisis, and this makes it difficult to gather sufficient financial and other resources for conservation.

Theory of Island Biogeography

The theory of **island biogeography** was first suggested by MacArthur and Wilson (1967) to explain variations in the numbers of species found on oceanic islands. In essence, the theory is based on differences in the species richness and rates of immigration and extinction among various kinds of islands. The theory predicts that (1) smaller islands support smaller populations, which are less viable and so have a higher extinction rate, compared with larger populations on larger islands; and (2) islands that are more distant from a mainland or from other islands will have a lower rate of immigration of new species, because longer gaps reduce the likelihood of colonization. The theory also predicts that, over a long period of time, an equilibrium condition will be established between these two influences, and this will result in fewer species occurring on islands that are relatively small and isolated, compared with those that are larger and closer to a mainland.

The theory has been tested many times by experiments and using field observations. One study by McNeil and Cody (1978) examined the numbers of plant species on 17 islands in St. Lawrence Islands National Park, in the region where Lake Ontario drains into the St. Lawrence River. They found a strong relationship between island area and the richness of plant species **(Figure 14.17)**.

The theory of island biogeography has been extended to other kinds of habitat "islands" that are surrounded by an inhospitable matrix, as would be the case of woodlots of various sizes and dispersion embedded in cornfields. In Section 14.5, we examine implications of predictions of the theory of island biogeography for the design of protected areas.

Keystone Species

Keystone species have a disproportionately large influence on the ecological structure and functionality of the community of which they are a component—much more so

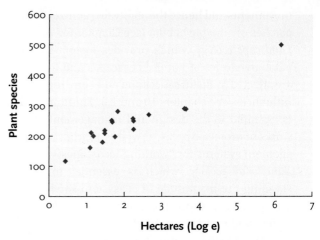

FIGURE 14.17 Relationship of Island Area to Plant Species Richness in the Thousand Islands National Park Species richness (S) is based on a thorough search of the terrain, and island area (A) is measured in hectares. The linear regression of the data is S = 57 $\log_e A$ + 121; r^2 = 0.88.

SOURCE: Based on data from McNeil J. and W.J. Cody. 1978. "Species-area relationships for vascular plants of some St. Lawrence River islands," *Canadian Field-Naturalist*, 92: 10–18.

than would be predicted based on their numbers or biomass (see Section 9.3). Consequently, if a keystone species is lost, its community undergoes a massive change. For instance, the few species of microbes that are important in nitrification and nitrogen-fixing may be extremely important to the productivity and nutrient cycling of their ecosystem, in ways that far exceed their contributions to the system in terms of biomass (see Chapter 4).

One of the best-known examples of a keystone species is the sea otter (*Enydra lutris*) of Pacific coastal waters, which was hunted almost to extinction in the 18th and 19th centuries (**Figure 14.18**; see also Chapter 9). However, it was protected in the early 20th century and has since increased over much of its original range, including to the west coast of Vancouver Island, where it was reintroduced during 1969 to 1972. The sea otter is a predator of benthic invertebrates, which it dives to collect and brings to the surface to eat. It is fond of sea urchins (*Strongylocentrotus* species), spiny invertebrates that feed on large seaweeds known as kelp (brown algae in the order Laminariales, including "giant kelps" in the genera *Macrocystis* and *Nereocystis* that can have fronds 30–80 m long). When sea otters are abundant, their "top–down" feeding depresses the population of sea urchins, which limits their grazing so that luxurious "forests" of the seaweeds can develop. The kelp forests are an important community because their complex structure provides habitat for many species. However, if sea otters are missing or rare, as they were when overhunted, the urchins are abundant, overgraze the kelps, and convert the ecosystem to a sparse and rocky "barren ground." Those degraded habitats were widespread in regions where the otters had been decimated, but the kelp forests are again widespread where the otters have recovered. More

Thomas Kitchin & Victoria Hurst/First Light

FIGURE 14.18 The Sea Otter (*Enydra lutris*) This marine mammal of Pacific coastal waters is a keystone species. If present, its feeding on herbivorous sea urchins allows lush kelp forests to develop.

recently, in the early 1990s, some populations of orca (*Orcinus orca*) in the Aleutian Islands began to prey on sea otters, depressing their abundance and allowing barren grounds to reappear.

Umbrella Species

Umbrella species are usually wide-ranging animals that have a large home range and are components of many different kinds of communities, which is why the term "umbrella" is used to describe them (Roberge and Angelstam, 2004). Because these species have such extensive and complex habitat needs, any conservation actions that are effective at sustaining them at a viable population level are also likely to achieve many additional benefits for biodiversity. Examples that are prominent in conservation planning in Canada include the grizzly bear (*Ursus arctos*), polar bear (*Ursus maritimus*; **Figure 14.19**), and timber wolf (*Canis lupus*).

Flagship Species

The notion of a **flagship species** has little to do with ecology or biology—rather, their importance is in the marketing of biological conservation. Flagship species are charismatic or otherwise "attractive" species that are used to profile the importance of conservation activities to the general public. Most are big animals such as top predators, or large herbivores. For instance, the giant panda (*Ailuropoda melanoleuca*) has become a symbol of the global conservation activities of the World Wildlife Fund (WWF). In Canada, flagship species are mostly used to profile conservation actions directed toward particular kinds of ecosystems, and they include alluring terrestrial animals such as the beaver (*Castor canadensis*), timber

Bill Freedman

FIGURE 14.19 The Polar Bear (*Ursus maritimus*) This large carnivore is an umbrella species, in the sense that it is a wide-ranging animal whose populations can persist only if they have access to extensive natural habitat. Conservation actions that are effective at sustaining polar bears are also likely to achieve many additional biodiversity benefits. It is also a flagship species, because it is a beautiful and fascinating animal and most people are supportive of actions to conserve its populations.

wolf, and peregrine falcon (*Falco peregrinus*), as well as marine animals such as the humpback whale (*Megaptera novaeangliae*), polar bear, and orca. Even the maple leaf (usually sugar maple, *Acer saccharum*) is sometimes used as a flagship icon in Canada, not least because it is featured on our country's flag.

Conservation Priorities

Limited financial and human resources are available to support all of the work needed to prevent the endangerment and extinction of elements of biodiversity.

The necessary actions include the designation and stewardship of protected areas, as well as research in conservation biology that identifies ways to better manage biodiversity on "working" ecoscapes. In such a constrained situation, it is necessary to undertake planning exercises to determine priorities, based on the knowledge of conservation biology, for the allocation of scarce resources.

Some researchers argue that we should focus on **hotspots of biodiversity**. These are regions that, at a global scale, support a relatively high density of endemic species or of biodiversity in general. For this reason, conservation action that that is focused on hotspots can result in disproportionately large fractions of species richness being sustained (compared with the relative area of the hotspot). This idea was first proposed by Myers et al. (1999), whose analysis suggested that up to 35 percent of terrestrial vertebrate species (mammals, birds, reptiles, and amphibians) and 44 percent of vascular plants are confined to 25 hotspots that represent only 1.4 percent of Earth's land surface. Clearly, those regions should be high priorities for global conservation actions, particularly in view of the fact that the natural ecosystems of the hotspots and many of the species they support are imperilled.

Most of the hotspots occur in tropical latitudes (none are in Canada) and most are forested ecosystems. They include areas of high endemic biodiversity such as the Atlantic forest of Brazil, the Caribbean Islands, Madagascar, the Philippines, New Zealand, and about 25 others **(Figure 14.20)**. Ongoing research is also identifying hotspots of marine biodiversity, particularly of tropical coral reefs and mid-latitude aggregations of species of large fish and marine mammals.

While recognizing the obvious benefits of conserving natural habitats in hotspots of the world, it is also necessary to work in other regions with less-focused concentrations of biodiversity, which are sometimes referred to as **coldspots of biodiversity** (Kareiva and Marvier, 2003). Although these regions support fewer endemic species, they nevertheless sustain important biodiversity and ecological values. For example, their extensive ecosystems provide crucial levels of ecosystem functions, such as carbon storage in biomass, nutrient cycling, control over erosion, moderation of the hydrological cycle, and other services that are beneficial to both the human economy and to all life on Earth. Moreover, at the national scale, it is important that natural heritage is conserved, even in countries that do not have globally significant hotspots. This is the case of Canada—our biodiversity is much less rich than that of tropical countries, but that in no way excuses Canada from working aggressively to conserve its indigenous biodiversity.

While hotspot and coldspot options are influential in planning for the conservation of biodiversity, too strong a reliance on either of them will inevitably be controversial. This is because all aspects of biodiversity contribute to ecosystem services, and they all have inherent value, and so it is tragic if any become greatly diminished or are irretrievably lost.

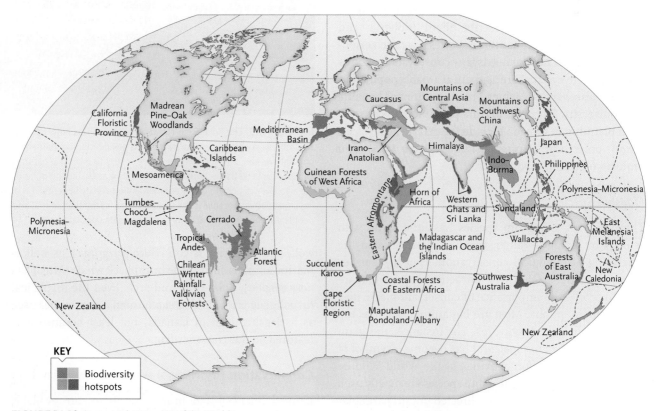

FIGURE 14.20 Terrestrial Hotspots of the World

SOURCE: © Conservation International.

14.5 Protected Areas

Protected areas are tracts of land or water that are set aside from intensive economic use, such as parks, ecological reserves, and wilderness areas. There are many kinds of protected areas, and the sorts of activities that are permitted inside them reflect a diversity of intentions. Some uses have a large economic impact, such as parks that are heavily devoted to tourism and outdoor recreation. Some parks allow consumptive uses, such as hunting, fishing, and even timber harvesting. Protected areas are also used for less-intrusive activities, such as education and ecological research.

However, in a biodiversity context the key role of protected areas is to sustain natural values that are incompatible with the intensive economic activities that occur on working ecoscapes. In this sense, protected areas are intended to (1) sustain self-organizing ecosystems that are representative of the natural types within an ecoregion, while also (2) protecting the habitat of rare or endangered species. In many cases, however, this role of conserving biodiversity is in conflict with other uses of protected areas. We will examine several examples of this kind of struggle later in this section.

It is important to understand, however, that protected areas are not the only way to conserve natural biodiversity—in fact, in isolation, they are not capable of accomplishing that goal. To the degree that is feasible and possible, it is also crucial that native species and natural communities also be accommodated in areas that are working for commercial purposes, such as in agriculture, forestry, fishing, mining, or urbanization. Within that larger context, the role of protected areas is to ensure that species and communities that are at risk in the "nonprotected" areas will still have suitable refuges of habitat.

Protected areas may be established by a variety of agencies, both public and private. For instance, Parks Canada, an agency of the federal government, has established 45 national parks (this number includes six national park reserves, which are not yet fully designated) in various regions of our country, plus four national marine conservation areas, while the Canadian Wildlife Service has designated 55 national wildlife areas (data as of 2013). All provincial and territorial governments also have designated systems of protected areas, as have some municipal governments.

In addition, the Nature Conservancy of Canada (NCC) and Ducks Unlimited Canada (DUC) are the leading non-governmental organizations (NGOs) that focus on acquiring private property to establish protected areas in Canada **(Figure 14.21)**. These are national NGOs, and there are also hundreds of smaller land trusts that operate more locally.

FIGURE 14.21 The Nature Conservancy of Canada (NCC) This is a Non-Governmental Organization (NGO) that acquires private property to establish protected areas in Canada. It is a national NGO, and hundreds of smaller land trusts also operate more locally in Canada. This protected area is on Brier Island, Nova Scotia.

Planning for Conservation

Ideally, the location, size, and dispersion of protected areas have been advised by a systematic process of **conservation planning**. The aim of conservation planning is to identify the most important places that should be set aside, within the context of a comprehensive network of protected areas. The **system plan** should capture those areas with the highest priority biodiversity values, while ensuring that all indigenous elements are conserved in the greater region, including in "working" areas. Key steps of conservation planning are the following (Margules and Pressey, 2000; NCC, 2010; see also **Figure 14.22**):

- *Assemble data on biodiversity for the planning region:* The most important kinds of information involve the spatial distributions of natural communities, as well as the locations of rare habitats and species at risk. The data should be **geo-referenced** (meaning the location and boundaries are established according to latitude and longitude) so that the information can be recorded on maps using a computerized geographic information system (GIS; see Chapter 13).
- *Identify conservation goals:* The broader goal is to ensure that all indigenous biodiversity values are accommodated within the planning region. Usually the focus is on natural communities and native species of the ecological region—these are the biodiversity targets to be conserved at viable levels of abundance. The biodiversity targets to be accommodated in protected areas must be identified, as well as those that can be met in working areas.

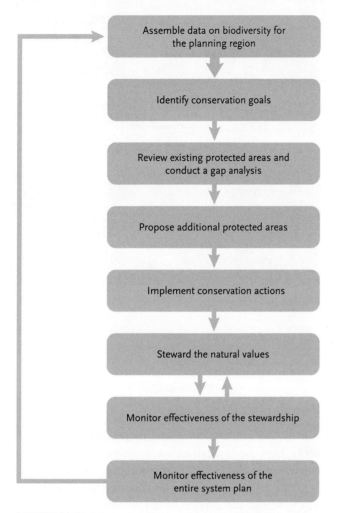

```
Assemble data on biodiversity for
the planning region

        ↓

Identify conservation goals

        ↓

Review existing protected areas and
conduct a gap analysis

        ↓

Propose additional protected areas

        ↓

Implement conservation actions

        ↓

Steward the natural values

        ↕

Monitor effectiveness of the stewardship

        ↓

Monitor effectiveness of the
entire system plan
```

FIGURE 14.22 Schematic Diagram of the Steps Needed to Achieve an Effective System Plan for Conservation See text for details.

- *Review existing protected areas:* If some protected areas are already established, then the biodiversity targets they support must be documented. A **gap analysis** is then done to identify the biodiversity targets that are not yet being adequately conserved in protected areas.
- *Propose additional protected areas:* The results of the gap analysis are used to plan the locations of additional areas to be protected, in order to ensure that all targets are being met. The system should have redundancy embedded, which will help to mitigate the potential effects of disturbances and other environmental changes. For example, if only one location is protected for a rare plant, the species could become extinct if that location is disturbed by a wildfire or another catastrophe. Protecting several critical habitats helps to decrease this risk of an irretrievable loss. An additional consideration is tenure of the land that is proposed for protection—whether the property is already owned by government (this is referred to as public land or as Crown land) or by private interests, and, if the latter, whether the owner is willing to sell or donate it to a conservation organization.

- *Implement conservation actions:* If a target property is owned by government, it can potentially be set aside as a protected area, assuming there are no irreconcilable conflicts with economic uses (such as permits to explore for or extract minerals, to harvest timber, or to graze livestock). If the property is privately owned, it can potentially be acquired for the purpose of establishing a protected area. This can be done by purchase or donation, either by a land-focused environmental charity such as the Nature Conservancy of Canada (NCC), or by a governmental agency (see Environmental Applications 14.2 for a discussion of the NCC).
- *Steward the natural values:* All protected areas must be managed appropriately to maintain the biodiversity and ecological values that they are intended to sustain. These ongoing actions are known as **stewardship**, and they are just as essential to conservation success as the act of designating protected areas. The intensity of stewardship can range from periodic monitoring of remote protected areas that are little affected by anthropogenic stressors, to more heroic measures such as restoring the depleted populations of endangered species or reconstructing rare ecological communities.
- *Effectiveness monitoring:* The effectiveness of the system plan in achieving its intent of conserving natural values must be monitored. There are two aspects of this: (1) stewardship activities should be monitored, and if found to be deficient they must be adaptively improved to address any emerged problems, and (2) the effectiveness of all actions on the working and protected areas must be evaluated, and any observed deficiencies addressed by implementing more effective conservation measures.

Conservation planning is undertaken by various agencies, with the ultimate goal of designing systems of protected areas that will be successful in conserving biodiversity. This goal may be relevant to various geographic scales—county, province, national, and global. In Canada, protected areas involve tracts that are controlled by governments (local, provincial, territorial, or federal), and also by Aboriginal authorities and private interests. Ideally, the system of protected areas, in concert with conservation actions on "working" ecoscapes, would be capable of sustaining all native species and natural ecosystems over the longer term, including terrestrial, freshwater, and marine systems.

This is, of course, an ideal model. In fact, no country has yet designed and implemented a comprehensive system of protected areas that sustains all indigenous biodiversity. Moreover, many existing protected areas have important management problems because they are too small to meet their conservation objectives, or they are affected by various degrading environmental stressors (see the case studies of national parks in "Stewardship of Protected Areas" on page 375).

Design of Protected Areas

From the perspective of biodiversity, the conservation objectives are the most important considerations in the design of a protected area. If the intent is to protect the critical habitat of one or more species at risk, then a protected area must be designed to include sustainable tracts of those targeted communities. On the other hand, if the goal is to maintain representative tracts of certain kinds of ecosystems, such as old-growth forest, then a protected area must be designed to accommodate the ecological conditions that are essential to maintaining that type against the inexorable effects of disturbances, climate change, and other environmental influences. The latter consideration acknowledges that a particular stand of old-growth forest cannot be preserved forever—rather, landscape-scale protected areas are required to conserve the ecological dynamics that allow stands of old-growth forest to develop.

Some theoretical considerations are also relevant to the design of protected areas. There are always limited resources available to establish these sorts of reserves. Therefore, to use the resources efficiently, networks of protected areas should be designed to optimize their size, shape, and position on the ecoscape so they can best deliver their intended function of conserving biodiversity.

Two of the design-related recommendations of conservation biologists are not controversial, because if followed they will always increase the likelihood of achieving success when designating a system of protected areas:

- *The number of protected areas:* The universal recommendation is to have as many protected areas as possible, given the various societal and economic constraints that may be operative in any context.
- *The size of protected areas:* They should be as large as possible, especially if large-scale ecological functions are to be maintained within their boundaries.

However, other aspects of the design of protected areas are actively debated by ecologists and conservation biologists, and the issues are not yet resolved. Much of the discussion of these controversial aspects of design is related to the theory of island biogeography, which we examined in the previous section. Here are some of the prominent questions:

- *Size versus number:* There may be a choice to be made between the size (area) and the number of protected areas. This being the case, is it preferable to have a large reserve, or a number of smaller ones of the same cumulative area **(Figure 14.23a)**? Conservation biologists identify this question with the acronym **SLOSS**, meaning single large or several small.

According to island biogeography, larger protected areas are a better choice because populations occurring in them are predicted to have a lower risk of extinction, compared with those in smaller reserves. However, separate protected areas also maintain discrete populations, which may provide a degree of helpful redundancy against a catastrophic loss of an endangered species in any one of them.

- *Interior habitat:* The shape of a protected area is an important consideration **(Figure 14.23b)**. So-called interior habitat is not affected by environmental conditions occurring at ecotones, such as a forest edge beside an adjacent pasture or wetland. Invasive species, predators, and parasites (such as cowbirds) are often more abundant in ecotone habitats than in interior ones. These can be important problems, and their influence may result in some species being able to survive and reproduce successfully only in interior habitats. In general, interior habitat is proportionately more abundant in protected areas that are larger and circular, because circles have a smaller ratio of edge to area than any other shape.
- *Distance between protected areas:* The distance between protected areas is also important. If a species becomes extirpated in a particular reserve, the likelihood of a natural recolonization is higher if it still persists in a nearby protected area. This could be a benefit of having protected areas located close to each other **(Figure 14.23c, d)**. On the other hand, proximity could also increase the likelihood of diseases or invasive species spreading among reserves.
- *Corridors:* A corridor is a connecting strip of habitat that is suitable for the movement of a species of interest (this attribute is sometimes referred to as **permeability**). Protected areas that are connected by corridors may have improved gene flow among

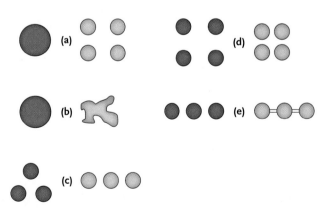

FIGURE 14.23 Conceptual Options for the Design of Protected Areas In each paired comparison, the cumulative area of each choice is assumed to be the same. See text for discussion of the benefits and risks of the paired choices.

SOURCE: Modified from Simberloff, D. 1988. "The contribution of population and community ecology to conservation science," *Annual Reviews of Ecology and Systematics*, 19: 473–511.

The Nature Conservancy of Canada: Conservation Science in the Private Sector

The Nature Conservancy of Canada (NCC) is an environmental charity, founded in 1962, whose mission is to work to conserve the indigenous bio-diversity of Canada (Freedman, 2013). The NCC raises funds from the public, governments, companies, and founda-tions and uses those monies to acquire private properties of high conservation value, and to then set them aside and steward them as protected areas. NCC does this because it and its supporters believe in the intrinsic value of bio-diversity. However, the organization does allow low-impact public access to most of its protected areas, so that people can enjoy and learn from the natural world. Because NCC is an environmental charity with limited funding, it is important that it uses its scarce resources effectively, and to accomplish that goal the organiza-tion engages in high-end conservation science.

The first level of conservation plan-ning at NCC occurs at the scale of ecoregions (the level below ecozones; see Chapter 11). Because most of the imperilled biodiversity of Canada is in its southern regions, this is also where NCC's ecoregional planning is focussed. The work is done with many partners; some provide funding, while others supply data on biodiversity within the ecoregion, collaborate with statistical and spatial analyses (the latter using GIS), or work with NCC to create protected areas. As of 2013,

NCC had completed or was working on 18 conservation blueprints **(Figure 1)**, each of which is an extensive and detailed planning document [see Henson et al. (2004) and Riley et al. (2007) for examples of conservation blueprints]. The blueprints provide carefully selected biogeographic tar-gets for conservation action, as well as indicators of progress and plans for moving forward. Ecoregions along the U.S. border are binational in scope—biodiversity knows nothing about political boundaries, and eco-regional planning respects that natural fact.

Once a conservation blueprint is completed for an ecoregion, another level of planning exercise is under-taken, referred to as a *natural area con-servation plan* (NACP). These have a more local focus, and typically result in a plan for assemblies of contiguous properties that, in aggregate, will con-serve an area known to be important for biodiversity. Usually, the area sus-tains species at risk or rare ecological communities, in addition to represent-ative tracts of less-threatened natural values. Each NACP has:

· a vision statement for the conservation action;
· a science-based rationalization of why it is an important place to create protected areas;
· highlights of specific properties that should be acquired;

· an explanation of the kinds of stewardship actions that are necessary in and around the reserve; and
· lists of the known or potential sources of funding to support the project.

The latter is no small consideration—the NACPs require millions of dollars to implement, and NCC is a charity that must raise these funds from various part-ners in its work and mission. As of 2013, NCC had prepared or was working on 90 NACPs, but additional ones will be added to this portfolio as the need and funding develop.

NCC also engages in considerable ecological research that is needed to guide its stewardship in managing pro-tected areas once they are acquired. In some cases, truly heroic stewardship is needed, such as actions to re-create areas of endangered communities, such as tallgrass prairie or Carolinian forest. Other stewardship activities might focus on reducing the abundance of invasive aliens that threaten native spe-cies or communities. These kinds of conservation actions cannot be suc-cessfully undertaken unless they are guided by ecological science, which often is region- or even site-specific. To this end, NCC employs its own in-house ecologists, while also working with a network of specialists in universities, governmental agencies, and the private sector.

---

otherwise isolated populations, and there may be a higher likelihood of recolonization after extirpation **(Figure 14.23e)**. However, there is also a risk that cor-ridors make it easier for diseases and invasive species to spread.

These sorts of design considerations are informative because they are based on ecological theory and empirical observations about environmental stressors and circum-stances. However, when establishing protected areas in the real world, these concerns are often trumped by

practical considerations, such as whether specific proper-ties of high conservation value are actually available to be purchased, so that they can be acquired to establish a protected area. In the case of lands already owned by a governmental agency, there may be conflicts with other potentially important uses of the land, such as timber harvesting, hunting, or mining. These economic conflicts could prevent a governmental agency from establishing a protected area, or one that is optimally designed for its size, shape, connectivity, and the sorts of ecological com-munities it sustains.

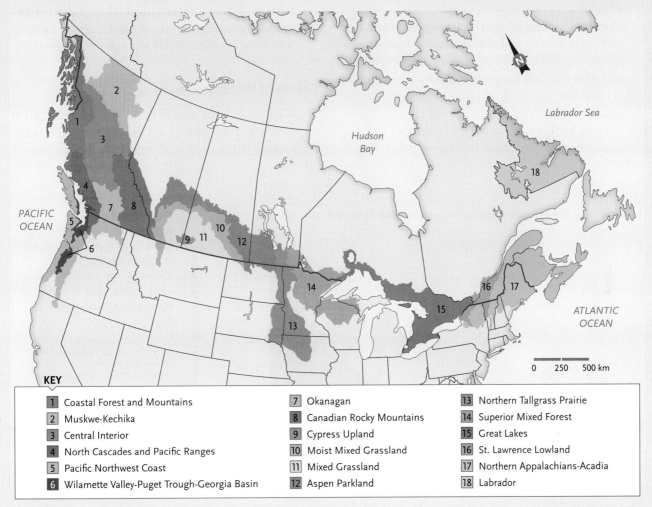

FIGURE 1 Ecoregions of Canada (and the Adjacent United States) Where the Nature Conservancy of Canada Has Completed or Is Working on Conservation Blueprints

SOURCE: Freedman, B. 2013. *A History of the Nature Conservancy of Canada*. Oxford University Press, Toronto, ON.

KEY

1	Coastal Forest and Mountains
2	Muskwe-Kechika
3	Central Interior
4	North Cascades and Pacific Ranges
5	Pacific Northwest Coast
6	Wilamette Valley-Puget Trough-Georgia Basin
7	Okanagan
8	Canadian Rocky Mountains
9	Cypress Upland
10	Moist Mixed Grassland
11	Mixed Grassland
12	Aspen Parkland
13	Northern Tallgrass Prairie
14	Superior Mixed Forest
15	Great Lakes
16	St. Lawrence Lowland
17	Northern Appalachians-Acadia
18	Labrador

The Nature Conservancy of Canada takes its conservation science seriously. This is necessary if it is to achieve success in its mission of private-sector conservation. It also assures the many sponsors of NCC that their funding is being well spent to conserve the threatened biodiversity of Canada.

Kinds of Protected Areas

Protected areas are properties or larger tracts of ecoscape that have been set aside from intensive economic use. However, there are various types of protected areas, which differ in the ways that they may be integrated into the human economy. The International Union for the Conservation of Nature recognizes the following categories of protected areas, which reflect the management intent of the reserve (IUCN, 2009):

- *Category Ia:* These are strictly protected **ecological reserves** that are set aside to conserve natural values, particularly biodiversity, and in which visitation is strictly limited and the only permitted activities are scientific monitoring and research.

- *Category Ib:* These are large **wilderness areas** that are managed to preserve their natural condition, with low levels of nonintensive, nonextractive visitation being permitted.

- *Category II:* These are co-managed for the conservation of natural ecosystems along with outdoor recreation and other compatible activities, as is typical of national parks and provincial parks.

- *Category III:* These are managed to conserve specific natural features, such as a prominent landform or other geological feature, or an ecological one such as a tract of old-growth forest. These protected areas are sometimes called *natural monuments* and they are usually relatively small and host a great deal of visitation.

- *Category IV:* These are **special management areas** for particular species or habitats, usually ones of economic importance, and are intended to achieve conservation through the protection and management of habitats; hunting, forestry, and some other extractive industries may be permitted.
- *Category V:* These are "protected landscapes and seascapes" that are co-managed to conserve those extensive regions together with their distinct cultural intersections with local peoples and their economic activities; these are sometimes referred to as "heritage areas."
- *Category VI.* These "managed-resource protected areas" are intended to conserve natural values, but in the context of the sustainable use of natural resources using traditional (non-industrial) management systems.

Extent of Protected Areas

There has been rapid growth in the numbers and extent of protected areas throughout the world **(Figure 14.24)**. There are now about 17×10^6 km² of IUCN categories I

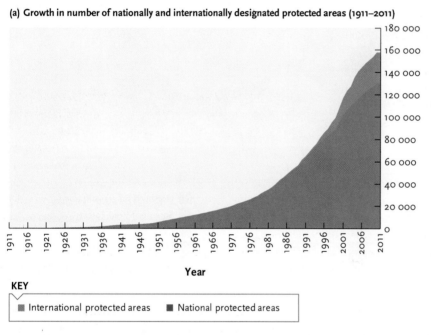

(a) Growth in number of nationally and internationally designated protected areas (1911–2011)

KEY

■ International protected areas   ■ National protected areas

FIGURE 14.24

Growth in the Numbers (a) and Extent (b) of Protected Areas in the World The database includes IUCN I–VI sites, but only those for which the year of designation is known (this excludes 43.7×10^3 sites).

SOURCE: IUCN and UNEP-WCMC (2012) The World Database on Protected Areas (WDPA): February 2012. Cambridge, UK: UNEP-WCMC. http://www.wdpa.org/Statistics.aspx.

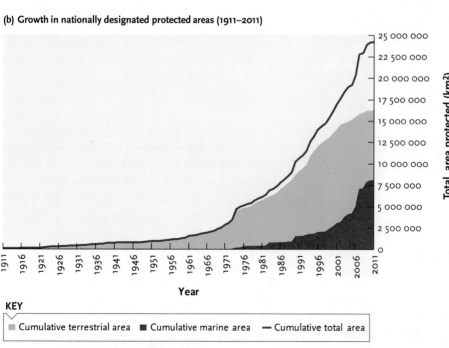

(b) Growth in nationally designated protected areas (1911–2011)

KEY

■ Cumulative terrestrial area   ■ Cumulative marine area   — Cumulative total area

to V protected areas in the terrestrial realm and 8×10^6 km² in the marine (2011 data). However, protected areas vary greatly in the effectiveness of the conservation that they provide. This is especially true in less-developed countries, where poaching (illegal harvesting) of animals and timber and other illicit activities may be rampant. This occurs because governmental priorities in developing countries do not necessarily focus on conserving bio-diversity; rather it is typically directed to achieve political stability, alleviating poverty, or otherwise directly improving the human condition, or in some cases as a corrupt way of gaining personal wealth. However, even in relatively developed countries like Canada it is common for there to be severe conflict between the need to conserve biodiversity in protected areas, and economic activities in those same reserves or in other natural habitats, as we examine later in the section.

In Canada, the largest kinds of protected areas are national parks, provincial parks, wilderness areas, and ecological reserves. As of 2011, about 10 percent of Canada's land area was in protected status, but only 0.7 percent of the marine area **(Table 14.4)**. Growth in the extent of protected areas in Canada is shown in **Figure 14.25**.

Stewardship of Protected Areas

Protected areas will never be successful in meeting their conservation objectives if their boundaries are merely proclaimed to exist. It is also essential that the ecological values of reserves are monitored to determine whether they are changing, and that appropriate management is undertaken when necessary. Collectively, those actions are referred to as stewardship.

For instance, if a species at risk is present in a protected area, its population and the condition of its habitat should be monitored, and if there are signs of degradation the causes should be identified and then mitigated, if possible. If the causes of a problem are not obvious, it may be necessary to undertake ecological research to

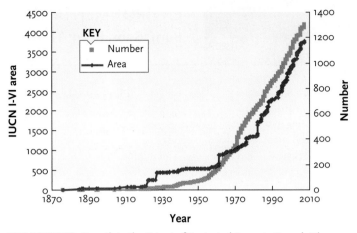

FIGURE 14.25 Growth in the Extent of Protected Areas in Canada The database includes IUCN I–VI sites. Area is in 10³ km².

SOURCE: Based on data from Canadian Council on Ecological Areas (CCEA). 2009. *Canadian Conservation Areas Database*. CCEA, Natural Resources Canada and Environment Canada, Ottawa, ON.

determine what the stressors are and how to decrease their intensity.

A comparable argument could be made for the stewardship of endangered communities in protected areas, such as tallgrass prairie or old-growth forest. The rare communities must be monitored, and if degrading changes are detected, research should be undertaken to understand their causes and consequences. It may then be necessary to actively manage the communities to maintain them in a healthy condition (see Environmental Applications 14.3).

Three broad types of anthropogenic stressors affect the biodiversity of protected areas: internal, surrounding, and regional stressors:

- Internal stressors originate with human activities occurring inside a protected area. In many parks they are typically associated with the influences of roads, hotels, ski facilities, golf courses, lawns, trails, and other infrastructure connected to tourism and outdoor recreation. In some countries, illegal harvesting of trees and wild animals may also be important.
- Some stressors originate in the locally surrounding area. This occurs because many protected areas are embedded within a landscape in which intensive economic activities are prominent, such as urbanization, agriculture, forestry, or mining. These anthropogenic land uses are incompatible with many of the natural values that protected areas are intended to conserve. Eventually, the protected area may become an ecological "island" of natural habitat, embedded within a "sea" of contrary habitats. Increasingly, the managers of protected areas view their responsibility to be one of engaging in partnerships with interested groups in the **greater protected area** to seek a sustainable balance between natural values and the regional human economy.

TABLE 14.4	Protected Areas in Canada

The data are for IUCN categories I–VI protected areas, and are current to 2011. *Percentage Protected* refers to the part of the national area (terrestrial or marine) that has been given protected status.

	Total Number	Total Area (10³ km²)	Percentage Protected
All Protected Areas	5832	1041	6.6
Terrestrial PAs	3256	104.5	9.8
Marine PAs	515	49.3	0.9

SOURCES: Based on data from United Nations Environment Programme — World Conservation Monitoring Centre (UNEP-WCMC). 2009. *World Database on Protected Areas (WDPA)*. UNEP-WCMC, Cambridge, UK. http://www.unep-wcmc.org/wdpa/.

Wildfire periodically affects certain kinds of natural communities, and species living in those habitats have evolved to be well adapted to that kind of disturbance. Jack pine (*Pinus banksiana*), for example, is a coniferous tree that is adapted to regenerating after stand-replacing burns. Its mature cones are serotinous, meaning they are retained on the branches for a number of years, but their scales are sealed shut by a resin that has a melting point of about 50°C. It typically takes a wildfire to reach that temperature and if this occurs, the cones open and their ripe seeds scatter to regenerate the next post-fire stand of jack pine.

There are many similar examples. The seeds of pin cherry (*Prunus pensylvanica*) are hard coated and long lived in the forest floor, where they may persist for more than 50 years. However, they are stimulated to germinate by exposure to environmental conditions that follow a wildfire, which helps the species to be prominent in the postfire succession (it is sometimes called "fire cherry").

Another case is fireweed (*Chamaenerion angustifolium*), a perennial herbaceous plant whose rhizomes may survive a light wildfire but, most importantly, the species produces highly dispersible seeds that are well adapted to colonizing recent burns, where they can establish and dominate the ground vegetation for a decade or more.

Because many species and ecological communities are adapted to wildfire, prescribed (or intentional) burns can be used as a tool to manage them in circumstances in which the natural fire regime is no longer operating well. This is generally relevant to conditions in which fires that are naturally ignited, usually by lightning, are routinely quenched to protect buildings or economically valuable forest.

However, if practised over a long time this firefighting can lead to an extensive build-up of large amounts of combustible biomass, which can set the stage for a dangerous conflagration. Such an occurrence happened near Kelowna, British Columbia, in August 2003, when an uncontrollable wildfire burned more than 250 km², some of it in residential areas, so that 239 homes were destroyed and 45 000 people were evacuated. That firestorm occurred during a lengthy drought and was wind driven, but the forest ecosystem was highly vulnerable because it had not had a wildfire for many decades and so was "overmature" with high fuel loads.

Prescribed burns can help to reduce dangerously large amounts of fuel, while also improving conditions for many species of plants and animals by opening up stands and enhancing regeneration.

Prescribed fire is also helpful in managing other kinds of ecological communities. Tallgrass prairie, for example, typically occurs in a climatic regime that is suitable for the development of habitats dominated by shrubs and even trees. However, the progression to later stages of succession is set back by periodic wildfires, which keep the habitat open and suitable for the plants and animals that are characteristic of tallgrass prairie. Originally, the wildfires were naturally ignited by lightning strikes, and then the Plains Indians took over by regularly burning the prairie to improve the habitat for the hunting of deer and other species. However, during the past century it became common to quench wildfires, and this practice allowed shrubs and trees to invade and become prominent in conserved remnants of tallgrass prairie, which is an endangered community that survives in only about 0.2 percent of its original extent in North America.

- Protected areas may also be affected by regional stressors, such as acid rain, ozone pollution, and climate change. Local anthropogenic stressors are cumulative upon the regional effects of these large-scale influences on environmental conditions.

Management Activities

The kinds of management activities that must be undertaken in protected areas can vary enormously. In extreme cases it is necessary to have armed patrols to monitor and prevent the poaching of animals or timber. Measures may also have to be taken to prevent the use of unauthorized motor transport, especially all-terrain vehicles (ATVs), which can damage the terrain and harass wildlife.

It may also be necessary to directly manage habitats to maintain them in a healthy ecological condition. For example, if natural disturbances are no longer functioning in a natural way, managers may have to simulate them to maintain certain communities. Some kinds of prairie must be periodically burned, or they will be degraded by incursions of shrubs and trees (Environmental Applications 14.3). In the past, naturally ignited wildfires would have provided that function, but today prescribed burns may be necessary. Moreover, some kinds of prairie communities were once maintained in good condition by periodic grazing by herds of wild bison, but today this function may be played by domesticated cattle.

Sometimes it is necessary to move or transplant individuals. For example, rare species may have become extirpated from particular areas. If suitable habitat still exists, it may be possible to reintroduce the lost species, either using individuals taken from other places where they are

leaf litter, and blackened soil surface help to advance the growing season for prairie species, which benefit and flourish to a much greater degree than prior to the burn.

Of course, prescribed burns have to be carefully controlled. This is done in several ways, including:

- training land stewards in the nuances of this land-management practice;
- burning only when the environmental conditions are suitable—not during a drought or when it is excessively windy;
- ensuring there are fire breaks with low fuel loads; and
- having firefighting equipment on hand in case things start to get out of control.

Prescribed burns are now routinely used by conservation agencies across Canada and around the world in ecosystems where the practice is suitable. For instance, Parks Canada has become a routine practitioner, as have some provincial governments and the Nature Conservancy of Canada. This "burning solution" is an excellent case of the application of ecological knowledge to dealing with important management problems in biological conservation.

FIGURE 1 A Prescribed Burn This management tactic is a valuable tool in the management of some kinds of ecological communities. In this image, a technician is igniting a springtime burn of mixedgrass prairie in Duck Mountain Provincial Park, Saskatchewan. The burn is intended to maintain the grassland against incursions of shrubs and trees.

To properly steward tracts of tallgrass prairie, ecosystem managers typically use prescribed burns **(Figure 1)** for two to three years in a row to rehabilitate shrub-invaded areas, and then every two to four years afterward to maintain them in good condition. The burning is done in the early springtime, typically in mid-April, when woody plants are beginning to flush out and are relatively vulnerable to fire. The resulting decrease in shrub dominance, reduction in accumulated

still abundant, or stock that has been captive-reared for the purpose of releasing into the wild. This tactic of restoration ecology has been done many times in Canada; for example:

- Pine marten (*Martes americana*) have been reintroduced to temperate forest habitat in Fundy and Kejimkujik National Parks in eastern Canada.
- Swift foxes (*Vulpes velox*) and black-footed ferrets (*Musetla nigripes*) have been released to shortgrass prairie in Grasslands National Park in southern Saskatchewan.
- Vancouver Island marmots (*Marmota vancouverensis*) have been captive-bred and released to montane forest–tundra habitat on southern Vancouver Island.
- Sea otters (*Enydra lutris*) from the Aleutians were released to waters off western Vancouver Island.

- Captive-bred peregrine falcons (*Falco peregrinus*) have been released at coastal breeding cliffs in Fundy National Park in New Brunswick.
- Prairie bison (*Bison bison bison*) have been introduced by the Nature Conservancy of Canada (NCC) to its shortgrass prairie reserve at Old Man on His Back Prairie Conservation Area in southwestern Saskatchewan **(Figure 14.26)**.
- Trumpeter swans (*Cygnus buccinator*) have been captive bred and released to wetlands in the Wye Marsh Wildlife Area in south-central Ontario.
- Burrowing owls (*Athene cunicularia*) have been released to dry grassland in southeastern British Columbia.
- Ginseng (*Panax quinquefolius*) has been reintroduced to various temperate-forest habitats in eastern Canada.

FIGURE 14.26 Sometimes Extirpated Species Are Reintroduced to Protected Areas These prairie bison (*Bison bison bison*) were released to the Old Man on His Back Prairie Conservation Area in southwestern Saskatchewan, a protected area established by the Nature Conservancy of Canada. The animals were obtained from Parks Canada, which had an excess of the animals in its Elk Island National Park in Alberta. Grazing by the bison is an important aspect of the stewardship of the shortgrass prairie in this area.

Bill Freedman

In some cases, restoration ecologists have worked to re-create facsimiles of endangered communities on degraded lands. For instance, ecologists with the NCC are working to enlarge a stand of rare Carolinian forest at its Clear Creek Protected Area in southern Ontario by planting suitable trees and other vegetation onto surrounding disused cornfields. At a site in southeastern Manitoba, NCC is re-creating endangered tallgrass prairie. And at its Cowichan Nature Reserve, NCC is expanding a rare stand of Garry oak forest by planting that tree and other suitable vegetation onto an old pasture. These are examples of heroic and expensive projects of restoration ecology, but they are worthwhile because they significantly expand the areas of endangered ecosystems, while providing additional habitat for a suite of their dependent plants and animals.

Sometimes, stewardship activities in support of an endangered species result in highly integrated programs of ecological monitoring, research, and applied management. These programs may occur in protected areas, in large regions around them, and sometimes far beyond. A well-known example is the globally endangered whooping crane, which in 1941 numbered only a perilously few 15 wild individuals, having been greatly diminished by excessive hunting and damage to its wintering and migratory habitats (BirdLife International, 2012). Today, thanks to aggressive conservation measures in Canada and the United States, this rare crane numbers about 437 wild birds plus 165 in captivity (in 2011). The numbers of whooping cranes are monitored on their breeding grounds, which are mostly in peaty wetlands

(a boreal habitat known as muskeg) in and near Wood Buffalo National Park in northern Alberta and the southwestern NWT. During their southward migration, the cranes use a number of wetlands as critical habitat, including Last Mountain Lake in Saskatchewan and Salt Plains National Wildlife Refuge in Oklahoma. The cranes winter at several places along the Texas Gulf Coast, particularly in the Aransas National Wildlife Refuge. Because of the importance of all of the breeding, migratory, and wintering habitats to these endangered birds, their locations have been a high priority for conservation, and most are now set aside in various kinds of protected areas.

Moreover, because so many species of cranes are endangered, a great deal of research has been done on the biology of their family (Gruidae), and particularly on their breeding. This sort of work has also been done with whooping cranes, and the knowledge gained has been applied to programs of captive breeding and release to the wild. This has allowed an additional breeding population to be established in the Necedah National Wildlife Refuge in Wisconsin. Remarkably, those cranes were trained to migrate to a wintering habitat in Florida by wildlife biologists flying with them in an ultra-light aircraft. Yet a third, nonmigratory population has been established with captive-bred birds near Kissimmee, Florida. To prevent the captive-bred birds from imprinting on humans, the wildlife biologists who work with the chicks fed them with crane-head puppets, and they used other fostering techniques developed through research into the ethology (behaviour) of the species **(Figure 14.27)**. These reintroductions are

FIGURE 14.27 The Whooping Crane (*Grus americana*) Because this species is critically endangered, heroic efforts have been made to increase its population. This image shows young captive-bred cranes being taught to migrate by a person flying an ultralight aircraft. The migration route is from a breeding centre in Wisconsin to wintering grounds in Florida.

showing signs of success, although they are hampered by the inexperience of the young cranes in their first nesting attempts, and by occasional events of mortality caused by severe weather on the wintering grounds.

Of course, not all research in conservation biology produces results that are useful in the applied sense. For instance, studies showed that whooping cranes lay one to three eggs, but it is rare for more than one young to survive. Knowing this, an attempt was made to increase the numbers of whooping cranes by taking "surplus" eggs from their nests and fostering them with wild sandhill cranes (*Grus canadensis*), a much more abundant species. In a sense, this innovative experiment worked, because the sandhill cranes incubated the eggs and raised the chicks, which then migrated with their foster parents. However, when the fostered whooping cranes became reproductively mature they chose sandhill cranes as their potential mates, having been imprinted on their parents. This meant that the experiment was a practical failure, because the additional whooping cranes did not contribute to the breeding population of their endangered species.

Conflicts with Other Uses of Protected Areas

In addition to stewarding species and habitats in protected areas, it is sometimes necessary to manage the activities of large numbers of visitors, as well as other anthropogenic influences. This is particularly the case of parks that serve purposes in addition to the conservation of biodiversity, such as the provision of venues and infrastructure to support tourism and outdoor recreation. These uses of parks may be economically important, but they can challenge their ability to conserve biodiversity. The degree to which this occurs largely depends on the kinds of activities that are allowed and the numbers of people engaging in them. National parks in southern Canada are typically well used by people and so they have embedded roads, campgrounds, interpretation facilities, and even resorts, golf courses, and other infrastructure to support tourism and recreation.

The ability of protected areas to conserve biodiversity may also be threatened by land-use activities in the areas around them. These external stressors may be associated with tourism, residential development, agriculture, forestry, mining, and hydroelectric facilities. In fact, all protected areas in southern regions of Canada are significantly affected by anthropogenic stressors originating both within and beyond their borders. This problem is illustrated by the cases of several national parks (Freedman, 2010):

- *Banff National Park* (BNP) in southwestern Alberta was established in 1885, making it the first national park in Canada (Page et al., 1996). It is also our most famous park because of its spectacular scenery, large animals that sometimes can be easily viewed, and

superb infrastructure supporting tourism and outdoor recreation. Those values attract visitors from across Canada and around the world—about four million people annually—generating more than $6 billion in economic activity. BNP covers a large area (6640 km^2) and so it is important in conserving natural ecological values of its region, a function that is further enhanced because it is bordered by other large protected areas—Jasper, Yoho, and Kootenay National Parks and Peter Lougheed Provincial Park, which together cover 26 000 km^2. The initial purpose of BNP was to protect scenic viewscapes and hot springs, and to develop the area for the economic benefits of tourism, which was rapidly becoming fashionable and accessible because of the construction of the first transcontinental railroads. It was not until several decades later that the purpose of national parks in Canada shifted toward the protection of natural values. The development of BNP has featured the construction of several villages, hotels, skiing facilities, golf courses, part of the Trans-Canada Highway and other major roads, the Canadian Pacific railway, and various other built structures. Moreover, natural habitats of much of the surrounding area, particularly eastward toward Canmore and Calgary, have been extensively converted into urbanized, tourism-related, agricultural, forestry, and industrial land uses, and additional changes are ongoing. The various facilities within the park, and its growing insularization by contrary land uses, severely threaten the conservation of some of its natural values. The economic developments in and around BNP are controversial, and were the subject of a federal task force led by Robert Page, an ecologist at the University of Calgary. That group was asked by Parks Canada to recommend changes to land use and other economic activities in the greater BNP region that would improve the sustainability of ecological, social, and economic values. The report of the task force (in 1996) concluded that economic development in the BNP region was approaching or had already exceeded what was sustainable, and that the ecological integrity of the national park was being threatened. Numerous recommendations were made for actions and policies to deal with the problems—in essence, that the pace and intensity of development be controlled, and in some places reversed. Although Parks Canada accepted those recommendations, the situation today has not changed much and the ecological values of Banff National Park remain threatened by incompatible land uses and other anthropogenic stressors (**Figure 14.28**).

- *Point Pelee National Park* (PPNP) is a small park in southwestern Ontario, covering only 15.5 km^2. It was established in 1918 and contains rare Carolinian

FIGURE 14.28 Banff National Park Part of the Trans-Canada Highway and a major railroad run through this national park. They are lethal hazards for large animals that might try to cross those transportation corridors (and also to people whose vehicles might collide with the animals). To reduce the hazard, Parks Canada has extensively fenced the sides of the highway and part of the railroad, and provided underpasses and overpasses (one is shown here) so the animals can safely get from one side of the corridor to the other.

Parks Canada Agency

forest, wetlands, and many species at risk. PPNP is used intensively for recreation, including bird-watching, picnicking, and hiking. To support these activities, which are important to the local economy, much of the limited area of the park is converted to roads, pathways, parking lots, campgrounds, an information centre, lawns, and other infrastructure that compete with use of the same landbase to support native biodiversity. Although much of PPNP is bordered by Lake Erie, all of its landward boundaries are adjacent to agricultural fields and residential developments, so the park is an ecological "island" surrounded by incompatible habitat. As a result of these many stressors, PPNP is losing some of the natural features that it is intended to conserve. The park has lost 10 of its original 21 reptile species, and 6 of 11 amphibians. Some habitats are being degraded by invasive alien plants, which are crowding out native plants—in fact, 37 percent of the vascular plants in PPNP are non-native.

- *Elk Island National Park* (EINP), located just east of Edmonton, was established in 1909, and covers 194 km². This park is almost rectangular in shape, is bounded by 2.2 m high fences strong enough to contain bison, and is surrounded by mostly incompatible agricultural land uses. In essence, EINP is an ecological "island" of natural fescue prairie, aspen parkland, and spruce boreal forest. The park is well known for its dense populations of large ungulates—bison, deer, elk, and moose, as well as bears, coyote, wolf, and abundant breeding and migratory birds. Of these, the plains and wood bison were introduced to

the park, as were beaver and trumpeter swans. Some of the larger animals are excessively abundant in relation to the carrying capacity of their limited habitats, and population surpluses have been dealt with by shipping animals elsewhere. This has recently included the sale of elk and bison to commercial interests, as well as providing animals for reintroduction to other protected areas. For example, plains bison from EINP were used to re-establish the species in Grasslands National Park and Old Man on His Back Prairie Conservation Area, both in southern Saskatchewan, and even to reintroduce bison to the steppes of the Yakutia region of Siberia. Because EINP is relatively small, its ungulates can be prevented from damaging their natural habitats only if park ecologists actively manage their populations within sustainable levels, and that requires an ongoing culling program.

- *Fundy National Park* (FNP) in New Brunswick was established in 1948 and it supports 206 km² of mostly forested terrain. This park is a popular summer destination, and its supporting facilities include campgrounds, lawns, roads, trails, interpretive facilities, a golf course, and a heated saltwater swimming pool. FNP is roughly rectangular in shape, with one side bordering the Bay of Fundy, but along the other three sides forestry is converting natural mixed-species forest into conifer plantations. This means that FNP is becoming insularized within a modified landscape that is hostile to some of its biodiversity values. There is concern that the park itself is not large enough to sustain viable populations of certain wide-ranging species, such as black bear, pine marten, and pileated woodpecker, or certain community types such as old-growth forest.

The national parks of Canada are commonly regarded as "jewels" in our system of protected areas. However, the parks we just examined, and many others, have formidable challenges if they are to sustain their native biodiversity. This is a typical context for the stewardship of protected areas—they are challenged by environmental stressors from contrary activities occurring inside them, on their surrounding ecoscape, and in the greater region. Because of these various stressors, proper stewardship is an essential component of successful conservation in protected areas. Key elements of that stewardship are ecological monitoring, research, and applied conservation actions.

14.6 Roles of Governments and Other Organizations in Conservation

People who understand issues associated with biodiversity believe that it is worthwhile and should be conserved. This is a broadly held public view, and it is increasingly being shared by politicians and other decision makers in society, who are beginning to undertake coordinated actions to help conserve biodiversity within their areas of responsibility.

At the international level, this awareness is represented by the *Convention on Biological Diversity* (CBD), a treaty under the auspices of the United Nations Environment Program (UNEP). The CBD was presented in 1992 at the "Earth Summit" sponsored by UNEP in Rio de Janeiro, Brazil. Canada signed on to the CBD at Rio and ratified it a few months later (we were the first developed country to do this). The vision of the CBD is to sustain life on Earth, and there are three broad objectives (CBD, 2010):

- the conservation of biodiversity;
- the sustainable use of biological resources; and
- the equitable sharing of benefits from the use of genetic resources (such as newly discovered medicines derived from wild organisms).

As a signatory nation to the CBD, Canada is obliged to assess the adequacy of its national efforts to conserve biodiversity, to use biological resources in a sustainable manner, and to identify and fill gaps in its policies and actions. One requirement is to develop a national strategy for implementation of the CBD, and this led to the *Canadian Biodiversity Strategy* (Environment Canada, 1995). This document outlines three strategic elements:

- recognition of jurisdictional and legislative responsibilities;

- the need for cooperation among various governments and other organizations in the development and implementation of policies and actions; and
- a vision for the conservation of biodiversity within the context of sustainable development in Canada.

The Canadian Biodiversity Strategy has five goals:

- Conserve biodiversity and use biological resources in a sustainable manner.
- Improve our understanding of ecosystems and increase our capability for resource management.
- Promote an understanding by the public of the need to conserve biodiversity and to use biological resources in a sustainable manner.
- Develop incentives and legislation toward these goals.
- Work internationally to promote these goals, and share benefits from the use of genetic resources.

The strategy also recognizes as guiding principles some of the qualities of biodiversity, ecology, and sustainable development that we have examined in this and other chapters:

- Biodiversity has instrumental, ecological, social-cultural, and intrinsic values.
- All life forms, including humans, are interconnected.
- Canadians depend on biodiversity and have an obligation to conserve it and use its products in a sustainable manner.
- Canadians should be encouraged to understand and appreciate the values of biodiversity and to participate in its conservation and that of biological resources.
- An ecological approach to resource management is necessary if biodiversity and biological resources are to be conserved.
- Decisions about development must reflect a balance of ecological, economic, social, and cultural values.
- Biodiversity and biological resources can be effectively conserved only where evolutionary forces are relevant and natural functions are able to operate in healthy ecosystems.
- In some cases, intensive management practices (such as captive breeding and release) may be needed to recover species at risk and other endangered biodiversity.
- Traditional ecological knowledge of indigenous and local communities is relevant.
- The conservation of biodiversity and of biological resources should be guided by the best available science, and be adaptive to the emergence of new knowledge and to changing environmental conditions.
- Successful conservation requires the sharing of knowledge and of costs and benefits among all levels of government and other organizations (the private sector, environmental charities, and universities).

Another federal response to Canada's responsibility to conserve biodiversity is the *Species at Risk Act* (SARA) of 2002, which has toughened the legal provisions in support of species that are designated as being at risk by COSEWIC. The provisions of SARA are especially strict with respect to species at risk and their habitat on lands falling within the jurisdiction of the federal government (in terms of either ownership or regulatory responsibility). However, SARA is weaker outside federal jurisdiction, such as on lands controlled by provincial, territorial, Aboriginal, municipal, or private entities. Although SARA has provisions that allow the federal government to intervene in such cases, it is not required to do so. However, the provinces and territories have also passed their own equivalents of SARA, which also helps to protect biodiversity at risk within their jurisdictions.

Environmental non-governmental organizations (ENGOs; these are environmental charities or non-profit organizations) also have an important role to play in the conservation of biodiversity. They do this in two broad ways:

- **Advocacy** involves activities that are intended to influence decisions and outcomes that might affect people or the environment. With respect to biodiversity, advocacy might be used to influence governmental policies and legislation, the activities of private companies, and even educational curricula. Advocacy is commonly pursued in a public way, such as by holding open meetings, staging demonstrations, and advertising in the mass media.
- **Direct action** refers to activities that result in immediate benefits. In the context of biodiversity it involves the implementation of conservation measures, such as the establishment of protected areas to benefit species at risk or rare communities.

Examples of national advocacy ENGOs with a biodiversity mandate are the Canadian Parks and Wilderness Society, Greenpeace, Nature Canada, the Sierra Club (Canada), and the World Wildlife Fund (Canada). These ENGOs lobby governments and the private sector to implement effective biodiversity agendas, while also engaging in public campaigns and supporting research toward those ends. The Nature Conservancy of Canada and Ducks Unlimited Canada are ENGOs that engage in direct action to establish and steward protected areas, and they are joined in this work by hundreds of more local land trusts.

In aggregate, the activities of governmental and non-governmental organizations add up to a lot of conservation action on behalf of the biodiversity of Canada. Nevertheless, much remains to be done. In fact, it is realistic to conclude that the condition of the biodiversity of Canada has recently been getting worse, rather than better. Each year, additional tracts of natural habitat are being destroyed and converted into anthropogenic land uses that are incompatible with native biodiversity, and the conservation status of many species at risk deteriorates.

Moreover, although Canada is a wealthy country, we do not have a national system plan for a comprehensive network of protected areas, and sufficient progress is not being made to set imperilled natural habitats aside from intensive economic development. In addition, many of the existing protected areas are too small or insularized to successfully conserve their inherent biodiversity values over the longer term.

Clearly, there is no reason for complacency here—much has yet to be done. The most direct role for ecologists is in providing the scientific advice and oversight that society needs to move effectively forward with the conservation of biodiversity. Ecologists should also have a prominent influence on the advocacy and direct actions that are leading the charge to protect the biodiversity of Canada and of the world.

14.7 Some Good News

Because so many reports about biodiversity are dismal, the global situation has been characterized as a "crisis." There are, however, important success stories. They involve species that were at the brink of extinction but were effectively protected and then had a substantial recovery. Although these successes are in a minority, they are instructive. We will end this chapter by examining some of the encouraging cases, because they show us how timely and effective conservation actions can fix desperate situations. These lessons are worth learning, because in modified form they can allow us to achieve conservation triumphs with species whose survival is at risk. The only exception, of course, is that of extinction, which is not reversible.

Conservation Successes

Grey Seal and Some Other Pinnipeds

The grey seal (*Halichoerus grypus*) occurs in temperate Atlantic waters, and for many years it had only an extremely small population in Canada because of excessive hunting in the past (Thompson and Harkonen, 2008; Freedman, 2010) **(Figure 14.29)**. It numbered only a few thousand animals in the 1950s, but because of protection from commercial hunting its abundance has grown rapidly and there are now more than 320 000 of them (in 2013).

Another case is the northern fur seal (*Callorhinus ursinus*) of the north Pacific, which was hunted for its fur and by the early 20th century was greatly depleted from an original several million to about 130 000 animals. In 1911 an international treaty was signed that regulated the

FIGURE 14.29 The Grey Seal (*Halichoerus grypus*) This mammal was rare in temperate Atlantic waters of Canada until about the 1950s. It has since increased rapidly in abundance and now numbers more than 320 000 animals. The largest breeding aggregation is on Sable Island off Nova Scotia, where these animals were photographed.

Bill Freedman

5–6 million. Because the hunting has been regulated during the past several decades, the abundance of this seal has increased to about six million (in 2013). The commercial hunting continues today—the quota for 2013 was 400 000, most of which would be young seals only several weeks old. This commercial seal hunt is one of the most controversial wildlife harvests in the world. Although its opponents claim the seals are being overexploited, this is not the case—they are one of the most populous large wild animals anywhere, and their abundance continues to grow despite the killing. Rather, the controversy is mostly about the ethics and aesthetics of the killing of the helpless babies of wild animals for commercial gain.

Grey Whale and Other Great Whales

Because the population of grey whales (*Eschrichtius robustus*) of the Pacific coast had been severely depleted by commercial overhunting, in 1949 the International Whaling Commission (IWC) banned further killing of the species. At that time there were only a few thousand of these whales surviving, but the ban has allowed them to increase to about their original abundance of 26 000 (Reilly et al., 2008; International Whaling Commission, 2010). However, populations of this species on both sides of the north Atlantic are extirpated, and another in the western Pacific numbers a critically endangered 120 animals.

The populations of all other large whales were also severely depleted by several centuries of commercial harvesting, and many species were endangered (**Figure 14.30**). In 1982, the IWC began a wide-scale moratorium on further hunting of whales, which was fully implemented in 1986, that greatly reduced the killing (it was not eliminated because several countries, notably Japan, Norway, and Iceland, are still engaged in limited commercial harvesting). The reduced hunting has allowed most

hunting, and over the following decades the population recovered to about one million. Since then, however, this seal has again declined, although not to the point of endangerment. The recent drop is due to a combination of factors, including commercial overharvesting of its food fish, entanglement in fishing gear, and predation by orcas.

An additional example is the harp seal (*Phoca groenlandica*) of the northwest Atlantic and eastern Arctic Oceans, which is commercially hunted mostly for its fur. This hunt has been ongoing for about two centuries, and as a result the abundance of harp seals in Canadian waters was taken to a relatively low population of about 1.7 million animals in the late 1980s from an original

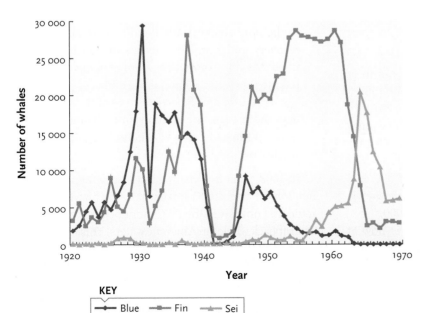

KEY
◆ Blue   ■ Fin   ▲ Sei

FIGURE 14.30 Numbers of Whales Killed in Antarctic Waters The data show the rise and collapse of whaling for three species of baleen whales. Note the limited hunting during World War II, and the sequential collapses of the stocks of blue, then fin, and then sei whales.

SOURCE: Based on data from Ellis, R. 1991. *Men and Whales.* Alfred A. Knopf, New York, NY.

The wolf (*Canis lupus*) is a large wild predator **(Figure 1)**. People have always been fascinated by these animals, perhaps because, like humans for much of our evolutionary history, wolves and other wild carnivores are cunning and dangerous animals. Wolves are also the progenitor of all of the astonishingly diverse breeds of dog (*Canis lupus familiaris*), which humans first began to domesticate more than 15 000 years ago. Most people who keep dogs as pets love them as faithful and unquestioning friends, and often that good feeling also transfers to a widespread admiration of wild wolves.

However, not all people admire wolves—opinions about these predators are remarkably capricious, ranging from deep attraction to intense repulsion, sometimes occurring in the same people, depending on circumstances. The reasons some people fear and loathe wolves are complex, but they typically involve a combination of anxiety about personal safety when the animals are nearby, and anger that these top predators kill and eat the same game animals that people hunt for food or as trophies, or the perception that wolves kill too many livestock. Because of the resulting antipathy to wolves, and the fact that their fur is valuable, they have been relentlessly hunted over most of their natural range throughout the Northern Hemisphere—they are killed by trapping, shooting, and poisoning. This hunting, along with habitat destruction by conversions to anthropogenic land uses, has caused populations of wolves to decline over most of their historical range. Wolves are now widely extirpated, and they occur in robust populations only in remote regions, such as the boreal forest and tundra of northern expanses of Canada, as well as montane forest in mountainous regions.

Many people are concerned about what is happening to the populations of wolves and other large predators. This includes some Canadian ecologists and wildlife biologists, who have transformed their apprehension of the future for large

Doug Morris

FIGURE 1 Wolf (*Canis lupus*) The original range of this predator encompassed most of North America, Eurasia, and northeastern Africa. Although still widespread, the modern range is much smaller, being limited to remote regions where it is not so intensively persecuted as a wild animal that is perceived to be a "pest."

whales to slowly increase, although not yet to their original abundance:

- The sperm whale (*Physeter catodon*) now numbers about one million, compared with its prewhaling abundance of two million (IWC, 2009; Freedman, 2010).
- The finback whale (*Balaenoptera physalus*) now numbers 163 000, compared with an initial 700 000.
- The blue whale (*Balaenoptera musculus*) is now at about 3000, compared with an original 250 000.
- The humpback whale (*Megaptera novaeangliae*) is now 64 000, compared with an initial 100 000.
- The bowhead whale (*Balaena mysticetus*) is now at about 12 000 (these are still taken in an Aboriginal hunt in northern Alaska, and a few also off Baffin Island).
- The right whale (*Balaena glacialis*) of the southern hemisphere now numbers about 7500 animals, but in the northwestern Atlantic they have shown little recovery and number only about 350 because of unsustainable mortality from entanglement in fishing gear and collisions with ships.
- The minke whale (*Balaenoptera acutorostrata*) numbers more than one million animals and it is the target of most ongoing whale hunting, although fin whales are also being taken.

In 2008, Japanese whaling interests announced their intention to harvest 935 minke whales, 50 fin whales, and, for the first time since the IWC moratorium was enacted, 50 humpback whales in Antarctic waters. This is obviously a commercial harvest, but because biological and ecological data are collected it is profiled as "scientific" whaling by the Japanese. Because of intense international controversy, the decision to harvest humpback whales was later reversed, but other species are still being taken.

carnivores into a dedication of their professional lives to helping society find an accommodation with these wild animals. One of the first of these people was Farley Mowat, who studied biology at the University of Toronto and spent two field seasons in boreal Keewatin (this is now continental Nunavut) doing research on wildlife, including wolves. He wrote several popular accounts of his experiences, including the famous book *Never Cry Wolf* (1963). Although that book contains some apparently fictionalized accounts of the behaviour of wolves, it nevertheless played a powerful role in helping to demystify these animals, which had long been stereotypically portrayed as vicious killers.

Douglas Pimlott was another influential researcher of wolves, although in a more rigorous context of ecology and wildlife biology than Mowat. Pimlott worked with the governments of Newfoundland and then Ontario, and then as a professor at the University of Toronto. He and his students did ground-breaking research on the behaviour and community ecology of wolves, working in and around Algonquin Provincial Park in central Ontario. Their work contributed greatly to our understanding of the conservation of wolves, and their role as top predators in controlling the abundance of certain prey species. Pimlott was also a devoted and effective advocate for wolves; he helped to eliminate the bounty on these animals in Ontario and provided a rational dissenting perspective to wolf-culling programs being undertaken elsewhere. He also worked more widely in conservation issues related to northern Canada, and is a founder of the modern environmental movement in our country.

John and Mary Theberge of the University of Waterloo, students of Pimlott, continued to study the behaviour and community ecology of wolves around Algonquin Park. They are also advocates of the animals, which were being killed by trappers and hunters when they wandered outside that park. Research by the Theberges suggested that the mortality was not sustainable, and that it was likely the Algonquin wolves would become both marginalized and hybridized by coyotes (*Canis latrans*) if the hunting was not stopped within a buffer zone around the park. Their advocacy on behalf of wolves created great difficulties for the Theberges, because they were criticizing policies of the provincial government, which was a key sponsor of their research, as well as powerful hunting and trapping constituencies. Fortunately, a "white knight" arrived to rescue their long-standing program of field research, in the form of support from the World Wildlife Fund (Canada). The WWF president at the time, Monte Hummel, was also a former student of Pimlott and is himself a prominent campaigner on behalf of conservation of the natural world, including wild carnivores.

The Theberges were able to continue their research and advocacy, eventually building up an impressive 40-year database and analysis of interactions of wolves and their prey (this includes the earlier studies led by Pimlott). Moreover, thanks to their research and advocacy, the provincial government enacted legislation to protect wolves in the area around Algonquin Park. This made Algonquin the first park in North America to have extended protection for a large carnivore beyond its boundaries. The Theberges have since retired from the University of Waterloo, but they remain engaged in wolf research and in advocacy for conservation, including for wolves, which are still being culled in parts of Canada as an action to favour larger populations of ungulates for hunting by people. Meanwhile other ecologists have taken up the mantle of wolf research in the Algonquin region, including Brent Patterson of Trent University and the Ontario Ministry of Natural Resources.

American Bison

The original abundance of the American bison or buffalo (*Bison bison*) was more than 60 million, making it one of the most populous large wild land animals in the world (Freedman, 1995; Gates and Aune, 2008). An eastern subspecies (*Bison bison pennsylvanicus*) inhabited forest openings, the plains bison (*B. b. bison*) occurred in the prairies, and the wood bison (*Bison bison athabascae*) was in the southern boreal forest of western Canada. The plains bison was especially abundant and it once migrated in colossal herds, with densities of 25–38 animals/ha, and moved over great fronts—one was described as being 40 km × 80 km in extent, another as 320 km long, and another as advancing over a 160-km expanse.

However, rapacious hunting caused the abundance of bison to precipitously decline. The eastern subspecies was extinct by the mid-19th century, and the plains bison perilously close to that end by the late 19th century. The plains bison had been subjected to an unsustainable market hunt for their hides and meat. Their extermination may also have been encouraged by governments of the time to foster agricultural development by disrupting the buffalo-dependent economy of the Plains Indians, making it easier to displace them with European colonists. The insatiable hunting caused the bison to rapidly decline, so that by the late 19th century there were only a few hundred animals left in the prairies of Canada and the United States.

Almost too late, several bison preserves were established and captive-breeding programs began. There are now about 100 000 wild bison and another 250 000 that are ranched as livestock. The largest populations of wild plains bison are in national parks and other extensive tracts of public land, and on several private ranches.

The wood bison are in and around Wood Buffalo National Park, as well as a transplanted group in Elk Island National Park. Although some bison populations suffer from introduced diseases such as bovine tuberculosis and brucellosis, and from genetic damage from interbreeding with domestic cows, the species now appears to be secure. Of course, it will never recover to anywhere close to its original abundance, because almost all its natural habitat has been converted to agricultural land uses.

Pronghorn Antelope (Antilocapra americana)

This endemic animal of the western plains may have originally numbered 35 million animals, but it was severely overhunted during the 19th century and its population was reduced to fewer than 20 000 (Hoffman et al., 2008). Fortunately, strong conservation measures were implemented, and this species now numbers as many as one million and again sustains a sport hunt.

American Beaver (Castor canadensis)

This large rodent was the most sought-after furbearer in the early fur trade, a commercial enterprise that stimulated much of the exploration of the interior of Canada and the central and western United States (Linzey et al., 2008). Beavers were excessively harvested everywhere, and they became extirpated from most of their original range by the first half of the 20th century. However, conservation measures implemented since then, along with much less demand for their fur because of changing fashions in clothing (especially regarding top hats), resulted in beavers recovering their abundance over most of their range where habitats are still suitable. In fact, beavers are now considered to be a pest in some areas because their engineering works may cause flooding of roads and other areas used by people.

Sea Otter (Enhydra lutris)

This furbearer of the Pacific coast was overhunted for its dense and lustrous fur during the 18th and 19th centuries (Doroff and Burdin, 2008). It became extirpated from almost all its original range, and at its lowest may have numbered fewer than a thousand animals. A moratorium was placed on further hunting in 1911, and this allowed the population to increase to the degree that about two-thirds of its original range is now occupied. The recovery in Canada was assisted by a reintroduction to the west coast of Vancouver Island, but the Canadian population is small and designated by COSEWIC as special concern.

Wild Turkey (Meleagris gallopavo)

This large landbird was extirpated from most of its original range by hunting and habitat loss, including from southern regions of Manitoba, Ontario, Quebec, and New

Brunswick (BirdLife International, 2008a). However, it has been widely reintroduced to many areas, including its former range in Canada and even beyond, to southern Saskatchewan, Alberta, and British Columbia. The wild turkey has now recovered to more than seven million wild animals, enough to support sport hunting in many regions (of course, domestic varieties are abundant, with about eight million being raised as food in Canada in 2006).

Cavity-Nesting Birds

The wood duck (*Aix sponsa*) was overhunted as food and for its beautiful feathers, and it also suffered extensive habitat loss from the drainage of wetlands and timber harvesting in swamps (BirdLife International, 2008b). The recovery of this cavity-nesting bird has been aided by regulation of its hunting as well as the widespread provision of nesting boxes in wetlands. Its abundance is now about 3.5 million. Nest-box programs also benefit other depleted cavity-nesting ducks, such as the common goldeneye (*Bucephala clangula*) and hooded merganser (*Lophodytes cucullatus*). An unrelated program of providing terrestrial nest-boxes has helped to increase the diminished populations of eastern bluebird (*Sialia sialis*) and western bluebird (*Sialia mexicana*).

Trumpeter Swan (Cygnus buccinator)

This largest native swan once bred extensively in western North America, but its populations were devastated by hunting for its meat and skin. However, this species was protected and has now recovered greatly in abundance, now numbering about 18 000 animals, including a reintroduced population in south-central Ontario (Moser, 2006; BirdLife International, 2008c).

Peregrine Falcon (Falco peregrinus) *and* Bald Eagle (Hialiaeetus leucocephalus)

These predatory birds suffered large population declines over most of their range because of the ecotoxicological effects of organochlorine chemicals, particularly the insecticides DDT and dieldrin and the industrial substances polychlorinated biphenyls (PCBs) (BirdLife International, 2008d, 2008e; Freedman, 2010). These chemicals caused toxicity to developing embryos and adults, which resulted in widespread reproductive failure in these and other species of birds. Almost all production and use of the organochlorines in North America was banned during the 1970s, and this has allowed the populations of affected species to recover. Because the eastern population of the peregrine falcon (*Falco peregrinus anatum*) had become critically endangered, its recovery was assisted by a program of captive breeding and release. The peregrine falcon now has a global population of more than 10 000 birds (it is one of the most widespread birds in the world), and the bald eagle more than 115 000 (it occurs only in North America).

American Ginseng (Panax quinquefolius)

This plant example involves an understorey species of temperate hardwood forests of eastern North America, which, beginning in the early 17th century, was excessively harvested because the rhizomes could be traded in China, where they are believed to be a tonic and to have other medicinal benefits. American ginseng is now widely cultivated for sale in traditional Chinese medicine, and so it is not at risk of extinction. However, its wild populations are still badly depleted (it is listed as endangered by COSEWIC), although efforts are beginning to enhance the species in some habitats by planting seeds or by out-planting seedlings.

Ongoing Challenges

These are some of the better known success stories of conservation in Canada and North America, and there are others from additional countries. There are useful lessons to be learned from these examples. However, even while some damages to biodiversity are being repaired, many other losses are ongoing. It is a key responsibility and opportunity for ecologists to be deeply engaged in the scientific activities that are needed to identify the ongoing problems of biodiversity and to recommend ways of avoiding or repairing those awful damages.

CHAPTER SUMMARY

(LO14.1)

- Extinctions have occurred throughout the history of life and ecosystems, at both a pervasive background rate and after-catastrophic mass events that carried away most of the species living at the time. Another mass extinction has been ongoing for the past several millennia, but especially quickly during the past two centuries, and this one is entirely anthropogenic.

(LO14.2)

- The modern extinction crisis is being caused mostly by the destruction of natural ecosystems, especially the conversion of low-latitude forests into land uses for agriculture, urbanization, and other anthropogenic purposes. Other important stressors are associated with invasive alien species and diseases, the excessive harvesting of species of economic importance, and pollution and climate change.

(LO14.3)

- Effective actions have been taken to conserve some species at risk and their habitats, and they now have much smaller likelihoods of being lost from Canada or indeed their global range. Examples of these "success stories" of conservation include the American bison, peregrine falcon, and whooping crane.

(LO14.4)

- Species at risk in Canada are identified and studied by the Committee on the Status of Endangered Wildlife in Canada (COSEWIC), which is developing lists of native taxa that are suffering from various degrees of conservation risk. There are also natural communities at risk, along with many of the species that need them as critical habitat, such as Carolinian forest and tallgrass prairie.

(LO14.5)

- Effective conservation of biodiversity requires the implementation of two clusters of solutions: (1) management practices on "working" ecoscapes that are sympathetic to the needs of indigenous biodiversity, and (2) the establishment of a system of protected areas that are set aside from intensive economic use. Protected areas accommodate the needs of biodiversity elements that are in conflict with certain economic activities, such as old-growth forests and certain wide-ranging species.

(LO14.6)

- All elements of society must work to conserve biodiversity. Government has the responsibility of monitoring conditions, doing research, managing habitats that it owns, and regulating all of society. Non-governmental conservation organizations engage in advocacy as well as direct action to create protected areas. The private sector, including individuals as well as corporations, has a responsibility to conserve biodiversity to the degree possible on property they own or manage. If all of society collaborates effectively, then the biodiversity crisis can be resolved as a key element of ecologically sustainable development.

QUESTIONS FOR REVIEW AND DISCUSSION

1. What are the several meanings of the word "conservation"?

2. What are "natural extinctions," and how do they provide context for the modern biodiversity crisis?

3. Explain the causes of the modern biodiversity crisis.

4. How do invasive aliens threaten the native biodiversity of Canada?

5. Explain the system used by COSEWIC (the Committee on the Status of Endangered Wildlife in Canada) to designate species at risk in Canada.

6. How is the theory of island biogeography relevant to conservation planning?

7. Choose a species listed by COSEWIC and prepare a report on key aspects of its biology, ecology, risk factors, and actions necessary for population recovery. You can get useful information from the COSEWIC website at http://www.cosewic.gc.ca, as well as other Web-based and library sources.

8. Explain the roles and responsibility of international, national, and regional organizations in the conservation of biodiversity. Include both governmental and non-governmental organizations.

9. Consider the following statement: "Conservation should be practised throughout working landscapes, but some large tracts must also be set aside as protected areas to ensure the survival of elements of biodiversity that are not compatible with economic activities." What, in the context of conservation biology, is meant by this statement?

Resource Ecology

LEARNING OBJECTIVES

After studying this chapter you should be able to:

1. Distinguish among the concepts of economic growth, economic development, sustainable development, and ecologically sustainable development.

2. Explain the differences between renewable and nonrenewable natural resources, including those based on biological or ecological stocks.

3. Discuss how management practices and systems can be used to increase the potential harvest of bioresources.

4. Describe cases of the depletion of potentially renewable resources, and explain why those damages occurred.

5. Describe renewable bioresources of Canada, and discuss whether those resources are being used in a sustainable fashion.

15.1 Natural Resources and Ecological Sustainability

In 1957, the first Earth-orbiting satellite, named *Sputnik*, was launched into space. Then, in 1961, Yuri Gagarin, a Russian cosmonaut, became the first person to orbit Earth. Those technological advances meant that people could view the first pictures of Earth taken from outer space **(Figure 15.1)**. Those compelling images provided an outlook of the utter isolation of Earth, a fact that was already well known but was starkly reinforced as a result of actually being seen.

The pictures resulted in a commonly expressed environmental metaphor of "spaceship Earth." This figure of speech is apt because it was plain to anyone viewing these images that the Earth, the only place in the universe known to support life and ecosystems, is exceedingly remote and seemingly floating in the immense, extremely dilute, black yet starry void of space.

This lucid image of our lonely planet affords context for the study of resource ecology—it helps us to understand that the resources needed to sustain life and ecosystems are mostly limited to the finite ones already contained on the planet. The only exception, and it is a crucial one, is the torrent of electromagnetic radiation that is continuously emitted by the Sun. A tiny fraction of that radiation reaches Earth, and in so doing provides warmth and the vital energy to drive photosynthesis.

All organisms must have access to certain goods and services that are provided by ecosystems. Photosynthetic autotrophs, such as plants and algae, need to appropriate sunlight, space, water, and nutrients (inorganic carbon, nitrogen, phosphorus, and so on). Heterotrophic organisms, such as animals and fungi, must have access to appropriate foods and other necessary aspects of their habitat.

The same is true of humans and their economy—there must be an adequate supply of all the necessities of life, such as food, materials, energy, and shelter. For a fully comfortable life, we also require access to the aesthetics of satisfaction and happiness. Of course, the resource needs of modern people are enormously more complicated than those of any other species. There are several core aspects to the complex needs of humans for natural resources:

• On a per capita basis, people use resources more intensively than do any other species.

FIGURE 15.1 Earth Images of Earth taken from space reinforce the metaphor of "spaceship Earth" as an isolated place whose resources are limited to those contained on the planet, with the key exception of sunlight. This March 2001 composite image was produced using data and images from several NASA satellites. It is late winter, and much of Canada is snow covered.

- We harvest an astonishing variety of natural resources from all accessible parts of the planet, exceedingly more so than any other species has ever done.

- In the process of using resources, they may become degraded, resulting in their stocks rapidly declining in amount and quality, a change that poses great risks for economic sustainability.

- We not only harvest raw foods, materials, and sources of energy from the environment and ecosystems, but also process them into manufactured goods such as processed foods, refined energy products, and machines. Many of these products are traded in an increasingly globalized economy.

- The release of large amounts of wastes and pollutants, which cause damage to the environment, is an inevitable consequence of the huge and increasing population of people, the intensification of their lifestyles, and the industrial and commercial activities associated with the manufacturing and trading of goods.

The stark fact is that we individual humans, and our collective economy, are utterly dependent on the environment and ecosystems to provide us with sustenance. This reality means that prudent questions about the long-term supply of resources are crucial to understanding whether the human economy is operating in a sustainable manner. This knowledge is vital, because many cases of environmental and economic calamities have been caused by the non-sustainable use of natural resources (see Environmental Applications 15.1 for one example).

The natural resources being considered are of two types: (1) **renewable resources**, which are sources of food, materials, or energy that are capable of regenerating after they are harvested, so potentially their stocks can always be available for use, and (2) **non-renewable resources**, which are present in a finite quantity on Earth, and therefore do not regenerate after they are extracted from the environment.

The science of ecology can be applied to dealing with vital problems related to the supply and quality of these natural resources. **Resource ecology** deals with the links between ecological knowledge and the management of natural resources, and it extends to framing the meaning and dimensions of economic sustainability.

In this chapter we will examine how ecological science informs our understanding of the process of **sustainable development**. This term refers to progress that is being made toward achieving a **sustainable economy**— one that can run forever because it is ultimately founded on the prudent use of renewable resources, meaning in ways that do not degrade their quantity or quality. We will also consider the even loftier idea of **ecologically sustainable development**. That process involves development toward an **ecologically sustainable economy**, which goes beyond mere resource sustainability to also include the need to maintain biodiversity and ecological functions at viable and necessary levels.

After we examine these themes, we will examine how the knowledge of applied ecology can help us design the harvesting and management systems used in agriculture, fisheries, forestry, and horticulture. We will finish by

gary yim/Shutterstock.com

FIGURE 1 Easter Island (Rapa Nui)

Easter Island, or Rapa Nui, is one of the most isolated places on Earth—it is a 164 km² volcanic island in the southern Pacific Ocean (Ponting, 1991; Diamond, 2004) **(Figure 1)**. The time of its discovery by wandering Polynesians is not certain, but it was likely around 300–400 CE. These colonizing people brought only banana, sweet potato, and chicken as useful crops, the warm-temperate climate of the island being unsuitable for their other more tropical foods, such as breadfruit and coconut. However, fish, porpoises, and other marine life were abundant in the near-shore waters. The Polynesian colonists hunted them from boats made of local trees, particularly the endemic palm, *Paschalococos disperta*, which is now extinct. By the 16th century, there was a flourishing economy on Easter Island, with a population of about 7000, and abundant food.

Life being relatively easy, the islanders had time to develop a cultural and religious tradition that involved carving great blocks of volcanic stone into human-headed monoliths (*moai*), which were dragged to coastal places and erected on massive stone bases. Both the monoliths (weighing up to 75 t) and their similarly heavy bases were carved at an inland quarry, and then laboriously moved to coastal sites by rolling them on logs cut from the forest. Unfortunately, Easter Island quickly became deforested by the excessive cutting of trees for use as rollers, as timber to construct fishing boats and dwellings, and as fuel. Once the vital forest resource disappeared, the core of the economy collapsed—most fishing became impossible because wooden boats were needed to safely pass through the oceanic surf, and it was difficult to cook food or heat homes because only shrubby and herbaceous biomass was available for use as fuel. The nuclear cultural activity of carving and erecting the great stone heads also ceased, because they could no longer be moved from the quarries.

Simply put, nonsustainable harvesting of trees caused a rapid collapse to occur in the economy of this prehistoric society. Undoubtedly, the islanders were aware of their remote and precarious circumstances—they may even have considered the need to conserve the last of the trees, but cut them anyway. The resulting disintegration of their economy and culture was so massive that, when the first Europeans arrived in 1772, the indigenous people were living in squalid dwellings of reeds and in a few caves, were engaged in warfare among rival clans, were likely cannibals, and no longer remembered who had erected the coastal monoliths.

The case of Easter Island has become a well-used metaphor for Earth as a planetary "island." This is because Earth also has limited stocks of nonrenewable resources, which are depleted as they are used, as well as renewable ones, which can become ruined by excessive harvesting. If those planetary resources become exhausted, the global human economy will collapse, just like that of the Easter Islanders. Those people had no alternative place rich in resources to which they could escape from their self-inflicted catastrophe. Similarly, there is no substitute for planet Earth.

examining case studies that illustrate severe problems that have arisen in many systems of resource harvesting and management, and how ecological knowledge can be used to prevent or repair those damages.

Economics and Ecology

Economics is the study of the ways that limited resources are produced, distributed, and consumed in an economy. Like ecology, economics is a highly interdisciplinary field and it can be studied at various scales. They range from small and local, such as an individual person or a particular household, to much larger, such as the economies of nations or of the global human enterprise. At any scale, an **economy** (or **economic system**) comprises all the interactions that occur at a defined level of society and that affect the production, distribution, and consumption of goods and services (together, these are **products**). This includes the influences of all people in the economy, as well as institutions such as governmental agencies, nongovernmental organizations, and private businesses.

The **goods** that are being traded are tangible things. They include raw natural resources such as petroleum, metal ore, timber, and harvested foodstuffs, as well as manufactured products such as gasoline, copper pipes, buildings, roads, vehicles, and ice cream. The **services** are related to functions within an economy, such as the harvesting of trees to manufacture into lumber and then furniture, the processing of wheat into flour and then cookies, the production of airplanes and computers, the construction of sewers and homes, and the provision of medical care and education by professionals. In fact, there is somewhat of a continuum between goods and services. For instance, a restaurant provides food and drink as physical goods, while also offering services such as the preparation of pizzas, washing of dishes, and provision of a pleasant ambiance.

Adam Smith (1723–1790), a Scot, provided an early definition of economics as "an inquiry into the nature and causes of the wealth of nations." He further elaborated the field in terms of the ways that heads of state and legislators work to supply a country with the revenues needed to deliver public services and employment for the populace. Smith also noted that the price of a good or service, and the profit to be made by its producers and vendors, is affected by the abundance of its supply relative to the demand for it from consumers. He believed that the market worked as an "invisible hand" in which the competing interests of sellers and buyers affect the benefits received by both sides—the seller realizes more profit if a product can be sold at a higher price, and the buyer saves money if it can be bought at a lower price. According to Smith, in an open marketplace, this relationship drives prices toward a "fair" valuation that benefits both parties and also results in improved products.

Today, economics is a highly interdisciplinary field that examines the ways that goods and services are produced, move within an economy, and are allocated in a predictable manner. This includes the influences of either scarcity or abundance of products, which affect the competition for access to them and thereby helps to set their price. However, there are additional influences on the price of goods and services, such as taxes on their use, subsidies of their costs, additional forms of governmental regulation (including bans on certain products), and the development of cheaper substitutes. Also important are the social customs, political influences, and other factors that influence the choices of consumers about their need for products and ability to pay for them (**Figure 15.2**).

Key premises of economics are that people will seek to enhance their wealth and lifestyle, and corporations will strive to maximize their profit, while governments hope to advance both of those goals. Therefore, the choices made by any of these entities will reveal how they value particular goods and services.

Economists have developed a number of processes and indicators for use in monitoring changes in conditions and for doing research on the consequences of alternative choices of regulation, policy, and other influences. **Valuation** is one of the key processes—it is a means by which the worth of a good or service is determined in monetary units (such as dollars). Valuation takes a number of factors into account, including the costs of production and distribution; the profit charged; the scarcity of a product compared with substitutes; the openness of the marketplace in terms of competition; effects of governmental regulation, subsidy, or taxation; and the worth of money itself, which changes over time, usually by a kind of devaluation called inflation. Ultimately, however, the value of a product is set by what consumers are willing or able to pay for it.

The **gross domestic product (GDP)** is the market value of all goods and services that are produced within a year by a country, or by the global economy. A relatively simple formula for calculating GDP is the summed value of the production of all goods and services + gross investment + governmental spending + exported products – imported ones. All of the units are measured in currency, such as dollars. The **gross national product (GNP)** is similar, but it is based on ownership and so it includes the value of products that are produced anywhere by citizens or companies owned in the home country, both domestically and in foreign locations. Both GDP and GNP are widely considered to be useful indicators of the economic condition of a country, under the assumption that growth in the GNP or GDP leads to a higher quality of living, all other things being equal. However, as we

FIGURE 15.2 Valuation The value of goods and services is set by a balance between the costs of production and delivery to consumers in a marketplace, and how much consumers are willing to pay. If you have ever bought food, clothing, or electronic goods, or have paid to rent accommodations to live in, or have paid someone to transport you somewhere (such as in a taxi or airplane), then you have participated in a marketplace for goods and services and have some understanding of how "fair" prices are set. This image shows a food market used by people living in a culture and an economy that is different from those of Canada—in the city of Cuzco in the highlands of Peru. There are many small-scale vendors in this market, competing to offer high-quality goods at the cheapest price at which they can make a fair profit, while their discerning customers are looking for the best quality at the most reasonable price.

Bill Freedman

examine later, these indicators are highly deficient from an environmental perspective, because they do not take proper account of resource depletion, pollution, and other important damages.

Economic indicators can be standardized as group functions, such as that of a country or the entire world, or as per capita rates as a way of understanding the intensity of consumption and the generation of wastes. For instance, the consumption of wheat may be expressed for all of Canada, or on a per capita basis by dividing by the number of Canadians. Similarly, emissions of CO_2, an important greenhouse gas, can be expressed for all of Canada in order to understand our national contribution to global emissions, or on a per capita basis to illustrate our intensity compared with typical people living in other countries.

Conventional and Ecological Economics

If economics is properly applied in the environmental realm, it can help us to understand and potentially manage the ways that people and industries cause damage by depleting natural resources, generating wastes, destroying biodiversity, and causing other kinds of degradation. These environmental damages could be assigned realistic costs, so that activities that cause them

would become less profitable, which would allow the market to work to improve conditions. That would result in a more sustainable economy, an overall improvement of society, and better prospects for the biosphere. This kind of full-cost accounting is known as **ecological economics** (or as **environmental economics**).

In economics as it is usually practised (i.e., **conventional economics**), valuation is assessed in a highly anthropocentric context, which reflects the perceived usefulness of goods or services to people. However, valuations may be highly dynamic, because they change over time in ways that echo the supply of a good or service compared to the demand for it. If a resource is abundant, then its valuation will be relatively low, and if it is scarce it will be more expensive. Moreover, if a necessary resource is in a limited supply, then great effort and expense will be expended to increase its stocks and to find less-costly substitutes. These conventional means of valuation perform relatively well when they are applied to goods and services that are directly needed by an economy, such as food, manufactured goods, physical infrastructure (e.g., buildings and roads), labour, expertise, and natural resources.

Conventional economics does not, however, perform so well when it is valuating goods and services for which there are no obvious or immediate markets. For instance, certain ecological functions are vital to a healthy performance of the biosphere. Such functions include the fixation of carbon dioxide and release of oxygen by vegetation, cleansing the environment of pollutants such as sulphur dioxide, and movement of water through the hydrologic cycle. Conventional economists treat these sorts of useful ecosystem functions as "externalities"—or benefits that are shared by society, but are not paid for and so are not included in the valuation of a tract of ecosystem. From an ecological perspective, however, these functions are vital both to the human economy and also to biodiversity at large, and they should be properly valuated and accounted for.

It is also common to not valuate certain kinds of environmental damage, such as:

- the extinction or endangerment of species and natural communities;
- damage caused by pollution to human health and to ecosystems, for example, by gaseous sulphur dioxide and ozone, by toxic metals, or by pesticides;
- the depletion of natural resources, which is not usually considered to be a "cost" of doing business, even though it threatens the sustainability of any dependent economic activity and is a grave risk to the livelihoods of future generations (these potential damages are known as "**opportunity costs**"); and
- socioeconomic inequalities, including poverty and the disenfranchisement and endangerment of indigenous peoples and other cultural groups.

These kinds of goods and services are appropriately valuated only if society judges them to be important. If their importance is acknowledged, then the cost of damage to them can be determined and used to adjust the calculation of profit associated with a threatening economic activity. For example, when petroleum is mined, its remaining stocks in the environment are diminished, so there is less available to be used in the future. Because petroleum is such an important source of energy and abundant substitutes are not yet fully available, and may never be, huge opportunity costs are associated with the depletion of this nonrenewable resource. However, conventional economics has not yet provided an agreed-upon way to calculate these opportunity costs, and so what we pay today for petroleum mostly reflects the direct costs of mining it and transporting it to a refinery (plus any royalties or other taxes levied by governments). This pricing system is inadequate because it passes the opportunity costs of depletion onto future generations, who may unfairly suffer as a result. Therefore, the people using the resource are not paying the full price—it is subsidized by opportunity costs that will be borne by future generations.

Similarly, a new housing development might cause damage to the scarce habitat of an endangered species.

However, conventional economics does not take that loss of biodiversity into account when determining the profit to be made from constructing and selling the new houses. Instead, the recourse is to rely on society to somehow prevent or manage the ecological damage. Typically, this is done by regulating certain economic activities that carry a risk of harming the environment. However, if effective regulation is not in place, which is remarkably often the case, then there is no reckoning of the cost of the ecological damage. Rather, it is considered to be a "**free good**" that can be shared with society and the biosphere, but without significant costs that are borne by the perpetrator.

Pollution is an additional example of not properly accounting for environmental damage **(Figure 15.3)**. It might appear sensible that to calculate profit, the cost of this sort of damage should be determined and subtracted from revenues gained from the economic activities that are causing the pollution to occur. In conventional economics, however, the deleterious activities may actually be regarded as being beneficial because they contribute to economic growth by adding to the GDP. For example, one of the largest oil spills ever to occur in North American waters was the grounding of the *Exxon Valdez* tanker in Alaska in 1989, which caused enormous damage by fouling marine habitats and killing hundreds of thousands of seabirds and numerous marine mammals, yet it actually increased the GDP of that year. This was because a great deal of money was spent on the clean-up of the spilled petroleum and to compensate people who were temporarily displaced from the local fisheries, and those expenditures contributed more than US$3 billion in economic activity to the GDP. More realistically, the

FIGURE 15.3 There Are No "Free Goods" In conventional economics, pollution and other kinds of environmental damage are viewed as "free goods (or externalities)." Their costs are not fully borne by the perpetrator, but rather are shared with all of society and with the biosphere. In ecological economics, the costs of environmental damage would be valuated and debited from the profit of the enterprise that was causing the harm to occur. This photo shows a landscape that has been severely degraded by pollution in the vicinity of Sudbury, Ontario.

huge costs associated with the clean-up and compensation of an environmental disaster should be viewed as a depletion of natural capital and a contribution to the "natural debt," rather than a helpful contribution to the GDP.

Fortunately, there is increasing recognition of the importance of environmental damages associated with resource depletion, pollution, and endangerment of biodiversity, and that benefits can be realized if ways are found to valuate them. Ecological economics is a relatively new way of thinking about valuations related to environmental damage (Costanza, 1991; Daly, 1996; Tietenberg, 2002; Daly and Farley, 2003). This novel field emerged as a conceptual fusion of economics and ecology (both names share the Greek root *oikos*, meaning household). The field of ecological economics seeks to examine and valuate the relationships of two kinds of systems—economies and ecosystems—in an objective and non-anthropocentric manner. It does this by using a variety of measures of scarcity and valuation to achieve a "full-cost" accounting of goods and services, such as

- the cost of repairing environmental damage associated with an economic activity, such as the production of a commodity (e.g., paper, metals, or food);
- a life-cycle assessment of the energy and material used to manufacture, transport, and eventually discard a product;
- surveys to determine how much money people would be willing to pay to ensure that an endangered species does not become extinct, or a natural community does not disappear;
- an evaluation of the costs of a project in restoration ecology that would produce an amount of comparable habitat to what is being destroyed by an economic activity, such as building a new subdivision; and
- the **ecological footprint** needed to support people living a certain lifestyle—this is the area of ecoscape needed to support the production of the energy and materials used by a person or an economy, and to treat any wastes.

Although the methodologies for making these sorts of valuations are controversial, they could potentially allow the marketplace to account for environmental damage as a cost of doing business, and as an expense to be reckoned when calculating profit. Most of the time this kind of full-cost accounting has not been done, so environmental damages were treated as free goods that did not detract from the profitability of an offending economic activity. There are many examples of these kinds of situations; they include ecological damage caused by pollution, clear-cutting, depletion of marine fisheries, urbanization, and other economic activities. If these damages were properly and sensibly valuated, they could be

offset in economic analyses of the costs and benefits associated with decisions about whether to undertake activities that carry risks of causing important environmental problems.

By allowing a full-cost accounting to be made, ecological economics helps us to understand the true consequences of economic activities. This knowledge would encourage people, corporations, and society at large to make choices that are less damaging to ecology and the environment.

Growth, Development, and Sustainability

Although economic growth and development are often confounded, in the sense of ecological economics, they are fundamentally different concepts.

Economic Growth

Economic growth merely refers to an economy that is increasing in size over time, in terms of attributes such as

- size of the human population;
- consumption of natural resources;
- manufacturing of goods;
- the supply of money; and
- production of waste materials and pollution.

Two commonly reported indicators of the growth of an economy are changes in the size of its population and the gross domestic product. GDP may be calculated in various ways, but a relatively simple equation is: GDP = consumption + gross investment + government spending + exports – imports.

Figure 15.4 shows recent growth of population (in **Figure 15.4a**) and GDP (in **Figure 15.4b**) for so-called developed (richer) and less-developed (poorer) countries. During the 53-year time period of record (1960 to 2012), the human population of currently developed countries increased by 49 percent, compared with a much faster 165 percent in less-developed countries, whose proportion of the global population increased from 45 percent to 82 percent **(Table 15.1)**. Less-developed countries also had a more rapid growth of GDP, which overall increased by 10.6 times, compared with 4.0 times in developed countries (note that because the GDP data are in constant dollars, the increases are not due to inflation). However, because the less-developed countries started from a much smaller base of GDP, their share of the global GDP increased from only 13 percent in 1960 to 25 percent in 2012. The data for Canada, by the way, are typical of developed countries **(Figure 15.4c)**, with the population growing by 2.0 times between 1960 and 2012, and GDP by 5.4 times.

Most politicians, economists, and businesspeople are enthusiastic advocates of economic growth. In general, they consider this to be a good way to increase the

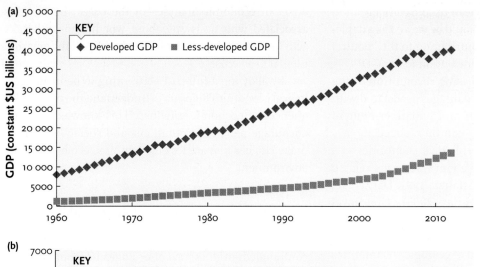

(a)

KEY
◆ Developed GDP ■ Less-developed GDP

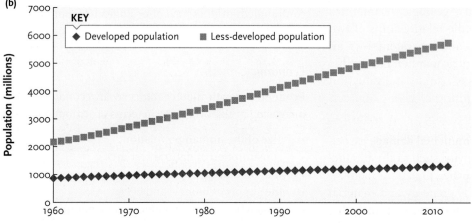

(b)

KEY
◆ Developed population ■ Less-developed population

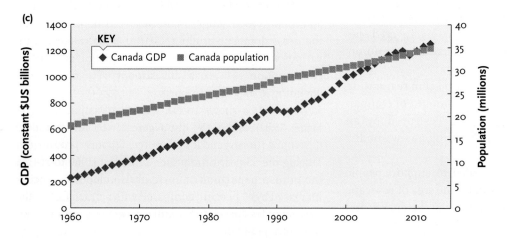

(c)

KEY
◆ Canada GDP ■ Canada population

FIGURE 15.4 Economic Growth The data show crude indicators of the growth of economies, separately for groups of countries that are relatively developed (or "high income" according to the World Bank classification, which in 2012 consisted of 1.3 billion people living in 69 wealthier countries) and less-developed (or "low and middle income," consisting of 5.8 billion in 144 countries). The population data are in millions, and gross domestic product (GDP) is in billions (10^9) of year-2005 U.S. dollars (these are "constant" dollars, in the sense of being adjusted for inflation, so that differences between years represent "real" growth). For context, the global population in 2012 was 7.1 billion, and the global GDP was US\$53.6 × 10^{12} (year 2012 US\$). GDP is the total expenditures for all final goods and services produced within an economy.

SOURCE: The World Bank. 2013. Data. (a) GDP (Constant \$US). http://data.worldbank.org/indicator/NY.GDP.MKTP.CD and (b) Population, total. http://data.worldbank.org/indicator/SP.POP.TOTL Accessed August, 2013.

amount of wealth in society, and thereby to help citizens have a greater capacity to purchase goods and services, which itself is considered an indicator of prosperity. Of course, for this to occur, the rate of increase in the size of an economy, as indicated by the GDP, must exceed that of population growth. In **Figure 15.5** we can see that much of the recent economic growth in developing countries, representing an overall increase of GDP of 11.6-fold between 1960 and 2012, was offset by a rise of population of 2.7-fold. Consequently, the growth of per capita GDP was 4.3-fold. In contrast, the more moderate 5.0 times increase of GDP in developed countries was largely

retained on a per capita basis (3.3 times) because of a much slower increase of population (1.5 times).

Although most leaders of society are eager proponents of economic growth, there are important problems inherent in the phenomenon. They arise because economic growth is typically achieved by increases in the following: population size, the consumption (and depletion) of natural resources, the generation of wastes, and many resulting environmental damages. From the perspective of ecological economics, these indicators of growth are symptomatic of grave difficulties, rather than being desirable attributes of an economy.

TABLE 15.1	**Economic Growth in Developed ("High Income") and Developing ("Low & Middle Income") Countries** The data show increases of both population and gross domestic product (GDP) over a 53-year period, as well as the percentage increases.					
	Population (billions)			GDP (Year-2005 US$ × 10¹²)		
	1960	2012	Increase	1960	2012	Increase
Developed	0.87	1.30	49%	8.00	40.05	400%
Developing	2.17	5.74	165%	1.18	13.69	1060%

SOURCE: Based on data from World Bank (2013); (a) GDP (Current $US). http://data.worldbank.org/indicator/NY.GDP.MKTP.CD and (b) Population, total. http://data.worldbank.org/indicator/SP.POP.TOTL Accessed August, 2013.

Economic Development

In marked contrast to economic growth, the process of **economic development** implies an improving efficiency in the use of materials and energy in an economy. Indicators of development include the following:

- decreased use of nonrenewable sources of energy, and their replacement by renewable supplies such as geothermal heat and the various direct and indirect forms of solar energy, including passive solar, hydro-electricity, wind, biomass, and photovoltaics (see the section on Natural Resources for details);
- increased use of renewable sources of materials, such as those manufactured from trees and other forms of biomass;

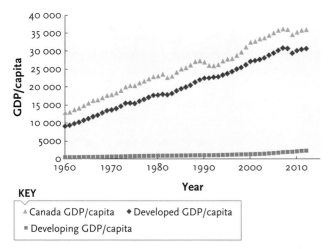

KEY
- ▲ Canada GDP/capita   ◆ Developed GDP/capita
- ■ Developing GDP/capita

FIGURE 15.5 Per Capita GDP The data show that, in absolute terms, relatively developed countries grew wealthier, on a per capita basis, much faster than did poorer (developing) countries during the study period. The data are in units of year-2005 US$ per capita.

SOURCE: Based on data from World Resources Institute (WRI). 2010. *EarthTrends database.* http://earthtrends.wri.org/.

- increased efficiency in all uses of resources, such as by improving the designs of machines and buildings to minimize their needs for energy and materials, by diligently recycling and reusing metals and other disused goods, and by less consumerism; and
- an improvement of social equity, so that progress is made toward an economy in which all people have access to the necessities and amenities of life, rather than just a minority of wealthy individuals (this is relevant at various scales, ranging from local communities, to national and global economies).

Sustainable Development

Sustainable development refers to progress being made toward a sustainable economy, which can operate without diminishing its essential base of natural capital. As such, a sustainable economy does not use resources faster than the rate at which they are being provided by the natural world, and so it does not compromise their availability to future generations. A sustainable economy must be fundamentally based on the use of renewable resources, because they are capable of regenerating after they are harvested. Nonrenewable resources cannot do this.

Nevertheless, there is also a role for nonrenewable resources in a sustainable economy. However, as their stocks become inevitably diminished by extraction, they must be replaced by an equivalent amount of a renewable substitute. For instance, electricity can be produced by burning coal or natural gas, but eventually these nonrenewable fuels will run out. The transition from the use of coal or gas to renewable energy resources might require linking their depletion to an offset gained by increasing the amount of an equivalent renewable resource, such as forest biomass. Enough trees could be planted to provide an increase of biomass that would offset both (1) the depletion of nonrenewable energy resources by the combustion of coal or gas (tree biomass can be used as a fuel), and (2) the emissions of CO_2 to the atmosphere, because that gas is fixed by growing trees into their biomass.

It would take a lot of forest to do this. For example, a study in New Brunswick found that the CO_2 emissions from even a relatively small coal-fired power plant (200 MW capacity) would require the off-setting CO_2-fixation services of 0.72×10^5 ha of conifer plantations established on higher-quality land (Freedman et al., 1992). Alternatively, because of the slower rate of productivity, 1.9×10^5 ha of natural afforestation would be required to offset the coal burning, or the ongoing fixation by 4.7×10^5 ha of existing mature natural forest.

As we previously noted, the human economy has been growing impressively during the past several centuries, and particularly in the last few decades (Figure 15.4).

However, any objective consideration of indicators related to the use of natural resources leads to the conclusion that not much of the economic growth has represented progress in terms of sustainable development. Obvious indicators of nonsustainability include the following:

- *Nonrenewable sources of energy*, such as petroleum, gas, coal, oil-sand, and nuclear power, account for 92 percent of the global consumption of primary energy (this refers to raw unprocessed fuels). In Canada this value is lower at 73 percent, largely because our country is relatively well endowed with hydroelectric resources (data for 2011; BP, 2013). During the 25-year period of 1987 to 2011, the global consumption of commercial energy increased by 60 percent (the increase was 34 percent in Canada). The heavy reliance on nonrenewable energy sources, all of which have relatively short **reserve lives** (calculated as the known recoverable reserves divided by the rate of mining), is an indication of nonsustainability of one of our most vital economic sectors—the provision and use of energy.

- *Fossil fuels* are crucial resources that are used for commercial energy and as feedstock to manufacture asphalt, plastics, and other synthetic materials. However, these nonrenewable resources have relatively short reserve lives, suggesting there will be future scarcities of these economically vital materials. The global reserve life of petroleum is about 59 years (in 2011), and it is 64 years for natural gas, and 218 years for coal **(Table 15.2)**. During the 20-year period of 1991 to 2011, the global mining of petroleum increased by a factor of 26 percent, gas by 63 percent,

and coal by 69 percent (in Canada, the increases were 85 percent, 40 percent, and –4 percent, respectively).

- *Metals* have many important uses in the economy, including the manufacturing of tools, machines, furniture, and buildings. However, metals are nonrenewable resources and their reserve lives are short, suggesting that the present rapid use threatens their future availability (although, unlike fossil fuels, the life span of metals in the economy can be extended by recycling of disused products). The global reserve life of aluminum ore is about 133 years (in 2011), and it is 43 years for copper, 79 years for iron, 22 years for lead, 49 years for nickel, and 17 years for zinc **(Table 15.2)**. In the 20 years between 1991 and 2011, the global production of aluminum increased by 42 percent, copper by 80 percent, iron by 21 percent, lead by 42 percent, nickel by 76 percent, and zinc by 65 percent (in Canada, the increases were 284 percent for aluminum and 211 percent for nickel; the other metals declined because some of the existing mines were exhausted and closed; Table 15.2).

- *Deforestation* is widespread and increasing. Only about 53 percent of the original forest cover of the world now survives, the rest having been converted to agricultural land uses, and to a much lesser extent to urbanized and industrial uses. In Canada, 91 percent of the original forest cover remains, although the amount is much less in southern regions, where most agricultural production occurs and most people live (WRI, 2010).

- *Marine fisheries* are showing enormous strain, and many of the most important stocks are greatly

TABLE 15.2 | Use of Fossil Fuels and Metals

The reserve life is calculated as the quantity of the resource that is considered to be economically recoverable divided by the amount mined per year; percentage change is the production in 2011 compared with 1991 (a 20-year period). Data for fossil fuels are for 2011, in tonnes of oil equivalent (toe; this standardization allows the data to be summed across the types of fossil fuels). Data for metals are for 2011.

Fossil Fuels	Global Production (10^6 toe/yr)	Reserve Life (Years)	Change (Percent)	Canada Production (10^6 toe/yr)	Reserve Life (Years)	Change (Percent)
Petroleum	3996	58.6	+26	172.6	163	+85
Natural Gas	2955	63.6	+63	144.4	12.5	+40
Coal	3956	218	+69	35.6	185	–4
Metals	(10^6 t/yr)	(Years)		(10^6 t/yr)	(Years)	
Aluminum	44.4	132	+140	3.0	0.0	+60
Copper	16.1	43	+80	0.55	13	–9
Iron	1090	79	+21	8.2	53	–36
Lead	4.70	22	+42	0.060	5.0	–80
Nickel	1.62	49	+76	0.158	21	–20
Zinc	12.0	17	+65	0.65	7.4	–44

SOURCES: Based on data from British Petroleum (2013) and U.S. Geological Survey 2013. Minerals Information. http://minerals.usgs.gov/minerals/index.html. Accessed February, 2013.

depleted or have collapsed because of excessive commercial fishing. This is particularly true of large, highly valued marine species. Over historical time scales, diadromous fish have declined by 96 percent (these are mostly migratory salmon), groundfish by 93 percent, reef fish by 89 percent, sharks by 87 percent, large pelagic fish by 76 percent (such as big tunas and billfish), and sea turtles by 96 percent (Lotze and Worm, 2009). The global catch of marine fisheries strongly increased from about 14×10^6 t in 1950 to an asymptote of $68–73 \times 10^6$ t since the late 1980s (70×10^6 t in 2005; WRI, 2010). The Food and Agriculture Organization of the United Nations considers that about 28 percent of fish stocks are severely damaged, while 19 percent are over-exploited, 8 percent are depleted, and 1 percent are recovering from depletion (based on 2007 data; Food and Agricultural Organization of the United Nations, 2009).

- *Agricultural land* is being extensively degraded by inappropriate management practices. Wood et al. (2000) estimated that 85 percent of agricultural land has already been degraded by erosion, salinization, compaction, or other problems. They estimated that soil degradation since 1950 had reduced potential global agricultural productivity by 13 percent. The damages are especially severe in poorer countries, which have less ability to mitigate the problems through improved management practices.

Clearly, the present human economy is characterized mostly by crude economic growth, which is achieved by population increases and the rapid mining and use of both nonrenewable and renewable resources. Although such growth can be maintained for some years, it is not sustainable over the longer term because of the integrated effects of resource depletion and environmental damage. Although it is seemingly heartening to know that many leading politicians, economists, and corporate spokespeople have openly avowed their support for the notion of sustainable development, they are mostly confusing it with "sustainable economic growth," which in a physical sense is an impossible phenomenon.

Ecologically Sustainable Development

However, there is an important problem with the definition that we just examined of a sustainable economy—one that can run forever without diminishing its base of natural capital. From an ecological perspective, this definition is too anthropocentric because it focuses on achieving a resource-neutral human economy. If that model were taken too far, the entire planet might become domesticated and converted to economic uses to service the human population. If that were to happen, grievous damage would be caused to the natural world.

For this reason, it is useful to consider the notion of an **ecologically sustainable economy**. This idea incorporates conventional resource sustainability, and so it too is an economy that is based on the use of renewable resources in ways that do not compromise their future availability. At the same time, however, the human economy would accommodate the needs of biodiversity, so that all species and natural ecosystems would be maintained at viable levels of abundance. This goal would be achieved in two major ways: (1) by conserving, to the degree possible, habitats on ecoscapes that are "working" to provide resources for the human economy, while also (2) designating networks of protected areas to accommodate those species and natural ecosystems whose viability is not compatible with intensive economic use (see also Chapter 14).

Capital and Natural Resources

An economy runs through the use of several types of **capital**, such as the following kinds:

- **Natural capital** (or **natural resources**) refers to sources of materials and energy that are harvested from ecosystems and the broader environment. There are two fundamental types: nonrenewable resources, which are always diminished by use, and renewable resources, which can regenerate after harvesting (these are examined in more detail later on);
- **Manufactured capital** is created by human ingenuity, and includes anything that is constructed from simpler resources, such as processed foods made from crops, lumber from logs, and metals from ore, as well as more complex goods made from these, such as machines and buildings.
- **Human capital** refers to the people who are participating in an economy, ranging from labourers performing relatively straightforward work, to highly trained professionals such as entertainers, engineers, lawyers, medical practitioners, economists, and ecologists.
- **Intellectual capital** is the knowledge that resides within an economy—the know-how of organizing a complex society and doing all the things that are required to keep people fed, healthy, safe, and content, and also to maintain the environment in good condition. Intellectual capital resides in the minds of people, and also in books and other media, including computerized resources on the World Wide Web.

All of these kinds of capital are vital to the functioning of an economy. In this chapter on resource ecology, however, we will focus on the harvesting and management of natural resources, and particularly on the biological and ecological varieties. Natural capital is harvested from the environment, and it includes many potentially renewable resources that are reaped from ecosystems. It is because of that latter connection, coupled with ecological damages that are associated with the harvesting and management of natural resources, that a commonly stated truism of ecology is that "economic systems and ecological systems are inextricably linked."

Natural Resources

As we previously noted, there are two kinds of natural resources: nonrenewable and renewable:

- *Nonrenewable resources* are present in a finite quantity on Earth, and they do not regenerate after they are extracted from the environment. This means that their use always diminishes the amount available to be harvested in the future—this inescapable depletion is inherent in the meaning of the word "mining" **(Figure 15.6)**. The prime examples of nonrenewable resources are metal ores and fossil fuels (coal, petroleum, oil-sand, and natural gas). Of course, the known stocks of nonrenewable resources can be increased by discoveries of additional exploitable quantities, and this helps to extend their calculated lifetimes (although the new findings do not change the physical amounts of the resources, which remain a finite quantity). In any event, the global stocks of nonrenewable resources are being rapidly depleted. Although metal ores can be mined only once from the environment, it is possible to extend their use in the economy by recycling them after some initial use. This process is done very efficiently for the most valuable metals, such as platinum and gold, but much less so for those that are cheaper, such as iron and aluminum. In contrast, fossil fuels used as sources of energy cannot be recycled within an economy—they flow through the system. In a sense, their content of potential energy and fixed carbon can be recycled by ecological and geological processes that occur outside the human economy, but these operate at exceedingly slow rates compared with the speed with which fossil fuels are now being mined and used.

- *Renewable resources* are sources of food, materials, or energy that are capable of regenerating after they are harvested, so potentially their stocks can always be available for use. Ultimately, a sustainable economy can be founded only on the prudent use of renewable resources. It must be remembered, however, that potentially renewable resources can be harvested too intensively (this is **overharvesting**) or inappropriately managed in other ways. If this happens, their stocks become diminished, and in severe cases may even disappear. The use of potentially renewable resources in such a wanton manner rejects their sustainability and is comparable to the mining of a nonrenewable resource. The most prominent examples of renewable resources are diverse manifestations of sunlight, which include:
  - direct solar energy, which can be absorbed and used as heat (this is known as passive solar);
  - wind, or movements of atmospheric mass that are driven by large-scale thermal gradients created by regional differences in the absorption of solar energy;
  - oceanic currents, which are flows of water that are solar-powered by thermal gradients in a manner analogous to wind;

FIGURE 15.6 Nonrenewable Resources These kinds of resources include fossil fuels and metals, which are depleted as they are mined from the environment. This photo shows a large open-pit mine for oil-sand near Fort McMurray in northern Alberta. The oil-sand is mined and then processed into synthetic petroleum.

Bill Freedman

- hydroelectricity, which is generated by tapping into the kinetic energy of water flowing from higher to lower altitude (the water having previously been lifted by the solar-driven hydrological cycle) **(Figure 15.7)**;
- photovoltaics, in which sunlight is directly converted into electricity; and
- biomass in its various forms, which are initially based on the fixation of inorganic carbon and water into simple sugars through sunlight-powered photosynthesis; examples are
  - agricultural crops, which are dependent on the fertility of soil and the ability of the environment to provide moisture;
  - tree biomass that is harvested as a source of energy or to manufacture lumber or paper;
  - wild animals that are hunted as food or for materials (such as fur), including deer, seals, ducks, fish, lobster, and oysters; and
  - wild plants that are gathered as food or medicine, such as blueberries, strawberries, and yew.

Bill Freedman

FIGURE 15.7 Renewable Resources These kinds of resources can regenerate after they are harvested, and so they are the fundamental basis of a sustainable economy. Much of the flow of the Churchill River in Labrador is already used to generate hydroelectricity. This place, known as Muskrat Falls, is the proposed site of an additional dam and hydroelectric generating station. The riverflow is regenerated through the hydrologic cycle, which is ultimately powered by absorbed solar energy.

A few types of renewable resources are not powered by solar energy. They include:

- geothermal energy, which is produced by the heat of radioactive decay occurring in Earth's core, and
- tidal movements of water, which are driven by the gravitational attraction between Earth and its moon and can be harnessed to generate electricity.

While many economic activities are dependent on the extraction of natural resources, the actual benefits may vary considerably depending on what is done with the harvested commodities. Local economic benefits may be limited if a primary resource (the form in which it exists at the time of harvesting) is exported somewhere else to be processed into **value-added products** (this is the increased value of a manufactured product over that of the materials from which it was produced). For instance, if raw logs are retained in an area for use in manufacturing such value-added products as sawn lumber, furniture, or guitars, the regional economic benefits are much greater. In fact, by encouraging value-added operations that use the entire tree, a large regional economy might be maintained even while having much smaller harvests of timber.

Of the various kinds of resources noted above, biomass is most directly a product of ecosystems. As such, biomass resources are the subject matter of the rest of this chapter. Biomass is harvested and used as the source of all of our food, much of our medicine and materials, and as a source of energy. Ecological knowledge is necessary to foster the productivity of **biological resources** (or **bioresources**), to set appropriate harvest limits, and to mitigate damages that are inevitably caused by harvesting and management. Moreover, the harvesting of any of the nonbiological resources noted above also carries the risk of causing many kinds of environmental damages, including to ecosystems and biodiversity.

Sustainability of the Human Enterprise

Ultimately, the longer-term sustainability of the human enterprise will be limited by the ability of the biosphere to deliver resources and to assimilate anthropogenic wastes. Essential nonrenewable resources are already being rapidly depleted, and the limits of some potentially renewable ones have been reached or exceeded, resulting in declines or collapses of their stocks. These changes are well documented and they are forewarnings of a potentially dire future for the human economy, unless it is transformed into a more sustainable enterprise.

Such a transformation will not be easy to achieve. It will involve less intensive and more efficient use of resources by wealthier nations, while lifting the peoples of poorer countries to an acceptable standard of living. Some of the necessary changes would be extreme, and might not be popular among much of the public or with many politicians, government bureaucrats, and leaders in business and industry. These shareholders might experience a degree of short-term pain, possibly over decades, to achieve the longer-term benefits of a sustainable economic system. The difficulties would be related to the abandonment of the paradigm of crude economic growth, less consumerism and diminished per capita use of natural resources, and a rapid stabilization and perhaps decrease of the human population. But the offsetting benefits would be enormous—a human economy that could sustain both present and future generations, as well as other species and natural ecosystems.

15.2 Harvesting and Managing Biological Resources

The discovery of improved ways of managing and harvesting biological resources is a major subject area of resource ecology. In the sense meant here, **management** involves actions that are undertaken to improve environmental conditions in ways that enhance the productivity or quality of a biological resource, while **harvesting** refers to the gathering of wild biomass or the reaping of a cultivated crop.

Often, various activities associated with harvesting and management are undertaken in a coordinated manner that is intended to increase the productivity and value of a biological resource—that is, as an **integrated system** (or an **integrated management system**). A key objective of an integrated system is to achieve resource sustainability—a level of harvesting that does not deplete the stocks of a bioresource. Usually, there are also considerations intended to keep associated environmental impacts within acceptable limits, including the need to ensure that biodiversity and environmental services are not compromised to an intolerable degree (while recognizing that some damage is inevitable).

In many cases, it is wild and unmanaged biological resources that are being harvested. Examples include much of the timber that is harvested in Canada, as well as wild stocks of fish and other hunted animals, such as deer, rabbits, furbearers, and seals. In all of these cases, there is reliance on natural processes and self-organizing ecosystems to continuously provide harvestable stocks of a bioresource. In an economic sense, the biomass is provided by "free" ecological services that require no investment from the human economy.

Often, however, management actions may improve the quantity or quality of a biological resource, usually by increasing its productivity, by enhancing recruitment, or by decreasing the natural mortality of economically desired species **(Figure 15.8)**. Improvements of the bio-resource might be reflected in larger stocks, faster productivity, or better quality in terms of the size or spe-

cies composition of the harvested organisms. The improvements might be achieved by influencing the biology of target populations to increase their yield, for instance, by selective breeding, or by mitigating environmental constraints on their productivity.

Ultimately, the potential productivity of an organism is determined by its genome, which sets the upper limits of developmental and growth rates that can be attained under optimal environmental conditions. It is rare, however, for that potential productivity to be realized, either in individual organisms, or their populations, or in multi-species communities. This is because of constraints posed by environmental conditions on recruitment, mortality, and productivity. In essence, management actions are intended to mitigate this reality by alleviating the intensity of environmental constraints, including biological ones. The management actions may result in higher rates of productivity of biological resources, resulting in larger harvests. Those benefits may, however, be somewhat offset by any environmental damages that are caused by the intensified management.

Maximum Sustainable Yield

For any biological resource, there is a theoretical upper limit of harvesting that can be made without compromising the sustainability of the stocks. This ideal is known as the **maximum sustainable yield (MSY)**. If the MSY is exceeded, then the productivity of the resource becomes diminished and the size of its stocks decreases at a rate that is strongly influenced by the degree by which the overharvesting is exceeding the MSY. The MSY is somewhat dependent on the abiotic environment, being relatively large if environmental conditions are optimal for crop productivity, and smaller if they are highly constraining.

An ideal model of MSY, occurring at a constant rate of harvesting regardless of population size, is illustrated in **Figure 15.9**. In the model, the productivity of the stock under resource-constrained conditions is described by the logistic equation that we previously examined in the context of population ecology (Chapter 5). The logistic equation is an equilibrium model of continuous change, and it is relevant to populations in which births and deaths occur continuously, but there is limited environmental capacity to sustain the population.

This MSY model describes the relationship between the growth rate of the population and the harvest rate ($F(N)$ and h, respectively; both on the vertical axis) with changes in the population size (N; horizontal axis). When the population is at carrying capacity (K), there is no net change in abundance, and no excess production is available to be harvested (i.e., beyond what the carrying capacity can support). For obvious reasons, there is also no productivity to be harvested when the population size is

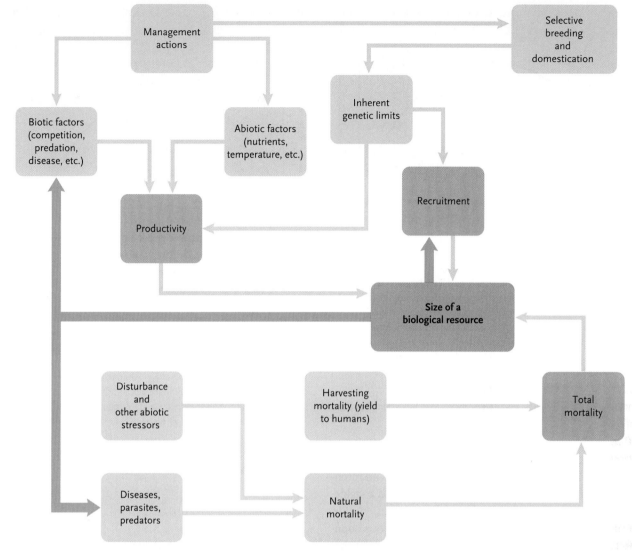

FIGURE 15.8 Conceptual Model of Constraints on the Productivity of a Biological Resource The size of a bioresource is influenced by the rates of mortality, recruitment, and productivity. Management actions can mitigate biotic and abiotic environmental factors, as well as some genetic constraints on productivity and recruitment. The rate of harvesting affects the total mortality rate.

SOURCE: Based on Begon, M., C.R. Townsend, and J.L. Harper. 2005. *Ecology: From Individuals to Ecosystems*, 3rd ed. Blackwell Publishing, Oxford, UK.

zero. When the population is at the top of the curve, growth rates are maximal and MSY (h_{max}, occurring when $N = \frac{1}{2}K$) can be achieved.

Note that a fixed intensity of the harvest rate (h) can intersect the curve at two places, and so there are two population equilibria: N_1 and N_2. Harvesting from the population (at a constant rate, h) when it is smaller than N_1 will drive the resource to extinction (this is indicated by the arrow pointing to the left), and so represents overexploitation. (Note also that at any particular population size, any effort of harvesting that is greater than the upper bound of the curve is also nonsustainable.) Harvesting (at h) when the population is larger than N_2 will drive the resource to N_2 and is a sustainable practice, although the yields are smaller than can potentially be achieved. Harvesting (at effort h) from a population that is larger than N_1 and smaller than N_2 will allow the population to

grow toward N_2 and is also sustainable. The MSY occurs at the apex of the curve. Note that if the harvesting effort changes, so do the two population equilibria.

Commercial interests that harvest biological resources generally maintain relatively fixed amounts of infrastructure, which might consist of personnel and machinery for harvesting biomass (such as fishing boats using a particular technology, or comparable machines in forestry). Because of these large investments in people and technology, there is a tendency for the harvesting effort to be relatively stable from year to year. Therefore, from the perspective of a resource manager, it may be more realistic to consider the effects of harvesting at a constant rate of effort, rather than at a constant yield (or amount).

Because the size of a harvest depends on the interaction of both the effort and the size of the stock, a constant

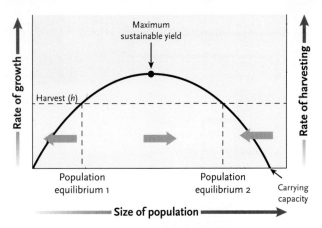

FIGURE 15.9 Maximum Sustainable Yield (MSY) This diagrammatic model of MSY is based on the productivity and harvesting of a single-species resource. The model shows that for any population size, a harvesting rate greater than the upper bounds of the curve would be nonsustainable, and if maintained would drive the population to extinction. In comparison, a harvesting rate smaller than MSY would force the population toward one of two equilibrium points. One of them is unstable because it forces the population to extinction, while the other is stable and sustainable because it is approached from two directions. Therefore, under conditions of a constant rate of harvesting there are several sustainable intensities of yield, the largest of which is the MSY.

SOURCE: Based on Clark, C.W. 1981. "Bioeconomics." Pp. 387–423 in: *Theoretical Ecology: Principles and Applications*. Blackwell Scientific.

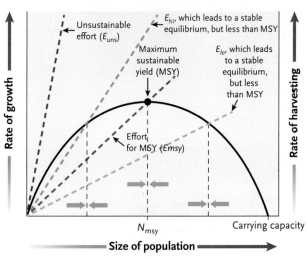

FIGURE 15.10 Maximum Sustainable Yield (MSY) under Constant Harvesting Effort Because the harvesting effort is constant, the yield varies depending on the size of the exploited population. The population growth model, *F(N)*, is based on the logistic equation. In the model depicted here, a single, stable equilibrium point is associated with all levels of harvesting that intersect the curve. At an effort of E_{msy} the maximum sustainable yield (h_m) is being harvested, and this MSY is achieved at a population of N_{msy}. Harvesting at E_{msy} when the population is larger or smaller than N_{msy} will result in movement of the population toward N_{msy}, indicating that this is a stable equilibrium point. Harvesting at efforts of E_{hi} or E_{lo} also leads to stable equilibrium points, but these have smaller sustainable yields than are achieved by harvesting at E_{msy}. Harvesting at E_{uns} does not intersect the curve and represents an unsustainable effort that would drive the stock to extinction.

SOURCE: Based on Clark, C.W. 1981. "Bioeconomics." Pp. 387–423 in: *Theoretical Ecology: Principles and Applications*. Blackwell Scientific.

harvesting effort results in a variable yield **(Figure 15.10)**. The constant-effort model predicts that there is an intensity of harvesting that will result in a MSY and a stable, equilibrium size of the stock being exploited. Within bounds set by the growth rate of the stock at various population sizes, there are also smaller levels of harvest that would be sustainable at other intensities of effort. However, greater intensities of harvest effort would not be sustainable, and would drive the stock to extinction.

There are also numerous, more-sophisticated models of population growth that consider multispecies stocks, changes in harvesting effort, environmental dynamics, regulatory strategies, and other variables associated with demographics, environmental conditions, technology, and regulation. These models (often referred to as dynamic pool models) have been developed for use primarily in the management of fisheries, but they can also inform the ways that other hunted animals and forests are managed. However, we will not examine these relatively advanced models, as they are beyond the scope of this introductory text. Specialized books in resource ecology and population ecology can be consulted for details.

For obvious reasons, the notion of MSY is intuitively attractive, and it has had great influence on the development of the theory and practice of fishery, wildlife, and forest management. MSYs are relatively easy to model in the ideal world of the logistic equation, in which the environment and its carrying capacity (*K*) are known and sometimes constant, and only one or a few species are growing without complex behaviour, such as social systems. In the real world, however, accurate MSYs are always difficult to determine. This is because environmental conditions are continually changing, sometimes in a dramatic manner, and there are corresponding adjustments by an interacting community of species.

For such reasons there is always uncertainty in the prediction of MSY and in understanding the degree to which it is limited by environmental factors. In essence, MSY is estimated using models of population growth, which can be modified (or parameterized) to account for the influence of environmental factors, including how they may be affected by both management activities and the harvesting rate. However, the models are always imperfect and so there is some degree of inaccuracy in their predictions.

Because of uncertainty in predicting the MSY, it is sensible to take a precautionary approach when setting the allowable harvest of a biological resource—it should be set low enough so that the stocks are not put at risk. This approach takes a prudent longer-term view and is more likely to be sustainable, although the harvest is not as large as might be physically possible. Unfortunately, such precautionary approaches are often not taken, as we will see later in Section 15.3 when we examine case studies of resource degradation caused by excessive harvesting. In those cases the strategy was to maximize the short-term revenue flows and profits, rather than to ensure an enterprise that sustained its vital resource base.

Another important problem with implementation of the MSY concept is associated with the fact that the logistic equation is an "instantaneous" model in which the balance between mortality and density-dependent recruitment is continuously maintained. The introduction of time lags (or delays), especially those associated with reproduction, can greatly destabilize such models. This problem can be especially severe in species that take a long time to become sexually mature. Moreover, changes in population size in the real world may be influenced by complex social behaviours, interactions with other species, environmental change, disturbances, and other unpredictable variables.

As such, MSY is best viewed as a way to gather insight into factors that influence the intrinsic rates of growth and mortality of simple populations and communities, including the effects of harvesting. Often, however, MSY models cannot be successfully applied to the management of real-world bioresources.

In any event, managers do need to regulate or adjust the rates of mortality that are associated with harvesting. They typically do this by controlling the harvesting effort, which is an integrated function of the methods (e.g., the types of fishing boats and their gear, or the weapons that hunters can use, such as bow-and-arrow or rifle) and intensity (e.g., the number of boats, or the number of hunting licences issued) of harvesting. In addition, various management tactics may be applied in an attempt to increase the productivity and sizes of the stocks of bioresources. In the remainder of this section we examine some factors (such as regeneration, productivity, and mortality) that affect the sustainable use of biological resources, including harvesting and management options that can affect the productivity and MSY.

Regeneration

After a biological resource is harvested, it is potentially capable of regenerating—this is the essence of its sustainability. The recovery may occur in various ways, including by the recruitment of new individuals into the population, as well as the regeneration of any that may have survived the harvest.

Natural regeneration is the spontaneous recovery of a bioresource after it has been harvested. It is the usual means of recovery following the harvesting of timber, fish, or deer and other terrestrial animals, although in some cases certain management actions may be used to enhance the regeneration.

After a timber harvest, for example, the trees may spontaneously regenerate in one or more of the following ways:

- **Vegetative regeneration** occurs when individuals of certain species survive the cutting and then recover by sprouting from their stump, roots, or rhizomes. Species of ash, aspen, maple, and other angiosperm trees ("hardwoods") are good at doing this, and their rapid vegetative regeneration may quickly restore another forest.
- **Advanced regeneration** refers to smaller individuals of tree species that are established under a mature forest canopy. After timber harvesting opens up the stand they become ecologically "released" from competitive stresses that were previously exerted by the mature trees. When this happens the smaller trees grow rapidly and can be prominent in the next stand.
- New seedlings can establish when timber harvesting opens up the forest canopy and creates a mosaic of microdisturbances of the forest floor. These conditions are favourable to the establishment of seedlings of many species of trees and other plants.

In some kinds of forest, these methods of natural regeneration can rather quickly re-establish a strong measure of ecosystem functioning on sites affected by timber harvesting and other disturbances. For instance, after the clear-cutting of mature hardwood forest in Nova Scotia of a type dominated by a mixture of hardwood species, the vigorous regeneration that occurred re-established a foliage biomass comparable to that of the original forest within only about five years (**Figure 15.11**; see also **Figure 10.12** in Chapter 10). This helped to quickly mitigate some of the environmental changes caused by the clear-cutting, such as warmed soil and disruption of the evaporation of water to the atmosphere (the rate of transpiration is strongly related to the amount of plant foliage on a site). The rate of biomass accumulation was also rapid in this forest type. However, not all kinds of forests in Canada regenerate as rapidly as this one did.

Sometimes, foresters might not consider the rate of natural regeneration to be fast enough, or the species mixture might be viewed as being less desirable from the perspective of the forest industry. To deal with those perceived problems, foresters might use various management tactics to improve the rate and quality of the postharvest recovery. They may use a prescribed burn or heavy machinery to scarify the ground surface, which breaks up the organic mat and exposes mineral soil that provides a better seedbed for the establishment of tree seedlings. Alternatively, they might plant seedlings of a preferred species, usually onto a scarified site and at a density intended to optimize the stand productivity.

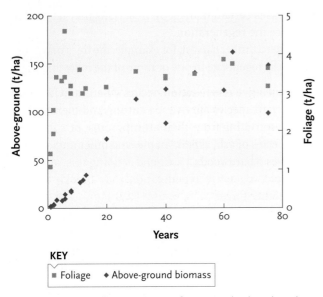

KEY
■ Foliage   ◆ Above-ground biomass

FIGURE 15.11 Rapid Regeneration of Biomass The data show the recovery of the aboveground biomass and foliage after clear-cutting stands of hardwood forest dominated by species that are capable of vegetative regeneration, such as red maple (*Acer rubrum*), sugar maple (*A. saccharum*), yellow birch (*Betula alleghaniensis*), and white ash (*Fraxinus americana*). The data were assembled by studying a chronosequence (time-series; Chapter 10) of stands of various ages after the clear-cutting of a mixed-species hardwood forest.

SOURCE: Based on data from Crowell, M. and B. Freedman. 1994. "Vegetation development during a post-clearcutting chronosequence of hardwood forest in Nova Scotia, Canada," *Canadian Journal of Forest Research*, 24: 260–271.

Similarly, after a harvest is made of fish or deer from some area, natural regeneration may be relied upon, or the recovery could be managed in some way. For instance, fishery managers may supplement the natural recruitment of wild salmon and trout by releasing large numbers of hatchery-raised fingerlings. This is an especially common practice for stocks that have been depleted by historical overharvesting or by damage caused to the breeding habitat.

In some cases the regeneration of depleted deer populations may be fostered by allowing only bucks (adult males) to be hunted. This takes advantage of the fact that the breeding system of deer is polygynous, with males mating with as many females (does) as they can (see Chapter 6). For this reason a deer population can tolerate a relatively high mortality rate of bucks from hunting, as long as enough of them survive to impregnate all of the does. However, if the hunting disproportionately kills the largest, strongest, fastest-growing, and otherwise "most fit" bucks (as happens with so-called "trophy hunting"), this management tactic could potentially degrade the genetic quality of an exploited population.

Limitations on Productivity

Various environmental factors may act as stressors that reduce the productivity of a bioresource (Chapter 2). If these limitations can be alleviated to any degree, the MSY may be increased. The stressors may be abiotic or biological in origin, and they may be mitigated using various interventions. Sometimes an intensive management system is used, which involves a variety of tactics used in a coordinated manner. In general, however, intensive management is done only with relatively high-value crops, such as in agriculture, aquaculture, or plantation forestry. It is used much less often with wild bioresources, such as hunted animals or in naturally regenerated forests.

The common sorts of environmental limitations and the associated management interventions include the following:

- **Abiotic stressors** include the limited availability of nutrients and moisture and extremes of climatic factors. Limitations of nutrients can potentially be mitigated by adding fertilizer or by incorporating nitrogen-fixing legumes into a crop rotation, while water stress may be alleviated by irrigation. The growing season for some high-value crops may be extended by cultivating them in greenhouses.
- **Interspecific competition** may occur between a crop and other species that are not viewed as being economically desirable. Non-crop plants are deemed to be "weeds," and in agriculture and forestry their influence may be reduced using an herbicide, or by mechanical methods such as tillage or the manual removal of offending plants.
- **Intraspecific competition** occurs within overly dense populations of a crop, and in such cases the density may be reduced by thinning. In agriculture and forestry this problem is managed primarily by planting to achieve an appropriate density. Likewise, the density of livestock is usually managed to avoid overgrazing of pastures. Sometimes, naturally regenerated populations of a crop species are excessively dense and they may be thinned to increase the overall productivity. For instance, overly dense populations of saplings in forestry may be thinned to enhance the stand productivity.
- Disease may be a problem for some bioresources and it may be managed by manipulating habitat to make it less suitable to the pathogen. Some diseases of animals may be treated with veterinary medicines, such as antibiotics. Fungal diseases of plants may be treated using fungicide.
- Losses of crop production to non-human consumers are an issue for many bioresources. Herbivorous animals may consume some crop production, sometimes killing the plants, and if the problem is severe it may be dealt with in various ways. For example, in agriculture, insecticide is routinely used to reduce the depredations of herbivorous insects. In aquaculture involving Atlantic salmon

(*Salmo salar*), insecticide is used to treat infestations of the sea-louse parasite (*Caligus* species). In forestry, fencing and other mechanical guards may be used to reduce the effects of browsing by large and small mammalian herbivores. Various crops as well as stored products may be protected from pest rodents using lethal traps and rodenticide.

- **Selective breeding** (or **cultural selection**) and **transgenic modification** are tactics that can reduce the vulnerability of crop varieties to many biotic stressors. Selective breeding has been used for millennia to develop "improved" varieties of crop plants and livestock. This process has resulted in a number of domesticated plant crops that, compared with their wild progenitors, are relatively tolerant of many environmental stressors and more responsive to fertilizer addition and other mitigations. Transgenic modifications are a more recent application of bioengineering, in which DNA coding for a trait that is beneficial in one species is incorporated into the genome of a different species, such as a crop plant, to realize an economically important benefit. (These are sometimes referred to as "**genetically modified organisms**" or **GMOs**, but that term is ambiguous because it could also logically apply to varieties that are affected by conventional selective breeding.) For example, varieties of maize (*Zea mays*) have been modified to include genes of *Bacillus thuringiensis* (*B.t.*). This is a soil bacterium that is toxic to many herbivorous insects, and its genes in maize confer a degree of resistance to pest insects. Another example is GMO varieties of soybean (*Glycine max*) and canola (*Brassica rapa*) that have been bioengineered to be tolerant of glyphosate, which allows that herbicide to be used to reduce the abundance of weeds in fields of those crop plants.
- Matching the crop with the regional and local environmental conditions is always an important consideration. This is particularly vital when choosing crops to grow in a larger region. It is the reason that plantations of black walnut (*Juglans nigra*) are not established in northern Ontario instead of black spruce (*Picea mariana*), and why peaches are not cultivated in northern Alberta, or barley in the Okanagan Valley of southern British Columbia. To some degree these large-scale considerations are made continually, and in the modern world they must track synoptic environmental changes, such as those in climate. Growing conditions are also important at a local scale, such as in low areas with wet soil, in better-drained higher places where drought may be an issue, in soils that are excessively acidic or calcareous, and so on.

Natural Mortality

Deaths caused by predators, parasites, diseases, accidents, and disturbances are referred to as **natural mortality**. Exploited stocks of bioresources are also subjected to **anthropogenic mortality** by harvesting. Any causes of mortality will affect the abundance of juvenile and adult organisms, and thereby the stocks of biological resources. Within this context, if natural causes of mortality can be reduced, larger harvests may be available to people.

There are various ways of decreasing natural mortality, although it can never be totally eliminated. For example:

- Severe infestations of herbivorous insects may cause mortality to agricultural and forestry crops. Sometimes, the problem can be dealt with by modifying the habitat to make it less suitable to the pest, but often this does not work well enough and pesticides may be used. Sprays of insecticide are routinely used in agriculture to reduce irruptions of arthropods, especially those that can devastate a crop, such as the migratory grasshopper (*Melanoplus sanguinipes*) and other locusts. In forestry, tens of millions of hectares of conifer forest in eastern Canada were sprayed with insecticides from the 1960s to 1993 to reduce the abundance of spruce budworm (*Choristoneura fumiferana*), a devastating herbivore of balsam fir (*Abies balsamea*) and white spruce (*Picea glauca*) (a cumulative area exceeding 118×10^6 ha was sprayed, including stands that were repeatedly treated in various years; Freedman, 2010). However, a similarly destructive irruption of the mountain pine beetle (*Dendroctonus ponderosae*) in western forests of lodgepole pine (*Pinus contorta*) cannot be managed in this way, because insecticide cannot be delivered to the beetle larvae, which live beneath the bark of the trees. Instead, great swaths of mature pine forest are affected by the beetle (16×10^6 ha in 2012), resulting in most of the trees being killed, and much of the dead timber later being salvaged by extensive clear-cutting **(Figure 15.12)**.
- Sometimes, large carnivores are considered to be important predators of livestock or of wild ungulates that are hunted by people. If those losses to natural predators are considered unacceptable, the carnivores may be killed by shooting, trapping, or poisoning. Wolf (*Canis lupus*) culls usually occur in situations where relatively small populations of woodland caribou (*Rangifer tarandus*) or moose (*Alces alces*) are being affected. An alternative tactic has been used in Yukon to increase the population of the endangered Chisana herd of caribou. In that case, pregnant does were captured and released into a large fenced enclosure built within the range of

FIGURE 15.12 The Mountain Pine Beetle (*Dendroctonus ponderosae*) An irruption of this native beetle is causing severe damage to montane pine forests in British Columbia. This landscape in the Thompson River region of British Columbia contains extensively killed stands of pine.

that herd, where their calves were protected from predation by wolves or grizzly bears (*Ursus arctos*) and also provided with supplemental food. This management increased the first-year survival of calves from about 15 percent under free-ranging conditions to 73 percent, and the supplemental recruitment is allowing the population to increase (Environment Yukon, 2007). In agricultural applications, access of predators to livestock may also be restricted using fences, or by guard animals such as dogs, donkeys, and llamas.

Harvest-Related Mortality

The rate of harvesting should be managed to ensure that the total mortality (natural plus that from the harvest) does not exceed the MSY. The harvest-related mortality is influenced by several factors related to the effort: (1) the numbers of harvesting units that are deployed, (2) the technology being used, and (3) the time they spend harvesting. Any of these factors can be regulated by resource managers to try to keep the harvest within a designated limit.

Various administrative and legal tools may be available to managers as they seek to regulate the harvesting effort. Relatively direct controls include:

- limiting the numbers of licences that are issued, which regulates the numbers of participants;
- regulating the harvesting methods that are allowed;
- specifying quotas for each harvesting unit;
- limiting the times during which harvesting can occur; and
- specifying the places where harvesting can take place.

A number of indirect mechanisms can also influence the harvesting rate, by affecting the operating costs:

- imposing taxes or other levies to increase the cost of certain harvesting methods that might be damaging to the habitat;
- subsidizing less-damaging methods;
- assessing fines for any aspect of noncompliance; and
- buying out excess harvesting capacity (of licences or equipment).

The influence of technology on the harvesting rate can be illustrated in various ways. Clearly, a person wielding an axe can cut down trees and de-limb the logs, which can then be hauled to a roadside using oxen or horses trained for that job. However, a person with a chainsaw can fell and de-limb trees much faster, and a skidding machine can get logs to the roadside quicker than a team of livestock. And the latest logging equipment can do these tasks even more rapidly—with only a single operator, these machines can fell and de-limb trees, cut them to a desired length, and then carry them to the roadside. Because machines of this sort can perform these tasks so efficiently, people using axes, chainsaws, and trained horses and oxen are now rarely employed in the logging industry.

In this context, the "efficiency" is measured as tonnes of wood delivered to a roadside landing per dollar of investment in the capacity to cut and haul the forest biomass. Moreover, the modern machines typically work most profitably when used to clear-cut all of the timber from a stand, rather than by harvesting trees using environmentally softer methods, such as selection cutting (we will examine these harvesting systems later). However, the greater environmental damages associated with clear-cutting compared with less-intensive harvesting systems are not fully accounted for when comparing the economic viability of the systems.

In a fishery, the simplest methods of harvesting involve people using hand-held equipment, such as jigs or a rod-and-reel (**Figure 15.13**). These methods are relatively well targeted to the species that are the object of the

FIGURE 15.13 **Fishing Methods Vary in Their Efficiency** Fishing with a rod and reel is not very efficient compared with the use of large ships deploying nets. However, recreational fishing provides much more value added to the economy, on a per-fish basis, compared with commercial fishing.

Yves Marcoux/First Light

fishery and undesired species can often be returned to the water. The most intensive methods use boats hauling large nets, such as bag-like trawls or seines, or wall-like drift-nets. These intensive technologies catch much more fish biomass per worker and per dollar of investment. However, depending on the stock being exploited, they may catch a much broader spectrum of species than is being commercially targeted.

The nontargeted mortality is referred to as **by-catch**, and it represents a kind of collateral damage that may be discarded as noneconomic "garbage." By-catch is particularly intense in shrimp trawling, which accounts for more than one-third of the global total, even though shrimp amount to only 2 percent of the commercial landings of marine animal biomass (Clucas, 1997). By-catch is also intense for some drift-net fisheries—these are gill-nets that float suspended in the water column, sometimes extending for tens of kilometres and representing a "wall-of-death" for creatures that swim into them, including dolphins and sea turtles (we examine this topic in more detail later in the chapter).

Clearly, the choice of the harvesting method has a great influence on the species and sizes of organisms that are harvested, and this is an important consideration in resource management. In a fishery, for instance, the mesh size of the net has a direct effect on the sizes of animals that are captured. Well-regulated fisheries generally do not permit the capture of undersized individuals, because they have a relatively low value on a per-weight basis than do larger animals, while also representing much of the future reproductive potential of the population.

In forestry, all species and sizes of trees are harvested in a clear-cut. However, alternative harvesting practices can be used that are more selective of species and sizes,

and that can favour the regeneration of the most desirable tree species, while also having fewer environmental impacts. The best of these practices is selection harvesting, which removes only some of the trees. When practised carefully, selection logging leaves the physical and ecological integrity of the managed forest substantially intact, even while timber is being harvested at intervals of one to several decades.

Managers sometimes issue licences that set a limit on the number of people or pieces of equipment that can be used to harvest a particular stock, in an attempt to ensure that an MSY is not exceeded. For example, the number of people allowed to hunt moose might be determined by a lottery, or a licence might be required to fish on a particular river. In a commercial harvest, a regulatory authority might also specify the kind of technology that may be used—such as the number of vessels using a particular kind of fishing gear.

The harvest-related mortality might also be managed by specifying the time that can be spent in the harvest. For example, waterfowl can be hunted only during the autumn, after they have bred and when their populations are relatively large. The only exceptions are for snow goose (*Chen caerulescens*) in some regions where they are abundant enough to be damaging their own habitat. Likewise, the hunting of deer is generally restricted to a period during the autumn, when their populations are largest, the mating season is over, and the animals are well fed in preparation for the winter. In coastal British Columbia and Alaska, the commercial fishery for prespawning herring (*Clupea pallasii*; their roe is a valuable product) is allowed to operate for only several hours or less on a few specified days, so as to help prevent overfishing of the limited breeding stock.

Unsustainable Harvesting

There are many examples of biological resources that have been depleted by nonsustainable use. Such overharvesting of a potentially renewable resource is comparable to the "mining" of a nonrenewable one, such as a metal or fossil fuel. The first occurrences of this sort of resource destruction are prehistoric, and include the numerous extinctions that occurred on various oceanic islands after they were discovered by people, and likely also those of many large animals when the Americas were initially colonized (Chapter 14).

More recently, in historical times, a number of Canadian species have been rendered extinct by overharvesting, including the great auk (*Pinguinus impennis*), Labrador duck (*Camptorhynchus labradorium*), passenger pigeon (*Ectopistes migratorius*), Eskimo curlew (*Numenius borealis*), deepwater cisco (*Coregonus johannae*), blue pike (*Stizostedion vitreum glaucum*), and Queen Charlotte Islands caribou (*Rangifer tarandus dawsoni*). There is a much longer list of Canadian species that have become endangered as a result of excessive harvesting, including some that were initially superabundant, such as the plains bison (*Bison bison bison*), northern right whale (*Eubalaena glacialis*), American ginseng (*Panax quinquefolius*), and many others. These species still survive in the wild, but in a small abundance that can no longer support commercial harvesting. They are often referred to as being **commercially extinct**.

Fortunately, the badly depleted stocks of some overharvested species have been rescued by effective conservation actions that allowed their populations to recover, sometimes to the degree that they regained their pre-exploitation abundance. Canadian examples noted in Chapter 14 include the harp seal (*Phoca groenlandica*), grey whale (*Eschrichtius robustus*), American beaver (*Castor canadensis*), wild turkey (*Meleagris gallopavo*), and various ducks and geese. Many other species, however, remain badly depleted.

In some cases, entire communities of economically important species have been devastated by excessive harvesting or by poor management. We examined some examples in Chapter 14, such as Carolinian forest of southern Ontario, dry coastal forests of Douglas fir (*Pseudotsuga menziesii*) and Garry oak (*Quercus garryi*) in southwestern British Columbia, all kinds of old-growth forest throughout Canada, tallgrass and other native grasslands in the Prairie provinces, and various kinds of fish, mollusc, and other aquatic communities.

The overexploitation of certain communities sometimes displayed a pattern of top-down degradation, which can be referred to as "**working-down**" the resource. Often, the original (or pre-exploitation) community was dominated by large, old-growth individuals of especially valuable species. These were selectively harvested in the initial phase of resource "development," which left smaller, younger individuals to dominate the postharvest community. Because these are often relatively fast-growing compared with old-growth individuals, the net productivity of the secondary community was not necessarily diminished. However, subsequent harvests often used intensive methods that were less selective and intended to recover as much biomass as possible. If those harvests were made on a sustainable basis, the regeneration might recover the secondary community, but never the original old-growth one because the rotations were too short to allow that older condition to redevelop. On the other hand, if the harvests were nonsustainable (and they commonly were), then the excessive harvesting mortality and inadequate recruitment would cause even the secondary communities to collapse in productivity and biomass.

In economic terms, this pattern of exploitation of mixed-species resources could be viewed as representing a series of harvests of commodities having increasingly smaller value (measured as value per individual, per weight, or per area harvested). First, the biggest individuals of the most desirable species were selectively harvested and quickly depleted. Then, smaller individuals of the most valuable species might be harvested and depleted, along with the largest ones of secondary species. The final stage typically involves an area-harvesting method that attempts to harvest all of the biomass for manufacturing into a bulk commodity.

This sequential process of working-down a biological resource can be illustrated by the commercial fishery of Lake Erie since 1880. Initially, the fishery landed mainly high-value species, but they were overfished and their stocks soon collapsed, although not all at the same time. Lake sturgeon (*Acipenser fulvescens*) and lake herring (*Coregonus artedii*) were the first to be extirpated from the lake **(Figure 15.14a)**, followed soon after by sauger (*Stizostedion canadense*) and blue pike (*Stizostedion vitreum glaucum*) **(Figure 15.14b**; the latter became globally extinct). Walleye (*Stizostedion vitreum vitreum*) and lake whitefish (*Coregonus clupeaformis*) have managed to survive, although in variable abundances **(Figure 15.14c)**. As these valuable larger species declined, they were replaced in the fishery by smaller species of lesser commercial value, such as yellow perch (*Perca flavescens*), rainbow smelt (*Osmerus mordax*), sheepshead (*Aplodinotus grunniens*), and white bass (*Morone chrysops*) **(Figure 15.14d, e)**. Interestingly, the aggregate landings did not change much over the 120 years of record **(Figure 15.14f)**, although there was a substantial degradation of the quality of the fish being caught.

A broadly similar pattern of working-down occurred during the harvesting of the great temperate forests of eastern Canada following the European colonization. In Nova Scotia, for example, the original forest was an older mixed-species community that was dominated by immense individuals of white pine (*Pinus strobus*), red spruce (*Picea rubens*), eastern hemlock (*Tsuga canadensis*), yellow birch (*Betula alleghaniensis*), and several other species. The first commercial harvest was selective for the largest white pines, which were tall and straight and highly prized for use as masts for the sailing ships of the time, particularly for naval vessels **(Figure 15.15)**. Following the depletion of these big trees, there was a more intensive harvest of the smaller pines and bigger red spruce, hemlock, and hardwood trees, which were used to manufacture large-dimension lumber for the construction of buildings, ships, and furniture. The secondary forest that regenerated was then harvested as soon as the trees were big enough to be sawn into lumber, so that the

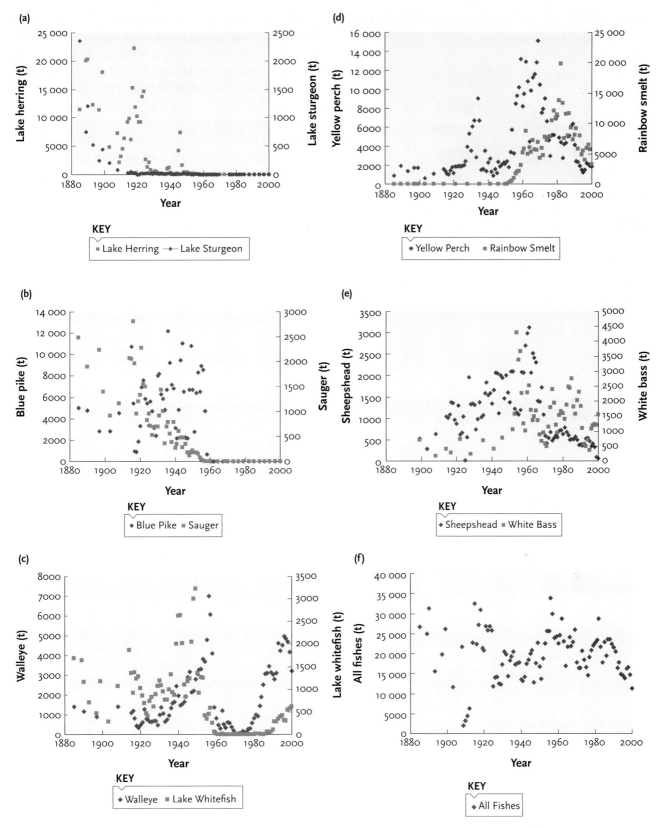

FIGURE 15.14 **Historical Changes in the Fishery of Lake Erie** The data show changes in the commercial landings of lake herring (*Coregonus artedii*), lake sturgeon (*Acipenser fulvescens*), blue pike (*Stizostedion vitreum glaucum*), sauger (*Stizostedion canadense*), walleye (*Stizostedion vitreum vitreum*), lake whitefish (*Coregonus clupeaformis*), yellow perch (*Perca flavescens*), rainbow smelt (*Osmerus mordax*), sheepshead (*Aplodinotus grunniens*), white bass (*Morone chrysops*), and all fish.

SOURCE: Based on data from Baldwin, N.A., R.W. Saalfeld, M.R. Dochoda, H.J. Buettner, and R.L. Eshenroder. 2002. *Commercial Fish Production in the Great Lakes 1867-2000*. Great Lakes Fishery Commission, Ann Arbor, MI. http://www.glfc.org/databases/commercial/commerc.php.

FIGURE 15.15 White Pine (*Pinus strobus*) Large, straight individuals of this species were an initial target of selective timber harvesting in eastern North America. After this primary resource was harvested, the working-down process switched to lower-value species, and eventually to area-harvesting methods such as clear-cutting. This white pine is growing in a region of Precambrian Shield in south-central Ontario.

Bill Freedman

original old-growth condition was never reattained. Late in the 19th century, a technology was developed to manufacture paper out of tree biomass, and this led to clear-cut harvesting of all trees for use as pulp, firewood, small-dimension lumber, and other uses for which relatively small and lower-quality trees are suitable. Today, forests are still extensive in Nova Scotia and they continue to support a large forestry-based industry, but the harvesting is almost entirely by clearcutting for the production of pulp, small lumber, and fuelwood. The harvest rotation is only 40–80 years, and there are hardly any stands older than 100 years.

Why Are Potentially Renewable Resources Overharvested?

An economy can function over the longer term only if it has sustained access to harvests of bioresources, which are required as sources of food, medicine, materials, and energy. Why is it, then, that so many biological resources, all of which are potentially renewable, are depleted through overharvesting or other damages, such as conversion into other land uses? Such mining of bioresources can be viewed only as being a foolish and maladaptive behaviour, yet it has happened many times and continues to occur.

The apparently self-destructive commercial activity of mining renewable resources can be rationalized in several ways. In the context of ecological economics, the reasons do not make much sense, but nevertheless they are the rationale for the wanton destruction of biological resources that are needed by both present and future generations of people. The reasons are as follows:

1. *Humans are self-viewed as being legitimately empowered.* People have long held an anthropocentric ethic that presumes they have the right to take whatever they want from the natural world for the purposes of subsistence or other economic benefits. For many people, this ethic is based on the biblical story of creation, in which God is believed to have directed humans to "be fruitful, and multiply, and replenish the earth, and subdue it" and to "have dominion over the fish of the sea, and over the fowl of the air, and over the cattle, and over all the earth and over every creeping thing that creepeth upon the earth" (Genesis 1:28). Lynn White (1967) labelled this as the **"Judeo-Christian ethic,"** although it is also held by other faiths, including Islam, whose beliefs include the account of human empowerment as described in Genesis. Clearly, from an ecological perspective, this is an arrogant attitude, but it is typical of the world's dominant cultures and religions. This commanding world view has had a profound influence on modern economic and technological ethics, and it serves to legitimize the mining of potentially renewable resources, as well as the collateral ecological damages that are often caused.

2. *Individuals and groups are self-interested.* Individual people, families, local societies, companies, and other groups are intrinsically self-interested. This attitude is the reason for many cases of irresponsible behaviour that may provide short-term benefits, even while damage is caused to other interests. In this context, the rapid depletion of both nonrenewable and renewable resources, as well as associated ecological damage, is often discounted as being unimportant. This is partly because the prevailing economic system treats both resources and environmental quality as being **common-property resources** (equity shared by all of society). Within such a context, self-interested individuals

or groups that are causing damage are able to off-load most of the consequences to the rest of society, and to the natural world. Garrett Hardin (1968) called this economic misadventure the "**tragedy of the commons.**" He explained it using the analogy of a publicly owned pasture (known as a commons) to which all local farmers had open access for grazing their livestock. Because each farmer is self-interested, they believed that they would benefit financially by grazing as many as possible of their own animals on the communally owned pasture. However, because all of the farmers did this, the pasture became badly degraded by overgrazing. Hardin's conclusion was that "freedom in a commons brings ruin to all," and this has proven true in the overharvesting of many renewable resources.

3. *Humans are socio-technologically empowered.* The defining attribute of modern Homo *sapiens* is our extraordinary and unprecedented ability to harvest natural resources, manufacture products, and increase our population and those of our mutualist species, while at the same time wreaking havoc on the natural world. In essence, these actions can occur because our species has achieved a high level of **cultural evolution.** This is not biological evolution, which is characterized by changes in the collective genetic information embedded among the individual genomes of a population. Rather, cultural evolution involves a progressive and adaptive improvement of the collective knowledge, means of social organization, and technological infrastructure of a society. For at least 99 percent of the history of *Homo sapiens*, all people were engaged in a hunting-and-gathering lifestyle, but then about 10 000 years ago the first inklings of agricultural practices were discovered and quickly became widespread (this is known as the Neolithic agricultural revolution). Since that time, there have been many additional and cumulative socio-cultural and technological improvements, all of which contributed to the extraordinary empowerment of the human population to exert its will over the biosphere. Today, if the right choices are made, people could implement a sustainable economy that would provide health and livelihoods for present and future generations, while also accommodating the needs of other species and natural ecosystems. Alternatively, choices might be made to continue overharvesting and degrading the natural capital of the planet, while causing a holocaust of biodiversity, or even to just blow everything up with a nuclear big bang. Any of these scenarios, and others, are plausible, in view of the present state of cultural evolution of our species.

4. *A cornucopian world view.* Many people perceive nature and its resources to be boundless—unlimited in extent, quantity, and productivity. This is referred to as the "cornucopian" world view (after the mythical "horn of plenty" that provides limitless food and other necessities). This view was relatively harmless when both the human population and our per capita use of resources were small. Today, however, it is clear that Earth has limited resources available for use by the human economy, and most of them are already depleted or are rapidly being depleted by excessive use.

5. *A false economy.* As we noted earlier in this chapter, the reckoning of profit by conventional economics often fails to capture important damages that commercial activities cause to the stocks and viability of natural resources, and also to biodiversity and ecological services. The billions of dollars spent to clean up the damage and to compensate individuals affected by the *Exxon Valdez* oil spill in 1989, or the *Deepwater Horizon* spill of 2010, should not be viewed as adding to the gross domestic product. Rather, they should be understood to be adding to the "natural debt" and so to be detracting from profit and not contributing to sustainable economic development. Another aspect of a false economy is the commonly held perception that investments of money in some economic sectors will accumulate profit faster than the rate at which many bioresources are growing. For example, an older forest might accumulate biomass at a rate of only 2–4 percent per year, whereas money invested in stock-based equities might return 10 percent per year. If this were true, then greater short-term profit might be made by liquidating (harvesting) a bioresource (such as a stand of forest) and then investing the money earned in a faster-growing sector of the economy. In fact, many regional and national economies have jump-started their economic growth by mining their "capital" of natural resources, including biological ones. Of course, this is an unrealistic financial system, because any sustainable economy ultimately depends on reliable flows of renewable resources.

The key lesson of ecological economics is that resource depletion and ecological damages detract from sustainable development. These damages are not free goods—in fact, they pose grave risks to future generations of people and to the natural world more generally. These ecological truths must become more widely acknowledged than they are at present. Once that is done, it will become possible to design and implement intelligent strategies to use natural resources sustainably.

In fact, that is what resource ecology and ecologically sustainable development are all about.

15.3 Resource Ecology in Practice

In this section, we will examine applications of the principles of resource ecology to the harvesting and management of a selection of biological resources that are important in the Canadian economy. This is a big subject area, so we cannot be exhaustive in the treatment. Rather, the intent is to provide an overview of key subject areas and their applications, with particular emphasis on forestry and fisheries.

Forests and Forestry

A forest is any tree-dominated ecosystem. However, some trees grow rather quickly, and if they are abundant a mature forest may develop within only a few decades following a stand-replacing disturbance. Nevertheless, it might take centuries for the old-growth character of late-successional forest communities to become expressed.

In general, forests have a complex physical structure, which is characterized by heterogeneity in both horizontal and vertical planes. The structural complexity involves the ways that biomass, especially of trees, is arranged within the community, as well as variations in the distributions of species. The occurrence of dead biomass, such as standing dead trees (snags) and slowly decomposing logs lying on the forest floor, may also be important. Older forests store a higher density of living biomass-carbon (expressed per unit area) than any other kind of ecosystem. Moreover, forest communities sustain a relatively high density of biodiversity, which might be measured as the number of species occurring per hectare (of all organisms, including plants, animals, and microbes).

Forests cover about 402 million ha of Canada, or 41 percent of the terrestrial area of our country (NRC, 2013). About 310 million ha are closed forest and 92 million ha are more open woodland and taiga. Forests are subjected to natural disturbances—in 2012, for example, wildfires affected about 2 million ha in Canada, and irruptions of tree-damaging insects about 9 million ha.

Forest Resources and Economy

Tree biomass is the most important bioresource that is harvested from forests **(Figure 15.16)**. It is used as a feedstock to manufacture lumber or paper, and as a source of bioenergy. Forest resources of secondary economic importance include hunted animals such as deer and fish, maple sugar and Christmas trees, as well as opportunities for outdoor recreation. In addi-

Bill Freedman

FIGURE 15.16 Forest Resources Are Important to the National Economy of Canada In recent years, about 0.5 million ha of mature forest have been harvested annually, about 90 percent by clear-cutting. This photo shows an area of clear-cut older-growth montane forest on central Vancouver Island.

tion, forests provide ecosystem functions that are important but not necessarily valuated, such as flows of clean water, storage of carbon, provision of oxygen, cleansing of the environment of pollutants, and control of erosion.

The forest resources of Canada are important to our national economy. In 2011, about 482 000 ha of forest were harvested (91 percent by clear-cutting; NRC, 2013). Trees were replanted on 63 percent of that harvested area (360 million seedlings were planted), and the rest of the area regenerated naturally. The value of harvested tree biomass was about $24 billion and of the subsequently manufactured products $53 billion. Together they contributed about 6 percent of the GDP of Canada (in 2011), including $16 billion to the balance of trade (this is the value of exports minus imports within the forest-products sector). About 185 000 Canadians are directly employed in the forest industries and another 283 000 are in jobs that are indirectly related. Canada is the world's leading producer of paper, accounting for 14 percent of global production, and we stand second in the production of pulp (11 percent) and lumber (14 percent).

Forest Harvesting and Management

Forestry is an applied science that is concerned with the harvesting and managing of trees and related forest resources. The field has a focus on the growing and nurturing of trees, also known as silviculture. Foresters and forest ecologists are also concerned with wildlife, protected areas, aquatic resources, recreational opportunities, carbon storage, and related topics.

FIGURE 15.17 A Shelterwood Cut This kind of timber harvest leaves 20–40 percent of the trees standing for as long as two decades. This encourages the establishment and growth of tree seedlings, after which the remaining trees are harvested. In this sense, it is a staged clear-cut, but because some trees are left standing the environmental effects are less than when all of the trees are harvested at the same time. This shelterwood cut in Nova Scotia supported more species of plants and birds than did more intensive clear-cuts made at the same time.

Forests may be harvested in various ways. By far the dominant system used in Canada is **clear-cutting**, in which all of the trees in an affected stand are harvested at the same time **(Figure 15.16)**. Several other harvesting methods are variations of clear-cutting. A shelterwood cut leaves 20–40 percent of the trees standing for several years to foster the establishment of tree seedlings, after which the remaining trees are harvested **(Figure 15.17)**. A seed-tree cut leaves some trees to provide seeds for the regenerating cutover. A commercial thin removes only some trees to reduce competition and encourage faster growth of the remaining trees, which after a decade or more are then clear-cut. Together, these kinds of clear-cuts account for about 95 percent of timber harvesting in Canada.

The other 5 percent is **selection-cutting** (or **uneven-aged management**), which takes only some of the larger trees during a harvest, so that the physical and ecological integrity of the stand is left substantially intact. Typically 120–40 percent of the trees are harvested at one time, depending on the forest community. This method is particularly suited to the management of older-growth forest in humid climatic regions (such as the temperate rain forest of coastal British Columbia), which are rarely affected by natural stand-replacing disturbances. Clear-cutting is somewhat more appropriate to forest types (such as boreal forest) that regenerate from periodic stand-replacing disturbances, such as those caused by wildfire or epidemics of tree-killing insects. Of course, all methods of timber harvesting result in substantial ecological changes, but they are much less with selection-cutting than with clear-cutting.

The intensity of post-harvest management in forestry also varies greatly. The low-intensity end of the spectrum relies on *natural regeneration* to establish the next forest (see Section 15.2). Natural regeneration can work well to establish a new forest after timber harvesting, especially in regions that do not experience severe drought in the growing season. In other regions, however, the establishment of new trees may be less than desired by foresters, resulting in "insufficiently regenerated" clear-cuts that have to be partially or totally planted with tree seedlings. Of course, natural regeneration requires no direct investment from the forest industry, because it relies on "free" ecological services to establish the postharvest forest.

At the other end of the spectrum of management intensity are systems that are used to establish a **plantation** on a clear-cut site **(Figure 15.18)**. In essence, a plantation is a "tree-farm" in which a crop of trees is sown and managed on a relatively short harvest rotation. A typical plantation may be established as follows:

- A clear-cut harvest is made of a natural stand of mixed-species forest.
- The clear-cut is then site-prepared for planting using a prescribed burn of the logging debris, or by large machines that crush the logging slash and scarify (expose mineral soil) parts of the forest floor.

Bill Freedman

FIGURE 15.18 **A Forestry Plantation** Plantations are anthropogenic forests that sustain a higher productivity of a tree crop than typically occurs in natural stands. Plantations are a result of the application of an agricultural model to forestry, but this agroforestry requires more intensive investment and management practices compared with reliance on natural regeneration. This 30-year-old spruce plantation is located in New Brunswick.

- The site is planted with tree seedlings, usually a species of conifer, at an optimal density.
- If the seedlings are subjected to intense competition from noncrop plants, they may be "released" by a herbicide treatment (usually glyphosate) that damages the weeds but not the conifers. Sometimes the release is by manual cutting of the "weeds."
- If, at the sapling stage of plantation development, the regenerating trees are too dense, there may be a precommercial thin to reduce the intensity of competition (i.e., some of the saplings are cut, but their biomass is not harvested).
- If the regeneration is too dense at the small-tree stage of development, there may be a commercial thin to reduce competition (the cut trees are large enough to be harvested).
- Once trees in the plantation are economically mature, they are clear-cut and the entire process is repeated.

Depending on the species and intended use of the biomass, the harvest rotation may range from only 20–40 years (for pulpwood) to as long as 60–100 years (for larger-dimension lumber).

During the process described above, attempts are made to quench fires that might threaten the plantation, and it may be necessary to use insecticide to protect the crop (and its financial investments) against insect pests that might kill the trees.

Forest Productivity

The productivity and biomass accumulation of the natural forests of Canada vary enormously, depending on the climate, site conditions (especially fertility and moisture status), the species of trees in the community, and the age of the stand. **Figure 15.19** compares the rate of biomass accumulation among four typical kinds of forest. The two boreal types typically regenerate after a stand-replacing disturbance, such as a wildfire. The boreal aspen type regenerates by prolific sprouting from the surviving rhizomes of burnt or cut trees, while the spruce re-establishes by seedlings.

According to the productivity models, biomass accumulation of the two boreal types becomes asymptotic (levels off) at about 200 years of age. This occurs mostly because the growth rates of individual trees slow down, while some trees are lost to natural mortality. The Acadian mixed-species forest occurs in a temperate climate region, but it grows on relatively infertile sites and its biomass accumulation becomes asymptotic at about 120 years. The coastal hemlock type grows in a humid climatic zone with a long growing season and only rare catastrophic disturbances, so it typically develops into an old-growth forest. This forest continues to accumulate tree biomass even after a stand age of 300 years, and the total amount of biomass is much larger than for the other types.

The effect of site quality is illustrated in **Figure 15.20**. Site quality is related to the soil depth, fertility, acidity, and moisture status. In the examples considered, which are both dominated by Douglas fir in British Columbia, higher-quality sites promote a faster growth of trees and a larger accumulation of stand biomass. However, trees growing in the humid coastal zone have a much longer and less-stressful growing season, and their productivity is much faster than occurs in the drier interior zone.

Trees growing in plantations are managed relatively intensively to promote a higher productivity. This effect is shown in **Figure 15.21** for several species of trees growing in Ontario. Remember, however, that the increased productivity of the plantations is gained as a result of costly investments of management, whereas

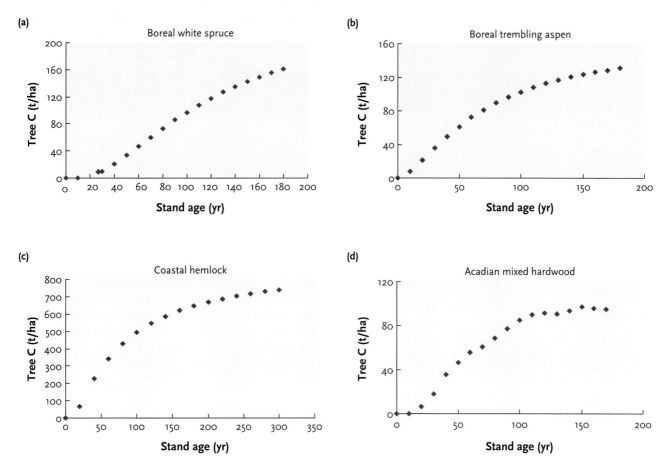

FIGURE 15.19 Biomass Accumulation in Four Kinds of Forest The data show the patterns of accumulation of tree biomass with increasing stand age for four types of forest: (a) white spruce (*Picea glauca*) in the boreal region, (b) trembling aspen (*Populus tremuloides*) in the southern boreal, (c) western hemlock (*Tsuga heterophylla*) in the humid coastal zone of British Columbia, and (d) mixed-species tolerant hardwoods (*Acer saccharum, A. rubrum, Betula alleghaniensis, Fraxinus americana*) in New Brunswick. The biomass is measured in tonnes of carbon per hectare, and it refers to all living tissues of trees, both above- and belowground. Note the changes in vertical scale for biomass. The data are predicted using stand-growth models, which are prepared for the major forest regions by governmental natural-resources agencies.

SOURCE: Based on data from data from Stinson and Freedman (2001).

the growth of naturally regenerated forests does not require that expense.

Environmental Impacts

Many environmental damages are associated with the harvesting and management of timber and other forest resources. Because this is a large subject area, we cannot explore it in depth; however, we can examine some of the key environmental effects of forestry that intersect with ecological values.

DAMAGE TO SITE QUALITY Timber harvesting has the potential to damage site quality, which could reduce the rate of productivity of future forests. One way for this to be caused is by the removal of nutrients along with harvested tree biomass—about 1.5 percent of the dry weight of plant biomass consists of nitrogen, 1.0 percent potassium, 0.5 percent calcium, 0.2 percent magnesium, 0.2 percent phosphorus, and 0.1 percent sulphur (these are data for entire plants, but concentrations in tree wood are smaller; Taiz and Zeiger, 2002). If the amounts of

nutrients removed with harvested biomass are large compared with the total site capital, particularly in soil, then there are risks for the inherent fertility of the site **(Figure 15.22).**

This is particularly true of the most intensive methods of timber harvesting, such as whole-tree clear-cutting, which removes all of the aboveground tree biomass (including nutrient-rich branches and foliage) and not just the stems as in a conventional clear-cut. If the purpose of a harvest is to recover as much biomass as possible, perhaps for use as bioenergy, then a whole-tree clear-cut yields 30–50 percent more biomass than would a stem-only harvest. However, the nutrient removal is increased by 100–200 percent, so the additional yield of biomass is gained at the ecological "expense" of much bigger removals of nutrients.

For instance, Freedman et al. (1986) studied four stands of hardwood forest and four of conifers in Nova Scotia, and found that on average a whole-tree clear-cut would remove 30 percent more biomass than a stem-only harvest, while the increase for nitrogen was 99 percent,

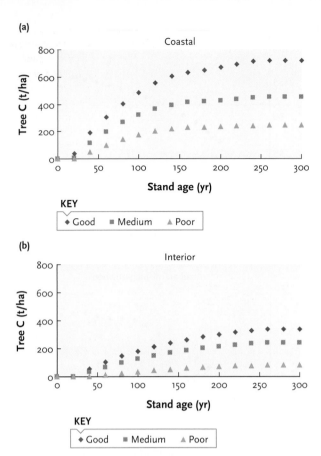

(a)

Coastal

KEY

♦ Good ■ Medium ▲ Poor

(b)

Interior

KEY

♦ Good ■ Medium ▲ Poor

FIGURE 15.20 Biomass Accumulation in Douglas Fir Forests
The data compare the accumulation of tree biomass with increasing stand age for six stand types, all dominated by Douglas fir (*Pseudotsuga menziesii*) in British Columbia. The sites are classified as being of good, medium, or poor quality, and are in either the humid coastal zone or the drier interior.

SOURCE: Based on data from Freedman, B. and Keith, T. 1996. *Planting Trees for Carbon Credits. A Discussion of the Issues, Feasibility, and Environmental Benefits.* Tree Plan Canada, Ottawa, ON.

phosphorus 94 percent, potassium 75 percent, calcium 54 percent, and magnesium 85 percent **(Table 15.3)**. Studies have been made of this issue in a number of sites, and it has generally been found that site nutrient depletion is a potentially important consequence after several harvest rotations, particularly if whole-tree clear-cuts are made.

The problem is likely to be especially acute for calcium removals in sites where the soil and bedrock are dominated by granite and related quartzitic rocks, which are deficient in this substance (such as occurs over most of the Canadian Shield). In addition to being a key nutrient for plants, calcium has a large influence on alkalinity, an attribute of soil and surface waters that helps to resist acidification (Sections 4.7 and 7.2). Lakes and rivers that are vulnerable to acidification are typically deficient in alkalinity, which could be made worse by large removals of calcium from their watershed with harvested forest biomass (Freedman et al., 1986; Jeziorski et al., 2008).

EROSION Forestry operations can cause severe erosion, especially from improperly constructed woodland roads and by clear-cutting steep slopes. Erosion associated with roads can usually be mitigated by installing small bridges or properly sized culverts that allow streams to pass beneath the roadbed. Because of their extreme vulnerability to erosion, trees on steep slopes should not be harvested—rather, they should be left to provide their vital environmental service of keeping the soil in place. On more moderate slopes, a useful mitigation against erosion is to leave uncut strips of forest,

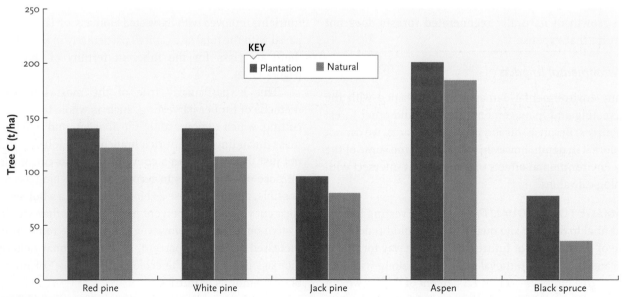

FIGURE 15.21 Biomass Accumulation in Natural Forest and in Plantations The data compare the accumulation of tree biomass in naturally regenerated forest and plantations of various species, all at stand ages of 80 years and on medium-quality sites in Ontario. Data are for red pine (*Pinus resinosa*), white pine (*Pinus. strobus*), jack pine (*Pinus. banksiana*), trembling aspen (*Populus tremuloides*), and black spruce (*Picea mariana*).

SOURCE: Based on data from Freedman, B. and Keith, T. 1996. *Planting Trees for Carbon Credits. A Discussion of the Issues, Feasibility, and Environmental Benefits.* Tree Plan Canada, Ottawa, ON.

(a) Variation in rotation length: fixed utilization

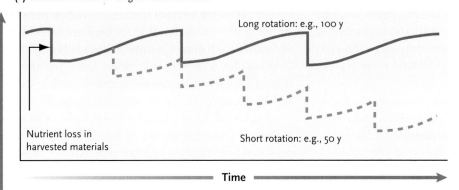

Long rotation: e.g., 100 y

Nutrient loss in harvested materials

Short rotation: e.g., 50 y

Time

(b) Variation in utilization: fixed rotation length

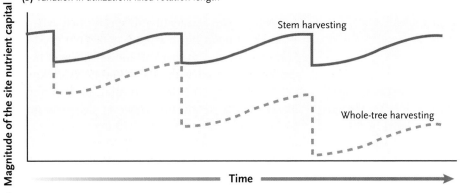

Stem harvesting

Whole-tree harvesting

Time

(c) Variation in rates of replacement of nutrient losses: fixed rotation and utilization

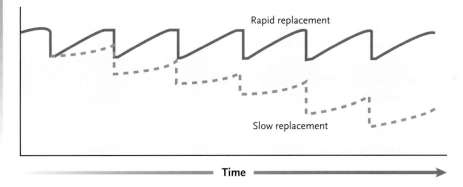

Rapid replacement

Slow replacement

Time

Magnitude of the site nutrient capital

FIGURE 15.22 Conceptual Effects of Timber Harvesting on Site Fertility Diagram (a) shows that a timber harvest removes a portion of the nutrient capital of a site, but that loss may be recovered during succession because of inputs with dustfall and precipitation from the atmosphere, as well as the weathering of soil minerals; however, if subsequent harvests are on too short a rotation, there will not be enough time for the nutrient losses to be fully replenished, so site fertility may become degraded; (b) a whole-tree clear-cut removes more nutrients than a conventional (stem-only) harvest, because foliage and other rich tissues are also removed; (c) an inherently fertile site (with rapid nutrient replacement by decomposition and other processes) can sustain a higher intensity of nutrient removals than a less-fertile one.

SOURCE: Kimmins, J.P. 1974. "Sustained yield, timber mining, and the concept of ecological rotation: a British Columbian view," *For. Chron.* 50: 27–31. Used with permission of the Canadian Institute of Forestry.

TABLE 15.3	**Biomass and Nutrient Removals by a Conventional and a Whole-Tree Clear-Cut**

The harvested stand in Nova Scotia was mature and dominated by red spruce (*Picea rubens*) and balsam fir (*Abies balsamea*). The tree stems and other aboveground biomass (branches and foliage) were weighed separately and subsampled to determine their water and nutrient contents. The percentage increase is that of the whole-tree removals compared with the stem-only ones. The forest floor and upper mineral soil are key components of the longer-term site capital of nutrients, which may become diminished by repeated removals with harvested biomass.

Compartment	Biomass (t/ha)	N (kg/ha)	P (kg/ha)	K (kg/ha)	Ca (kg/ha)	Mg (kg/ha)
Trees above ground	153	239	35	133	337	37
Stems	118	120	18	76	219	20
Branches and foliage	35	119	17	57	118	17
Increase	30%	99%	94%	75%	54%	85%
Forest floor (8 cm)	45	900	62	110	290	32
Mineral soil (to 30 cm)	170	3 860	1 220	13 300	5 460	1 740

SOURCE: Based on data from Freedman, B., R. Morash, and A.J. Hanson. 1981. "Biomass and nutrient removals by conventional and whole tree clear-cutting of a red spruce balsam fir stand in central Nova Scotia," *Canadian Journal of Forest Research*, 11: 249–257.

known as **riparian buffers**, beside watercourses. Nevertheless, when working in steep terrain, some amount of erosion is inevitable from disturbances associated with forestry. Severe erosion can strip away the soil, even to bedrock, which can make the local regeneration of trees impossible.

Eroded materials that reach watercourses eventually settle out in slow-moving reaches of streams and rivers, or in lakes, in a process called **sedimentation**. The gravelly spawning habitat (known as redds) of salmonid fish can be destroyed if there is excessive sedimentation of fine particles, which in-fill the interstices of the rocky beds. Aquatic habitat is also damaged if excessive amounts of logging debris (known as slash) are deposited into streams, where it may block the movements of fish and other animals.

Forestry and Biodiversity

Timber harvesting severely disturbs a forest ecosystem, and it profoundly changes habitat conditions for the animals, plants, and microorganisms that lived in the original mature community. However, at the same time, habitat is created for a variety of other species that are adapted to disturbance. The challenge for forestry operations is to ensure that species that are dependent on older habitats do not become endangered because of the regional diminishment of their habitat from too much timber harvesting.

It is not enough to achieve this goal only in particular stands of habitat, because they will change over time in response to either natural environmental influences or to anthropogenic ones, including the harvesting of trees. Therefore, this broad goal of conserving biodiversity must be met at a larger spatial scale—that of landscape (Chapter 13). For this to happen, it is important that not all stands of mature or older-growth forest are harvested. Large tracts should be set aside as protected areas to accommodate both the elements of biodiversity whose needs are not compatible with forestry operations, as well as the ecological dynamics that result in older-growth ecosystems. At the same time, certain modifications of harvesting practices can mitigate some effects on habitat, allowing higher levels of biodiversity to be supported in "working" areas. If these steps are taken in a balanced manner at the landscape scale, then commercial forestry operations can be conducted, even while native biodiversity is sustained at a viable level of abundance. Moreover, in a forestry context, this is the essence of ecological sustainability, in the sense that we previously examined.

The effects of forestry on biodiversity are too large a subject area to investigate in detail in a text like this one. There are two reasons: (1) there are many ways of harvesting timber and of managing regenerating forests, and (2) the resulting ecological effects vary enormously depending on the kinds of species and communities that are being affected. Rather than examining this complexity in depth, we will draw out some ecological generalities by focusing only on timber harvesting, and especially clear-cutting, which is the dominant method used in Canada, and on effects on vertebrate animals, especially birds.

In general, when a stand of forest is clear-cut, a community of birds that occurs in mature habitat is totally displaced by a different one that prefers younger vegetation. This effect is illustrated by a study in Nova Scotia that compared the avian species present in mature stands of mixed-species hardwood forest and recent clear-cuts of that community **(Table 15.4)**. The mature stands had somewhat more abundant and species-rich avian communities, supporting an average of 660 (range 515–815) pairs of breeding birds per km^2 and a richness of 12 (9–16) species, compared with 588 (435–745) pairs/km^2 and 8 (7–10) species in the clear-cuts (none of the differences are statistically significant). However, these community-level indicators do not tell us anything about the species of birds that were present in the forest and clear-cuts, which in fact were almost completely different. The mature forest was dominated by American redstart, black-throated green warbler, hermit thrush, least flycatcher, ovenbird, and red-eyed vireo. In contrast, the most prominent birds in the clear-cuts were chestnut-sided warbler, common yellowthroat, dark-eyed junco, song sparrow, and white-throated sparrow. All of the birds in this study are native species, which is typical of the avifaunal communities of regions in Canada where forestry is carried out.

Table 15.4 also presents data for a shelter-wood cut and a strip-cut, both of which provide habitat that is intermediate in structure between clear-cuts and mature forest. These stands supported a mixture of birds typical of either mature or younger habitats.

Susan Hannon (2005) of the University of Alberta also studied a wide range of harvest types in northern Alberta, including stands that had been selectively harvested, a method that leaves numerous trees standing and much of the physical integrity of the forest intact. That work also found that the relatively open-treed harvested stands supported a mixture of species typical of younger or older habitats. However, some birds that occur in older forest were not present in the selectively harvested stands. As such, Hannon's research suggests that selective cutting, a relatively "soft" method of timber harvesting, is an effective mitigation for some species of birds, but not for all of them. Because the latter species are dependent on older forest, they must be sustained on the landscape by ensuring that a network of protected areas is designated to accommodate their needs.

TABLE 15.4 | Birds in Various Forest Habitats

The mature forest consisted of mixed-species stands dominated by maples and birches in Nova Scotia. The harvested stands were 3–5 years old and were regenerating naturally. The clear-cuts had all trees removed, while about 40 percent of the trees were retained on the shelter-wood cut, and the strip-cut area had alternating 30 m wide strips of mature forest and linear clear-cuts. There are three replicates of the mature forest and clear-cuts. The avian data are in pairs of breeding birds per km². Only abundant species are listed.

Species	Mature Forest			Clear-Cuts			Shelter-Wood Cut	Strip-Cut
Plot Number	1	2	3	4	5	6	7	8
Common snipe (*Capella gallinago*)	0	0	0	10	15	0	0	0
Ruby-throated hummingbird (*Archilochus colubris*)	0	0	0	25	30	15	0	0
Least flycatcher (*Empidonax minimus*)	290	120	0	0	0	0	140	60
Hermit thrush (*Catharus guttatus*)	60	40	30	0	0	0	0	15
Veery (*Catharus fuscescens*)	50	10	0	25	0	0	0	15
Solitary vireo (*Vireo solitarius*)	60	30	0	0	0	0	0	15
Red-eyed vireo (*Vireo olivaceous*)	80	50	30	0	0	0	80	30
Black-and-white warbler (*Mniotilta varia*)	15	50	40	0	0	0	0	70
Northern parula (*Parula americana*)	15	30	40	0	0	0	0	10
Black-throated green warbler (*Dendroica virens*)	50	30	30	0	0	0	0	15
Chestnut-sided warbler (*Dendroica pensylvanica*)	0	0	0	100	40	190	110	50
Ovenbird (*Seiurus aurocapillus*)	150	120	200	0	0	0	0	60
Mourning warbler (*Oporornis philadelphia*)	0	0	0	0	0	90	80	20
Common yellowthroat (*Geothlypis trichas*)	0	0	0	25	300	130	80	0
American redstart (*Setophaga ruticilla*)	15	80	100	0	0	0	30	90
Rose-breasted grosbeak (*Pheucticus ludovicianus*)	15	10	0	0	0	0	0	0
Dark-eyed junco (*Junco hyemalis*)	15	20	15	50	70	30	0	25
White-throated sparrow (*Zonotrichia albicollis*)	0	20	0	90	190	100	30	0
Song sparrow (*Melospiza melodia*)	0	0	0	90	70	0	0	0
Total density	**815**	**660**	**515**	**435**	**745**	**585**	**550**	**425**
Species richness	**12**	**16**	**9**	**10**	**8**	**7**	**7**	**13**

SOURCE: Based on data from Freedman, B., R. Morash, and A.J. Hanson. 1981. "Biomass and nutrient removals by conventional and whole tree clear-cutting of a red spruce balsam fir stand in central Nova Scotia," *Canadian Journal of Forest Research*, 11: 249–257.

Hannon identified a number of specialists of older forest, including brown creeper (*Certhia familiaris*), red-breasted nuthatch (*Sitta canadensis*), boreal chickadee (*Parus hudsonicus*), golden-crowned kinglet (*Regulus satrapa*), Swainson's thrush (*Catharus ustulatus*), black-throated green warbler (*Dendroica virens*), and bay-breasted warbler (*Dendroica castanea*). Hannon mostly studied songbirds, but some larger forest birds are also specialists that require older-growth forest, including the northern spotted owl (*Strix occidentalis caurina*) and marbled murrelet (*Brachyramphus marmoratus*) in British Columbia **(Figure 15.23)**.

As clear-cuts regenerate, birds typical of mature forest begin to invade the community as soon as appropriate habitat develops for them during succession. However, species do this at different times, so in stands of intermediate structure there is a mixture of bird species typical of both mature and younger habitats. This effect is apparent in a study of post-clear-cutting stands of black-spruce boreal forest in northern Ontario (Welsh and Fillman, 1980). The uncut forest was dominated by Tennessee warbler (*Vermivora peregrina*), yellow-rumped warbler (*Dendroica coronata*), least flycatcher (*Empidonax minimus*), Nashville warbler (*Vermivora ruficapilla*), Cape

Tim Zurowski/All Canada Photos

FIGURE 15.23 The Marbled Murrelet (*Brachyramphus marmoratus*) This seabird is at conservation risk throughout its range in western North America, mostly because of the loss of its breeding habitat of old-growth forest through timber harvesting. It is a critically endangered species in southern British Columbia.

May warbler (*Dendroica tigrina*), and ruby-crowned kinglet (*Regulus calendula*). These species invaded regenerating clear-cuts as they matured, but at different times. The Tennessee and Nashville warblers did so first, breeding in stands only 5 years old, while least flycatcher, Cape May warbler, and ruby-crowned kinglet did so later, at 11 years.

The clear-cuts examined in this study had embedded remnants of trees that had not been harvested, and this may have allowed some of the forest birds to reinvade relatively early. Interestingly, the highest levels of avian abundance and species richness occurred not in the mature spruce forest, but in stands of an intermediate age following clear-cutting (17–19 years old). This was presumably because of a greater habitat complexity and better availability of invertebrate foods for breeding birds in the transitional stands. Similar observations have been made in other studies of post-clear-cutting recovery, such as one in eastern hardwood forest, where the richness of the avian community peaked at 20–40 years (Morgan and Freedman, 1986; see **Figure 10.16**). These observations are compatible with the intermediate disturbance hypothesis that we examined in Chapter 9.

The most intensively managed habitats in forestry are plantations, which begin as clear-cuts and when mature support a cohort of trees of the same age and species, which are evenly spaced in rows and have a dense canopy whose shade does not allow much vegetation to grow on the forest floor. As such, plantations have a relatively simple structure, in both the physical sense and in terms of their plant community. Nevertheless, some birds are able to breed abundantly in forestry plantations.

This is illustrated in **Figure 15.24** for conifer plantations of various ages in New Brunswick, and stands of natural forest of the kind that had been clear-cut and converted. These data show that the youngest plantations, aged less than five years, had a relatively low abundance and richness of breeding birds, but as the trees grew larger these community indicators increased. In fact, plantations aged 13–21 years maintained a higher abundance and species richness of birds than did the natural mixed-species forest. The most abundant birds in the older plantations

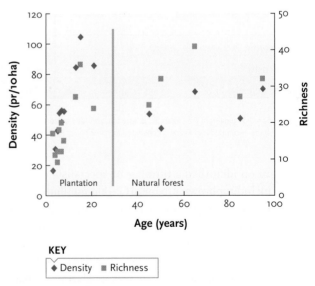

FIGURE 15.24 Bird Communities in Conifer Plantations and Natural Forest The data are the densities of breeding birds and the numbers of species present. Stands aged up to 21 years are spruce plantations, while those 45–95 years old are natural mixed-species forest. The study area is in southern New Brunswick.

SOURCE: Based on data from Johnson, G.A.M. and B. Freedman. 2002. "Breeding birds in forestry plantations and natural forest in the vicinity of Fundy National Park, New Brunswick," *Canadian Field-Naturalist*, 116: 475–487.

were yellow-bellied flycatcher (*Empidonax flavifrons*), magnolia warbler (*Dendroica magnolia*), yellow-rumped warbler (*Dendroica coronata*), palm warbler (*Dendroica palmarum*), common yellowthroat, and white-throated sparrow, most of which also occurred in the natural forest, but in lower abundances.

Although maturing plantations can support abundant avifauna, there is an important guild of birds that do not use them much as breeding habitat—these are species that require tree cavities as a component of their habitat. Cavity-dependent species use these hollow features as places in which to nest, and also for roosting at night. The most prominent group of birds that do this is woodpeckers, of which 12 species breed in Canada, and all of which excavate cavities in heart-rotted trees. In addition, many other species are secondary users of cavities that woodpeckers have excavated but then abandoned, or they use naturally formed tree hollows.

Trees with cavities are regular components of the habitat in older natural forests, but they are rare in plantations because the older trees or snags with cavities are either harvested or are deemed to be "noncommercial" or hazardous and are knocked down while preparing the site for planting to conifer seedlings. **Figure 15.25** shows that conifer plantations studied in New Brunswick have almost no snags, which are important sources of cavity trees, whereas they are abundant in the natural forest, although to varying degrees among stands. In that region,

stands with a higher abundance of snags had suffered damage from windstorms or insect infestations within the past decade or so.

The importance of cavities to some species of birds was shown by a field experiment that involved placing artificial nest-boxes in a variety of plantations in New Brunswick (**Figure 15.26**; Woodley et al., 2006). In the plantations, birds used the artificial cavities for nesting or roosting at a rate of 6.9/10 ha, compared with only 0.3/10 ha in the natural forest, where cavities were abundant. These data suggest that cavities are a limiting resource for a variety of species in plantations, and that is a reason so few of them breed in that kind of anthropogenic forest.

Because plantations are intended to be harvested by clear-cutting on a relatively short rotation, they will never develop cavity-trees and so will not be able to support species of birds that depend on cavities. However, to some degree this problem can be mitigated in simple ways, such as by leaving existing cavity-trees standing during a clear-cut, and by embedding "islands" of uncut forest within harvested tracts for the purpose of supporting large trees that can eventually develop cavities. In Nova Scotia, for example, it is now required that at least 10 mature trees per ha be left standing on harvested sites, arranged within no-harvest clumps with at least 30 trees in each, and at least 1 clump per 8 ha, located no more than 200 m apart, and within 20 m of a forested edge (NSDNR, 2009). These sorts of mitigations are being tried

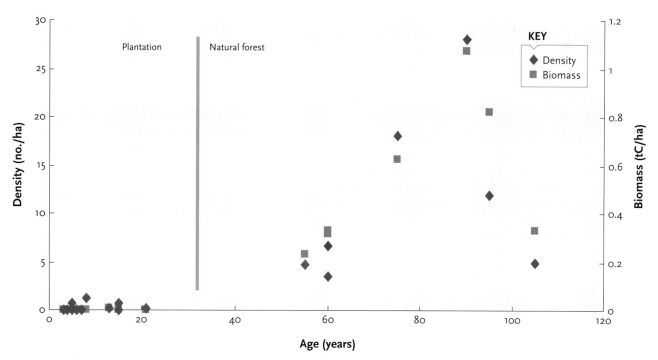

FIGURE 15.25 Snags in Conifer Plantations and Natural Forest The data are the density and biomass of snags (standing dead trees). Stands aged up to 21 years are spruce plantations, while those older than 55 years are natural mixed-species forest. The study was done in southern New Brunswick.

SOURCE: Based on data from Fleming, T.L. and B. Freedman. 1998. "Conversion of natural, mixed-species forests to conifer plantations: Implications for dead organic matter and carbon storage," *Ecoscience*, 5: 213–221.

FIGURE 15.26 Tree Cavities Are a Limiting Resource for Dependent Species in Plantations This phenomenon was studied in plantations of various age in New Brunswick by providing artificial cavities and comparing their use with stands of natural forest.

Bill Freedman

in various other jurisdictions, and they show promise in accommodating the needs of some cavity-dependent birds.

Another aspect of clear-cuts is that they create distinct edge habitat (ecotones) between forested and harvested areas. In agricultural and urbanized areas, edge habitats may be problematic for birds because they are places where their nests can suffer intense predation from foxes, skunks, crows, and other predators. Edges are also habitats with greater vulnerability to the brown-headed cowbird (*Molothrus ater*), a parasite that lays its eggs in the nests of other birds, whose own young usually die while the parents raise the cowbird chick. Hannon (2005) reported on a range of studies of reproductive success near edges in a forestry context, but found no consistent effect. This may be partly due to the fact that the study areas were relatively remote, so there were no predators such as the feral cats that are often found close to human settlements, and cowbirds were not abundant.

Forestry operations also affect aquatic habitats. Streams running through managed areas are at risk of being damaged in various ways, particularly by:

- the sedimentation of eroded fine materials, which can deposit and in-fill areas of gravelly substrate that are critical habitats used for spawning by salmonid fish;
- **turbidity**, or the suspension of eroded clay-sized materials, which can impede feeding by fish that are visual predators, and also interfere with their gill function;
- the deposition of excessive woody logging debris, which can block the movements of local fish and also prevent the long-distance migrations of **anadromous** species (these are born in freshwater but migrate to

the sea where they spend most of their adult life, then migrate back to their natal stream to breed);

- the removal of shading provided by riparian trees, which can result in excessive warming of water during the summer, even to levels that are lethal to fish and other aquatic organisms;
- the leaching of nutrients from disturbed areas, which can potentially degrade habitats by eutrophication; and
- a reduction of inputs of finer organic debris from riparian vegetation, such as foliage, which is a critical input of external fixed energy (as allochthonous dead biomass) that sustains most of the secondary and tertiary productivity of stream ecosystems in forested terrain (which are largely heterotrophic in their energetics).

As we previously examined, much of the erosion associated with forestry is caused by the improper construction of logging roads. This damage is now routinely mitigated (but not entirely prevented) by provincial regulations that require the installation of properly sized culverts that allow streams to pass freely beneath roads. Additional measures that help to protect aquatic habitat include bans on felling trees into streams, on depositing large amounts of logging debris, and against running logging machines along stream-courses. Another key measure is to leave riparian buffer strips of uncut forest beside waterbodies in logged areas.

The need for and specifications of riparian buffers are regulated by provincial and territorial governments, which have various names for these features, such as buffer zone, riparian reserve zone, and special management zone. As is often the case where provincial/territorial jurisdictions are involved, the guidelines and regulations vary quite a bit (O'Carroll, 2004). The Northwest Territories is the only jurisdiction that requires no-logging reserve zones around all streams, lakes, and wetlands (with a width of at least 60 m; this and the following criteria are the minimum required widths). Manitoba requires a 100 m special management zone (SMZ) around these kinds of waterbodies, within which selective harvesting can be done, whereas British Columbia and Ontario have a 30 m SMZ requirement, and other provinces have even less stringent criteria. In Nova Scotia, the SMZ is 20 m on both sides of streams, and there must be an additional 1 m for each 2 percent increase in slope over 20 percent, to a maximum of 60 m. New Brunswick requires a 15 m SMZ on both sides of small streams, but that doubles for stand types with a high risk of suffering wind damage after timber harvesting. Although the SMZ for Ontario is 30 m, it is 2000 m in streamside corridors in northwestern Ontario that are used by woodland caribou (*Rangifer tarandus*) during their migrations.

Of course, riparian buffers not only help to mitigate the effects of clear-cutting on streams, but also provide linear stretches of mature forest that survive the local timber harvesting. In this sense, riparian buffers also provide older conserved habitat for terrestrial biodiversity. However, the buffer width that is needed to protect water quality is typically much less than what is needed to conserve the habitat of terrestrial species that are dependent on riparian forest—that typically requires a buffer of 100 m or more (Richardson, 2003; O'Carroll, 2004).

Emulating Natural Disturbances

The disturbance of mature forest by clear-cutting has some broad similarities to wildfire, but there are also key differences (McRae et al., 2001). Both are stand-replacing disturbances that kill the most prominent organisms in the community—the trees—after which a secondary succession begins (Section 10.5). The initial stages of recovery are dominated by ruderal plants, which are low-growing, early-successional species that are intolerant of competition. As biomass accumulates and site resources become limiting, the ruderals become replaced by more competitive species until eventually a community typical of mature and then old-growth forest is re-established. In general, changes in animal populations occur in response to the development of physical and vegetational attributes of their necessary habitat, with some species preferring younger conditions, and others older ones.

The size and shape of a wildfire are highly situational, being affected by factors that influence the vulnerability of the forest community to burning (including its species composition, stand age, fuel loading, and site moisture) as well as the immediate weather conditions (especially wind speed and recent drought). Depending on these influences, a natural wildfire ignited by lightning may cover tens of thousands of hectares, or only a few, while its boundaries are typically ragged and complex, and there will be many unburned "skips," often of relatively moist habitat.

In contrast, clear-cuts are usually much smaller than areas burned by wildfire and are more uniformly arranged on the landscape, often occurring as a regular mosaic of rectangular blocks. Over a number of years, however, clear-cut areas may progress as a front of affected stands, as timber harvesting "eats away" at the original natural forest on the landscape (except for areas that are deliberately set aside as protected). In regions where there are many smaller parcels of privately owned land, timber harvesting and other land uses result in an especially complex mosaic of stands of varying character, but if larger blocks are being managed as a single unit, as is typical of Crown land and large private holdings, the stand types are usually larger and more uniform.

There are other important differences between wildfire and clear-cutting. Snags and large woody debris, which are critical habitat for many animals, may be abundant after wildfires but not after clear-cuts. In addition, if a plantation is established after a clear-cut, the resulting forest will be highly uniform in its physical structure and community make-up, whereas regenerating burned areas are more complex in these and other ecological attributes.

Emulation forestry is a relatively new concept of modelling systems of timber harvesting and management in ways that imitate the natural disturbance regime of a forest type, and to which its constituent species are presumably well adapted. For instance, the types of forest that develop after a stand-replacing disturbance, such as a wildfire, might be viewed as being relatively compatible with clear-cutting. Forests of that kind include boreal communities dominated by jack pine (*Pinus banksiana*), black spruce, or trembling aspen, as well as montane stands of ponderosa pine (*Pinus ponderosa*) or interior Douglas fir, and temperate forests of white pine or red pine (*Pinus resinosa*).

These natural forests are periodically affected by stand-replacing wildfires, followed by regeneration by the establishment of a cohort of seedlings, which eventually develops an even-aged mature forest similar to the original. In these cases, the natural disturbance regime can to a degree be emulated by clear-cutting, followed by a light prescribed burn and establishment of a new cohort of trees by either seeding-in from nearby mature forest or by planting seedlings. The emulation can be further improved if a reasonable number of standing dead trees and tree-islands are left to imitate "skips" in a wildfire—these also contribute to site regeneration by acting as a source of seeds.

In contrast, old-growth forests typically develop in a climatic regime that is consistently humid, so that stand-replacing disturbances are rare. Instead, the disturbance regime involves the deaths of individual old trees, which create gaps in the canopy below which smaller trees compete to fill the vacated space. This gap-phase disturbance regime results in the development of a highly complex ecosystem in which broad ranges of sizes and ages of trees are represented, including some that are extremely old, and usually various species are present. Old-growth forest also has big snags and abundant large-woody debris (dead logs) lying on the ground.

If timber harvesting in this ecosystem is to emulate the natural disturbance regime, then the best system to use is selection harvesting every several decades. Only some of the larger trees are taken during a particular harvest, so that the forest will always be physically intact and will retain the diversity of ages, sizes, and species that characterize the old-growth condition. Therefore, clear-cutting is not an appropriate way to emulate the natural disturbance regime of old-growth forest, but selection harvesting can achieve that benefit to some degree.

The advantage of emulation forestry is that it can sustain many of the biodiversity and other ecological values of the forest type that is being harvested and managed, even while the human economy benefits from sustainable flows of timber and other economic products.

Marine Bioresources

Marine bioresources are stocks that can be harvested as sources of food, chemicals, energy, or materials. They include the following:

- seaweeds (macroalgae) that are harvested from coastal waters and used as sources of industrial chemicals known as phycocolloids (agar, alginate, and carrageenans) and as minor sources of food and medicine;
- invertebrates, particularly edible species of crustaceans and molluscs;
- fish, which are used as food for people, and also to produce feed for raising fish in aquaculture and livestock in agriculture **(Figure 15.27)**;
- seabirds, which are a minor food crop in some places, although the greatest harvesting-related mortality is associated with their by-catch in commercial fisheries; and
- marine mammals, which are harvested for their meat, fur, and other products.

These marine bioresources are harvested from coastal waters throughout most of Canada, but especially in the boreal and temperate zones. Some countries also have high-seas fisheries. Canada has a marine coastline of about 265×10^3 km (16 percent of the global total), territorial marine waters of 0.2×10^6 km^2 (14 percent of global; territorial waters extend out 18.2 km from the coast), and it claims an additional exclusive economic zone (EEZ) of 3.0×10^6 km^2 (3 percent of global; the EEZ extends from 18.2 to 320 km), most of which is on continental shelf (WRI, 2010). An EEZ is designated to allow a country to manage its coastal resources and to prevent marine pollution.

Harvesting and Management

Most harvesting of marine biological resources in Canada involves the capture of wild animals—a sort of oceanic hunting. The Canadian capture fishery in 2011 had landings of 851×10^3 t and a value of $2.11 billion (DFO, 2013c). Of these totals, 704×10^3 t and $1.83 billion were taken in Atlantic and northern waters, and 147×10^3 t and $0.28 billion in the Pacific. Canada also has freshwater fisheries, with landings of 25.5×10^3 t and a value of $58 million. The most prominent species in the marine fisheries are summarized in **Table 15.5**.

A wild-capture fishery relies on "free" ecological services to produce the biomass that is harvested. In essence,

FIGURE 15.27 Industrial Fishing The technologies used in industrial fishing are highly efficient ways to catch marine fish. This load of fish was caught using a pelagic trawl.

naturally produced stocks of bioresources are harvested, and then allowed to self-regenerate. Other than attempting to regulate the harvest within limits that should not exceed the productivity of the stock, or its MSY, there is almost no management of the regeneration of capture fisheries. Nevertheless even estimating an accurate MSY and then regulating the harvesting are not easy things to do, as we will see below when we examine case studies.

However, certain stocks of anadromous salmon may be managed in ways beyond just regulating the harvest. This is done by enhancing their recruitment in streams and rivers by the release of captive-reared fingerlings, or by managing the freshwater breeding habitat to mitigate the effects of land-based activities, such as those associated with forestry or urbanization.

In addition, the **aquaculture** industry is rapidly growing in Canada and in other countries. Between 1950 and 2010, the global production of animal biomass in aquaculture increased by more than 80-fold, and in Canada by 55-fold (WRI, 2010; DFO, 2013a). Aquaculture

TABLE 15.5	The Most Prominent Marine Bioresources in Canada

The data are commercial landings (in 10³ t) of wet biomass in Pacific or Atlantic plus northern waters in 2011.

Species	Atlantic	Pacific
Groundfish	88.6	90.0
Cod (*Gadus morhua*)	13.0	—
Haddock (*Melanogrammus aeglefinus*)	15.2	—
Redfish (*Sebastes* spp.)	13.8	18.0
Pacific halibut (*Hippoglossus stenolepis*)	—	4.1
Atlantic halibut (*Hippoglossus hippoglossus*)	2.5	—
Flatfish (*Pleuronectes* spp.)	8.3	10.0
Turbot (*Reinhardtius hippoglossoides*)	13.9	—
Hake (*Merluccius* spp.)	11.2	45.7
Pelagics	183.8	46.4
Herring (*Clupea harengus*)	134.4	—
Pacific herring (*Clupea pallasii*)	—	7.8
Mackerel (*Scomber scombrus*)	11.4	—
Swordfish (*Xiphias gladius*)	1.6	—
Pacific salmon (*Oncorhynchus* spp.)	—	20.7
Capelin (*Mallotus villosus*)	32.4	—
Tuna (*Thunnus* spp.)	0.7	4.5
Shellfish	413.6	10.3
Clams and mussels (various species)	26.7	1.9
Scallop (*Placopecten magellanicus*)	59.9	—
Lobster (*Homarus americanus*)	66.5	—
Shrimp (*Pandalus borealis*)	150.8	—
Queen crab (*Chionoecetes opilio*)	84.1	—
Seaweed (various species of kelps)	14.9	—
TOTAL	703.9	146.6

SOURCE: Based on data from Department of Fisheries and Oceans (DFO). 2010. Statistical Services. Ottawa, ON. http://www.dfo-mpo.gc.ca/communic/statistics/main_e.htm.

Alexandra Morton

FIGURE 15.28 Aquaculture Is the Rearing of Fish under Controlled Conditions This is an aerial view of a facility for rearing Atlantic salmon (*Salmo salar*) in open-water net-pens in the Broughton Archipelago of British Columbia.

is essentially the "farming" of aquatic organisms, and it uses intensive management practices that are intended to maximize the productivity of the species being cultivated. At least this is the case in Canada and other wealthier countries—in developing nations, much of the aquaculture involves less-intensive practices, but it is undertaken over larger areas.

Atlantic salmon is the most commonly reared species in aquaculture in Canada (**Figure 15.28**). Its rearing typically involves the following practices:

- Adult fish are kept in captivity in a land-based hatchery facility. They are of a genetic lineage that is considered to have high potential for survival and productivity under the environmental conditions in which the cultivation pens are located. In late autumn, the males are stripped of milt (sperm) and the females of ova and these are mixed to achieve fertilization and the eggs are incubated in the hatchery.

- The hatched fry are fed on a nutritionally superior artificial medium, which is modified to meet their changing dietary requirements as they grow.

- When the small fish are 1–1.5 years old (about 15 cm long; at this stage they are called smolts), they are transferred to much larger rearing pens in saltwater. The pens are usually of a floating, 10–20 m deep, open-mesh, netted construction and located in a shallow, semi-sheltered, coastal embayment.

- The fish are kept at a dense level of stocking in the sea-pens and are fed to satiation with fish meal and fish oil obtained from marine fisheries (about one-third of the global marine wild-fishery catch is manufactured into products for use in finfish aquaculture); after 1.5 to 2.5 years they attain a harvest weight of 3 to 5 kg (but up to 10 kg).

- At any time during the process, medicine may be required to treat contagious diseases. Antibiotics such as oxytetracycline are used to treat bacterial infections. Insecticides are used to treat infestations of sea lice (*Caligus* species and *Lepeophtheirus salmonis*), which are crustacean ectoparasites. Antifoulants such as organotin and copper-based compounds may be used to keep the net mesh clean so that the cages do not become excessively heavy with fouling biomass, and also to allow water to circulate through the pens. If wild carnivores, such as seals or sea lions, try to eat the caged salmon, they may be shot as vermin (a licence is required to do this).

The use of this intensive management system results in high rates of salmon production and an abundant and nutritious food for people. However, there are also important environmental impacts of aquaculture systems, which we examine later as a case study.

The most prominent species grown in aquaculture in Canada are Atlantic salmon (production in 2009 was 109×10^3 t, of which 86 percent was grown in British Columbia and the rest in Atlantic waters; DFO, 2013a), mussels (mostly *Mytilus edulis*; 24×10^3 t), and oysters (*Crassostrea virginica* on the Atlantic coast and *C. gigas* on the Pacific; 10×10^3 t). The total value of the aquaculture crops was $1.0 billion.

For wild fisheries, management of the harvesting rate (or fishing mortality) is the major tool used to try to prevent overharvesting. The first step toward determination of a sustainable level of harvesting is to apply the principles and methods of population ecology to estimate the biomass and productivity of the biological stock, as well as the natural rate of mortality. If these are known, then the biomass and productivity that remain after natural mortality is accounted for can be allocated to anthropogenic harvesting—this would be the maximum sustainable yield available to a typical capture fishery.

Conceptually, this is a simple process. However, fishery ecologists do not yet have a sufficient understanding of the biological and environmental factors that affect the productivity of populations of most marine species of commercial importance. Because of this lack of reliable knowledge, the available population models suffer from a degree of inaccuracy, and they may predict MSYs that are too large to be sustainable, or in some cases smaller than could be harvested without placing the stock at risk. A major part of the problem is the unpredictability of changes in environmental conditions—these influence recruitment into populations as well as the growth rate of individuals. Because many important changes in key environmental variables are unpredictable (or stochastic), they are impossible to accurately model (other than in a probabilistic sense, which is not good enough for real-world setting of harvest quotas).

Moreover, it is extremely difficult to field-test the predictions of population-dynamic models that are used to assess the size and productivity of commercial stocks. This requires, for example, the need to estimate the numbers of fish in management zones. "Counting fish" is an extraordinarily difficult task—it is fraught with uncertainty and so the resulting estimates may be substantially inaccurate. We cannot discuss this subject area in much detail here, but the estimates of stock biomass and productivity are usually made using indirect methods and they involve various key assumptions, which typically require knowledge based on:

- *the biology and life history of the exploited species*, including the age at first maturity (when spawning begins), the frequency of spawning, age-related fecundity (larger, older animals often produce many more offspring than smaller, younger ones), recruitment success (especially the survival of eggs and larvae) and growth rate under various environmental conditions, and natural rates and causes of juvenile and adult mortality;
- *the age structure of populations in particular years*, which must be known to predict the productivity of a stock; if the field-determined age-class structure is different from that used in a population-dynamic model to predict the size and productivity of a stock, then the assessment will be inaccurate;
- *catch-per-unit effort (CPUE), and a presumed statistical relationship* between *CPUE and the stock biomass*; of course, the kind of effort used to catch the fish must be adjusted for its efficiency—effort based on rod-and-reel fishing is extraordinarily different in efficiency than net-based methods, such as trawls; and
- *assessment of the size and biomass of schools of fish using sonar-based technology*, which again is based on presumed statistical relationships between sonar-estimated densities and the actual stock biomass.

Once fisheries ecologists have used these methods to predict a **total allowable catch (TAC)** from a biological stock, it is possible to recommend quotas. It must be understood, however, that quotas are only partly based on recommendations made by scientists from the predictions of stock-assessment models—economic and social considerations are also important influences. In practice, these non-science pressures often result in decisions to allow larger quotas than are recommended by fishery ecologists (while recognizing that the scientists do not always agree among themselves). When this happens, it is usually because the decision maker, typically a non-science bureaucrat or a politician, has been influenced to do so by economic and political pressures that are brought to bear by commercial and labour-related interests.

In any event, once a TAC is recommended, the amount of harvesting mortality can be set, which is essentially done by regulation of the harvesting effort. This can be achieved by regulating the enterprise in a number of interacting ways:

- Only certain kinds of harvesting units may be permitted for use—for example, regulations may specify certain kinds or sizes of fishing boats and the sorts of gear they are allowed to deploy.
- The number of harvesting units may be regulated, usually by a licensing system.
- The amount of time that each unit can spend harvesting may be limited; this is usually done by setting a season, which may be long or short. In certain

herring fisheries of western North America the harvesting time may be only a few hours per year.

- A quota may be assigned to each harvesting unit, and once it is achieved, its harvesting must stop.
- There may also be restrictions on the sizes of organisms that can be harvested. In the Atlantic lobster fishery, for example, animals smaller than a regulated carapace length must be returned to the ocean, while for net fisheries the permissible mesh size sets a lower limit on the size of fish that are caught.

Of course, it is not enough to just have regulations—the catches must also be monitored and noncompliance punished in some meaningful way. Some of the tools that managers can use to do this include the following:

- the withdrawal of licences in cases of egregious noncompliance with regulations;
- fines for lesser cases of noncompliance; however, the fines must be consequential, otherwise they could just be absorbed by the enterprise as an affordable cost of doing business;
- providing subsidies for operators who voluntarily engage in less-damaging harvesting methods; the subsidies influence their profit by reducing their net operating costs; and
- if there is excessive harvesting capacity in the aggregate fishery, either in terms of equipment or licences, then the regulator might purchase and retire the excess capacity.

If used effectively, these various considerations and measures should result in predictable and sustainable harvests being made of marine biological resources. As is well known, however, this has often not been the case, and many potentially renewable harvests of marine bioresources have been ruined by excessive harvesting. There is a remarkable litany of examples of this sort of wanton damage, as summarized in recent books and scientific reviews (Busch, 1985; Ellis, 1991, 2003; Kurlansky, 1997; Jackson et al., 2001; Pauly et al., 2002; Myers and Worm, 2003; Hutchings and Reynolds, 2004; Clover, 2006; Worm et al., 2006, 2009; Roberts, 2007).

In the following sections, we will examine a number of case studies that are relevant to nonsustainable harvests of marine bioresources in Canada. These cases are selected to illustrate important points about nonsustainability, as well as the environmental damages that are inherent in all cases of excessive harvesting or inappropriate management of marine biological resources.

The Bowhead Whale

The bowhead whale (*Balaena mysticetus*) has the most northern range of the large cetaceans, occurring in arctic and boreal waters of the northern hemisphere

FIGURE 15.29 Bowhead Whales (*Balaena mysticetus*) This species was made endangered by an intensive commercial hunt in Arctic waters, but it was protected and has since recovered much of its original abundance over part of its range.

NOAA Photo Library, Image anim0842

(Reilly et al., 2008). It is a filter-feeder, mostly on large planktonic crustaceans known as krill **(Figure 15.29)**. Bowheads are often relatively abundant near the edges of sea-ice, but they also occur in open water during the brief arctic summer. They can achieve a remarkable longevity for a wild mammal of more than 100 years, and have a generation time of about 52 years.

The bowhead whale was hunted primarily for its fat, which was valuable as an oil-lamp fuel and for making smokeless candles, and also for its baleen. (Commonly referred to as "whalebone," baleen is actually a strong and flexible keratin-rich material found in the mouths of various kinds of whales; it is an adaptation for filtering small food items from immense gulps of seawater, and in the past had many uses in manufacturing.) The bowhead and more temperate right whale (*Eubalaena glacialis*) were the first large cetaceans to be hunted because they swim slowly, usually float when killed, and inhabit coastal waters.

The commercial hunting of bowhead whales began in the northeastern Atlantic around 1611, particularly around the Arctic island of Spitzbergen and to its south in the Barents Sea. The first hunting of bowheads in North America was by Basque seamen off Labrador in the 16th century. One of their key whaling stations was at Red Bay, where between about 1530 and 1600 they killed thousands of bowheads and right whales as the animals migrated through the Strait of Belle Isle between Newfoundland and southern Labrador. The dead animals were towed to Red Bay, where the baleen was removed and the blubber flensed from the body and rendered into oil in large iron cauldrons known as try-pots. The pre-hunting populations of bowheads in the northern Atlantic Ocean were about 24 000 in the Spitsbergen-Barents Sea and 12 000 in the northwestern Atlantic, but after a number of decades of hunting they were severely depleted by overharvesting.

In 1848, whalers discovered a "new" population of bowhead whales in waters of the northern Pacific Ocean, in a region encompassing the Bering, Chukchi, and Beaufort seas (the latter includes waters of northwestern Canada). The initial population of this Bering-Chukchi-Beaufort (BCB) stock was 10 000–20 000 animals. Relatively good data exist for the hunting of bowheads in the north Pacific, and they show a rapid increase in the harvest, followed by a collapse as the stocks were depleted **(Figure 15.30)**. There were large variations in the annual harvest during the early years of the hunt, primarily because the sailing ships of the time were not effective at penetrating pack ice, which was severe in some years. Over the period of time covered by **Figure 15.30**, a total of 20 735 bowheads were recorded as landed. However, the kill was actually considerably larger than this because some mortally wounded animals were not retrieved by the whalers, particularly in difficult sea-ice conditions.

Throughout the history of bowhead hunting, and for that matter all whaling prior to about 1950, there was no ethic of conservation among the commercial whale hunters. They killed every animal that they could, regardless of species, rarity, or trend in population status. The intent was to convert whales into money and profit as quickly as possible. Sustainability was not a significant issue in the whaling industry, and certainly not an operational consideration.

The hunting of the BCB bowheads had essentially ceased by the 1930s, and in 1946 the newly created International Whaling Commission (IWC) banned further exploitation of these animals. This action allowed the stocks to increase, and the present abundance is about

10 000 animals, similar to the pre-exploitation population of bowheads in the BCB region.

Since 1985, the IWC has allowed Aboriginal peoples in northern Alaska to engage in a traditional hunt of bowheads. Between 2000 and 2011, they harvested a total of 1276 animals (IWC, 2013). For the first time, in 2011, there was also a large kill by Aboriginal people in eastern Siberia (Russia), when 128 animals were landed. However, even with this Aboriginal hunting, the population of bowheads in the BCB region is increasing at a rate of about 3 percent per year. Bowheads are also being taken from the much smaller population in the eastern Arctic of Canada; between 1991 and 2011, 10 animals were landed, although considerably more than this were struck and likely killed, but not retrieved.

Some key lessons to be learned from the history of the hunting of bowhead whales, and of commercial whaling in general, are the following:

- The hunting of all the populations was not sustainable—an effort was made to kill as many as possible of any whales that were encountered;
- Consequently, as each "new" stock was discovered it was rapidly overharvested and depleted to commercial extinction;
- Eventually the hunting stopped because of the combined influences of nonprofitability and a ban by the IWC; these circumstances have allowed the surviving bowheads to rebuild their abundance.

Today, bowhead whales in the BCB region are considered to no longer be at risk (Reilly et al., 2008). The separate population in Arctic waters of eastern Canada and Greenland is also increasing, and may no longer be at risk, while that of the northeastern Atlantic off Spitsbergen and in the Barents Sea is still greatly depleted.

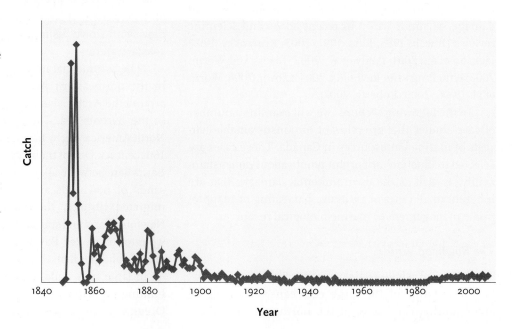

FIGURE 15.30 Annual Catch of Bowhead Whales in the Western Arctic The data are the numbers of whales landed, but the total annual kill was larger (but unknown) because many animals are struck but not landed.

SOURCES: Based on data from Cushing, D.H. 1988. *The Provident Sea*. Cambridge University Press, Cambridge, UK; International Whaling Commission (IWC). 2000. *Aboriginal subsistence whaling catches since 1985*. IWC, Cambridge, UK.

Atlantic Cod

Atlantic cod (*Gadus morhua*) is an amphi-Atlantic species, meaning it occurs in boreal and north-temperate waters of the continental shelves of both North America and Europe. It has long been an important food fish, and when the first European mariners explored the coastal waters off what is now eastern Canada they were astonished by the immense numbers of cod **(Figure 15.31)**. In 1497, John Cabot wrote in his journal that the Grand Banks were so "swarming with fish [that they] could be taken not only with a net but in baskets let down [and weighted] with a stone."

(a)

(b)

FIGURE 15.31 **The Historical Cod Fishery** The historical fishery for Atlantic cod (*Gadus morhua*) was much less intensive than modern industrial fishing, in terms of the total harvest of fish biomass and damage caused to habitat, although it still depleted some inshore stocks. (a) Split cod drying on wooden flakes at Quidi Vidi, Newfoundland, around 1886. (b) Two large "mother cod" that were caught in a nearshore trap near Battle Harbour, Labrador, in 1903. The larger fish weighed 27 kg and was 1.6 m long.

The largest cod stocks were on the Grand Banks off Newfoundland, a relatively shallow (25–110 m deep), productive marine ecosystem of about 250 000 km². However, cod were also abundant on banks off Labrador, Nova Scotia, and New England and in the Gulf of St. Lawrence.

Soon after these immense and productive fishing grounds were discovered, fleets of sailing vessels arrived from Europe to harvest cod and other groundfish (species that feed on or near the bottom). In 1600, about 650 ships were fishing in the region, and in 1800 there were about 1600 vessels (Mowat, 1984; Hutchings and Myers, 1995). The typical landings during 1750–1800 were about 190 000 t per year, increasing to 400–460 000 t/yr during 1800–1900, and almost 1 million t/yr in 1899–1904 (Mowat, 1984; Cushing, 1988).

During the earlier times, the fishers worked with hand-lines (a single hook-and-line that is hand-jigged), long-lines (lines with numerous baited hooks set between floating buoys), seines (bag-like nets), and near-shore traps (netted entrapments). Most of the individual fishers worked from a small dory (a stackable wooden boat with high sides, and often pointed at both ends), which on the banks would be launched from a mother ship, such as one of the illustrious schooners that were built in and sailed out of Nova Scotia and Newfoundland. These fishing methods are not particularly efficient, but the aggregate harvesting effort was large and so, therefore, were the catches. By the early 20th century, stocks of cod in many near-shore waters were depleted, although those on the banks remained robust.

During the 20th century, more efficient technologies were developed and their use resulted in a major intensification of the cod fishery (and almost all commercial fisheries). Particularly important innovations were: the changeover from wooden sailing vessels to increasingly powerful, steel-hulled, motorized ships; the invention of new netting technologies (especially monofilament gill nets and pelagic trawls); the use of sonar equipment to locate schools of fish; and the installation of on-ship methods to process and freeze fish, which allowed large vessels to remain at sea for an extended time.

These hugely effective improvements resulted in much larger harvests of cod and other fish in the northwest Atlantic, particularly during the 1960s, when most of the fishery was an essentially unregulated enterprise that was open to all countries **(Figure 15.32)**. However, the immense catches were not sustainable, and the stocks plummeted.

The collapse of the cod stocks resulted in a crisis in the fishery-dependent economy of coastal regions of Atlantic Canada. In response to this socioeconomic and ecological calamity, in 1977 the Government of Canada proclaimed a 320 km-wide exclusive economic zone (EEZ). This allowed the federal Department of Fisheries and Oceans (DFO) to regulate the entire cod fishery and to allocate quotas. Those

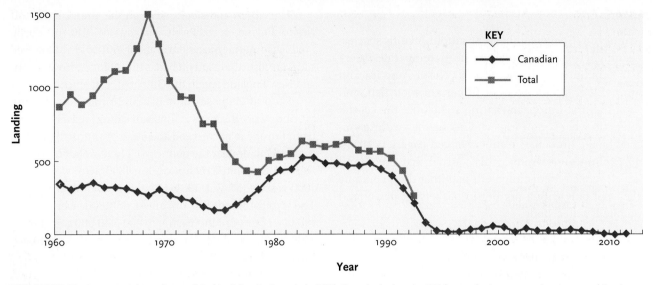

FIGURE 15.32 Commercial Landings of Cod in Atlantic Canada In 1977, Canada declared a 320 km exclusive economic zone, resulting in higher catches by Canadian fishers. However, the stocks then collapsed further, and in 1992 a moratorium was placed on most cod fishing. There have been variable quotas and by-catch since then. Data are in 10^3 tonnes.

SOURCE: Based on data from Department of Fisheries and Oceans (DFO). 2010. Statistical Services. Ottawa, ON. http://www.dfo-mpo.gc.ca/communic/statistics/main_e.htm.

measures resulted in a moderate increase in landings, mostly by Canadian fishers, but the harvesting was still excessive and soon there was an even more ruinous collapse of the stocks (**Figure 15.32**). In 1992, DFO declared a moratorium on commercial cod fishing, a ban that has substantially remained in place ever since (in 2013, there was a relatively small commercial quota of 10 800 t, mostly as by-catch in fisheries directed to other species, plus a small food fishery by local people; DFO, 2013c).

It was initially hoped that reduced fishing pressure resulting from the 1992 moratorium would allow the cod stocks to recover, but this has not yet happened. The reasons for a lack of substantial recovery are not fully understood. However, they are probably due to some combination of the following factors:

- Only small populations of cod are old enough to spawn, relative to the carrying capacity of their habitat.
- Undue fishing pressure continues through recently permitted legal harvesting for recreational and commercial purposes, as well as by-catch in fisheries directed at other species.
- Excessive mortality from natural causes occurs, which may be caused by increased predation of eggs and larvae of cod by other fish, which are themselves no longer subjected to intense predation by cod. Predation by the increasingly larger populations of harp and grey seals, which feed on older cod, may also be important in some areas.

It is hoped, despite these factors, that the cod stocks will eventually recover to the point where they could again be an abundant renewable resource.

At the time that the cod stocks collapsed in the late 1980s, there was controversy about the cause (Hutchings and Myers, 1995; Hutchings and Reynolds, 2004). Some fishery ecologists suggested that environmental factors, such as several years of unusually cold water in the southward-flowing Labrador current, could have been a factor. Others blamed the burgeoning populations of harp seals (*Phoca groenlandica*), which consume more than one million t of food per year, although they mostly eat crustaceans and small fish such as Arctic cod (*Boreogadus saida*) and capelin (*Mallotus villosus*). However, it is now clear that it was overfishing that caused this resource calamity to occur—the stocks of cod were being harvested much faster than they could regenerate, particularly during the 1970s and 1980s, and this caused them to undergo a rapid and precipitous decline.

Several factors caused the nonsustainable harvesting to occur. One was the essentially unregulated fishery until 1977, when Canada proclaimed its 320 km EEZ (as did other coastal nations at that time). Another was the apparent use of inaccurate stock-assessment models to predict the MSY of the cod stocks. These models overestimated the fish biomass and resulted in the setting of quotas that were too large to be sustainable. Many people also thought that poorly regulated non-Canadian fishers were catching too many fish (even though Canadians landed 85 percent of the cod in the northwest Atlantic between 1977 and 1991, in a more-or-less regulated fishery). Finally, politicians and other decision makers were influenced by various socioeconomic interests (i.e., by the concerns of fishers and their businesses) that were opposed to cutting the quotas to the degree the fishery scientists were recommending, which resulted in excessive harvests being allowed in the years immediately preceding the moratorium.

All of these factors, and others, resulted in unsustainably intense harvesting of a potentially renewable resource. That overexploitation has apparently ruined what was once one of the greatest marine fisheries in the world. Recovery of the cod stocks may yet be possible, but so far it has not occurred.

Pacific Salmon

Pacific salmon comprise a group of species of salmonid fish (family Salmonidae) in the genus *Oncorhynchus*, most populations of which are anadromous **(Figure 15.33)**. Depending on the life history of the species, and sometimes on the particular geographic population, the downriver migration from freshwater to the ocean may be undertaken by recently hatched larvae, or by 1- to 2-year-old animals known as smolts. During their migration the larvae or smolts become physiologically tolerant of seawater, and they then spend one to several years in coastal or pelagic habitats. When the salmon become sexually mature adults, they migrate up to thousands of kilometres back to their natal stream to breed. They often return to the same reach of the stream, navigating using smell and other environmental cues, and battling river currents, rapids, and waterfalls to reach an upstream gravel spawning bed (known as a redd). There the adults breed and, in most species, die soon afterward.

Migrating salmon are a crucial food for various other animal species, including bears and eagles, and they have long provided sustenance for Aboriginal people on the Pacific Coast and on inland rivers. The migrating adults are also a "nutrient pump" that delivers phosphorus and nitrogen to upriver habitats, a function that enhances the overall productivity of their ecosystem (see Chapter 4).

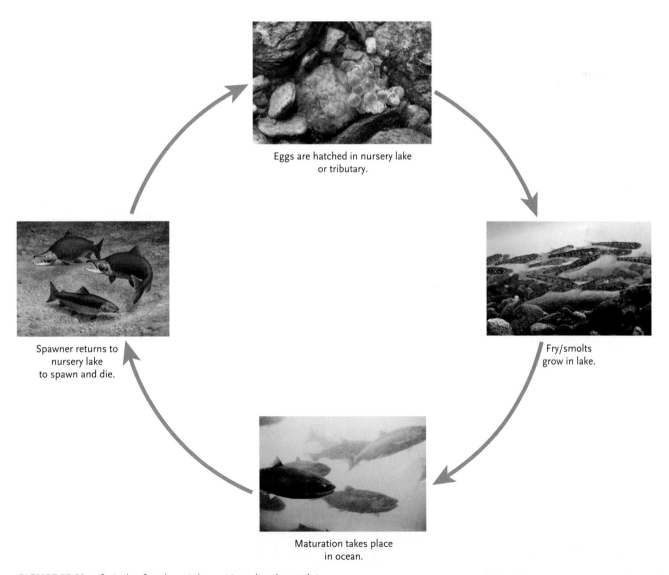

Eggs are hatched in nursery lake or tributary.

Fry/smolts grow in lake.

Maturation takes place in ocean.

Spawner returns to nursery lake to spawn and die.

FIGURE 15.33 Life Cycle of Sockeye Salmon (*Oncorhynchus nerka*)

SOURCES: Photographs, clockwise from top, Photos.com; Sergey Gorshkov/Minden Pictures/Getty Images; Paul Edmondson/Photographer's Choice RF/Getty Images; WALTER A. WEBER/National Geographic Stock.

Pacific salmon have complex life histories, which vary remarkably among the species and often among geographic populations. There is a strong genetic component to the variation among populations, which has presumably arisen because of natural selection by the specific regimes of environmental conditions that have influenced their evolution. In general, the genetic differences are not sufficient to allow discrete populations to be assigned a taxonomic designation, such as variety or subspecies. Nevertheless, the genetic differences are considered important in terms of management and conservation, and so the different populations are referred to as being **evolutionarily significant units** (or **ESUs**). Having noted this, a few of the ESUs are differentiated enough to have been named as varieties, such as the kokanee type of sockeye salmon.

Seven species of *Oncorhynchus* are indigenous to the coastal waters and rivers of British Columbia (DFO, 2002):

- Chinook salmon (*O. tshawytscha*) is the largest species, weighing 3 to 50 kg as spawning adults. Some stocks migrate in the spring, but most do so in the summer or autumn. In the Fraser River, various stocks are present from March to November, but the peaks of abundance are from early July to early October. In general, the spring migrants breed in the headwaters of larger rivers, and the fall ones in smaller coastal rivers. The smolts of spring- and summer-run stocks usually migrate to the ocean at about one year of age, and those of fall-runs within a few days or months of hatching. However, several of the life-history complexes may occur together in the same breeding habitat. The adults spend from one to seven years at sea before returning to their natal river to breed and die.
- Sockeye salmon (*O. nerka*) weigh 3–8 kg. The hatchling fry migrate immediately to the ocean, or to large lakes, where they feed on zooplankton. Kokanee salmon are an entirely freshwater variety, and they may mingle with sea-run sockeyes or occur in landlocked lakes. Marine sockeyes mature at two to six years of age, but typically when four years old.
- Chum salmon (*O. keta*) weigh 3–10 kg and spawn during the summer and autumn in lower reaches of coastal streams and rivers (they have little ability to navigate steep rapids or waterfalls). This widely distributed species may have composed half of the salmon biomass in pre-European contact times. The newly hatched fry spend little time in freshwater, migrating soon after birth to the ocean, where they spend two to six years as pelagic adults.
- Coho salmon (*O. kisutch*) weigh 3–6 kg and maintain a larger number of distinct breeding populations in British Columbia than any other species of salmon. The young generally spend one year in freshwater,

but this may be extended to two to three years in northern rivers, and in some coastal ones the hatchling fry migrate immediately to the ocean. Juvenile coho defend a territory in their stream, and intraspecific competition for the limited carrying capacity may limit their population density. Adults inhabit coastal waters, and they typically breed at three years of age.
- Pink salmon (*O. gorbuscha*) are the smallest and most abundant species of salmon, weighing 1.5–3 kg. The hatchling fry migrate immediately to saltwater, and the fish spend two years in pelagic habitats feeding on zooplankton before migrating as adults to breed in their natal stream. In the Fraser River, migrating pinks are abundant in odd-numbered years (such as 2013), and much less so in even ones.
- Cutthroat trout (*O. clarki*; formerly placed in the genus *Salmo*) weigh 2–4 kg and occur in most coastal watercourses and also in major rivers. The young spend one to two years in freshwater, and the adults occur mostly in or near the estuary of their natal river, spawning after three to four years of age (this species is iteroparous, meaning it can breed several times in different years).
- Steelhead trout (*O. mykiss*; formerly in *Salmo*; the nonmigratory form is known as rainbow trout) typically weigh about 4 kg but may exceed 25 kg. Young fish spend one to three years in freshwater before running to the ocean as smolts. The adults live in pelagic habitats, typically migrating and spawning after two to three years at sea. About one-fifth of adults, mostly females, spawn more than once. So-called "winter-run" populations migrate upriver during November to May, and "summer-run" ones from April to October, but in both types the actual spawning occurs from January to May.
- Atlantic salmon (*Salmo salar*) is a non-native species that has been transplanted to the Pacific Coast for use in aquaculture. Escaped animals now appear to be breeding in a few places in the wild (see the following case study).

Pacific salmon can be extraordinarily abundant and accessible for harvesting during their migrations, and for this reason they have provided crucial subsistence for Aboriginal fishers for thousands of years. Some species are also harvested at sea. During the past century or so, however, salmon have been subjected to extremely intensive commercial and sport fisheries. Because each species has a different life history, as well as behavioural and ecological distinctions, the timing of the harvesting varies among them, and sometimes even for their populations. The places where the harvesting occurs and the technologies used also vary among the species and stocks of Pacific salmon.

Commercial harvesting of salmon in coastal waters and rivers of what is now British Columbia began in the late 19th century. Between 1894 and 1899, the average harvest of Pacific salmon was about 16 000 t/yr (DFO, 2010b). Most of the harvest was canned (about 93 percent), and the rest was sold fresh, smoked, dry-salted, or pickled in brine. The commercial landings of all species since 1972 are shown in **Figure 15.34**. Although the catches can be rather variable from year to year, it is clear that the stocks are declining. The diminishing catches have resulted in DFO imposing severe restrictions on harvesting the remaining stocks.

The various species of Pacific salmon have declined for different various reasons, but there are two clusters of major factors: (1) damage to the freshwater breeding habitats and (2) excessive commercial fishing.

1. *Damage caused to freshwater breeding habitat.* The declines of salmon have been aggravated by severe damage caused to much of their critical freshwater habitat in rivers and streams. For example, the construction of hydroelectric dams on rivers blocks the passage for migrating fish and can wipe out historical breeding stocks. The construction of logging roads and the clear-cutting of timber have also caused severe damage in many areas. Those practices erode soil from steep slopes in mountainous regions, causing severe degradation of salmon habitat by the siltation of gravel spawning beds in streams and rivers. Tangles of logging debris may also block salmon migrations in streams. In addition, some historically productive rivers have been degraded by pollution from pulp mills and mines, and by discharges of urban and agricultural sewage.

2. *Excessive commercial fishing.* Overharvesting results from an excessive industrial capacity to catch fish, meaning there are too many boats equipped with sophisticated harvesting technology, and too many people whose livelihood depends on commercial fishing. The key issues are the following:

   • Fishing pressures are compounded by jurisdictional conflicts among governments. For example, certain stocks are "shared" between Canada and U.S. states, particularly those whose adults migrate south along the coast toward their breeding rivers. However, effective and equitable comanagement strategies do not always exist. Certain migrating management units (local breeding populations) may be initially harvested by American fishers in Alaska, then by Canadian fishers in British Columbia, then potentially in Washington, Oregon, and even northern California. Moreover, the Government of British Columbia has stated its belief that the Government of Canada (through DFO) has negotiated too small an allocation of salmon for British Columbian fishers, because Canada harvests less than the relative amount of reproduction of the salmon that occurs in provincial rivers.

   • In many areas, Aboriginal fishers believe that they have never relinquished their right to

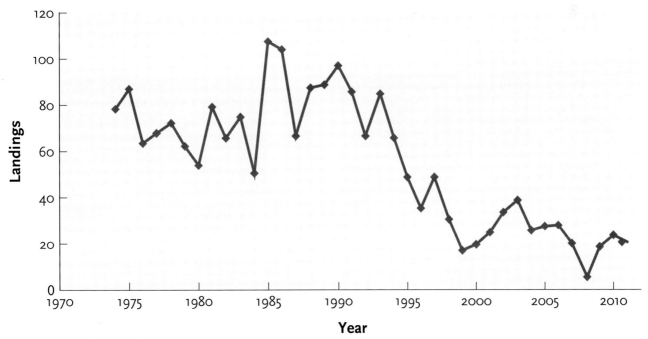

FIGURE 15.34 Commercial Landings of Salmon in British Columbia Salmon landings are variable, but the overall trend is of a substantial decline. Data are in 10³ tonnes.

SOURCE: Based on data from Department of Fisheries and Oceans (DFO). 2010. Statistics. Ottawa, ON. http://www.dfo-mpo.gc.ca/stats/stats-eng.htm Accessed February, 2013.

FIGURE 1 Daniel Pauly

It is well known that many fisheries are failing, usually because these renewable bioresources have been degraded by irresponsible overharvesting. Many people are deeply concerned about the ruination of these vital resources, and about the collateral ecological harm that is caused by industrial methods of harvesting and management. These latter damages include effects on native species and natural communities, as well as those caused to ecosystem functions such as productivity and clean-environment services. A number of Canadian ecologists who are specialists in the study of fish and other aquatic biota have devoted their careers to documenting the causes and consequences of these ecological tragedies (and others that have not yet occurred but are moving in that direction), as well as understanding the ways of recovering the degraded stocks.

These people are ecological heroes because they are champions of both resource sustainability and the need to maintain healthy ecosystems. These ecologists work in universities, environmental organizations, and governmental research laboratories and policy divisions. There are too many of these scientists to mention by name, but several are briefly profiled here. They are all professors who have devoted their great opportunity of academic freedom to engage in research to document and understand aquatic resource calamities. They are also engaged in honest and effective public advocacy to ensure that society moves toward improved management of its limited stocks of biological resources, and of its natural heritage of indigenous biodiversity.

Ransom Myers was a population ecologist who worked on oceanic fisheries, initially as a scientist with the federal Department of Fisheries and Oceans (DFO) and then as a professor at Dalhousie University. He and his students undertook highly regarded research that documented collapses of specific fish stocks, as well as global declines of other marine bioresources. One special contribution of Myers was to bring these important resource issues to the attention of politicians and regulators, as well as to the broader public. He was a leader in high-profile outreach from the academic community, and helped to focus the attention of society on the critical task of conserving both marine resources needed as food and the biodiversity of the oceans. In 2005, *Fortune* magazine nominated Myers as one of its "10 people to watch" globally because of his powerful influence on marine policy issues. Unfortunately, Myers died suddenly of cancer in 2007. However, there are valuable lessons to be learned from his work as an ecologist. Among these are the value of high-quality research, enthusiastic support of

harvest salmon in waters within their traditional range of resource harvesting. They believe that they should be allowed to catch as many fish as they wish, restricted perhaps only by the greater needs of conservation. However, non-Aboriginal fishers also believe that they have a legitimate right to harvest salmon, and that management rules should apply to everyone. This circumstance can result in conflicts between Aboriginal governments and federal, provincial, or state authorities that have the responsibility to set population-level quotas. The problem is compounded by the fact that the rights of Aboriginal persons to harvest salmon are not always well defined, and their traditional rights may not be specifically guaranteed by negotiated treaties.

- Certain fishing nations of East Asia have engaged in a relatively uncontrolled high-seas fishery for salmon in international waters. Their harvesting compromises efforts to conserve the stocks in the coastal waters and breeding rivers in Canada and the United States. This issue has been partly resolved through international agreements, although excessive pelagic harvesting of salmon and other fish continues.

There is also economic competition between powerful interest groups, such as the commercial and recreational fishing industries. On a per-fish basis, the economic impact of salmon caught by recreational fishers is much larger than in the industrial fishery. This is because recreational fishers spend a lot of money on travel, equipment, lodging, guides, and other expensive needs that are associated with their sport fishing. These expenditures contribute a large amount of "value added" to individual fish that are caught by recreational fishers. The conflicting interests of commercial and recreational fishers have

students and colleagues, scientific integrity, and the need for at least some professors to be engaged in public discussions of issues of the day that fall within the domain of their expertise.

Jeff Hutchings, also a professor at Dalhousie and a colleague of Myers, was a key participant in research that documented the ecological and anthropogenic causes of the collapse of cod stocks in the northwest Atlantic, a resource tragedy that had awful economic consequences for the region. At the time, Hutchings and Myers were working for DFO, where bureaucratic interests were profiling the collapse of cod as a somewhat natural phenomenon from which the stocks would quickly recover. Hutchings and Myers publicly opposed those views, because their interpretation of the ecological data clearly showed that the damage was anthropogenic. It had been caused by overfishing, much of it occurring within the context of quotas set by DFO that were too large to be sustainable, and that were often overruled by politicians who used their authority to set quotas even larger than what DFO was recommending. In 1995, Hutchings won a prize as a whistle blower for the effectiveness with which he

communicated evidence about the cod calamity to both scientists and the public. Hutchings continues to work on issues related to aquatic biodiversity and resources, and has been heavily engaged in the COSEWIC process by which species at risk are designated in Canada.

Daniel Pauly is a French-born fishery ecologist at the University of British Columbia **(Figure 1)**. He takes an international approach to his research, being engaged in projects around the world, all with the common thread of studying marine bioresources, documenting threats to their sustainable use, and proposing management and policy solutions to those important problems. Pauly is the leader of a collaborative international venture known as the *Sea Around Us Project*, which is using GIS (geographic information systems) to map global fisheries catches since 1950 as a way of documenting and mitigating the damaging effects of this industrial activity. His work has focused on collapses of fishery resources, risks to critical marine habitats (such as reefs, seamounts, and upwellings), and damage caused to marine biodiversity at the levels of species and communities. Pauly has won many professional awards,

is an advisor to governments, and a frequent commentator in the media on issues related to the marine realm.

Boris Worm and *Heike Lotze* are part of a younger cohort of professors whose enterprise is focused on identifying, and then repairing, the damages that the human economy is causing to the marine realm. They work at Dalhousie University, and both are interested in Canadian and international marine issues, particularly collapsing stocks of bioresources and damage caused to biodiversity. Like the others noted above, Lotze and Worm are engaged with a broad network of collaborators, including scientists in universities and governments from around the world, as well as a large coterie of graduate students. Worm and Lotze have similar motivations in their professional life. They have a love and fascination with science and with the natural world, and a deep concern about terrible damages that are being caused to vital resources and to biodiversity. But neither they nor the other ecologists mentioned in this section are just complainers about these important problems—they are leading the charge to find ways to fix these damages and are demanding that those fixes be rapidly implemented.

resulted in economic and political pressures on politicians and resource managers that make it difficult for those authorities to impose realistic limits on the total fishing effort, and so the overfishing of many stocks persists.

The case of Pacific salmon is yet another distressing example of a phenomenon that is becoming much too familiar in modern times—the decline of a potentially renewable natural resource. Excessive harvesting and habitat damage, which are causing the decline of salmon, must be managed more effectively if their stocks are to recover to their historical abundance.

Salmon Aquaculture

Salmon aquaculture, which is mostly based on the cultivation of Atlantic salmon, is carried out on both the Atlantic and Pacific Coasts **(Figure 15.35)**. This intensive method of fish production has rapidly increased since the mid-1980s, but it may now be levelling off **(Figure 15.36)**.

The value of the production of Atlantic salmon in Canadian aquaculture was $607 million in 2011 ($435 million in British Columbia and $172 million in Atlantic Canada), compared with a wild salmon fishery of $31 million (DFO, 2013a, b).

Advocates of aquacultural systems point to the fact that they are highly productive of nutritious food, which helps to replace some of the collapsed yields of wild fisheries. Aquaculture also provides employment opportunities in coastal communities. While these benefits are real, aquaculture also causes some important ecological damages. For this reason, the establishment or expansion of aquaculture facilities may be bitterly resisted by various interest groups, including some local people (but not all of them), environmental organizations, Aboriginal peoples, commercial and recreational fishers, and some fishery scientists. The cultivation of fish in shallow-water net-pens is particularly contentious; closed-tank facilities on land or in the ocean are much less controversial.

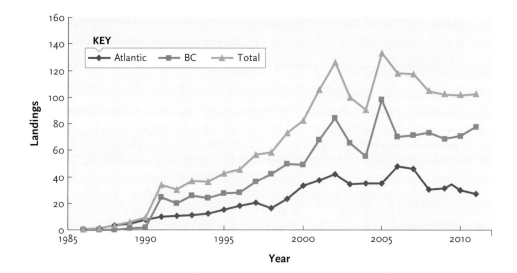

FIGURE 15.35 Production of Atlantic Salmon in Aquaculture in Canada Data are in 10³ tonnes.

SOURCE: Based on data from DFO (2010B).

The most important environmental issues associated with salmon aquaculture are the following:

- *Location:* Fish farms are typically located in shallow protected embayments, which are also prime locations for some wild fisheries, recreational activities, and the viewscapes of residential properties, resulting in conflicts with these alternative uses.
- *Benthic impacts:* If local tidal flushing is not vigorous, uneaten food and fish excrement will accumulate in large amounts around the sea cages, resulting in severe ecological damage by smothering, deoxygenation, hydrogen sulphide, and eutrophication.
- *Chemical inputs:* Various toxic chemicals are used in salmon aquaculture, such as organotin and cupric compounds that are used as antifoulants to keep net-meshes clean (this allows water to pass through and prevents the cages from becoming too heavy with attached biomass), pesticides used to treat infestations of parasitic copepods known as sea lice, and medicines used to treat bacterial infections.
- *Parasite transmission to wild fish:* It appears that sea lice (*Lepeophtheirus salmonis* and *Caligus clemensi*) infestations in penned salmon may be transmitted to wild fish that occur in the vicinity of aquaculture facilities, or that migrate past the cages **(Figure 15.36)**. This can be especially debilitating or lethal to juvenile life-history stages, which because of their small size cannot tolerate many parasites. This stress has been attributed as the cause of a collapse of runs of pink salmon in the Broughton Archipelago (Morton et al., 2004; Krkošek et al., 2005).
- *Disease transmission to wild fish:* Penned Atlantic salmon are also vulnerable to infectious salmon anemia, a lethal hemorrhagic disease caused by the virus *Isavirus*, which is directly transmitted fish-to-fish or by contact with contaminated netting or other equipment (Raynard et al., 2001; Cipriano, 2002).

Alexandra Morton

FIGURE 15.36 Fry of Pink Salmon (*Oncorhynchus gorbuscha*) Fouled with Sea Lice (*Caligus clemensi*) These wild young fish were migrating from their natal river to the ocean in coastal British Columbia, but they passed near an aquaculture facility for rearing Atlantic salmon (*Salmo salar*), where they picked up the crustacean parasites. The load of sea lice on these fish is likely to be lethal.

The only available treatment is to eradicate infected stock, which is an economic catastrophe to the grower. The virus can survive in seawater, so it is possible that it might spread to wild salmon in the vicinity of an aquaculture facility.

- *Escapes:* Penned salmon sometimes break out of damaged pens. When this happens on the Atlantic coast, the escapees may interbreed with endangered populations of wild salmon (such as those of the Bay of Fundy), potentially affecting the genetic integrity of those rare ESUs. When escapes occur on the Pacific Coast, there is a possibility of establishment of wild breeding populations, which would compete with indigenous Pacific salmon. In fact, observations have been made of wild juvenile Atlantic salmon in various places, which confirms the occurrence of feral breeding populations in British Columbia (Volpe et al., 2000).

- *Feed:* Salmon are carnivores and must be provided with a high-quality feed, most of which is manufactured from meal and oil obtained from wild-caught fish, although because of assimilation and food-web inefficiencies, most of the energy content of the feed does not end up in the biomass of the salmon. According to the World Wildlife Fund, fish caught to manufacture fishmeal and oil for aquaculture represent one-third of the global fish harvest.

These are all important issues, and only some of them are resolvable. As with any economic activity, some degree of environmental damage is inevitably caused by salmon aquaculture. Nevertheless, it is clear that aquaculture is a viable enterprise and it will continue to be undertaken in environments where it is feasible. The key to sustainability rests in finding an appropriate balance between the benefits to the human economy that are realized through the production of a renewable bioresource and associated employment opportunities, and the damages caused to biodiversity and other components of the natural environment. Of course, this is true of all activities that contribute to the human economy.

By-Catch

Fishing effort directed to certain marine species also results in the inadvertent harvesting of other species. This incidental take is referred to as by-catch, and it is usually lethal for the affected individuals. By-catch is also associated with lost or discarded fishing gear, such as "ghost nets" that continue to kill marine biota until they eventually wash up on shore or sink to the bottom.

Particularly intense by-catch occurs in shrimp trawling, in which nontarget species may account for as much as 95 percent of the harvested biomass, with an average of 85 percent (Clucas, 1997). Shrimping is responsible for more than one-third of the global by-catch, even though the commercial shrimp harvest is only 2 percent of the total landings of marine animal biomass. In various Canadian fisheries in the northwest Atlantic, an average of 10 percent of the total catch was discarded back to the ocean during a monitoring period in 1994 (Clucas, 1997; DFO, 2010c). The highest by-catch rates were 23 percent in the fishery for lobster, 21 percent in those for haddock and pollock, 20 percent for sea scallop, and 18 percent for cod and queen crab.

By-catch has been a huge issue for fisheries that use drift-nets—these are gill-nets that float suspended in the water column, sometimes extending for tens of kilometres and representing a "wall of death" for creatures that swim into them. Dolphins and sea turtles have been severely affected as by-catch in pelagic drift-nets, and this is a key reason that harvesting method was banned in international waters in 1992 (drift-nets are still permitted in some coastal waters, but only in fisheries where the by-catch is relatively low).

By-catch is an important conservation risk for some marine species. For instance, the barndoor skate (*Dipturus laevis*) has declined precipitously and is now endangered in Canadian Atlantic waters because of excessive by-catch mortality in trawls directed at other species (Casey and Myers, 1998; Cheung et al., 2005). Each year, a number of northern right whales, a critically endangered species, become entangled in fishing gear on the Atlantic coast, as do other cetaceans. Large numbers of seabirds are also killed when they are snagged in fishing nets. For example, all of the 21 species of albatrosses (family Diomedeidae) are at conservation risk, and a leading cause of their declines is unsustainable mortality associated with the seabirds being caught in fishing nets or snagged on long-line hooks when they try to take the bait (there are additional important stressors for these seabirds, including alien mammalian predators that have been introduced to some of their nesting islands, declining stocks of their marine foods because of overfishing, and pollution).

Because by-catch is widely recognized as an important ecological problem, steps are being taken to mitigate some of the damages that are caused. For example, because of controversial mortality caused to the endangered Kemp's Ridley (*Lepidochelys kempii*) and other sea turtles in U.S. waters, shrimp trawls are now required to incorporate turtle-exclusion devices (TEDs) that divert these animals from the rest of the catch, which is retained in the net.

Similarly, by-catch of small cetaceans has been a major problem with tuna fisheries in Pacific waters, because these marine mammals often co-school with yellowfin tuna (*Thunnus albacares*) as they both hunt small baitfish. If a purse seine is set around such a co-school, the dolphins may drown when the net is closed and hauled in to harvest the tuna; particularly vulnerable species are the spotted dolphin (*Stenella attenuata*) and spinner dolphin (*S. longirostris*). This is now much less of a problem than in the past because methods have been developed to release the dolphins, and in some regions it has been made illegal to set purse seines on co-schooling tuna and dolphins.

Other mitigations that can reduce by-catch include requiring net-mesh sizes that capture only larger fish, while allowing smaller ones to escape (although in a heavily laden net many of the smaller fish may also be retained), and the use of various kinds of by-catch reduction devices (BRDs) that help to focus the harvesting on the target species. Many fisheries are also making greater commercial use of the by-catch, so that the inadvertently harvested biomass is not wasted.

The Marine Stewardship Council and other advocacy and research groups are working hard to require fishery managers to reduce the rates of by-catch. One of their most successful tools is the certification of seafood as being harvested with low levels of by-catch. It must be recognized, however, that some degree of by-catch is inevitable. All enterprises that harvest resources from the natural world cause some degree of collateral environmental damage, and by-catch is one of the key impacts of industrial fishing.

15.4 Integrated Resource Management

As we have repeatedly stressed, all systems used to harvest and manage bioresources cause environmental damages of varying kinds and to various degrees. In a general sense, the key damages include the following:

- *degradation of the primary resource* by overharvesting or inappropriate management, which diminishes the economic sustainability of the enterprise (timber, for example, is the primary resource in forestry; in fishing, it is fish);
- *damage caused to secondary resources*, which may be economically important in their own right and might also support commercial or subsistence harvesting (for instance, in a forested region, secondary resources might include hunted species such as deer and trout, as well as opportunities for outdoor recreation);
- *effects on ecological services*, such as carbon storage in the ecosystem, productivity in general, and the provision of reliable and clean flows of freshwater;
- *effects on biodiversity*, such as the endangerment of native species, or the excessive diminishment of natural communities; and
- *societal damages*, which can be various and are mostly borne by local people, including those whose culture and traditional livelihoods become disrupted when industrial resource-harvesting enterprises move into their area; in Canada, it is Aboriginal peoples who are usually most strongly affected in this manner.

To varying degrees, these kinds of environmental damages can be prevented or at least substantially mitigated by adopting a collaborative and broad-reaching approach known as **integrated resource management** (or **IRM**). IRM starts by identifying all of the key stakeholders and issues in a geographic area that has been defined for the purpose of using this approach, including those where bioresources are extensively harvested. The partnership of stakeholders then collaborates to find ways to manage economic activities in a manner that is deemed acceptable by a consensus of the parties.

IRM approaches have been used in Canada in landscapes in which forestry is the primary economic activity. In this context, foresters work with other interested parties to develop integrated management plans that accommodate the harvesting of timber from the landscape, while also sustaining other important forest values. Typically, the IRM plan focuses on discovering ways that forestry can be conducted while still ensuring that the landscape continues to support a sizable abundance of hunted terrestrial animals such as deer, elk, and bears, and aquatic ones such as trout and salmon. Substantial efforts are also made to accommodate nonconsumptive uses of the forest estate, such as outdoor recreation and ecotourism. Protected areas may also be accommodated in IRM plans.

For this integrated system of management to work well, the partners must acknowledge the forest industry as a legitimate player, and that it has a need to harvest trees from the landscape (as does society at large). At the same time, the forestry interests must understand that other views about use and functioning of the forest are also valid, and that they must be accommodated to a mutually acceptable degree. This may require the following sorts of accommodations:

- Less (or even no) clear-cutting is done; instead, timber is harvested using selective methods that have softer environmental impacts.
- Strict rules are required for timber harvesting and road building to decrease their ecological effects, such as cavity-tree retention, leaving uncut groups of trees embedded in clear-cuts, maintaining riparian buffers, careful installation of culverts at stream crossings, and other sensible practices.
- Ecological surveys should be undertaken to identify critical habitats that should not be harvested, such as deer yards (these are important wintering habitats in regions where a deep snowpack accumulates) and ecological communities that support rare or endangered species.
- In some regions it is important to protect tracts of old-growth forest, and for this to be successful it is necessary to set aside protected areas that are large enough to conserve the ecological dynamics that allow this special ecosystem to develop. This means protected areas must be big enough to allow the natural disturbance regime to operate, but at a scale that will sustain a viable abundance of old-growth tracts.
- Local people should continue to have access to acceptable and dependable livelihoods, which might involve employment in forestry for some of them, but could also include traditional economic and subsistence activities such as hunting, fishing, trapping, and guiding.

It is not easy to balance all of these interests and needs in a way that is satisfactory to everyone, but if it can be done, there may be a lasting peace in the forest.

Typically, because of its size and influence, the forest industry is the most powerful interest in this sort of partnership. However, the activities of industrial forestry are increasingly being closely scrutinized by society because of the ecological and other environmental damages that they cause. This is resulting in closer regulation of forestry activities, as well as better-informed choices by consumers in favour of "greener" forest products. These emerging interests are economically powerful, and they are bringing the forest industry to the table as a partner in the development of working IRM partnerships. By cooperating in this way, the forest industry is attempting to come to grips with important controversies that are arising from its woodland and manufacturing operations.

The IRM model is also relevant to fisheries, agriculture, horticulture, and other systems that involve the harvesting of wild biomass or the cultivation of crops. The key steps in a successful application of IRM are the identification of the interested parties, the discovery of their particular concerns, and the collaborative development of accommodations that would achieve a consensus about an appropriate IRM system to implement.

Society expects that the vast ecosystems of Canada will always deliver a wide range of goods and services. These include the large economic benefits that come from sustainable harvests of biomass as sources of food, materials, and energy, while also satisfying other economic and ecological needs. Even while bioresources are used in these ways, the greater landscapes and seascapes are expected to always provide important ecological services, such as carbon storage and a clean environment, and to sustain native biodiversity at viable levels of abundance. In fact, the vision expressed in this paragraph is precisely that of ecological sustainability. The model is portable to the harvesting and management of any kind of bioresource.

CHAPTER SUMMARY

(LO15.1)

- Economic growth is due to increases in population and in per capita consumption of natural resources and generation of wastes. In contrast, economic development implies an increasing efficiency in the operation of an economy, so that results are obtained with less consumption of natural resources and fewer wastes. Sustainable development is reflected in progress toward an economy that is based on the use of renewable natural resources, so that ultimately the use of natural capital is not greater than its rate of regeneration. Ecologically sustainable development includes this prudent vision for the human economy, while at the same time requiring measures that would sustain biodiversity at viable levels of abundance, as well as ecosystem services at necessary levels of functioning.

(LO15.2)

- Nonrenewable resources cannot regenerate after they are extracted from the environment, and they include fossil fuels and metals. Renewable resources can regenerate, and include all forms of solar energy (biomass, flowing water, photovoltaics, wind, and others). However, for renewable resources to be sustained, the rate of harvest must not exceed that of the regeneration. This includes biological stocks such as harvests of particular species, and ecological ones such as the harvesting of trees from entire stands of forest.

(LO15.3)

- The productivity of bioresources can be managed in various ways to mitigate the constraints associated with abiotic environmental factors and biotic ones such as competition and predation. These sorts of management actions are especially frequently used in agriculture, aquaculture, and forestry, but they may also be integrated into management systems for bioresources harvested from the wild.

(LO15.4)

- Although bioresources are potentially renewable, they can be degraded and even destroyed by overharvesting or other kinds of inappropriate management activities. This generally happens because too much emphasis is placed on immediate profit in a commercial enterprise, without due regard for the costs of environmental damage and nonsustainability.

(LO15.5)

- Key bioresources of Canada are examined as case studies, with a focus on those harvested from forests (such as tree biomass) and the ocean (such as fish). The lack of sustainable management is described for these cases, a problem that has resulted in severe depletion of important bioresources. Necessary changes in harvesting and management systems are explained that would make their use more sustainable.

QUESTIONS FOR REVIEW AND DISCUSSION

1. What are natural resources? How are nonrenewable and renewable resources different? Why are biological resources potentially renewable, and what factors can interfere with their sustainable use?

2. In the context of ecological economics, explain what is meant by the following terms: economic growth, economic development, sustainable development, and ecologically sustainable development.

3. You have been given the responsibility of managing a large tract of forest that is currently in a natural condition. It is a big area—at a landscape scale—perhaps 20 km by 20 km (40 000 ha) in extent. The natural disturbance regime involves periodic wildfires at a rotation of 50–100 years. Explain how you would manage this area to ensure a sustainable flow of timber, while also maintaining opportunities for hunters and fishers, and ensuring viable abundances of native species and natural ecosystems, both in the "working" habitats used primarily for forestry and in protected areas.

4. This is essentially the same question as in (3) above, but in this case the forested landscape is in a consistently humid climatic region, so that wildfires and other kinds of stand-replacing disturbances are uncommon and the natural forest is in a predominantly old-growth condition. How would you manage this forest to achieve objectives similar to the ones in question 3?

5. This is also essentially the same question as in (3) above, but it involves the harvesting and management of fish from one of (you can choose): (a) a large lake, (b) a Pacific fishery for salmon, or (c) an Atlantic fishery for cod or lobster.

6. To a substantial degree, fishery biologists and ecologists understand the reasons for the decline of many stocks of Pacific salmon. If this is the case, why have the necessary actions not all been implemented that would allow the salmon to recover?

7. The cultivation of Atlantic salmon in aquaculture can yield large amounts of high-quality biomass, and could replace much of the depleted productivity of wild fisheries. Why, then, is there so much controversy about salmon aquaculture? What ecological risks are inherent in this technological means of fish production?

Paleoecology:
Lessons from the Past

LEARNING OBJECTIVES

After studying this chapter you should be able to:

1. Define paleoecology and describe its major strengths and assumptions.

2. Explain some of the advantages an ecologist would have by extending the monitoring window back into time.

3. Describe the field of dendrochronology and summarize how its approaches can be used by ecologists.

4. Outline the basic principles used in sedimentary analyses and describe the major indicators used by paleoecologists, and the value of multiproxy approaches.

5. Outline the critical roles that paleoecologists have played in environmental debates, such as lake acidification and climatic change.

6. Understand complexities involved in studying the effects of multiple stressors on ecosystems.

16.1 What Is Paleoecology?

Paleoecology is the branch of ecology that deals with populations, communities, and ecosystems that existed in the past. Although fossils of long-ago biota are the mainstay of many investigations in paleoecology (see Ecology in Depth 16.1 for a case related to dinosaur ecology), the field also uses a wide variety of proxy data to reconstruct historical ecosystems and their associated environmental conditions. Proxy data are measured factors or other observations that are used by paleoecologists to infer the values of variables of interest that cannot be easily measured.

The principles used in paleoecology are the same as those used generally by ecologists. However, paleoecologists have the advantage of being able to extend the observational window far back in time, and so allow hypotheses to be examined in a historical context. Moreover, if we understand the causes and consequences of past ecological changes, we can better anticipate those of the future. To have this capacity greatly increases our ability to understand the structure and function of the natural world, as well as some of the important environmental problems that humans are causing. In this sense, paleoecology is not

just about studying what has already happened—it also helps us to better understand current conditions and allows us to better prepare for the future.

Of course, the study of paleoecology has difficulties, such as dealing with incomplete records (i.e., not all aspects of the ecosystem are preserved) and other problems that affect the integrity of paleoecological data. Nevertheless, paleoecological research can yield impressive records of changes in the distribution and abundance of organisms and communities, as well as changes in environmental conditions.

This knowledge can allow paleoecologists to conduct "natural experiments" that involve statistical and mathematical analyses of biological and environmental factors, which can be used to propose the likely causal mechanisms of change. This is not the same as running a contemporary experiment, in which conditions may be carefully manipulated in a randomized block design, and the results then analyzed by statistical tests of significance. Nevertheless, important insights are gained from examination of the fossil record.

A number of disciplines fall under the umbrella of the paleo-sciences: in this chapter we focus on studies that link

ECOLOGY IN DEPTH 16.1
Paleoecology of Dinosaurs
by Philip J. Currie (University of Alberta)

When one thinks of ecology, one does not usually think about extinct animals and plants. This is particularly true of dinosaurs, which are ancient beasts that have been studied for only about 150 years, and are often rare as fossils. In fact, few people are even aware that different species of dinosaurs lived at different times in different places.

Alberta has one of the finest, richest dinosaur sites in the world **(Figure 1)**. In fact, the badlands of Dinosaur Provincial Park (a UNESCO World Heritage Site) have produced a greater diversity of dinosaur species than any other single place or geological formation. Moreover, among the hundreds of excavated dinosaur skeletons are the fossil remains of plants, invertebrates (including shellfish and insects), fish, alligators, crocodiles, lizards, pterosaurs, snakes, turtles, as well as ancient birds and mammals. To put this remarkable paleofauna in perspective, it existed in a paleoecosystem that lasted for less than two million years, yet about 5 percent of all known species of dinosaurs from the entire world are found in this Park.

The first ecological studies in Dinosaur Provincial Park began in the 1960s, when paleontologists realized that they had a large enough sample and good enough field data to study the geographic and stratigraphic distribution of fossils. One study looked at differences in species associations from the west of the Park to the east, and from the lowermost (oldest) to the uppermost (youngest) layers of rock. A following study focused on the relative numbers of carnivores versus herbivores, as a way to tease out information on the physiology of the carnivores. A third study tried to associate specific types of dinosaurs with particular environments. These and other studies came up with more questions than answers, but they focused subsequent specimen and data collection into specific areas of paleoecological research that showed promise in terms of yielding a scientific understanding of the extinct animals and their ecosystem.

More than 40 species of dinosaurs have been identified from the Park, and (on average) tens of skeletons (representing young and old individuals, males and females) have been found for each species. In addition, there are probably 10 bonebeds for every skeleton that has ever been found in the Park. A bonebed is an accumulation of bones from multiple individuals that are mixed up together. They can form in many different ways, but in most cases are created when bones are washed out of the river banks and are then hydraulically concentrated in pockets of quiet water downstream.

Individual bones can be used to identify the types of animals. Some teeth and bones can be identified to the level of species, and virtually all can be referred to the general types (usually at the family level) of

FIGURE 1 Excavating a Dinosaur Skeleton This field crew from the University of Alberta is excavating a dinosaur skeleton in Dinosaur Provincial Park. More than 700 dinosaur skeletons have been found in this area within the past century.

biological and ecological responses to past environmental influences. Furthermore, planet Earth is more than 4.6 billion years old, with the earliest forms of life identified from material dating back over 3.5 billion years. Paleoecologists have worked on material from these earliest times of biological genesis and evolution, although the records become more fragmented and difficult to interpret as one moves back to the most ancient reaches of life. This chapter will focus on relatively recent paleoecological applications, particularly studies that postdate the most recent Wisconsinan glaciation (i.e., the past 13 000 years or so), and with special attention to anthropogenic effects on ecosystems during the past several centuries.

The Importance of Paleoecology

One of the biggest challenges faced by ecologists is the lack of long-term monitoring data. Such data are vital to answering important questions, such as:

- How have populations, communities, and ecosystems changed over time?
- Are any of the changes cyclical?

animals that they represent. The bonebeds comprise bones of animals of all sizes, and do not have the same size bias that more complete skeletons do. And because literally millions of fossil bones are exposed in Dinosaur Provincial Park at any time, statistically meaningful sample sizes can be collected much more readily than of skeletons. The bonebed studies sometimes reveal other aspects of the ecosystem than skeletons do, and include remains of the small species of animals that are not dinosaurs.

Footprints, especially those in trackways, are not common in Dinosaur Provincial Park, but they do provide another way of independently checking aspects of the ecosystem **(Figure 2)**. As one geologist noted: if you don't have footprints, how do you know that all the dinosaur skeletons were not just washed into the area by the ancient rivers?

Dinosaur eggshells are rare in the Park because there was enough acid in the soil during the Cretaceous to dissolve the material before it had a chance to be preserved. Fortunately, however, there were some paleo-waterbodies where the shells of snails and clams reduced the acidity of the water enough for eggshells of dinosaurs to be preserved, which showed that dinosaurs laid laying eggs in the region. Another contemporary dinosaur site at Devil's Coulee, 300 km to the south, had the right soil conditions and preserved nests of eggs, some of which contain the fossils of embryonic dinosaurs.

Stomach contents and coprolites (feces) provide other lines of paleoecological

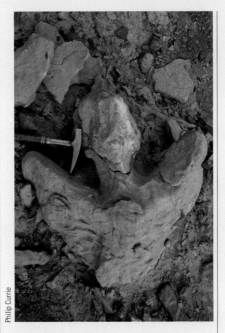

Philip Currie

FIGURE 2 A Dinosaur Footprint This specimen is the infilling of an ancient tyrannosaurid footprint, and as such represents a natural cast of a dinosaur foot.

evidence. One massive coprolite from the Park was clearly from a tyrannosaur like *Gorgosaurus*, because it was full of broken bone fragments of a herbivorous dinosaur. Coprolites also represent a specialized kind of microenvironment that preserves things in different ways, and fossilized muscle tissue (presumably of the animal that was eaten) was also recovered from that tyrannosaurid coprolite.

Fossilized skin impressions are sometimes collected with the skeletons of large dinosaurs. Some specimens even preserve fossilized keratin in the form of the horny beaks of bird-like dinosaurs (ornithomimids) and duck-billed (hadrosaurian) dinosaurs, and these provide clues about their diet. The keratinous parts of toenails of the carnivorous dinosaurs have also been recovered, and show that their bony claws were extended into needle-sharp points. In 2012, the feathers were first reported on a carnivorous dinosaur skeleton from Dinosaur Provincial Park. Although feathers had been known since 1996 to exist on small carnivorous dinosaurs from China, their discovery in the Park was the first for a whole family of dinosaurs (the Ornithomimidae). The ecological implications are profound because insulating feathers of these dinosaurs indicate they were warm-blooded animals.

Of course, terrestrial ecosystems also have plants. Relatively little was known about ancient vegetation from the Park until recently, because large plant fossils are rarer than dinosaur bones; the chemistry of the ancient soils caused plant biomass to decompose before it had a chance to fossilize. However, spores and pollen from plants, although microscopic, are amazingly persistent and are abundant in the rocks (Section 16.3). To date, palynological studies have identified about 500 species of plants in Dinosaur Provincial Park.

Dinosaur Provincial Park is not the only dinosaur-based ecosystem that has been studied, but it is certainly the best known in the world. Even after more than a century of research at this site, new discoveries are reported every year.

- What has caused the changes to occur? How important have natural influences been, as opposed to anthropogenic ones?

To provide robust and defensible answers to these sorts of questions, long-term observational data (i.e., a monitoring database) are needed. However, direct observations are usually only of a short-term duration, often a few decades or years or even less. For many ecological and environmental issues, short-term data are insufficient, and so indirect proxy methods must be used to examine a longer period of time.

Fortunately, a number of "natural archives" contain an excellent and accessible record of past ecological and environmental conditions. In some cases, this historical information occurs in isolated samples, such as bones found in a specific deposit, which represent a "time capsule" of a certain period of time. Such finds are important and form a mainstay of information used in disciplines such as paleontology. However, the focus of this chapter will be on more continuous records of ecological change, such as those archived in cores of lake sediment and in tree rings. Using these kinds of records, paleoecologists

A CANADIAN ECOLOGIST 16.1
Philip J. Currie: Dinosaur Sleuth

Eva Koppelhus

FIGURE 1 Philip Currie Collecting Dinosaur Fossils in Mongolia

Philip Currie is a professor at the University of Alberta, where he holds the Canada Research Chair in Dinosaur Paleobiology **(Figure 1)**. Before this academic appointment, he helped found

the Royal Tyrrell Museum of Palaeontology in Drumheller, Alberta, where he was the curator of dinosaurs. Currie has been a driving force in building Alberta's international reputation as a centre of excellence in paleontology—more than 5 percent of the world's known species of dinosaur occur in the province. Currie's fieldwork has resulted in the naming of 25 species of dinosaurs.

Dinosaur fossils have been found on every continent, and so Currie's research has taken him around the world. For example, in the 1980s he was a codirector of the Canada–China Dinosaur Project, the first such partnering between China and the West since the 1920s. This collaborative work described some of the first dinosaurs with feathers, thus showing evolutionary links to birds. Two of the richest sites where Currie does field research—Dinosaur Provincial Park in Canada and the Nemegt Formation in Mongolia—are the best known ecosystems that were dominated by dinosaurs. Research at these locations provides clues to the complex interactions that occurred among dinosaurs, birds,

mammals, and the plants that lived in their ancient ecosystems. One ostrich-mimic dinosaur (ornithomimid) with a broken arm was found associated with a layer of plants, and it was jokingly suggested that it lay down on the bed of plants to die.

Currie has also used his many fossil discoveries to study dinosaurian migrations and herding behaviour, and to challenge the long-standing belief that carnivorous dinosaurs were solitary, rather than social predators. One pack of the tyrannosaurid dinosaur *Albertosaurus*, for example, died en masse 70 million years ago. The site, found originally in 1910 but not excavated until much later, has now produced evidence of more than 20 individuals ranging in age from two years old to a large adult of 24 years.

Currie's diverse and numerous discoveries have made him a celebrity among scientists, and he is frequently interviewed in documentaries, as well as in newspapers, radio, and television shows. By describing the ancient past and its species, he has provided important insights into evolutionary and environmental change.

can reconstruct changes over known periods of time. This approach is highly relevant to many of the topics discussed in this text, including the ecological damage being caused by pollution and other anthropogenic stressors.

The basic approaches used by paleoecologists are firmly grounded in many of the scientific principles defined in this book. Paleoecologists often use the **principle of uniformitarianism**, which stated plainly is "The present is the key to the past." This important idea was developed by Charles Lyell (1797–1875), an English naturalist/geologist who was one of Charles Darwin's most influential mentors. The importance of uniformitarianism arises from the reasonable assertion that, if we understand how organisms respond to their environmental influences today, then to some degree their fossil remains can be used to reconstruct their past communities and the environments in which they lived.

The **principle of superposition** is also important. It states that in a sequence of sedimentary deposits, the oldest beds are at the bottom and the youngest are at the top. This assumes that the layers were originally deposited

on horizontal planes, and that geological forces have not caused them to be grossly deformed or overturned. As such, the relative ages of the rocks is related to their position in the sedimentary layers.

Of course, many of the ecological communities studied by paleoecologists are no longer present. This is either because species have become extinct or environmental conditions have changed to such a degree that modern analogues of the ancient communities no longer exist. In these cases, paleoecologists must base their reconstructions on whatever information is available, and they may make reasonable deductions based on the morphology of comparable species or other helpful information they can recover.

Paleoecologists always work with incomplete data. Nevertheless, having some reliable data is always better than having none at all. If direct observational data are not available, then inferences provided by paleoecologists are valuable because they contribute to an improved understanding of many fundamental and applied ecological problems.

16.2 Environmental Change

Environmental factors are in a continuous state of change. Some changes are natural and beyond the control of humans, while others are related to anthropogenic influences. If we are to understand the causes and consequences of anthropogenic damages caused to ecosystems, then we must first appreciate the natural influences that result in conspicuous environmental change.

Some of the biggest natural environmental changes are related to climate. For example, just 15 000 years ago, almost all of Canada **(Figure 16.1)**, large parts of the northern United States, and regions of northern Eurasia and elsewhere were covered by massive ice sheets, up to several kilometres thick. In fact, many times during the past two million years, ice sheets covered large parts of those regions, then retreated, and returned. Clearly, humans had no influence on the extensive changes in climate that caused those colossal glacial events to occur.

The physical causes of those remarkable climatic changes are now reasonably well understood. They include a spectrum of factors, often working in concert. For example, the planet's movements about its axis and around the Sun exhibit periodic changes, called Milankovitch cycles. They are named after Milutin Milanković (1879–1958), a Serbian engineer and mathematician who recognized the significance of those patterns for the global climate system.

Three major cycles in Earth's orbital movements are recognized:

1. eccentricity or orbital shape, which measures the departure of Earth's orbit around the Sun from a circular path to one that is ellipsoidal;
2. obliquity, which measures changes in the tilt of Earth's axis; and
3. precession, sometimes referred to as "wobble," which measures changes in axial rotation.

These orbital cycles affect the amount and location of solar energy reaching Earth's surface. Moreover, because the cycles occur on different time scales, there are periods in which they have diminished each other's effects or reinforced them, resulting in substantial changes in climate.

There are also natural variations in the Sun's output of energy. For example, sunspot cycles occur about every 11 years—these correlate with solar intensity. Other natural influences on global climate include volcanic eruptions that eject fine aerosols of ash and sulphate particulates into the stratosphere, where they reflect some incoming solar energy and may cause cooling. This was demonstrated by the massive eruption of Mount Pinatubo in the Philippines in 1991, which resulted in a detectable cooling of the global climate for about two years. Of course, changes in the composition of Earth's atmosphere, such as increases in the concentrations of

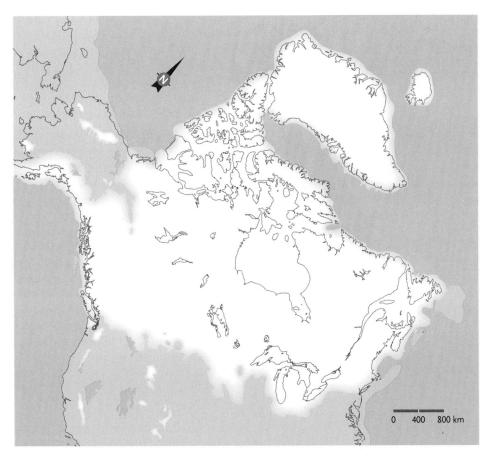

FIGURE 16.1 Maximal Extent of the Wisconsinan Glaciers in Canada, about 20 000 Years Ago Almost all of what is now Canada was covered by glacial ice, several kilometres thick in places, and even extending onto what are now shallow continental-shelf marine waters. A few nonglaciated places, especially in the northwest, were continuously vegetated. These are called refugia (singular refugium).

SOURCE: Dyke, A.S., A. Moore, and L. Robertson. 2003. *Deglaciation of North America*. Open File 1574, Geological Survey of Canada, Natural Resources Canada, Ottawa, ON. http://geopub .nrcan.gc.ca/moreinfo_e.php?id=214399.

0   400   800 km

The Fossil Forest of Axel Heiberg Island

A striking example of ancient climate change in Canada is reflected by the extraordinary remains of lush forests of the middle Eocene epoch, from about 45 million years ago. This paleo-forest is located in what is now the High Arctic tundra of Axel Heiberg Island, at a far-northern latitude of 80°N and about 1500 km north of the modern treeline (Basinger, 1991; Jahren, 2007). The ancient forest was first identified by a helicopter pilot and geologists working with the Geological Survey of Canada, who noticed the ancient stumps when they flew over the area. However, much of what we know about the phenomenon is based on the work of James Basinger of the University of Saskatchewan and his many colleagues.

Paleobotanical evidence shows that this age-old forest was dominated by dawn redwoods (*Metasequoia*) that were as tall as 30 m and had diameters exceeding 1 m. Other trees adapted to a warm temperate climate were also present, including species of fir (*Abies*), pine (*Pinus*), cypress (*Taxodium*), walnut (*Juglans*), and ginkgo (*Ginkgo*), with an understorey of alder (*Alnus*) and birch (*Betula*). The fossil woody debris includes logs and stumps still rooted in ancient soil, and of size providing an astonishing contrast to the small tundra plants that now characterize this polar latitude, which are shorter than 10 cm. The paleo-biomass is in a mummified (dried) form and remarkably well preserved, a consequence of the swamp forest having been rapidly buried by an event of sediment deposition, which prevented the organic material from decomposing. The fossil-bearing beds are now being exposed by erosion of the overlaying sedimentary materials.

Plate-tectonic evidence shows that, even 45 million years ago, Axel Heiberg Island was at a similar location in the High Arctic as it is today. Clearly, however, the polar regions were much warmer then. In fact, the planet was experiencing a period of warmth that is referred to as a "Greenhouse Earth," as opposed to the "Icehouse" of the most recent hundreds of thousands of years.

At 80°N, however, this Arctic region has always experienced prolonged times of winter darkness. How did the large trees survive the extended lack of sunlight? Tree-ring analysis of their mummified wood provides the answer—the early rings laid down when the light was rapidly increasing in the springtime did not grade slowly into the latewood rings of autumn, but rather the seasonal growth ended abruptly **(Figure 1)**. This shows that the trees quickly "shut down" into a dormant state when the photoperiod was diminishing as the long "winter" approached. Unlike modern trees growing in cold climates, these warm-temperate Eocene trees appear to not have needed an extended period of physiological hardening prior to the onset of their extended dark season.

Hans Dommasch/James Basinger

FIGURE 1 Fossilized Wood The annual growth rings in a fossil log show that this conifer tree grew rapidly in a warm, moist climate, and that its seasonal growth ended abruptly when the long winter darkness began at this high latitude.

The Axel Heiberg paleo-forest and sediments of comparable age on nearby Ellesmere Island have also yielded an interesting zoological history, represented by fossil teeth and bones of warm-climate alligators, turtles, hippopotamus, rhinoceros, rodents, and birds. This further confirms the ecological and climatic interpretations made from the paleo-botanical evidence

Paleoecologists have used a variety of methods to determine that the fossil Eocene forest grew in a climatic regime with an average annual temperature of about 12°C (as opposed to −20°C now), and that even the "winter" was above freezing. This suggests a climate similar to that experienced today from about South Carolina to northern Florida. However, the fossil record from other places reveals that, during these times of global warmth, it was the polar regions that were most strongly affected, while equatorial regions were little changed. Therefore the transfer of the heat of absorbed solar radiation from low to high latitudes, which is a major component of the Earth's climate system, was different in the Eocene. This may be partly explained by slightly different spatial configurations of the continents, which resulted in patterns of oceanic and wind currents that were unlike those of today. There is also evidence that the atmospheric concentration of carbon dioxide, an important greenhouse gas, may have been at least twice as great during the Eocene as today.

The ancient forests of Axel Heiberg Island give us insight into a time in Earth's history when the global climate supported warmth-loving species in the polar regions. Today, anthropogenic activities are causing increases to occur in the concentrations of greenhouse gases, which will also result in a period of global warming. We may have embarked on an uncontrolled experiment with the global climate system, with uncertain but likely profound consequences.

greenhouse gases, can also have effects on climate. We examined this in Chapter 4 and will do so again later in this chapter.

Some of the most striking illustrations of natural environment change come from paleoecological studies in the High Arctic, where ancient coniferous forests covered parts of Axel Heiberg Island about 45 million years ago (see Ecology in Depth 16.2). Another example is that of a fossil beaver pond on Ellesmere Island dating to about four million years ago, when the climate was more temperate than today (Tedford and Harington, 2003; Dawson and Harington, 2007; **Figure 16.2**).

16.3 The Toolkit

A wide variety of paleoecological data is available to reconstruct past ecological and environmental conditions. Only a few approaches can be highlighted here, but they are representative of the methods that are being used.

Richard Harington

(a)

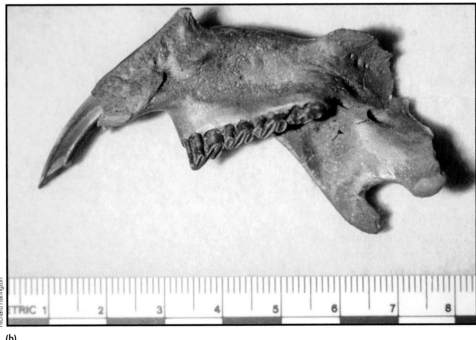

Richard Harington

(b)

FIGURE 16.2 Arctic Beavers
About four million years ago the climate of the present high arctic of canada was warm enough to support beavers. (a) This excavation site of a paleo-beaver pond from the early Pliocene (four million years ago) is on Ellesmere Island in the High Arctic, with Strathcona Fiord in the background. Paleoecologists have determined, based on proxy data gathered at this site, that the average temperature was about 10°C warmer than now in the summer, and 15°C warmer in winter. (b) The left lower jaw with teeth of *Dipoides*, an extinct species of beaver, was found at this site. (c) On the next page, an artist's conception of what this currently High Arctic region would have looked like about four million years ago. The vegetation responded to the warmer climate by growth that was much more lush than occurs today.

FIGURE 16.2 (Continued)

Painting "Early Pleistocene Beaver Pond in the High Arctic" by George Teichman, reproduced with permission from the Canadian Museum of Nature.

(c)

Once we have learned about these methods, we will examine some of their applications to research, with a focus on studies that have a Canadian context.

Tree Rings

Paleoecologists can use the known relationships between plant growth and environmental factors in a variety of ways. One commonly used approach is **dendrochronology**, or the information contained in annual tree-ring couplets. This method is especially effective in regions that experience strong seasonal contrasts, such as all of Canada. While this method seems fairly straightforward, like most paleoecological approaches, information must be interpreted cautiously. Tree-ring analyses are based on the premise that annual growth rings will reflect variations of key environmental factors that affect growth, such as temperature, precipitation, herbivores and pollution **(Figure 16.3)**.

Many species of trees can live for several centuries, and some for much longer—a bristlecone pine (*Pinus longaeva*) may be the world's oldest living organism at about 5062 years of age (Brown, 2013). In Canada, some of the oldest living trees are a subalpine larch (*Larix lyallii*; aged 1917 years old) from Kananaskis, Alberta; a yellow cypress (*Chamaecyparis nootkatensis*; 1636 yr) on Vancouver Island, British Columbia; and an eastern white cedar (*Thuja occidentalis*; 1653 yr; **Figure 16.4**) growing on the Niagara Escarpment in southern Ontario. The dendrochronology of these long-lived plants contains an archive of past environmental conditions. Moreover, because dead tree trunks may be preserved in lake sediment and

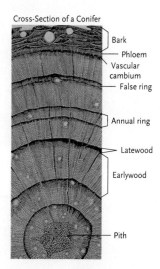

Cross-Section of a Conifer

Bark
Phloem
Vascular cambium
False ring
Annual ring
Latewood
Earlywood
Pith

FIGURE 16.3 Section of a Tree Showing Growth Rings One annual growth ring consists of a couplet of earlywood when the tree was growing rapidly in the spring and early summer, plus latewood from much slower growth later in the season. The vascular cambium is a region of living cells where growth actually occurs. False rings are sometimes formed during times of unseasonable cold or drought.

SOURCE: National Oceanic and Oceanographic Administration (NOAA). 2008. *Paleoclimatology Slides*, National Climatic Data Center, NOAA, Washington, DC. http://www.ncdc.noaa.gov/paleo/slides/slideset/18/index.html.

in bogs, and also as building material in older buildings, the tree-ring record can sometimes be extended far beyond the chronology of living trees using a process known as cross-dating. Such continuous records are now available for several regions of the world, and they may provide a record dating back as much as 10 000 years.

FIGURE 16.4 An Ancient Cedar This eastern white cedar (*Thuja occidentalis*) growing on a cliff on the Niagara Escarpment of southern Ontario was dated by dendrochronology to be over 1000 years old. This species has provided some of the oldest known trees in eastern North America.

taken from each tree being sampled. Because there can be considerable variability among individual trees, 20 or more trees are typically sampled at each study site. If a tree is dead, an entire cross-sectional disc of the trunk may be removed using a saw.

Several tree-ring characteristics are important in paleo-ecological studies. The width of the rings is almost always useful. This is due to the well-founded assumption that wider rings are laid down during periods of faster growth and so represent environmental conditions that are relatively conducive to the well-being of the tree. The strongest indicators of local environmental conditions are gained by coring trees that are living close to the limit of their tolerance, such as near treeline in a mountainous area.

One of the main uses of dendrochronology is to reconstruct past climatic conditions, based on the assumption that growth is faster and rings wider when temperature and precipitation are at optimal levels. **Figure 16.6** shows a crosssection of a spruce tree collected near Inuvik in the subarctic Mackenzie Delta of the Northwest Territories. Note the variable widths of the tree rings, which provide paleoclimatic information for this site. Of course, there are complications when using dendrochronology data. For example, biotic factors can change, such as the effect of age or competition on productivity, but these factors can usually be accounted for. In addition to simply tracking the size of the growth rings, information can be gleaned from the wood density and its chemical and isotopic composition.

Figure 16.7 shows how tree rings have been used to track past flooding events of the Red River Valley in Manitoba, which are recurrent hazards in that region (St. George, 2009). Knowledge of past floods is important to both public safety and the insurance industry, which needs to know the frequency of the disasters against which it provides indemnity. During severe floods, the river inundates trees in its floodplain and causes them to develop unusual anatomical features within their annual growth rings.

In addition, fire history can often be deduced by searching for fire scars on tree-trunks **(Figure 16.8)**. These are areas of the trunk that were charred during a past fire that injured but did not kill the tree. Tree rings have also been used to reconstruct information concerning historical irruptions of pest insects, such as spruce

FIGURE 16.5 Coring a Tree An increment borer that resembles a hollow drill is used to obtain a tree core about 4 mm in diameter. It consists of a borer, handle, and spoon that allow the core to be removed from a tree without causing any long-term damage. The inset image shows a tree core being removed from the increment borer using the spoon.

To sample a living tree, a dendrochronologist typically uses a hand-held increment borer to remove a thin core of wood, about the thickness of a pencil, from the trunk **(Figure 16.5)**. This is usually done at a height of about 1.5 m (known as breast height), and typically two orthogonal cores (i.e., at right angles from each other) are

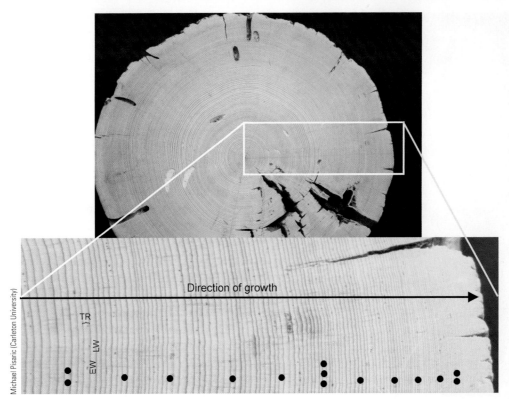

Michael Pisaric (Carleton University)

Direction of growth

TR

EW LW

FIGURE 16.6 Close-Up of a Cross-Section of a White Spruce (*Picea glauca*) Tree The tree was sampled in the Mackenzie Delta near Inuvik, Northwest Territories, an area with the northernmost tree growth in Canada. An individual tree ring (TR) is composed of light-coloured low-density cells known as earlywood (EW) and darker and denser cells called latewood (LW). A couplet of one earlywood and latewood band represents one year of growth (TR). The first complete ring at left represents the year 1745 and is the oldest growth of the tree in the image. The most recent growth of the tree is at the right of the image and dates to the 1800s. Dots on the image represent decades (single dot), 50 years (two dots), and a century (three dots). The sample dates from 1668–1883. Particularly narrow rings occur in 1763, 1785, and 1802. Also note the generally narrow rings following 1830—this period of slow growth coincides with the final stages of a relatively cool climatic period known as the Little Ice Age.

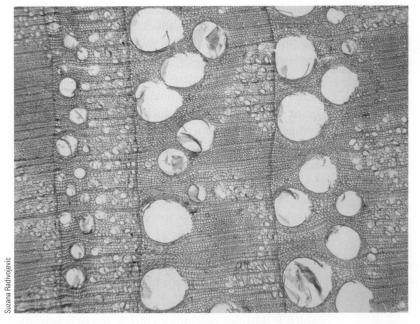

Suzana Radivojevic

FIGURE 16.7 Anomalous Tree Rings The image shows a microscopic thin section of normal and flood-damaged tree rings from a bur oak (*Quercus macrocarpa*) collected beside the Red River, Manitoba. The left ring, formed during 1862, contains shrunken earlywood vessels and anomalous latewood, indicating stress induced by flooding in that year. Rings formed in 1827 and 1828 (to the right) have larger vessels and represent normal rings.

budworm (Blais, 1965), as well as the effects of caribou trampling roots (Morneau and Payette, 2000).

Growth rings from organisms other than trees can also be used by paleoecologists. For example, the field of **sclerochronology** uses information contained in the pattern of growth increments of a variety of hard-bodied organisms, such as marine corals. Scientists have also learned ways to tap the information contained in the growth patterns on mollusk shells and in the inner ear bones (otoliths) of many fish species.

Sediment: A Window on the Past

Perhaps the most common method of reconstructing past terrestrial vegetation is by studying pollen grains that are preserved in sedimentary deposits, such as the

FIGURE 16.8 **Fire Scars** This image shows a series of fire scars on a ponderosa pine (*Pinus ponderosa*) tree growing in El Malpais National Monument in New Mexico. This tree has recorded multiple scars from low-severity fires.

material that accumulates at the bottom of lakes, oceans, and peat bogs. Similar approaches are used to study pollen in sediments from all of those environments, but we will focus on lake sediments here, a field of research called paleolimnology.

A characteristic feature of much of Canada is the great numbers of lakes on the landscape, many of which are a legacy of the past ice age **(Figure 16.1)**. As the ice sheets expanded, they greatly modified the morphology of the landscape, much like immense bulldozers. The glaciers scraped away the soil under their massive weight, scoured the bedrock surface, enlarged river valleys, and excavated basins that would later become the lakes of today. Once the climate warmed, the great ice sheets melted and retreated, exposing the many lakes that are an important natural feature and resource of Canada.

Lakes are not static features of the landscape. They are continuously draining through effluent streams while receiving water and sediment from their watershed, and slowly accumulating inorganic sediment and biological remains **(Figure 16.9)**. This material comes from two main sources:

- **autochthonous** material that originates within the lake itself, such as algal and invertebrate remains, dead fish, and chemical precipitates; and
- **allochthonous** material that has come from outside the lake, such as foliage and pollen grains of terrestrial vegetation, soil particles, and airborne substances.

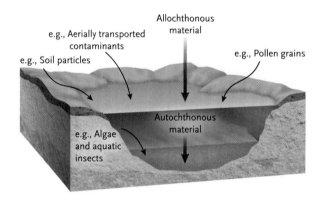

FIGURE 16.9 **Schematic of a Lake Gradually Filling with Sediment** Natural sedimentation is a cumulative process in a lake. It can yield time-dependent profiles that are repositories of information about ecological and environmental changes that have occurred in the lake and its surrounding watershed and region. The paleolimnological record (i.e., from the sediment, which accumulates constantly) is composed of material from both allochthonous and autochthonous sources (see the text for details).

Sediment therefore contains a diverse array of materials from many sources, including dead biomass. This is the reason sediment can provide such a rich historical record about changes in lake organisms and processes, as well as those of the watershed and even the landscape. The "words" of this historical "book" are represented by physical, chemical, and biological indicators (proxy data) that are preserved in sediment. In this chapter we will focus on biological indicators, but sediment also archives an extensive library of indicators that are physical (e.g., evidence of past erosion events) and chemical (e.g., records of contaminants such as mercury, lead, and organic pollutants such as DDT and PCBs).

The task of the paleoecologist is to remove a core of this sediment profile, then to extract and quantify the proxy data, and finally to interpret the information in a meaningful and defensible manner **(Figure 16.10)**. Under ideal circumstances, the sediment record preserves a stratigraphic (layered) sequence that represents a depth-time profile. The deeper you go into the profile, the older is the sediment, until bedrock is reached, which marks the origin of the lake (in most of Canada that would indicate the time of the retreat of the most recent glaciation). Of course, problems are sometimes encountered. The sediment profile may have been mixed by physical processes such as currents, or by burrowing aquatic animals (referred to as bioturbation), thus blurring the historical record. However, paleoecologists often have independent ways to assess the historical integrity of a stratigraphic record. For instance, the age

of layers within a profile can be reliably dated using methods based on the rate of radioactive decay of certain isotopes, such as carbon-14 (^{14}C or radiocarbon) and lead-210 (^{210}Pb).

The portfolio of biological indicators preserved in sediment is remarkably varied and often remarkably complete. Some indicators are preserved as microfossils that are typically identified and enumerated using a microscope. They include pollen grains of vascular plants, siliceous cell walls of diatoms and scales of chrysophytes (phytoplankton), and the chitinous exoskeletal parts of invertebrates. Sometimes, there is a biogeochemical historical record, such as fossil pigments that can be linked to cyanobacteria (blue-green algae) and other photosynthetic organisms.

Of course, recovering indicators in a sedimentary profile is only the first part of the study. Continuing with the "book" analogy, we may now have recovered a series of "words"—the indicators, such as species of diatoms and their relative abundances. To interpret this information in a meaningful ecological context we must also know the environmental optima and tolerances of

(a)

(b)

FIGURE 16.10 **Methods in Paleolimnology** (a) Removing a short core of surface sediment from a lake; (b) a short sediment core. A core of ~40 cm would typically cover the most recent two centuries or so of sediment accumulation for typical Canadian lakes. Longer cores, extending to the end of the continental Ice Age, can be retrieved using different kinds of sediment corers.

the species. For example, if we are presented with information about the presence of a polar bear (*Ursus maritimus*) or a black bear (*U. americana*), we could deduce meaningful information about the environments and ecosystems that these species represent. We would know that the polar bear is from an Arctic habitat, and because most of its diet is based on seals, it would have lived near an ocean or a large bay such as Hudson's Bay. In comparison, the presence of a black bear would indicate temperate regions and a mostly forested landscape. These examples illustrate the principle of uniformitarianism, which means that what we observe in the present is a key to understanding the past, and vice versa.

The larger the number of indicators that we have to work with, the more refined our ecological inferences can become. For this reason, much of paleoecology has been moving toward integrated or multiproxy approaches, in which a suite of microbial, plant, and animal indicators, as well as chemical and physical ones, is gathered and interpreted. Nevertheless, certain taxa are more reliable indicators than others.

For example, the polar bear is a specialist in hunting seals, and so its niche is relatively narrow, whereas the black bear is omnivorous and eats a wide range of plant and animal foods, depending on habitat conditions. As a result, polar bears are a rather specific indicator of changes (often referred to as a specialist) in their prey and environmental conditions necessary to hunt them (such as extensive and persistent sea ice), whereas black bears provide more generalist inferences about their landscape-scale ecosystem. In this sense, knowledge of the historical presence of humans might not be very informative about environmental conditions, because our species is a generalist omnivore that is capable of living in an astonishing variety of environments, ranging from the tropics to polar regions.

Figure 16.11 provides a conceptual summary of some of these relationships. If the abundance of most species is plotted relative to an environmental variable, such as lakewater pH or temperature for an aquatic organism, the relationship often approximates a bell-shaped curve **(Figure 16.11a)**. Most species would be particularly competitive at a certain pH level, and that would likely be its optimum pH within its range of habitats. However, a species would also be able to survive at pH levels higher and lower than its optimum, which is shown as tolerance in the figure. A specialist has a relatively narrow tolerance whereas a generalist has a broader one **(Figure 16.11b)**.

These are reasons different species have varying optima and tolerances to environmental factors, and why this ecological information is critical for interpreting the paleoecological record. Once the environmental optima

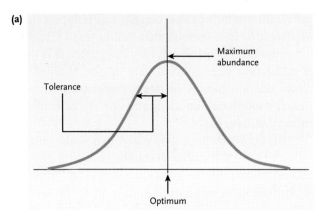

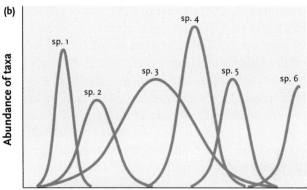

FIGURE 16.11 Conceptual Diagram of Environmental Optima and Tolerances Species differ in their tolerances to environmental factors (such as temperature and pH) in individualistic ways that often approximate a bell-shaped curve (or a unimodal, or Gaussian distribution). Diagram (a) shows this for a particular species. Diagram (b) compares various species, showing that they have different optima and tolerances. For example, if the environmental variable of interest was lakewater pH (on the *x*-axis), then species 1 has its optimum in low-pH waters, while species 5 has its optimum in higher-pH habitats. Species 3, however, has a circumneutral optimum and a broader tolerance—it is more of a generalist with respect to pH. A paleoecologist can use these known relationships to reconstruct past environmental conditions based on the presence and relative abundance of fossils of these species.

SOURCES: (a) Based on Jongman, R.H.G., C.J.F. ter Braak, and O.F.R. van Tongeren (eds.). 1995. *Data Analysis in Community and Landscape Ecology.* Cambridge University Press, Cambridge, UK. (page 19); (b) Based on Smol, J.P. 2008. *Pollution of Lakes and Rivers: A Paleoenvironmental Perspective*, 2nd Edition. Wiley-Blackwell Publishing, Oxford, UK. (page 81).

and tolerances of species are understood, they can be used in paleoecological reconstructions.

For some indicators, the characterization of environmental optima has been taken to a highly quantitative level. One of the examples presented later in this chapter (see "Acidification of Lakes") will show how fossil algae in dated cores of lake sediment were used to determine how and which lakes had acidified due to acid rain, and to what degree. Although it should not be surprising that lakewater pH will affect algal species in different ways, one might ask how paleoecologists can interpret these relationships in a manner that stands up to scientific and sometimes political scrutiny. In essence, it is done by calibrating the historical data on the basis of the known relationships of species to present-day environmental conditions—an application of the principle of uniformitarianism.

This approach begins by studying how the surface sediment reflects the present conditions, and using that information to calibrate historical observations. Suppose we are trying to reconstruct trends in lakewater pH using data on fossil diatom communities near the large smelters at Sudbury, Ontario. Hundreds of diatom species live in the lakes and ponds in that region, each with its own optima and tolerances to pH, nutrients, and other environmental factors. The typical approach used by a paleoecologist would be to examine a suite of calibration lakes in the study region that span a gradient of the environmental variable of interest, which in this case is pH. In this example, let us assume that 80 calibration lakes have been chosen with present lakewater pH values that range from 4.5 to 8.0. Other water-quality data, such as metal concentrations and nutrients, would also be gathered. Ideally, several years of monitoring data would be examined so that interyear variability can be assessed. These data would result in a matrix that lists the 80 calibration lakes with their associated environmental data.

The next step is to develop a second data matrix involving species of diatoms. To do this, each calibration lake would be sampled for its uppermost sediment (the surface 1 cm or so, which was laid down in the past two to three years). The sample would be taken near the centre of the lake, a location that integrates the entire waterbody and so provides a representative place for sampling. Back in the laboratory, the species of diatoms would be identified and enumerated so that their relative abundances can be estimated (typically using percentage data) in all of the calibration lakes.

Finally, using a variety of statistical approaches, the environmental optima and tolerances of the diatom species are estimated, in this case with a focus on lakewater pH. This allows a quantitative transfer function to be developed that relates the abundances of the various diatom species to the lakewater pH levels. Broadly defined, a **transfer function** is a mathematical model, also called an inference model, that describes the relationship between biological taxa (or other proxy data) and environmental data. It is used to infer past values of environmental variables from fossil assemblages. The end result is a "paleo-pH meter" that allows historical pH values to be inferred from the fossil diatom communities that are recovered from layers of sediment.

Identifying and enumerating fossils and other indicators in sediment profiles is only part of the story. It is also necessary to develop a chronology of the sedimentary profiles, so that changes of environmental and community factors can be put into a perspective of time. A variety of dating techniques is available, but the most commonly used methods are based on radioisotopes, such as carbon-14 dating for material ranging from about 500 to 40 000 years in age, and lead-210 for sediment younger than about 150 years.

For most of the remainder of this section, we shall focus on lake sediments, but any stratigraphic deposit likely contains important historical information that can be of value to ecologists. For example, one recent case study is a deposit of several decades of bird droppings that were recovered from a chimney on the campus of Queen's University (see Ecology in Depth 16.3).

Palynology: The Study of Pollen and Spores

The most commonly used method of reconstructing past terrestrial vegetation is **palynology**, or the study of pollen and spores (see also Chapter 10). Pollen grains are the male reproductive cells of conifers and flowering plants, which for species that are anemophilous (i.e., pollinated by the wind) are released in immense numbers (as can be attested to by those who suffer from hay fever, which is an allergic reaction to certain species, particularly ragweed or *Ambrosia*).

Most aerial pollen grains are not successful in fertilizing a plant ovum—many land on foliage, soil, rocks, or the surface of lakes, where they sink to the bottom and become incorporated into the sediment. A pollen grain has a biopolymer coat called sporopollenin that resists degradation and remains well preserved in sediment, even for millennia. Mosses and fungi produce spores, which are also well preserved in sediment. Because many plant genera and species produce distinct pollen, their presence and relative abundance can be estimated by identifying grains preserved in sediment **(Figure 16.12)**. In addition to pollen and spores, the sediment may contain larger identifiable plant fossils (referred to as macrofossils because they can be seen with the naked eye), such as foliage, seeds, and twigs, that also help to identify paleocommunities. Pollen, spores, and macrofossils allow inferences to be made about past changes in the local terrestrial vegetation.

Pollen analyses have been used to track the revegetation and successional changes that occurred in landscapes following deglaciation. For instance, if a sediment core retrieved from a lake spans a record dating to the period of deglaciation (about 12 000 years ago), the pollen record would show when the denuded landscape left by the retreating ice sheets was colonized by northward-migrating plants.

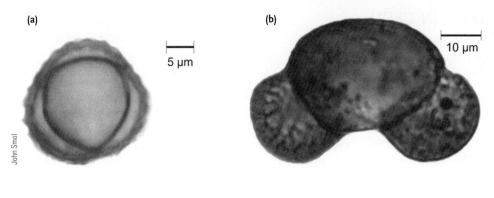

FIGURE 16.12 Microscopic Images of Fossil Pollen Grains Recovered from Lake Sediment (a) A marked increase in the pollen of *Ambrosia* (ragweed) in lake sediment cores from eastern Canada indicates the arrival of European settlers, as this genus is abundant in culturally modified landscapes, such as open fields following deforestation; ragweed is also a major allergen and cause of hay fever; (b) *Pinus* (pine) pollen grain. Scale bars are shown to the right.

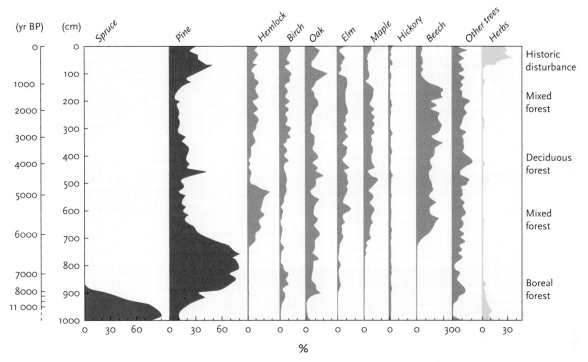

FIGURE 16.13 Pollen Diagram from van Nostrand Lake, Ontario Recent times are at the top of the diagram, and older at the bottom. See text for further explanation.

SOURCE: McAndrews, J.H. *North American Pollen Database* http://www.ncdc.noaa.gov/paleo/napd.html.

Figure 16.13 is a simplified pollen diagram from a sediment core retrieved from van Nostrand Lake, located just north of Toronto (McAndrews, 1970). The diagram shows the 11 most abundant pollen categories that were enumerated, and it divides the 12 000-year record from the lake into major zones of vegetation history: spruce, pine, maple-beech, and ragweed (its pollen makes up most of the "herbs"). The pollen grains that dominated the earliest "communities" were from spruce plus various sedges and grasses, which suggests that the pioneering vegetation was an open spruce-forest and tundra. This vegetation indicates subarctic conditions that are much cooler than those currently occur near Toronto.

Then, between about 10 500 and 9500 years ago, a pine-dominated boreal forest characterized the vegeta-tion, suggesting warmer and drier conditions. The post-glacial succession then continues to a third major stage of mixed deciduous–coniferous temperate forest with beech, birch, elm, maple, and oak, as well as hemlock and pine that are especially abundant at the beginning and the end of this zone. This hardwood-dominated forest is comparable to the temperate forests that are now charac-teristic of southern Ontario. There are other significant changes in the paleoflora, such as a decline in hemlock pollen about 4600 years ago, which may be linked to a pathogen that affected that species (similar to the decline in elm that has occurred in many areas because of mor-tality caused by the introduced Dutch elm disease fungus in the 20th century; see Chapter 10).

The influence of modern agriculture and its associ-ated forest clearing is indicated near the surface of the

The Poop on Chimney Swifts

The chimney swift (*Chaetura pelagica*) is a migratory bird that, after wintering in the upper Amazon basin, breeds throughout eastern North America, including southern Canada east of Saskatchewan. Although its original nesting and roosting habitat consisted of hollow trees and caves, since the late 17th century it has often used chimneys as sites for those purposes. Typically one pair breeds per chimney, but groups of chimney swifts may congregate to roost in larger chimneys (over 10 000 birds in some cases), especially during migration. The birds are remarkably well adapted for a "clinging lifestyle." They can grasp walls using long claws on their feet, while using their stiff tail feathers as a prop **(Figure 1)**.

Although this species was common in the first half of the 20th century, its numbers have been rapidly declining, and it is now listed as threatened in Canada. Many other aerially insectivorous birds,

such as flycatchers, nighthawks, and swallows, are also in decline. The cause of the declines of these birds is poorly understood and likely multifaceted, but a probable stressor is a reduced abundance of their prey of flying insects. As with most species at risk, historical monitoring data on either the swifts or their insect prey are not of sufficient duration to pinpoint exact causes of the changes.

While engaged in conservation activities for chimney swifts in Kingston, Ontario, the history of the birds on the campus of Queen's University was discovered by local naturalists. Documentation of high swift numbers came from a paper published in 1952 that described the banding of thousands of birds per night between 1928 and 1947 at a large chimney in Fleming Hall, a stately building on campus **(Figure 2)**. However, swifts had not been recently observed near or in that chimney, and

a roof-top investigation revealed that it had been capped in 1993. When this was discovered, the Kingston Field-Naturalists were given permission by the university to un-cap the chimney as a conservation measure. To their surprise, they found a 2 m thick deposit of swift droppings (or guano) at the interior base of the chimney. Most people who find several metres of bird guano would say "Someone has to clean this poop up!" Paleoecologists, on the other hand, might say "This is very interesting" and then engage in a study.

It was reasoned that, if the guano deposit was relatively undisturbed by mixing processes, it should contain an archival record of past swift diets as well as other environmental data (Nocera et al., 2012). The guano deposit was sampled at 1 cm intervals, each of which represented time going back into history. The researchers knew that the surface layer was 1993, the year the chimney had been capped. Historical documents showed that Fleming Hall was originally the central heating plant for the university, but the chimney had been decommissioned in 1928 when a different steam plant was built, which meant that year was the earliest time that guano could have accumulated in the disused chimney. In addition, Fleming Hall had a fire in 1933, which was marked by a thin layer of charcoal in the guano deposit. Estimates of intermediate dates were made by measuring the amount of the isotope cesium-137 (^{137}Cs) in the profile. Briefly, ^{137}Cs is a man-made isotope that can be directly linked to aboveground nuclear bomb testing. That practice began in the 1950s, peaked in 1963, and then sharply declined and stopped as treaties between the USSR and the United States banned further atmospheric bomb tests. These various temporal data were used to develop a depth-time profile of the archive of guano.

Bruce Di Labio

FIGURE 1 A Chimney Swift (*Chaetura pelagica*) This bird is clinging to the vertical wall of a chimney using its short legs and long claws, and propping its spine-tipped tail against the wall beneath.

core by a large increase in ragweed and other types of forbs (herbaceous dicotyledonous plants) and grasses. These indicate species related to disturbances and that are abundant in agricultural and urbanized areas.

Reconstructing Changes in Lakes and Rivers

Pollen analyses provide information on what happened in the terrestrial part of the watershed, but what about the lake itself? To understand changes in aquatic

Chris Grooms

(a)

Chris Grooms

(b)

FIGURE 2 Fleming Hall and the Large Chimney That Contained the Guano Deposit
(a) After excavating into the chimney and up through the guano deposit, samples were taken from the face of the deposit, using a stainless steel tray (b).

Microscopic analysis of the 1 cm sections of guano showed that the deposit was almost exclusively made up of the chitinous remains of insects. The most frequent insects were beetles (Coleoptera) and true bugs (Hemiptera), but their proportions had changed over time. Beetles are a better quality food source (because of a higher caloriic density) than bugs. In the mid- and late-1940s, beetles formed almost 70 percent of the swift diet, but this was halved in the 1950s. Beetles became more common again in the mid-1970s. These changes in food type and quality were confirmed by other indicators related to analyses of nitrogen isotopes.

The next step was to determine why the diet of swifts had changed over time. The potential causative factors were explored by sending samples of the guano to the University of Ottawa for analyses of trace contaminants. The variations of insect abundance in the diet showed correlations with the presence of the insecticide DDT and its primary metabolite, DDE. It appears that when DDT use had increased, the beetle populations had decreased. At the same time, the abundance of bugs in the swift diet increased; this group of insects is known to quickly develop resistance to this group of insecticides. At about the time diet was changing, the local population of swifts began its rapid decline.

Additional studies using these and similar approaches are needed before a definitive conclusion can be made regarding the demise of aerially insectivorous birds, but dietary change may provide an explanation. Moreover, this study further illustrates the remarkable chain of effects that DDT applications may have on nontarget organisms. Of course, dietary changes and pollutants are likely interacting with other factors, such as habitat loss and climate change, in depressing swift populations. All of our planet's ecosystems are being subjected to multiple stressors.

communities, we can examine autochthonous indicators that are preserved in sedimentary profiles. This is called paleolimnology, a branch of **limnology** (the study of lakes and rivers) that uses proxy data based on biological, chemical, and physical indicators in sediment cores to reconstruct changes in aquatic ecosystems.

The most widely used proxy data in paleolimnology are based on the siliceous cell walls of microscopic diatom algae (Bacillariophyceae). Diatoms are a remarkably diverse group that often dominates the species richness and sometimes the productivity of the phytoplankton, as well as the shallow-water littoral zone. There are thousands of species of diatoms, each with its own optima and tolerances for environmental variables such as water pH, nutrient concentration, and climatic factors. The cell walls of diatoms are composed of two overlapping siliceous valves known as frustules (vaguely resembling a set of Petri dishes), which preserve well in sediment. Furthermore, the taxonomy of diatoms is based on the size, shape, and sculpturing of their frustules **(Figure 16.14)**. Therefore, the parts of diatoms that are extracted from dated layers of sediment can be used to reconstruct their past communities as well as historical environmental conditions. The siliceous cell-surface scales of some golden-brown algae (Chrysophyceae) are also identifiable and can be used in paleolimnological reconstructions.

Various invertebrate remains can also be recovered from sediment, such as the chitinous body parts of Cladocera (water fleas), including prominent genera such as *Daphnia* and *Bosmina* **(Figure 16.15)**. Cladocerans are

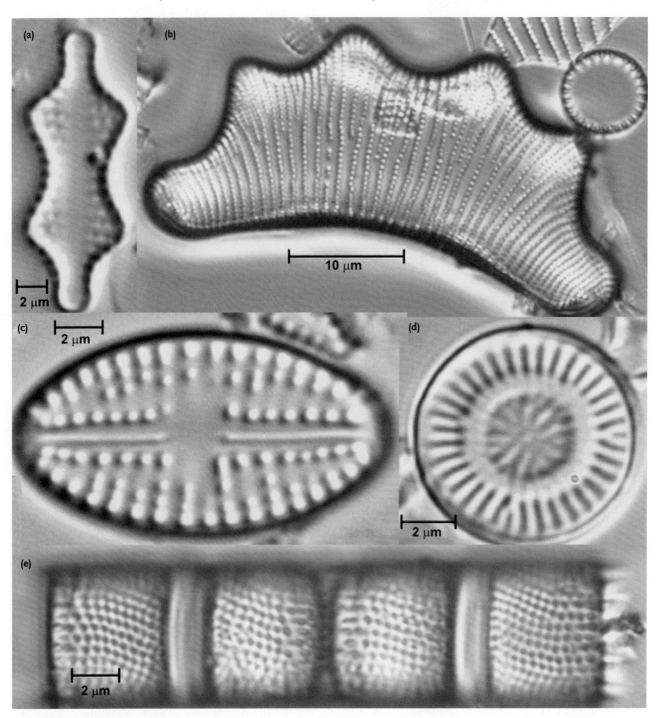

FIGURE 16.14 Micrographs of Fossil Diatom Valves Recovered from Lake Sediment (a) *Staurosira construens* var. *binodis*; (b) *Eunotia serra* var. *tetraodon*; (c) *Navicula farta*; (d) *Cyclotella pseudostelligera*; (e) *Aulacoseira subarctica*.

SOURCES: Photographs (a), (c), (d), (e), K. Rühland, Queen's University; (b) A. Paul, Queen's University.

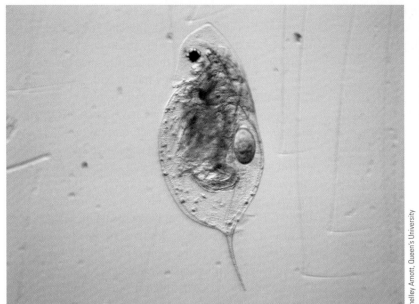

(a)

FIGURE 16.15 Cladocerans as Paleo-Indicators
(a) Micrograph of a living water flea, *Daphnia mendotae*, which is common in many lakes; (b) fossil body parts, such as this postabdominal claw from a daphniid collected from lake sediment, can be used to indicate changes in invertebrate populations and in environmental conditions.

Shelley Arnott, Queen's University

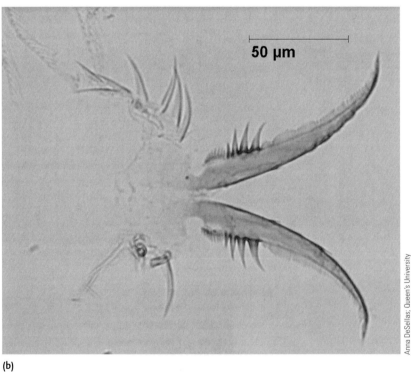

50 µm

(b)

Anna DeSellas, Queen's University

an important food-web link between phytoplankton (their food) and larger invertebrates and smaller fish (their predators). As such, understanding changes in cladocerans provides information about their community.

Lakes and rivers also support many aquatic insects, whose larval stages may be abundant in sediment. Midges (Chironomidae) are often the most abundant insect larvae in Canadian lakes, and their species may be identified by their hard, chitinous mouth parts, which preserve well in sediment. Particular midge species are indicators of temperature and so have been useful in studies of paleoclimate. Species of midges also have different

tolerances and optima of oxygen concentrations, and have been used to track changes in that important factor, particularly in studies of **eutrophication** (or nutrient enrichment; Section 16.4).

16.4 Paleoecology and Environmental Issues

Paleoecology has helped us to better understand some important environmental problems. In the sections that follow, we will examine case studies employing paleolimnological methods to examine environmental issues: acidification, calcium declines in lakes, eutrophication, depletion of Pacific salmon, and climate change.

Acidification of Lakes

Lake acidification became an issue in Canada in the early 1970s. Acidification caused by atmospheric deposition is due to anthropogenic emissions of gaseous sulphur dioxide (SO_2) and oxides of nitrogen (NO and NO_2; these are collectively referred to as NO_x). These and other atmospheric substances can acidify aquatic and terrestrial habitats when deposited in large amounts in the following ways:

- as "acid rain," or acidic rain and snow that are rich in sulphuric acid (H_2SO_4) and nitric acid (HNO_3);
- by the direct (or dry) deposition of atmospheric SO_2 and NO_x, which then become oxidized in water or soil into the acidic compounds sulphate (SO_4^{-2}) and nitrate (NO^{3-}), respectively;
- by the deposition of ammonium (NH_4^+) in precipitation and ammonia (NH_3) gas, which become oxidized to nitrate, generating acidity.

In addition to these atmospheric influences, some surface waters have been acidified by a phenomenon known as acid-mine drainage. This occurs when sulphide minerals (such as iron sulphide, FeS_2) are exposed to oxygen, causing them to react and produce sulphate (SO_4^{-2}), ionic iron (Fe^{2+}), and acidity. This problem occurs whenever sulphide-bearing minerals are exposed to oxygen, and it is often associated with coal mining.

The acidification of ecosystems is an important environmental problem because it causes toxicity to many kinds of biota. In Canada, acidification is an extensive issue over much of the eastern provinces, where lakes on the Precambrian Shield acidify easily because they naturally have low levels of alkalinity (HCO_3^-) and base cations such as calcium, which are key to neutralizing acid inputs. Acidification may also be severe near smelters that emit SO_2 into the atmosphere. The most toxic effects of acidification to most aquatic biota, and especially to fish, are caused by aluminum ions (Al^{+3}) that become solubilized from watershed soils by acidity, rather than direct toxicity caused by hydrogen ions (H^+).

Although the phenomenon of acidifying deposition from the atmosphere is well understood, the issue and its mitigation were embroiled in political and scientific debate, especially in the 1980s. It is clear that many lakes in parts of eastern Canada and upstate New York are now acidic, but there have been polarized discussions about the causes and history of the problem. Although some of the lakes are naturally acidic (such as those in bogs), many others have acidified because of anthropogenic influences, especially atmospheric depositions, although land-use activities may also have had some effect.

Because no one was measuring lakewater pH or aquatic communities in the lakes in the late 1800s, before the time of marked anthropogenic influences, there are no monitoring data to isolate the specific causes of acidification. However, paleoecology has provided some crucial information to help settle the controversy.

Paleo-acidification studies have taken advantage of limnological indicators that are closely linked to lakewater acidity, such as certain species of chrysophytes, diatoms, and invertebrates. For example, calibration studies of modern surface-sediment show that species of *Eunotia* diatoms are often abundant in acidic lakes, while most *Cyclotella* are not and so would be expected to decline as acidification progresses. Based on this sort of knowledge about diatom communities in lakes that vary in acidity, paleolimnologists have developed mathematical models (or transfer functions, as discussed earlier) that allow the historical pH values of lakes to be reconstructed, sometimes to within only 0.2 pH units.

A case study of fossil chrysophyte algae in a sediment core taken from a lake near a smelter at Sudbury is presented in **Figure 16.16**. That smelter operated between 1913 and 1972. It emitted large amounts of SO_2 to the atmosphere, which was deposited to local lakes and caused them

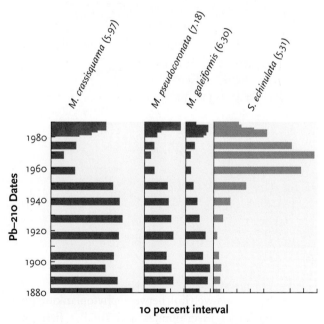

FIGURE 16.16 Acidification and Recovery Shown by a Profile of Fossil Algae Baby Lake is located near the Coniston smelter at Sudbury, Ontario, which began operation in 1913. The profile shows the acidification of this lake, as well as a recovery following the closing of the smelter in 1972. Only the four dominant chrysophyte species are shown, along with their abundance-weighted mean pH values shown in brackets. The three taxa at the left (coloured in blue) are characteristic of circumneutral waters, while the one on the right (coloured in orange) is common in acid lakes.

SOURCE: With kind permission from Springer Science+Business Media: Data from Dixit, A.S., Dixit, S.S. and Smol, J.P. (1992) "Algal microfossils provide high temporal resolution of environmental trends," *Water, Air, and Soil Pollution*, 62: 75–87.

to become severely acidic. The fossil-algal profile tracks the acidification of the lake through changes in four dominant chrysophytes in a sediment core, which was dated using the ^{210}Pb method (Dixit et al., 1992). The three taxa on the left are characteristic of circumneutral waters (pH ~6–7), while the one on the right is an indicator of acidic conditions. An obvious change in the algal community began in the 1940s, peaked around the time of closing of the smelter in 1972, and then declined somewhat afterward. The algal-inferred acidification indicates an initial pH of about 6.5 to a low of pH 4.2 around 1975. After the smelter closed there was a striking recovery of pH, as indicated by both pH measures and the return of the circumneutral taxa (Dixit et al., 1992).

Fish populations are greatly depleted or even absent from severely acidified lakes. The loss of fish is an ecological problem as well as one for recreational fisheries. Unfortunately, there is usually little or no information about the historical communities of acidic lakes that currently lack fish. Although fish scales and bones are sometimes preserved in sediment, they are often too rare to allow for a detailed paleoecological assessment. Instead, indirect ways have been developed to indicate historical fish populations.

One approach is to examine the remains of phantom-midges (*Chaoborus*), whose relatively big larvae are an important food of fish. There are five widespread species of *Chaoborus* in eastern North America and, of these, *C. americanus* is especially sensitive to mortality from planktivorous fish and so it does not coexist with them. Therefore, remains of *C. americanus* in a historical sediment layer are an indicator that the lake was fishless at that time. This is shown in the fossil *Chaoborus* profile for Swan Lake **(Figure 16.17)**, for which monitoring and

paleolimnological data show there was acidification caused by the deposition of SO_2 from nearby smelters in the Sudbury area. The lake is currently fishless, but the fossil *Chaoborus* analysis indicates that it lost its fish in the 1940s, because that is when *C. americanus* began to thrive (Uutala and Smol, 1996).

Paleolimnological studies have been carried out in various regions, and have been helpful in showing that widespread acidification has been caused by anthropogenic emissions of SO_2 and NO_x. These approaches have also been used to identify naturally acidic lakes, such as many in Nova Scotia that are influenced by organic acids leaching from bogs (Ginn et al., 2007). However, not all of the acidic lakes in that province are naturally acidic, and paleolimnological studies have also identified ones that are more recently acidified because of acid rain, such as several lakes in Kejimkujik National Park.

Such data are important from a lake-management perspective, because knowing the preindustrial conditions is critical to determining whether a restoration program might be justified. If a lake is naturally acidic, it would not be an appropriate candidate for a liming program to mitigate the effects of acid rain. Similarly, if a lake is shown to be naturally fishless, it should not be stocked with fish because its ecosystem is supporting communities that developed for millennia in their absence and so would be irretrievably damaged if fish were introduced.

Aquatic Osteoporosis: Calcium Declines in Lakes

Environmental stressors rarely occur in isolation—often, several anthropogenic influences occur simultaneously and they may synergistically interact to cause more serious damage to ecosystems. One such issue is that of calcium declines in softwater lakes, which have naturally dilute concentrations of ions and are common in regions of granitic bedrock, such on the Precambrian Shield.

Calcium is essential for all life forms, although species differ in their requirements for this nutrient. In humans and other animals, calcium deficiency may lead to bone disorders such as osteoporosis. Freshwater crustaceans also have a high demand for calcium to harden their chitinous exoskeleton. Laboratory and field-based studies have shown that if calcium availability declines below certain thresholds, larger zooplankton such as *Daphnia pulex* can no longer reproduce and become extirpated.

There are several potential causes of calcium declines in lakes. The ultimate source of calcium is the bedrock and soil in the watershed, and if there is much limestone ($CaCO_3$) or dolomite ($Ca,MgCO_3$), then there will be ample supplies of this nutrient. However, calcium-rich minerals and glacial debris are uncommon on most of the Precambrian Shield and other granitic regions.

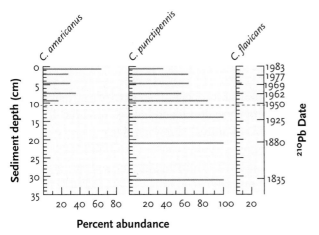

FIGURE 16.17 Changes in Phantom-Midge Fossils in a Dated Sediment Core Because *Chaoborus americanus* cannot coexist with fish, the profile indicates that Swan Lake became fishless in the 1940s as a result of acidifying deposition of SO_2 from smelters at nearby Sudbury.

SOURCE: Uutala, A.J. and J.P. Smol. 1996. "Paleolimnological reconstructions of long-term changes in fisheries status in Sudbury area lakes," *Canadian Journal of Fisheries and Aquatic Sciences*, 53: 174–180. © 2008 NRC Canada or its licensors. Reproduced with permission.

Nevertheless, for millennia even those calcium-depauperate regions had an adequate supply to satisfy the needs of dependent organisms, such as the large *Daphnia* species. More recently, however, the natural stocks of calcium have become depleted by anthropogenic influences, particularly by acidic precipitation and logging.

One of the environmental impacts of the acidification of soil is an increase of the solubilization of base cations (such as Ca^{2+} and Mg^{2+}) and their leaching out of the watershed. In the early stages of acidification, this may result in calcium levels increasing in surface waters, but once the catchment becomes depleted, the input to lakes declines and the concentrations may fall below the levels needed by some organisms.

The problem of calcium depletion can be made worse by logging of a watershed. Trees need large amounts of calcium—it occurs in especially high concentrations in their foliage and bark (see **Table 15.3** in Chapter 15). Therefore, if trees are harvested, calcium is being removed from the watershed. Although new trees and other vegetation will regrow in a logged area, they too need calcium, and will remove it from the soil. By combining the effects of acid rain and timber harvesting, we have an example of a multiple stressor, resulting in a cumulative effect on calcium declines.

But how widespread is the problem of calcium decline? We can survey a large number of lakes and show that their calcium levels are now dilute, but how do we know that this was not always so? Because long-term monitoring data are lacking, we must use a paleoecological approach. This involves examining long-term trends in biotic paleo-indicators known to have a high calcium requirement, such as *Daphnia* fossils, which have been shown to be declining in many softwater lakes **(Figure 16.18)**. This poses risks for species with a high calcium requirement, such as vertebrate animals, crustaceans such as crayfish and *Daphnia*, and mollusks such as snails and clams.

In addition, the calcium supply is closely tied to the amount of alkalinity present in a lake, which is the key component of the acid-neutralizing capacity (ANC) of waterbodies with a circumneutral pH. Once the ANC becomes exhausted, a lake or river rapidly acidifies (see also Chapter 4).

Eutrophication of Lakes: The Problem of Overfertilization

One of the most common problems of freshwater ecosystems is caused by overfertilization with nutrients, which leads to excessive productivity or *eutrophication* (see Environmental Applications 2.1). The productivity of most temperate lakes, such as those in Canada, is primarily limited by the supply of phosphorus (occurring as phosphate, PO_4^{-3}), with other nutrients such as nitrogen (usually as nitrate, NO_3^-) being of secondary importance. The

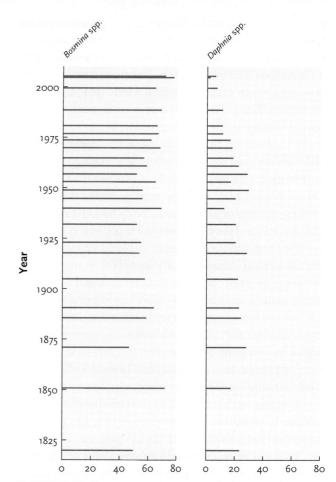

FIGURE 16.18 Changes in Dominant Zooplankton Fossils since the Early 1800s Large *Daphnia* species, which are often keystone zooplankton in many lakes, have a higher calcium requirement than the smaller *Bosmina* crustaceans. Plastic Lake has not yet acidified, but water-quality measurements dating to the 1970s show that its calcium levels have been steadily dropping. The decline in the abundance of *Daphnia* fossils matches that of lakewater calcium concentration.

SOURCE: Jeziorski, A., N.D. Yan, A.M. Paterson, A.M. DeSellas, M.A. Turner, D.S. Jeffries, W. Keller, R.C. Weeber, R.C. McNicol, M.E. Palmer, K. McIver, K. Arseneau, B.K. Ginn, B.F. Cumming, and J.P. Smol. 2008. "The widespread threat of calcium decline in fresh waters," *Science*, 322: 1374–1377.

most common anthropogenic sources of nutrient loading are runoff of agricultural and horticultural fertilizer and the dumping of untreated sewage of livestock and people.

Phosphorus loading causes eutrophication by stimulating the growth of phytoplankton and larger aquatic plants (or macrophytes). To a certain point, increased primary productivity may be desirable, but if excessive it causes serious ecological, aesthetic, and economic problems. Large increases of algal biomass, known as blooms, can result in foul-tasting and smelly water that is unsuited for drinking or recreation. When the organic matter sinks to the bottom of the lake and decomposes, it can deplete the oxygen supply, killing fish and other animals.

Paleoecology has played a key role in studies of the history of eutrophication in lakes. Various algal groups, such as diatoms, have been studied to develop transfer functions that allow past lakewater phosphorus concentrations to be inferred, using comparable approaches to those described for work on acidification. These ecological reconstructions have also provided insights into the resistance of freshwater ecosystems—the amount of stress they can tolerate before environmental problems become evident.

For example, the major changes in diatom communities over the past three centuries were studied in a dated sediment core from Gravenhurst Bay in southern Ontario (**Figure 16.19**). The diatom-inferred total phosphorus concentrations show that eutrophication of this bay began in the mid-19th century, and that it has recently recovered as a result of sewage treatment and other mitigations to reduce nutrient inputs to Lake Muskoka.

Increased nutrient loading has additional ecological repercussions, including declines in deepwater oxygen concentrations, which can have serious negative implications for fish and other biota. Algal indicators are not useful in reconstructing oxygen in deeper waters, but certain benthic insects, such as chironomid larvae, do have varying tolerances to oxygen concentration. For instance, some *Chironomus* species can tolerate anoxic conditions (these are called bloodworms due to their red-coloured hemoglobin that binds oxygen), whereas *Heterotrissocladius* species require much higher O$_2$ levels (Brodersen et al., 2004). Information like this, collected from many lakes, allows a transfer function to be developed that infers historical oxygen levels on the basis of fossil head-capsules of chironomid species found in dated layers of sediment.

For example, based on chironomid fossils in a core from Gravenhurst Bay, researchers found that deepwater O$_2$ concentrations dropped rapidly with the advent of cultural eutrophication. Unlike the recovery observed in the diatom assemblage of the surface waters following reduced nutrient inputs, the deepwater O$_2$ concentrations did not quickly recover to their pre-eutrophication levels (Little et al., 2000).

Reconstructing Long-Term Trends in Pacific Salmon

Nutrient enrichment is often associated with human activities, such as sewage dumping and agricultural runoff. However, there are also natural sources of nitrogen and phosphorus that may elevate nutrient concentrations in lakes and rivers. For example, certain migratory animals, such as Pacific salmon (*Onchorhynchus* species), act as "nutrient pumps" to increase the fertility of aquatic and terrestrial ecosystems and thereby enrich their productivity (**Figure 16.20**). In fact, for some west-coast lakes, over 50 percent of the entire nutrient budget comes from decaying salmon carcasses (Finney et al., 2000) (**Figure 16.21**).

In some regions, stocks of these fish are apparently declining because of overfishing, habitat destruction, water pollution, and perhaps climate change (which itself may now be mostly anthropogenic) (see Chapter 15). A historical context for these changes is needed in order to fully understand their causes and consequences, in both ecological and economic terms (Lotze and Worm, 2009).

Paleoecologists have studied these phenomena in several ways. Although salmon fossils, such as bones and scales, are rare in lake sediment, other proxies can be used to reconstruct their past abundances. Because salmon are predators in the marine food web, they accumulate a

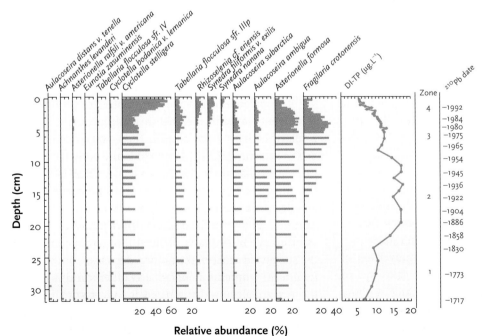

FIGURE 16.19 Changes in Diatom Communities That Indicate Eutrophication The data cover the past three centuries and are inferred from a dated sediment core from Gravenhurst Bay, an embayment of Lake Muskoka, Ontario. The data indicate the original diatom assemblages before cultural eutrophication (Zone 1), during the period of nutrient inputs by sewage and other sources (Zone 2), and recovery following mitigation efforts (Zones 3 and 4). The diatom-inferred total phosphorus concentration (DI-TP) is shown to the right.

SOURCE: Little, J., R. Hall, R., R. Quinlan, and J.P. Smol. 2000. "Past trophic status and hypolimnetic anoxia during eutrophication and remediation of Gravenhurst Bay, Ontario: Comparison of diatoms, chironomids, and historical records," *Canadian Journal of Fisheries and Aquatic Sciences*, 57, 333–341. © 2008 NRC Canada or its licensors. Reproduced with permission.

Keith Douglas/First Light

FIGURE 16.20 Sockeye Salmon (*Oncorhynchus nerka*) Spawn in Freshwater Streams Juvenile fish migrate to the ocean, where they feed and grow for several years. When they are mature, the fish migrate back to their natal stream to spawn, completing their life cycle. In addition, their return migration results in a large "biopumping" of oceanic nutrients to the headwaters of streams and adjacent forested habitat, which enriches their productivity (see also Chapter 15).

Irene Gregory-Eaves, McGill University

FIGURE 16.21 Carcasses of Sockeye Salmon along the Adams River of British Columbia After spawning, the adults die and the nutrients present in their abundant carcasses can significantly fertilize the nursery streams and lakes.

relatively high proportion of a heavy nitrogen isotope, ^{15}N, in their body relative to the more abundant and lighter ^{14}N. This "heavier" nitrogen signal is expressed as a ratio of ^{15}N/^{14}N, or its notation δ^{15}N. This signal is transported in the bodies of migrating salmon to their natal breeding habitat, where they spawn. The fish die soon after spawning, releasing the heavier δ^{15}N into the nursery habitat, where it becomes incorporated into the sedimentary record and can be measured in dated cores to obtain an indication of the size of historical salmon returns. In addition, diatom species composition in dated sediment profiles can be used to infer changes in marine-derived nutrients, and so also track historical salmon returns.

These methods have been used to study runs of sockeye salmon at a lake in Alaska. This lake was of interest because there is a record of fish catches going back to the late 1800s, as well as data on escapement (i.e., the numbers of salmon that reached the nursery lake)

dating back to the early 1900s. Those longer-term data are critical for evaluating the reliability of paleoecological tools. The δ^{15}N in dated lake sediment clearly drops after commercial fishers began to harvest the salmon **(Figure 16.22)**. This pattern was also reflected by increases in diatom species that indicate lower nutrient concentrations, such as *Cyclotella pseudostelligera*, while those indicative of more fertile waters decline (such as *Stephanodiscus* species and *Fragilaria crotonensis*). For the period of concurrent records, the paleoecological data match the known catch and escapement data for the lake.

The paleo-inferred indicators of returning salmon fluctuated markedly even before commercial fishing was a major activity. For example, there were decreases in sedimentary δ^{15}N in the early 1800s and early 1700s, with associated changes in the species composition of diatoms that indicate lowering nutrient concentrations due to smaller fish runs. These observations indicate that salmon had previously declined markedly, even without interference by humans. Natural changes in climate are the suspected cause of the natural decreases, but since no long-term temperature data are available for this region, the researchers used the paleoclimatic record inferred from local tree-ring analyses to examine this idea. In fact, the data showed that the periods of natural salmon

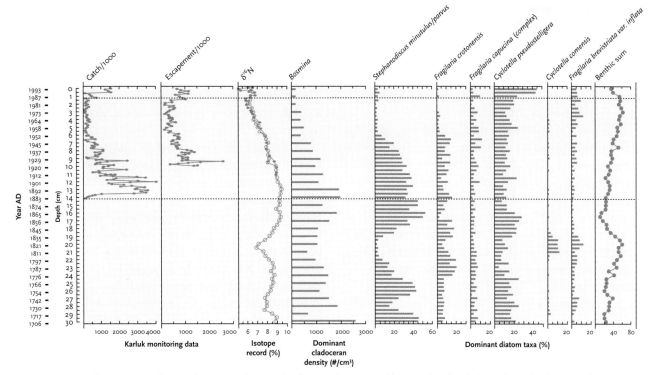

FIGURE 16.22 Changes in Sockeye Salmon Populations The figures show several historical and paleolimnological indicators of the abundance of sockeye salmon in Karluk Lake on Kodiak Island, Alaska, over the past three centuries. The routine collection of data on the commercial fishery began in 1882 and is shown to the left, as are escapement data since 1921 for migrating fish that reached the lake. The sediment-derived $\delta^{15}N$ data and relative abundances of certain prominent diatom species are also presented.

SOURCE: Finney, B.P., I. Gregory-Eaves, J. Sweetman, M.D. Douglas, and J.P. Smol. 2000. "Impacts of climatic change and fishing on Pacific salmon abundance over the past 300 years," *Science*, 290 795–799.

declines coincided with those of narrower tree-rings indicative of a cooler climate. These various observations have helped us to better understand environmental influences on salmon populations and ecological consequences of their declines.

Historical and Modern Climate Change

Climate varies according to a variety of natural cycles, and paleoecology has played a role in describing and studying those changes, especially the causes and magnitude of natural variability. However, as described more fully in Section 3.5, humans are undertaking large but unintentional modifications of the global climate system through large and accelerating releases of greenhouse gases to the atmosphere, particularly carbon dioxide from fossil-fuel combustion and deforestation. To place recent climate change into an appropriate context, data on longer-term changes are required.

Among the best environmental time series we have available are those for temperature and other climatic variables, such as precipitation. However, those data cover too short a period of time to provide insight into some important questions. Given that Daniel G. Fahrenheit (1686–1735) and Anders Celsius (1701–1744) did not develop their temperature scales until the 18th century, it should be no surprise that only a few reliable

records date back even to the 1700s. In Canada, only a few temperature data extend to the 19th century, and for most regions there are only short time series available.

However, climate exerts a strong influence on the distribution and abundances of species, including many whose fragments are preserved in sedimentary profiles. By knowing the ecological optima of those organisms, including the influences of climatic factors, paleoecologists can reconstruct past climatic conditions. Some of the inferences are direct, meaning the data for certain species are closely linked to particular climatic factors, such as temperature. In most cases, however, the species are related to environmental variables that are indirectly linked to climate.

In this section we will explore two such applications: (1) reconstruction of the historical frequency of droughts in the prairie region using the salinity optima of aquatic biota, and (2) tracking changes in lake-ice cover in the Arctic.

Drought in the Prairies

The prairie regions of Canada and the adjacent United States are the "bread baskets" of North America, and are major exporters of grain to other countries. However, periodic droughts in the prairies have had devastating effects on agriculture. To better understand this phenomenon and its consequences, we need to determine the historical frequency of drought so that recent conditions can be placed within a context of natural variation. Although it may seem counterintuitive to use lakes to track changes in drought on land, decreased precipitation and increased evaporation result in many changes in waterbodies. These are often expressed together, as a ratio of precipitation to evaporation, or P:E.

Lakes with a closed basin (i.e., with no inlet or outlet streams) and a small watershed are especially sensitive to changes in P:E. The effects of drought on such lakes are comparable to leaving a pot of soup on a stove at low heat—if you return to the soup every 15 minutes or so, you will notice two things: (1) as some of the water evaporates, the height of liquid in the pot decreases; and (2) if you taste the soup at intervals, you will notice it getting saltier because water is being lost and leaving dissolved substances behind.

Similar changes occur in a closed-basin lake when the P:E declines—the surface level drops and salinity increases **(Figure 16.23)**. Both of these changes are closely tracked by a variety of aquatic species that leave fossils in lake sediment. For example, certain diatoms are adapted to living in shallow water, while others occur in deeper conditions; species also vary in their tolerance of salinity. Therefore, we might expect a shift to shallow-water and salt-tolerant species as lake levels decrease and salinity increases.

One such paleolimnological study of a prairie lake identified diatom taxa in a dated sediment core, and reconstructed lakewater salinity in 10-year intervals going back about 2400 years **(Figure 16.24)**. This research used transfer functions developed using methods similar to those described earlier for acid-rain studies, but focusing on salinity optima. Past events of high salinity indicate a decrease in P:E caused by drought, while lower salinity indicates wetter and/or cooler conditions. The persistent drought of the 1930s—these are known as the "dust-bowl years"—is clearly evident in the diagram. What is most

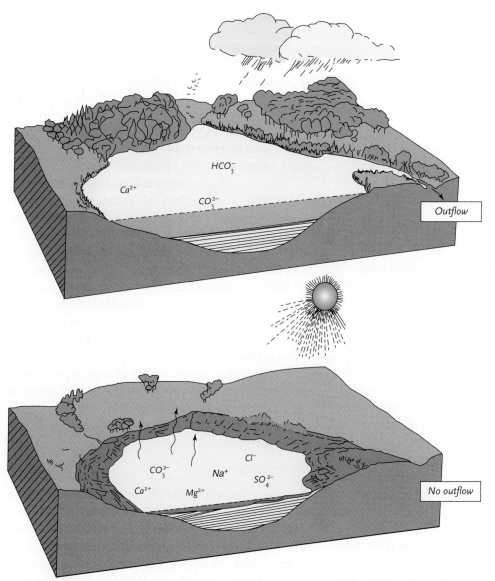

FIGURE 16.23 Changes in a Closed-Basin Lake with Shifts in Precipitation (P) and Evaporation (E) The upper diagram summarizes lake conditions during relatively wet periods, when P:E is higher and as a result lake levels are high and salinity is low. The lower diagram shows the same lake under drought conditions, when P:E decreases so that the water level is lower and salinity higher. Species of diatoms and other aquatic organisms track these environmental changes, and their fossil remains can be used to reconstruct a chronology of historical changes that are due to periods of drought.

SOURCE: Smol, J.P. and B.F. Cumming, B.F. 2000. "Tracking long-term changes in climate using algal indicators in lake sediments," *Journal of Phycology*, 36: 986–1011, John Wiley and Sons.

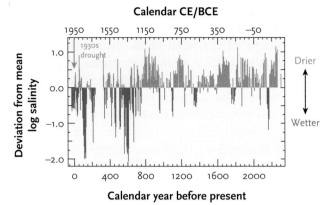

Calendar CE/BCE

FIGURE 16.24 Reconstruction of Past Salinity of a Prairie Lake
The data are based on fossil diatoms recovered from a dated lake sediment core taken from Moon Lake, North Dakota. A diatom-based transfer function was used to reconstruct past lakewater salinity, based on the species composition of diatom assemblages preserved in the surface (modern) sediments from a variety of prairie lakes. The mean diatom-inferred salinity for the profile is shown as 0.0. Positive deviations from the mean salinity are shown in orange and indicate saltier conditions associated with drought. Negative deviations are in blue and indicate wetter conditions. The 1930s drought is clearly discernible, but it is dwarfed by droughts that occurred in the past, such as the pronounced increases in diatom-inferred salinity around 800 years ago.

SOURCE: Based on data from Laird, K.R., S.C. Fritz, K.A. Maasch, and B.F. Cumming. 1996. "Greater drought intensity and frequency before AD 1200 in the Northern Great Plains, USA," *Nature*, 384: 552–555.

striking, however, is that some droughts over the past two millennia were more intense and of longer duration than those of the most recent century, suggesting that this prairie region is naturally prone to severe droughts.

This study provides a sober warning about our perhaps optimistic view on the agricultural capability of this vital grain-growing region. It appears that when European settlers first arrived in the prairies, the region was experiencing an unusually "moist" climate, based on the data for Moon Lake. However, the salinity reconstruction suggests that for large periods in the past, the region would not have been able to sustain agriculture because of widespread and persistent droughts. Given that one of the most common predictions of recent climate models for this region is for an increased frequency of drought, this does not bode well for the security of high levels of agricultural production in the prairies.

Climate Change in the Arctic

Polar regions are especially sensitive to climatic change because of a variety of positive feedback mechanisms, many of which are related to the surface albedo (or reflectivity). If you were to approach two parked cars on a hot sunny day, one that is white (i.e., high albedo) and one black (low albedo), and put your hand on each, you would find that they differ markedly in temperature. The black car would be hotter because it has absorbed much more of the incoming solar radiation, and the white one cooler because it is more reflective.

The Arctic, with its extensive areas of snow and ice for much of the year, also has a relatively high albedo and much of the incoming solar radiation is reflected rather than absorbed. However, with the climate warming, the time during which the surface of land and ocean is covered by reflective snow and ice is greatly lessened, thus decreasing the regional albedo. The lower albedo results in more heating, and therefore more melting of the ice and snow, thus further reducing the albedo. This process is a positive feedback system that accelerates a warming climate.

Because of its climate sensitivity, regions such as the Canadian Arctic can be considered to be like "miner's canaries" of the planet, in the sense that they are expected to respond relatively early and at a strong intensity to climate change. Because about half of Canada's landmass is in the Arctic, it is important that we know how climate change is affecting its ecosystems. Unfortunately, long-term monitoring records of the surface temperature are sparse from polar regions, and so paleoecological approaches are critical for defining the historical magnitudes of climate change in that region.

Because most of the Arctic is well north of treeline, there is little potential to use dendrochronology, although some paleoclimatic records have been extracted from the wood of low-growing arctic willow (*Salix arctica*) and a few other long-lived plant species. A more important source of paleoenvironmental data is from ice cores taken from glaciers on Greenland and several Arctic islands, as well as in high-alpine areas. As useful as these ice-core data are, we will not discuss them in detail here because our theme is ecology, and not just environmental reconstruction. Rather, we will focus on aquatic sediment, because lakes and ponds are abundant in the Arctic and they yield information on both environmental and ecological changes.

Changes in ice and snow cover are often overriding factors affecting the limnological conditions of Arctic lakes. Under very cold conditions, a polar lake may be covered by ice and snow for all but a few weeks of the year. In fact, some of the deepest lakes may have floating ice throughout the summer, with only a moat of ice-free water near the shore **(Figure 16.25)**. Because algae, mosses, and vascular plants are photosynthetic, they require light, and under these conditions only taxa adapted to shallow-water conditions and an ephemeral ice-free littoral zone will thrive. However, if the climate warms, more of the ice cover will melt, so there will be additional open-water habitat for photosynthetic organisms, and eventually the lake may become ice-free for an extended period during the summer. These changes will be reflected in the kinds of organisms that the lake can support.

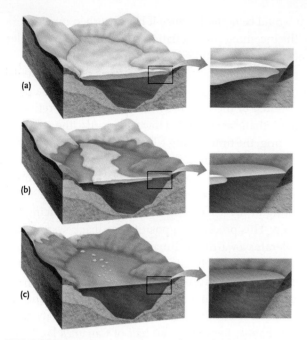

FIGURE 16.25 Indicators of Climate Change The figures show effects of climate-related changes in ice and snow cover on limnological properties of Arctic and alpine lakes, and on their dominant organisms. This schematic model shows changing ice and snow conditions on a polar lake during (a) relatively cold, (b) moderate, and (c) and warm conditions. During colder years, a permanent raft of ice and snow may persist throughout the short summer, precluding the development of large populations of open-water phytoplankton and restricting much of the primary production to a shallow open-water moat along the shore. With warmer conditions, more of the lake becomes available for algal and plant growth.

SOURCE: Based on Smol, J.P. 1988. "Paleoclimate proxy data from freshwater arctic diatoms," *Verhandlungen der Internationale Vereinigung von Limnologie*, 23: 837–844.

In much of the Arctic the most frequent kind of standing water is shallow ponds, which are more sensitive bellwethers of climatic change than deeper lakes. Even small changes in temperature will affect the ice-free period of shallow ponds, and hence the length of their growing season for primary producers. These changes are reflected in the composition of diatom communities and other indicators, which paleolimnologists can use to reconstruct trends in climate. Because of their small volume, shallow ponds are also more greatly affected by changes in the P:E ratio.

A study of dominant diatom species in sediments of a pond on Ellesmere Island found a greater diversity of shallow-water diatoms in the more recent sediments. The species thriving in the more recent sediments are typically found living on mosses and other complex substrates, which were replacing other diatom taxa that are characteristic of unvegetated environments, indicating that ice-free conditions were becoming more extended as the climate warmed **(Figure 16.26a)**. For comparison, a much deeper lake further south in the mainland

Northwest Territories also had a profile that indicates recent warming, but the species changes are expressed by variations of the open-water phytoplankton community rather than a littoral one **(Figure 16.26b)**. The marked increase in *Cyclotella* suggests longer ice-free conditions in the deepwater lake, and possibly an increased depth of thermal stratification.

Paleolimnological assessments can also be used to study indirect effects of climate change, such as the flooding of terrestrial ecosystems by marine storm surges (see Ecology in Depth 16.4).

These studies illustrate how ecological information preserved in lake and pond sediments can be used to track past changes in climate. There are additional approaches that can be used, such as tree-ring and pollen analysis, which we discussed earlier in this chapter. Furthermore, the chitinous mouth parts of chironomid insects are frequently used as paleoclimatic indicators,

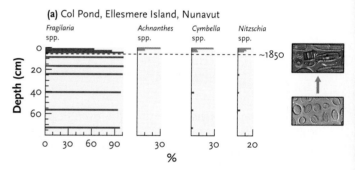

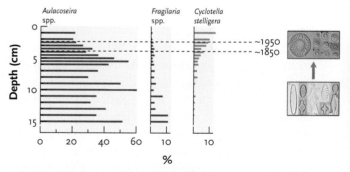

FIGURE 16.26 Climate-Related Changes in Diatoms in Two Waterbodies in the Arctic (a) Changes in dominant species of diatoms in a sediment core representing the past few millennia in Col Pond, Ellesmere Island, Nunavut. The figure highlights the marked changes occurring in post-1850 sediment, which indicate decreased ice cover and other effects related to climate warming; (b) changes in diatoms in a sediment core from much deeper Slipper Lake, located on the mainland of the Northwest Territories, highlighting the marked increase in *Cyclotella* diatoms in recent sediment, which indicates decreased ice cover and possibly increased thermal stratification with recent warming. Approximate dates are shown to the right of the profiles.

SOURCE: Used with permission of Ecological Society of America, from Smol, J.P. and M.S.V. Douglas. 2007. "From controversy to consensus: Making the case for recent climatic change in the Arctic using lake sediments," *Frontiers in Ecology and the Environment*, 5(9): 466–474; permission conveyed through Copyright Clearance Center, Inc.

Traditional Ecological Knowledge (TEK) Meets Paleoecology: The Impacts of a Major Storm Surge on Coastal Ecosystems of the Mackenzie River Delta

A storm surge occurs when strong winds cause oceanic water to build up, move toward land, and then flood low-lying areas. These events are especially severe if the timing of the windstorm coincides with that of a twice-daily high tide. Storm surges can damage coastal ecosystems and urban and industrial infrastructure. Due to the combined effects of climate change (e.g., sea-level rise, increased frequency of major storms, decreased sea ice cover), storm surges are expected to increase in frequency at high latitudes, such as the Arctic. However, because we have few historical records of storm surges in polar regions, how do we know if they are increasing in magnitude and frequency? Paleoecology can provide some answers.

The Mackenzie Delta, which is on the coast of the Beaufort Sea, is the largest delta system in Canada. The area is of ecological, cultural, and economic importance to the Inuvialuit and to economic interests related to the exploration and extraction of fossil fuels. Therefore, understanding the magnitude and frequency of storm-surge events is important for assessing environmental change and planning for potential economic development.

A partnership of university and government scientists and hunter-and-trapper committees of the Mackenzie Delta region has been examining the effects of a recent storm surge that flooded marine water onto more than 130 km² of the outer delta, as well as the historical occurrence of such events

(Pisaric et al., 2011; Kokelj et al., 2012). This project combined the methodologies and knowledge of dendrochronology, paleolimnology, and traditional ecological knowledge (TEK). It developed from a workshop in which Inuvialuit land users had identified major landscape impacts from a massive storm surge that occurred in September 1999.

For two days, sustained winds of >60 km/hr (with gusts to 80 km/hr) resulted in a surge of marine water greater than 2 m in height that inundated low-lying terrain up to 20 km inland from the coast of the Beaufort Sea. That extensive inundation of seawater killed much of the affected vegetation and resulted in an extensive "dead zone" that represented the extent of the saltwater intrusion **(Figure 1)**.

Dead zone impacted by inundation of saline water

Unaffected zone beyond limit of salt water inundation

Joshua Thienpont

FIGURE 1 A Storm Surge In 1999, a major windstorm caused a storm surge to occur and the resulting intrusion of marine water resulted in widespread death of vegetation (the brown area) across the outer reaches of the northwestern Mackenzie Delta. Even 10 years later in this image, little recovery had occurred.

(Continued)

Based on the knowledge of the region held by the local Inuvialuit, the effects of that 1999 storm surge were unprecedented within traditional memory.

Paleoecology provided a second avenue for tracking historical storm surges, in addition to the information provided by the traditional knowledge of local residents. There are about 25 000 lakes in the Mackenzie Delta region, many of which are in the impacted zone. Analyses of water chemistry revealed that those lakes still had elevated salinity a decade after the storm surge. Because diatoms and other aquatic organisms often have strict tolerances of salinity, analyses of sediment cores from within the marine intrusion zone would likely archive a signal of the 1999 storm surge as an increase in salt-tolerant species.

As is shown in the diatom profile from an affected lake, the 1999 storm surge did have a marked effect on lake ecology **(Figure 2)**. Because no other significant marine incursions were noted in the more than 1000 years of sediment accumulation in that lake core, the 1999 event was unprecedented at that time scale. A "reference" lake sampled just outside the marine intrusion zone showed no recent increase in salt-tolerant diatoms.

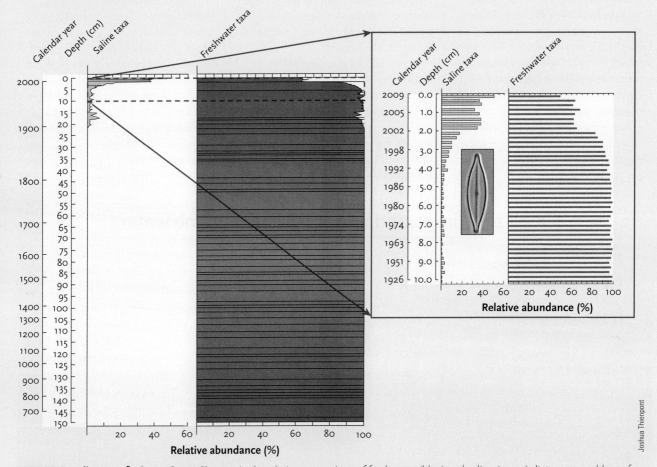

FIGURE 2 Indicators of a Storm Surge Changes in the relative proportions of freshwater (blue) and saline (green) diatom assemblages from a core of lake sediment taken from the marine-inundated "dead zone" of the Mackenzie Delta show that the 1999 flooding was unprecedented. Left: a profile extending to about 700 AD. Right: a detailed profile of the more recent sediments, with an example of a salt-tolerant diatom.

SOURCE: Based on data from Pisaric, M.F.J., Thienpont, J.R., Kokelj, S.V., Nesbitt, H., Lantz, T.C., Solomon, S., and Smol, J.P. 2011. "Impacts of a recent storm surge on an Arctic delta ecosystem examined in the context of the last millennium," *Proceedings of the National Academy of Sciences*, 108: 8960–8965.

with many Canadian examples. In fact, this method was developed in eastern Canada (Walker et al., 1991) and then became extensively used elsewhere to provide important climatic perspectives, such as in the Maritimes (e.g., Walker and Cwynar, 2006). Given the continuing debate and concerns related to climate change, and whether it is being caused by anthropogenic influences, paleoclimatic studies have an important role to play in these scientific, social, and political discussions.

Paleoecology and Environmental Issues

We live in a constantly changing environment. Some of the changes are natural, but others are clearly linked to human activities. Without long-term monitoring data, we cannot place the environmental changes into an appropriate context. Advances in paleoecological approaches during the past several decades are helping to resolve this difficulty, and they are now being integrated into many environmental and ecological assessments. The most reliable paleoecological assessments are based on multi-proxy approaches that use a variety of evidence to reach defensible conclusions.

This chapter has provided a sampling of approaches and applications used in paleoecology, although other sections of this book touch on relevant issues and methodologies (such as Chapter 10, which examines the history of insect irruptions and postglacial succession, and Chapter 14, which deals with the overkill hypothesis of megafaunal extinctions at the end of the Pleistocene).

Additional paleoenvironmental methods include the use of chemical approaches to track past contaminant levels (such as those of DDT and mercury) in sediment cores and museum specimens of birds. Novel molecular approaches are also being used, such as the sampling of ancient DNA. With the increasing prominence of environmental and ecological problems, there has never been a more pressing need for these types of long-term data, and so we can expect to see continuing advances in paleoecology.

CHAPTER SUMMARY

(LO 16.1)

- Paleoecology deals with populations, communities, and ecosystems that existed in the past. Paleoecologists examine biomass and fossils of long-ago biota in dated samples of the environment (such as lake or oceanic sediment), and relate these to past environmental conditions, such as in climate or acidity. An additional technique is to examine indicators of past growth rates, such as is revealed by historical patterns of tree-ring widths.

(LO 16.2)

- One of the biggest challenges faced in the ecological and environmental sciences is the lack of reliable long-term monitoring data. Such data are critical for establishing background or reference (i.e., pre-impact) conditions, and for determining the trajectories of ecosystem changes in response to natural and anthropogenic stressors. Paleoecological approaches are useful in providing this kind of information, and in showing how populations, communities, and ecosystems have changed over time.

(LO 16.3)

- Dendrochrology uses the size, density, and other characteristics (e.g., chemical and isotopic composition) of annual growth rings on trees to reconstruct paleoecological information. Much of this work has focused on climatic reconstructions, because tree growth is often closely linked to variables such as temperature and precipitation.

(LO 16.4)

- Lake sediments slowly accumulate over time and so a depth-time profile steadily accumulates. Sediments include two

sources of paleoecological indicators: (1) allochthonous ones from outside the lake, such as charcoal deposits and pollen and spores of terrestrial plants, and (2) autochthonous material from within the lake itself, such as algal remains and chemical precipitates. Paleolimnologists can use this information from dated sediment cores to reconstruct past ecological and environmental conditions. Multiproxy approaches are especially useful, because inferred trends can be confirmed using a number of independent indicators.

(LO 16.5)

- Paleoecologists have played critical roles in a number of environmental debates. For example, especially in the 1980s and early 1990s, there was much controversy as to whether currently acidic lakes were naturally so or had been acidified due to anthropogenic influences. By using diatom-based pH inferences from dated sediment cores, as well as other indicators, paleolimnologists could show that many lakes had acidified because of exposure to atmospheric influences. Similarly, work on paleoclimatology has been used to show that recent climatic changes can be linked to increased concentrations of greenhouse gases.

(LO 16.6)

- An important consideration in all ecological studies is to appreciate the complexities of the effects of multiple stressors on ecosystems. Typically, several environmental stressors are acting simultaneously on an ecosystem. For example, the combined effects of acidic deposition and logging have exacerbated the recently described problem of calcium depletion on softwater lakes and soils.

QUESTIONS FOR REVIEW AND DISCUSSION

1. Explain the principle of uniformitarianism, and discuss some of its limitations.
2. Provide examples of multiple stressors, and explain how climate warming might exacerbate some of those problems.
3. A major research area in paleoecology is the reconstruction of climate change using proxy data from lake sediment. Describe other environmental changes that were not covered in this chapter that you might be able to track using indicators extracted from lake sediment.

Ecology and Society

LEARNING OBJECTIVES

After studying this chapter you should be able to:

1. Explain why the knowledge of ecology influences our understanding of sustainability and guides the process of sustainable development.

2. Define ecological integrity and explain its key indicators.

3. Describe the importance of monitoring and research in understanding the causes and consequences of changes in environmental quality.

4. Explain the process of environmental impact assessment as it is practised in Canada.

5. Understand how ecologists play a vital role in advising and managing key aspects of sustainable development in Canada.

17.1 Ecology and Sustainability

Ecology is a vital scientific discipline. There are two reasons why this is true:

1. The knowledge of ecology is essential to understanding the existence and evolution of life, and the ways that organisms have spontaneously organized into ecosystems that occur at various hierarchical levels, the largest of which is the biosphere.

2. The wisdom of ecology is indispensable to guiding the development of the human economy along an ecologically sustainable pathway that can forever provide people with a superior quality of life, while also sustaining the global biodiversity of species and natural ecosystems.

Ecologists seek to contribute knowledge that is relevant to both of these kinds of values. They do this primarily by engaging in fundamental and applied research.

Fundamental Research

Like many scientists, individual ecologists became interested in their profession because they have a deep and abiding interest in "big questions" about existence and life. They have a curiosity about the natural world—how it came to be present, and how it is organized and

functions. These are primary, existential questions, and scientific work that is designed to investigate them is known as **fundamental research** (sometimes referred to as basic or curiosity-driven research). All ecologists have devoted their professional lives to improving our understanding of the natural world, and they typically pursue their work with energy and determination.

Because of the nature of the subject area, ecologists are interested in research that investigates the influence of environmental factors on the distribution and abundance of free-living organisms and their self-organizing populations, communities, and ecoscapes. This research is of great intrinsic worth because it helps us to understand the natural world, while also providing vital insight into the station and role of our own species. From this perspective, it is difficult to understand how some people might not view fundamental research, and the knowledge it provides, as being worthwhile.

Remarkably, however, many people do hold such a view—that curiosity-driven research is not as valuable as work that is directly intended to solve a practical problem (the latter is **applied research**, which we examine in the next section). Some of the people who feel this way are highly influential in society—they include many politicians, senior bureaucrats in government, businesspeople, and religious leaders. The reasons for their attitude about fundamental research are varied and complex, but the most crucial one is a deeply held belief in the necessity of being engaged in practical work that directly contributes to solving real-world problems. It is also not helpful that some religious people hold faith-based opinions about creation and evolution that disagree with those of biologists and most other scientists, and that are often the basis of hypotheses that they investigate in fundamental research.

The most important reason why critics of fundamental research are in error (outside of discussions about evolution) is that they do not understand or acknowledge the many cases in which insights gained from pure scientific investigations have indirectly resulted in important applied advances. This includes notable discoveries in fields ranging from genetics to medical biology to engineering and technology. There are legions of examples that demonstrate this fact, including several with Canadian storylines:

- the discovery in 1921 by Frederick Banting (1891–1941) and Charles Best (1899–1978) of the University of Toronto that insulin can be used to treat diabetes, a disease that previously was almost incurable; the lives of millions of diabetics have been saved by this research, which originated with fundamental studies in animal physiology;
- the invention of the Java programming language in 1991 by James Gosling, a Canadian who created the original design of the system and implemented an enabling compiler and other technology; the work originated with theoretical approaches to computer science; and
- the discovery in the 1960s by David Schindler and colleagues that phosphate is the usual limiting factor for the productivity of freshwaters; this allowed the problem of eutrophication of lakes and rivers to be tackled by removing phosphorus from detergent and by treating sewage to reduce its nutrient content before the effluent is discharged to the environment; the key research began as studies of nutrient cycling in oligotrophic lakes in northwestern Ontario (see Environmental Applications 2.1 and A Canadian Ecologist 17.1).

Applied Research

It is important to understand that most ecologists today are not only fascinated by fundamental research—also interested in applied work, which contributes to the resolution of environmental problems that pose clear and present dangers to two vital goals: (1) the sustainability of the human economy, and (2) the continued viability of biodiversity, including natural ecosystems. Within that context, applied ecological research involves extremely big questions—ones about the meaning and limits of sustainability (Section 1.2 and Chapter 15).

Of course, ecological knowledge derived from research is also important at a finer level. It can be applied to practical, everyday issues that are related to our need to have the necessities and amenities of life. These issues include the production and management of resources that are required as foods, materials, and energy, as well as for the ways that we design our urban and industrialized land uses, and also for the aesthetics of pleasure and satisfaction. In this sense, the applied wisdom of ecology is vital to solving important problems related to the quality and sustainable use of natural resources, including bioresources associated with agricultural production, forests, fisheries, and hunted wildlife. It is also vital to understanding the causes and consequences of pollution (**Figure 17.1**). Of all the ways of knowing, ecology has the most to contribute to the vital societal objective of ecological sustainability.

Moreover, applied ecological knowledge is crucial to the conservation of Earth's biodiversity. This includes actions to implement networks of protected areas, and to appropriately steward them so their natural values do not become degraded over time (see Section 14.5). Applied ecological knowledge is also needed to develop management systems that will sustain more of native biodiversity on landscapes and seascapes that are "working" to directly support the human economy—the places where we engage in agriculture, forestry, fisheries, and other kinds of resource management.

It is obvious that applied research in ecology is important and vital to sustainable development. However, fundamental research also plays a key role in our society. The purview of science is not just to assist the human economy by discovering superior technologies related to materials, energy, and the handling of information. Science also plays a special role in improving our fundamental understanding of how and why the natural world exists and functions, and in providing context for humans within that magnificent and unique realm. Curiosity-driven research in ecology helps us to understand those imperative questions, in ways that the more narrowly focused endeavours of applied work cannot.

Ecology and Sustainability

In Chapter 15 we examined ideas about sustainable development, which refers to progress being made toward a human economy that can run forever because it is ultimately founded on the wise use of renewable resources. We also examined the even higher altitude idea of ecologically sustainable development, which includes but goes beyond resource sustainability for humans to include the vital need to maintain biodiversity and ecological services at viable abundances.

Within this context of sustainability, the knowledge of ecology is crucial to setting limits to growth of the human economy, and to finding accommodations for the

FIGURE 17.1 Natural Pollution An aerial view of plumes rich in sulphur dioxide at the Smoking Hills, Northwest Territories. The plumes originate in smouldering beds of bituminous shale, which have spontaneously ignited, so the pollution is "natural" rather than anthropogenic. Studies of the resulting ecological changes at the Smoking Hills are of fundamental value because they allow us to better understand how the pollution-related stressors affect the structure and function of natural ecosystems. In addition, the research is of applied use because it helps us to understand the potential effects of comparable anthropogenic pollution, such as that associated with releases of sulphur dioxide from smelters, oil-sand processing facilities, and coal-fired power plants.

genuine rights of coexistence of other species and natural ecosystems. Clearly, if the recommendations of ecologists and other environmental specialists are not heeded with respect to ecologically sustainable development, then the bitter alternative must be nonsustainability—which is not acceptable for many obvious reasons.

The human enterprise is currently on a nonsustainability trajectory. Simply put, the core evidence of this fact is the following (see Chapter 15 for details):

- *Population:* The human population is unprecedentedly large (about 7.1 billion in 2013), and it continues to increase (by 1.14 percent per year; UNPF, 2012); the abundances of our mutualist species are also huge and growing (such as cows, pigs, chickens, potatoes, wheat, maize, and so on).
- *Resources:* The stocks of both nonrenewable and renewable resources are being rapidly depleted; within only decades the human economy will become severely limited by the available supplies of fossil fuels and certain metals, and likely also by the amounts of water, high-quality agricultural land, stocks of wild fish, and timber.
- *Pollution:* Some kinds of pollution are causing widespread damage to bioresources and to wild ecosystems (such as acid rain and ground-level ozone), while others (carbon dioxide and other greenhouse gases) may be affecting global environmental functions such as climate.
- *Damage to biodiversity:* Apart from risks to the human economy caused by growing populations, diminishing

resources, and pollution, the biodiversity of Earth is increasingly threatened by extinctions and endangerment caused by the destruction of natural ecosystems, damage by invasive aliens, and other anthropogenic stressors.

It is important to understand that these factors interact in a nonlinear way to result in cumulative environmental and ecological damages. For example, a human population may be growing in size, and at the same time becoming more affluent, so that the per capita use of resources, generation of wastes, and destruction of natural ecosystems is also increasing. In such a case there is a multiplicative relationship among the factors. In a general sense, the collective effect of humans on the biosphere is a function of two factors: the size of the population and the per capita environmental impact. The population varies greatly among and within countries, as does the per capita impact, depending on the nature and degree of economic and technological development.

Paul Ehrlich, an American ecologist, expresses this relationship using a simple "impact formula", as follows:

$I = P \times A \times T$, where

I = the total environmental impact of a human population

P = the size of that population

A = an estimate of the affluence in terms of per capita consumption of resources

T = the technological development of the economy, in terms of environmental impact per unit of consumption

David Schindler: A Champion of Ecology and Environment

David Schindler

FIGURE 1 David Schindler

David Schindler is an aquatic ecologist, with wide-ranging experience working in northern lakes and rivers **(Figure 1)**. His early career was spent as a scientist with the Freshwater Institute of the federal Department of Fisheries and Oceans, and he then took up a position at the University of Alberta. Schindler's career has been distinguished by outstanding research done in collaboration with numerous colleagues in government and academia, as well as a willingness to serve as an environmental advisor to governmental and non-governmental organizations, and to engage in high-profile public advocacy on important issues.

Much of Schindler's early work was done at the Experimental Lakes Area (ELA) in northwestern Ontario. That area was set aside from commercial development in 1967 under a cooperative agreement among the governments of Canada and Ontario and several forestry companies. The intent was to reserve a large block of landscape, including its lakes and their watersheds, for the purposes of large-scale experimental research. This work has largely involved entire lakes being manipulated in ways that test hypotheses about the anthropogenic causes and consequences of aquatic pollution. Initially the ELA contained 17 watersheds with 46 oligotrophic lakes; in 2013, the research area included 58 designated lakes. The ELA has become famous as one of the world's leading field stations, dedicated to long-term environmental monitoring and ecosystem-scale research on anthropogenic impacts on freshwater ecosystems.

In 1968, David Schindler was designated as the first lead scientist at the ELA. At the time, economic and ecological damages caused by eutrophication were a high-profile issue, particularly in parts of the Great Lakes. There was great pressure on politicians to deal with this problem, but they were receiving conflicting advice from scientists about how to do it. Schindler and his colleagues helped to settle that controversy through an insightful series of experiments that involved fertilizing entire lakes with various mixtures of nutrients. Their work demonstrated that phosphate is the primary limiting nutrient for the eutrophication of oligotrophic waterbodies (see Environmental Applications 2.1). Once this was known, it became possible to prevent this environmental problem by removing phosphorus from household detergent and to treat sewage to reduce its nutrient content before the effluent is discharged into an aquatic environment.

Calculations based on this **IPAT** formula clearly show that wealthy countries with a high level of technological development have a disproportionately larger environmental impact than do poorer ones, when expressed on a per capita basis. Consider, for example, the data presented in **Figure 17.2**, which compares simple indicators of the environmental impact of Canada with that of China and India, the two most-populous countries in the world. In this assessment, the use of commercial (primary) energy and the gross domestic product (GDP) are presented as indicators of the intensity of environmental impact of both national economies and individual people (per capita data). Energy use is a useful metric because it is associated with most activities that occur in an economy, such as harvesting resources, manufacturing goods and providing services, transportation, and recycling or disposing of disused materials. Gross domestic product represents the sum of all economic activities in a country, each of which results in some amount of environmental impact.

The data in **Figure 17.2** indicate that Canada, with a population of about 35 million (in 2013), supports far fewer people than do China (1370 million) or India (1220 million). However, the per capita data for energy use and GDP indicate that an average Canadian affects the environment considerably more intensely than do people living in China or India. This difference is a consequence of the prosperous nature of the typical Canadian lifestyle—sometimes referred to as "affluenza."

However, if the per capita energy use or GDP of the three countries is multiplied by their population, the national indicators of "environmental impact" are rather similar. This comparison tells us that although Canada has a relatively small population, the intensive lifestyle of Canadians means that our aggregate influence on the environment is large and roughly comparable to that of India or China. Arguably, with the concept of lifestyle intensity in mind, Canada might be considered to be as overpopulated as either of those countries.

Schindler was also heavily engaged in whole-lake experiments that revealed many of the important effects of acidification on low-alkalinity waterbodies. In those studies, lakes were monitored for several years to establish baseline conditions, and then were deliberately acidified and the changes in physical-chemical limnology and biology observed. That research provided key information about the critical thresholds of acidification that resulted in large changes in the communities of phytoplankton, zooplankton, benthic organisms, and fish in oligotrophic lakes, as well as functional changes, such as in productivity and nutrient cycling. That work at ELA, plus a great deal of research done elsewhere in Canada and in other countries, helped to provide impetus for governmental regulation of the emissions of acidifying gases to the atmosphere, particularly sulphur dioxide.

Schindler stayed involved with ELA programs after his move to the University of Alberta in 1989, where he further expanded his research interests to the study of mountain lakes, northern rivers, the biomagnification of persistent organochlorines, effects of climate change and ultraviolet radiation on lakes, global carbon and nitrogen budgets, and environmental consequences of oil-sand development in northern Alberta. His teaching has reflected the two focal areas of his career: (1) the science of limnology and aquatic ecology, and (2) the philosophy, sociology, and politics of the intersection of science and public policy. Schindler's extraordinary career is demonstrated by hundreds of journal publications and a prolific network of colleagues and graduated students. In recognition of such achievements he has been awarded 11 honorary doctoral degrees by various universities and more than 30 academic awards and prizes.

The narrative of Schindler's career provides abundant evidence that well-designed and carefully executed research in ecology is crucial to identifying the causes and consequences of environmental problems and to finding ways to avoid or fix them, and that objective professional opinions and forceful advocacy can influence public attitudes and environmental policy in meaningful ways.

David Schindler is not the only ecologist to have worked at the ELA. Hundreds of researchers have worked there and their aggregate work represents an immense contribution to our knowledge about the functioning of freshwater ecosystems and the effects on them of environmental stressors. Unfortunately, in 2012 the Government of Canada announced its plans to summarily close down the ELA research centre, a decision that represented an enormous blow to the conduct of ecological and environmental science in Canada. There was intense public opposition to that federal move, but as of this writing it appears that the ELA and its world-class research facilities will be "saved" by funding provided by the provinces of Ontario and Manitoba. Their support will allow the International Institute for Sustainable Development of Winnipeg to take over responsibility for running the ELA and its core programs.

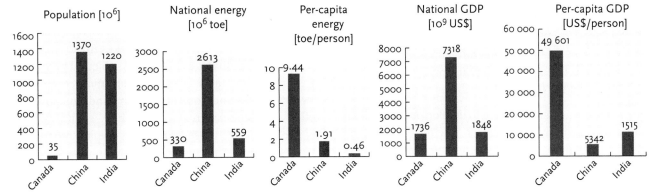

FIGURE 17.2 Comparison of Simple Indicators of the Environmental Impacts of Canada, China, and India The environmental impacts of countries, and of their individual citizens, can be roughly compared using energy and gross domestic product as simple indicators. The environmental impacts of individuals are compared using per capita metrics. Energy use is in standardized units of tonnes of oil (petroleum) equivalent (toe).

SOURCE: Based on Central Intelligence Agency. 2012. *The World Factbook*. CIA, Langley, VA. https://www.cia.gov/library/publications/the-world-factbook/fields/2119.html Primary energy data from: British Petroleum (BP). 2013. *Statistical Review of World Energy 2012*. http://www.bp.com/bodycopyarticle.do?categoryId=1&contentId=7052055 Accessed February 2013.

Many environmental scientists, including ecologists, believe that if the present, apparently nonsustainable pathway of the human economy is adhered to, the enterprise could collapse because of the consequences of excessive growth, insufficient resources, and environmental and ecological degradation. Such a calamity would cause misery for multitudes of people, and it would also be terrible for other species and natural ecosystems. If this awful outcome is to be avoided, society will have to heed the advice of ecologists and other environmental specialists about sensible and precautionary use of the limited resources and ecosystems of Earth. At the same time, we must do all that is necessary to conserve the planet's natural heritage of biodiversity. These are big challenges, but they can and must be met.

17.2 Ecological Integrity

A number of specialized terms have come into common use for the purpose of indicating changes in environmental conditions. These expressions are useful notions that help us understand the consequences of changes that may be occurring in ecosystems and the environment in general. Although the terms cannot be precisely defined, we can develop a customary understanding of what they mean:

- **Environmental quality** is related to the intensity of environmental stressors, particularly anthropogenic ones, such as toxic chemicals and disturbances, as well as their effects on people, economic values, and biodiversity.
- **Ecological integrity (EI)** is related to environmental quality, but it has a focus on changes in wild populations and natural ecosystems, rather than on people and their economy. A high level of EI would represent a low degree of system-level damage caused by anthropogenic stressors to populations and communities (additional interpretations are examined below).
- **Ecosystem health** does not differ substantially from ecological integrity, although it typically has more of a focus on the functional attributes of ecosystems.

These concepts are all used to develop environmental **indicators**. Typically, an indicator is a relatively simple measurement that is intended to represent complex aspects of environmental quality or ecological integrity. Such indicators are often sensitive to variations of the intensity of stressors, and changes in them may serve as early warnings of much larger, impending damage. As we will see in the next section, well-chosen indicators are important components of environmental monitoring programs.

An indicator of ecological integrity must be associated with a number of factors that are related to the structure and function of ecosystems. Obviously, intense environmental stressors associated with human activities pose a risk of causing damage to ecological integrity **(Figure 17.3)**. However, the changes are complex because stressors may cause damage to some species, communities, and ecological functions, while at the same time enhancing others. Nevertheless, it is reasonable to suggest that *higher values* for any of the following characteristics would imply greater ecological integrity (Freedman, 1995, 2010; Karr, 2004):

- resistance, or tolerance of the effects of intensified stressors;
- resilience, or an ability to recover from a disturbance or other reductions of stress;
- complexity in ecological structure and function, including the biodiversity that is supported;
- presence of large species **(Figure 17.4)**;
- presence of top carnivores;
- controlled nutrient cycling—the system is not "leaky" of its accumulated nutrient capital;
- dominance of native species rather than alien ones;
- the ecosystem is not being subjected to strong anthropogenic influences—natural environmental factors are the primary controls of its structure and function, so the ecosystem is self-organized rather than anthropogenic;
- management is not required to maintain attributes that are considered desirable, for instance, to maintain the habitat of an endangered species;

Where did these various indicators come from? In essence, they have emerged from studies of the effects of intensified stress by pollution, climate change, disturbance, and other factors on the structure and function of ecosystems **(Table 17.1)**. In previous chapters we examined examples of these kinds of studies, such as the effects of pollution at the Smoking Hills or near smelters (Chapter 2), of harvesting of bioresources in forestry and fisheries (Chapter 15), and whole-ecosystem experiments such as those at the Experimental Lakes Area.

Ecosystems that are chronically subjected to intense stress (e.g., climate-stressed desert or tundra) eventually develop stable conditions of structure and function that reflect limitations imposed by their environmental regime. Typically, those ecosystems are low in species richness, simple in structure and function, and dominated by long-lived plants that are short in stature. These ecosystems also have low rates of functional properties such as productivity, decomposition, and nutrient cycling. It is important to understand, however, that in situations where environmental stressors are natural in origin, there are no implications for ecological integrity.

Consider, for example, the effects of severe climate at high altitude on mountains, or at high latitude in the Arctic.

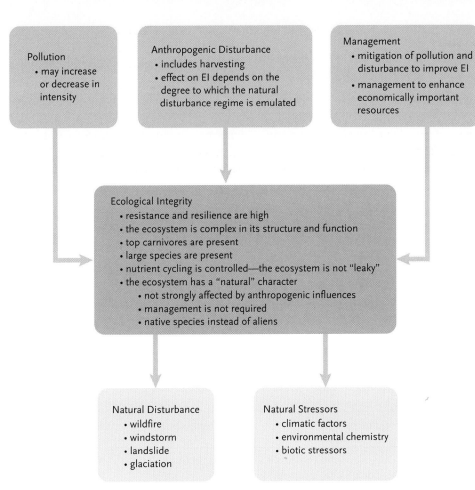

Pollution
- may increase or decrease in intensity

Anthropogenic Disturbance
- includes harvesting
- effect on EI depends on the degree to which the natural disturbance regime is emulated

Management
- mitigation of pollution and disturbance to improve EI
- management to enhance economically important resources

Ecological Integrity
- resistance and resilience are high
- the ecosystem is complex in its structure and function
- top carnivores are present
- large species are present
- nutrient cycling is controlled—the ecosystem is not "leaky"
- the ecosystem has a "natural" character
  - not strongly affected by anthropogenic influences
  - management is not required
  - native species instead of aliens

Natural Disturbance
- wildfire
- windstorm
- landslide
- glaciation

Natural Stressors
- climatic factors
- environmental chemistry
- biotic stressors

FIGURE 17.3 Influences on **Ecological Integrity** Ecological integrity (EI—the blue box) is related to the degree of naturalness of an ecosystem. EI may be degraded by anthropogenic pollution and disturbance, and also by management to enhance the productivity of economically important bioresources (orange boxes). However, management to lessen the impacts of any of those anthropogenic stressors may result in an improvement of EI. Natural disturbances and stressors also affect ecosystems, but do not necessarily degrade EI.

FIGURE 17.4 **Ecological Integrity** Ecological integrity is related to the amount of system-level damage that has been caused to populations and communities by anthropogenic stressors. Ecosystems that support large animals and top predators, such as this breaching humpback whale (*Megaptera novaeangliae*) in the Bay of Fundy, have a high level of ecological integrity.

TABLE 17.1	Effects of Intensified Stress
	This table shows the general trends observed in ecosystems that have been subjected to an intensified regime of environmental stress associated with pollution, climate, disturbance, or other factors.

Ecological Energetics

- Community respiration increases.
- The ratio of production:respiration becomes unbalanced (P:R becomes >1 or <1).
- The ratios of production:biomass (P:B) and respiration:biomass (R:B) increase, indicating that more energy is diverted into maintaining structural attributes related to biomass.
- The export of biomass increases.
- Exogenous sources of fixed energy (from outside the ecosystem) may become more important than endogenous ones (internal to the ecosystem).

Nutrient Cycling

- The rate of nutrient turnover increases (recycling of organically bound forms to inorganic ones that are available for uptake by autotrophs or for leaching out of the system).
- Nutrient losses from the ecosystem increase—the system becomes "leaky" of its accumulated nutrient capital.

Community Structure

- The proportion of r-strategists and ruderals increases while K-strategists and competitors decrease.
- The size of dominant organisms decreases.
- The life spans of organisms or of their parts (such as leaf longevity) decrease.
- Food chains become shorter because of reduced energy flow to higher trophic levels and/or greater sensitivity of predators to an intensified stressor regime.
- Species richness/diversity decreases and dominance increases; at the community level there is decreased redundancy of functional attributes, but if the original diversity was low because of dominance by competitors, the reverse may occur.
- There is a general biotic impoverishment by the extirpation of sensitive species and increased dominance by a relatively few tolerant ones; the prominence of alien species increases.

General System-Level Trends

- The ecosystem becomes more open, with inputs and outputs becoming relatively more important as internal cycling becomes reduced.
- Successional trends may reverse, with a reversion to earlier stages.
- The efficiency of resource use declines.
- There is a decrease in positive symbioses such as mutualisms, and an increase in negative ones such as disease and parasitism.
- Functional properties (such as community-level metabolism) may be more resistant to intensified stress than are species composition and other structural properties.

SOURCE: Based on data from Odum (1985), Schindler (1990), Freedman (1995, 2010).

In both cases, ecosystem development is restricted to a tundra that supports relatively few species of short stature, low productivity, and slow nutrient cycling. However, the natural tundra would not be viewed as having a lower level of EI than a tropical rainforest, even though the latter sustains much more biodiversity, higher productivity and biomass, and faster decomposition and nutrient cycling.

In contrast, exposure of either of those ecosystems to intense anthropogenic stressors, perhaps associated with pollution or disturbances, would result in changes that degrade ecological integrity. Those effects might include diminished structural or functional complexity, reduced numbers of large species or of top predators, or increased prominence of alien species. As we examine later, these sorts of anthropogenic changes are usually considered to represent damage and so they degrade ecological integrity and environmental quality.

In fact, the conservation of ecological integrity has a degree of legal standing in Canada: it is a key aspect of the legislated mandate of Parks Canada for its management of national parks. According to the *Canada National Parks Act* (Parks Canada, 2000a), the "maintenance or restoration of ecological integrity, through the protection of natural resources and natural processes, shall be the first priority of the Minister when considering all aspects of the management of parks" (Section 8.2). In this context, Parks Canada defines EI as follows: "'ecological integrity' means, with respect to a park, a condition that is determined to be characteristic of its natural region and likely to persist, including abiotic components and the composition and abundance of native species and biological communities, rates of change, and supporting processes."

Therefore, a national park would be judged to have a higher level of ecological integrity if it supports native plants and animals that are expected to live in its eco-region, if their populations are likely to survive into the future, and if the patch dynamics of communities on the ecoscape continue to be dependent on natural influences, such as wildfire, windstorms, and biotic interactions.

In 1998, Parks Canada commissioned a Panel on the Ecological Integrity of Canada's National Parks to provide a high-level review of its policies and approach for maintaining EI in national parks, and to recommend improvements. The panel consisted of arms-length ecologists and other relevant specialists (i.e., from outside Parks Canada), and it found that the EI of most national parks was being threatened and damaged by a variety of internal and external stressors (Parks Canada, 2000b). The internal stressors are mostly associated with tourism and transportation infrastructure, and depending on the particular national park they might include highways, railroads, golf courses, hotels, skiing facilities, campgrounds, and even entire towns. The external stressors, which occur in the areas surrounding the parks, but threaten them indirectly, are typically associated with logging, mining, agriculture,

tourism, and urbanization. The external stressors threaten to insularize the affected parks and the species and ecological communities that they are intended to conserve (see the case studies in Chapter 14).

Threats to the EI of national parks are particularly severe in southern regions of Canada, where the human population is largest and the economic infrastructure most intensively developed. This is also true for protected areas that are managed by other organizations that seek to conserve native species and natural habitats, such as provincial parks authorities and the Nature Conservancy of Canada.

To deal with these threats to natural values and other aspects of environmental quality, a number of integrated actions must be implemented by responsible authorities **(Figure 17.5)**. These actions include increasing the environmental literacy of citizens so they will be more likely to adopt a lifestyle that causes less environmental damage, while also regulating the kinds of activities that people and companies are allowed to undertake, and ensuring that society is provided with suitable advice by ecologists and other specialists. In the next section, we examine the roles of ecological monitoring and research as vital components of this synthesis of helpful actions toward improved sustainability.

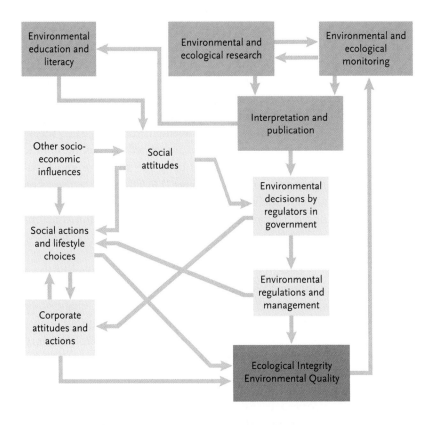

FIGURE 17.5 Influences on Environmental Quality This is a conceptual model of the many influences on environmental quality (EQ), an important component of which is ecological integrity (EI; orange box). Changes in EQ and EI are detected by monitoring programs, with research being undertaken to understand the causes and consequences of changes in conditions. Results of the monitoring and research programs are objectively interpreted by ecologists and other specialists (although their analysis may be conditioned to some degree by social and cultural influences) and are reported to both the scientific community and the public using various media (journals, books, the Internet, and others). The analyses are also communicated to decision makers in government, who may implement regulations and management actions that affect environmental quality. Public environmental literacy is another key component—it is achieved through the educational system, by outreach activities of governmental agencies and private companies, by actions of non-governmental organizations, and by the mass media. Environmental literacy affects social attitudes about the environment, which may result in appropriate choices of lifestyle and a public influence on the policies and actions of governments and corporations.

SOURCE: Modified from Freedman, B. 1995. *Environmental Ecology. The Impacts of Pollution and Other Stresses on Ecosystem Structure and Function.* 2nd ed. p. 459, Copyright Academic Press, San Diego, CA, 1995.

17.3 Monitoring and Research

There is increasing concern in society about damage being caused to ecosystems and to the environment more generally. To better identify and track those changes, various organizations are undertaking programs of monitoring and research. These include governmental agencies, private companies, **environmental non-governmental organizations** (**ENGOs**, or environmental charities), and groups working in universities.

At the federal level, Environment Canada is the organization that is most actively engaged in environmental monitoring and research. In addition, Natural Resources Canada provides information about non-renewable and some renewable resources, while the Department of Fisheries and Oceans deals with fisheries and marine environments, the Canadian Forest Service provides data relevant to commercial forests, Parks Canada examines changes in national parks, and Health Canada deals with environmental influences on human health. All of the provincial and territorial governments have comparable agencies that deal with the corresponding issues within their own jurisdictions.

Several ENGOs are also heavily involved in monitoring and research. For instance, NatureServe Canada is a network of eight **conservation data centres** that collect data on the distribution and abundance of species at risk and on communities and other kinds of biophysical habitat types. Other relevant ENGOs include the Nature Conservancy of Canada, which is engaged in biophysical monitoring in its own network of protected areas and their surrounding lands, and the World Wildlife Fund of Canada, which has funded work on endangered species and ecosystems.

Some important monitoring programs organized by ENGOs mobilize large numbers of citizens to collect the data. One such example are the annual Christmas counts of birds, which have been ongoing since 1900 and have built up a terrific database that allows trends of winter-time populations of many species of birds to be tracked. These counts involve thousands of volunteer birders counting all of the birds observed in a fixed 24-km diameter circle on a particular date close to Christmas. The data are posted on-line in an open-access format and can be analyzed to show changes over time in the distribution and abundance of the various species that spend the winter in particular places or regions. The original Christmas counts of wintering birds have been augmented by additional volunteer databases for migrating and breeding ones, and there are similar projects that count fish, insects, earthworms, and water quality. Other volunteer projects monitor climate change by collecting data on the first date of flowering of certain plants and the dates that ice forms and thaws on lakes.

Canadian universities also have considerable expertise on environmental and ecological issues. Although some university-based ecologists are involved in long-term monitoring programs, most professors and graduate students are engaged in research into the causes and ecological consequences of environmental changes. The university community is not always deeply involved in long-term monitoring because of the relatively short time frames of student research projects, and often of the research funding and directions of professors. It is more the purview of government to undertake long-term monitoring programs (although this responsibility is not always fully met).

In general, the intent of monitoring and research programs is to detect or predict threats to environmental quality, and to find ways to avoid or repair them to the degree possible. Ecologists have an important role to play in these programs, because many indicators that are being examined are ecological in character, such as populations of wild organisms, the extent of certain habitats or communities, productivity and carbon storage, pollutant residues in biota and the environment, and so on.

However, the objectives of monitoring programs can vary enormously in their scale and intent. Most are relatively focused, smaller-scale programs that are associated with the need to manage protected areas or to ensure that particular industrial facilities are complying with environmental regulations. Other programs are intended to examine changes that might be occurring over large regions or entire countries, and even globally. In either case, the resulting data and knowledge are used to guide decision making in government and industry, to assist the work of ENGOs, and to provide materials for environmental education.

Environmental monitoring involves repeated measurements of variables that are related to either the abiotic (inorganic) environment or to the structure and functioning of ecosystems **(Figure 17.6)**. Of course, ecosystems are extremely complex and not everything can be monitored. Therefore, monitoring programs require that limited numbers of representative indicators be sensibly chosen for sampling.

Research is integral to monitoring programs because it investigates questions that are relevant to the possible causes and consequences of environmental changes, or to other aspects of the structure and functioning of ecosystems. Research might be undertaken in the laboratory or in the field, and it may involve experiments or the investigation of patterns of covariation of biotic and abiotic variables (such as by gradient or multivariate analyses).

Environmental Indicators

Environmental indicators are relatively simple measurements that are intended to represent complex aspects of environmental quality. Indicators are often highly

FIGURE 17.6 Environmental Monitoring Monitoring involves repeated measurements of variables related to either the abiotic environment or to the structure and functioning of ecosystems. This apparatus is used to monitor the chemistry of precipitation. A sensor detects when it is raining or snowing, and causes the tent-like cover to be lifted from the top of the white bucket, which collects the precipitation as it falls. When the rain or snow stops, the lid is replaced in the original position, so the sample is not contaminated by dustfall. The apparatus is designed to sample "wet-only" precipitation, which is a core indicator of the acidity and other chemical attributes of rain and snow.

sensitive to changes in the intensity of stressors. Two examples of ecological indicators are chemical residues in organisms and changes in the abundance of species known to be sensitive to certain stressors, such as those particularly affected by acidification or by clear-cutting.

Residues of chemicals in the tissues of top predators are often used as an indicator of the degree of contamination of their ecosystem, especially for persistent substances that biomagnify to particularly high concentrations in carnivores, such as organochlorines (e.g., DDT, PCBs, dioxins, and furans). **Figure 17.7** shows how the residues of PCBs and DDE (a metabolic breakdown product of DDT) have been declining since the 1970s in eggs of herring gulls (*Larus argentatus*) breeding in Toronto harbour. The data are derived from a monitoring program run by the Canadian Wildlife Service to track residues of persistent organochlorine chemicals following bans on their production and use that were enacted by Canada and the United States in the 1970s.

Changes in the abundance of species are often monitored, because widespread declines are worrisome and should be dealt with by discovering the causes and taking appropriate conservation action. For instance, the population status of the grizzly bear (*Ursus arctos*) is considered an indicator of the health of the communities and extensive landscape that it depends on. Other indicator species are spotted owl (*Strix occidentalis*) living in western tracts of old-growth forest, pileated woodpecker (*Dryocopus pileatus*) and pine marten (*Martes americana*) in other forests, salmon and trout in certain aquatic ecosystems, and orca (*Orcinus orca*) and whales in their coastal marine ecosystems. **Figure 17.8** shows that many species of landbirds that breed in the boreal region of Canada are suffering population declines, with nonmigratory residents and short- and long-distance migrants being affected in similar proportions. **Figure 17.9** shows a more encouraging change—substantial increases in the global population of the whooping crane (*Grus americana*), a critically endangered species.

Additional examples of ecological monitoring data were presented in previous chapters. For instance, changes in biomass and communities during succession were examined in Chapter 10, and alterations in the numbers of protected areas and of certain species in Chapter 14. Additionally, changes in the abundance of economically important cod, salmon, and whales were described in Chapter 15, and in diatoms, pollen, and other paleo-indicators in Chapter 16.

Sometimes, **composite indicators** are monitored to track changes in environmental quality. These involve summing the data of a number of different metrics to produce an artificial variable that integrates changes in all of them. Because composite indictors allow complex changes to be presented in a simple manner, they are especially useful for advising the general public. Several composite indicators are routinely used to monitor changes in socioeconomic conditions. Here are some examples:

- *Stock market indices* are based on the sum of the equity values of a group of listed companies. The most prominent one in Canada is for the Toronto Stock Exchange (TSX), whose S&P/TSX Composite Index is based on the stock prices of the largest Canadian-based companies listed on its exchange, which represent about 70 percent of the total market value of all its listed companies.
- The *consumer price index* (*CPI*) is a measure of the prices of goods and services that are routinely purchased by consumers in Canada. It is determined by measuring the retail prices of a representative "shopping basket" of specific goods that is periodically sampled across the country.
- The *human development index* (*HDI*) is intended to provide an objective indicator of the socioeconomic

FIGURE 1 Anne Salomon

Anne Salomon **(Figure 1)** is an assistant professor at Simon Fraser University. She is an applied marine ecologist, in the sense that her research is intended to advance our understanding of how human-caused disturbances alter the productivity, biodiversity, and resilience of coastal ecosystems and human well-being to inform ecosystem approaches to marine conservation. In particular, Salomon and her students engage in research about trophic cascades triggered by predator depletion and recovery mechanisms driving alternative community state dynamics, the effects and design of marine protected areas, and the resilience of social-ecological systems. Her approach is highly collaborative, engaging coastal human communities and government agencies in collaborative research and monitoring to find sustainable outcomes to problems of resource use and the conservation of biodiversity.

Salomon's research on trophic dynamics has investigated both top-down and bottom-up influences. For example, she has worked on the effects of keystone predators such as sea otters on the food web of coastal kelp forests, including implications for the recovery of economically and culturally important shellfish like sea urchins and clams and endangered species like northern abalone. Another approach has involved the empirical and theoretical examination of ecological communities inside and adjacent to marine reserves. Salomon and her colleagues have shown that food webs can change dramatically inside reserves, where the recovery of previously harvested predatory fish can trigger a cascade of effects.

In 2013, Salomon was named a Pew Fellow as part of an international programme in marine conservation supporting the research of global leaders working to preserve and protect the world's oceans and marine species. She was also awarded the International Recognition of Professional Excellence Prize by the International Ecology Institute in Germany. This award is given to an ecologist under 40 years of age who has published uniquely independent research representing an important scientific breakthrough.

Salomon believes that understanding the dynamics of coastal ecosystems at appropriate scales of space and time is vital to the design of practical approaches to the conservation of both bio-resources and biodiversity, and that the collaboration of local human communities is necessary for success. Salomon has worked in partnership with coastal First Nations in Alaska and British Columbia on a diversity of coastal research initiatives integrating experimental field ecology, archaeology, satellite remote sensing, stable isotopes, and traditional ecological knowledge. Her approach represents a helpful fusing of research designed to contribute to basic ecological knowledge, while at the same time working toward the resolution of important conservation problems.

---

harvesting yields a commodity (tree biomass) that has direct value as a material that can be manufactured into value-added products such as lumber and paper, or that can be used for bioenergy, while also yielding secondary benefits from employment and tax revenues. There would also, however, be some economic disbenefits from the timber harvesting. This might perhaps be associated with decreased potential for outdoor recreation because the aesthetics of timber-harvested lands are often perceived as being degraded compared with those of intact forest, as well as the diminished value of the carbon credits provided by the landscape (because of decreased biomass on harvested sites). Again, any decision to harvest the timber, or to not do so, would reflect a balance of these and other ecological and socio-economic considerations.

Of course, another consideration when judging the importance of ecological change and damage is what it may mean in terms of sustainability. Judgments of the "quality" of change are related to important ideas in environmental reporting and monitoring, such as environmental quality and ecological integrity (Section 17.2).

Along these lines, environmental quality is damaged by anthropogenic influences that result in:

- increased exposure to potentially toxic chemicals;
- disturbances that are more frequent or different in intensity than those occurring naturally;
- changes in regional or global climate; and
- increases in the numbers of endangered species and decreases in the extent of natural ecosystems.

In addition, ecological integrity would be damaged by anthropogenic influences that result in:

- mortality of dominant organisms in affected communities;
- a reduction of biomass storage;
- the leakage of nutrients from the ecosystem;
- a greater preponderance of alien species compared with native ones; and
- an increased intensity of management in order to maintain desired attributes of the ecosystem.

These sorts of changes would be viewed as representing environmental and ecological damages, even if there were presumed "benefits" to the human economy.

17.5 Environmental Impact Assessment

All human activities carry some degree of risk of causing damage to the environment, including to its ecological components. **Environmental impact assessment (EIA)** is a planning process that helps to identify and evaluate environmental problems that are potentially involved with a proposed economic activity, and to find ways to avoid or mitigate them if possible. This does not mean that environmental damage will not be caused by the development—some amount of harm is inevitable.

Because an EIA considers ecological and physical-chemical environmental consequences, as well as socio-economic effects, its process is a highly multi- and interdisciplinary activity. **Multidisciplinary** means that various fields of study are engaged, including chemistry, ecology, economics, geography, geology, sociology, and others. **Interdisciplinary** means that a diversity of kinds of knowledge is used in an integrated manner, rather than (or in addition to) a disconnected approach.

An EIA may be undertaken to examine various kinds of planned activities that might affect environmental quality. In Canada, they might include:

- *an individual project*, such as a proposal to construct a pipeline, power plant, dam, airport, school, or highway;
- *an integrated scheme*, such as a proposal to develop a pulp mill with its included plans for wood supply and forest management, an industrial park consisting of various enterprises and businesses, and other complex developments that involve numerous projects that are undertaken in a coordinated manner; and
- *a governmental policy* that carries a risk of substantially affecting the environment, such as a strategy to increase the fossil-fuel, metal-mining, or agricultural sectors of the economy, or to increase the rate of immigration to a region or to the country as a whole.

Within this context, the spatial scale of an EIA can vary greatly. It can range from an examination of the risk to a small wetland posed by the proposed construction of a building nearby, to the examination of a complex mega-project to build a large hydroelectric dam and reservoir in a region that is currently wilderness.

EIA is based on the premise that any proposed development, program, or policy carries inherent risks for the welfare of people, their economy, and other species and ecosystems. For instance, an EIA of a proposed coal-fired generating station would have to study its emissions of chemicals to the atmosphere, such as sulphur dioxide, carbon dioxide, mercury vapour, and particulates. The predicted effects on local and regional air quality would have to be compared with levels that are known to already occur in the region (to determine the cumulative impacts; see Environmental Applications 17.1), as well as those that are known to cause toxicity to sensitive biota. Of course, the predicted effects on air quality would also have to be compared with any environmental criteria that are regulated by governments. Construction of the power plant might also damage areas of natural habitat, and that ecological effect would have to be quantified and its importance evaluated before permission is given to start the project. Interestingly, under Canadian EIA law and practice, there would not be a need to study the plans to mine and transport coal to the power plant—that would be a separate proposal and EIA process.

In Canada, environmental impact assessments for proposals that involve federal funding or jurisdiction are regulated under the *Canadian Environmental Assessment Act* (CEAA), which was enacted in 1992. Initially, the CEAA required that EIA studies be done on a wide range of projects involving the federal government, but in 2013 the act was greatly weakened so that only big projects are considered (Essentially, this was done because the federal government-of-the-day viewed the EIA process as unduly interfering with industrial projects needed for economic growth and employment.). Provinces and territories also have legislated requirements for EIA, as do some local levels of government, such as municipalities and Aboriginal peoples.

Typically, the most stringent regulatory standards for pollutants apply to the maximum exposures that people can experience without a significant risk to their health. There are also criteria to protect wild species and ecosystems, but they are less exacting, meaning that higher exposures are tolerated. For example, the Canadian guideline for uranium in drinking water is 0.02 mg/L (Health Canada, 2008), but that for the protection of aquatic life is 40 mg/L for a short-term exposure (<1–4 days) and 5.5 mg/L for a long-term exposure (CCME, 2009). Note that the criteria for aquatic life accommodate the fact that, in terms of the cumulative dose received, a longer-term exposure to a low concentration may be as important as a shorter exposure to a higher concentration.

Bill Freedman

Bill Freedman

FIGURE 17.12 Valued Ecosystem Components Environmental impact assessments often focus on the examination of likely effects of a proposed development on a selected set of valued ecosystem components (or VECs). A VEC is considered important because it is a bioresource, a species, or community that is at risk, of aesthetic value, or of cultural significance to an Aboriginal community or other local people. The Baird's sandpiper (*Calidris bairdii*, top) and the green heron (*Butorides virescens*, bottom) would be considered VECs for an EIA in Canada because they are rare in parts of their range and are sought after for viewing by naturalists.

Any economic development is likely to affect a wide variety of species and communities. However, it is not possible to study all of the potential effects on such ecological values. Instead, EIAs are usually restricted to examining the likely effects on a carefully selected set of **valued ecosystem components** (or **VECs**) **(Figure 17.12)**. A VEC is considered to be important for one or more of these reasons:

- It is a bioresource, such as a commercial forest, or a hunted stock of birds, mammals, or fish.
- It is a species or community that is rare or otherwise at risk.
- It is of aesthetic importance, such as a prominent viewscape that local people or tourists like to visit.
- It is of cultural significance to an Aboriginal community or other local people.

The initial phase of an EIA is known as a **screening**. It is important because it helps to determine the level of assessment of a proposed development—whether a relatively minor review or a full assessment is necessary. Once this is decided by a regulatory authority, a **scoping exercise** is undertaken to identify the potentially important intersections of project-related activities and stressors with VECs or human socioeconomic welfare. In essence, a scoping evaluates the intersections of the predicted spatial and temporal boundaries of stressors associated with the proposed development with those where VECs and people occur. If potential interactions are identified, the assessors must determine whether significant damage is likely to be caused.

If enough time and funding are available, it may be possible to conduct simulation modelling or field or laboratory research to investigate the potential interactions between project-related stressors and VECs. Often, however, this cannot be done because there is insufficient funding to do the work, or the EIA must be completed relatively quickly. If this is the case, then assessments of the likely environmental effects may be based on the expert opinions of ecologists and other professionals. Those opinions should be founded on careful and objective review of the best scientific information that is available. However, even well-funded and properly designed and executed research may yield uncertain results. This is especially true of ecological damage that might be caused by exposure to a low intensity of project-related stressors.

Planning Options

If potentially important risks to human welfare or VECs are identified, a number of planning options must be considered. There are three broad choices:

- *Prevent or avoid*: One option is to avoid the predicted damage by ensuring that people or VECs do not suffer a significant exposure to damaging stressors related to the project. This can be done by modifying the characteristics of the development, or even by choosing to cancel the project if there is a severe conflict with human welfare or ecological values. Because prevention and avoidance may involve substantial costs, they may be viewed as a less-desirable option by proponents of a development. Cancelling a project is also controversial, because substantial economic prospects may be foregone (this is known as an opportunity cost). Nevertheless, it is always prudent to identify and take as many precautions as possible before undertaking a development.
- *Mitigate*: Another option is to mitigate the predicted damages, or to repair or offset them to the degree that is possible. **Mitigation** is mainly relevant to damage that is caused to VECs and to low-level risks caused

ENVIRONMENTAL APPLICATIONS 17.1
Cumulative Environmental Effects

Environmental impact assessment (EIA) is a planning activity that is used to identify and evaluate environmental problems that may be caused by a proposed economic activity. According to the *Canadian Environmental Assessment Act*, this includes the need to evaluate **cumulative environmental impacts**, or those resulting from the effects of a proposed undertaking within some defined area, over and above those caused by any past, existing, and imminent developments and activities. The concept of cumulative effects recognizes that the environmental effects of separate anthropogenic influences will combine and interact to cause changes that may be different from those occurring separately. It is prudent and sensible to consider all of the anthropogenic influences when examining the potential effects of a newly proposed project or activity.

Assessment of cumulative impacts requires knowledge of both the likely effects of a proposed development, as well as those of other anthropogenic activities in a study area, and additional ones that are likely to occur. If all of this is known, then the incremental effects of a proposed undertaking can be evaluated for their relative importance. Cumulative effects can result from multiple pathways, and they may be manifested in physical, biological, and socioeconomic damages.

There are a number of examples of cumulative environmental effects that are primarily ecological and have occurred in Canada (and were examined in various chapters of this book):

- aggregate damage caused to populations of migratory salmon in the Fraser River watershed in British Columbia as a result of commercial fishing in the open Pacific or in the river itself, along with sport and subsistence fishing, and degradation of freshwater habitat through influences such as the dumping of sewage, agricultural erosion and pesticides, warmer temperatures and woody debris in streams caused by forestry operations, risks of sea-louse infection from aquaculture in coastal waters, and warming oceanic waters caused by climate change;
- incremental losses of wetlands in the Prairie provinces caused by various agricultural practices, such as drainage, excessive fertilization with nutrients, toxicity caused by pesticides, and trampling by cattle, along with drying caused by periodic droughts whose frequency may become exacerbated by anthropogenic climate change;
- losses of biodiversity throughout Canada, but particularly in southern regions, caused by deforestation to develop land for urbanized and agricultural uses, fragmentation by roads and transmission corridors, disturbances by forestry and mining, and various kinds of pollution;
- ecological degradation in a region of boreal forest in northern Alberta in which there are diverse anthropogenic stressors associated with timber harvesting, exploration and mining for oil and gas, oil-sand extraction and processing, and pipelines and roads to service all of those economic activities; and
- threats to the ecological integrity of national parks that are associated with the development of internal infrastructure to support tourism, such as campgrounds, interpretation centres, roads and trails, golf courses, and skiing facilities, along with economic activities in the surrounding area such as forestry and agriculture, as well as regional influences such as acid rain and climate change.

A requirement that environmental impacts be studied in a cumulative manner acknowledges the complexity of ecosystems and the fact that all aspects of their structure and function are affected by a diverse array of influences.

to people. For example, a wetland may be unavoidably destroyed by a development, but the damage may be offset by creating or enhancing a comparable wetland somewhere else. Similarly, if the habitat of a rare species is threatened by a development, it may be possible to move the population that is at risk to another suitable place, or to create or enhance a habitat elsewhere, so that no net damage is caused. Mitigations are a common response to conflicts between project-related stressors and VECs, but they are not perfect and there is often some degree of residual damage.

- *Accept the damages*: The third option is for decision makers to choose to allow a proposed project to cause some or all of the predicted damages to human welfare or VECs. This choice is often favoured by the proponents of projects, because of their belief that the socioeconomic benefits provided by their development would be greater than the cost of environmental damages that are predicted.

Inevitably, environmental impact assessments find that proposed developments carry some risks of causing damage. In almost all cases the development is allowed to move forward, but with important predicted damages being avoided or mitigated to a degree considered feasible, in both technological and economic terms. However, there will always be some damages that cannot be avoided or mitigated—these are environmental "costs" of a development.

Once the actual development of a project begins, it may be necessary to undertake compliance monitoring to ensure that regulatory criteria for pollution or health hazards are being met. If potential ecological damages were identified during the EIA, it is prudent to monitor those effects, although this is not always required. Ideally, the monitoring would be designed to test the predictions of the impact assessment, and to identify unanticipated "surprises" so they could be mitigated in a timely fashion.

A properly designed monitoring program would begin prior to the implementation of a project, so that baseline conditions could be established. There should also be monitoring of nearby nonaffected indicators, which provide a reference comparison to those affected by project-related stressors. Once the development proceeds, the monitoring should continue for a long enough period to determine whether important damage is being caused. If monitoring discovers that damage is occurring that was not predicted by the EIA, then the project operations might be changed to avoid or mitigate those unanticipated effects, or they might just be accepted as an ecological "cost" of development.

Examples of Impact Assessments

Environmental impact assessments are routinely conducted in all regions of Canada. They are required and scrutinized by various levels of government. The proponents of a project are usually a company or a governmental agency, and the EIA is typically undertaken by in-house professionals or by one or more private consulting firms (the latter would be viewed as having greater independence than in-house staff). The proposed developments vary enormously in their scale, complexity, and potential environmental effects. The following case studies are brief examples of Canadian EIAs that had significant ecological dimensions.

Diamond Mines in the Northwest Territories

This development proposed the construction of mines to extract diamonds from several columnar deposits, known as kimberlite pipes, located about 300 km northeast of Yellowknife. Because kimberlite is softer than the surrounding granitic rocks, glaciers and other erosive forces have worn it away to form basins that support natural lakes. Those waterbodies would be drained and thus destroyed—along with their aquatic biota—to develop open-pit mines. Ore might also eventually be mined in underground shafts, and there would be large amounts of waste rock and tailings to be disposed of on land. In addition, huge amounts of gravel are needed to construct roads and ground-pads for buildings, and that aggregate would be obtained from local eskers, which are long, sinuous hills that provide critical denning habitat for grizzly bear, wolf, and other animals. Moreover, the mine and its network of roads are a potential hazard to herds of woodland caribou (*Rangifer tarandus*) that migrate

through the region. Aboriginal peoples hunt in the region for country foods (these are harvested from the land) and furs to sell, and those activities would be interfered with by the development. Finally, the region proposed for mining was a non-roaded wilderness, and conservation interests, led by the World Wildlife Fund, objected to the approval of the development unless a system of protected areas was established to ensure the landscape viability of both natural ecosystems and large carnivores, such as grizzly bear, wolf, and wolverine (*Gulo gulo*).

The diamond mines passed their EIA and were allowed to proceed, subject to various restrictions, such as a ban on local hunting by mine employees, specified methods for the disposal of mining and tailings wastes, and actions to protect surface waters (other than the several lakes that must be destroyed to develop the mines and to dispose of waste tailings). A monitoring program was required to detect unanticipated damage to water or atmospheric quality, or to wildlife. At the same time the government of the Northwest Territories committed to setting aside protected areas in the larger region, although this has not yet been fully done. The mine opened in 1998.

Crude Oil on the Grand Banks

Large reservoirs of petroleum have been discovered on the Grand Banks, a region of continental shelf east of Newfoundland. A consortium of companies sought to develop this valuable resource by constructing the Hibernia project. This is an immense submersible platform located in 80-m-deep water to which petroleum is fed from a network of wells located on the seabed and eventually taken away by a fleet of tankers.

The development is subjected to risks associated with environmental hazards, such as hurricane-force winds and waves that sometimes affect the region and enormous icebergs from the eastern Arctic that pass through in some years. The ecosystem of the Grand Banks is considered highly vulnerable to petroleum spills, as it supports a large fishery as well as important biodiversity, including abundant seabirds and marine mammals. Because the proposed Hibernia project included close monitoring of weather and icebergs, and rigorous systems to avoid icebergs and prevent spills of petroleum, it was considered by regulators to provide an acceptable degree of environmental safety and it passed through its impact assessment. It began producing petroleum in 1997.

Al-Pac Pulp Mill

This was a proposal to construct a mill to produce pulp in northern Alberta. The principal issues in the EIA were the potential effects on the Peace–Athabasca River system, including ecological damage that might be caused by the depletion of dissolved oxygen to decompose organic matter in effluent waters, and the contamination of fish with residues of persistent organochlorines, including dioxins and furans (these would have been produced in extremely small concentrations during the chlorine-bleaching process, but are known to biomagnify by thousands of times in aquatic food webs, endangering top predators and perhaps humans).

Remarkably, the terms of reference of the EIA deliberately excluded the potential environmental effects of the wood-supply plan for the mill, which would be one of the largest in the world. The mill had access to about 55 000 km^2 of boreal mixedwood forest in a region that at the time was a largely unroaded wilderness. About half of the area is capable of producing merchantable wood, and the management plan called for clear-cutting about 1 percent of the area annually on a 60- to 70-year rotation. In essence, the appointed federal–provincial EIA review panel was asked to consider the question: "Will the proposed mill harm the Athabasca River?" However, the panel had difficulty addressing that specific question, in part because there was so little baseline information about the riverine ecosystem.

In view of the insufficient materials presented for its consideration, the panel recommended that the mill not be built, and that a series of ecological studies be undertaken to better document the baseline conditions of the Athabasca River before the proposal was reconsidered. The judgment of the panel was initially accepted by the Alberta premier at the time, Don Getty. Soon after, however, he declared the panel's judgment to be "flawed" and he hired a Finnish consulting firm to review its report; however, they supported the panel's findings. The government then declared the previous formal EIA process to have been only a preliminary "environmental review." The premier and his Minister of Environment, Ralph Klein, then appointed a technical panel of three government employees to address a modified technological system that the mill proponents claimed would produce no dioxins and furans. Although the novel technology had not yet been tested at a commercial scale, the technical panel agreed with its zero-organochlorine assertion. The premier then ordered that a permit be issued to allow the mill to be constructed, and the facility began production in 1993. This was done regardless of the public controversy about potential effects of the mill on the Athabasca River, as well as the unconsidered ecological effects of converting an immense wood-supply area to timber production.

At the same time, the provincial and federal governments co-funded an integrated research program known as the Northern River Basins Study, which was charged with documenting the ecology of the Athabasca River, even while the pulp mill was being constructed and operated. As it turned out, the new bleaching technology did result in immeasurable organochlorine production, and it has subsequently been adopted in many other pulp mills. Nevertheless, the interference by politicians in the EIA process, borne out of economic aspirations and political values, resulted in this being one of the most flawed environmental assessments ever undertaken for a large project in Canada.

Twinning of the Trans-Canada Highway in Banff National Park

This was a proposal to "twin" or double the capacity (from two to four lanes) of an existing 18 km stretch of the Trans-Canada Highway running through Banff National Park in southwestern Alberta (eventually, all 45 km of the highway in Banff were twinned). The larger highway would contribute to the fragmentation of populations of certain species of large animals, including ungulates such as elk (*Cervus canadensis*) and moose (*Alces alces*) and large carnivores such as black bear (*Ursus americanus*), grizzly bear, timber wolf, and coyote (*Canis latrans*). It would also increase their risks of suffering collisions with vehicles, which are also a risk to people travelling on the highway.

The proposed mitigations included the installation of 2.4-m-high fencing along both sides of the highway to prevent random crossings by large animals and to guide them to safe passages, which were provided by the installation of 22 underpasses and 2 overpasses (these are for the entire 45 km of highway within the park; see **Figure 17.13**). Although little information was available at the time about the efficacy of the proposed mitigations to allow safe crossings, the twinning project made it through its EIA and construction began in 1995. Subsequent

Jeff Whyte/Shutterstock.com

FIGURE 17.13 A Wildlife Overpass When the part of the Trans-Canada Highway that runs through Banff National Park was twinned to increase its capacity, a number of mitigations were constructed to reduce the risks to both people and large animals from vehicular collisions. This image shows a wildlife "overpass" that was installed to allow wildlife to move across the highway. An extensive barrier of fencing on both sides of the road directs animals to the overpass, which they can use to traverse the dangerous barrier to their movements, while at the same time reducing the risk to people of collisions with large animals.

research has shown that the roadside fencing has reduced the numbers of collisions with large ungulates by about 96 percent, and both the underpasses and overpasses appear to be working well to provide safe passage for the target species.

Grande-Baleine Hydroelectric Complex

Rivers flowing into James and Hudson Bays from north-western Quebec have enormous potential for the production of hydroelectricity, but to develop them for this purpose dams must be constructed and huge reservoirs flooded. The Grande-Baleine proposal involved the construction of three generating stations with a capacity of 3212 MW. It would flood reservoirs about 1667 km² in area and would also affect the landscape by the construction of roads and high-voltage transmission lines. The most important environmental impacts were associated with the creation of such immense reservoirs, which would destroy extensive terrestrial and wetland habitats, convert rivers into artificial lakes, and enormously affect the local aquatic biota, including that of nearby reaches of Hudson Bay. The movements of local herds of woodland caribou and fur-bearing mammals would also be affected. There were also cultural and socioeconomic consequences for Aboriginal peoples living in the region.

These and other potential effects were examined during the environmental impact assessment, including plans to avoid or mitigate damages to whatever extent was considered feasible. The proposal was highly controversial, largely because it was being resisted by the local Cree nation, which felt aggrieved by the environmental implications and lack of local benefits from previous hydro developments in the region. Ultimately, the proposed hydro development did not go forward, not because it would have failed its EIA, but because commitments to purchase the electricity in the northeastern United States were insufficient to support the business plan.

Eradication of Diseased Bison

Some of the bison (*Bison bison*) in the southern part of Wood Buffalo National Park and in its vicinity in northern Alberta and the southwestern NWT are infected with bovine tuberculosis and brucellosis. Because of this, Agriculture Canada proposed to slaughter as many of the bison as possible as a measure to prevent the spread of these infectious diseases to herds of cattle to the south of the region. The bison to be culled were hybrids of indigenous wood bison (*B. b. athabascae*) of the region and plains bison (*B. b. bison*) that had been introduced to the area in the 1920s. There was no intent to cull the populations of "pure" wood bison that roamed farther to the north. Nevertheless, the proposal engendered great controversy and it was opposed by conservationists and local

Aboriginal peoples. Although the proposal managed to successfully pass its impact assessment, it was suspended by the Minister of the Environment, largely because of the powerful opposition it faced.

A Peat Mine in Nova Scotia

This was a relatively small proposal to mine peat as an industrial fuel from a bog. The major issue in the impact assessment was the fact that the bog intended for destruction was one of only a few places where the thread-leaved sundew (*Drosera filiformis*; **Figure 17.14**) occurred in Canada. This rare carnivorous plant is endangered in Canada and also in much of its range in the eastern United States. Because the proposed mine site supported the largest known population of the rare plant in Canada, the provincial Minister of Environment did not allow a mine to be developed at that location.

17.6 Ecology as a Career

A professional ecologist is a highly qualified scientist, typically with a master's degree (M.Sc.) or a doctorate (Ph.D.) in some aspect of ecology. However, some people with an undergraduate degree (B.Sc.) and substantial work experience also consider themselves to be ecologists.

Nevertheless, it is important to understand that most ecologists are self-proclaimed to be of that profession—not many of them are actually certified as being a specialist practitioner of ecology. However, since 1961 the Ecological Society of America, a U.S. organization, has offered a service by which ecologists can be certified at various professional levels—*associate ecologist*, *ecologist*, and *senior ecologist*. The certification is based on the kinds of classes that a person has taken toward college or university degrees, relevant work experience, publications or reports that have been written, and other pertinent information.

Typically, this certification would be sought only by ecologists for whom it would represent a professional advantage, such as those employed in the private sector, including the environmental consulting industry. In fact, most highly qualified practitioners of ecology are not certified in this way, including almost all professors who teach the subject in universities and colleges in Canada.

In addition, some professional societies of specialists in the broader environmental field in Canada offer alternative certifications that ecologists might hold. They include those of registered professional biologist (R.P.Bio.), registered professional forester (R.P.For.), and registered professional wetland scientist (R.P.Wetl.Sci.).

Most ecologists live and work in relatively developed countries, such as Canada, but they can also be found in less-developed ones. In general, the global community

Bill Freedman

FIGURE 17.14 The Thread-Leaved Sundew (*Drosera filiformis*; below) and Its Bog Habitat The largest known population of this carnivorous plant in Canada occurs on a site in southwestern Nova Scotia that was proposed for a peat mine. An environmental impact assessment predicted that the mining would obliterate the most important population of this endangered species, and as a consequence the government of Nova Scotia did not allow the mine to proceed.

Bill Freedman

of ecologists has developed a commonly used approach and toolkit of methodologies for use in their fieldwork, data analysis, and preparation of scientific reports, papers published in journals, and books. As a result, ecologists working in various parts of the world can understand the essentials of the issues and studies of their far-flung colleagues. The only real barrier to collective understanding and communications is differences in language rather than in scientific principles or approaches. Nevertheless, much ecological work has a local and ecoregional context, and therefore many practitioners have developed expertise at those levels, rather than at national or global ones.

The following is a list of the more frequent kinds of careers in which ecologists are engaged **(Figure 17.15)**:

- a scientist working in a governmental agency whose mandate includes some aspect of ecology (e.g., bio-diversity, bioresources, or the broader environmental field), such as Canadian Forestry Service, Canadian Wildlife Service, Environment Canada, Natural Resources Canada, Parks Canada, or their provincial, territorial, or First-Nations equivalents;

- a scientist working in the private sector, either to provide in-house expertise for a company that is engaged in managing ecosystems or biodiversity, or working in a consulting firm that provides those services;

- a scientist working for an ENGO whose activity intersects with the conservation of biodiversity or other ecological values, such as the Canadian Parks and Wilderness Society (CPAWS), the Canadian Wildlife Federation (CWF), Ducks Unlimited Canada (DUC), Nature Canada, the Nature Conservancy of Canada (NCC), the Sierra Club of Canada, the World Wildlife Fund Canada

FIGURE 17.15 Ecologists Doing Fieldwork Ecologists can work in various kinds of jobs, ranging from instructors at colleges and universities, to consultants and scientists in the private sector. This photo shows ecologists doing fieldwork as part of an environmental impact assessment of a proposed hydroelectric development on the Churchill River in Labrador.

Bill Freedman

- the management of ecological functions such as productivity, hydrology, erosion, nutrient cycling, and carbon fixation and storage relevant to offsetting emissions of greenhouse gases;
- monitoring or mitigating ecological damage caused by pollution, disturbances, and other anthropogenic influences; and
- planning and stewardship to conserve biodiversity in protected areas, including tracts of representative ecosystems as well as the habitats of species at risk.

Many other ecologists, particularly those working in universities, are engaged in research that is undertaken for the inherent sake of curiosity—their interests help us to better understand the natural world. Their "pure" academic research has great intrinsic value, and this alone is sufficient to make it worthwhile, even while acknowledging that it may also sometimes result in knowledge that is important in an applied context.

(WWF), or similar ENGOs working at provincial or international levels; and

- a professor or instructor working in a college or university who is involved in developing and teaching classes in ecology or related subjects, often while also running a research program and training senior students to do scientific investigations.

Many professional ecologists are engaged in applied work that is related to important issues or tasks, such as the following:

- the management of bioresources of economic importance, such as those in forestry, fisheries, and hunting;
- environmental impact assessments of the potential ecological effects of proposed development activities;

17.7 Conclusions

Earth and its biosphere are the only place in the universe that is definitely known to sustain life and ecosystems. It is the purview of ecology, and of ecologists, to study this grand living system. The ultimate goal is to understand the influence of environmental factors on the abundance and distribution of organisms and of higher levels of the ecological hierarchy, such as populations, communities, and ecoscapes.

Ecology is also a vital endeavour because of its central importance in defining and setting the limits of an ecologically sustainable human enterprise. In essence, such an economy would be capable of running forever because it is founded on the prudent use of natural resources, especially renewable ones that are being used at rates that are smaller than their productivity, while also conserving other species and natural ecosystems at viable levels of abundance and distribution.

CHAPTER SUMMARY

(LO 17.1)

- The knowledge of ecology is vital to defining a proper vision of an ecologically sustainable human economy, and to marking progress toward that necessary goal.

(LO 17.2)

- Ecological integrity (EI) is related to environmental quality, but with a focus on changes in wild populations and natural ecosystems. High levels of EI are indicated by greater

complexity, dominance by native species, self-organized communities, and ecoscapes that are characteristic for the prevailing environmental regimes.

(LO 17.3)

- Monitoring and research are vital to understanding the occurrence, causes, and consequences of environmental and ecological changes that occurring naturally, or are caused by anthropogenic influences.

- Environmental impact assessment is a planning process that is intended to identify and mitigate, to the degree considered feasible, the environmental and ecological effects associated with a proposed economic activity. In Canada, EIA is normally engaged in studying the potential effects of proposed developments, and sometimes also larger-scale integrated developments and governmental policies.

- Ecologists play a vital role in guiding the sustainable development of Canada and other countries by being involved in identifying changes in biodiversity and other key aspects of ecosystems, by conducting research that helps to understand the causes and consequences of environmental problems, and by engaging in educational and advocacy activities that helps society-at-large to understand and deal with these important issues.

QUESTIONS FOR REVIEW AND DISCUSSION

1. What are the key differences between fundamental and applied research in ecology? Explain why both of these kinds of research, and the knowledge they provide, are important.

2. What is ecological integrity, and how is it different from environmental quality?

3. Consider a park or other protected area with which you are familiar. What are the most important challenges to its ecological integrity?

4. Explain the rationale and general process of environmental impact assessment, and when it must be done. Make sure that you explain the role of ecological studies in the process.

5. What factors must be considered when judging whether an ecological change should be viewed as representing "damage"?

6. Why is the knowledge of ecology important to sustainable development?

References

Chapter 1

Commoner, B. 1971. *The Closing Circle: Nature, Man and Technology*. New York: Alfred Knopf.

Cox, R. M. and T. C. Hutchinson. 1979. Metal co-tolerances in the grass *Deschampsia caespitosa*. *Nature* (London), 279, 231–233.

Freedman, B. 2010. *Environmental Science. A Canadian Perspective* (5th ed.). Toronto, ON: Pearson Education Canada.

Freedman, B. and T. C. Hutchinson. 1980a. Pollutant inputs from the atmosphere and accumulations in soils and vegetation near a nickel-copper smelter at Sudbury, Ontario, Canada. *Canadian Journal of Botany*, 58, 108–132.

Freedman, B. and T. C. Hutchinson. 1980b. Long-term effects of pollution near a nickel-copper smelter at Sudbury, Ontario, Canada, on surrounding forest communities. *Canadian Journal of Botany*, 58, 2123–2140.

Odum, E. P. and G. W. Barrett. 2005. *Fundamentals of Ecology* (5th ed.). Belmont, CA: Thomson Brooks/Cole.

Vitousek, P. M., P. R. Ehrlich, A. H. Ehrlich, and P. A. Matson. 1986. Human appropriation of the products of photosynthesis. *BioScience*, 36, 368–373.

Whitby, L. M. and T. C. Hutchinson. 1974. Heavy metal pollution in the Sudbury mining and smelting region of Canada. II. Soil toxicity tests. *Environmental Conservation*, 1, 191–200.

Chapter 2

Campbell, S. E. 1979. Soil stabilization by a prokaryotic desert crust: Implications for Precambrian land biota. *Origins of Life and Evolution of Biospheres*, 9, 335–348.

Freedman, B. 1995. *Environmental Ecology* (2nd ed.). San Diego, CA: Academic Press.

Freedman, B. 2010. *Environmental Science. A Canadian Perspective* (5th ed.). Toronto, ON: Pearson Education Canada.

Golubic, S., E. I. Friedmann, and J. Schneider. 1981. The lithobiotic ecological niche, with special reference to microorganisms. *Journal of Sedimentary Research*, 51, 475–478.

Kidd, K. A., P. J. Blanchfield, K. H. Mills, V. P. Palace, R. E. Evans, J. M. Lazorchak, and R. W. Flick. 2007. Collapse of a fish population after exposure to a synthetic estrogen. *Proceedings of the National Academy of Sciences USA*, 104, 8897–8901.

LaPaix, R., B. Freedman, and D. Patriquin. 2009. Ground vegetation as an indicator of ecological integrity. *Environmental Reviews*, 98: 124–135.

Schindler, D. W. 1990. Experimental perturbations of whole lakes as tests of hypotheses concerning ecosystem structure and function. *Oikos*, 57, 25–41.

Schindler, D. W., R. E. Hecky, D. L. Findlay, M. P. Stainton, B. R. Parker, M. J. Paterson, K. G. Beaty, M. Lyng, and S. E. M. Kasian. 1990. Eutrophication of lakes cannot be controlled by reducing nitrogen input: Results of a 37-year whole-ecosystem experiment. *Proceedings of the National Academy of Science*, 105, 11254–11258.

Wainwright, M., N. C. Wickramasinghe, J. V. Narlikar, and P. Rajaratnam. 2003. Microorganisms cultured from stratospheric air samples obtained at 41 km. *FEMS Micorbiology Letters*, 218, 161–165.

Chapter 3

Arft, A. M., M. D. Walker, J. Gurevitch, M. Alatalo, S. Bret-Harte, M. Dale, M. Diemer, F. Gugerli, G. H. R. Henry, M. H. Jones, R. D. Hollister, I. S. Jonsdottir, K. Laine, E. Levesque, G. M. Marion, U. Molau, P. Mølgaard, U. Nordenhall, V. Raszhivin, C. H. Robinson, G. Starr, A. Stenstrom, M. Stenstrom, O. Totland, P. L. Turner, L. J. Walker, P. J. Webber, J. M. Welker, and P. A. Wookey. 1999. Responses of tundra plants to experimental warming: Meta-analysis of the International Tundra Experiment. *Ecological Monographs*, 69, 491–511.

Blasing, T. J. 2013. Recent Greenhouse Gas Concentrations. Carbon Dioxide Information Analysis Center, U.S. Department of Energy, Oak Ridge, TN. Retrieved March 2013 from http://cdiac.ornl.gov/pns/current_ghg.html.

Bridgham, S. D., J. P. Megonigal, J. K. Keller, N. B. Bliss, and C. Trettin. 2006. The carbon balance of North

American wetlands. *Wetlands*, 26, 889–916.

Freedman, B. and T. Keith. 1995. *Planting Trees for Carbon Credits. A Discussion of the Issues, Feasibility, and Environmental Benefits*. Ottawa, ON: Tree Canada Foundation.

Freedman, B., G. Stinson, and P. Lacoul. 2009. Carbon credits and the conservation of natural areas. *Environmental Reviews*, 17, 1–19.

Freedman, B., P. N. Duinker, R. Morash, and U. Prager. 1982. *Forest Biomass and Nutrient Studies in Central Nova Scotia*. Information Report M-X-134. Fredericton, NB: Maritimes Forest Research Centre, Canadian Forestry Service.

IPCC (Intergovernmental Panel on Climate Change). 2007. *Climate Change 2007 Synthesis Report*. Oxford, UK: Oxford University Press.

Keeling, R. F., S. C. Piper, A. F. Bollenbacher, and J. S. Walker. 2012. Atmospheric CO_2 Records from Sites in the SIO Air Sampling Network. Oak Ridge, TN: Oak Ridge National Laboratory, Carbon Dioxide Information Analysis Center. http://cdiac.ornl.gov/trends/co2/ sio-keel.html.

Krebs, C. J., Boutin, S., and R. Boonstra. 2001. Ecosystem Dynamics of the Boreal Forest: The Kluane Project. New York: Oxford University Press.

Maessen, O., B. Freedman, M. L. N. Nams, and J. Svoboda. 1983. Resource allocation in high arctic vascular plants of differing growth form. *Canadian Journal of Botany*, 61, 1680–1691.

Natural Resources Canada. 2013. National Forest Carbon Monitoring, Accounting and Reporting System. Retrieved March 2013 from http://cfs.nrcan.gc.ca/pages/93?lang=en_CA.

Oberbauer, S. F., C. E. Tweedie, J. M. Welker, J. T. Fahnestock, G. H. R. Henry, P. J. Webber, R. D. Hollister, M. D. Walker, A. Kuchy, E. Elmore, and G. Starr. 2007. Tundra CO_2 fluxes in response to experimental warming across latitudinal and moisture gradients. *Ecological Monographs*, 77, 221–238.

Odum, E. P. 1983. *Basic Ecology*. New York: Saunders College Publishing.

Odum, E. P. and G. W. Barrett. 2005. *Fundamentals of Ecology* (5th ed.). New York: Thomson Brooks/Cole.

Smithwick, E. A. H., M. E. Harmon, S. M. Remillard, S. A. Acker, and J. F. Franklin. 2002. Potential upper bounds of carbon stores in forests of the Pacific Northwest. *Ecological Applications*, 12(5), 1303–1317.

Walker, M. D., C. H. Wahren, R. D. Hollister, G. H. R. Henry, L. E. Ahlquist, J. M. Alatalo, M. S. Bret-Harte, M. P. Calef, T. V. Callaghan, A. B. Carroll, H. E. Epstein, I. S. Jonsdottir, J.A. Klein, B. Magnusson, U. Molau, S. F. Oberbauer, S. P. Rewa, C. H. Robinson, G. R. Shaver, K. N. Suding, C. C. Thompson, A. Tolvanen, Ø. Totlandt, P. L. Turner, C. E. Tweedie, P. J. Webber, and P. A. Wookey. 2006. Plant community responses to experimental warming across the tundra biome. *Proceeding of the National Academy of Science*, 103, 1342–1346.

Whittaker, R. H. and G. E. Likens. 1975. The biosphere and Man. In H. Lieth and R. H. Whittaker (Eds.). *Primary Productivity of the Biosphere.* (pp. 305–328). New York: Springer-Verlag.

Chapter 4

Blasing, T. J. 1985. Background: Carbon cycle, climate, and vegetation responses. In *Characterization of Information Requirements for Studies of CO2 Effects. Water Resources, Agriculture, Fisheries, Forests, and Human Health*, DOE/ER-0236. (pp. 9–22). Washington, DC: U. S. Department of Energy.

Boden, T. A., G. Marland, and R. J. Andres. 2012. *Global, Regional, and National Fossil-Fuel CO_2 Emissions.* CDIAC (Carbon Dioxide Information Analysis Center). Oak Ridge, TN: Oak Ridge National Laboratory, U.S. Department of Energy. Retrieved from http://cdiac .ornl.gov/trends/emis/tre _glob_2009.html.

CDIAC (Carbon Dioxide Information Analysis Center). 2013a. *Global CO_2 Emissions from Fossil-Fuel Burning, Cement Manufacture, and Gas Flaring: 1751–2009.* CDIAC, Oak Ridge, TN. Retrieved October 2013 from http://cdiac.ornl.gov/ftp/ ndp030/global.1751_2009.ems.

CDIAC (Carbon Dioxide Information Analysis Center). 2013b. *National CO_2 Emissions from Fossil-Fuel Burning, Cement Manufacture, and Gas Flaring: 1751–2009.* CDIAC, Oak Ridge, TN. Retrieved October 2013 from http://cdiac.ornl.gov/ftp/ ndp030/nation.1751_2009.ems.

Cox, R. M. and T. C. Hutchinson. 1979. Metal co-tolerances in the grass *Deschampsia caespitosa. Nature*, 279, 231–233.

Freedman, B. 2010. *Environmental Science. A Canadian Perspective* (5th ed.). Don Mills, ON: Pearson Education Canada.

Gresh, T., J. Lichatowich, and P. Schoonmaker. 2000. An estimation of historic and current levels of salmon production in the Northeast Pacific ecosystem: Evidence of a nutrient deficit in the freshwater systems of the Pacific Northwest. *Fisheries*, 25, 15–21.

Houghton, R. A. 2008. *Annual Net Flux of Carbon to the Atmosphere from Land-Use Change: 1850–2005.* CDIAC (Carbon Dioxide Information Analysis Center), Oak Ridge, TN. Retrieved January 2013 from http://cdiac.ornl.gov/ trends/landuse/houghton/ houghton.html.

Hutzinger, O. (Ed.). 1982. *The Handbook of Environmental Chemistry.* New York: Springer-Verlag.

Keeling, R. F., S. C. Piper, A. F. Bollenbacher, and J. S. Walker. 2009. Atmospheric CO2 Records from Sites in the SIO Air Sampling Network. Oak Ridge, TN: Oak Ridge National Laboratory, Carbon Dioxide Information Analysis Center. http://cdiac.ornl.gov/ trends/co2/sio-keel.html.

Likens, G. E. and F. H. Bormann. 1999. *Biogeochemistry of a Forested Ecosystem* (2nd ed.). New York: Springer-Verlag.

Moore, J. W. and D. E. Schindler. 2004. Nutrient export from freshwater ecosystems by anadromous sockeye salmon (*Oncorhynchus nerka*). *Canadian Journal of Fisheries and Aquatic Science*, 61, 1582–1589.

Solomon, A. M., J. R. Trabolka, D. E. Reichle, and L. D. Voorhees. 1985. The global cycle of carbon. In *Atmospheric Carbon Dioxide and the Global Carbon Cycle* (pp. 1–12). Washington, DC: U.S. Department of Energy.

United States Census Bureau. 2013. International Programs United States Department of Commerce, Washington, DC. Retrieved January 2013 from http://www.census.gov/ population/international/data/ worldpop/table_history.php.

USDA. 2009. *Soil Science Glossary.* Washington, DC: United States Department of Agriculture, Natural Resources Conservation Service. http://soils.usda.gov.

Wetzel, R. G. 1975. *Limnology.* Toronto, ON: Saunders.

Chapter 5

Albano, D. J. 1992. Nesting mortality of Carolina chickadees breeding in natural cavities. *The Condor*, 94, 371–382.

Bérubé, C. H., Festa-Bianchet, M., and J. T. Jorgenson. 1999. Individual differences, longevity, and reproductive senescence in bighorn ewes. *Ecology*, 80, 2555–2565.

Bowen, W. D., J. McMillan, and R. Mohn. 2003. Sustained exponential growth of grey seals at Sable Island, Nova Scotia. *ICES Journal of Marine Science*, 60, 1265–1274.

(b) Modified from Menu, S., G. Gauthier, and A. Reed. 2002. Changes in survival rates and population dynamics of greater snow geese over a 30-year period: Implications for hunting regulations. *Journal of Applied Ecology*, 39, 91–102.

Brattey, J., N. G. Cadigan, K. Dwyer, B. P. Healey, M. J. Morgan, E. F. Murphy, D. Maddock Parsons, and D. Power. 2008. Assessments of the cod (*Gadus morhua*) stock in NAFO Divisions 2J3KL (April 2007 and April 2008). *Canadian Science Advisory Secretariat Research Document 2008/086*, Ottawa, ON: Fisheries and Oceans Canada.

Caswell, H. 1989. *Matrix Population Models.* Sunderland, MA: Sinauer Associates.

Claessen, D., A. M. de Roos, and L. Persson. 2000. Dwarfs and giants: Cannibalism and competition in size-structured populations. *American Naturalist*, 155, 219–237.

Fisher, R. A. 1930. *The Genetical Theory of Natural Selection.* Oxford, UK: Clarendon Press.

Fryxell, J. M., J. B. Falls, E. A. Falls, and R. J. Brooks. 1998. Long-term dynamics of small-mammal populations in Ontario. *Ecology*, 79(1), 213–225.

Garcia, S., P. Sparre, and J. Csirke. 1989. Estimating surplus production and maximum sustainable yield from biomass data when catch and effort time series are not available. *Fisheries Research*, 8, 13–23.

Gause, G. F. 1932. Experimental studies on the struggle for existence. I. Mixed population of two species of yeast. *Journal of Experimental Biology*, 9, 389–402.

Gause, G. F. 1934. *The Struggle for Existence.* Baltimore, MD: Williams and Wilkins.

Gause, G. F. 1935. Vérifications expérimentales de la Théorie Mathématique de la Lutte Pour la Vie. Paris, France: Hermann.

Gotelli, N. J. 2008. *A Primer of Ecology* (4th ed.). Sunderland, MA: Sinauer.

Holling, C. S. 1959. The components of predation as revealed by a study of small mammal predation of the European pine sawfly. *Canadian Entomologist*, 91, 293–320.

Hutchings, J. A. 1999. The influence of growth and survival costs of reproduction on Atlantic cod, *Gadus morhua*, population growth rate. *Canadian Journal of Fisheries and Aquatic Sciences*, 56, 1612–1623.

Hutchings, J. A. and M. E. B. Jones. 1998. Life history variation and growth rate thresholds for maturity in Atlantic salmon, *Salmo salar*. *Canadian Journal of Fisheries and Aquatic Sciences*, 55 (Supplement 1), 22–47.

Hutchings, J. A., C. Walters, and R. L. Haedrich. 1997. Is scientific inquiry incompatible with government information control? *Canadian Journal of Fisheries and Aquatic Sciences*, 54, 1198–1210.

Hutchings, J. A., R. A. Myers, V. B. García, L. O. Lucifora, and A. Kuparinen. 2012. Life-history correlates of extinction risk and recovery potential. *Ecological Applications*, 22, 1061–1067.

Krebs, C. J. 2009. *Ecology: The Experimental Analysis of Distribution and Abundance*. San Francisco, CA: Benjamin Cummings.

Lack, D. 1947. *Darwin's Finches*. Cambridge, UK: Cambridge University Press.

Leslie, P. H. 1945. On the use of matrices in certain population mathematics. *Biometrika*, 35, 183–212.

Lieske, D. 1997. Population dynamics of urban merlins. M.Sc. Thesis, University of Saskatchewan.

Loery, G., K. H. Pollock, J. D. Nichols, and J. D. Hines. 1987. Age-specificity of black-capped chickadee survival rates: Analysis of capture-recapture data. *Ecology*, 64, 1038–1044.

Loison, A., M. Festa-Bianchet, J.-M. Gaillard, J. T. Jorgenson, and J.-M. Jullien. 1999. Age-specific survival in five populations of ungulates: Evidence of senescence. *Ecology*, 80, 2539–2554.

Lotka, A. J. 1925. *Elements of Physical Biology*. Baltimore, MD: Williams and Watkins.

MacArthur, R. H. 1958. Population ecology of some warblers of northeastern coniferous forests. *Ecology*, 39, 599–619.

MacArthur, R. H. 1972. *Geographical Ecology*. New York: Harper and Row.

Mahoney, N., E. Nol, and T. C. Hutchinson. 1997. Food-chain chemistry, reproductive success, and foraging behaviour of songbirds in acidified maple forests of central Ontario. *Canadian Journal of Zoology*, 75, 509–517.

Myers, R. A., G. Mertz, and P. S. Fowlow. 1997. Maximum population growth rates and recovery times for Atlantic cod, *Gadus morhua*. *Fishery Bulletin*, 95, 762–772.

Neal, D. 2004. *Introduction to Population Ecology*. Cambridge, UK: Cambridge University Press.

Oliphant, L. W. and E. Haug. 1985. Productivity, population density and rate of increase of an expanding Merlin population. *Raptor Research*, 19, 56–59.

Parsons, L. S. 1993. *Management of Marine Fisheries in Canada*. Ottawa, ON: NRC Press.

Ramsay, S. M., D. J. Mennill, K. A. Otter, L. M. Ratcliffe, and P. T. Boag. 2003. Sex allocation in black-capped chickadees *Poecile atricapilla*. *Journal of Avian Biology*, 34, 134–139.

Rosenzweig, M. L. and R. H. MacArthur. 1963. Graphical representation and stability conditions of predator–prey interactions. *American Naturalist*, 47, 209–223.

Schluter, D. 2000. *The Ecology of Adaptive Radiation*. Oxford, UK: Oxford University Press.

Schluter, D. and J. D. McPhail. 1992. Ecological character displacement and speciation in sticklebacks. *American Naturalist*, 140, 85–108.

Smith, C. and P. Reay. 1991. Cannibalism in teleost fishes. *Reviews in Fish Biology and Fisheries*, 1, 41–64.

Smith, S. M. 1995. Age-specific survival in breeding black-capped chickadees (*Parus atricapillus*). *The Auk*, 112, 840–846.

Swain, D. P. and A. F. Sinclair 2000. Pelagic fishes and the cod recruitment dilemma in the Northwest Atlantic. *Canadian Journal of Fisheries and Aquatic Sciences*, 57, 1321–1325.

Swain, D. P. and G. Chouinard. 2008. Predicted extirpation of the dominant demersal fish in a large marine ecosystem: Atlantic cod (*Gadus morhua*) in the southern Gulf of St. Lawrence. *Canadian Journal of Fisheries and Aquatic Sciences*, 65, 2315–2319.

Volterra, V. 1926. Fluctuations in the abundance of a species considered mathematically. *Nature*, 118, 558–560.

Williams, G. C. 1966. *Adaptation and Natural Selection*. Princeton, NJ: Princeton University Press.

Worm, B., R. Hilborn, J. K. Baum, T. A. Branch, J. S. Collie, C. Costello, M. J. Fogarty, E. A. Fulton, J. A. Hutchings, S. Jennings, O. P. Jensen, H. K. Lotze, P. M. Mace, T. R. McClanahan, C. Minto, S. R. Palumbi, A. M. Parma, D. Ricard, A. A. Rosenberg, R. Watson, and D. Zeller. 2009. Rebuilding Global Fisheries. *Science*, 325, 578–585.

Chapter 6

Alcock, J. 2009. *Animal Behavior* (9th ed.). Sunderland, MA: Sinauer Associates.

Alonzo, S. H. 2008. An inordinate fondess for behavioural ecology. *Trends in Ecology and Evolution*, 23, 600–601.

Arnqvist, G. and L. Rowe. 2005. *Sexual Conflict*. Princeton, NJ: Princeton University Press.

Arnqvist, G. and L. Rowe. 1995. Sexual conflict and arms races between the sexes: A morphological adaptation for control of mating in a female insect. *Proceedings of the Royal Society of London (B)*, 261, 123–127.

Baker, R. L. and B. P. Smith. 1997. Conflict between antipredator and antiparasite behaviour in larval damselflies. *Oecologia*, 109, 622–628.

Barette, C. and D. Vandal. 1990. Sparring, relative antler size, and assessment in male caribou. *Behavioural Ecology and Sociobiology*, 26, 383–387.

Berdoy, M., J. P. Webster, and D. W. Macdonald. 2000. Fatal attraction in rats infected with *Toxoplasma gondii*. *Proceedings of the Royal Society of London (B)*, 267, 1591–1594.

Biological Sciences Electron Microscopy Laboratory, Texas Tech University. Retrieved August 2013 from http://www.devbio.biology.gatech.edu/?page_id=34.

Biron, D. G., F. Ponton, L. Marche, N. Galeotti, L. Renault, E. Demey-Thomas, J. Poncet, S. P. Brown, P. Jouin, and F. Thomas. 2006. "Suicide" of crickets harbouring hairworms: A proteomics investigation. *Insect Molecular Biology*, 15, 731–742.

Blackmore, C. J. and R. Heinsohn. 2007. Reproductive success and helper effects in the cooperatively breeding grey-crowned babbler. *Journal of Zoology*, 273, 326–332.

Borgerhoff Mulder, M. 2005. Human Behavioural Ecology. In *Encyclopedia of Life Sciences*. Chichester: John Wiley & Sons.

Brooks, D. R. and D. A. McLennan. 1991. *Phylogeny, Ecology, and Behavior: A Research Program in Comparative Biology*. Chicago, IL: University of Chicago Press.

Brooks, D. R. and D. A. McLennan. 2002. *The Nature of Diversity: An Evolutionary Voyage of Discovery.* Chicago, IL: University of Chicago Press.

Brown, J. L., E. R. Brown, S. D. Brown, and D. D. Dow. 1982. Helpers: Effects of experimental removal on reproductive success. *Science*, 215, 421–422.

Cartar R. V. 2004. Resource tracking by bumble bees: Responses to plant-level differences in quality. *Ecology*, 85, 2764–2771.

Cézilly, F., A. Grégoire, and A. Bertin. 2000. Conflict between co-occurring manipulative parasites? An experimental study of the joint influence of two acanthocephalan parasites on the behaviour of *Gammarus pulex*. *Parasitology*, 120, 625–630.

Chapman, T., B. J. Crespi, B. D. Kranz, and M. P. Schwarz. 2000. High relatedness and inbreeding at the origin of eusociality in gall-inducing thrips. *Proceedings of the National Academy of Sciences (USA)*, 97, 1648–650.

Chapman, T. W., B. J. Crespi, and S. P. Perry. 2008. The evolutionary ecology of eusociality in Australian gall thrips: A "model clades" approach. In J. Korb and J. Heinze (Eds.) *Ecology of Social Evolution.* (pp. 57–82). Berlin: Springer-Verlag.

Chase, R. and K. C. Blanchard. 2006. The snail's love-dart delivers mucus to increase paternity. *Proceedings of the Royal Society B*, 273, 1471–1475.

Clout, M. N., G. P. Elliott, and B. C. Robertson. 2002. Effects of supplementary feeding on the offspring sex ratio of kakapo: A dilemma for the conservation of a polygynous parrot. *Biological Conservation*, 107, 13–18.

Clutton-Brock, T. H. and A. C. J. Vincent. 1991. Sexual selection and the potential reproductive rates of males and females. *Nature*, 351, 58–60.

Dawkins, R. 1976. *The Selfish Gene.* Oxford, UK: Oxford University Press.

De Moraes, C. M., W. J. Lewis, P. W. Paré, H. T. Alborn, and J. H. Tumlinson. 1998. Herbivore-infested plants selectively attract parasitoids. *Nature*, 393, 570–573.

Despland, E. and S. Hamzah. 2004. Ontogenetic changes in social behaviour in the forest tent caterpillar, *Malacosoma disstria*. *Behavioral Ecology and Sociobiology*, 56, 177–184.

Doherty, P. F., G. Sorci, J. A. Royle, J. E. Hines, J. D. Nichols, and T. Boulinier. 2003. Sexual selection affects local extinction and turnover in bird communities. *Proceedings of the National Academy of Science*, 100, 5858–5862.

Emlen D. J. 1997. Diet alters male horn allometry in the beetle *Onthophagus acuminatus* (Coleoptera, Scarabaeidae). *Proceedings of the Royal Society of London (B)*, 264, 567–574.

Emlen, D. J., J. Marangelo, B. Ball, and C. W. Cunningham. 2005. Diversity in the weapons of sexual selection: Horn evolution in the beetle genus *Onthophagus* (Coleoptera: Scarabaeidae). *Evolution*, 59, 1060–1084.

Fisher, R. A. 1930. *The Genetical Theory of Natural Selection.* Oxford, UK: Clarendon Press.

Fitzpatrick, M. J., Y. Ben-Shahar, H. M. Smid, L. E. M. Vet, G. E. Robinson, and M. B. Sokolowski. 2005. Candidate genes for behavioural ecology. *Trends in Ecology and Evolution*, 20, 96–104.

Freeman, D. C., E. D. McArthur, K. J. Miglial, M. J. Nilson and M. L. Brown. 2007. Sex and the lonely *Atriplex*. *Western North American Naturalist*, 67, 137–141.

Gardner A., J. Alpedrinha, and S. A. West. 2012. Haplodiploidy and the evolution of eusociality: Split sex ratios. *American Naturalist*, 179: 240–256.

Gibbs, H. L., M. D. Sorenson, K. Marchetti, M. D. Brooke, N. B. Davies, and H. Nakamura. 2000. Genetic evidence for female host-specific races of the common cuckoo. *Nature*, 407, 183–186.

Godin, J.-G. J. and L. A. Dugatkin. 1996. Female mating preference for bold males in the guppy, *Poecilia reticulata*. *Proceedings of the National Academy of Science*, 93, 10262–10267.

Godin, J.-G. J. and S. E. Briggs, 1996. Female mate choice under predation risk in the guppy. *Animal Behavior*, 51, 117–130.

Grimson, M. J. and R. L. Blanton. SEM of Dictyostelium developmental stages.

Gwynne, D. T. 1997. Glandular gifts. *Scientific American*, 277, 46–51.

Gwynne, D. T. and L. W. Simmons, 1990. Experimental reversal of courtship roles in an insect. *Nature*, 346, 172–174.

Gwynne, Darryl T. 2001. *Katydids and Bush-crickets: Reproductive Behavior and Evolution of the Tettigoniidae.* Ithaca, NY: Cornell University Press.

Hames, R. 2001. Human Behavioral Ecology. In M. J. Smelser and P. B. Baltres (Eds.), *International Encyclopedia of the Social and Behavioral Sciences.* (pp. 6946–6951). London, UK: Elsevier.

Hamilton, W. D. and M. Zuk. 1982. Heritable true fitness and bright birds: A role for parasites? *Science*, 218, 384–387.

Harpending, H. 2002. Kinship and population subdivision. *Population and Environment*, 24, 141–147.

Hughes, W. O. H., B. P. Oldroyd, M. Beekman, and F. L. W. Ratnieks. 2008. Ancestral monogamy shows kin selection is key to the evolution of eusociality. *Science*, 320, 1213–1216.

Hutchings, M. R., I. J. Gordon, I. Kyriazakis, E. Robertson, and F. Jackson. 2002. Grazing in heterogeneous environments: Infra- and supra-parasite distributions determine herbivore grazing decisions. *Oecologia*, 132, 453–460.

Karban, R. 1982. Increased reproductive success at high densities and predator satiation for periodical cicadas. *Ecology*, 63, 321–328.

Karban, R. 2008. Plant behaviour and communication. *Ecology Letters*, 11, 727–739.

Karban R., J. Maron, G. W. Felton, G. Ervin, and H. Eichenseer. 2003. Herbivore damage to sagebrush induces resistance in wild tobacco: Evidence for eavesdropping between plants. *Oiko*, 100, 325–332.

Kelly, C. D. 2006a. Fighting for harems: Assessment strategies during male-male contests in the sexually dimorphic Wellington tree weta. *Animal Behaviour*, 72, 727–736.

Kelly, C. D. 2006b. Replicating empirical research in behavioral ecology: How and why it should be done but rarely ever is. *Quarterly Review of Biology*, 81, 221–236.

Krakauer, A. H. 2005. Kin selection and cooperative courtship in wild turkeys. *Nature*, 434, 69–72.

Kuzdzal-Fick, J. J., K. R. Foster, D. C. Queller, and J. E. Strassmann. 2007. Exploiting new terrain: An advantage to sociality in the slime mold *Dictyostelium discoideum*. *Behavioral Ecology*, 18, 433–437.

Lefèvre, T., C. Lebarbenchon, M. Gauthier-Clerc, D. Misse, R. Poulin, and F. Thomas. 2009. The ecological significance of manipulative parasites. *Trends in Ecology and Evolution*, 24, 41–48.

Lima, S. L., T. J. Valone, and T. Caraco. 1985. Foraging-efficiency-predation-risk trade-off in the grey squirrel. *Animal Behaviour*, 33(1), 155–165.

Lockwood, J. 2004. The orgy in your backyard. *New York Times*, May 20.

Lyon, B. E., J. M. Eadie, and L. D. Hamilton. 1994. Parental choice selects for ornamental plumage in American coot chicks. *Nature*, 371, 240–243.

Macchiusi, F. and R. L. Baker. 1992. Effects of predators and food availability on activity and growth of *Chironomus tentans* (Chironomidae, Diptera). *Freshwater Biology*, 28, 207–216.

Mennill, D. J., L. M. Ratcliffe, and P. T. Boag. 2002. Female eavesdropping on male song contests in songbirds. *Science*, 296, 873–873.

Moller A. P. 1991. Sexual selection in the monogamous barn swallow (*Hirundo rustica*) I. Determinants of tail ornament size. *Evolution*, 45, 1823–1836.

Otronen, M. 1990. Mating behavior and sperm competition in the fly, *Dryomyza anilis*. *Behavioral Ecology and Sociobiology*, 26, 349–356.

Owens, I. P. F. 2006. Where is behavioral ecology going? *Trends in Ecology and Evolution*, 21, 356–360.

Parker, G. A. 1970. Sperm competition and its evolutionary consequences in the insects. *Biological Reviews (Cambridge)*, 45, 525–567.

Parrott, M. L., S. J. Ward, and P. D. Temple-Smith. 2007. Olfactory cues, genetic relatedness and female mate choice in the agile antechinus (*Antechinus agilis*). *Behavioral Ecology and Sociobiology*, 61, 1075–1079.

Poulin, R. 2006. *Evolutionary Ecology of Parasites* (2nd ed.) Princeton, NJ: Princeton University Press.

Preston, B. T., I. R. Stevenson, J. M. Pemberton, and K. Wilson. 2001. Dominant rams lose out by sperm depletion. *Nature*, 409, 681–682.

Proctor, H. C. 1991. Courtship in the water mite *Neumania papillator*: Males capitalize on female adaptations for predation. *Animal Behavior*, 42, 589–598.

Queller, D. C., F. Zacchi, R. Cervo, S. Turillazzi, M. T. Henshaw, L. A. Santorelli, and J. E. Strassmann. 2000. Unrelated helpers in a social insect. *Nature*, 405, 784–787.

Queller, D. C. and J. E. Strassmann. 2003. Eusociality. *Current Biology*, 13, R861–R863.

Rasmann, S., G. T. G. Köllner, J. Degenhardt, I. Hiltpold, S. Toepfer, U. Kuhlmann, J. Gershenzon, and T. C. J. Turlings. 2005. Recruitment of entomopathogenic nematodes by insect-damaged maize roots. *Nature*, 434, 732–737.

Rodd, F. H., K. A. Hughes, G. F. Grether, and C. T. Baril. 2002. A possible non-sexual origin of mate preference: Are male guppies mimicking fruit? *Proceedings of the Royal Society of London (B)*, 269, 475–481.

Rowe, L., G. Arnqvistb, A. Sihc, and J. J. Krupac. 1994. Sexual conflict and the evolutionary ecology of mating patterns: Water striders as a model system. *Trends in Ecology and Evolution*, 9, 289–293.

Sherman, P. W. 1977. Nepotism and the evolution of alarm calls. *Science*, 197, 1246–1253.

Sibley, R. and R. Smith (Eds.). 1985. *Behavioural Ecology: Ecological Consequences of Adaptive Behaviour*. Oxford, UK: Blackwell Scientific Publications.

Strassmann, J. E. and D. C. Queller. 2007. Altruism among amoebas. *Natural History*, 116, 24–29.

Tarpy, D. R. and T. D. Seeley. 2006. Lower disease infections in honeybee (*Apis mellifera*) colonies headed by polyandrous vs monandrous queens. *Naturwissenschaften*, 93, 195–199.

Thorne, B. L., N. L. Breisch, and M. L. Muscedere. 2003. Evolution of eusociality and the soldier caste in termites: Influence of intraspecific competition and accelerated inheritance. *Proceedings of the National Academy of Science*, 100, 12808–12813.

Tibbetts, E. A. and J. Dale. 2004. A socially enforced signal of quality in a paper wasp. *Nature*, 432, 218–222.

Trivers, R. and D. Willard. 1973. Natural selection of parental ability to vary the sex ratio of offspring. *Science*, 179, 90–92.

Welch, A. M., R. D. Semlitsch, and H. C. Gerhardt. 1998. Call duration as an indicator of genetic quality in male gray tree frogs. *Science*, 280, 1928–1930.

West-Eberhard, M. J. 1979. Sexual selection, social competition, and evolution. *Proceedings of the American Philosophical Society*, 123, 222–234.

Wilkinson, G. S. 1984. Reciprocal food sharing in the vampire bat. *Nature*, 308, 181–184.

Wilkinson, G. S., D. C. Presgraves, and L. Crymes. 1998a. Male eye span in stalk-eyed flies indicates genetic quality by meiotic drive suppression. *Nature*, 391, 276–279.

Wilkinson, G. S., H. Kahler, and R. H. Baker. 1998b. Evolution of female mating preferences in stalk-eyed flies. *Behavioral Ecology*, 9, 525–533.

Williams, G. C. 1966. *Adaptation and Natural Selection*. Princeton, NJ: Princeton University Press.

Wilson, M. and M. Daly. 1997. Life expectancy, economic inequality, homicide, and reproductive timing in Chicago neighbourhoods. *British Medical Journal*, 314, 1271–1274.

Zahavi, A. 1975. Mate selection—A selection for a handicap. *Journal of Theoretical Biology*, 53, 205–214.

Chapter 7

Aerts, R. 1996. Nutrient resorption from senescing leaves of perennials: Are there general patterns? *Journal of Ecology*, 84, 597–608.

Ahrens, C.D. 2012. *Essentials of Meteorology* (6th ed.). Belmont, CA: Cengage Learning, Brooks/Cole.

Aronson, J., J. Kigel, A. Shmida, and J. Klein. Adaptive phenology of desert and Mediterranean populations of annual plants grown with and without water stress. 1992. *Oecologia*, 89(1), 17–26.

Brown, G. W., W. R. Brown, and P. P. Cohen. 1959. Comparative biochemistry of urea synthesis. II. Levels of urea cycle enzymes in metamorphosing *Rana catesbeiana* tadpoles. *Journal of Biological Chemistry*. 234, 1775–1780.

Butler, P. J. and D. R. Jones. 1997. Physiology of diving of birds and mammals. *Physiological Reviews*, 77, 837–899.

Chen, L., A. L. DeVries, and C. C. Cheng. 1997. Convergent evolution of antifreeze glycoproteins in Antarctic notothenioid fish and Arctic cod. *Proceedings of the National Academy of Science*, 94, 3817–3822.

Coley, P.D., J. P. Bryant, and F. S. Chapin. 1985. Resource availability and plant anti-herbivore defense. *Science*, 230, 895–899.

Cooper, G.M. 2000. *The Cell: A Molecular Approach* (2nd ed.). Sunderland, MA: Sinauer Associates.

Danks, H. V. 2004. Seasonal adaptations in arctic insects. *Integrative and Comparative Biology*, 44, 85–94.

Danks, H. V., O. Kukal, and R. A. Ring. 1994. Insect cold-hardiness: Insights from the Arctic. *Arctic*, 47, 391–404.

Davenport, J. A. 1992. *Animal Life at Low Temperature*. London, UK: Chapman and Hall.

Dawson, W. R. and G. A. Bartholomew. 1956. Relation of oxygen consumption to body weight, temperature, and temperature acclimation in lizards *Uta stansburia* and *Scelopwus occidentalis*. *Physiological Zoology*, 29, 40–51.

Degnan, K. J., K. J. Karnaky, and J. A. Zadunaisky. 1977. Active chloride transport in the in vitro opercular skin of a teleost (*Fundulus heteroclitus*), a gill-like epithelium rich in chloride cells. *Journal of Physiology*, 271, 155–191.

Dejours, P. 1975. *Principles of Comparative Respiratory Physiology*. Amsterdam: North Holland Publishing.

Dittmer, H. J. 1937. A quantitative study of the roots and root hairs of a winter rye plant (Secale cereale). *American Journal of Botany*, 24, 417–420.

Duguay, S. M., K. Arii, M. Hooper, and M. J. Lechowicz. 2001. Ice storm damage and early recovery in an old-growth forest. *Environmental Monitoring and Assessment*, 67, 97–108.

Ehleringer, J. R. and Monson, R. K. 1993. Evolutionary and ecological aspects of photosynthetic pathway variation. *Annual Review of Ecology, Evolution and Systematics*, 24, 411–439.

Evert, R. F. and S. E. Eichhorn. 2013. In Raven: *Biology of Plants* (8th ed.). New York: W.H. Freeman and Company Publishers.

Ewart, K. V., Q. Lin, and C. L. Hew. 1999. Structure, function and evolution of antifreeze proteins. *Cellular and Molecular Life Sciences*, 55, 271–283.

Freedman, B., P. N. Duinker, H. Barclay, R. Morash, and U. Prager. 1982. *Forest Biomass and Nutrient Studies in Central Nova Scotia. Part 1. Biomass and Nutrient Standing Crop Equations.* Information Report M-X-134. Fredericton, NB: Maritimes Forest Research Centre, Canadian Forestry Service.

Gershenzon, J. 1994. The cost of plant chemical defense against herbivory: A biochemical perspective. In E. A. Bernays (Ed.). *Insect-Plant Interactions.* (pp. 105–173). Boca Raton, FL: CRC Press.

Giron, D., W. Kaiser, N. Imbault, and J. Casas. 2007. Cytokinin-mediated leaf manipulation by a leafminer caterpillar. *Biology Letters*, 3, 340–343.

Gorham, E., J. A. Janssens, and P. H. Glaser. 2003. Rates of peat accumulation during the postglacial period in 32 sites from Alaska to Newfoundland, with special emphasis on northern Minnesota. *Canadian Journal of Botany*, 81, 429–438.

Heinrich, B. and G. A. Bartholomew. 1971. An analysis of pre-flight warm-up in the sphinx moth *Manduca sexta. Journal of Experimental Biology*, 55, 233–239. Retrieved October 2013 from http://jeb.biologists.org/cgi/content/abstract/55/1/223.

Hejl, A. M, F. A. Einhellig, and J. A. Rasmussen. 1993. Effects of juglone on growth, photosynthesis and respiration. *Journal of Chemical Ecology*, 19, 559–568.

Hill, R. W. 1975. Daily torpor in *Peromyscus leucopus* on an adequate diet. *Comparative Biochemistry and Physiology—Part A: Physiology*, 51, 413–423.

Hill, R. W., G. A. Wyse, and M. Anderson. 2008. *Animal Physiology.* Sunderland, MA: Sinauer Associates.

Hoar, W. S. 1960. *Comparative Biochemistry*, vol. 1. M. Florkin and H. S. Mason, (Eds.). New York: Academic Press.

Hochachka, P. W. and G. N. Somero. 2002. *Biochemical Adaptation: Mechanism and Process in Physiological Evolution.* New York: Oxford University Press.

Jurik, T. W., J. A. Weber, and D. M. Gates. 1984. Short-term effects of CO_2 on gas exchange in leaves of big-toothed aspen (*Populus grandidentata*) in the field. *Plant Physiology*, 75, 1022–1026.

Kaiser, W., E. Huguet, J. Casas, C. Commin, and D. Giron. 2010. Plant green-island phenotype induced by leaf-miners is mediated by bacterial symbionts. *Proceedings of the Royal Society, London B* 277 (1692), 2311–2319.

Kilgore, D. L. and K. Schmidt-Nielsen. 1975. Heat loss from ducks' feet immersed in cold water. *The Condor*, 77, 475–478.

Kooyman, G. L. and P. J. Ponganis. 1998. The physiological basis of diving to depth: Birds and mammals. *Annual Review of Physiology*, 60, 19–32.

Lambers, H., F. S. Chapin III, and T. L. Pons. 1998. *Plant Physiological Ecology.* New York: Springer-Verlag.

Lausen, C. L. and R. M. R. Barclay. 2003. Thermoregulation and roost selection by reproductive female big brown bats (*Eptesicus fuscus*) roosting in rock crevices. *Journal of Zoology, London*, 260, 235–244.

Lawton, J. H. and S. E. Hartley 1987. Effects of different types of damage on the chemistry of birch foliage, and the responses of birch feeding insects. *Oecologia*, 74(3), 432–437.

Lenfant, C., K. Johansen, and J. D. Torrance. 1970. Gas transport and oxygen storage capacity in some pinnipeds and the sea otter. *Respiration Physiology*, 9, 277–286

Loik, M. E. and P. S. Nobel. 1993. Freezing tolerance and water relations of *Opuntia fragilis* from Canada and the United States. *Ecology*, 74, 1722–1732.

Long, S. P., E. A. Ainsworth, A. D. B. Leakey, J. Nösberger, and D. R. Ort. 2006. Food for thought: Lower-than-expected crop yield stimulation with rising CO_2 concentrations. *Science*, 318, 1918–1921.

Marchand, P. J. 1996. *Life in the Cold: An Introduction to Winter Ecology* (3rd ed.). Hanover, NH: University Press of New England.

Marchand, P. J. and B. F. Chabot. 1978. Winter water relations of tree-line plant species on Mt. Washington, New Hampshire. *Arctic and Alpine Research*, 10, 105–116.

Minorsky, P. V. 2002. Global warming: Effects on plants. *Plant Physiology*, 129, 1421–1422.

Pallardy, S. G. 2008. *Physiology of Woody Plants* (3rd ed.). Burlington, MA: Academic Press.

Ponganis, P. J., G. L. Kooyman, and M. A. Castellini. 1993. Determinants of the aerobic dive limit of Weddell seals: Analysis of diving metabolic rates, postdive end tidal PO_2's, and blood and muscle oxygen stores. *Physiological Zoology*, 66: 732–749.

Randall, D., W. Burggren, and K. French. 2002. *Eckert Animal Physiology: Mechanisms and Adaptations* (5th ed.). New York: W. H. Freeman and Co.

Regniere, J. and B. Bentz. 2007. Modeling cold tolerance in the mountain pine beetle, *Dendroctonus ponderosae. Journal of Insect Physiology*, 53, 559–572.

Reynolds, J. E. III and S. A. Rommel (eds). 1999. Biology of Marine Mammals, Washington, DC: Smithsonian Institution Press.

Rietveld, W. J. 1983. Allelopathic effects of juglone on germination and growth of several herbaceous and woody species. *Journal of Chemical Ecology*, 9, 295–308.

Sage, R.F. 2004. The evolution of C4 photosynthesis. *New Phytologist*, 161, 341–370.

Schmidt-Nielsen, B. and K. Schmidt-Nielsen. 1951. A complete account of the water metabolism in kangaroo rats and an experimental verification. *Journal of Cellular and Comparative Physiology*, 38, 165–181.

Schmidt-Nielsen, K., F. R. Hainsworth, and D. E. Murrish. 1970. Countercurrent heat exchange in the respiratory passages. Effect on water and heat balance. *Respiration Physiology*, 9(2), 263–276.

Seiger, D.S. 1998. *Plant Secondary Metabolism.* Norwell, MA: Kluwer Academic Publishers.

Sherwood, L. and R. Kell. 2009. *Human Physiology: From Cells to Systems.* Toronto, ON: Nelson.

Sherwood, L. 2010. *Human Physiology* (1st ed.). Toronto, ON: Nelson Education.

Shively, S. B. and J. B. Weaver. 1939. Amount of underground plant materials in different grassland climates. *Nebraska Conservation Bulletin*, 21, 1–68.

Southon, I. W. and J. Buckingham. 1989. *Dictionary of Alkaloids.* London, UK: Chapman & Hall.

Storey, K. B. and J. M. Storey. 1996. Natural freezing survival in animals. *Annual Review of Ecology and Systematics*, 27, 365–386.

Strimbeck, G. R., T. D. Kjellson, P. G. Schaberg, and P. F. Murakami. 2008. Dynamics of low-temperature acclimation in temperate and boreal conifer foliage in a mild winter climate. *Tree Physiology*, 28, 1365–1374.

Szent-Gyorgyi, A. 1960. *Introduction to a Submolecular Biology.* New York: Academic Press.

Tarnocai, C. 2009. The impact of climate change on Canadian peatlands. *Canadian Water Resources Journal*, 34, 453–466.

Tubiello, F. N., J.-F. Soussana, and S. M. Howden. 2007. Crop and pasture response to climate change. *Proceedings of the National Academy of Sciences of the United States of America*, 104, 19686–19690.

Valentine, J. F. 2001. *Grazing Management* (2nd ed.). San Diego, CA: Academic Press.

Vogel, S. 2009. Leaves in the lowest and highest winds: Temperature, force and shape. *New Phytologist*, 183, 13–26.

Vogel, S. 2012. *The Life of a Leaf.* Chicago, IL: University of Chicago Press.

Way, D. A. and R. F. Sage 2008. Thermal acclimation of photosynthesis in black spruce [*Picea mariana* (Mill.) B.S.P.] *Plant, Cell and Environment*, 9, 1250–1262.

Whitehead, H. 2002. Sperm whale *Physeter macrocephalus.* In W. Perrin, B. Würsig, and J. Thewissen (Eds.) *Encyclopedia of Marine Mammals.* (pp. 1165–1172). New York: Academic Press.

Wikipedia. 2013. Growing-degree day. Retrieved March 2013 from http://en.wikipedia.org/wiki/Growing-degree_day.

Willmer, P., G. Stone, and I. Johnston. 2000. *Environmental Physiology of Animals.* Oxford, UK: Blackwell Science.

Wood, C. M. and D. G. McDonald 1982. Physiological mechanisms of acid toxicity in fish. In R. E. Johnson (Ed.), *Acid Rain/Fisheries, Proceedings of an International Symposium on Acidic Precipitation and Fishery Impacts in North-eastern North America.* (pp. 197–226). Bethesda, MD: American Fisheries Society.

Woodward, F. I. 1987. *Climate and Plant Distribution.* Cambridge, UK: Cambridge University Press.

Zhang, X., F. W. Zwiers, G. C. Hegerl, F. H. Lambert, N. P. Gillett, S. Solomon, P. A. Stott, and T. Nozawa. 2007. Detection of human influence on twentieth-century precipitation trends. *Nature*, 448, 461–465.

Chapter 8

Alm, G. 1959. Connection between maturity, size and age in fishes. Annual Report of the Institute of Freshwater Research, Drottningholm, 40, 5–145.

Arnqvist, G. and L. Rowe. 2005. *Sexual Conflict.* Princeton, NJ: Princeton University Press.

Aubin-Horth, N., C. R. Landry, B. H. Letcher, and H. A. Hofmann. 2005a. Alternative life histories shape brain gene expression profiles in males of the same population. *Proceedings of the Royal Society B*, 272, 1655–1662.

Aubin-Horth, N., B. H. Letcher, and H. A. Hofmann. 2005b. Interaction of rearing environment and reproductive tactic on gene expression profiles in Atlantic salmon. *Journal of Heredity*, 96, 261–278.

Barot, S., M. Heino, L. O'Brien, and U. Dieckmann. 2004. Long-term trend in the maturation reaction norm of two cod stocks. *Ecological Applications*, 14, 1257–1271.

Barot, S., M. Heino, M. J. Morgan, and U. Dieckmann. 2005. Maturation of Newfoundland American plaice (*Hippolossoides platessoides*): Long-term trends in maturation reaction norms despite low fishing mortality? *ICES Journal of Marine Science*, 62, 56–64.

Beaumont, H. J. E., J. Gallie, C. Kjost, G. C. Ferguson, and P. B. Rainey. 2009. Experimental evolution of bet hedging. *Nature*, 462, 90–93.

Bell, G. 1980. The costs of reproduction and their consequences. *American Naturalist*, 116, 45–76.

Bennett, P. M. and I. P. F. Owens. 2002. *Evolutionary Ecology of Birds: Life Histories, Mating Systems and Extinction.* Oxford, UK: Oxford University Press.

Beverton, R. J. H. 1992. Patterns of reproductive strategy parameters in some marine teleost fishes. *Journal of Fish Biology*, 41 (Supplement B), 137–160.

Beverton, R. J. H. and S. J. Holt. 1959. A review of the lifespans and mortality rates of fish in nature, and their relation to growth and other physiological characteristics. *CIBA Foundation Coloquia on Ageing*, 54, 142–180.

Bielak, A. T. and G. Power. 1986. Changes in mean weight, sea-age composition, and catch-per-unit-effort of Atlantic (*Salmo salar*) angled in the Godbout River, Quebec, 1859–1983. *Canadian Journal of Fisheries and Aquatic Sciences*, 43, 281–287.

Brokordt, K. B., H. E. Guderley, M. Guay, C. F. Gaymer, and J. H. Himmelman. 2003. Sex differences in reproductive investment: Maternal care reduces escape response in the whelk, *Buccinum undatum. Journal of Experimental Marine Biology and Ecology*, 291, 161–180.

Capinera, J. L. 1979. Qualitative variation in plants and insects: Effect of propagule size on ecological plasticity. *American Naturalist*, 117, 724–737.

Charnov, E. L. 1993. *Life History Invariants: Some Explorations of Symmetry in Evolutionary Ecology.* Oxford, UK: Oxford University Press.

Coates, D. 1988. Length-dependent changes in egg size and fecundity in females, and brooded embryo size in males, of fork-tailed catfishes (Pisces: Ariidae) from the Sepik River, Papua New Guinea, with some implications for stock assessments. *Journal of Fish Biology*, 33, 455–464.

Cole, L. C. 1954. The population consequences of life history phenomena. *Quarterly Review of Biology*, 29, 103–137.

Coltman, D. W., P. O'Donoghue, J. T. Jorgenson, J. T. Hogg, C. Strobeck, and M. Festa-Bianchet. 2003. Undesirable evolutionary consequences of trophy hunting. *Nature*, 426, 655–658.

Consuegra, S., C. G. De Leaniz, A. Serdio, and E. Verspoor. 2005. Selective exploitation of early running fish may induce genetic and phenotypic changes in Atlantic salmon. *Journal of Fish Biology*, 67 (Suppl. 1), 129–145.

Crump, M. L. 1981. Variation in propagule size as a function of environmental uncertainty for tree frogs. *American Naturalist*, 117, 724–737.

Cunningham, E. J. A. and A. F. Russell. 2000. Egg investment is influenced by male attractiveness in the mallard. *Nature*, 404, 74–77.

Dobson, F. S. and M. K. Oli. 2008. The life histories of orders of mammals: Fast and slow breeding. *Current Science*, 95, 862–865.

Dufresne, F., G. J. FitzGerald, and S. Lachance. 1990. Age and size-related differences in reproductive success and reproductive costs in threespine stickleback (*Gasterosteus aculeatus*). *Behavioral Ecology*, 1, 140–147.

Dunlop, E. S., B. J. Shuter, and M. S. Ridgway. 2005. Isolating the influence of growth rate on maturation patterns in the smallmouth bass (*Micropterus dolomieui*). *Canadian Journal of Fisheries and Aquatic Sciences*, 62, 844–853.

Dutil, J.D. 1986. Energetic constraints and spawning interval in the anadromous Arctic charr (*Salvelinus alpinus*). *Copeia*, 1986, 945–955.

FAO (Food and Agriculture Organization of the UN). 2002. Report of the second technical consultation on the suitability of the CITES criteria for listing commercially-exploited aquatic species. FAO Fisheries Report No. 667.

Festa-Bianchet, M. B., J.-M. Gaillard, and J. T. Jorgenson. 1998. Mass- and density-dependent reproductive success and reproductive costs in capital breeder. *American Naturalist*, 152, 367–379.

Fisher, R. A. 1930. *The Genetical Theory of Natural Selection*. Oxford, UK: Oxford University Press.

Fleming, I. A. 1996. Reproductive strategies of Atlantic salmon: Ecology and evolution. *Reviews in Fish Biology and Fisheries*, 6, 379–416.

Fox, C. W. and M. E. Czesak. 2000. Evolutionary ecology of progeny size in arthropods. *Annual Reviews in Entomology* 45, 341–369.

Fox, M. G. 1994. Growth, density, and interspecific influences on pumpkinseed sunfish life-histories. *Ecology*, 75, 1157–1171.

Fox, M. G. and A. Keast. 1991. Effect of overwinter mortality on reproductive life history characteristics of pumpkinseed (*Lepomis gibbosus*) populations. *Canadian Journal of Fisheries and Aquatic Sciences*, 48, 1791–1799.

Gadgil, M. and W. Bossert. 1970. Life historical consequences of natural selection. *American Naturalist*, 104, 1–24.

Gaillard, J.-M., D. Pontier, D. Allainé, J. D. Lebreton, J. Trouvilliez, and J. Clobert. 1989. An analysis of demographic tactics in birds and mammals. *Oikos*, 56, 59–76.

Gaston, K. J. and T. M. Blackburn. 1995. Mapping biodiversity using surrogates for species richness: Macro-scales and New World birds. *Proceedings of the Royal Society B*, 262, 335–341.

Grift, R. E., A. D. Rijnsdorp, S. Barot, M. Heino, and U. Dieckmann. 2003. Fisheries-induced trends in reaction norms for maturation in North Sea plaice. *Marine Ecology Progress Series*, 257, 247–257.

Grime, J. P. 1977. Evidence for the existence of three primary strategies in plants and its relevance to ecological and evolutionary theory. *American Naturalist*, 111, 1169–1194.

Grime, J. P. 2002. *Plant Strategies and Vegetation Processes, and Ecosystem Properties* (2nd ed.). Toronto, ON: John Wiley & Sons.

Gross, M. R. 1979. Cuckoldry in sunfishes (*Lepomis*: Centrarchidae). *Canadian Journal of Zoology*, 57, 1507–1509.

Gross, M. R. 1982. Sneakers, satellites and parentals: Polymorphic mating strategies in North American sunfishes. *Zeitschrift fur Tierpsychologie*, 60, 1–26.

Gross, M. R. 1985. Disruptive selection for alternative life histories in salmon. *Nature*, 313, 47–48.

Gross, M. R. 1996. Alternative reproductive strategies and tactics: Diversity within sexes. *Trends in Ecology and Evolution*, 11, 92–98.

Hamon, T. R., C. J. Foote, R. Hilborn, and D. E. Rogers. 2000. Selection on morphology of spawning wild sockeye salmon by a gillnet fishery. *Transactions of the American Fisheries Society*, 129, 1300–1315.

Handford, P., G. Bell, and T. Reimchen. 1977. A gillnet fishery considered as an experiment in artificial selection. *Journal of the Fisheries Research Board of Canada*, 34, 954–961.

Hanssen, S. A., H. Engebretsen, and K. E. Erikstad. 2002. Incubation start and egg size in relation to body reserves in the common eider. *Behavioral Ecoogy and Sociobiology*, 52, 282–288.

Haugen, T. O. 2000. Growth and survival effects on maturation pattern in populations of grayling with recent common ancestors. *Oikos*, 90, 107–118.

Haugen, T. O. and L. A. Vøllestad. 2000. Population differences in early life-history traits in grayling. *Journal of Evolutionary Biology*, 13, 897–905.

Hazel, W. N., R. Smock, and M. D. Johnson. 1990. A polygenic model for the evolution of and maintenance of conditional strategies. *Proceedings of the Royal Society of London B*, 242, 181–187.

Heath, D. D., L. Rankin, C. A. Bryden, J. W. Heath, and J. M. Shrimpton. 2002. Heritability and Y-chromosome influence in the jack male life history of Chinook salmon (*Oncorhynchus tshawytscha*). *Heredity*, 89, 311–317.

Heino, M., U. Dieckmann, and O. R. Godo. 2002. Measuring probabilistic reaction norms for age and size at maturation. *Evolution*, 56, 669–678.

Hirshfield, M. F. and D. W. Tinkle. 1975. Natural selection and the evolution of reproductive effort. *Proceedings of the National Academy of Sciences of the U. S. A.*, 72, 2227–2231.

Houde, A. E. and J. A. Endler. 1990. Correlated evolution of female mating preferences and male patterns in the guppy. *Poecilia reticulata*. *Science*, 248, 1405–1408.

Hunt, J. and L. W. Simmons. 2001. Status-dependent selection in the dimorphic beetle *Onthophagus taurus*. *Proceedings of the Royal Society B*, 268, 2409–2414.

Hutchings, J. A. 1991. Fitness consequences of variation in egg size and food abundance in brook trout, *Salvelinus fontinalis*. *Evolution*, 45, 1162–1168.

Hutchings, J. A. 1993. Adaptive life histories effected by age-specific survival and growth rate. *Ecology*, 74, 673–684.

Hutchings, J. A. 1996. Adaptive phenotypic plasticity in brook trout, *Salvelinus fontinalis*, life histories. *Écoscience*, 3, 25–32.

Hutchings, J. A. 1999. The influence of growth and survival costs of reproduction on Atlantic cod, *Gadus morhua*, population growth rate. *Canadian Journal of Fisheries and Aquatic Sciences*, 56, 1612–1623.

Hutchings, J. A. 2005. Life history consequences of overexploitation to population recovery in Northwest Atlantic cod (*Gadus morhua*). *Canadian Journal of Fisheries and Aquatic Sciences*, 62, 824–832.

Hutchings, J. A. 2006. Survival consequences of sex-biased growth and the absence of a growth-mortality trade-off. *Functional Ecology*, 20, 347–353.

Hutchings, J. A. 2009. Avoidance of fisheries-induced evolution: Management implications for catch selectivity and limit reference points. *Evolutionary Applications*, 2, 324–334.

Hutchings, J. A. and D. J. Fraser. 2008. The nature of fisheries- and farming-induced evolution. *Molecular Ecology*, 17, 294–313.

Hutchings, J. A. and D. W. Morris. 1985. The influence of phylogeny, size and behaviour on patterns of covariation in salmonid life histories. *Oikos*, 45, 118–124.

Hutchings, J. A. and M. E. B. Jones. 1998. Life history variation and growth rate thresholds for maturity in Atlantic salmon, *Salmo salar*. *Canadian Journal of Fisheries and Aquatic Sciences*, 55 (Suppl. 1), 22–47.

Hutchings, J. A. and R. A. Myers. 1993. Effect of age on the seasonality of maturation and spawning of Atlantic cod, *Gadus morhua*, in the Northwest Atlantic. *Canadian Journal of Fisheries and Aquatic Sciences*, 50, 2468–2474.

Hutchings, J. A. and R. A. Myers. 1994. The evolution of alternative mating strategies in variable environments. *Evolutionary Ecology*, 8, 256–268.

Hutchings, J. A., R. A. Myers, V. B. Garcia, and L. O. Lucifora. 2010. Life history correlates of extinction risk in vertebrates. *Ecological Applications*, 22, 1061–1067.

Jansen, W. A. 1996. Plasticity in maturity and fecundity of yellow perch, *Perca flavescens* (Mitchill): Comparisons of stunted and normal-growing populations. *Annales Zoologici Fennici*, 33, 403–415.

Jensen, A. L. 1997. Origin of the relation between K and Linf and synthesis of relations among life history parameters. *Canadian Journal of Fisheries and Aquatic Sciences*, 54, 987–989.

Jetz, W., C. H. Sekercioglu, and K. Böhning-Gaese. 2008. The worldwide variation in avian clutch size across species and space. *PloS Biology*, 6, 2650–2657.

Jones, J. W. 1959. *The Salmon*. London, UK: Collins.

Kamler, E. 1992. *Early Life History of Fish: An Energetics Approach*. London, UK: Chapman & Hall.

Kendall, N. W., J. J. Hard, and T. P. Quinn. 2009. Quantifying six decades of fishery selection for size and age at maturity in sockeye salmon. *Evolutionary Applications*, 2, 523–536.

Koops, M. A., J. A. Hutchings, and B. K. Adams. 2003. Environ-mental predictability and the cost of imperfect information: Influences on offspring size variability. *Evolutionary Ecology Research*, 5, 29–42.

Koslow, J. A., J. Bell, P. Virtue, and D. C.Smith. 1995. Fecundity and its variability in orange roughy: Effects of population density, condition, egg size, and senescence. *Journal of Fish Biology*, 47, 1063–1080.

Kudo, S. 2001. Intraclutch egg-size variation in acanthosomatid bugs: Adaptive allocation of maternal investment. *Oikos*, 92, 208–214.

Kuparinen, A. and J. A. Hutchings. 2012. Consequences of fisheries-induced evolution for population productivity and recovery potential. *Proceedings of the Royal Society B*, 279, 2571–2579.

Lack, D. 1947. The significance of clutch size. I. Intraspecific variations. *Ibis*, 89, 302–352.

Law, R. 1979. Optimal life histories under age-specific predation. *American Naturalist*, 114, 399–417.

Law, R. 2000. Fishing, selection, and phenotypic evolution. *ICES Journal of Marine Science*, 57, 659–668.

Law, R. and C. A. Rowell. 1993. Cohort-structured populations, selection responses, and exploitation of the North Sea cod. In T. K Stokes, J. M. McGlade, R. Law (Eds.), *The exploitation of evolving resources*. (pp. 155–174). Berlin: Springer-Verlag.

Leggett, W. C. and J. E. Carscadden. 1978. Latitudinal variation in reproductive characteristics of American shad (*Alosa sapidissima*): Evidence for population specific life history strategies in fish. *Journal of the Fisheries Research Board of Canada*, 35, 1469–1478.

Lidgard, D. C., D. J. Boness, W. D. Bowen, J. I. McMillan, and R. C. Fleischer. 2004. The rate of fertilization in male mating tactics of the polygynous grey seal. *Molecular Ecology*, 13, 3543–3548.

MacArthur, R. H. and E. O. Wilson. 1967. *The Theory of Island Biogeography*. Princeton, NJ: Princeton University Press.

Mainguy, J., S. D. Côté, E. Cardinal, and M. Houle. 2008. Mating tactics and mate choice in relation to age and social rank in male mountain goats. *Journal of Mammalogy*, 89, 626–635.

Maynard Smith, J. 1982. *Evolution and the Theory of Games*. Cambridge, UK: Cambridge University Press.

Musick, J. A., M. M. Harbin, S. A. Berkeley, G. H. Burgess, A. M. Eklund, L. Findley, R. G. Gilmore, J. T. Golden, D. S. Ha, G. R. Huntsman, J. C. McGovern, G. R. Sedberry, S. J. Parker, S. G. Poss, E. Sala, T. W. Schmidt, H. Weeks, and S. G. Wright. 2000. Marine, estuarine, and diadromous fish stocks at risk of extinction in North America (exclusive of Pacific salmonids). *Fisheries*, 25, 6–30.

Myers, R. A. 1984. Demographic consequences of precocious matu-ration of Atlantic salmon (*Salmo salar*). *Canadian Journal of Fisheries and Aquatic Sciences*, 41, 1349–1353.

Myers, R. A., J. A. Hutchings, and R. J. Gibson. 1986. Variation in male parr maturation within and among populations of Atlantic salmon, *Salmo salar*. *Canadian Journal of Fisheries and Aquatic Sciences*, 43, 1242–1248.

Näslund, I., E. Degerman, and F. Nordwall. 1998. Brown trout (*Salmo trutta*) habitat use and life history in Swedish streams: Possible effects of biotic interactions. *Canadian Journal of Fisheries and Aquatic Sciences*, 55, 1034–1042.

Neff, B. D. and R. Knapp. 2009. Paternity, parental behavior and circulating steroid hormone concentrations in nest-tending male bluegill. *Hormones and Behaviour*, 56, 239–245.

Olsen, E. M., G. R. Lilly, M. Heino, M. J. Morgan, J. Brattey, and U. Dieckmann. 2005. Assessing changes in age and size at maturation in collapsing populations of Atlantic cod (*Gadus morhua*). *Canadian Journal of Fisheries and Aquatic Sciences*, 62, 811–823.

Olsen, E. M., M. Heino, G. R. Lilly, M. J. Morgan, J. Brattey, B. Ernande, and U. Dieckmann. 2004. Maturation trends indicative of rapid evolution preceded the collapse of northern cod. *Nature*, 428, 932–935.

Partridge, L. 1988. The rare-male effect: What is its evolutionary significance? *Philosophical Transactions of the Royal Society B*, 319, 525–539.

Pauly, D. 1980. On the interrelationships between natural mortality, growth parameters, and mean environmental temperature in 175 fish stocks. *Journal du Conseil, Conseil International pour l'Exploration de la Mer*, 39, 175–192.

Pianka, E. R. 1970. On r and K selection. *American Naturalist*, 104, 592–597.

Pianka, E. R. 1978. *Evolutionary Ecology* (2nd ed.). New York: Harper & Row.

Piché, J., J. A Hutchings, and W. Blanchard. 2008. Genetic variation in threshold reaction norms for alternative reproductive tactics in male Atlantic salmon, *Salmo salar*. *Proceedings of the Royal Society B: Biological Sciences*, 275, 1571–1575.

Pietsch, T. W. 2005. Dimorphism, parasitism, and sex revisited: Modes of reproduction among deep-sea ceratioid anglerfishes (Teleostei: Lophiiformes). *Ichthyological Research*, 52, 207–236.

Poulin, R. and W. J. Hamilton. 2000. Egg size variation as a function of environmental variability in parasitic trematodes. *Canadian Journal of Zoology*, 78, 564–569.

Purchase, C. F. and J. A. Hutchings. 2008. A temporally stable spatial pattern in the spawner density of a freshwater fish: Evidence for an ideal dispotic distribution. *Canadian Journal of Fisheries and Aquatic Sciences*, 65, 382–388.

Quinn, T. P., P. McGinnity, and T. F. Cross. 2006. Long-term declines in body sizes and shifts in run-timing of Atlantic salmon in Ireland. *Journal of Fish Biology*, 68, 1713–1730.

Quinn, T. P., S. Hodson, L. Flynn, R. Hilborn, and D. E. Rogers. 2007. Directional selection by fisheries and the timing of sockeye salmon (*Oncorhynchus nerka*) migrations. *Ecological Applications*, 17, 731–739.

Reynolds, J. D., N. K. Dulvy, N. B. Goodwin, and J.A. Hutchings. 2005. Biology of extinction risk in marine fishes. *Proceedings of the Royal Society B*, 272, 2337–2344.

Reznick, D. N., H. Bryga, and J. A. Endler. 1990. Experimentally-induced life history evolution in a natural population. *Nature*, 346, 357–359.

Ricker, W. E. 1981. Changes in the average size and average age of Pacific salmon. *Canadian Journal of Fisheries and Aquatic Sciences*, 38, 1636–1656.

Rijnsdorp, A. D. 1993. Fisheries as a large-scale experiment on life-history evolution: Disentangling phenotypic and genetic effects in changes in maturation and reproduction of North Sea plaice, *Pleuronectes platessa* L. *Oecologia*, 96, 391–401.

Rijnsdorp, A. D., R. E. Grift, and S. B. M. Kraak. 2005. Fisheries-induced adaptive change in reproductive investment in North Sea plaice (*Pleuronectes platessa*)? *Canadian Journal of Fisheries and Aquatic Sciences*, 62, 833–843.

Roff, D. A. 1984. The evolution of life history parameters in teleosts. *Canadian Journal of Fisheries and Aquatic Sciences*, 41, 989–1000.

Roff, D. A. 1986. Predicting body size with life-history models. *BioScience*, 36, 316–323.

Roff, D. A. 1992. *The Evolution of Life Histories*. New York: Chapman and Hall.

Roff, D. A. 1996. The evolution of threshold traits in animals. *Quarterly Review of Biology*, 71, 3–35.

Roff, D. A. 2002. *Life History Evolution*. Sunderland, MA: Sinauer.

Rowe, L. 1994. The cost of mating and mate choice in water striders. *Animal Behaviour*, 48, 1049–1056.

Schaffer, W. M. 1974. Selection for optimal life histories: The effects of age structure. *Ecology*, 55, 291–303.

Sears, R. 2002. Blue Whale, *Balaenoptera musculus*. In W. F. Perrin, B. Wursig, and J. G. M. Thewissen (Eds.) *Encyclopedia of Marine Mammals*. (pp. 112–116). San Diego, CA: Academic Press.

Seger, J. and H. J. Brockmann. 1987. What is bet-hedging? *Oxford Surveys in Evolutionary Biology*, 4, 182–211.

Sheriff, M. J., C. J. Krebs, and R. Boonstra. 2009. The sensitive hare: Sublethal effects of predator stress on reproduction in snowshoe hares. *Journal of Animal Ecology*, 78, 1249–1258.

Shuster, S. M. and M. J. Wade. 2003. *Mating Systems and Strategies*. Princeton, NJ: Princeton University Press.

Simons, A. M. and M. O. Johnston. 2006. Environmental and genetic sources of diversification in the timing of seed germination: Implications for the evolution of bet hedging. *Evolution*, 60, 2280–2292.

Sinclair, A. F., D. P. Swain, and J. M. Hanson. 2002. Measuring changes in the direction and magnitude of size-selective mortality in a commercial fish population. *Canadian Journal of Fisheries and Aquatic Sciences*, 59, 361–371.

Smith, C. C. and S. D. Fretwell. 1974. The optimal balance between size and number of offspring. *American Naturalist*, 108, 499–506.

Smith, T. D. 1994. *Scaling Fisheries: The Science of Measuring the Effects of Fishing, 1855–1955*. Cambridge, UK: Cambridge University Press.

Stearns, S.C. 1983. The influence of size and phylogeny on patterns of covariation among life-history traits in the mammals. *Oikos*, 41, 173–187.

Stokes, T. K., J. M. McGlade, and R. Law. 1993. *The Exploitation of Evolving Resources*. Berlin: Springer-Verlag.

Svärdson, G. 1949. Natural selection and egg number in fish. Annual Report of the Institute of Freshwater Research, Drottningholm, 29, 115–122.

Swain, D. P., A. F. Sinclair, and J. M. Hanson. 2007. Evolutionary response to size-selective mortality in an exploited fish population. *Proceedings of the Royal Society B*, 274, 1015–1022.

Taborsky, M. 2001. The evolution of bourgeois, parasitic, and cooperative reproductive behaviors in fishes. *Journal of Heredity*, 92, 100–110.

Tomkins, J. L. and W. Hazel. 2007. The status of the conditional evolutionarily stable strategy. *Trends in Ecology and Evolution*, 22, 522–528.

Weir, L. K. 2008. Consequences of the intensity of male-male competition on the mating system of Atlantic salmon (*Salmo salar*). Ph.D. Thesis. Halifax, NS: Dalhousie University.

Westoby, M., E. Jurado, and M. Leishman. 1992. Comparative evolutionary ecology of seed size. *Trends in Ecology and Evolution*, 7, 368–372.

Whitehead, H. and J. Mann. 2000. Female reproductive strategies of cetaceans: Life histories and calf care. In J. Mann, R. C. Connor, P. L. Tyack, and H. Whitehead (Eds.). *Cetacean Societies: Field Studies of Dolphins and Whales* (pp. 219–246). Urbana IL: University of Chicago Press.

Williams, G. C. 1957. Pleiotropy, natural selection, and the evolution of senescence. *Evolution*, 11, 398–411.

Williams, G. C. 1966. Natural selection, the cost of reproduction, and a refinement of Lack's principle. *American Naturalist*, 100, 687–690.

Wilson, A. J., J. A. Hutchings, and M. M. Ferguson. 2003. Selective and genetic constraints on the evolution of body size in a stream-dwelling salmonid fish. *Journal of Evolutionary Biology*, 16, 584–594.

Wootton, R. J. 1998. *Ecology of Teleost Fishes*. Dordrecht, Germany: Kluwer Academic Publishers.

Chapter 9

Abraham, K. F., R. L. Jefferies, and R. F. Rockwell. 2005. Goose-induced changes in vegetation and land cover between 1976 and 1997 in an arctic coastal marsh. *Arctic, Antarctic, and Alpine Research*, 37, 269–275.

Beisner, B. E., D. T. Haydon, and K. Cuddington. 2003. Alternative stable states in ecology. *Frontiers in Ecology and the Environment* 1, 376–382.

Bergerud, A. T. 1974. Decline of caribou in North America following settlement. *Journal of Wildlife Management*, 38, 757–770.

Bergerud, A. T., W. J. Dalton, H. Butler, L. Camps, and R. Ferguson. 2007. Woodland caribou persistence and extirpation in relic populations on Lake Superior. *Rangifer*, Special Issue 17, 57–78.

Bertness, M. D. and R. Callaway. 1994. Positive interactions in communities. *Trends in Ecology and Evolution*, 9, 191–193.

Boutin, S., C. J. Krebs, R. Boonstra, M. R. T. Dale, S. J. Hannon, K. Martin, A. R. E. Sinclair, J. N. M. Smith, R. Turkington, M. Blower, A. Byrom, F. I. Doyle, C. Doyle, D. Hik, L. Hofer, A. Hubbs, T. Karels, D. L. Murray, V. Nams, M. O'Donoghue, C. Rohner, and S. Schweiger. 1995. Population changes of the vertebrate community during a snowshoe hare cycle in Canada's boreal forest. *Oikos*, 74, 69–80.

British Columbia Ministry of Forests. 1996–1999. *The Biogeoclimatic Zones of British Columbia*. From http://www.for.gov.bc.ca/hfd/library/documents/treebook/biogeo/biogeo.htm.

Brooker, R. W., F. T. Maestre, R. M. Callaway, C. J. Lortie, L. A. Cavieres, G. Kunstler, P. Liancourt, K. Tielbörger, J. Travis, F. Anthelme, C. Armas, L. Coll, E. Corcket, S. Delzon, E. Forey,

Z. Kikvidze, J. Olofsson, F. Pugnaire, C. I. Quiroz, P. Saccone, K. Schiffers, M. Seifan, B. Touzard, and R. Michalet. 2008. Facilitation in plant communities: The past, present, and the future. *Journal of Ecology*, 96, 18–34.

Brown, J. H. and D. W. Davidson. 1977. Competition between seed-eating rodents and ants in desert ecosystems. *Science*, 196, 880–882.

Brown, J. H., D. W. Davidson, and O. J. Reichman. 1979. An experimental study of competition between seed-eating desert rodents and ants. *American Zoologist*, 19, 1129–1143.

Bruno, J. F., J. J. Stachowicz, and M. D. Bertness. 2003. Inclusion of facilitation into ecological theory. *Trends in Ecology and Evolution*, 18, 119–125.

Callaway, R. M. 1995. Positive interactions among plants. *Botanical Review*, 61, 306–349.

Carpenter, S. R., J. F. Kitchell, and J. R. Hodgson. 1985. Cascading trophic indirections and lake productivity. *BioScience*, 35, 634–639.

Clements, F. E. 1916. *Plant Succession: An Analysis of the Development of Vegetation*. Publication No. 242, Washington, DC: Carnegie Institute.

Clements, F. E. 1936. Nature and structure of the climax. *Journal of Ecology*, 24, 252–284.

Connell, J. H. 1961a. The effects of competition, predation by *Thais lapillus* and other factors on natural populations of the barnacle, *Balanus balanoides*. *Ecological Monographs*, 31, 61–104.

Connell, J. H. 1961b. The influence of interspecific competition and other factors on the distribution of the barnacle, *Chthamalus stellatus*. *Ecology*, 42, 710–723.

Connell, J. H. 1975. Some mechanisms producing structure in natural communities: A model and evidence from field experiments. In M. L. Cody and J. M. Diamond, (Eds.) *Ecology and Evolution of Communities*. (pp. 460–490). Cambridge, MA: Belknap Press.

Connell, J. H. 1978. Diversity in tropical rain forests and coral reefs. *Science*, 199, 1302–1310.

COSEWIC. 2002. *Assessment and Update Status Report on the Woodland Caribou, Rangifer tarandus caribou, in Canada*. Ottawa: Committee on the Status of Endangered Wildlife in Canada.

Cranston, B. and L. Hermanutz. 2009. The stress gradient hypothesis: Facilitation at the forest-tundra transition zone in Labrador. Poster at INTECOL in Brisbane, Australia.

Darwin, C. 1859. *On the Origin of Species by Means of Natural Selection, or the Preservation of Favoured Races in the Struggle for Life* (1st ed.). London: John Murray.

Davidson, D. W. 1977a. Foraging ecology and community organization in desert seed-eating ants. *Ecology*, 58, 724–737.

Davidson, D. W. 1977b. Species diversity and community organization in desert seed-eating ants. *Ecology*, 58, 711–724.

Ellis, J. C., M. J. Shulman, M. Wood, J. D. Witman, and S. Lozyniak. 2007. Regulation of intertidal food webs by avian predators on New England rocky shores. *Ecology*, 88, 853–863.

Emery, N. C., P. J. Ewanchuk, and M. D. Bertness. 2001. Competition and salt marsh plant zonation: Stress tolerators may be dominant competitors. *Ecology*, 82, 2471–2485.

Estes, J., M. Tinker, T. Williams, and D. Doak. 1998. Killer whale predation on sea otters linking oceanic and nearshore ecosystems. *Science*. New Series, Vol. 282 No. 5388, 473–476.

Gause, G.F. 1932. Experimental studies on the struggle for existence. *Journal of Experimental Biology*, 9, 389-402.

Gause, G.F. 1934. *The Struggle for Existence*. Baltimore: Williams & Wilkins.

Gause, G.F. 1935. Behaviour of mixed populations and the problem of natural selection. *The American Naturalist*, 69, 596–609.

Gibbons, D. W., J. B. Reid, and R. A. Chapman. 1993. *The New Atlas of Breeding Birds in Britain and Ireland, 1988–1991*. London, UK: T. & A. D. Poyser.

Gleason, H. A. 1926. The individualistic concept of the plant association. *Torrey Botanical Club Bulletin*, 53, 7–26.

Gleason, H. A. 1939. The individualistic concept of the plant association. *American Midland Naturalist*, 21, 92–110.

Goldberg, D. E., R. Turkington, and L. Olsvig-Whittaker. 1995. Quantifying the community-level consequences of competition. *Folia Geobotanica and Phytotaxonomica*, 30, 231–242.

Goldberg, D. E., R. Turkington, L. Olsvig-Whittaker, and A. R. Dyer. 2001. Density-dependence in an annual plant community: Variation among life history stages. *Ecological Monographs*, 71, 423–446.

Grace, J. B. and R. G. Wetzel. 1981. Effects of size and growth rate on vegetative reproduction in *Typha*. *Oecologia*, 50, 158–161.

Gregory, R. 1994. Species abundance patterns of British birds. *Proceedings of the Royal Society, London, Series B*, 257, 299–301.

Grime, J. P. 1977. Evidence for the existence of three primary strategies in plants and its relevance to ecological and evolutionary theory. *Am. Nat.* 111, 1169–1194.

Hairston, N. G., F. E. Smith, and L. B. Slobodkin. 1960. Community structure, population control, and competition. *American Naturalist*, 94, 421–425.

Handa, I. T. and R. L. Jefferies. 2000. Assisted revegetation trials in degraded salt-marshes of the Hudson Bay lowlands. *Journal of Applied Ecology*, 37, 944–958.

Hope-Simpson, J. F. 1940. Studies of the vegetation of the English chalk: vi. Late stages in succession leading to chalk grassland. *Journal of Ecology*, 28, 386–402.

Hubbell, S. P. 2001. *The Unified Neutral Theory of Biodiversity and Biogeography*. Princeton Monographs No. 32. Princeton, NJ: Princeton University Press.

Keddy, P. A. 1990. Competitive hierarchies and centrifugal organization in plant communities. In J. Grace and D. Tilman (Eds.), *Perspectives on Plant Competition*. (pp. 265–289). New York: Academic Press.

Koplin, J. R. and R. S. Hoffmann. 1968. Habitat overlap and competitive exclusion in voles (*Microtus*). *American Midland Naturalist*, 80, 494–507.

Krebs, C. J., S. Boutin, R. Boonstra, A. R. A. Sinclair, J. N. M. Smith, M. R. T. Dale, K. Martin, and R. Turkington. 1995. Impact of food and predation on the snowshoe hare cycle. *Science*, 269, 1112–1115.

Krebs, C. J., S. Boutin, S., and R. Boonstra. 2001. *Ecosystem Dynamics of the Boreal Forest: the Kluane Project*. New York: Oxford University Press.

Lamb, E. G. and J. F. Cahill. 2008. When competition does not matter: Grassland diversity and community composition. *American Naturalist*, 171, 777–787.

Lamb, E. G., S. W. Kembel, and J. F. Cahill. 2009. Shoot, but not root, competition reduces community diversity in experimental mesocosms. *Journal of Ecology*, 97, 155–163.

Lamb, E. G., S. W. Kembel, and J. F. Cahill. 2009. Shoot, but not root, competition reduces community diversity in experimental mesocosms. *Journal of Ecology*, 97, 155–163.

Lubchenco, J. 1978. Plant species diversity in a marine intertidal community: Importance of herbivore food preferences and algal competitive abilities. *American Naturalist*, 112, 23–39.

MacArthur, R. H. 1958. Population ecology of some warblers of northeastern coniferous forests. *Ecology*, 39, 599–619.

MacArthur, R. H. and E. O. Wilson. 1967. *The Theory of Island Biogeography*. Monographs in Population Biology No. 1. Princeton, NJ: Princeton University Press.

MacDougall, A. S. and S. D. Wilson. 2007. Herbivory limits recruitment in an old-field seed addition experiment. *Ecology*, 88, 1105–1111.

Marquis, R. J. and C. J. Whelan. 1994. Insectivorous birds increase growth of white oak through consumption of leaf-chewing insects. *Ecology*, 75, 2007–2014.

McGill, B. J. 2003. A test of the unified neutral theory of biodiversity. *Nature*, 422, 881–885.

McLaren, J. R. and R. L. Jefferies. 2004. Initiation and maintenance of vegetation mosaics in an Arctic salt marsh. *Journal of Ecology*, 92, 648–660.

Menge, B. A. and J. P. Sutherland. 1987. Community regulation: Variation in disturbance, competition, and predation in relation to environmental stress and recruitment. *American Naturalist*, 130, 730–757.

Ministry of Forests and Range. 2009. Biogeoclimatic Zones of British Columbia. Retrieved October 2013 from http://www.for.gov.bc.ca/hfd/library/documents/treebook/biogeo/biogeo.htm.

Molenda, O., A. Reid, and C. J. Lortie. 2012. The alpine cushion plant *Silene acaulis* as foundation species: A plant and bug's-eye view to facilitation and microclimate. *PLOSONE*, 7, e37223.

Paine, R. T. 1966. Food web complexity and species diversity. *American Naturalist*, 100, 65–75.

Pojar, J. and D. V. Meidinger. 1991. *Ecosystems of British Columbia*. B. C. Ministry of Forests, Forest Science Program, Special Report Series 6. Retrieved October 2013 from http://www.for.gov.bc.ca/hfd/pubs/Docs/Srs/Srs06.htm.

Rajaniemi, T. K., R. Turkington, and D. E. Goldberg. 2009. Population- and community-level consequences of regulation in an annual plant community under different resource levels. *Journal of Vegetation Science*, 20, 836–846.

Reid, A. M. and C. J. Lortie 2012. Cushion plants are foundation species with positive effects extending to higher trophic levels. *Ecosphere*, 3, 11.

Ripple, W. J., E. J. Larsen, R. A. Renkin, and D. W. Smith. 2001. Trophic cascades among wolves, elk and aspen on Yellowstone National Park's northern range. *Biological Conservation*, 102, 227–234.

Robertson, G. P., M. A. Huston, Evans F. C., & J. M. Tiedje. 1988. Spatial variability in a successional plant community: Patterns of nitrogen availability." *Ecology*, 69 (5), 1517–1524.

Rosenzweig, M. L. and Z. Abramsky. 1986. Centrifugal community organization. *Oikos*, 46, 339–348.

Sale, P. F. and W. A. Douglas. 1984. Temporal variability in the community structure of fish on coral patch reefs and the relation of community structure to reef structure. *Ecology*, 65, 409–422.

Scheibling, R. A. and R. L. Stephenson. 1984. Mass mortality of *Strongylocentrotus droebachiensis* off Nova Scotia, Canada. *Marine Biology*, 78, 153–164.

Sharam, G. J., A. R. E. Sinclair, and R. Turkington. 2009. Serengeti birds maintain forests by inhibiting seed predators. *Science*, 325, 51.

Shilo-Volin, H., A. Novoplansky, D. E. Goldberg, and R. Turkington. 2005. Density regulation in annual plant communities under different resource levels. *Oikos*, 108, 241–252.

Simenstad, C. A., J. A. Estes, and K. W. Kenyon. 1978. Aleuts, sea otters, and alternate stable-state communities. *Science*, 200, 403–411.

Sinclair, A. R. E., C. J. Krebs, J. M. Fryxell, R. Turkington, S. Boutin, R. Boonstra, P. Lundberg, and L. Oksanen. 2000. Testing hypotheses of trophic level interactions using experimental perturbations of a boreal forest ecosystem. *Oikos*, 89, 313–328.

Sinclair, A. R. E., S. A. R. Mduma, and J. S. Brashares. 2003. Patterns of predation in a diverse predator-prey system. *Nature*, 425, 288–290.

Sousa, W. P. 1979. Disturbance in marine intertidal boulder fields: The nonequilibrium maintenance of species diversity. *Ecology*, 60(6), 1225–1239.

Sousa, W. P. 1979b. Experimental investigations of disturbance and ecological succession in a rocky intertidal algal community. *Ecological Monographs*, 49, 227–254.

Spedding, C. R. W. 1971. *Grassland Ecology*. Oxford, UK: Clarendon Press.

Stenseth, N. C. 2002. The story of an ecosystem: A ten-year study of a Canadian forest shows the way ahead for ecology. *Nature* 416, 679–680.

Stoecker, R. E. 1972. Competitive relations between sympatric populations of voles (*Microtus montanus* and *M. pennsylvanicus*). *Journal of Animal Ecology*, 41, 311–319.

Tansley, A. G. 1917. On competition between *Galium saxatile* L. (*G. hercynicum* Weig.) and *Galium sylvestre* Poll. (*G. asperum* Schreb.) on different types of soil. *Journal of Ecology*, 5, 173–179.

Tansley, A. G. and R. S. Adamson. 1925. Studies of the vegetation of the English chalk. III The chalk grasslands of the Hampshire-Sussex border. *Journal of Ecology*, 13, 177–223.

Townsend, C. R., J. L. Harper, and M. Begon. 2000. *Essentials of Ecology*. Oxford, UK: Blackwell Science.

Turkington, R., E. John, C. J. Krebs, M. Dale, V. O. Nams, R. Boonstra, S. Boutin, K. Martin, A. R. E. Sinclair, and J. N. M. Smith. 1998. The effects of NPK fertilization for nine years on the vegetation of the boreal forest in northwestern Canada. *Journal of Vegetation Science*, 9, 333–346.

Turkington, R., E. John, S. Watson, and P. Seccombe-Hett. 2002. The effects of fertilization and herbivory on the herbaceous vegetation of the boreal forest in northwestern Canada: A ten-year study. *Journal of Ecology*, 90, 325–227.

Welden, C. W. and W. L. Slauson. 1986. The intensity of competition versus its importance: An overlooked distinction and some implications. *Quarterly Review Biology*, 61, 23–44.

Werner, P. A. and W. J. Platt. 1976. Ecological relationships of co-occurring goldenrods (*Solidago*: Compositae). *American Naturalist*, 110: 959–971.

Whicker, A. D. and J. K. Detling. 1988. Ecological consequences of prairie dog disturbances. *BioScience*, 38, 778–785.

Whittaker, R. H. 1956. Vegetation of the Great Smokey Mountains. *Ecological Monographs*, 26, 1–80.

Whittaker, R. H. 1975. *Communities and Ecosystems* (2nd ed.). New York: Macmillan.

Williams, C. B. 1964. *Patterns in the Balance of Nature and Related*

Problems of Quantitative Biology. London, UK: Academic Press.

Wittmer, H. U., A. R. E. Sinclair, and B. N. McLellan. 2005. The role of predation in the decline and extirpation of woodland caribou. *Oecologia,* 144, 257–267.

Zeevalking, H. J. and L. F. M. Fresco. 1977. Rabbit grazing and species diversity in a dune area. *Vegetatio,* 35, 193–196.

Chapter 10

Bergeron P. and E. Bourget. 1986. Shore topography and spatial partitioning of crevice refuges by sessile epibenthos in an ice-disturbed environment. *Marine Ecology Progress Series,* 28, 129–145.

Bergeron, Y. and A. Leduc. 1999. Relationships between change in fire frequency and mortality due to spruce budworm outbreak in the southeastern Canadian boreal forest. *Journal of Vegetation Science,* 9, 492–500.

Bergsma, B. M., J. Svoboda, and B. Freedman. 1984. Entombed plant communities released by a retreating glacier at central Ellesmere Island, Canada. *Arctic,* 37, 49–52.

Blais, J. R. 1965. Spruce budworm outbreaks in the past three centuries in the Laurentide Park, Quebec. *Forest Science,* 11, 130–138.

Blais, J. R. 1981. Mortality of balsam fir and white spruce following a spruce budworm outbreak in the Ottawa River watershed in Quebec. *Canadian Journal of Forest Research,* 11, 620–629.

Bormann, F. H. and G. E. Likens. 1979. *Pattern and Process in a Forested Ecosystem.* New York: Springer-Verlag.

Brooks, M. and M. Lusk. 2008. *Fire Management and Invasive Plants: A Handbook.* United States Fish and Wildlife Service, Arlington, VA.

Bruce, J. 2009. *Identifying Forest Wind Throw in Nova Scotia due to Hurricane Juan using Landsat Satellite Imagery.* Truro, NS: Nova Scotia Department of Natural Resources, Forestry Branch .

Canadian Forest Service (CFS). 2012. The *State of Canada's Forests, Annual Report 2012.* Ottawa, ON: Natural Resources Canada, CFS.

Clements, F. E. 1916. *Plant Succession: An Analysis of the Development of Vegetation.* Publication No. 242, Washington, DC: Carnegie Institute.

Clements, F. E. 1936. Nature and structure of the climax. *Journal of Ecology,* 24, 252–284.

Connell, J. H. and R. O. Slatyer. 1977. Mechanisms of succession in natural communities and their role in community stability and organization. *American Naturalist,* 111, 1119–1144.

Cowles, H. C. 1899. The ecological relations of the vegetation of the sand dunes of Lake Michigan. *Botanical Gazette,* 27, parts 2, 3, 4, 5.

Crocker, R. L. and J. Major. 1955. Soil development in relation to vegetation and surface age at Glacier Bay, Alaska. *Journal of Ecology,* 43, 427–448.

Damman, A. W. H. 1971. Effect of vegetation change on the fertility of a Newfoundland forest site. *Ecological Monographs,* 41, 253–270.

Freedman, B. 2010. *Environmental Science. A Canadian Perspective* (5th ed.). Toronto: Pearson Education Canada.

Freedman, B., C. Stewart, and U. Prager. 1985. *Patterns of Water Chemistry of Four Drainage Basins in Central Nova Scotia.* Technical Report IWD-AR-WQB-85–93. Moncton, NB: Water Quality Branch, Inland Waters Directorate, Environment Canada.

Freedman, B., R. Morash, and D. S. MacKinnon. 1993. Short-term changes in vegetation after the silvicultural spraying of glyphosate herbicide onto regenerating clearcuts in central Nova Scotia. *Canadian Journal of Forest Research,* 23, 2300–2311.

Gleason, H. A. 1926. The individualistic concept of the plant association. *Torrey Botanical Club Bulletin,* 53, 7–26.

Gleason, H. A. 1939. The individualistic concept of the plant association. *American Midland Naturalist,* 21, 92–110.

Grignon, T. 1992. The dynamics of *Rubus strigosus* (*Michx.*) in post-clearcut mixedwood and softwood forests of Nova Scotia. M.Sc. Thesis, Department of Biology. Halifax, NS: Dalhousie University.

Grime, J. P. 2002. *Plant Strategies and Vegetation Processes, and Ecosystem Properties* (2nd ed). Toronto: John Wiley & Sons.

Holling, C. S. 1973. Resilience and stability of ecological systems. *Annual Reviews in Ecology and Systematics,* 4, 1–23.

Jasinski, J. P. P. and S. Payette. 2005. The creation of alternative stable states in the southern boreal forest, Quebec, Canada. *Ecological Monographs,* 75, 561–583.

Jones, G. A. and G. H. R. Henry. 2003. Primary plant succession on recently deglaciated terrain in the Canadian High Arctic. *Journal of Biogeography,* 30, 277–296.

Kettela, E. 1983. *A Cartographic History of Spruce Budworm Defoliation from 1967 to 1981 in Eastern North America.* Information Report DPC-X-14. Fredericton, NB: Maritimes Forest Research Centre, Canadian Forestry Service.

Krause, H. H. 1982. Nitrate formation and movement before and after clear-cutting of a monitored watershed in central New Brunswick, Canada. *Canadian Journal of Forest Research,* 12, 922–930.

La Farge, C., K.H. Williams, and J.H. England. 2013. Regeneration of Little Ice Age bryophytes emerging from a polar glacier with implications of totipotency in extreme environments.

Lauzon-Guay, J.-S., R. E. Scheibling, and M. A. Barbeau. 2008. Modeling phase shifts in a rocky subtidal ecosystem. *Marine Ecology Progress Series,* 375, 25–39.

Lees, J. C. 1981. *Three Generations of Red Maple Stump Sprouts.* M-X-119. Fredericton, NB: Canadian Forestry Service, Maritimes.

Lewontin, R. C. 1969. The meaning of stability. In *Diversity and Stability in Ecological Systems.* (pp. 13–24). Brookhaven Symposium in Biology, 22. Brookhaven, NJ.

Lieffers, V. J., S. E. Macdonald, and E. H. Hogg. 1993. Ecology of and control strategies for *Calamagrostis canadensis* in boreal forest sites. *Canadian Journal of Forest Research,* 23, 2070–2077.

Likens, G. E., F. H. Bormann, R. S. Pierce, and W. A. Reiners. 1978. Recovery of a deforested ecosystem. *Science,* 199, 492–496.

MacLean, D. A. 1984. Effects of spruce budworm outbreaks on the productivity and stability of balsam fir forests. *Forestry Chronicle,* 60, 273–279.

MacLean, D. A. 1988. Effects of spruce budworm outbreaks on vegetation, structure, and succession of balsam fir forests on Cape Breton Island, Canada. In M. J. A. Werger, P. J. M. van der Aart, H. J. During, and J. J. A. Verhoeven (Eds.), *Plant Form and Vegetation Structure.* (pp. 253–261). The Hague, The Netherlands: SPB Academic Publishers.

Macpherson, E. A., R. Scrosati, and P. Chareka. 2008. Barnacle recruitment on ice-scoured shores in eastern Canada. *Journal of the Marine Biological Association of the United Kingdom,* 88, 289–291.

Mallik, A. U. 1993. Ecology of a forest weed of Newfoundland: Vegetative regeneration strategy of *Kalmia angustifolia*. *Canadian Journal of Botany*, 71, 161–166.

Marks, P. L. 1974. The role of pin cherry (*Prunus pensylvanica*) in the maintenance of stability in northern hardwood ecosystems. *Ecological Monographs*, 44, 73–88.

May, M. R. 1977. Thresholds and breakpoints in ecosystems with a multiplicity of stable states. *Nature*, 269, 471–477.

McRae, D. J., L. C. Duchesne, B. Freedman, T. J. Lynham, and S. Woodley. 2001. Differences between wildfire and clear-cutting and their implications in forest management. *Environmental Reviews*, 9, 223–260.

Minchinton, T. E., R. E. Scheibling, and H. L. Hunt. 1997. Recovery of an intertidal assemblage following a rare occurrence of scouring by sea ice in Nova Scotia, Canada. *Botanica Marina*, 40, 139–148.

Morrison, R. G. and G. A. Yarranton. 1973. Diversity, richness, and evenness during a primary sand dune succession at Grand Bend, Ontario. *Canadian Journal of Botany*, 51, 2401–2411.

Morrison, R. G. and G. A. Yarranton. 1974. Vegetational heterogeneity during a primary sand dune succession. *Canadian Journal of Botany*, 52, 397–410.

Prager, U. and F. B. Goldsmith. 1977. Stump sprout formation by red maple (*Acer rubrum*) in Nova Scotia. *Proceedings of the Nova Scotia Institute of Science*, 28, 93–99.

Proceedings of the National Academy of Sciences. Retrieved October 2013 from http://www.pnas.org/content/early/2013/05/22/1304199110.abstract.

Reiners, W. A., I. A. Worley, and D. B. Lawrence. 1971. Plant diversity in a chronosequence at Glacier Bay, Alaska. *Ecology*, 52, 55–69.

Reynolds, J. W. 1977. *The Earthworms (Lumbricidae and Sparganophilidae) of Ontario*. Toronto: Life Sciences Miscellaneous Publications, Royal Ontario Museum.

Scheibling, R. 1986. Increased macroalgal abundance following mass mortalities of sea urchins (*Strongylocentrotus droebachiensis*) along the Atlantic coast of Nova Scotia. *Oecologia (Berlin)*, 68, 186–198.

Simenstad, C. A., J. A. Estes, and K. W. Kenyon. 1978. Aleuts, sea otters, and alternate stable-state communities. *Science*, 200, 403–410.

Taylor, S. J., T. J. Carleton, and P. Adams. 1987. Understorey vegetation change in a *Picea mariana* chronosequence. *Vegetatio*, 73, 63–72.

Tilman, D. 1982. *Resource Competition and Community Structure*. Princeton, NJ: Princeton University Press.

Tilman, D. 1990. Mechanisms of plant competition for nutrients: The elements of a predictive theory of competition. In Grace, J.B. and D. Tilman (Eds.) *Perspectives on Plant Competition*. (pp. 117–141). New York: Academic Press.

Tomlinson, S., E. Matthes, P. J. Richardson, and D. W. Larson. 2008. The ecological equivalence of quarry floors to alvars. *Applied Vegetation Science*, 11, 73–82.

Wikipedia. 2012. *List of wildfires*. Retrieved January 2012 from http://en.wikipedia.org/wiki/List_of_wildfires#North_America .

Chapter 11

Commission for Environmental Cooperation (CEC). 1997. *Ecological Regions of North America: Toward a Common Perspective*. Montreal, PQ: CEC.

Ecological Stratification Working Group. 1995. *A National Ecological Framework for Canada*. Ottawa: Environment Canada.

Freedman, B. 2010. *Environmental Science. A Canadian Perspective* (5th ed.). Toronto: Pearson Education Canada.

NOAA (National Oceanographic and Atmospheric Administration). NOAA Okeanos Explorer Program, INDEX-SATAL 2010, NOAA/OER. Retrieved October 2013 from http://www.photolib.noaa.gov/htmls/expl2184.htm.

Odum, E. P. and G. W. Barrett. 2004. *Fundamentals of Ecology*. Florence, KY: Brooks.

Scott, G. A. J. 1995. *Canada's Vegetation: A World Perspective*. Montreal: McGill-Queen's University Press.

The State of Canada's Environment, 1996. 1996. Her Majesty the Queen in Right of Canada, Environment Canada.

USDA. 2009. *Major Biomes Map*. United States Department of Agriculture, Natural Resources Conservation Service. Washington, DC. Retrieved October 2013 from http://soils.usda.gov/use/worldsoils/mapindex/biomes.html.

Wiken, E., D. Gauthier, I. Marshall, K. Lawton, and H. Hirvonen. 1996. *A Perspective on Canada's Ecosystems: An Overview of the Terrestrial and Marine Ecozones*. Occ. Pap. No. 14, Ottawa: Canadian Council on Ecological Areas.

Wilkinson T., E. Wiken, J. Bezaury-Creel, T. Hourigan, T. Agardi, H. Herrmann, L. Janishevski, C. Madden, L. Morgan, and M. Padilla. 2009. *Marine Ecoregions of North America*. Montreal, PQ: Commission for Environmental Cooperation.

Chapter 12

Canadian Animal Health Institute (CAHI). 2008. *Latest Pet Population Figures Released*. Guelph, ON: CAHI.

Canadian Endangered Species Conservation Council (CESCC). 2006. *Wild Species: The General Status of Species in Canada*. Retrieved October 2009 from http://www.wildspecies.ca/wildspecies2005/index.cfm?lang5e.

Cardinale, B. J., J. E. Duffy, A. Gonzalez, D. U. Hooper, C. Perrings, P. Venail, A. Narwani, G. M. Mace, D. Tilman, D. A. Wardle, A. P. Kinzig, G. C. Daily, M. Loreau, J. B. Grace, A. Larigauderie, D. S. Srivastava, and S. Naeem. 2012. Biodiversity loss and its impact on humanity. *Nature*, 486, 59–67.

Census of Marine Life (CoML). 2010. *A Decade of Discovery*. Retrieved February 2010 from http://www.coml.org.

Centre for Applied Conservation Research. 2007. *Endemic Taxa of British Columbia*. Faculty of Forestry, University of British Columbia, Vancouver, BC. Retrieved October 2009 from http://www.forestbiodiversity inbc.ca/manage_approach_species_endemic.asp.

Cheliak, W. M. and B. P. Dancik. 1982. Genic diversity of natural populations of a clone-forming tree *Populus tremuloides*. *Canadian Journal of Genetics & Cytology*, 24, 611–616.

Comiskey, J. A., T. C. H. Sunderland, and J. L. Sunderland-Groves (Eds.). 2003. *Takamanda: The Biodiversity of a Tropical Forest*. Washington, DC: Smithsonian Institution.

de March, B. G. E., L. D. Maiers, and M. K. Friesen. 2002. An overview of genetic relationships of Canadian and adjacent populations of belugas (*Delphinapterus leucas*) with emphasis on Baffin Bay and Canadian eastern Arctic populations. The North Atlantic Marine Mammal Commission (NAMMCO), *Scientific Publication*, 4, 17–38.

Eldredge, L. G. and N. L. Evenhuis. 2003. *Hawaii's Biodiversity: A Detailed Assessment of the Numbers of Species in the Hawaiian Islands.* Bishop Museum, Occasional Papers 76, 1–28. Honolulu, HI.

Elton, C. S. 1958. *The Ecology of Invasions by Plants and Animals.* Chicago, IL: University of Chicago Press.

Environment Canada. 1995. *Canadian Biodiversity Strategy, Canada's Response to the Convention on Biological Diversity.* Biodiversity Convention Office, Environment Canada. Retrieved October 2009 from http://www.cbin.ec.gc.ca/documents/national_reports/cbs_e.pdf.

Environment Canada. 1997. *The State of Canada's Environment.* State of the Environment Reporting Organization. Ottawa, ON: Environment Canada.

Erwin, T. L. 1983. Beetles and other insects of tropical forest canopies at Manaus, Brazil, sampled by insecticidal fogging. In S. L. Sutton, T. C. Whitmore, and A. C. Chadwick (Eds.) *Tropical Rain Forest: Ecology and Management.* (pp. 59–75). Boston, MA: Blackwell.

Freedman, B. 2010. *Environmental Science. A Canadian Perspective* (5th ed.). Toronto: Pearson Education Canada.

Gentry, A. H. 1986. Endemism in tropical vs. temperate plant communities. In M.E. Soule (Ed.) *Conservation Biology.* (pp. 153–181). Sunderland, MA: Sinauer Associates.

Gentry, A. H. 1988. Tree species of upper Amazonian forests. *Proceedings of the National Academy of Sciences,* 85, 156–159.

Goodman, S. M. and J. P. Benstead. 2004. *The Natural History of Madagascar.* Chicago: University of Chicago Press.

Groombridge, G. 1992. *Global Biodiversity.* London, UK: Chapman & Hall.

Hamlin, K. L. and J. A. Cunningham. 2009. *Monitoring and Assessment of Wolf-Ungulate Interactions and Population Trends within the Greater Yellowstone Area, Southwestern Montana, and Montana Statewide.* Helena, MT: Montana Department of Fish, Wildlife, and Parks, Wildlife Division.

Heywood, V. H. (Ed.). 1995. *Global Biodiversity Assessment.* Cambridge, UK: Cambridge University Press.

Holmes, R. T., T. W. Sherry, and F. W. Sturges. 1986. Bird community dynamics in a temperate deciduous forest: Long-term trends at Hubbard Brook. *Ecological Monographs,* 56, 201–220.

Hubbell, S. P. and R. B. Foster. 1983. Diversity of canopy trees in a neotropical forest and implications for conservation. In S. L. Sutton, T. C. Whitmore, and A. C. Chadwick (Eds.) *Tropical Rain Forest: Ecology and Management.* (pp. 25–41). Boston: Blackwell Scientific Publishers.

Hughes, J. B., G. C. Daily, and P. R. Ehrlich. 1997. Population diversity: Its extent and extinction. *Science,* 278, 689–692.

International Union for the Conservation of Nature (IUCN). 2009. *2008 IUCN Red List Summary Statistics.* Retrieved October 2009 from: http://cms.iucn.org/about/work/programmes/species/red_list/2008_red_list_summary_statistics.

Janzen, D. H. 1987. Insect diversity in a Costa Rican dry forest: Why keep it, and how. *Biological Journal Linnaean Society,* 30, 343–356.

Leigh, E. G. 1982. Why are there so many kinds of tropical trees? In E. G. Leigh, A. S. Rand, and D. M. Windsor (Eds.) *The Ecology of a Tropical Forest.* (pp. 63–66). Washington, DC: Smithsonian Institution Press.

MacArthur, R. E. 1955. Fluctuations of animal populations and a measure of community stability. *Ecology,* 36, 533–36.

MacKinnon, K., G. Hatta, H. Halim, and A. Mangalik. 1996. *The Ecology of Kalimantan.* Singapore: Periplus Editions.

May, R. M. 1973. *Stability and Complexity in Model Ecosystems.* Princeton, NJ: Princeton University Press.

McCann, K. S. 2000. The diversity–stability debate. *Nature,* 405, 228–233.

Miller, K. and L. Tangley 1991. *Trees of Life.* Boston, MA: Beacon Press.

Mitton, J. B. and M. C. Grant. 1996. Genetic variation and the natural history of quaking aspen. *BioScience,* 46, 25–31.

Murray, B. W., S. Malik, and B. N. White. 1995. Sequence variation at the major histocompatibility complex locus DQB in beluga whales (*Delphinapterus leucas*). *Molecular Biology and Evolution,* 12, 582–593.

Myers, N. 1983. *A Wealth of Wild Species.* Boulder, CO: Westview Press.

Newman, D. and G. Cragg. 2007. Natural products as drugs over the past 25 years. *Journal of Natural Products,* 70, 461–477.

Paijmans, J. 1970. An analysis of four tropical rain forest sites in New Guinea. *Journal of Ecology,* 58, 77–101.

Patenaude, N. J., J. S. Quinn, P. Beland, M. Kingsley, and B. N. White. 1994. Genetic variation of the St. Lawrence beluga whale population assessed by DNA fingerprinting. *Molecular Ecology,* 3, 375–381.

Pimm, S. L., L. Dollar, and O. L. Bass. 2006. The genetic rescue of the Florida panther. *Animal Conservation,* 9, 115–122.

Primack, R. B. and P. Hall. 1992. Biodiversity and forest change in Malaysian Borneo. *BioScience,* 42, 829–837.

Staicer, C. 2001. *User's manual: Forest Bird Monitoring and Research Program at Kejimkujik National Park.* Research Report to Parks Canada, Atlantic Region. Halifax, NS: Department of Biology, Dalhousie University,

Stupka, A. 1964. *Trees, Shrubs, and Woody Vines of Great Smoky Mountains National Park.* Knoxville, TN: University of Tennessee Press.

Terborgh, J., S. K. Robinson, T. A. Parker, C. A. Muna, and N. Pierpont. 1990. Structure and organization of an Amazonian forest bird community. *Ecological Monographs,* 60, 312–238.

Thiollay, J.-M. 1992. Influence of selective logging on bird species diversity in a Guaianan rain forest. *Conservation Biology,* 6, 47–63.

Thorington, R. W., B. Tannenbaum, A. Tarak, and R. Rudran. 1982. Distribution of trees on Barro Colorado Island: A five hectare sample. In C. E. G. Leigh, A. S. Rand, and D. M. Windsor (Eds.). *The Ecology of a Tropical Forest.* (pp. 83–94). Washington, DC: Smithsonian Institution Press.

Turkington, R., E. John, S. Watson, and P. Seccombe-Hett. 2002. The effects of fertilization and herbivory on the herbaceous vegetation of the boreal forest in northwestern Canada: A ten-year study. *Journal of Ecology,* 90: 325–227.

Vasseur, L., L. W. Aarssen, and D. D. Lefebvre. 1991. Allozymic and morphometric variation in *Lemna minor* (Lemnaceae). *Plant Systematics and Evolution,* 177, 139–148.

Vitousek, P. M. 1988. Diversity and biological invasions of oceanic islands. In E. O. Wilson (Ed.). *Biodiversity.* (pp. 181–189). Washington, DC: National Academy Press.

Whitten, A. J., S. J. Damanik, J. Anwar, and N. Hisyam. 1987. *The Ecology of Sumatra.* Yogyokarta, Indonesia: Gadjah Mada University Press.

Wilson, E. O. (editor). 1988. *Biodiversity.* Washington, DC: National Academy Press.

World Resources Institute (WRI). 2009. *EarthTrends Environmental Information.* Retrieved October 2009 from http://earthtrends.wri.org.

Yeh, F. C., D. K. X. Chong, and R.-C. Yang. 1995. RAPD variation within and among natural populations of trembling aspen (*Populus tremuloides* Michx.) from Alberta. *Journal of Heredity*, 86, 454–460.

Chapter 13

Alftine, K. J. and G. P. Malanson. 2004. Directional positive feedback and pattern at an alpine tree line. *Journal of Vegetation Science*, 15, 3–12.

Anonymous. 2012. Yellowstone to Yukon Conservation Initiative: Our Vision. Retrieved August 2013 from http://y2y.net/our-vision.

Bennett, A. F., K. Henein, and G. Merriam. 1994. Corridor use and the elements of corridor quality—chipmunks and fencerows in a farmland mosaic. *Biological Conservation*, 68, 155–165.

Bosakowski, T. and D. G. Smith. 1997. Distribution and species richness of a forest raptor community in relation to urbanization. *Journal of Raptor Research*, 31, 26–33.

Botkin, D. 1990. *Discordant Harmonies: A New Ecology for the Twenty-First Century.* New York: Oxford University Press.

Broadfoot, J. D., R. C. Rosatte, and D. T. O'Leary. 2001. Raccoon and skunk population models for urban disease control planning in Ontario, Canada. *Ecological Applications*, 11, 295–303.

Clevenger, A. P., B. Chruszcz, K. Gunson, and J. Wierzchowski. 2002. *Roads and Wildlife in the Canadian Rocky Mountain Parks—Movements, Mortality and Mitigation.* Banff, AB: Research Report prepared for Parks Canada.

Delcourt, H. R., P. A. Delcourt, and T. Webb. 1983. Dynamic plant ecology: The spectrum of vegetational change in space and time. *Quaternary Science Review*, 1, 153–175.

Dessler, A. and E. A. Parson. 2006. *The Science and Politics of Global Climate Change: A Guide to the Debate.* Cambridge, UK: Cambridge University Press.

Fahrig, L. 2001. How much habitat is enough? *Biological Conservation*, 100, 65–74.

Fonseca, M. S. and S. S. Bell. 1998. Influence of physical setting on seagrass landscapes near Beaufort, North Carolina, USA. *Marine Ecology-Progress Series*, 171, 109–121.

Forman, R. T. T. 1995. *Landscape Mosaics: The Ecology of Landscapes and Regions.* Cambridge, UK: Cambridge University Press.

Forman, R. T. T. and M. Godron. 1986. *Landscape Ecology.* New York: John Wiley & Sons.

Fortin, M. J. and M. R. T. Dale. 2005. *Spatial Analysis: A Guide for Ecologists.* Cambridge, UK: Cambridge University Press.

Freedman, B. and T. C. Hutchinson. 1980. Long-term effects of smelter pollution at Sudbury, Ontario, on forest community composition. *Canadian Journal of Botany*, 58, 2123–2140.

Fritz, R., R. Suffling, and A. K. Younger. 1993. Influence of fur trade, famine and forest fires on moose and caribou populations in northwestern Ontario from 1786–1911. *Environmental Management*, 17, 477–489.

Fudge, D., B. Freedman, M. Crowell, T. Nette, and V. Power. 2007. Road-kill of mammals in Nova Scotia. *Canadian Field-Naturalist*, 121, 265–273.

Gagne, S. A. and L. Fahrig. 2010. The trade-off between housing density and sprawl area: Minimising impacts to forest breeding birds. *Basic and Applied Ecology*, 11, 723–773.

Greater Fundy Ecosystem Project. 2009. *About the Greater Fundy Ecosystem Project.* Retrieved September 2009 from http://www.unbf.ca/forestry/centers/fundy.

Hanrahan, J. L., S. V. Kravtsov, and P. J. Roebber. 2009. Quasi-periodic decadal cycles in levels of lakes Michigan and Huron. *Journal of Great Lakes Research*, 35, 30–35.

Hessburg, P. F, J. K. Agee, and J. F. Franklin. 2005. Dry forests and wildland fires of the inland Northwest USA: Contrasting the landscape ecology of the pre-settlement and modem eras. *Forest Ecology and Management*, 211, 117–139.

Hills, G. 1961. The ecological basis for natural resources management. In *The Ecological Basis for Land-use Planning.* (pp. 8–49). Toronto, ON: Research Branch, Ontario Department of Lands and Forests.

Hodgson, J. A., A. Moilanen, B. A. Wintle, C. D. Thomas. 2011. Habitat area, quality and connectivity: Striking the balance for efficient conservation. *Journal of Applied Ecology*, 48, 148–152.

Holling, C. S. 1992. Cross-scale morphology, geometry, and dynamics of ecosystems. *Ecological Monographs*, 62, 447–502.

Laurence, W. F. 2007. Ecosystem decay of Amazonian forest fragments: Implications for conservation. In T. Tscharntke, C. Leuschner, M. Zeller, E. Guhardja, and A. Bidin, (Eds.). *The Stability of Tropical Rainforest Margins: Linking Ecological, Economic and Social Constraints of Land Use and Conservation.* (pp. 11–37). Berlin, Germany: Springer.

Law, B. S. and C. R. Dickman. 1998. The use of habitat mosaics by terrestrial vertebrate fauna: Implications for conservation and management. *Biodiversity and Conservation*, 7, 323–333.

Levin, S. A. 1992. The problem of pattern and scale in ecology. *Ecology*, 73, 1943–1967.

Lindeman, R. L. 1942. The trophic-dynamic aspect of ecology. *Ecology* 23, 399–418.

Ludwig, J. A., B. P. Wilcox, D. D. Breshears, D. J. Tongway, and A. C. Imeson. 2005. Vegetation patches and runoff-erosion as interacting ecohydrological processes in semiarid landscapes. *Ecology*, 86, 288–297.

Lutz, S. G. 1997. *Pre-European Settlement and Present Forest Composition in King's County, New Brunswick, Canada.* Master of Forestry Thesis. Fredericton, NB: University of New Brunswick.

McArthur, R. H. and E. O. Wilson. 1967. *The Theory of Island Biogeography.* Princeton, NJ: Princeton University Press.

McGarigal, K. 2009a. *FRAGSTATS Spatial Pattern Analysis Program for Categorical Maps.* Landscape Ecology Program, University of Massachusetts, Amherst. Retrieved January 12, 2009 from http://www.umass.edu/landeco/research/fragstats/fragstats.html.

McGarigal, K. 2009b. *What Is Landscape Ecology?* Retrieved January 12, 2009 from http://www.umass.edu/landeco/about/landeco.pdf.

Naiman, R. J., G. Pinay, C. A. Johnston, and J. Pastor. 1994. Beaver influences on the long-term biogeochemical characteristics of boreal forest drainage networks. *Ecology*, 75, 905–921.

Nakamura, F., F. J. Swanson, and S. M. Wondzell. 2000. Disturbance regimes of stream and riparian systems—A disturbance-cascade perspective. *Hydrological Processes*, 14, 2849–2860.

Odum, E. P. and H. T. Odum. 1959. *Fundamentals of Ecology* (2nd ed.). Philadelphia, PA: W. B. Saunders.

Odum, H. T. 1957. Trophic structure and productivity of Silver Springs, Florida. *Ecological Monographs*, 27, 55–112.

Ontario's Woodland Caribou Conservation Plan. 2009. Ontario Ministry of Natural Resources. Queen's Printer for Ontario.

Payette, S., M. J. Fortin, and I. Gamache. 2001. The subarctic forest-tundra: The structure of a biome in a changing climate. *BioScience,* 51, 709–718.

Pidwirny, M. et al. 2009. *Remote Sensing. The Encyclopedia of Earth.* Retrieved January 12, 2010 from http://www .eoearth.org/article/Remote_sensing.

Puric-Mladenovic, D. and S. Strobl. 2012. Designing natural heritage systems in southern Ontario using a systematic conservation planning approach. *Forestry Chronicle,* 88, 22–35.

Quinn, T. P., S. M. Carlson, S. M. Gende, and H. B. Rich. 2009. Transportation of Pacific salmon carcasses from streams to riparian forests by bears. *Canadian Journal of Zoology,* 87, 195–203.

Rapport, D. J. 1997. Transdisciplinarity: Transcending the disciplines. *Trends in Ecology and Evolution,* 12, 289.

Rhemtulla, J. M., R.J. Hall, E. S. Higgs, and S. E. Macdonald 2002. Eighty years of change: Vegetation in the montane ecoregion of Jasper National Park, Alberta, Canada. *Canadian Journal of Forest Research,* 32, 2010–2022.

Roland, J. 1993. Large-scale forest fragmentation increases the duration of tent caterpillar outbreak. *Oecologia,* 93, 25–30.

Rothamsted Research. 2009. *Broadbalk.* Rothamsted Research. Retrieved January 12, 2010 from http://www .rothamsted.bbsrc.ac.uk/resources/ ClassicalExperiments .html#Broadbalk.

Schindler, D. E., M. D. Scheuerell, J. W. Moore, S. M. Gende, T. B. Francis, and W. J. Palen. 2003. Pacific salmon and the ecology of coastal ecosystems. *Frontiers in Ecology and the Environment,* 1, 31–37.

Schindler, D. W., R. E. Hecky, D. L. Findlay, M. P. Stainton, B. R. Parker, and M. J. Paterson. 2008. Eutrophication of lakes cannot be controlled by reducing nitrogen input: Results of a 37-year whole-ecosystem experiment. *Proceedings of the National Academy of Sciences (United States),* 105, 11254–11258.

Schmitt, D. and R. Suffling. 2006. Managing eastern North American woodlands in a cultural context. *Landscape and Urban Planning,* 78, 457–464.

Stoate, C., A. Baldi, P. Beja, N. D. Boatman, I. Herzon, A. van Doorn, G. R. de Snoog. L. Rakosyi, C. Ramwell. 2009. Ecological impacts of early 21st century agricultural change in Europe—A review. *Journal of Environmental Management,* 91(1), 22–46.

Storfer, A., M. A. Murphy, J. S. Evans, C. S. Goldberg, S. Robinson, S. F. Spear, R. Dezzani, E. Delmelle, L. Vierling, and L. Waits. 2007. *Heredity,* 98, 128–142.

Suffling, R. 1995. Can disturbance determine vegetation distribution during climate warming? A boreal test. *Journal of Biogeography,* 22, 501–508.

Suffling, R. and A. Perera. 2004. Characterizing natural forest disturbance regimes. In A. Perera, L. J. Buse, and M. G. Weber (Eds.). *Emulating Natural Forest Landscape Disturbances: Concepts and Applications.* (pp. 43–54). New York: Columbia University Press.

Suffling, R. and C. Wilson. 1994. The use of Hudson's Bay Company records in climatic and ecological research, with particular reference to the Great Lakes Basin. In R. I. MacDonald (Ed.). *Great Lakes Archaeology and Paleoecology: Proceedings of a Symposium.* (pp. 295–319). Waterloo, ON: Quaternary Sciences Institute, University of Waterloo.

Suffling, R., B. Smith, and J. Dal Molin. 1982. Estimating past forest age distributions and disturbance rates in northwestern Ontario—A demographic approach. *Journal of Environmental Management,* 14, 45–56.

Tanner, J. E. 2006. Landscape ecology of interactions between seagrass and mobile epifauna: The matrix matters. *Estuarine Coastal and Shelf Science,* 68, 404–412.

Trombulak, S.C. and C. A. Frissell. 2000. Review of ecological effects of roads on terrestrial and aquatic communities. *Conservation Biology,* 14, 18–30.

Turner, M. G. 1989. Landscape ecology— The effect of pattern on process. *Annual Review of Ecology and Systematics,* 20, 171–197.

Turner, M. G. 2005. Landscape ecology: What is the state of the science? *Annual Review of Ecology Evolution and Systematics,* 36, 319–344.

Turner, M. G., W. H. Romme, R. H. Gardner, and W. W. Hargrove. 1997. Effects of fire size and pattern on early succession in Yellowstone National Park. *Ecological Monographs,* 67, 411–433.

Turner, M.G. 2010. Disturbance and landscape dynamics in a changing world. *Ecology,* 91, 2833–2849.

Van Wagner, C. E. 1978. Age-class distribution and the forest fire cycle. *Canadian Journal of Forest Research,* 8, 220–227.

Weaver, J. L., P. C. Paquet, and L. F. Ruggiero. 1996. Resilience and conservation of large carnivores in the Rocky Mountains. *Conservation Biology,* 10, 964–976.

Chapter 14

Baillie, J. E. M., C. Hilton-Taylor, and S. N. Stuart (Eds.). 2004. *A Global Species Assessment.* Cambridge, UK: IUCN— The World Conservation Union.

Bambach, R. K., A. H. Knoll, and S. C. Wang. 2004. Origination, extinction, and mass depletions of marine diversity. *Paleobiology,* 30, 522–542.

BirdLife International 2008a. *Meleagris gallopavo.* 2008 IUCN Red List of Threatened Species. http://www .iucnredlist.org.

BirdLife International. 2008b. *Aix sponsa.* 2008 IUCN Red List of Threatened Species. http://www.iucnredlist.org.

BirdLife International. 2008c. *Cygnus buccinator.* 2008 IUCN Red List of Threatened Species. http://www .iucnredlist.org.

BirdLife International. 2008d. *Falco peregrinus.* 2008 IUCN Red List of Threatened Species. http://www .iucnredlist.org.

BirdLife International. 2008e. *Haliaeetus leucocephalus.* 2008 IUCN Red List of Threatened Species. http://www .iucnredlist.org.

BirdLife International. 2012. *Grus americana.* IUCN Red List of Threatened Species—Version 2012.2. Retrieved February 2013 from http://www.iucnredlist.org/ details/106002796/0.

Blockstein, D. E. and H. B. Tordoff. 1985. Gone forever. A contemporary look at the extinction of the passenger pigeon. *American Birds,* 39, 845–851.

Canadian Council on Ecological Areas (CCEA). 2011. Canadian Conservation Areas Database. CCEA, Natural Resources Canada and Environment Canada, Ottawa, ON.

Canadian Endangered Species Conservation Council (CESCC). 2006. *Wild Species: The General Status of Species in Canada.* Retrieved October 2009 from http:// www.wildspecies.ca/ wildspecies2005.

Chapman, F. 1907. *The Warblers of North America.* New York: D. Appleton & Co.

Committee on the Status of Endangered Wildlife in Canada (COSEWIC). 2013. *Canadian Wildlife Species at Risk, January, 2013.* Retrieved

Glossary

abiotic Nonliving things, phenomena, processes, and their influences. Compare with **biotic**. p. 29

abiotic stressor A stressor that is associated with nutrients, moisture, or a climatic factor. p. 496

acclimation A process of physiological conditioning to prevailing or anticipated environmental conditions, as when plants acclimate to dry or cold conditions. p. 171

acclimatization Adjustments made by an organism in response to changes in the natural environment, such as seasonal change. p. 171

accuracy The degree to which a measurement or observation reflects the true value of the subject. p. 15

acidosis A decrease in blood pH below the normal range. p. 188

active layer Seasonally thawed ground that overlies the permafrost of cold regions. p. 344

adaptation A genetically controlled trait that increases the fitness of its bearer and that evolved for that specific role. p. 24

advanced regeneration Refers to small individuals of tree species that are established in a mature forest; the small individuals survive a disturbance and then are ecologically released from stresses previously exerted by the mature trees, so they can grow rapidly and be prominent in the next stand. p. 313

advocacy Activities that have the intention of influencing decisions and outcomes that affect people or the environment; with respect to biodiversity, advocacy might be undertaken to influence governmental policies and legislation, the activities of private companies, and even educational curricula. p. 470

aerobic metabolism Metabolic reactions that involve oxygen. p. 160

afforestation The establishment of a forest on land that is currently in a nonforested land use, such as an agricultural field. p. 55

age at maturity The age at which an organism reproduces for the first time (becomes sexually mature). p. 215

age-specific fecundity (age-specific fertility) The birth rate attained by individuals of a particular age. p. 106

age-specific fertility See **age-specific fecundity**. p. 106

age-specific survival The probability of an individual surviving from birth to the particular age. p. 107

aggradation phase A stage of secondary succession that immediately follows the reorganization phase, and is characterized by a steady accumulation of biomass because of positive ecosystem-level net production (productivity exceeds respiration). See also **reorganization phase**. p. 314

agroecosystem An ecosystem managed for the production of food. p. 356

albedo Reflectivity. p. 51

alien See **non-native**. p. 382

alkalosis An increase in blood pH above the normal range. p. 188

allelopathy A competitive interaction between plants that is mediated by one species releasing toxic secondary compounds into the soil, which other species cannot tolerate. p. 206

allochthonous Material that originates from outside a waterbody. Compare with **autochtonous**. p. 545

allopatric Refers to populations or species that occupy geographically separate ranges. Compare with **sympatric**. p. 122

alpha (α) diversity The variety of organisms occurring in a particular place or habitat; sometimes called local diversity. See also **beta (β) diversity**, **species diversity**, **species richness**, and **evenness**. p. 389

alternative stable states (or **multiple stable states**) The view that more than more than one type (state) of stable community may persist under similar abiotic and environmental conditions; a succession that does not necessarily result in the recovery of the original type of community. p. 276

altruism Helping behaviour that increases the recipient's direct fitness while decreasing that of the donor. p. 147

ammonification Part of the nitrogen cycle, in which organic-N is oxidized to ammonia, which acquires a hydrogen ion (H^+) to form ammonium (NH_4^+). p. 82

ammonotelic An animal that produces ammonia as the primary nitrogenous waste product. p. 181

anadromous Refers to fish that migrate to breed in freshwater, then migrate to the sea where they spend most of their adult life. p. 239

anaerobic Environmental conditions in which O_2 is not available. p. 78

anaerobic metabolism Metabolic reactions that occur without oxygen, or with an insufficient supply of that gas. p. 160

animal ecology The study of the populations, ecophysiology, productivity, and behaviour of wild animals and their communities. p. 17

antagonistic pleiotropy Occurs when a single gene that influences multiple phenotypic traits has a beneficial influence on a trait in early life (e.g., fecundity) but a negative one on another trait (e.g., survival) later on. p. 226

anthropocentric worldview A worldview that places the needs and aspirations of people at the centre of moral consideration, and regards our species as being more important and worthwhile than other living entities. Compare with **biocentric worldview** and **ecocentric worldview**. p. 584

anthropogenic Associated with an influence of humans or their economy. p. 9

anthropogenic biome A biome whose characteristics are greatly influenced by stressors or management associated with humans. Compare with **natural biome**. p. 343

anthropogenic mortality Deaths caused by harvesting or some other human influence. Compare with **natural mortality**. p. 497

applied ecology The integration of ecological knowledge with economic needs, such as finding improved ways to cultivate crops or to mitigate environmental damage. p. 16

applied research Research that is directly intended to solve a practical problem. Compare with **fundamental research**. p. 258

aquaculture The cultivation of aquatic organisms using various management practices. p. 516

aquifer An underground bed or layer of earth, gravel, or porous stone that can store and yield water. p. 407

asymmetric competition A condition in which one species exploits a particular resource more efficiently than another, but both may persist in the community. p. 266

atmosphere The envelope of gases, plus much smaller amounts of suspended particulates and droplets, that envelop Earth. p. 11

autecology The study of relationships of individual organisms, or of particular populations or species, with their environment. Compare with **synecology**. p. 16

autochthonous Material that originates within a waterbody. Compare with **allochthonous**. p. 545

autotroph Refers to "self-feeding organisms," such as plants and algae that are able to utilize sunlight to drive the fixation of carbon dioxide and water into simple organic compounds. See also **heterotrophic**. p. 45

base cation (or **base**) Refers to potassium, sodium, calcium, and/or magnesium. p. 86

behaviour Adjustment of state in response to changes in the environment; the actions of organisms, including their conscious or unconscious, deliberate or involuntary reactions to other organisms, abiotic stimuli, and other circumstances. p. 14

behavioural ecology The study of behaviour and its associated structures and biological processes, with reference to their adaptive consequences. p. 17

behavioural thermoregulation The regulation of body temperature through changes in body position or movement to a different location. p. 171

benthic zone The bottom habitat of waterbodies and oceans, including the sediment and immediately overlying water. p. 350

beta (β) diversity The variety of organisms occurring in different habitats or in a region; sometimes called regional diversity. See also **alpha (α) diversity**, **species richness**, and **evenness**. p. 389

bet-hedging strategy A life history that reduces the variance in genotypic/individual fitness over generations, even if this would entail a "sacrifice" of the expected fitness within any particular generation, as an adaptive trait to deal with environmental change and unpredictability. p. 220

biocentric worldview A worldview that in addition to humans considers that individual organisms of other species have intrinsic value, and so they deserve to have moral standing; moreover, in the case of sentient animals there is a special obligation to avoid causing unnecessary suffering while in pursuit of a human interest. Compare with **anthropocentric worldview** and **ecocentric worldview**. p. 584

bioconcentration The tendency of certain substances to occur in larger concentrations in organisms than in their ambient, nonliving environment. Compare with **biomagnification**. p. 37

biodiversity (biological diversity) The richness of biological variation, at all levels of biological organization; all of the populations (and genes), species, and communities in a particular area. p. 369

biological conservation The conservation of the natural world, particularly biodiversity and the services it provides. p. 432

biological resource (bioresource) Any biomass that is harvested as a source of food, material, or energy. p. 491

biomagnification The tendency for certain persistent chemicals to occur in their highest concentrations in top predators, such as organochlorines and methyl-mercury. Compare with **bioconcentration**. p. 37

biomagnify See **biomagnification**. p. 37

biomass The accumulated productivity of ecosystems; the mass of living matter in a given area or in a volume of water. p. 45

biome An ecosystem that exists over an extensive geographic range, occurring anywhere in the world that environmental conditions are suitable for its development. p. 13

biosphere All space occupied by life on Earth. p. 8

biotic An organic influence, meaning it is exerted by one or more organisms. Compare with abiotic. p. 29

bog An infertile, acidic, unproductive wetland that develops in cool but wet climates. Compare with **fen**. p. 351

bottom–up hypothesis (resource-control) A model based on the idea that community organization is determined by the effects of plants on herbivores, and of herbivores on carnivores, and the carnivores are self-regulating. Compare with **top–down hypothesis**. p. 286

brood parasite An individual that exploits the parental care of another individual other than its parents; may parasitize the parental care of the same or other species. p. 138

buffer A chemical that causes the pH of a solution to remain at a particular value. p. 188

bulk flow Movement of fluid from one compartment to another as a result of differences in hydrostatic and colloid osmotic pressure. p. 176

by-catch Nontargeted mortality, usually used in reference to a fishery. p. 499

capture efficiency The effect of a single predator on the per capita growth rate of its prey. p. 124

carnivore An animal that eats animal tissue. Compare with **herbivore** and **omnivore**. p. 59

carrying capacity The largest population size that a habitat can sustain without becoming degraded. p. 101

caste A biologically distinct group within a species of eusocial organism, such as a soldier or worker. p. 148

centrifugal organization A model of community organization in which the most competitive species occupies core habitat, while others become more prominent as one moves toward harsher conditions in peripheral habitats. p. 254

character displacement A divergence in the phenotypic attributes of similar species as a result of competition occurring when they co-occur in a place or habitat. p. 122

chemical energy Energy that is stored in bonds occurring among the atoms that comprise molecules. p. 48

chemoautotrophs Microorganisms that utilize potential energy of sulphides and certain other inorganic chemicals to drive their fixation of energy through chemosynthesis. Compare with **photoautotrophs**. p. 57

chemosynthesis Autotrophic productivity that utilizes energy released during the oxidation of sulphides and certain other inorganic chemicals to drive biosynthesis. Compare with **photosynthesis**. p. 57

chronic A longer-term or continuous influence. p. 36

chronosequence A series of communities of various ages that have regenerated from a similar kind of disturbance, and are studied as a progression to infer patterns of ecological change occurring during a succession. p. 316

clear-cutting The harvesting of all trees in an affected stand at the same time. Compare with **selection-cutting**. p. 505

climatic climax According to the Clementsian view of succession, this is the "potential vegetation" of a site, which would be attained if succession were able to run its full course without an intervening disturbance that truncates the sere. See also **climax**. p. 306

climax (or climax community) A predictable end-point community of a succession in which a community has reached a steady state under a particular set of environmental conditions. p. 250

clone A group of genetically uniform organisms. p. 371

closed population One that is isolated from other groups of the same species, such that there is no movement of individuals between them. Compare with **open population**. p. 97

closed system A situation in which there is no gain in mass, energy, or information, and also no loss. See also **open system**. p. 74

coarse scale Related to observing in relatively little detail over relatively large areas. Compare with **fine scale**. p. 394

coefficient of relatedness (or coefficient of relationship) Defined as two times the coefficient of kinship, which itself is the probability that alleles at any random locus chosen from two individuals are identical by descent. p. 148

coevolution The linked evolution of one or more biological attributes, including that of two or more species. p. 139

cohort A group of individuals that were born at about the same time. p. 108

cohort life table The age-specific survival and fecundity schedule of a cohort. See also **cohort** and **life table** and compare with **static life table**. p. 108

coldspots of biodiversity Regions with less-focused concentrations of biodiversity. Compare with **hotspots of biodiversity**. p. 456

commensalism A relationship in which one organism benefits without harming the other. p. 264

commercial extinction (economic extinction) Occurrence of a bioresource in an abundance that has become too small to support commercial harvesting. p. 520

common-property resource Equity that is shared by a group or even all of society. See also **tragedy of the commons**. p. 502

community A group of organisms that live together in the same place and time and that interact directly or indirectly; a community consists of plants, animals, fungi, and bacteria. p. 8

community ecology Examines interactions occurring among populations of various species within an ecological community. p. 17

competition An interaction that occurs when two or more organisms require a common resource that is in short supply compared with the biological demand; it occurs when an organism uses more energy to obtain, or maintain, a unit of resource because of interference from other individuals, of the same or different species, than it would otherwise do. p. 6

competition coefficient A mathematical constant that reflects the competitive ability of a species. p. 117

competitive exclusion The great diminishment or extirpation of a species in a community because of the competitive dominance of another species. p. 265

competitive release The expansion of a species' distribution in the absence of a competitor. p. 265

competitor A species that is relatively effective at acquiring scarce resources, often to the detriment of less-competitive species. p. 232

composite indicator An artificial variable that integrates changes in a number of different metrics to broadly track changes in all of them. See also **multimetric indicator**. p. 577

connectivity The permeability of the landscape between patches, which is related to corridors, the matrix, and how closely adjacent the patches are; permeability will vary among species. See also **permeable**. p. 401

conservation (1) Sustainable use of a renewable natural resource; or (2) stewardship of the natural world. p. 16

conservation data centre An organization that collects data on the distribution and abundance of species at risk and of communities and other kinds of biophysical habitat types. p. 576

conservation ecology The application of ecological knowledge to the stewardship of biodiversity and protected areas. p. 16

conservation planning Planning that seeks to identify the most important places that should be set aside, within the context of a comprehensive system of protected areas. p. 457

conspecific Refers to members of the same species. p. 135

constraints of reproduction Inherent limitations on reproduction (and on fitness), owing to costs associated with energetic, ecological, or genetic factors. p. 224

consumer-control hypothesis See **top–down hypothesis**. p. 286

contamination The presence of a substance, but at a concentration or intensity that is too low to result in a measurable biological or ecological effect. Compare with **pollution**. p. 37

control A non-manipulated treatment in an experiment. p. 21

convenience polyandry Polyandry occurring when females re-mate to avoid costs of rejecting matings. p. 141

conventional economics Economics as it is usually practised, with valuation being assessed primarily in an anthropocentric context. Compare with **ecological economics**. p. 483

convergent evolution Evolution by different species, sometimes occurring in widely spaced places, but subjected to similar regimes of environmental conditions and natural selection, so that the evolutionary responses are parallel (or convergent). p. 341

conversion A change in character of an ecosystem from one type to another, often in reference to a change from a natural to an anthropogenic ecosystem. p. 124

corridor A linear feature that differs from the matrix on either side and that may provide connectivity between separated patches of habitat. p. 401

cost of reproduction Effort or resource allocation that is required to support reproduction. p. 224

counter-current flow A flow of fluids in opposite directions in tubules or vessels in close proximity. p. 184

counter-current heat exchange A heat conservation mechanism that occurs when an artery and vein are in close proximity, so heat is exchanged between the two, resulting in less loss to the environment. p. 168

crown fire A fires that burns the forest canopy, and in Canadian forests generally kills the trees, and so it is a stand-replacing disturbance. p. 410

crust The outermost layer of the solid sphere of Earth, and composed mostly of crystalline and sedimentary rocks. p. 13

cryoprotectant A compound that helps reduce the freezing point of water and prevents the formation of ice crystals in body fluids. p. 169

cryptic herbivore Small consumers, typically herbivores, that are not visually abundant in a community but have a major impact on community structure. p. 279

cumulative environmental impacts Environmental impacts resulting from the effects of a proposed undertaking within some defined area, on top of those caused by any past, existing, and imminent developments and activities. See also **environmental impact assessment**. p. 589

cyclic phenomena Regular and predictable temporal changes in the structure or function of a system. p. 418

damped oscillation Repetitive temporal variation about a central (average) value that becomes progressively less over time, and is eventually asymptotic with the mean as a point of equilibrium. Compare with **stable limit cycle**. p. 103

data deficient A COSEWIC designation that applies when the available information is not sufficient to resolve an assessment of conservation status of a species (or taxon). p. 451

decomposition (mineralization) The oxidation of dead organic matter into simpler compounds, and ultimately to carbon dioxide, water, and other simple inorganic molecules. p. 76

deductive logic Reasoning that involves making an initial assumption, or several of them, and then drawing conclusions. p. 19

deforestation The permanent conversion of a forest into a nonforested land use, for example, into agricultural production. Compare with **afforestation**. p. 442

deglaciation The meltback of glacial ice. p. 318

dendrochronology The branch of science that uses annual tree-ring couplets to age trees and reconstruct past environmental conditions. p. 542

denitrification Part of the nitrogen cycle, in which nitrate is converted by bacteria into either N_2 or N_2O, which are released to the atmosphere. p. 83

density-independent model of population growth An exponential model of population growth, in that the per capita growth rate does not vary with the density of the population. See also **exponential model of population growth**. p. 97

determinate growth Growth of individuals that ceases after a certain age. p. 106

deterministic (1) Refers to age-specific rates of survival and fecundity that are fixed at constant values. (2) Relating to a specific input variable to a system, giving a specific and predictable output. p. 114

detritivore Organisms that feed on dead organic matter. p. 59

devegetation A severe disturbance that removes vegetation cover from an affected site, p. 315

direct action In the context of biodiversity, this refers to activities that result in immediate benefits, as occurs when protected areas are established to benefit species at risk or rare communities. p. 470

direct fitness Genes contributed by an individual to its population via its personal reproduction (its surviving offspring). Compare with **indirect fitness**. p. 148

disclimax A climax community that occurs in a situation with an unusual disturbance or environmental regime. See also climax. p. 306

disease A biological relationship that involves a pathogenic microorganism infecting a plant or animal, making the host ill or sometimes killing it; some other diseases may be caused by abiotic factors, such as toxic substances. p. 6

disturbance A discrete event; a discrete occurrence that disrupts a population or community and thereby changes substrates, resource availability, and the physical environment, and often provides opportunity for colonization by new individuals. p. 6

dominance-controlled community A situation in which early colonizers of a recently disturbed habitat are dissimilar ecologically, and as the community matures it will become progressively more dominated by competitively superior species. See also **founder-controlled community**. p. 259

dominant species A species having the highest abundance or biomass in a community, and thereby having a major influence on community structure. p. 258

doubling time The length of time required for an initial quantity to double in amount or size. p. 98

ecocentric worldview A worldview that includes the biocentric one but goes further by also affording inherent value to species and higher-order ecological levels, including natural communities and ecoscapes, as well as functional attributes such as clean-environment services and carbon storage. Compare with **anthropocentric worldview** and **biocentric worldview**. p. 584

ecological economics A conceptual fusion of economics and ecology, whose distinction is that it seeks to examine and valuate the relationships of economic systems and ecological systems in an objective and nonanthropocentric manner. Compare with **conventional economics**. p. 483

ecological energetics Study of the energy inputs, outputs, and transformations within ecosystems, including those involving biologically fixed energy. p. 45

ecological footprint The area of ecoscape that is needed to support the production of the energy and materials used by a person, city, or another economic unit, as well as assimilate any resulting wastes. p. 484

ecological function (or **ecological process**) Flows and/or transformations of energy, materials, and species occurring among landscape elements. p. 407

ecological genetics See **molecular ecology**. p. 17

ecological integrity (EI) An indicator related to environmental quality, but with a focus on changes in wild populations and natural ecosystems, rather than on humans and their economy; indicators of high levels of EI include dominance by native species, self-organized communities, and ecoscapes that are characteristic for the prevailing natural environmental regimes. See also **ecosystem health**. p. 433

ecological region See **ecoregion**. p. 357

ecological reserve A protected area established to conserve natural values, particularly biodiversity, and in which visitation is strictly limited and the only permitted activities are scientific monitoring and research. p. 461

ecologically sustainable development An economy that is making progress toward ecological sustainability. See also **ecologically sustainable economy** and compare with **sustainable development**. p. 25

ecologically sustainable economy An economy that is resource sustainable, and that also maintains biodiversity and ecological services at viable levels of abundance. Compare with **sustainable economy**. p. 25

ecologist A scientist who studies some aspect of ecology. p. 17

ecology The study of the relationships of organisms and their environment. p. 5

economic development Progress made in structuring an economy toward a greater use of renewable resources and other improvements. Compare with **sustainable development** and **economic growth**. p. 487

economic growth An economy that is increasing in size over time, in terms of its human population, consumption of resources, manufacturing of goods, supply of money, and generation of waste materials and pollution. Compare with **economic development** and **sustainable development**. p. 485

economics An interdisciplinary field whose principal goal is to understand the ways that scarce resources (goods and services of various kinds) are allocated among competing uses within an economy. p. 482

economy (economic system) A system comprising all of the institutions and interactions occurring at a defined level of society and that affect the production, distribution, and consumption of goods and services. p. 482

ecophysiology See **physiological ecology**. p. 159

ecoregion (ecological region) Extensive regions of general similarity; terrestrial ecoregions are classified according to their physiography, climate, and biological characteristics, and marine ones by physiography, oceanography, and biological attributes. p. 357

ecoscape A heterogeneous terrestrial and/or aquatic area with repeated forms at any appropriate scale. See also **landscape** and **seascape**. p. 8

ecosystem (ecological system) A generalized term that cannot be precisely defined, but is a space in which organisms are interacting with environmental factors, and is delimited for the purposes of studying it. p. 6

ecosystem approach A holistic way of understanding ecological systems, which considers all individuals, populations, communities, and environments to be intrinsically connected and interdependent, although in varying degrees. p. 8

ecosystem ecology (functional ecology) Examines the flows of energy and nutrients among organisms and the abiotic environment. p. 17

ecosystem health An indicator related to and not substantially different from ecological integrity, but with more of a focus on the functional attributes of ecosystems. See also **environmental quality** and **ecological integrity**. p. 572

ecotone An edge or zone of transition between discrete habitat types, such as between a forest and a wetland, or between neighbouring patches on a landscape. See also **edge**. p. 41

ecotypic variation See **population diversity**. p. 374

ecozone Extensive ecological regions that are distinguished and mapped largely on the basis of their ecological similarities, particularly their dominant late-successional biota, the most prominent species, and their "enduring" environmental features related to bedrock, soil types, climate, and topography. p. 357

ectotherm An animal that relies on the environment as a heat source. p. 162

edaphic climax A climax community that is primarily determined by local soil conditions. See also **climax**. p. 306

edge (1) A linear place where a landscape patch abuts one or more other land-cover units. (2) The collective occurrence of edges in a landscape. See also **ecotone**. p. 399

electromagnetic energy Energy associated with entities called photons, which have properties of both waves and particles and travel at an unvarying velocity known as the speed of light (3×10^8 m/s). p. 46

emergent property (1) An attribute of life or ecosystems that cannot be predicted from knowledge of the parts, and that exists only if the system is operating as an integrated whole. (2) A complex pattern or phenomenon that arises from a multiplicity of relatively simple interactions or phenomena. p. 8

emulation forestry (emulation silviculture) Modelling timber-harvesting and management systems to imitate the natural disturbance regime of a forest type. p. 515

endangered A species that is at imminent risk of extinction or extirpation in all or an important portion of its range. p. 450

endemic A taxon (species or subspecies) with a local or restricted distribution. p. 347

endogenous Influences that are internal to the ecosystem (or organism) being studied, especially ones that are biological in origin. Compare with **exogenous**. p. 418

endotherm An animal that obtains its body heat from its own metabolism. p. 163

energy A fundamental physical entity, simply defined as the capacity of a body or system to accomplish work. p. 46

energy budget A physical budget of a system that describes the rates of input and output of energy and any internal transformations among its states, including changes in stored amounts. p. 51

entropy A physical attribute related to the degree of randomness of the distributions of matter and energy. See also **second law of thermodynamics**. p. 49

environmental ecology Study of ecological responses to environmental stressors, with a focus on anthropogenic pollution and disturbance. p. 16

environmental factor (or **influence**) Influences that affect individual organisms, populations, communities, or ecoscapes (landscapes and seascapes), or functions such as productivity, decomposition, and nutrient cycling. p. 5

environmental gradient See **gradient**. p. 250

environmental impact assessment (EIA) A planning process that helps to identify and appraise environmental problems that are potentially involved with a proposed economic activity, and to find ways to avoid or mitigate them if possible. p. 587

environmental influence See **environmental factor**. p. 29

environmental monitoring Repeated measurements of variables related to either the abiotic (inorganic) environment or to the structure and functioning of ecosystems. p. 576

environmental non-governmental organization (ENGO) An environmental charity, such as the Nature Conservancy of Canada or the World Wildlife Fund. p. 576

environmental quality An indicator of the intensity of environmental stressors, particularly anthropogenic ones, as well as their effects on people, economic values, and other species and ecosystems. See also **ecological integrity** and **ecosystem health**. p. 572

enzyme A protein that catalyzes a biochemical reaction. p. 162

equilibrium A condition in which competing influences are in balance, resulting in a relative constancy of conditions. p. 118

equilibrium framework A view that communities are relatively constant in their species composition and resistance to changes in environmental stressors. See also **non-equilibrium framework**. p. 253

estivation A drop in metabolic rate and body temperature for two or more consecutive days during the summer months. p. 168

euphotic zone The upper waters of a lake or ocean that support a positive net production by phytoplankton, meaning their gross photosynthesis is less than their respiration. p. 351

eutrophic Waterbodies that have a large nutrient supply and so are highly productive. Compare with **oligotrophic** and **mesotrophic**. p. 350

eutrophication An increase in the productivity of waterbodies, caused by an increase in the supply of nutrients. p. 33

evaporation The change of state of water from a liquid or solid to a gas. p. 11

evapotranspiration The evaporation of water from a landscape. See also **evaporation** and **transpiration**. p. 51

evenness A measure of how similarly abundant species are within a community; it is a measure of unpredictability—the higher the unpredictability, the higher the evenness. See also **species diversity** and **species richness**. p. 387

evolution (biological evolution) Change in the collective genetic information of a population or of higher-order groupings (such as species), occurring from generation to generation. p. 24

evolutionarily significant unit (ESU) A local population that is genetically distinct, but not sufficiently so to be assigned taxonomic rank. p. 524

evolutionary ecology An overarching theme that provides context for much of ecology; the core area is evolutionary aspects of adaptive ecological change, including interactions with selective forces. p. 16

evolutionary radiation A proliferation of species (or of other taxa), often occurring relatively quickly, and in response to the opening up of new ecological space or by novel adaptive changes and opportunities. p. 433

exogenous Influences that are external to the system (or organism) being studied. Compare with **endogenous**. p. 418

experiment An investigation that is designed to provide evidence relevant to testing a hypothesis. p. 21

exponential model of population growth A model that assumes that population is increasing at a constant rate. See also **density-independent model of population growth**. p. 97

exposure The intensity of an interaction of an organism or an ecosystem with an environmental stressor or a regime of stressors. p. 35

extinct A species (or taxon) that no longer exists anywhere in the world. p. 381

extirpated (extirpation) Refers to a species (or taxon) that formerly occurred in some region, but now survives only elsewhere; a local extinction. p. 381

extreme environment Habitat with severe environmental conditions, so that life is barely viable. p. 32

facilitation The positive effect of one species upon another, or the enhancement of the conditions for one species by the activities of another. p. 249

facilitation model A model of succession that suggests that early species in a sere are important in changing abiotic conditions in ways that enhance the environmental setting for species that invade later. Compare with **tolerance model** and **inhibition model**. p. 311

fact An event or thing that is true—it is known to have happened or to exist. p. 20

fecundity (fertility) The number of offspring produced by an individual in a single breeding season. p. 215

fen A wetland that develops in cool and wet climates, but is less acidic and more productive than a bog because it has a better nutrient supply. Compare with **bog**. p. 351

feral See **naturalized**. p. 437

fine scale Related to observing in relatively great detail over relatively small areas. Compare with **coarse scale**. p. 394

fire intensity The rate of energy release per unit of burnt area during a wildfire. Compare with **fire severity**. p. 410

fire severity The degree to which an ecosystem is disrupted by mortality of its organisms as a result of a wildfire. Compare with **fire intensity**. p. 410

first law of thermodynamics A physical principle stating that energy may be transformed among its various states, but it is never created or destroyed, so that the energy content of the universe remains constant. See also **second law of thermodynamics**. p. 49

fitness The proportionate contribution that an individual's offspring make to the genetic make-up of subsequent generations. p. 24

flagship species Charismatic or otherwise "attractive" species that are used to profile the importance of conservation activities. p. 455

flow-through system See **open system**. p. 51

food chain A linear model of feeding relationships within a group of species. Compare with **food web**. p. 64

food web A representation of the feeding relationships of an ecosystem, including all of its food chains. p. 64

forest ecology Investigation of ecosystems dominated by trees, including non-treed successional stages that are recovering from a disturbance of a mature forest. p. 17

founder-controlled community A situation in which most of the early invaders to a gap are similar in their dispersal ability, tolerance to local conditions, growth rates, and competitive abilities, making such a community quite diverse and the composition of later seral stages primarily dependent upon the founder species. See also **dominance-controlled community**. p. 258

fragmentation The process whereby individual patches of a given type become increasingly separated in space through landscape change. p. 396

free good A value that exists, but in which there has been no significant investment of money. p. 484

freshwater ecology (limnology) The study of lakes, ponds, rivers, streams, and wetlands. p. 17

functional attribute Rate functions, such as productivity, nutrient flux, water flow, and other variables that are commonly reported as change of the amount per unit area and time. p. 6

functional group A group of species that perform similar ecological functions within a community. Compare with **guild**. p. 253

functional response Refers to the ways that a predator or herbivore varies its consumption of food according to the abundance of that resource. Compare with **numerical response**. p. 124

fundamental niche The complete range of conditions under which a species can establish, grow, and reproduce when it is free from interference from other species that might limit it in any way. Compare with **realized niche**. p. 260

fundamental research (basic research or **curiosity-driven research)** Research that is undertaken primarily to examine a question about the natural world or life—how it came to exist, is organized, and functions. Compare with **applied research**. p. 258

gamma diversity The richness of different communities within a larger study region, such as a landscape or seascape. p. 389

gap analysis In the context of conservation planning, this compares a list of biodiversity targets to those already captured in existing protected areas; the residuals are targets for the implementation of additional reserves. p. 458

gap-phase microsuccession A small-scale succession that follows a microdisturbance occurring in an otherwise intact community. p. 299

generation time The average age of reproductive individuals in a population. p. 109

genetically modified organism (GMO) An organism whose genome has been modified by genetic engineering that has resulted in the incorporation of DNA of another species. See also **transgenic modification**. p. 497

genome The specific genetic information encoded within the DNA (deoxyribonucleic acid) of an organism; sometimes also used in reference to a population or species. p. 23

geographical information system (GIS) A computer program that overlays digital maps or images of some part of the surface of Earth to reveal and create further information. p. 396

geo-referenced Refers to a location being established using a coordinate system, such as latitude and longitude. p. 456

GIS See **geographical information system**. p. 396

glaciation An extensive expansion of glacial cover during a period of climatic cooling. p. 301

good An economic term referring to tangible things being traded in an economy, such as raw natural resources or manufactured products. Compare with **service**. p. 482

greater protected area Refers to a protected plus a designated region of its surrounding terrain, which are co-managed as a single ecological system. p. 463

greenhouse effect A physical process by which infrared-absorbing (or "greenhouse") gases (such as H_2O and CO_2) in the atmosphere help to keep Earth warm. p. 53

greenhouse gas (GHG) A gas (such as water vapour or carbon dioxide) that absorbs infrared energy within the spectral range that Earth emits, and by doing so diminishes the ability of the planet to cool itself of the heat of absorbed solar radiation. p. 53

gross domestic product (GDP) The total value of all goods and services produced within an economy in a year. p. 482

gross national product (GNP) The total value of all goods and services that are produced by citizens of a country or by companies owned in it, both domestically and in foreign countries. Compare with **gross domestic product**. p. 481

gross primary production (GPP) The total fixation of solar energy by primary producers within an ecosystem. p. 57

ground fire A relatively uncommon type of fire that is limited to burning the organic matter of the forest floor and soil. p. 410

ground truthing The testing of a prediction by the examination of actual conditions in nature, such as when an air-photo interpretation is tested by the examination of actual ecological conditions in the field. p. 420

group selection Evolutionary change that involves change in the genetic information of a population because of benefits realized by a group, regardless of effects on the fitness of the individuals involved. p. 25

growing-degree days (GDDs, also known as **growing-degree units**, **GDUs)** A measure of the cumulative heat available during a day or over a growing season. p. 202

growing-degree units (GDU) See **growing-degree days**. p. 202

guild All species in a community that use the same resource base in a similar way, e.g., all seed-eating animals, even though they may not be taxonomically related. Compare with **functional group**. p. 253

harvest rate The number of individuals, or biomass, removed from a population relative to the number or amount that is available to be harvested. p. 100

harvesting The gathering of wild biomass or the reaping of a cultivated crop. p. 492

herbivore An animal that eats plants and plant tissues. Compare with **carnivore** and **omnivore**. p. 59

herbivory A biological relationship that involves animals eating the tissues of plants. p. 6

heterotherm (or poikilotherm) An animal that allows its body temperature to fluctuate with that of its environment. p. 163

heterotroph An organism that feeds on organic materials (any kind of biomass, living or dead) as a source of energy and nutrients; organisms that are not capable of fixing solar energy into biomass, such as animals, fungi, and most bacteria. See also **autotroph**. p. 46

heterotrophic Refers to organisms that can survive only if they have access to organic matter as a source of nutrition. Compare with **autotroph**. p. 10

hibernation (or seasonal torpor) A drop in metabolic rate and body temperature for two or more consecutive days during the winter months. p. 166

Holocene biodiversity event See **modern biodiversity crisis**. p. 435

homeotherm An animal that regulates its body temperature within a narrow range independent of that of its environment. p. 163

homogecene A colloquial term for the widespread introductions of many alien species throughout most of the inhabited regions of the world. p. 305

hotspots of biodiversity Regions that, at a global scale, support a relatively high density of endemic species. Compare with **coldspots of biodiversity**. p. 456

human capital The people who are participating in an economy, including their skill sets. p. 489

humus Amorphous, partially decomposed organic matter—a persistent component of soil that is important in tilth and fertility. p. 89

hydrological cycle (or water cycle) Refers to movements of water among its various compartments in the environment. p. 11

hydrology Study of the properties, distribution, and effects of water on the surface, in the soil and rocks, and in the atmosphere. p. 407

hydrosere A sere that begins with a lake, which gradually in-fills and develops into a wetland, and perhaps eventually into a forested habitat. p. 308

hydrosphere Consists of water occurring in various compartments—on the surface of the planet, in rocks, and in the atmosphere. p. 11

hyperionic Having an ionic pressure greater than that of another fluid. p. 178

hyperosmotic Having an osmotic pressure greater than that of another fluid. p. 178

hyperthermia A rise in body core temperature above normal. p. 166

hyposmotic Having an osmotic pressure less than that of another fluid. p. 177

hypothermia A drop in body core temperature below normal. p. 168

hypothesis A proposed explanation of a phenomenon or its cause. p. 20

importance of competition The effect of competition on a population or community, relative to other environmental factors. p. 267

inclusive fitness The sum of an individual's direct and indirect fitness. See also **direct fitness** and **indirect fitness**. p. 148

indeterminate growth Growth of individuals that continues throughout their life. Compare with **determinate growth**. p. 215

index of biotic integrity (IBI) A multimetric indicator in ecology that is based on metrics of species richness, relative abundances of functional groups, trophic structure, and sometimes the incidence of developmental abnormalities associated with pollution. p. 579

indicator A relatively simple measurement that is intended to represent complex aspects of something else, such as environmental quality or ecological integrity. p. 572

indirect fitness Fitness gained by an individual that helps non-descendant kin. Compare with **direct fitness** and see also **altruism**. p. 148

individual organism (individual) A living entity that is genetically and physically discrete. p. 7

individualistic (or continuum) hypothesis A view of community organization proposed by Henry Gleason that considers the community to be a coincidental assemblage of species that have similar environmental requirements; while they interact, there is no predictable or repeatable end-point of succession. Compare with **organismal hypothesis**. p. 250

inductive logic Reasoning in which conclusions about natural phenomena are based on the gathering of evidence based on experience and the results of experiments. p. 19

inhibition model A model of succession that suggests that early-establishing species resist invasions of later ones, so the latter can penetrate the community only when early ones die. Compare with **facilitation model** and **tolerance model**. p. 311

inorganic (abiotic or nonliving) Refers to environmental influences that are nonbiological in origin. p. 6

inorganic nutrient Chemicals that autotrophs need to support their biosynthesis and metabolism, including carbon, nitrogen, phosphorus, potassium, and others. p. 71

instrumental value (utilitarian value) Value that exists because something is useful to humans and their economy. p. 380

insularization The process of development of islands of habitat by removal of much of the connecting matrix. See also **fragmentation**. p. 416

integrated resource management (IRM) A collaborative and broad-reaching approach that identifies all stakeholders and issues in an area that has been defined for the purpose of using this approach, then finds ways to manage economic activities in a manner that is deemed acceptable to a consensus of the parties. p. 530

integrated system (integrated management system) A system in which various activities associated with harvesting and management are undertaken in a coordinated manner, so as to increase the productivity and value of a biological resource. p. 492

intellectual capital The knowledge that resides within an economy and that is essential to organizing a complex society and doing all of the things that are required to keep people fed, healthy, safe, and content, and also keep the environment in good condition. p. 489

intensity of competition The degree to which competition for a limited resource reduces performance below the physiological maximum achievable in a given environment. p. 267

interdisciplinary Refers to knowledge that engages many subject areas in an integrated manner, as in ecology and environmental studies. p. 13

interference competition Involves action by an individual to reduce the access of others to a resource. p. 116

interior habitat Habitat within a patch or community that is distinct from that occurring in its ecotone or edge. p. 401

intermediate disturbance hypothesis A hypothesis that species diversity in communities is highest under conditions of an intermediate level of disturbance, rather than at lower or higher levels of disturbance. p. 272

intersexual selection Sexual selection within a sex, such as by direct competition. p. 141

interspecific competition Competition occurring among individuals of different species. Compare with **intraspecific competition**. p. 116

intrasexual selection Sexual selection occurring as a consequence of interactions between the sexes, such as mate choice. p. 141

intraspecific competition Competition occurring among individuals of a species. Compare with **interspecific competition**. p. 116

intrinsic rate of population growth The difference between the instantaneous rates of birth and death. p. 97

intrinsic value (inherent value) Value that is due to unique and irreplaceable qualities, that exists "for its own sake." p. 383

invasive alien Non-native organisms that can become abundant in natural habitats and cause ecological damage. p. 37

ionoconformer An animal that conforms to the ionic composition and concentration of its environment. p. 177

ionoregulation The process of maintaining a constant ionic concentration in a body fluid. p. 178

ionoregulator An animal that regulates the ionic composition and concentration of its body fluids. p. 177

IPAT A formula that allows the total environmental impact of a human population to be calculated, based on the multiplication of its size, affluence in terms of per capita consumption of resources, and technological development of the economy, in terms of environmental impact per unit of consumption. p. 570

irruption A rapid increase to an extremely high population level. p. 96

island biogeography An ecological theory that seeks to explain variations in the numbers of species found on oceanic islands based on their area, isolation, and related factors. p. 454

isocline A series of lines that have the same slope. p. 118

isostasy An elastic rebound of Earth's crust following its release by deglaciation from the immense weight of up to several kilometres of overlying ice during continental glaciation. p. 321

isozyme (or isotype or isoenzyme) Variations within the structure of a single enzyme. p. 173

iteroparous Refers to a species in which individuals are capable of reproducing more than once in their life. Compare with **semelparous**. p. 106

Judeo-Christian ethic An ethic that presumes that humans have the right to take whatever they want from the natural world for the purposes of subsistence or other economic benefits, based on a literal interpretation of the biblical myth of creation and Genesis 1:28. p. 502

keystone species Species that have a disproportionately large influence on the ecological structure and functionality of their community. p. 258

kin selection Selection in the context of increasing indirect fitness. See also **indirect fitness**. p. 148

kinetic energy Energy that exists in two basic forms that involve mass in motion; thermal energy or heat, which involves atomic or molecular vibration, and mechanical energy, which involves mass in motion through space. p. 48

landscape A larger-scale, heterogenous integration of community-level patches in a terrestrial environment, with repeated forms at any appropriate scale. p. 8

landscape demographics Demographics that operate at a large scale, such as the attributes of a metapopulation. p. 414

landscape ecology Integrated, scale-related study of the structural and functional attributes and changes of ecosystems. p. 16

landscape element Patches, corridors, and networks that are the basis of landscape structure. p. 397

landscape function Ecosystem functions (services) operating at the level of a landscape, such as hydrology, productivity, large-scale movements, and disturbances. p. 411

landscape structure A spatial pattern of elements that is dependent on influences of factors such as the underlying geology, topography, and disturbance history. p. 397

leaching A process that involves percolating water dissolving chemicals out of soil and carrying them to deeper layers. p. 41

lentic ecosystem An aquatic ecosystem that occurs in a basin and whose hydrology does not include strong water flows, such as a lake or pond. Compare with lotic ecosystem. p. 350

Leslie matrix See **transition matrix**. p. 111

life form A grouping of organisms based on similarities of their dominant morphological and physiological traits, regardless of their evolutionary relatedness. p. 340

life history The attributes of the life cycle through which an organism passes (or more precisely, a genotype), with particular reference to strategies that influence its survival and reproduction. p. 213

life table A data matrix with columns of data on age-specific survival and fecundity (or fertility). p. 107

life-history invariants The constancy, or invariance, in the associations between various life-history traits that may reflect adaptive processes of a broad and universal nature across species. p. 234

limnology The study of inland waters, such as lakes and rivers. See also **freshwater ecology**. p. 551

lithosere A sere that begins on an exposed rocky surface. p. 309

lithosphere The surface layer of Earth's solid sphere, consisting of the crust and the upper mantle. p. 13

littoral zone A distinct shallow-water habitat that occurs along the shores of ponds and lakes. p. 350

logarithmic series A community in which a graph plotting the abundance of species is characterized by having a large number of rare species and few common ones. p. 254

logistic model of population growth A model that predicts an S-shaped or sigmoidal pattern of population increase, which starts slowly, increases, then slows and becomes asymptotic at the carrying capacity. p. 101

log-normal distribution A community in which a graph plotting the abundance of species in abundance classes is normally distributed when the x axis is plotted on a logarithmic scale rather than on an arithmetic one. p. 254

longevity (life span) The length of time that an organism lives. p. 215

longitudinal study A longer-term or continuous study of a particular place or experiment. p. 412

lotic ecosystem An aquatic ecosystem that is characterized by flowing water, such as a stream or river. Compare with lentic ecosystem. p. 351

macronutrient These are needed by plants in relatively large quantities, and include carbon (about 50% of dry biomass), oxygen (40%), hydrogen (6%), nitrogen and potassium (1–2%), and calcium, magnesium, phosphorus, and sulphur (0.1%–0.5%). Compare with **micronutrient**. p. 71

management Actions that are undertaken to improve environmental conditions so as to enhance the productivity or quality of a biological resource. p. 492

manipulative experiment An experiment that involves modifications of one or more variables that are hypothesized to influence natural phenomena. p. 21

mantle The region of Earth's solid sphere between the core and crust, and composed of minerals in a hot, plastic state known as magma. p. 13

manufactured capital Something created by human ingenuity and made from simpler resources, such as processed foods, textiles, lumber, metals, and more complex commodities such as machines and buildings. p. 489

marine ecology The study of any aspects of ecology in the oceanic realm. p. 17

marker (genetic marker) A genetic element (allele, locus, DNA sequence, or chromosome feature) of an individual that can be detected by cytological, molecular, or phenotypic methods. p. 387

marsh A productive wetland, typically dominated by species of monocotyledonous angiosperm plants (such as bulrush, cattail, and reed) that grow as tall as several metres above the water surface. p. 351

mass extinction An event of catastrophic damage of epic proportions, which causes the extinction of a large fraction of species existing at the time. p. 433

mass-specific metabolism Metabolic rate expressed per unit of mass (for example: mL O_2 consumed/unit time/unit of mass). p. 160

mathematical ecology Involves the use of quantitative models; sometimes also includes **statistical ecology**. p. 16

matrix A predominant cover or community type on a landscape, in which are embedded island-like blocks (patches) of other kinds of ecosystem. p. 401

maximum per capita rate of growth (intrinsic rate of population growth) The highest per-individual rate of growth that a population can achieve, limited only by the biological attributes of a species. Compare with **realized per capita rate of population growth**. p. 98

maximum sustainable yield (MSY) A theoretical upper limit of harvesting of a biological resource that will result in the largest sustainable long-term yield. p. 104

mechanical energy Energy associated with mass that is in motion through space. p. 48

mesotrophic Waterbodies that have a moderate nutrient supply and so have an intermediate level of productivity. Compare with **eutrophic** and **oligotrophic**. p. 350

meta-analysis A statistical process that combines and compares results from different studies in order to identify common patterns or disagreements among them. p. 195

metabolic disturbance (or metabolic disorder) Changes in acid-base status due to the addition or removal of organic acids or bases to the blood or hemolymph. p. 188

metabolic rate The rate at which an organism uses energy, which may be measured by oxygen consumption, excretion of carbon dioxide, heat production, or the difference in the caloric contents of ingested food and excreted feces. p. 160

metabolic water Water obtained from the reduction of oxygen at the end of the electron transport chain of metabolism. p. 180

metapopulation A regional population; spatially separated subpopulations that are linked by dispersal, leading to gene flow among them. p. 402

microbial ecology The study of the populations, ecophysiology, and productivity of microorganisms and their communities, often with a focus on functional processes such as decomposition and nutrient cycling. p. 17

microdisturbance Disturbance that is local in scale, such as the death of a large tree within an otherwise intact forest. Compare with **stand-replacing disturbance**. p. 299

micronutrient These are needed by plants in relatively small quantities, 0.01% to several ppm, and include boron, chlorine, copper, iron, manganese, molybdenum, and zinc. p. 71

microsuccession Smaller-scale succession that follows a microdisturbance. p. 299

mineralization See **decomposition**. p. 76

minerotrophic Wetlands whose hydrology and nutrient supply are substantially derived from flows of ground water. Compare with **ombrotrophic**. p. 351

minimum viable area (MVA) The least area of suitable habitat that would allow a population at risk to persist in the wild, or for an imperilled community type to survive. p. 453

minimum viable population (MVP) The least abundance that would allow a population to persist in the wild. p. 453

mitigation An action that helps to avoid or repair an ecological or other environmental damage. p. 588

modern biodiversity crisis (Holocene biodiversity event) An ongoing mass extinction that is being caused by the activities and influences of modern people. p. 435

molecular ecology (ecological genetics) A recently emerged field in which the methodologies of molecular biology (in population genetics, phylogenetics, and genomics) are used to investigate certain kinds of ecological and evolutionary questions in a field setting. p. 17

monoclimax According to the Clementsian view of succession, this is the climax community that eventually develops, which is primarily influenced by climatic conditions. See also **climax**. p. 306

monoculture An agricultural ecosystem in which only a single crop is grown. Compare with **polyculture**. p. 356

mosaic A spatially integrated complex of patches, corridors, and networks that gives a landscape its ecological character. See also **shifting mosaic**. p. 287

MSY See **maximum sustainable yield**. p. 104

multidisciplinary Various fields of study are engaged, including chemistry, ecology, economics, geography, geology, sociology. Compare with **interdisciplinary**. p. 587

multimetric indicator A composite indicator that is developed using metrics whose data were transformed into a unitless score before being aggregated. See also **composite indicator**. p. 578

multiple stable states (or alternative stable states) The view that more than one type (state) of stable community may persist under similar abiotic and environmental conditions. p. 276

mutualism A mutually beneficial biological interaction. p. 264

natural biome A biome whose characteristics are not significantly influenced by stressors or management associated with humans. Compare with **anthropogenic biome**. p. 343

natural experiment Involves studying gradients in nature or other differences in environmental conditions and ecological change, and then developing explanations for the observed patterns using statistical analyses. p. 21

natural history The investigation of organisms in their wild habitats, also often extending to an interest in all natural phenomena, even astronomy; studies in natural history are relatively simple, with few or no quantitative data, and a rigorous scientific methodology is not used. p. 5

natural mortality Deaths caused by predators, parasites, diseases, accidents, or other disturbances. Compare with **anthropogenic mortality**. p. 497

natural regeneration The spontaneous recovery of a biological resource after it has been harvested. p. 495

natural selection An important cause of evolutionary change, in which organisms have an increased likelihood of leaving descendants (of having fitness) if their specific genetically based phenotypic attributes are better suited to coping with the constraints and opportunities presented by their environment, compared with other individuals in their population. p. 24

natural stressor A stressor that is not caused by a human influence. p. 36

natural world In the context of ecology, this refers to indigenous biodiversity and related values, such as self-organizing ecosystems, their environmental conditions, and the services that are provided. p. 432

naturalized An alien species that can persist and regenerate in native habitats. p. 437

negative feedback system A means of regulating a variable by means of a detector, a set-point, an integrator, and various controlled outputs that keep the parameters within limits. p. 164

negative-pressure ventilation The filling of a lung as a result of air being drawn into it by suction. p. 185

net primary production (NPP) The difference between gross primary production and respiration. See also **gross primary production** and **respiration**. p. 57

net reproductive rate The average number of offspring produced over the lifetime of an individual. p. 109

network A series of interconnected linear elements on a landscape, often surrounding patches of another type. p. 403

neutral model A model proposed by Stephen Hubbell in which all individual organisms in a community are treated as essentially ecologically identical, i.e., all individuals of all species have the same parameters of ecological behaviour, such as birth rate and death rate; complex interactions such as competition are permitted among individuals, provided that they all follow the same rules. p. 256

new ecology An approach to ecology that emphasizes complexity over reductionism, change over stable states, and an ecological world that includes the human economy and activities. p. 254

niche (1) The ecological role of a species in a community; it describes all of the environmental factors that limit the distribution, growth, and reproduction of a species. (2) The physical space occupied by an organism or species. See also **fundamental niche** and **realized niche**. p. 260

nitrification Part of the nitrogen cycle, in which bacteria oxidize ammonium to nitrate. p. 76

nitrogen fixation Part of the nitrogen cycle, in which the strong triple bond of N_2 gas is cleaved to form NH_3 or NO. p. 81

non-equilibrium framework A view that communities are not constant in species composition and never reach a stable condition because they are always responding to changes in environmental conditions or recovering from disturbances. Compare with **equilibrium framework**. p. 253

non-native (or alien) A species that is not part of the indigenous biota, having been introduced by humans. p. 382

nonrenewable resource (nonrenewable capital) A resource that is present in a fixed quantity and is diminished by use. p. 25

nonshivering thermogenesis An increase in heat production due to an increase in the metabolic rate. p. 165

nucleation A successional process in which communities begin as small patches that grow increasingly larger until they eventually coalesce. p. 323

null hypothesis A hypotheses that is formulated so that it can be disproved through research. p. 20

numerical response A response of the abundance of a predator or herbivore to a change in their consumption of food. Compare with **functional response**. p. 124

nuptial gift A gift of food or other fitness-enhancing product, typically from the male, that is delivered orally or into the female's genital tract. p. 142

nutrient Substances needed for the healthy physiology and growth of organisms. p. 71

nutrient budget An estimate of the rates of input and output of nutrients for an ecosystem, and amounts and transfers among its compartments, such as plants, animals, dead organic matter, and soil. p. 75

nutrient cycling The movements, transformations, and recycling of nutrients in ecosystems. p. 74

obligatory water loss Water loss in feces, urine, and across cutaneous and gas exchange surfaces in animals. p. 180

old-growth forest Older stands of forest, which typically have a complex structure, with many species of trees present, of various sizes and ages, and supporting a large amount of biomass, including much dead organic matter. p. 347

oligotrophic Waterbodies that have a sparse nutrient supply and so are relatively unproductive. Compare with **eutrophic** and **mesotrophic**. p. 350

ombrotrophic A wetland whose hydrology and nutrient supply is cut off from flows of groundwater, so the only inputs are derived from precipitation and other atmospheric sources. Compare with **minerotrophic**. p. 351

omnivore An animal that feeds at more than one level of the food web. Compare with **herbivore** and **carnivore**. p. 59

open population One from which individuals are free to leave and into which others can immigrate from other populations. Compare with **closed population**. p. 97

open system A situation in which there is a gain in mass, energy, or information, and/or a loss. p. 45

operational sex ratio The ratio of females to males, of individuals that are available to mate. p. 142

opportunity cost The value of a foregone choice as a consequence of having made a decision to pursue some other option. p. 484

optimal behaviour Behaviour that maximizes fitness. p. 136

organic matter The biomass, or the living and recently dead tissues of organisms, and longer-dead and more humified organic materials present on and in the soil or sediment. p. 314

organismal (or community unit) hypothesis A view of community organization proposed by Frederic Clements that views the community as acting like a superorganism, in that it is a highly organized and closely integrated entity composed of mutually interdependent species, and individual species are to some varying degree coadapted to one another. Compare with **individualistic hypothesis**. p. 250

osmoconformer An animal that conforms to the osmotic concentration of its environment. p. 177

osmoregulation The process of maintaining a constant body fluid osmotic pressure. p. 178

osmoregulator An animal that regulates the osmotic concentration of its body fluids. p. 177

overharvesting (overexploitation) Harvesting a potentially renewable natural resource (such as a biological one) at a rate that exceeds its regeneration, so that the stocks become depleted in quantity and/or quality. p. 381

oxidative capacity The maximum scope of oxygen utilization in aerobic metabolism. p. 160

paleoecology The branch of ecology that deals with populations, communities, and ecosystems that existed in the past. p. 16

paleolimnology The branch of aquatic science that deals with reconstructing the histories of inland waters, such as lakes and rivers; paleolimnologists typically use the physical, chemical, and biological information preserved in sediment profiles to reconstruct past ecological and environmental conditions. p. 545

paludification A process in which the organic forest floor retains so much water that trees die from the waterlogging, so that a peat-rich, boggy wetland known as muskeg develops. p. 320

palynology The branch of science that deals with the study of pollen grains and spores. p. 548

paradigm A set of assumptions, concepts, practices, and values that constitutes an understanding of the natural world and is shared by an intellectual community. p. 21

parameter Numbers that remain constant in a mathematical equation. Compare with **variable**. p. 98

parasitism A biological relationship that involves one species of animal feeding on another, usually much larger one, but usually not killing it. p. 6

parent material Minerals and rocks from which soil is derived. p. 88

parental care Behaviour of a parent that is directed at offspring to increase their fitness. p. 142

parental investment Investment by a parent in the fitness of offspring, at a cost of not investing in future offspring. p. 142

partial pressure The pressure attributed to a specific gas found within an atmosphere; the product of the gas fraction and the atmospheric pressure. p. 183

patch A contiguous areal unit representing a single land-cover class, or a stand of a particular community that is distinguished from its surroundings by discontinuities of environmental influences. p. 397

patch dynamics Temporal change in the dynamics of communities or patches on a landscape. See also **patch**. p. 411

pattern The spatially repeated occurrence of landscape elements. p. 393

pelagic zone Deep open waters, with little influence of shorelines or shallow habitats. p. 350

per capita rate of population growth The intrinsic rate of population increase expressed on a per-individual basis. See also **intrinsic rate of population growth**. p. 101

permafrost Subsoil in cold regions that is frozen for at least three continuous years. See also **active layer**. p. 344

permanent wilting point A degree of wilting, or desiccation, from which a plant tissue, or an entire plant, cannot recover if given access to water. p. 196

permeable In the context of conservation biology, this refers to habitat that is suitable for the movement of a species of interest; in landscape ecology it is the degree to which a matrix environment is suitable for organisms to use as they travel among patches of appropriate habitat on a landscape. See also **connectivity**. p. 402

permeability The degree to which organisms can move between patches of habitat. Compare with **connectivity**. p. 459

phenology The seasonal progression of developmental events, such as the production of leaves or of flowers, or of comparable events in animals. p. 202

phenotype The expression of the genetic potential of an individual. p. 23

phenotypic plasticity The variable expression of the genotype, occurring in response to vagaries of environmental conditions. p. 24

philopatry The property of an organism remaining in or returning to its natal area. p. 152

photoautotrophs (phototrophs) Green plants, algae, and certain bacteria that utilize sunlight to drive photosynthesis. See **phototroph**. Compare with **chemoautotrophs**. p. 11

photorespiration Reactions that occur when the Rubisco enzyme involved in the dark reaction of C3 photosynthesis binds to oxygen, instead of to carbon dioxide, causing some of the carbon fixed in photosynthesis to be lost and released as carbon dioxide. Photorespiration reduces the efficiency of carbon fixation in the C3 or Calvin cycle. p. 192

photosynthesis Autotrophic productivity that uses visible electromagnetic energy (usually sunlight) to drive biosynthesis. Compare with **chemosynthesis**. p. 10

physiological ecology Involves study of the adaptive biochemistry and physiology of organisms in response to environmental conditions. p. 17

plant ecology The study of the populations, ecophysiology, and productivity of wild plants and their communities. p. 17

plantation A tree farm, in which a crop of trees is sown and managed. p. 505

pleiotropy A single gene influencing multiple phenotypic traits. p. 225

poikilotherm See **heterotherm**. p. 163

pollution The presence of a substance at a high enough concentration or intensity to result in a measurable biological or ecological damage. p. 37

polyclimax Multiple end-states of succession that are possible depending on variations of such key factors as topography, slope and exposure, the local regime of moisture and nutrients in soil, and the kinds of disturbances that affect the community. See also **climax**. p. 306

polyculture An agricultural ecosystem in which several crops are grown together. Compare with **monoculture**. p. 356

polynya An ice-free area in a high-latitude ocean (Arctic or Antarctic) that provides critical habitat for marine birds and mammals. p. 365

population Individuals of the same species that are co-occurring in space and time. p. 7

population diversity Diversity that is related to the variation in genetic and phenotypic characters that exists among discrete populations of a species. p. 374

population dynamics Changes in the size and age composition of populations, as well as processes influencing those changes. p. 104

population ecology Study of the population dynamics of species, including environmental influences on those changes. p. 17

population-replacing disturbance A disturbance that affects only a particular species within a community. p. 300

positive-pressure ventilation The filling of a lung as a result of air being forced into it under pressure. p. 185

postcopulatory sexual selection Events occurring after fertilization in which the paternity of certain males is biased over that of others. See also **sperm competition**. p. 146

potential energy A stored ability to perform work, which can occur only if the potential energy becomes transformed into kinetic or electromagnetic energy. p. 48

precipitation Water settling gravitationally from the atmosphere as rain or snow. p. 12

precision The degree of repeatability of measurements. p. 15

predation A biological relationship that involves one species of animal killing and eating another kind. p. 6

primary forest (frontier forest) Forest that occurs in large blocks of self-organizing ecosystems, often in an old-growth condition, and that sustains all of the appropriate species, including wide-ranging animals. See also **old-growth forest**. p. 347

primary producer Autotrophic organisms, which form the biological foundation of ecological productivity. p. 57

primary succession A succession that occurs in situations where a disturbance was severe enough to destroy all organisms on the affected terrain, and so obliterated the inherent ability to regenerate, so that colonization is necessary. Compare with **secondary succession**. p. 317

principle of limiting factors An ecological theory that suggests that primary productivity is limited by whichever necessary metabolic requirement is present in the least supply relative to the demand. p. 31

principle of superposition An assumption made in geology that states that in a sequence of layered (and undeformed) sedimentary rocks, the oldest beds are at the bottom and the youngest are at the top. p. 538

principle of uniformitarianism A theory that is most simply described as "the present is the key to the past," and that is the basis of most paleoecological research. p. 538

product An economic term referring to a good or service. See also **good** and **service**. p. 482

production The total productivity, usually calculated as the productivity multiplied by the area being considered. p. 61

productivity The rate at which energy is fixed in ecosystems, standardized to time and area. p. 45

protected area Tracts of natural habitat that are set aside from intensive economic use, such as parks, ecological reserves, and wilderness areas. p. 444

provenance See **population diversity**. p. 374

proxy data (1) Data indirectly measuring a cause-and-effect relationship between two or more variables, such as tree-ring counts as a predictor of tree age; or (2) data obtained by scientists such as paleoecologists to reconstruct past ecological and environmental conditions, e.g., using fossil pollen to reconstruct past terrestrial vegetation and then using that information to reconstruct past climate. p. 535

psammosere A sere that begins on a sandy substrate. p. 309

punctuated equilibrium An extended predominance of slow variations interspersed by rare but massive events of fast change. p. 584

Q_{10} The rate of change in a reaction over a 10°C range of temperature. p. 162

rank abundance A graph of the relative abundance of each species in a community, listed in the order of most abundant to least. p. 254

rarefaction A technique for assessing species richness based on the results of cumulative sampling, usually done using a rarefaction curve, which is a plot of the number of species as a function of the sampling effort. p. 388

realized niche The observed resource used by a species in nature, in which the potential distribution is restricted by competition and other biotic interactions. Compare with **fundamental niche**. p. 260

realized per capita rate of population growth The per-individual rate of growth of a population. Compare with **maximum per capita rate of growth**. p. 101

reciprocity (or reciprocal altruism) Help that increases a recipient's direct fitness and that is paid back at a later time by the recipient to the donor. p. 148

recovery strategy All species listed by COSEWIC as endangered or threatened must have a recovery strategy developed that would promote an increase of the population to a more sustainable level. p. 451

reference condition The normal and natural conditions for a site or region, given the environmental circumstances, including the disturbance regime. p. 579

refugium (plural, refugia) A place that has escaped regional ecological change and therefore provides a habitat where species may survive; often used in reference to glacial refugia. p. 539

remote sensing Measurements that are made from afar, often in reference to aerial photography or satellite images. p. 420

renewable resource (renewable capital) A resource that can regenerate after harvesting. p. 25

reorganization phase A stage of secondary succession that immediately follows a disturbance event, and during which there may be a further loss of biomass because of negative ecosystem-level net production (respiration exceeds productivity); it is then followed by an accumulation of biomass during the aggradation phase. See also **aggradation phase**. p. 314

reproductive skew Asymmetry in reproductive success within a sexually competing or social group. p. 140

reproductive success The number of progeny that an individual has during its lifetime. See also **fitness**. p. 136

reproductive value The average expected reproduction of individuals from their present age onward, given that they have survived to their present age. p. 115

research In ecology, it is a systematic activity undertaken in the laboratory or in the field, which may involve experiments or the investigation of patterns of covariation of biotic and abiotic variables to investigate questions relevant to factors affecting the distribution and abundance of organisms, populations, communities, or ecoscapes. p. 3

reserve life This is calculated as the known recoverable reserves of a nonrenewable resource divided by the rate of mining. p. 488

resilience The speed and degree to which an organism, population, community, or ecoscape can recover to its original condition following an event of disturbance or after an intense stressor relaxes. p. 38

resistance (or tolerance) The ability of an organism or an ecological variable to function in a "healthy" manner within a range of intensities of environmental stressors, without undergoing change that would be judged as representing damage. p. 298

resource conservation The harvesting and management of renewable resources in ways that ensure that the harvest does not exceed the rate of renewal; may also refer to actions that help to prolong the lifetime of nonrenewable resources. p. 432

resource ecology The branch of ecology that deals with linkages between ecological knowledge and the management of natural resources, including the meaning and dimensions of economic and ecological sustainability. p. 480

respiration (R) The mobilization of fixed energy needed by organisms to support the physiology required to maintain a healthy condition. p. 57

respiratory acidosis An increase in the acidity (lowering of the pH) of the blood because of a high concentration of absorbed CO_2, which forms carbonic acid. p. 188

respiratory disturbance (or respiratory disorder) Changes in acid-base status due to changes in the carbon dioxide partial pressure of the blood or hemolymph. p. 188

respiratory pigment A molecule that is capable of binding and transporting oxygen within the circulatory system. p. 185

response A biological or ecological change that has occurred as a result of an interaction with an environmental stressor or a regime of stressors. p. 35

response time The length of time required for a population to change in reaction to an altered environmental circumstance. p. 103

restoration ecology Use of ecological knowledge and practices to repair damaged habitats or ecosystems. p. 17

return frequency (or rotation) The length of time between successive disturbance events. p. 302

riparian (riparian zone) Related to river and stream banks; the transition zone between a stream and adjacent land, often but not always synonymous with flood plain. p. 351

riparian buffer (buffer zone, riparian reserve zone, special management zone) Uncut strips of forest left beside a lake or on both sides of a watercourse. p. 510

rotation See **return frequency**. p. 302

ruderal A species that is adapted to recently disturbed habitats with abundant resources, so that stress and competition are not intense. p. 232

runaway sexual selection Sexual selection through female mating preferences for certain male traits, in which a positive feedback loop is created that favours males with the trait as well as females that prefer these males. p. 144

science The use of objective and systematic methodologies to better understand the character and dynamics of the natural world, including the discovery of general principles. p. 18

scientific method Begins with a researcher identifying a question about a natural phenomenon, then formulating hypotheses in the context of existing theory, then running experiments or doing other research to test null hypotheses in an attempt to falsify the original hypothesis. p. 20

scientific revolution Occurs when a well-established theory is rigorously tested and then collapses under the weight of new facts and observations that it cannot explain. p. 21

sclerochronology The use of calcified structures, such as fish otoliths, mollusk shells, and corals, to reconstruct environmental conditions. p. 544

scoping exercise A phase of an environmental impact assessment that is undertaken to identify the potentially important intersections of project-related activities and stressors with valued ecological components or human socio-economic welfare. p. 588

scramble (or exploitation) competition Competition whereby individuals reduce the access of others to a resource by consuming some of it, but not involving direct or indirect actions to reduce access to the resource. p. 116

screening The initial phase of an environmental impact assessment that helps to determine the level of assessment of a proposed development—whether a relatively minor review or a full assessment is necessary. p. 588

seascape A larger-scale integration of various kinds of community-level patches in a marine environment. p. 8

second law of thermodynamics A physical principle stating that transformations of energy occur spontaneously only under conditions in which there is an increase in the entropy (or randomness) of the universe. See also **first law of thermodynamics** and **entropy**. p. 49

secondary compounds Complex biochemicals made by plants that are not essential to the life of the plant. p. 206

secondary metabolites See **secondary compounds**. p. 206

secondary sexual character Traits that distinguish the two sexes of a species, but that are not directly part of the gamete-producing or -receiving systems; they are derived by sexual selection. See also **sexual selection**. p. 141

secondary succession A succession that includes regeneration by organisms that survived a disturbance, as well as those that invaded. Compare with **primary succession**. p. 324

secular change Change in a consistent direction. p. 419

sedimentation The deposition of eroded fine materials from water as its velocity slows down. p. 510

seed bank An enduring population of viable seeds in the surface litter and soil. p. 313

selection-cutting (uneven-aged management) Harvesting only some of the larger trees, so the physical and ecological integrity of the stand is left substantially intact. Compare with **clear-cutting**. p. 505

selective breeding (cultural selection) The deliberate breeding of individuals that are viewed as having desirable traits; this is the principal means of the evolution of domesticated varieties and species. p. 497

self-organization Refers to a system that develops in a natural fashion, rather than by anthropogenic influences. p. 408

semelparous Refers to a species in which individuals die after a single reproductive event. p. 106

SER model An acronym for stressor—exposure—response, used in reference to the relationship of environmental stressors and biological or ecological responses. p. 35

seral stage A community type occurring within a succession. See also **sere**. p. 305

sere A series of community types that make up a successional sequence. See also **seral stage**. p. 305

serotiny An adaptation of certain species of pines (*Pinus*) in which the cones and their viable seeds are held persistently aloft on branches for several years, to eventually be dispersed when a fire melts a wax that had sealed the scales together, allowing them to spread so the seeds can scatter and establish a regenerating cohort. p. 313

service An economic term referring to functions within an economy, such as the harvesting of trees to manufacture into lumber, the processing of wheat into flour and then cookies, and the production of airplanes and computers. Compare with **good**. p. 482

sexual antagonism Genes that enhance the fitness of one sex but harm the other. p. 145

sexual conflict Conflict between the sexes over decisions that differentially affect their fitness, such as how much to invest in offspring and whether or not to mate. p. 141

sexual dimorphism Sex difference in structure or size. p. 141

sexual selection Selection in the context of competition to maximize the number of fertilizations or matings, or to maximize these with the best mates. p. 135

shifting cultivation A subsistence agricultural system practised in the tropics, in which trees of the original (primary) forest are felled, the woody debris burned, and the land used to grow a mixture of crops for several years; by this time fertility declines and weeds become abundant, so the land is abandoned for a lengthy fallow period during which a secondary forest regenerates, while other primary forest is felled and cultivated. Compare with **slash-and-burn**. p. 444

shifting mosaic A landscape-scale model of succession that describes a diverse array of communities (patches) of various postdisturbance ages occurring over a large area. See also **mosaic**. p. 299

significant figures The number of digits used when reporting data from observations or calculations. p. 15

silviculture Refers to management practices in forestry, such as planting seedlings, thinning, and pesticide use. p. 330

size at maturity The size (weight, length, height) at which an organism reproduces for the first time (becomes sexually mature). Compare with **age at maturity**. p. 215

slash-and-burn A relatively intensive subsistence or commercial agricultural system practised in the tropics that results in a longer-term conversion of the land to crop production; it starts with cutting and burning the natural forest, but the land is then used continuously, without an extended fallow period during which a secondary forest regenerates. Compare with **shifting cultivation**. p. 444

SLOSS debate (single large or several small) A debate within the scientific community as to whether biodiversity is best protected by a single large protected area or several small ones of equivalent total area. p. 459

social selection Selection on individuals to reproduce within a group where there is competition to mate or to produce offspring. p. 154

soil A complex matrix covering terrestrial landscapes and consisting of rocks, organic matter, moisture, gases, and organisms. p. 88

soil order The highest level in the classification of soil types. p. 90

soil profile The vertical stratification that soils develop, with horizons that are distinct in colour, chemistry, and texture. p. 89

solar constant The input of solar energy to Earth, measured at the average distance from the Sun and just beyond the atmosphere, and having a value of 8.21 J/cm².min (1.96 cal/cm².min). p. 51

special concern (formerly referred to as **vulnerable**) A species (or taxon) that is at risk of becoming threatened because of small or declining numbers or occurrence in a limited range. p. 446

special management area A type of protected area that is managed to support particular species or habitats, usually ones of economic importance, and intended to achieve conservation through the protection and management of habitats; however, forestry, hunting, and some other extractive industries may be permitted. p. 462

species An aggregation of individuals (and populations) that are capable of interbreeding and producing fertile offspring. p. 7

species diversity An indicator of the number of species in a local area (α diversity) or region (β diversity), but also taking into account their relative abundances (or evenness). See also **alpha (α) diversity**, **species richness**, and **evenness**. p. 254

species richness The number of species in a community, or in a designated geographical area, such as a park. Compare with **species diversity** and **evenness**. p. 254

sperm competition Competition among the sperm of different males for fertilizations of the same female's eggs. p. 141

stability Refers to constancy over time, including resistance to environmental change and the degree of resilience after a perturbation. p. 40

stable age distribution A distribution in which the relative numbers of individuals in each age class are similar from one generation to the next. p. 108

stable equilibrium A state of equilibrium that returns to its original condition after it has been displaced. Compare with **unstable equilibrium**. p. 120

stable limit cycle Indefinite repetitive temporal variation about a central (average) value. Compare with **damped oscillation**. p. 103

stand An easily defined area, often of forest, that is relatively uniform in species composition or age and that can be studied or managed as a unit. p. 397

stand age-class distribution The proportion of patches (communities within a sere) within classes of stand age. p. 415

stand-replacing disturbance An extensive disturbance that damages entire communities and sometimes even a landscape. Compare with **microdisturbance**. p. 299

stasis An extended period of biological or ecological quiescence. p. 583

state space A configuration of discrete states that is used as a simple model. p. 117

static life table A life table based on the enumeration of all individuals in a population at a particular time. Compare with **cohort life table**. p. 108

statistical ecology The application of statistical methodologies to examining and explaining patterns and processes. p. 16

step-cline A zone of rapid change in environmental conditions. p. 306

stewardship All management activities that are needed to maintain protected areas, with particular attention to biodiversity and other ecological values. p. 458

stochastic change Change that is apparently random. p. 418

stochastic modelling A modelling methodology of scenarios that allows the most likely outcomes and their statistical variation to be computed. p. 423

stochasticity Refers to patterns that are not predictable. 104

stratosphere The atmospheric layer above the troposphere, extending to about 51 km above the surface. p. 11

stress tolerator A species that is adapted to environments that are difficult in terms of climate, moisture, and nutrient supply, but that are stable because they are infrequently disturbed. p. 232

structural attribute Amounts, such as biomass, density, species richness, and other variables that are commonly reported in units of quantity per area. p. 6

succession The process of community-level recovery following a disturbance. p. 6

supercooling Cooling of a solution to below its freezing point but without freezing actually occurring. p. 170

surface fire Fires that combust shrubs and ground vegetation but do not ladder into the canopy, so most trees survive the event. p. 410

sustainable development Progress made in structuring an economy toward a greater use of renewable resources and other improvements, with the ultimate goal of having an economy that can potentially run forever. Compare with **economic development** and **economic growth**. p. 480

sustainable economy An economy that can run forever because it is fundamentally based on the prudent use of renewable resources. Compare with **ecologically sustainable economy**. p. 25

swamp A forested wetland, flooded seasonally or permanently. p. 351

symbiosis Any close biological interaction occurring between species. p. 264

sympatric Refers to geographic areas where populations or species co-occur. Compare with **allopatric**. p. 122

synecology The study of relationships occurring within and among ecological communities. Compare with **autecology**. p. 16

system plan A plan for protected areas that captures areas that support the highest priority biodiversity values, while ensuring that all indigenous elements are conserved in the greater region. p. 457

systems ecology Uses a holistic approach to investigate the attributes of ecosystems. p. 16

taxon Any taxonomic unit, such as variety, subspecies, or species. p. 449

theoretical ecology The identification of theories regarding the organization and functioning of ecosystems, and then using rigorous methodologies to test their veracity; the field is particularly relevant to population ecology and biogeography. p. 16

theory A unifying principle that explains a body of knowledge (facts based on observational and experimental evidence and any laws that are based on them). p. 20

thermal energy Also known as heat, and associated with the vibration and rotation of atoms or molecules. p. 48

thermoneutral zone A range of environmental temperature within which the metabolic rate of homeotherms is independent of changes in environmental temperature. p. 166

thermoregulation The ability to maintain the core temperature of the body within a narrow range. p. 163

threatened A species (or taxon) that is likely to become endangered unless factors affecting its risk are mitigated. p. 450

tilth A property of soil that relates to the capacity to retain moisture and nutrients and to have an aggregated particle structure that allows easy root penetration and good aeration. p. 90

time lag A delay in the realization of an anticipated event or result. p. 102

tolerance (or resistance) The ability of an organism or an ecological variable to function in a "healthy" manner within a range of intensities of environmental stressors, without undergoing change that would be judged as representing damage. p. 38

tolerance model A model of succession that suggests that a predictable sequence of species occurs in succession because they vary in their abilities to utilize the available resources, with early species being relatively intolerant of competition, and becoming replaced by others that are more tolerant of competitive interactions. Compare with **facilitation model** and **inhibition model**. p. 311

top predator Predators that feed at the top of their food web, but that do not themselves have natural predators. p. 64

top–down hypothesis (consumer-control) A model of community organization based on the idea that carnivores affect the species composition and abundance of their herbivore prey, and that herbivores affect plants. Compare with **bottom–up hypothesis**. p. 286

torpor (or daily torpor) Controlled reduction in metabolism and body temperature on a daily basis. p. 165

total allowable catch (TAC) The amount of harvesting of a biological resource that is being permitted, usually following the advice of scientists about the sustainable yield. Compare with **maximum sustainable yield**. p. 518

trade-off In the study of life histories, a trade-off implies that an increase in the value of one trait (and its potential importance in terms of influencing fitness) can be achieved only if there is a concomitant reduction in that of another one. p. 222

tragedy of the commons An environmental metaphor associated with the degradation of a common-property resource, in which individuals justify overexploitation because they can share the degradation with many others. See also **common-property resource**. p. 503

trait Any characteristic or attribute of an organism. p. 136

transgenic modification An application of bioengineering, in which DNA of one species is incorporated into the genome of another one in order to realize an economic benefit. See also **genetically modified organism**. p. 497

transition matrix (Leslie matrix) Rows and columns of parameters (a matrix) that describe how age-class abundance changes from one time step to the next. p. 111

transpiration The evaporation of water from plants. Compare with **evapotranspiration**. p. 12

trophic cascade A model of community organization involving top–down control, such that a change in the rate of consumption at a higher trophic level results in a series of changes in species abundances that cascade down through lower trophic levels. p. 284

trophic structure The relative productivities and abundances of primary producers, herbivores, carnivores, and detritivores in an ecosystem, often represented using so-called trophic pyramids. p. 66

troposphere The lower atmosphere, extending from the surface to 7 km at the poles and 17–20 km at the equator. p. 11

turbidity The load of suspended fine-sized particulates in water. p. 351

Type-I survival A survival schedule in which a species exhibits relatively high survival during young and intermediate ages, after which survivorship declines steeply as the maximum longevity is approached. Compare with **Type-II survival**. p. 107

Type-II survival A survival schedule in which a species exhibits a constant rate of mortality throughout life. Compare with **Type-I survival**. p. 107

umbrella species Wide-ranging animals that utilize a large home range and are components of many communities; because of their extensive and complex habitat needs, any conservation actions that are effective at sustaining a viable population of them are also likely to achieve many other biodiversity benefits. p. 455

unstable equilibrium A state of equilibrium that can be upset if excessively displaced, so that it does not return to its original condition but instead moves to a new one. Compare with **stable equilibrium**. p. 120

urban ecology The study of biodiversity and ecological functions in urbanized habitats, with a focus on problems that can be mitigated by naturalization and the establishment of protected areas. p. 17

ureotelic An animal that produces urea as the primary nitrogenous waste product. p. 181

uricotelic An animal that produces uric acid as the primary nitrogenous waste product. p. 181

valuation A means by which the worth of a good or service is determined in monetary units, such as dollars. p. 482

value-added product The increased value of a product over that of the materials from which it was produced. p. 491

valued ecosystem component (VEC) An ecological component that is considered important in an environmental impact assessment because it is a bioresource, a species or community that is at risk, is of aesthetic importance, or is of cultural significance to an Aboriginal community or other local people. p. 588

variable Numbers that change in a mathematical equation. Compare with **parameter**. p. 98

vegetative regeneration Regrowth of individuals of certain plant species that survive a disturbance and then regenerate by sprouting from the rhizomes or roots. p. 312

viability selection Natural selection that maximizes survival of the individual. p. 135

weathering Chemical reactions in which insoluble minerals in rocks and soil become available for biological uptake through chemical reactions that make them water-soluble. p. 76

weed A plant that is unwanted by people in a management-related context. p. 232

wilderness Wild and uninhabited tracts that are little used by people, especially not for resource extraction and other intensive activities. p. 433

wilderness area A type of protected area that is managed to preserve its natural condition, with low levels of nonintensive, nonextractive visitation being permitted. p. 461

work In the sense of physics, this is the consequence of a force that is applied over a distance. p. 46

working-down The sequential harvesting of a previously nonexploited multispecies biological resource; initially the best individuals are harvested, then secondary species, and eventually nonselective area-harvesting methods are used. p. 500

Name Index

Life history, 213–247
  alternative, 238–241
    "The Best of a Bad Situation," 238, 239
    environmentally determined tactics,
      238, 239
    environment and genotypes, interaction
      between, 240–241
    extreme, 239
    frequency-dependent selection, 240
    genetically determined strategies,
      240, 241
    threshold traits, 240–241
  bet hedging, 220–222
  cost of reproduction, 224–226
  defined, 213
  differences occurring among species, 214
  fundamentals of, 213–222
  genetics and, 242
  harvest-induced evolution of, 241–245
    age and size at maturity, 241, 242–243
    consequences on life history, 243–245
  natural selection on, 226–234
    age and reproductive effort at maturity,
      227–230
    growth rate, 230
    life-history invariants, 234
    plant-focused classification, 232, 233–234
    r and K-selection, 230–232
  offspring size and number, 234–237
    optimal egg size, 235–237
  trade-offs, 222–224
  traits
    differences occurring among
      species, 214
    population growth rate linked to,
      217–219
    related to fitness, 215
    variabilty in, 215–217, 218
Life History Evolution (Roff), 242
Lifespan, 215
Life tables, 107–109
Light-dependent reaction, 191
Lignin, 208
Limnology, 551
Linear population growth, 99
Lithosere, 309
Lithosphere, 13
Little Ice Age, 544
Littoral zone, 350
Logarithmic series, 254–256
Logic, 19
Logistic model of population growth, 101
Logistic population growth, 100–106
  density-dependent per capita growth rate
    (r), 101–102
  sustainable rates of harvesting and,
    104–106
  time lags and oscillations of abundance,
    102–104
Longevity, 215
Longitudinal studies, 412
Lotic ecosystems, 351
Lotka-Volterra competition model, 116–117
Lower Critical Temperature (LCT), 166, 167
Lower incipient lethal limits, 166
Luvisol, 91

M

Mackenzie River Delta, 543, 563–564
Macrofossils, 548

Macronutrients, 71
Magma, 13
Magnesium (Mg), 71, 73
Major histocompatibility complex
    (MHC), 145
Managed-resource protected areas, 462
Management
  of biological resources, 492–504
    harvest-related mortality, 498–499
    limitations on productivity, 496–497
    maximum sustainable yield, 492–495
    natural mortality, 497–498
    overharvesting, 502–503
    regeneration, 495–496
    unsustainable harvesting, 499–502
  defined, 492
  integrated system of, 492
Manganese (Mn), 71
Manipulative experiment, 21
Mantle, 13
Manufactured capital, 489
Marine biomes, 352–355
  continental shelf waters, 353–355
  ocean, 352–353, 354
Marine bioresources, 516–530
  Atlantic cod, 521–523
  bowhead whale, 519–520
  by-catch, 529–530
  harvesting and management, 516–519
  Pacific salmon, 523–527
  salmon aquaculture, 527–529
Marine ecology, 17
Marine ecoregions, 360, 362
Marine ecozones, of Canada, 365, 366–367
  Arctic archipelago, 365
  Arctic basin, 365, 366
  Atlantic marine, 367
  characteristics of, 360
  distribution of, 357
  northwest Atlantic, 366
  Pacific, 365
Marine environments, 177–178
Marine fisheries, nonsustainability and,
    488–489
Marine Stewardship Council, 530
Maritime Provinces, 87
Markers, 387
Marmots, 465
Marshes, 351–352
Marten, pine, 465
Mass extinctions, 433–434
Mass-specific metabolism, 160
Mathematical Ecology (Pielou), 18
Matrix, 401, 403, 404–406, 407
Matrix community, 403
Maturity, age at, 214
Mauna Loa, Hawaii, 54
Maximum per capita rate of growth, 98
Maximum sustainable yield (MSY), 104–105,
    492–495
Mean, 15
Measuring biodiversity, 385–390
  diversity of species, 387–389
  genetic-level biodiversity, 387
  richness of communities, 389, 390
Mechanical energy, 48
Megafauna, 438–439
Menge-Sutherland model of community
    structure, 290
Mesophyll, 197
Mesotrophic waterbodies, 350

Metabolic disturbances (or disorders), 188
Metabolic rate, 160
Metabolic water, 180
Metabolism
  of diving mammals, 188
  mass-specific, 160
  scaling and, 162
Metals, nonsustainability and, 488
Metapopulations, 402
Methane (CH$_4$), 10, 25, 54, 58, 77, 82, 201
Microbial ecology, 17
Microbial loop, 64–65
Microdisturbances, 299
Micronutrients, 71–73
Microorganisms, in extreme
    environments, 32
Microsuccessions, 299
Migratory birds, decline in (case study), 583
Migratory Birds Convention Act, 432
Migratory songbirds, 146, 147
Milankovitch cycles, 539
Milkweeds, 209
Mineralization, 76
Minerotrophic ecosystem, 351
Minimum viable area (MVA), 408, 453
Minimum viable population (MVP), 453
Minke whale, 164, 472
Miramichi fire, 325
Mires, 351–352
Mississagi-Chapleau fire, 325
Mitigation, 588, 589
Mitochondria, 160
Mixedwood plains ecozone, 358, 365
Modelling, in landscape ecology, 423
Modelling Evolution (Roff), 242
Modern biodiversity crisis, 435–449. See also
    Anthropogenic extinctions and
    endangerments
  cause of, 436–437
  defined, 435
  elements of, 435–436
  global data on species at risk, 437–438
Molecular ecology, 17
Molybdenum (Mo), 71
Monitoring and research, 576–583
  case studies, 581–583
    acid rain, 581
    anthropogenic climate change,
      582–583
    decline in migratory birds, 583
    organochlorines, 581–582
    stratospheric ozone, 582
  ENGOs in, 576
  environmental indicators, 576–580
    composite, 577–578
    defined, 572
    intensified stress and, 572, 574
    multimetric, 578–579
    multivariate, 579–580
    relationship between, 580–583
Monocultures, 356
Montane cordillera ecozone, 359, 364–365
Montane forest, 345
Moraine, 88
Mortality
  anthropogenic, 497–498
  harvest-related, 498–499
  natural, 497–498
Mosaic, 403, 404–406, 407
Mountain pine beetle and antifreeze, 172
Mouse, house, 447